# Touring British Antique Shops

*Written & Compiled by*

***Carol Fisher***

ISBN 0951 9653-2-8





Published by Carol Fisher Publishing
PO Box 531, Melksham
Wiltshire SN12 8SL

Distributed in the U.S.A. by
Seven Hills Distributors
49 Central Avenue
Cincinnati, OH45202

Printed by Butler & Tanner, Great Britain

Cover Picture: Looe Harbour. By courtesy of the Cornwall Tourist Board

# Contents

# List of Maps

**London**

# MAP KEY

**Numbers refer to maps list**

# Introduction

Thank you for choosing this book and a heartfelt welcome to the touring world of British antiques. People in the antiques business are not a great amorphous mass with a pigeonhole label instead they are more likely to be highly individualistic, just like those adventurous types who seek them out – the customers. Dealers seem more independent, and sometimes even more downright eccentric, than folk in other businesses. Many appear to work for the love of beautiful and interesting things rather than much expectation of growing rich. Even now, after years of recession, many of the characters are still larger than life and few have grown wealthy. They continue to work from the crack of dawn, and often earlier, till late at night for the kind of rewards that any rational city businessman would not cross the road for. Despite all this they tend to be a generous, humorous bunch of people always ready for a chat and a drink.

And what of the shop and the stock? Well some are the size of cricket pitches, others half a telephone box but even if you found two places with apparently identical stock, the shops will be different for the owners themselves are as diverse as life itself. In this guide there are shops that have stock for as little as 50p and others whose minimum prices start at £50,000 so there is something for every pocket. Some establishments look like museums or public galleries, others appear to be little more than junk shops. There are dealers who carefully concentrate on a particular area of the antiques field, others have truly given in to a severe case of the magpie instinct. But whatever the set-up you will usually find something interesting, desirable or unusual.

How did the book come about? Well, in 1991 we thought that, after 15 years in the antiques publishing field ourselves, it might be nice to produce a guide that, as well as being a handy reference work, would make antiques buying trips far more pleasurable and encourage more people to search for and buy antiques. So the pilot edition came out in June 1992 with just 12 selected touring areas. It was not meant to be comprehensive, just a trial and the tours didn't even go west of Taunton or north of York. From the surprisingly rapid sales that followed we were encouraged to produce a second edition, two years later, with a vastly expanded scope: the number of tours doubled to 24 and this time covered the whole of England. That edition received very wide acclaim being reviewed by most of the antiques press here and overseas and was selling in at least 11countries. In fact this is the only British antiques directory to be listed in the prestigious U.S. Maloney's Resources Directory.

This new volume has been expanded yet again and now includes not just the whole of England, but also Scotland, Wales and Ulster. The number of tours has again doubled, now to 51 (plus London) and the maps have been made more logical and clearer. Despite the massive increase in content, the weight has also been kept down to maintain the book's portability – an essential for the touring person. The edition has been specially bound for easy folding.and unfolding with wipe-clean cover – ideal for carrying in the car.

If this is the first time you have seen this guide, don't worry it is clear and simple to use. London is split into nine main antiques areas with accompanying street maps. However once outside the capital, the volume is divided into 51 planned routes covering more than 1100 towns, villages and hamlets throughout Britain and Northern Ireland. The tours are vastly different in duration, character and content, hopefully to cater for every taste. All routes come complete with a generous historic and touring commentary, being limited only by the space available and the book format. It was hard work producing this but if you have as much fun using the book as we had writing it, we will be well satisfied.

It is advisable to spend some time just browsing. From the many readers' reports it appears that whatever your purpose, a combination of searches will quickly isolate the best areas for you. The place index and the specialist stock index should be consulted in full conjunction with the maps' list and contents page. A word about navigation: much effort has gone into producing 60 accurate detailed maps with scale bars but this has meant that where too much data had to go in certain confined areas then some artistic licence had to be allowed and the shape of roads or location of towns modified with clarity and ease of use the main objective. So the maps should be treated as schematic although perfectly adequate, we think, for touring.

To make the shop listings as accurate as possible free entry forms were sent out to more than 6000 dealers and, unless we had other reliable information, the tours were made up only from completed forms. Some

only provided partial information and in this case it is reflected in their listing. Whilst this has been done to ensure accuracy, remember, to maintain an accurate direrctory is a continuous, never-ending job, like painting the Forth Bridge. Inevitably between the date of the return of forms and publication, there may have been changes. Thus if you are travelling any distance to see a particular shop, best telephone first. Some shops may occasionally close during their stated opening hours, after all many dealers work alone and may be out after a special piece, delivering or collecting, possibly at an auction or antiques fair. Maybe they just need a bit of undisturbed time to themselves with an icepack on their heads whilst they attempt to do their accounts. Another important point: we sent out 6000 forms but did not receive them all back, some dealers have probably gone out of business but many of the non-returnees probably just never got round to completing it. This means that there may be more shops in some places than we have listed. If you come across any of these, do us a favour, ask them to return their form!

Now whether you are a potential buyer, dealer, a library or tourist officer, if you find that we could not say anything about your favourite place, please feel free to make criticisms, helpful comments, or suggest improvements. In particular we would like to know HOW exactly you use the guide and whether it fulfilled your expectations. If you are a dealer and do not see yourself in this volume and want to appear in the next, the preparations have already started, so please contact us or fill in the form at the back. If you would like to go on our mailing list for information on the publication of future editions, please tell us and should you wish to distribute the book tell us that too! On pages 494 and 495 are two forms, Dealer & Shops Information and Readers Remarks to make things easier for you to have a listing or let us know what you think of the book, good, bad or indifferent. Incidentally, the best suggestions for improvements will receive a free copy of the next guide. In the mean time I hope that you find the book most useful and enjoyable. Good hunting!

# Abbreviations

| | |
|---|---|
| ABA | Antiquarian Booksellers Association |
| ATCC | Antique Tools Collectors Club |
| ATD | Art Teachers Diploma |
| BA | Booksellers Association |
| BABADA | Bath & Bradford-on-Avon Antique Dealers Association |
| BADA | British Antique Dealers Association |
| BAFRA | British Antique Furniture Restorers Association |
| BHI | British Horological Institute |
| BJA | British Jewellers Association |
| BNTA | British Numismatic Traders Association |
| BT | Book Trust |
| BWCMG | British Watch & Clocks Makers Guild |
| CADA | Cotswolds Antique Dealers Association |
| CADO | Cliffe Antique Dealers Association (Lewes, Sussex) |
| CINOA | Confederation Internationale des Negociants en Oeuvres d'Art |
| CMJ | Company of Master Jewellers |
| CTS | China Trade Society |
| Cumbria ADA | Cumbria Antique Dealers Association |
| FATG | Fine Arts Trade Guild |
| DADA | Dorking Antique Dealers Association |
| FPPF | Federation of Professional Picture Framers |
| GA | Gemmological Association of Great Britain |
| GMC | Guild of Master Craftsmen |
| HADA | Highlands Antique Dealers Association |
| IADA | Irish Antique Dealers Association |
| IBD | Institute of British Designers |
| ILAB | International League of Antiquarian Booksellers |
| IMCOS | International Map Collectors Society |
| LAPADA | London and Provincial Antique Dealers Association |
| NADA | Nottingham Antique Dealers Association |
| NAG | National Association of Goldsmiths |
| NAWCCC | National Association of Watch & Clock Collectors (USA) |
| OMRS | Orders Medals Research Society |
| PAADA | Petworth Art & Antique Dealers Association |
| PADA | Portobello Antique Dealers Association |
| PBFA | Provincial Book Fairs Association |
| PCCGB | Print Collectors Club of Great Britain |
| PTS | Philatelic Trade Society |
| RSA | Royal Society of Art |
| SLAD | Society of London Art Dealers |
| TATHS | Tool & Trade History Society |
| TVADA | Thames Valley Antique Dealers Association |
| WADA | Warwick Antique Dealers Association |

*Note: Some abbreviations may be prefixed M or F denoting Member of Fellow.*

# London

The first record of settlement in **London** was in AD43 when the Romans set up a stronghold called *Londinium* at what is now Cornhill. Then it was just a small hill by a narrow part of the Thames overlooking the surrounding flat land. This stronghold became the centre of the road network that the Romans built throughout England.

By the time that Boudicca (Boadicea) launched her rebellion against the Romans in AD60, *Londinium* was a thriving town. However, Boudicca attacked it and reduced it to ashes. The Romans rebuilt the town and it continued to flourish, becoming the administrative centre for the province. City walls were built, which may still be seen in places, and so was the largest basilica outside of Rome itself.

After the Romans left England in the fifth century, London declined for some years but its fortunes revived with the coming of the Saxons. It was ideally situated for trade with Europe and it continued to prosper until the Normans arrived. William the Conqueror confirmed its pre-eminence when he was crowned at **Westminster Abbey** and made London his capital.

The city had two centres of power. **The City**, the centre of wealth and trade, and **Westminster**, the seat of royal power. The earliest surviving map of London, showing the city in 1558, gives an idea of how small it was. There was only one bridge spanning the Thames and east of the **Tower of London** and north of **Clerkenwell** there were farms and orchards. West of what is now **Aldwych** the only buildings were alongside the river. At that time the population stood at about 90,000 people but by the end of the 16th century it had more than doubled to 200,000.

Over the following two centuries, in spite of the Great Fire and the plague, London grew outwards. Villages like **Highgate** and **Islington** also spread. Development started on a larger scale south of the Thames giving a need for more bridges. Both **Westminster** and **Blackfriars Bridges** were completed in the mid 18th century.

The coming of the railways started a massive expansion in the capital. As the hub of a great empire and an international financial centre, the demand for labour grew. Public transport allowed workers to travel into the City from their homes in the suburbs. Before this people had always had to live close to their place of employment.

London's last great disaster was the blitz during the Second World War. The bombing started on 7th September 1940 and between then and 11th May 1941, 18,800 tons of high explosive bombs were dropped. Many people spent their nights in shelters or tube stations. While many of the stations were safe because they were so deep underground, others were not. A direct hit was scored on **Marble Arch** tube station resulting in many casualties and at **Balham**, in South London, a bomb fractured a water main, the station flooded and a number of people were drowned. By the end of the war, of the City's 677 acres, 164 had been laid waste, Throughout the whole of London, more than 15,000 people were killed and over three and a half million houses had been destroyed.

# Barnes and Chiswick

**Barnes** still retains much of the character of a rural village. It has a village green with a pond and the Sun Inn by the green dates from the 18th century. Until the early 19th century the area was quite inaccessible as the only routes were either from the river or across **Barnes Common** which was marshland until it was drained in the mid 19th century. It was in 1827 that a road was constructed to give access from **Hammersmith Bridge**. The railway arrived in 1846, giving rise to wide-scale development of the area.

There are a number of historic houses in Barnes including Milbourne House originally built in the 15th century but with little of the original fabric remaining. Now much of it dates from the 16th century and it has an 18th century facade. One of its most famous inhabitants was the novelist Henry Fielding.

Across the river from Barnes, **Chiswick** was also a very rural area until the mid 19th century

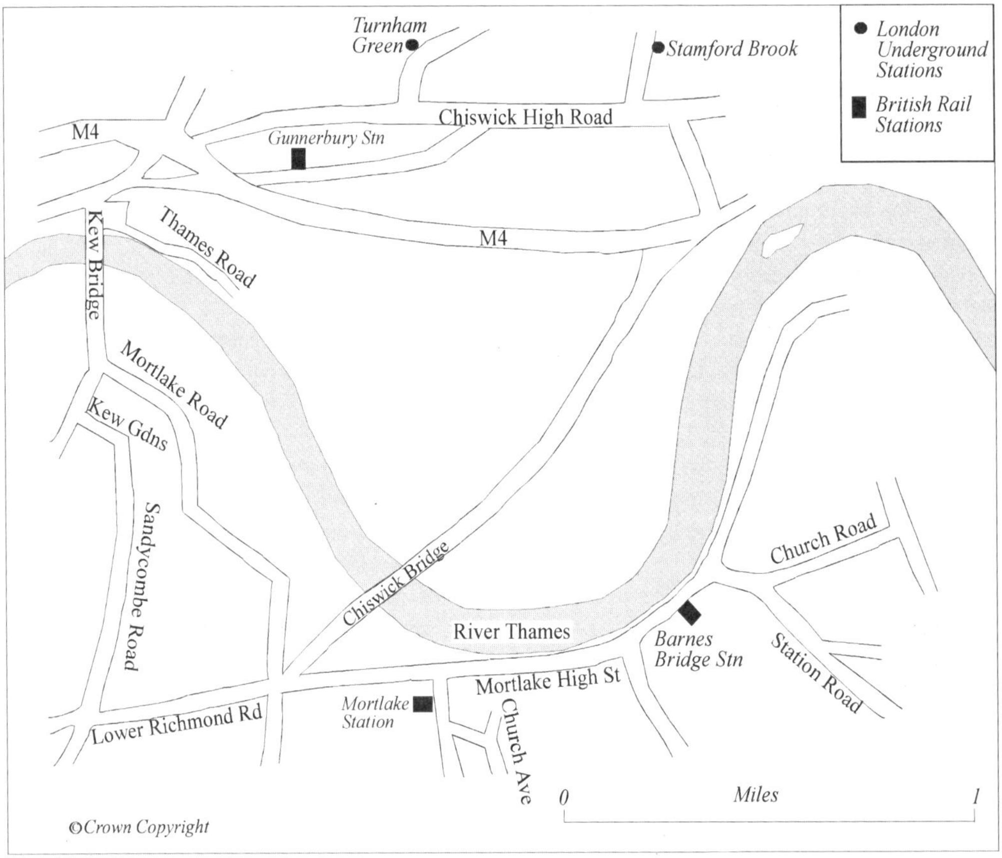


and the coming of the railways. From earliest times there were a number of settlements mostly along the river, with the origins of Chiswick itself in **Church Street** and **Chiswick Lane**.

Chiswick House in **Burlington Lane**, half a mile from the station, was completed in 1729 by the third Earl of Burlington. Built in the Italian style, the house was used solely to display the Earl's library and art collection. He lived in a house nearby that has since been demolished.

## ANTIQUE DEALERS

### LONDON SW13 (0181)

**Barnes Gallery,** 51 Church Road, SW13 9HH TEL: 741 1277 PARKING: Easy MIN: £100 MAX: £2000 PERIOD: 20th century SPECIALIST: Figurative, living artists GENERAL: Paintings, sculpture & paints OTHER INFO: Barnes has a charming village atmosphere with many antiques shops & galleries.

**Christine Bridge Antiques,** 78 Castelnau, SW13 9EX TEL & FAX: 741 5501 mobile: 0831 126668 ASSNS: LAPADA PARKING: Own carpark OPEN: Anytime by appt only MIN: £50 MAX: £24,000 PERIOD: 18th-19th century SPECIALIST: 18th century collectors glass, 19th century coloured glass GENERAL: Small decorative antiques.

**The Dining Room Shop**, 62-64 White Hart Lane, SW13 0PZ TEL: 878 1020 FAX: 878 7404 PARKING: Easy OPEN: Mon-Fri 10-5.30, Sat 10.15-5.30 MIN: £1 MAX: £50,000 PERIOD: 18th-20th century SPECIALIST: Dining room furniture, china, glass, silver GENERAL: Wine & food prints, decorative table accessories OTHER INFO: Oxford & Cambridge boat race finish nearby.

**Paul Foster's Bookshop,** 46-52 Church Road, SW13 0DQ TEL: 748 1858 ASSNS: PBFA PARKING: Easy OPEN: Tues-Sat 10.30-6 MIN: 20p MAX: £2000 PERIOD: 17th-20th century GENERAL: Secondhand, out of print, rare & antiquarian books.

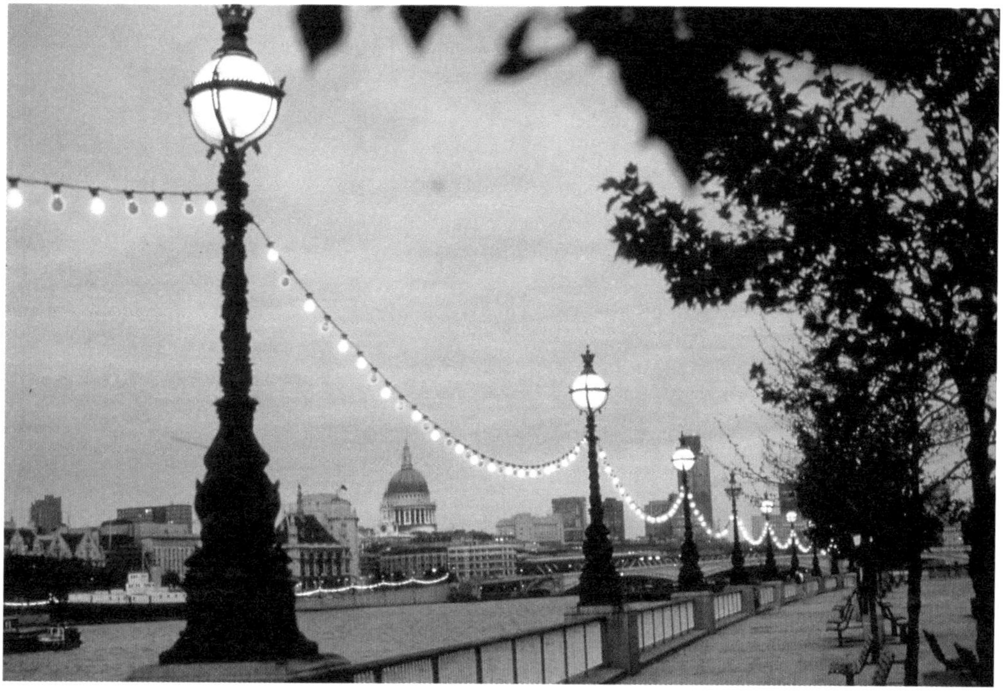

*St Paul's and the City of London seen from the South Bank of the River Thames*

**Joy Macdonald**, 50 Station Road, Barnes, SW13 0LP TEL: 876 6184 PARKING: Easy OPEN: 10-5.30 (resident) MIN: £20+ PERIOD: 18th-20th century SPECIALIST: Large English & French gilt mirrors GENERAL: French fruitwood country tables, unusual decorative items inc chandeliers.

**New Grafton Gallery,** 49 Church Road, SW13 9HH TEL: 748 8850 FAX: 748 9818 PARKING: Easy OPEN: Tues-Sat 10-5.30 MIN: £100 MAX: £4000 SPECIALIST: 20th century British paintings.

**Wren Antiques**, 49b Church Road, Barnes, SW13 9HH TEL: 741 7841 PARKING: Easy OPEN: 10-5 MIN: £50 MAX: £3000 PERIOD: 18th-19th century SPECIALIST: Chandeliers GENERAL: General antiques.

## LONDON SW14 (0181)

**Age of Elegance,** 61 Sheen Lane, SW14 8AB TEL: 876 0878 PARKING: Medium OPEN: Mon, Wed, Fri, Sat 12-6 MIN: £3 MAX: £400 PERIOD: 19th century SPECIALIST: Door furniture, fittings GENERAL: Collectables, old & interesting things.

**William Sheppee**, 1a Church Avenue, SW14 8NW TEL: 392 2379 FAX: 878 9903 PARKING: Own carpark OPEN: Mon-Fri 8.30-5.30 MIN: £5 MAX: £5000 PERIOD: 19th century GENERAL: Indian & colonial furniture, architectural items, treen OTHER INFO: Close M3 & M4 motorways.

## LONDON SW15 (0181)

**RA Barnes Antiques**, 26 Lower Richmond Road, Putney, SW15 1JP TEL: 789 3371 PARKING: Easy OPEN: 10-5.30 MIN: £20+ MAX: £3000+ PERIOD: 18th-20th century SPECIALIST: Wedgwood, Chinese, Art Nouveau, brass, glass GENERAL: Furniture, paintings, copper, treen, English & Continental pottery & porcelain OTHER INFO: Good pubs etc overlooking River Thames.

**The Clock Clinic Ltd**, 85 Lower Richmond Road, Putney, SW15 1EU TEL: 788 1407 FAX: 780 2838 ASSNS: LAPADA PARKING: Medium OPEN: Tues-Fri 9-6, Sat 9-1 MIN: £350 MAX: £20,000 PERIOD: 17th-19th century SPECIALIST: English longcase clocks GENERAL: Antique clocks & barometers overhauled & guaranteed OTHER INFO: Look for our blue bollards, next to Half Moon, famous for jazz.

## LONDON W4 (0181)

**JD Marshall**, 38 Chiswick Lane, W4 2JQ TEL: 742

8089 PARKING: Own carpark OPEN: Tues-Fri 10-6, Sat 10-5 MIN: £10 MAX: £60,000 PERIOD: 18th-19th century SPECIALIST: Decorative objects, bronzes, furniture, lighting GENERAL: French furniture & objects OTHER INFO: Just off M4, 20 mins Heathrow, Fouberts Hotel, plenty of restaurants.

**The Old Cinema**, 160 Chiswick High Road, W4 1PR TEL: 995 4166 FAX: 995 4167 ASSNS: LAPADA PARKING: Easy OPEN: Mon-Sat 9.30-6, Sun 12 noon-5 MIN: £50 MAX: £25,000 PERIOD: 18th-20th century GENERAL: Furniture SPECIALIST: Architectural items.

**Strand Antiques**, 166 Thames Road, Chiswick TEL: 994 1912 PARKING: Easy OPEN: Seven days 12-5 MIN: £1 MAX: £500 PERIOD: 18th-19th century SPECIALIST: Glass GENERAL: General antiques OTHER INFO: 8 dealers by the many Thames riverside pubs on Strand on the Green.

## LONDON W6 (0181)

**Richard Miles**, TEL: 748 6385 FAX: 741 2574 OPEN: By appt only MIN: £100 MAX: £50,000 PERIOD: 18th-19th century SPECIALIST: Anglo Indian & Chinese Colonial furniture, country house, Gothic & unusual woods.

**Paravent,** c/o Flat 10, Ranelagh Gardens, Stamford Brook Avenue, W6 0YE TEL: 748 6323 ASSNS: Worshipful Company of Furniture Makers OPEN: Must phone first for appt MIN: £500 MAX: £10,000 PERIOD: 18th-20th century SPECIALIST: Screens 18th century, leather GENERAL: Decorative screens, other decorative furniture.

# Bermondsey

*A view of Tower Bridge. By courtesy of the London Tourist Board*

In 1082 the building of an abbey was started in Bermondsey by a branch of the Benedictines. Various grants of land were given to the abbey, first by William Rufus and then by Henry I. King Stephen exempted it from paying taxes, granted it the right to hold courts of law and gave it more land nearby. The abbey flourished until the time of the Dissolution of the Monasteries when the buildings were sold and demolished. Some of the stones were used in building Bermondsey House which once stood on the site of the present day **Bermondsey Square**.

By the 18th century the area was still very rural although leather tanneries had been set up in **Long Lane** and there was other development along the river bank. However by the mid 19th century parts of Bermondsey had degenerated into dismal slums.

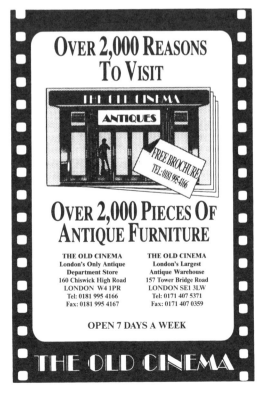

**Tower Bridge** connects **Tower Hill** to Bermondsey. One of London's most distinctive landmarks, it was constructed between 1886 and 1894. Directly across the river from Bermondsey stands the **Tower of London** started by William the Conqueror and said to be the best example of a medieval fortress in Britain. The outer walls enclose an area of 18 acres and it is encircled by a deep moat. During its thousand year history it has served as a palace, prison, royal armoury, mint, treasury and library. However, the Tower is best known as a place of tragedy and suffering. The two princes were kept here by Richard III until they disappeared, thought murdered. Anne Boleyn and Catherine Howard, wives of Henry VIII, were executed here as was Lady Jane Grey and the Earl of Essex. Many others were also imprisoned here and then executed either on Tower Hill or Tower Green.

On a happier note, the Crown Jewels are kept here and are on display to the public (patience is required as, in summer, the queues can be very long). Most the Jewels date from after the Restoration of the monarchy as Parliament ordered the destruction of the royal regalia after the execution of Charles I. One of the most famous of the jewels is the diamond, Koh-i-Noor, which is supposed to bring bad luck, but to men only; it is said to be lucky for women so it has been worn by all the queens (and queen consorts, i.e. the wives of kings) since Queen Victoria.

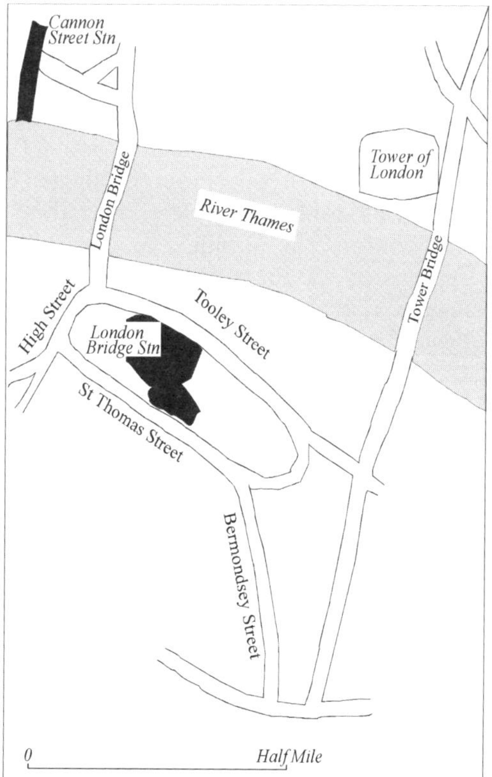




# ANTIQUE DEALERS

## LONDON SE1 (0171)

**Bermondsey Antiques Market**, Corner of Long Lane & Bermondsey Street TEL: 351 5353 FAX: 351 5350 OPEN: Fri 4am-2pm MIN: £5 MAX: £5000 PERIOD: 17th-20th century GENERAL: 150+ dealers with extensive selection of the unusual & collectable antiques OTHER INFO: 2 cafés serving very early breakfasts, bureau de change. Tubes: Borough, Tower Hill or London Bridge.

**Bermondsey Antique Traders,** 158 Bermondsey Street, SE1 3TQ TEL & FAX: 378 1000 ASSNS: LAPADA PARKING: Own carpark OPEN: Mon-Sat 9.30-5 Sat 10.30-3.30 MIN: £50 MAX: £5000+ PERIOD: 18th-20th century SPECIALIST: Furniture OTHER INFO: Close to Tower Bridge.

**The Old Cinema**, 157 Tower Bridge Road, SE1 3LW TEL: 407 5371 FAX: 403 0359 ASSNS: LAPADA PARKING: Easy OPEN: Mon-Sat 9.30-6, Sun 12 noon-5 MIN: £50 MAX: £25,000 PERIOD: 18th-20th century GENERAL: Furniture SPECIALIST: Victorian furniture.

# Camden Passage & Islington

Originally owned by the canons of St Paul's, **Islington**, by the 16th century, boasted some wonderful mansions two of which were owned by Henry VIII who came here to hunt. Queen Elizabeth I often visited Sir John Spenser at Canonbury House and Sir Walter Raleigh, who had a house in **Upper Street**. However, Islington continued as a rural village well into the 19th century. As with so many other places, the railways brought about a huge increase in population and terraces of houses were built.

Upper Street was the start of the **Great North Road** and a major coaching route. The Angel, Islington, was a coaching inn and the nearest staging post to London. However, the Angel, Islington, is a misnomer because it stood just outside the Islington parish boundary. The original Jacobean inn was demolished in 1819 and rebuilt. Just eighty years later it was rebuilt again as Lyons Corner House. Near the Angel tube station and running parallel to Upper Street is **Camden Passage**, once called Pullens Row, and the major centre for antiques in this area.

## ANTIQUE DEALERS

### LONDON N1 (0171)

**After Noah,** 121 Upper Street, N1 1QP TEL & FAX: 359 4281 PARKING: Medium OPEN: Mon-Sat 10-6, Sun 12-5 MIN: £1 MAX: £3000 PERIOD: 19th-20th century SPECIALIST: American Shaker mission & Pennsylvania furniture GENERAL: Contemporary & antique furniture especially wrought iron beds, Arts & Crafts, mosaic tables, jewellery, toys.

**At The Sign of the Chest of Drawers**, 281 Upper Street, N1 2TZ TEL: 359 5909 FAX: 359 5909 PARKING: Medium OPEN: Seven days 10-6 MIN: £1 MAX: £1500 PERIOD: 19th-20th century SPECIALIST: Antique pine & country furniture. OTHER INFO: Good restaurants, theatres.

**Banbury Fayre,** 6 Pierrepoint Arcade, Camden Passage, N1 TEL: 0181-852 5675 ASSNS: CPTA PARKING: Easy OPEN: Wed 7-4, Sat 7-5 MIN: £8 MAX: £250 PERIOD: 19th-20th century SPECIALIST: Collectables, ships memorabilia, Boer War items GENERAL: Collectables.

**William Bedford plc**, 46 Essex Road, N1 8LN TEL: 226 9648 FAX: 226 6225 ASSNS: LAPADA, CPTA PARKING: Own carpark OPEN: Tues-Sat 9.30-5.30 IN: £500 MAX: £120,000 PERIOD: 17th-19th century SPECIALIST: Dining room & library furniture GENERAL: English, Irish, Continetal furniture & works of art. Bespoke reproductions.

**Bushwood Antiques**, 317 Upper Street, N1 TEL: 359 2095 FAX: 704 9578 ASSNS: LAPADA PARKING: Medium OPEN: 9.30-5.30 MIN: £250 MAX: £10,000 PERIOD: 18th-19th century SPECIALIST: Furniture GENERAL: Clocks, lighting, objets d'art in 14,000+ sq ft showroom.

**Patric Capon,** 350 Upper Street, N1 0PS TEL: 354 0487 & 0181-467 5722 FAX: 0181-295 1475 ASSNS: BADA PARKING: Easy OPEN: Wed & Sat MIN: £1000 MAX: £30,000 PERIOD: 18th-19th century SPECIALIST: Fine clocks, barometers, furniture.

**Cat Box Antiques & Collectables**, York Arcade, 80 Islington High Street, N1 8EA TEL: 0181-744 9277 ASSNS: CPTA PARKING: Medium OPEN: Wed, Sat 8.30-4 MIN: £40 MAX: £500 PERIOD: 19th century to 1960's SPECIALIST: Cat objects of all kinds (ceramics, prints, some dog items, jewellery, etc) OTHER INFO: Exhibits at National & Supreme Cat Shows. York Arcade is near Tourist Info Bureau.

**Peter Chapman Antiques**, 10 Theberton Street, N1 0QX TEL: 226 5565 FAX: 348 4846 ASSNS: LAPADA, CPTA PARKING: Easy OPEN: Mon-Sat 9.30-6 MIN: £50 MAX: £15,000 PERIOD: 18th-19th century SPECIALIST: Furniture, paintings, objets d'art, lanterns, mirrors, decoratives. Restoration service. No reproductions.

**Charlton House Antiques,** 7 Charlton Place, Camden Passage, N1 8AQ TEL & FAX: 226 3141 ASSNS: CPTA PARKING: 9-5.30 MIN: £50 MAX: £10,000 PERIOD: 19th-20th century GENERAL: English & Continental furniture OTHER INFO: Camden Passage has a street market & 150 shops.

**Commemoratives**, 3 Pierrepoint Arcade, Camden Passage, N1 8EF ASSNS: Eggcupp Collectors Club of GB PARKING: Medium OPEN: Wed, Sat 10-5 & by appt MIN: £1 MAX: £100 PERIOD: 19th-20th century SPECIALIST: Eggcups, thimbles, egg timers, Torquay ware, novelty collectables.

**Dome Antiques (Exports) Ltd**, 75 Upper Street, N1 0NU TEL: 226 7227 FAX 704 2960 PARKING: Medium OPEN: 9-5 MIN: £500 MAX: £10,000 PERIOD: 18th-19th century GENERAL: Desks, dining tables & chairs, bookcases, occasional tables, etc OTHER INFO: Opposite Camden Passage.

**Vincent Freeman Antiques**, Camden Passage, N1 2UD TEL: 226 6178 FAX: 226 7231 PARKING: Medium OPEN: Tues-Wed, Fri-Sat 10-5 MIN: £50+ MAX: £20,000+ PERIOD: 19th century SPECIALIST: Antique cylinder & disc music boxes GENERAL: Furniture & objects.

**Get Stuffed**, 105 Essex Road, N1 5SL TEL: 226 1364 FAX: 359 8253 PARKING: Medium OPEN: Mon 12-4.30, Tues, Wed, Fri 10.30-4.30, Thurs 10.30-1, Sat 12-3 MIN: £25 MAX: £25,000 PERIOD: 19th-20th century SPECIALIST: Glass domes GENERAL: All aspects of taxidermy.

**Graham Gallery**, 104 Islington High Street, Camden Passage, N1 8EG TEL: 354 2112 FAX: 704 0728 ASSNS: LAPADA PARKING: Medium OPEN: Tues-Sat 10-5 MIN: £100 MAX: £100,000 PERIOD: 19th-early 20th century SPECIALIST: Unique fine English marquetry furniture, stylish silver, romantic Victorian oils OTHER INFO: Next to Frederick famous restaurant.

**Gordon Gridley Antiques**, 28 & 41 Camden Passage, Islington, N1 8EA TEL: 226 0643 ASSNS: CPTA PARKING: Medium OPEN: Tues-Sat 10-4.30 MIN: £50 MAX: £20,000 PERIOD: 17th-19th century SPECIALIST: Folk art & naïve paintings, English ironstone GENERAL: English & Continental furniture, paintings, sculpture, metalware, decorative objects OTHER INFO: 1000 sq ft warehouse at rear. 2 internationally famed restaurants.

**Hart & Rosenberg**, 2-3 Gateway Arcade, 355 Upper Street, Camden Passage, N1 0PD TEL: 359 6839 FAX 0181-676 8984 ASSNS: CPTA PARKING: Easy OPEN: Tues, Fri 10.30-5, Wed 9-5, Sat 10-5 & by appt MIN: £50 MAX: £4,000 PERIOD: 17th-20th century SPECIALIST: Oriental ceramics GENERAL: English & Continental ceramics, works of art & decoratives OTHER INFO: Opposite Business Design Centre, close to Angel tube station.

**Heritage Antiques**, 112 Islington High Street, N1 8EG TEL: 226 7789 ASSNS: LAPADA PARKING: Easy OPEN: Wed & Sat & by appt MIN: £20 MAX: £5000 PERIOD: 17th-19th century SPECIALIST: Metalware GENERAL: Oak & decorative items.

**House of Steel**, 400 Caledonian Road, N1 1DN TEL: 607 5889 FAX: 607 5889 PARKING: Own carpark OPEN: Mon-Fri 9-5 & by appt MIN: £5+ MAX: £3000 PERIOD: 19th-20th century SPECIALIST: Metal antiques, ornamental & architectural metalware, fireplaces, railings, gates, garden furniture, lighting, steel tables & chairs OTHER INFO: Reproductions in cast steel, brass.

**Diana Huntley**, 8 Camden Passage, N1 3ED TEL: 226 4605 FAX: 359 0240 ASSNS: LAPADA PARKING: Medium OPEN: Tues, Fri 10-4, Wed 7.30-4, Sat 9-4 MIN: £100 MAX: £10,000 PERIOD: 19th century SPECIALIST: European porcelain GENERAL: Meissen, Minton, Coalport, Wedgwood, Derby services.

**Inheritance**, 8-9 Gateway Arcade, Camden Passage, N1 8EG TEL & FAX: 226 8305 PARKING: Easy OPEN: 10-5 PERIOD: 17th-19th century SPECIALIST: 19th century paintings GENERAL: Paintings, furniture, Oriental porcelain, silver.

**Intercol London**, Upper Gallery, 11 Camden Passage, N1 8DY TEL: 349 2207 FAX: 346 9539 ASSNS: CPTA PARKING: Easy OPEN: Wed, Sat 9-5 MIN: £5+ MAX: £5,000 PERIOD: 18th-20th century SPECIALIST: Playing cards, maps, money.

**Islington Antiques**, 14 Essex Road, N1 8LN TEL: via 226 6867 PARKING: Easy OPEN: Seven days 9-6 MIN: £15 MAX: £2,000 PERIOD: 19th century

SPECIALIST: Original antique pine furniture.

**Cassandra Keen**, 18 Georgian Village, Camden Passage, NI 8EA TEL: 359 6534 ASSNS: LAPADA PARKING: Medium OPEN: Wed 7-3, Sat 8-4 MIN: £100 MAX: £1,500 PERIOD: 18th-early 20th century SPECIALIST: French mirrors & fin de siècle lighting GENERAL: Across the board.

**Jane House Antiques**, 15 Camden Passage, N1 8EH TEL: 359 1343 PARKING: Easy OPEN: Tues-Sat 10-4.30 MIN: £400 MAX: £7000 SPECIALIST: Georgian & Victorian furniture.

**Japanese Gallery**, 23 Camden Passage, N1 8EA TEL: 226 3347 ASSNS: CPTA PARKING: Easy OPEN: 9.30-4.30 MIN: £5 MAX: £10,000 PERIOD: 19th-20th century SPECIALIST: Japanese woodcut prints GENERAL: Japanese arts, porcelain, pottery, screens, furniture OTHER INFO: Framing & free authentification.

**Jubilee Photographica**, 10 Pierrepoint Row, Camden Passage, N1 TEL: 607 5462(home) FAX: Yes PARKING: Medium ASSNS: CPTA OPEN: Wed, Sat 10.30-3.30 & by appt MIN: 5p snaps MAX: £1500 PERIOD: 18th-20th century SPECIALIST: Daguerrotypes, Ambrotypes, Tintypes, all types of paper prints, stereocards, viewers, categorised cartes de visite. Photoframes, graphoscopes, magic lanterns & slides OTHER INFO: Photo dating service.

**Thomas Keen Antiques**, 11 Theberton Street, N1 0QY TEL: 226 0626 FAX: 354 5625 ASSNS: LAPADA PARKING: Easy OPEN: 10-5.30 MIN: £10 MAX: £20,000 PERIOD: 17th-18th century GENERAL: English furniture.

**Carol Ketley**, 4-5 Pierrepoint Arcade, N1 8EF TEL: 359 5529, (0831) 827284 ASSNS: LAPADA PARKING: Medium OPEN: Wed 8-3, Sat 10-4 MIN: £5+ MAX: £800 PERIOD: 19th century SPECIALIST: Decanters, glassware, pottery, inexpensive decorative furniture OTHER INFO: 300 dealers in Camden Passage, market days Wed & Sat.

**Sara Lemkow & Rookery Farm Antiques**, 12 Camden Passage, N1 8ED TEL: 359 0190 FAX: 704 2095 ASSNS: CPTA PARKING: Medium OPEN: 10-5 MIN: £15 MAX: £1000 PERIOD: 18th-19th century SPECIALIST: Pine furniture, oil lamps, GENERAL: Kitchenalia, scales, copper & brass.

**Michael Lewis**, 16 Essex Road, N1 8LN TEL: 359 7733 ASSNS: LAPADA, CPTA PARKING: Easy OPEN: Sat 8-6, Sun 8-5 & by appt MIN: £5 MAX:

£10,000 PERIOD: 18th-19th century SPECIALIST: British & Irish period pine & country furniture.

**London Militaria Market**, Angel Arcade, Camden Passage, N1 TEL: (01628) 822503 FAX: (01628) 822503 PARKING: Medium OPEN: 8-2 MIN: £1 MAX: £2000+ PERIOD: 19th century SPECIALIST: Military helmets, badges, uniforms, regimental brooches, medals, swords, aviation items OTHER INFO: 35 dealers from all over England.

**Finbar Macdonnell**, 17 Camden Passage, NI TEL: 226 0537 PARKING: Medium OPEN: 10-6 MIN: £5 MAX: £1000 PERIOD: 17th-20th century GENERAL: Prints, caricatures, Vanity Fair, Japanese OTHER INFO: Big market Wed & Sat AM.

**The Mall Antiques Arcade**, Camden Passage, N1 TEL: 351 5353 FAX: 351 5350 PARKING: Easy OPEN: Tues, Thurs, Fri 10-5, Wed 7.30-5, Sat 9-6 MIN: £5 MAX: £25,000 GENERAL: English & Continental furniture, porcelain, silver, Art Deco & Nouveau, glass, jewellery, prints, lighting & Oriental art OTHER INFO: Prime trading is on Weds being Camden Passage market day.

**Laurence Mitchell Antiques Ltd**, 13 & 27 Camden Passage, N1 8EA TEL: 359 7599 PARKING: Medium OPEN: 10-5, Wed 8-5 MIN: £100 MAX: £20,000 PERIOD: 18th-19th century SPECIALIST: Probably largest UK stock of Meissen GENERAL: General, porcelain, works of art, decorative furniture.

**Jacqueline Oosthuizen Antiques**, 1st Floor (upstairs), Georgian Village, Camden Passage, N1 8EA TEL: 352 6071, 226 5393 FAX: 376 3852 ASSNS: LAPADA PARKING: Easy OPEN: Wed & Sat 8-4 MIN: £28 MAX: £3000 PERIOD: 18th-19th century SPECIALIST: Staffordshire figures 1760-1890, cotestate jewellery.

**Peter Oosthuizen & De Verzamelaar**, 1st Floor (upstairs), Georgian Village, Camden Passage, NI 8EA TEL: 359 3322 FAX: 376 3852 PARKING: Easy OPEN: Wed, Sat 8-4 MIN: £10 MAX: £2000 PERIOD: Late 19th-early 20th century SPECIALIST: Dutch Art Nouveau ceramics & Boer War memorabilia.

**Marcus Ross Antiques**, 14 & 16 Pierrepoint Row, Camden Passage, N1 8EF TEL: 359 8494 FAX: 359 0240 PARKING: Medium OPEN: Tues-Wed, Fri-Sat 10-5 MIN: £50 MAX: £10,000 PERIOD: 17th-19th century SPECIALIST: Japanese Imari, Chinese export GENERAL: European porcelain, small furniture.

**Style Galleries**, 1 Georgian Village, Camden Passage, N1 TEL: 359 7867, (0831) 229640 PARKING: Easy OPEN: Wed 9-4, Sat 9.30-4.30 MIN: £150 MAX: £15,000 PERIOD: 19th-20th century SPECIALIST: Art Nouveau/Deco GENERAL: Pewter, WMF Liberty, bronze, ivories, Lalique Loetz lighting OTHER INFO: We are the gallery which published reprint of WMF 1906 catalogue.

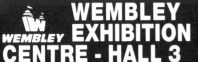

**Tadema Gallery**, 10 Charlton Place, Camden Passage, N1 8AJ TEL: 359 1055 FAX: 704 9335 ASSNS: LAPADA PARKING: Medium OPEN: Wed, Fri, Sat 10-5 MIN: £150 MAX: £20,000 PERIOD: 20th century SPECIALIST: Abstract art & jewellery from Art Nouveau to artist designed pieces circa 1960.

**Titus Omega,** Shop 18, Georgian Village, Camden Passage, N1 TEL: 704 8003 OPEN: Wed 8-3, Sat 9-4 MIN: £50 MAX: £5000 GENERAL: General antiques.

**Turn On Lighting**, 116-118 Islington High Street, Camden Passage, N1 8EG TEL & FAX: 359 7616 ASSNS: Decorative Arts Society, Historic Lighting Club PARKING: Easy OPEN: Tues-Sat 10.30-5 MIN: £250 MAX: £1000 PERIOD: 18th-20th century SPECIALIST: Lighting c.1840-1940 OTHER INFO: Juggling shop & school on Upper St, N1.

**Yesterday Child**, Angel Arcade, 118 Islington High Street, N1 8EG TEL & FAX: (01908) 583403 PARKING: Medium OPEN: Wed, Sat 9-3 MIN: £100 PERIOD: 20th century SPECIALIST: Enormous stock of antique dolls & miniatures.

**Michael Young,** 22 The Mall, 359 Upper Street, N1 0PD TEL: 226 2225, mobile: (0385) 228686 PARKING: Medium OPEN: Wed & Sat 7-4 MIN: £50 MAX: £2500 PERIOD: 18th-20th century SPECIALIST: Propellor aircraft, pond yachts GENERAL: Furniture, marine aviation, boys toys.

## LONDON NW1 (0171)

**Victorian Fireplace Co**, 53 West Yard, Camden Lock, NW1 8AF TEL: 482 2543 FAX: (0191) 417 9946 PARKING: Medium OPEN: Wed-Sun 10.30-5 MIN: £95 MAX: £600 PERIOD: 19th-20th century SPECIALIST: Original Victorian, Edwardian fireplaces & accessories OTHER INFO: Camden Lock Market wonderful Sat & Sun

# Chelsea and Knightsbridge

The village of **Chelsea** was mentioned in the Domesday Book but it was not until the 16th century that it became fashionable. Sir Thomas More, later to be executed in the Tower of London, had a house here as did Henry VIII, the Duke of Norfolk and the Earl of Shrewsbury. In the 19th century, residents like Whistler and Rossetti gave the area a more Bohemian character and led to the founding of the Chelsea Arts Club, still going strong today.

The most well-known building in Chelsea is probably the **Royal Hospital** founded by Charles II, and designed by Sir Christopher Wren, to care for sick and aged soldiers. The building was finished in 1692 and it has had few alterations since. In May every year since 1913, except during the war, the Royal Horticultural Society has held their flower show in the grounds.

The main road through Chelsea, running from **Sloane Square** to **Fulham**, is the **King's Road**. Originally this was a private road used by Charles II to go to Hampton Court. It only became a public thoroughfare in 1830. One of the many businesses that occupied premises here was Thomas Crapper, makers of water closets, whose name introduced a new word into the English language.

Sloane Square, like many of the streets in the area, is named for Sir Hans Sloane who bought the manor of Chelsea in 1712. He had two daughters who each inherited half of his estate. One married Lord Cadogan and the other George Stanley who came from Paultons in Hampshire. These names are also reflected in the streets.

**Belgravia**, north of Sloane Square, takes its name from Belgrave in Leicestershire, where the Grosvenor family, owners of the land, had an estate. Right into the 18th century this was an area of fields and the haunt of footpads. The first houses were built in 1726 in what is now **Grosvenor Place**. Few other buildings were constructed, however, until the first half of the 19th century when Lord Grosvenor leased the land to Thomas Cubitt for development. It quickly became fashionable and has remained so.

**Knightsbridge** was a village as early as the 11th century. Famous for its taverns in the 17th century, it was also a popular place for duels and highwaymen. The village green, commemorated in the name **Knightsbridge Green**, was situated where the Scotch House stands today. Harrods, another famous landmark, stands on the **Brompton Road**. In 1849 Henry Harrod took a small grocer's shop which his son, Charles, bought from him in 1861. He rapidly expanded the business in terms of staff numbers, premises and range of stock. Unfortunately, in December 1883, a fire totally destroyed the shop. Charles Harrod impressed his customers by still delivering all their orders in time for Christmas. The store was rebuilt in 1884 and five years later he sold it. Without him sales began to fall and so he was brought back for a further two years. The famous frontage was completed in 1905 and the remaining rebuilding and redesigning work was finished in 1939. It is now one of the world's largest stores.

## ANTIQUE DEALERS

### LONDON SW1 (0171)

**Anno Domini Antiques**, 66 Pimlico Road TEL: 730 5496 ASNS: BADA PARKING: Medium OPEN: 10-1, 2.15-6 MIN: £20 MAX: £20,000 PERIOD: 18th-19th century SPECIALIST: Glass, pictures, celery vases GENERAL: Furniture, mirrors, screens, decorative items.

**Hilary Batstone Decorative Antiques,** 51 Kinnerton Street, SW1X 8EA TEL: 259 6070 ASSNS: LAPADA PARKING: Medium OPEN: Mon-Fri 10-5 MIN: £100 MAX: £10,000 PERIOD: 18th-19th century GENERAL: Decorative furniture, textiles, lighting & accessories.

**Andre de Canqueray**, 227 Ebury Street, SW1W 8UT TEL: 730 5000 FAX: 730 7199 PARKING: Easy OPEN: 10-6 MIN: £100 MAX: £10,000 PERIOD: 18th-19th century GENERAL: French antiques OTHER INFO: Next to Boucherie Lamartine Roux-owned La Poule au Pot, French provincial food.

**Chaucer Fine Arts Ltd**, 45 Pimlico Road, SW1W 8NE TEL: 730 2972 & 5872 FAX: 730 5861 PARKING: Medium OPEN: Mon-Fri 10-6 by appt

*Covent Garden Market. By courtesy of the London Tourist Board*

PERIOD: 18th century SPECIALIST: Italian & Italianate Old Master paintings & works of art.

**Christopher Edwards,** 8 Holbein Place, SW1W 8NL TEL & FAX: 730 4025 PARKING: Easy OPEN: Mon-Fri 10-6, Sat 11-5 MIN: £100 MAX: £20,000 PERIOD: 19th-20th century SPECIALIST: 19th century architect designed furniture & objects.

**Galerie Moderne Ltd**, 10 Halkin Arcade, Motcomb Street, SW1X 8JT TEL: 245 6907 FAX: 245 6341 PARKING: Medium OPEN: Mon-Fri 10-6 & by appt MIN: £500 PERIOD: 20th century SPECIALIST: Pre-war Rene Lalique glass including vases, scent bottles, tableware, lighting fixtures, designs, car mascots, jewellery & statuettes. 20th century porcelain by Sevres OTHER INFO: Carlton Tower, Sheraton, Park Tower & Lowndes hotels.

**Joss Graham Oriental Textiles,** 10 Eccleston Street, SW1W 9LT TEL & FAX: 730 4370 PARKING: Medium OPEN: Mon-Sat 10-6 MIN: £5 MAX: £5000 PERIOD: 18th-20th century SPECIALIST: All kinds of exotic textiles & costume, eg Indian, Ottoman, Asian, Oriental, African, etc GENERAL: Tribal art, inc. jewellery, wood carvings, kilims, floor coverings, etc OTHER INFO: Textiles restoration & conservation facilities. Green tea with cardomon served to our visitors. 5 mins from Victoria coach, train & underground stations.

**Rosemary Hamilton,** 44 Moreton Street, SW1V 2PB TEL: 828 5018 FAX: 828 1325 PARKING: Easy OPEN: 9.30-5.30 MIN: £5 MAX: £950 PERIOD: 19th-20th century GENERAL: Cushions, porcelain, lamps, prints, small furniture OTHER INFO: Small street, village atmosphere, most people say they didn't know we existed.

**Ross Hamilton Ltd**, 95 Pimlico Road TEL: 730 3015 FAX: 730 3015 ASSNS: LAPADA PARKING: Easy OPEN: Mon-Fri 9.30-6, Sat 11-2 MIN: £200 MAX: £150,000 PERIOD: 17th-19th century SPECIALIST: Mostly English & Continental furniture GENERAL: Paintings, bronzes, porcelain, works of art & lacquer OTHER INFO: Several interior design & contemporary furniture designers' showrooms nearby

**Heraz**, 25 Motcomb Street, SW1X 8JU TEL: 245 9497 FAX: 235 7416 PARKING: Medium OPEN: Mon-Fri 10-6 MIN: £100+ PERIOD: 17th-19th century SPECIALIST: Textiles, cushions GENERAL: Antique Oriental, European, Aubusson & needlework carpets. Restoration & cleaning.

**Christopher Hodsoll Ltd**, 91 Pimlico Road, SW1W 8PH TEL: 730 3370 FAX: 730 1516 PARKING: Medium OPEN: Mon-Fri 9.30-6.30, Sat 10-4 MIN: £190 MAX: £250,000 PERIOD: 17th-20th century SPECIALIST: Own range of reproduction light fittings & furniture GENERAL: Furniture, works of art OTHER INFO: Business taken over from world famous Geoffrey Bennison who trained owner as interior decorator

**The Horseman's Bookshop**, 1 Lower Grosvenor Place, Buckingham Palace Road, SW1W 0EL TEL: 834 5606 FAX: 233 8001 ASSNS: ABA, Booksellers Assn of GB PARKING: Difficult OPEN: Mon-Fri 9-5.30, Sat 9-1 MIN: £2 MAX: £500 PERIOD: 17th-20th century SPECIALIST: Equine & equestrian world OTHER INFO: GB's only horse bookshop. Royal warrant holders to HM The Queen, HRH Prince Philip. Britsh Horse Society Award of Merit.

**Christopher Howe**, 36 Bourne Street, Belgravia, SW1W 8JA TEL: 730 7987 FAX: 730 0157 PARKING: Easy OPEN: Mon-Fri 9.30-6 MIN: £100 MAX: £100,000 PERIOD: 18th-19th century SPECIALIST: Enormous stock (1,500 sq ft separate warehouse) of English, Continental furniture & lighting

**Christopher Hull Gallery**, 17 Motcomb Street, SW1X 8LB TEL: 235 0500 PARKING: Easy OPEN: Mon-Fri 10-6, Sat 10-1 MIN: £500 MAX: £ 50,000 PERIOD: 20th century SPECIALIST: Modern British paintings & sculpture GENERAL: Artists of promise.

**Sally Hunter Fine Art**, 11 Halkin Arcade, Motcomb Street, SW1X 8JT TEL: 235 0934 PARKING: Medium OPEN: Mon-Fri 10-6 MIN: £200 MAX: £2000 SPECIALIST: 20th century British art OTHER INFO: Knightsbridge shopping: Harrods, Harvey Nichols, and galleries. Hotels: Carlton Tower, Berkeley, Hyde Park etc.

**David James**, 8 Halkin Arcade, Motcomb Street, SW1X 8JT TEL & FAX: 235 5552 OPEN: Mon-Fri 11-6 & by appt to 6pm MIN: £500 MAX: £30,000 PERIOD: 19th century SPECIALIST: Victorian watercolours & furniture GENERAL: Edwardian furniture & Victorian engravings OTHER INFO: 2 mins from Carlton Tower Hotel & 5 mins from Harrods.

**Lucy Johnson Antiques,** London SW1 TEL & FAX: 465 5743 PARKING: Own carpark OPEN: By appt PERIOD: 17th-18th century SPECIAL-

IST: William & Mary and Queen Anne furniture, delftware.

**Keshishian**, 73 Pimlico Road, SW1 TEL: 730 8810 FAX: 730 8803 PARKING: Easy ASSNS: BADA OPEN: Mon-Fri 9.30-6, Sat 10-5 PERIOD: 17th-20th century SPECIALIST: Rare antique carpets GENERAL: Period tapestries, Arts & Crafts to Art Deco, Aubusson carpets.

**Dominic King Antique Glass**, 85 Ebury Street, Belgravia, SW1W 4QY TEL: 824 8319/8310 ASSNS: Glass Assn, Glass Circle PARKING: Medium OPEN: Mon-Thurs 10-6 MIN: £20 MAX: £950 PERIOD: 18th-19th century SPECIALIST: 18th century drinking glasses & decanters GENERAL: Bristol & Stourbridge coloured glass, Victorian Hyacinth & Celery glasses. Wine related antiques, all glass pre 1900 especially dated & sealed wine bottles OTHER INFO: 5 mins from some of the world's greatest antiques. Queen's Gallery, Buckingham Palace, Victoria Station.

**Kojis Antique Jewellery Ltd**, Harrods, Fine Jewellery Room, Brompton Road, SW1X 7XL TEL: 730 1234 extn 4072 FAX: 589 0655 PARKING: Difficult OPEN: Mon, Tues, Sat 10-6, Wed-Fri 10-7 MIN: £30 MAX: £50,000+ PERIOD: 6000BC-1600AD SPECIALIST: Antiquities & ancient jewellery, collectable watches, antique, estate & designer jewellery.

**Leuchars & Jefferson**, 11 West Halkin Street, Belgrave Square, SW1X 8JL TEL: 235 2656 FAX: 823 1409 PARKING: Easy OPEN: 9.30-6 PERIOD: 18th century SPECIALIST: Fine furniture, Regency furniture & works of art OTHER INFO: Close to Mosiman's.

**M & D Lewis,** 84 Pimlico Road, SW1 TEL: 730 1015 FAX: 823 6090 PARKING: Medium OPEN: Mon-Fri 9.30-5.30, Sat 9.30-12 noon MIN: £1000 MAX: £86,000 PERIOD: 18th-20th century SPECIALIST: English & Continental furniture, etc GENERAL: Established suppliers to both British & American decorators. Extensive stock of Victorian bronzes & mirrors OTHER INFO: Adjacent to Wren's famous Chelsea Hospital & Physic Garden.

**Lion Witch & Lampshade**, 89 Ebury Street, SW1W 9QU TEL: 730 1774 PARKING: Easy OPEN: Mon-Tues, Thurs-Fri 10.30-5.30, Wed pm only MIN: £5 MAX: £1500 PERIOD: 18th-20th century SPECIALIST: Lighting GENERAL: Un-

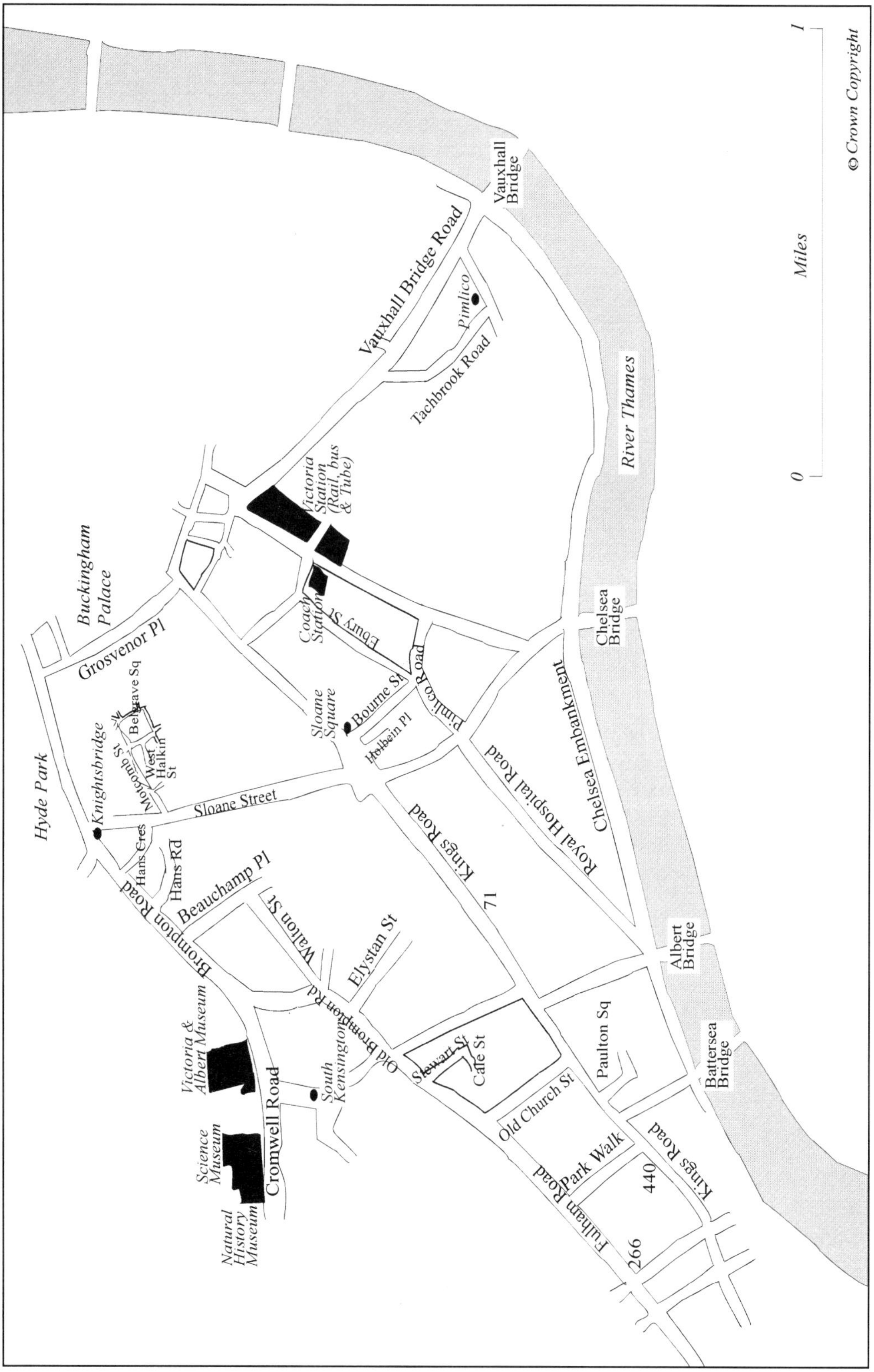
Hyde Park
Buckingham Palace
Grosvenor Pl
Knightsbridge
Belgrave Sq
Motcomb St
West Halkin St
Sloane Street
Hans Cres
Hans Rd
Beauchamp Pl
Brompton Road
Walton St
Elystan St
Victoria & Albert Museum
Cromwell Road
South Kensington
Science Museum
Natural History Museum
Old Brompton Rd
Stewart St
Cale St
Old Church St
Park Walk
Fulham Road
266
440
Kings Road
71
Paulton Sq
Sloane Square
Bourne St
Holbein Pl
Pimlico Road
Royal Hospital Road
Chelsea Embankment
Ebury St
Coach Station
Victoria Station (Rail, bus & Tube)
Vauxhall Bridge Road
Tachbrook Road
Pimlico
Vauxhall Bridge
Chelsea Bridge
Albert Bridge
Battersea Bridge
River Thames
0
Miles
1
© Crown Copyright

*Westminster Abbey. By courtesy of the London Tourist Board*

usual decorative objects OTHER INFO: Inexpensive hotels in Ebury Street.

**Mason,** 145 Ebury Street, SW1X 1HS TEL: 730 8331 FAX: 730 8334 PARKING: Easy OPEN: 10-1, 2-5 MIN: £100 MAX: £30,000 PERIOD: 18th century SPECIALIST: Chinese & Japanese works of art.

**McCed,** 8 Holbein Place, SW1W 8NL TEL & FAX: 730 4025 PARKING: Easy OPEN: Mon-Fri 10-6, Sat 11-5 MIN: £100 MAX: £20,000 PERIOD: 19th-20th century SPECIALIST: Lighting, leather chairs GENERAL: Architect inspired furniture & objects, mirrors, seating.

**McClenaghan,** 69 Pimlico Road, SW1W 8NE TEL & FAX: 730 4187 PARKING: Medium OPEN: Mon-Fri 10-6, Sat 11-5 or by appt MIN: £300 MAX: £15,000 PERIOD: 19th century SPECIALIST: English furniture, lighting & objects.

**Lennox Money (Antiques) Ltd**, 93 Pimlico Road, SW1W 8PH TEL: 730 3070 FAX: 259 9563 PARKING: Medium OPEN: Mon-Fri 9.45-6, Sat 11-1 MIN: £250 MAX: £15,000 PERIOD: 18th-19th century SPECIALIST: Indian Colonial furniture, hanging lanterns GENERAL: Furniture & objects, lighting OTHER INFO: Nearest tube Sloane Square.

**The Old Ephemera & Newspaper Shop,** 37 Kinnerton Street, SW1X 8ED TEL: 235 7788 ASSNS: PBFA, Ephemera Society PARKING: Medium OPEN: Mon, Wed, Fri 11-6, Tues, Thurs 11-4 MIN: 50p MAX: £1000 PERIOD: 17th-20th century SPECIALIST: Birthday edition newspaper service GENERAL: Ephemera & antiquarian newspapers 1642 to 20th century, magazines, photographs, books & prints.

**Ossowski,** 83 Pimlico Road, SW1W 8PH TEL: 730 3256 FAX: 823 4500 ASSNS: BADA PARKING: Medium OPEN: Mon-Fri 10-6 MIN: £2000 MAX: £20,000 PERIOD: 18th century SPECIALIST: English giltwood mirrors, consoles, 17th-18th century wood carvings.

**Parker Gallery**, 28 Pimlico, SW1W 8LJ TEL: 730 6768 FAX: 259 9180 ASSNS: BADA, SLAD PARKING: Medium OPEN: Mon-Fri 9.30-5.30, Sat by appt MIN: £38 MAX: £20,000 PERIOD: 18th-20th century SPECIALIST: Marine, military, topographical, sporting oils, watercolours & prints. Ship models, marine curios, maps, caricatures OTHER INFO: Army Museum.

**Geoffrey Rose Ltd**, 77 Pimlico Road, SW1W 8PH TEL: 730 3004 PARKING: Difficult OPEN: Mon-

Fri 10.15-1, 2.15-6, most Sats 10.15-1 MIN: £500 MAX: £5,000 PERIOD: 18th-early 19th century GENERAL: English furniture OTHER INFO: Opposite modern furniture of Queen's nephew, Richard Linley.

**Seago,** 22 Pimlico Road, SW1W 8LJ TEL: 730 7502 FAX: 730 9179 ASSNS: BADA PARKING: Own carpark OPEN: Mon-Fri 9.30-5.30 PERIOD: 17th-19th century SPECIALIST: Garden sculpture.

**Peta Smyth Antique Textiles**, 42 Moreton Street, SW1V 2PB TEL: 630 9898 FAX: 630 5398 ASSNS: LAPADA, GMC PARKING: Medium OPEN: 9.30-5.30 MIN: £5 MAX: £15,000 PERIOD: 17th-19th century SPECIALIST: European early textiles GENERAL: Needlework, tapestries, cushions, fabrics.

**Henry Sotheran**, 80 Pimlico Road, SW1W 8PL TEL: 730 8756 FAX: 823 6090 OPEN: Mon-Fri 10-6, Sat 10-4 MIN: £5 MAX: £5,000+ PERIOD: 17th-19th century SPECIALIST: John Gould, David Roberts, Piranesi GENERAL: Architecture, travel & topography, natural history, antique prints OTHER INFO: Pimlico Road known as decorators alley, near Sloane Square tube.

**Gerald Spyer & Son (Antiques) Ltd**, 18 Motcomb Street, Belgrave Square, SW1X 8LBTEL: 235 3348 FAX: 823 2234 PARKING: Easy OPEN: Mon-Fri 10-6 MIN: £250 few ornaments MAX: £135,000 PERIOD: 18th-early 19th century SPECIALIST: Decorative English furniture GENERAL: English furniture, giltwood mirrors, ornaments & some decorative pictures OTHER INFO: Next to Knightsbridge & Sloane Square areas.

**Trove**, 71 Pimlico Road, SW1W 8NE TEL: 730 6514 PARKING: Medium OPEN: Mon-Fri 10-6, Sat 10-1 PERIOD: 17th-19th century SPECIALIST: Blue John GENERAL: Antique furniture, bronzes, decorative objects.

## LONDON SW3 (0171)

**Norman Adams Ltd**, 8-10 Hans Road, SW3 1RX TEL: 589 5266 FAX: 589 1968 ASSNS: BADA, CINOA PARKING: Difficult OPEN: Mon-Fri 9-5.30 MIN: £400 MAX: £100,000+ PERIOD: 18th century SPECIALIST: Fine English furniture GENERAL: Mirrors, chandeliers, clocks, barometers OTHER INFO: Down west side of Harrods.

**Aesthetics,** V2 Antiquarius, 131-141 Kings Road, SW3 4PWTEL: 352 0395 FAX: 376 4057ASSNS: LAPADA PARKING: Medium OPEN: Mon-Sat 10-6 PERIOD: 19th-20th century SPECIALIST: Items in the aesthetic style GENERAL: Silver, ceramics, decorative art 1860-1960.



**Antiquarius**, 131-141 Kings Road, SW3 4PW TEL: 351 5353 & 352 6688 FAX: 351 5350 PARKING: Easy OPEN: Mon-Sat 10-6 MIN: £5 MAX: £50,000 GENERAL: 120+ dealers offering jewellery, clocks, watches, silver, glass, antiquarian books, boxes, ceramics, porcelain, prints, paintings, collectables.

**Apter-Fredericks Ltd,** 265-267 Fulham Road, SW3 6HYTEL: Mon-Fri 9.30-5.30 PERIOD: 18th century SPECIALIST: English furniture.

**HC Baxter & Sons**, 53 Stewarts Grove, SW3 6PU TEL: 352 9826ASSNS: BADA, LAPADA PARKING: Medium OPEN: Wed, Thurs 9-5 & by appt MIN: £1000 MAX: £50,000 SPECIALIST: English furniture 1730-1830 OTHER INFO: South Kensington near Victoria & Albert Museum etc.

**Joanna Booth**, 247 Kings Road, Chelsea, SW3 5EL TEL: 352 8998 FAX: 376 7350 ASSNS: BADA PARKING: Medium OPEN: Mon-Sat 10-6 MAX: £30,000 PERIOD: 17th-18th century SPECIALIST: Tapestry, textiles, Old Master drawings GENERAL: Furniture, sculpture, drawings, French books.

**Chelsea Clocks & Antiques**, Stand H3-4, Antiquarius, 135-143 Kings Road, SW3 4PWTEL: 352 8646 FAX: 376 4591 PARKING: Medium OPEN: 10-5.30 MIN: £10 MAX: £5000 PERIOD: 19th-20th century SPECIALIST: Clocks, barometers, boxes GENERAL: Scales, brass & small collectables.

**Chenil Galleries**, 181-183 Kings Road, Chelsea,

SW3 TEL: 351 5353 FAX: 351 5350 PARKING: Easy OPEN: Mon-Sat 10-6 MIN: £20 MAX: £100,000 PERIOD: 18th-20th century SPECIALIST: 30+ dealers offering Art Nouveau, Art Deco & fine art GENERAL: 18th-19th century paintings, clothing, textiles. Furniture, porcelain, silver, collectables.

**Michael Foster**, 118 Fulham Road, Chelsea, SW3 6HU TEL: 373 3636 FAX: 373 4042 ASSNS: BADA PARKING: Medium OPEN: 9.30-6 PERIOD: 18th-early 19th century SPECIALIST: Dining tables, sofa tables GENERAL: English furniture & works of art.

**Green & Stone**, 259 Kings Road, SW3 5EL TEL: 352 6521 FAX: 351 1098 ASSNS: FATG PARKING: Medium OPEN: 9-5.30 MIN: £1,000 MAX: £20,000 PERIOD: 19th century SPECIALIST: Antique artist & writing implements GENERAL: Antique glass, lustre china, decorative French brocante, English watercolours.

**E Hollander Ltd**, 84 Fulham Road, Chelsea, SW3 6HR TEL: 589 7239 FAX: 584 8479 ASSNS: BADA BHI MIN: £250 MAX: £75,000 PERIOD: 17th-19th century SPECIALIST: Clocks & Barometers GENERAL: Scientific instruments, sundials with the accent on English 18th century OTHER INFO: Full restoration service.

**Stephanie Hoppen Ltd**, 17 Walton Street TEL: 589 3678 FAX: 584 3731 PARKING: Medim OPEN: Mon-Fri 10-6, Sat 11-4 MIN: £200 MAX: £5000 PERIOD: 18th-20th century SPECIALIST: Exciting living artists, painters from times past GENERAL: Oils & watercolours, some prints.

**Malcolm Innes Gallery,** 172 Walton Street, SW3 2JL TEL: 584 0575 FAX: 589 1066 ASSNS: SLAD, Edinburgh Art Galleries Assn PARKING: Difficult OPEN: 9.30-6 MIN: £100 MAX: £15,000 PERIOD: 19th-20th century SPECIALIST: Scottish, sporting, military oils, watercolours & prints.

**Anthony James & Son Ltd**, 88 Fulham Road, Chelsea, SW3 6HR TEL: 584 1120 FAX: 823 7618 ASSNS: BADA CINOA PARKING: Easy OPEN: Mon-Fri 9.30-5.45 & by appt MIN: £300 MAX: £100,000 PERIOD: 18th-19th century SPECIALIST: Furniture.

**John Keil Ltd,** 154 Brompton Road, SW3 1HX TEL: 589 6454 FAX: 823 8235 PARKING: Medium OPEN: Mon-Fri 9-6 MIN: £1000 MAX: £400,000 PERIOD: 17th-19th century SPECIALIST: English furniture & objets d'art.

**Stanley Leslie**, 15 Beauchamp Place, SW3 1NQ TEL: 589 2333 FAX: 589 3530 PARKING: Easy OPEN: 9-6 PERIOD: 18th-20th century GENERAL: Antique & modern silver & silverplate, cutlery, crystal etc.

**Peter Lipitch Ltd,** 120-124 Fulham Road, SW3 6HU TEL: 071-373 3328 FAX: 373 8888 ASSNS: BADA PARKING: Easy OPEN: 9.30-5.30 PERIOD: 18th century SPECIALIST: Fine English furniture.

**The Map House**, 54 Beauchamp Place, SW3 1NY TEL: 589 4325 FAX: 589 1041 ASSNS: ABA PARKING: Difficult OPEN: Mon-Fri 9.45-5.45, Sat 10.30-5 MIN: £5 MAX: £75,000 PERIOD: 16th-19th century SPECIALIST: Antique maps, prints, atlases OTHER INFO: 5 mins from Harrods.

**McKenna & Co,** 28 Beauchamp Place, Knightsbridge, SW3 1NJ ASSNS: LAPADA, NAG PARKING: Difficult OPEN: Mon-Sat 10-5.45 MIN: £20 MAX: £20,000 PERIOD: 19th-20th century SPECIALIST: Jewellery GENERAL: Gifts, etc OTHER INFO: 2 blocks from Harrods, same street as San Lorenzo, the restaurant patronised by (famously) Princess Diana.

**Merola,** 178 Walton Street, SW3 2JL TEL: 589 0365 PARKING: Medium OPEN: 10-6 MIN: £30 MAX: £2000 PERIOD: 20th century SPECIALIST: Vintage designer costume jewellery 1920s to present day OTHER INFO: Walton Street is renown as an area for its good restaurants, small specialist antiques & interior decorating shops.

**Number 12**, Cale Street, Chelsea Green, SW3 3QU TEL: 581 5022 FAX: 581 3968 ASSNS: LAPADA PARKING: Easy OPEN: 10-5.30 MIN: £10 MAX: £20,000 PERIOD: 17th-18th century SPECIALIST: French provincial furniture.

**Jacqueline Oosthuizen**, 23 Cale Street, SW3 3QR TEL: 352 6071 FAX: 376 3852 ASSNS: LAPADA PARKING: Own carpark OPEN: Mon-Fri 10-6 & by appt MIN: £28 MAX: £9000 PERIOD: 18th-19th century SPECIALIST: Staffordshire figures 1760-1890, cottages, animals, toby jugs. Antique & estate jewellery OTHER INFO: Many small hotels, museums etc. Kings Road.

**Prides of London**, 15 Paulton House, Paulton Square, SW3 5DU TEL: 586 1227 PARKING: Easy OPEN: By appt MIN: £1000 MAX: £25,000+ PERIOD: 18th-19th century SPECIALIST: Regency brass inlaid furniture GENERAL: English furniture, objets d'art.

**The Purple Shop**, Antiquarius, 15 Flood Street, Chelsea, SW3 5ST TEL: 352 1127 FAX: 351 5350 PARKING: Medium OPEN: 10.30-5.30 MIN: £20 MAX: £5000 PERIOD: 19th-20th century SPECIALIST: Art Nouveau, Art Deco, gentlemen's jewellery GENERAL: Antique & period jewellery OTHER INFO: Café on site, good antiques area.

**Rogers de Rin**, 76 Royal Hospital Road, Chelsea, SW3 4HN TEL: 352 9007 FAX: 351 9407 ASSNS: LAPADA PARKING: Easy OPEN: Mon-Fri 10-5.30, Sat 10-1, Sun 11-5 MIN: £100 MAX: £5000+ PERIOD: 18th-19th century SPECIALIST: Wemyss ware, objets de vitrine, curiosities, Regency taste, tortoiseshell, tea caddies, Russian boxes, Staffordshire animals OTHER INFO: Situated between Tante Claire & Foxtrot Oscar restaurants.

**Julian Simon Fine Art Ltd**, 70 Pimlico Road, SW1W 8LS TEL: 730 8673 FAX: 823 6116 ASSNS: BADA, LAPADA PARKING: Medium OPEN: Mon-Fri 10-6, Sat 10-4 MIN: £1000 MAX: £150,000 PERIOD: 18th-early 20th century SPECIALIST: English & Continental paintings.

**Robert Stephenson Oriental Carpets**, 1 Elystan Street, Chelsea Green, SW3 3NT TEL: 225 2343 PARKING: Medium OPEN: Mon-Fri 9.30-5.30, Sat 10-1 MIN: £100 MAX: £25,000 PERIOD: 19th-20th century SPECIALIST: Room sized carpets, East European flatweaves GENERAL: Carpets, rugs & runners from Persia, India, Turkey. Kilims. Cleaning & repairs. OTHER INFO: Relaxing village atmosphere, ideal shopping area.

**OF Wilson Ltd**, Queens Elm Parade, Old Church Street, Chelsea, SW3 6EJ TEL: 352 9554 FAX: 351 0765 PARKING: Easy OPEN: Mon-Fri 9.30-5.50, Sat 10.30-1 MIN: £250 MAX: £50,000 PERIOD: 18th-19th century SPECIALIST: Marble & stone mantels GENERAL: Continental furniture, painted & gilt furniture & mirrors, chandeliers.

**Clifford Wright Antiques Ltd**, 104-106 Fulham Road, SW3 6HS TEL: 589 0986 FAX: 589 3565 ASSNS: BADA, Master Carvers Assn PARKING: Easy OPEN: 9-5.30 MIN: £1,000 MAX: £185,000 SPECIALIST: 18th century carved giltwood mirrors & consoles GENERAL: 18th & 19th century furniture & works of art.

# Covent Garden to Bloomsbury

**Covent Garden** was owned by the Abbey of St Peter and consisted mainly of fields up until the Dissolution of the Monasteries. Then it was granted to the Earl of Bedford, John Russell, who built a house on the site of what was later **Southampton Street**. In the early 17th century Inigo Jones was commissioned to design fine houses to the north of Bedford House. These were constructed around a piazza and showed a strong Italian influence. Their foreign style militated against them and the area never became truly fashionable. In 1670 the Earl of Bedford was granted a licence to hold a flower and vegetable market there. This market continued for 300 years and it was only in 1974 that it moved to a new purpose-built site at Nine Elms on the south side of the river.

One of the most notorious slums in London could be found in the area. **Seven Dials**, described by Dickens, was sited where **Mercer, Monmouth** and **Earlham Streets** now meet. Development was completed in the early 18th century and intended to be a fashionable address, however it became a place for the poorest of the poor as well as cut-throats and thieves. Everything was largely cleared out when **Shaftesbury Avenue** and **Charing Cross Road** were built.

**The Strand**, in earlier centuries, ran by the river but by the Middle Ages land had been reclaimed and bishops' palaces ran alongside the Thames. After the Dissolution of the Monasteries these church estates went to the Crown and were given to court favourites who built their own magnificent mansions there. Today the street pattern between the Strand and the river owes much to these 16th century estates because roads ran up to or around estates, ending abruptly or turning corners in an apparently inexplicable manner.

Nearby **St Martin's Lane** was constructed in the early 17th century and immediately became a 'good' address. Mozart, as a child, played in **Cecil Court**, a small lane now connecting St Martin's Lane to **Charing Cross Road,** although the latter was only built in the late 19th century.

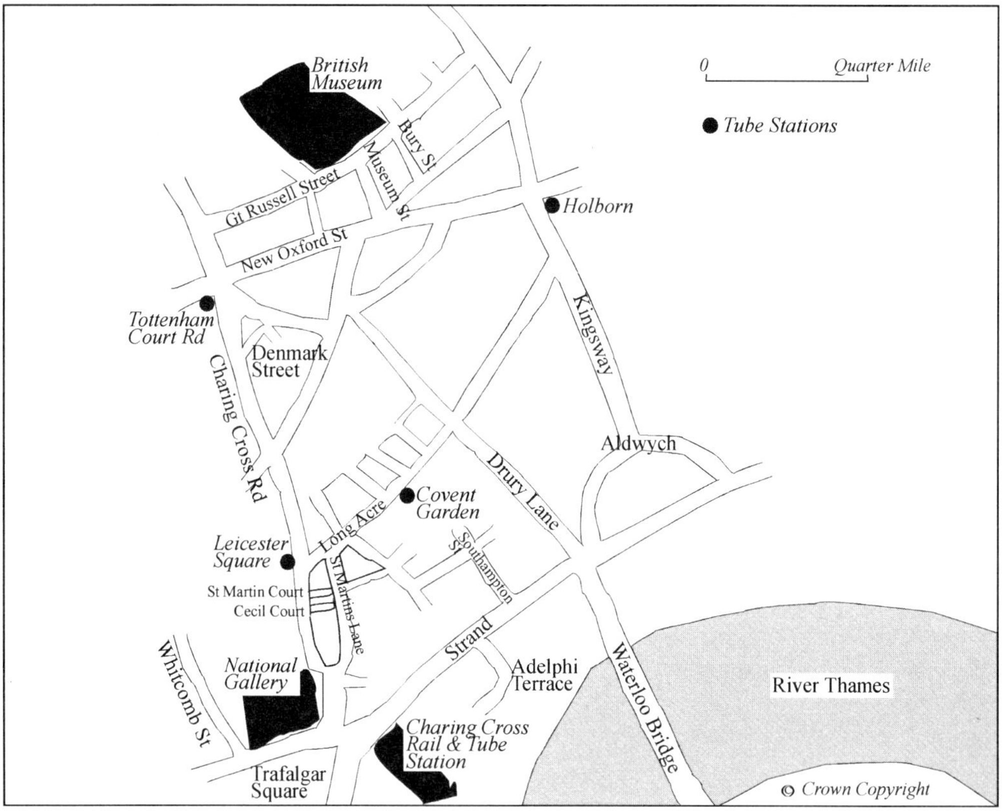

**New Oxford Street** runs along the northern side of Covent Garden, at the top of Charing Cross Road. It was built in 1847 as an extension to **Oxford Street** which was originally a Roman road running from Hampshire to Suffolk. North of New Oxford Street is the area known as **Bloomsbury.** This was developed by the Dukes of Bedford, the Russell family, who played such a large part in the development of Covent Garden. In the early 20th century the area became associated with the Bloomsbury Group, people like E.M. Forster, Virginia and Leonard Woolf, Lytton Strachey and John Maynard Keynes.

Bloomsbury is also the home of the British Museum, founded in 1753. It started when Sir Hans Sloane left his collection of books and antiquities to the nation on the condition that £20,000 was paid into his estate. Since then the museum has expanded and now offers a superb collection of antiquities including the Elgin Marbles, the Rosetta Stone, the Sutton Hoo treasure and two of the four existing copies of Magna Carta.

## ANTIQUE DEALERS

### LONDON WC1 (0171)

**Abbott & Holder**, 30 Museum Street, WC1A 1LH TEL: 637 3981 PARKING: Medium OPEN: Mon-Sat 9.30-6 MIN: £10 MAX: £10,000 PERIOD: 18th-20th century SPECIALIST: British watercolours & drawings GENERAL: Pictures OTHER INFO: The Coffee Gallery.

**Classic Collection**, 2 Pied Bull Yard, Bury Place, WC1A 2JR TEL: 831 6000 FAX: 831 5424 PARKING: Medium OPEN: 9-5.30 PERIOD: 19th-20th century GENERAL: Collectable cameras & optical toys.

**George & Peter Cohn**, Unit 21, 21 Wren Street, WC1X 0HF TEL: 278 3749 PARKING: Own carpark OPEN: Mon-Fri 9.30-4 PERIOD: 19th century SPECIALIST: Chandeliers & antique lights. Restoration & cleaning.

**JA L Franks**, 7 New Oxford Street, WC1A 1BA TEL: 405 0274 FAX: 430 1259 PARKING: Difficult OPEN: Mon-Fri 10.30-5.30 MIN: £2 MAX: £1,000 PERIOD: 17th-20th century SPECIALIST: Postcards, cigarette cards, antique maps.

**Jessop Classic**, 67 Great Russell Street, WC1 TEL: 831 3640 FAX: 831 3956 PARKING: Difficult OPEN: Mon-Sat 9-5.30 MIN: £10 MAX: £10,000+ PERIOD: 19th-20th century SPECIALIST: Antique & classic cameras, optical toys, magic lanterns, second-hand camera books & lenses OTHER INFO: British Museum closeby.

**The Marchant Bookshop,** 39 Burton Street, WC1H 9AL TEL: 387 7989 PARKING: Easy OPEN: Mon-Fri 11-6.30, Sat 11-3 MIN: £1 MAX: £500 PERIOD: 17th-20th century SPECIALIST: English & American literature GENERAL: Books on most subjects inluding large Australian section.

**The Print Room**, 37 Museum Street, WC1A 1LP TEL: 430 0159 FAX: 831 2874 PARKING: Easy-underground carpark OPEN: Mon-Fri 10-6, Sat 10-4 MIN: £2 MAX: £10,000 PERIOD: 17th-19th century SPECIALIST: Caricatures, botanicals, Hogarth, topography GENERAL: Original antique prints & maps OTHER INFO: Opposite British Museum, Museum Tavern pub.

**SJ Shrubsole Ltd**, 43 Museum Street, WC1A 1LY TEL: 405 2712 PARKING: Medium OPEN: Mon-Fri 9-5.30 MIN: £50 MAX: £50,000 PERIOD: 17th-18th century SPECIALIST: Fine early silver GENERAL: Georgian silver & old Sheffield plate.

### LONDON WC2 (0171)

**Apple Market**, 41 The Market, Covent Garden, WC2E 8RF TEL: 836 9136 FAX: via 240 5770 ASSNS: Antiques & Collectables Committee PARKING: Difficult OPEN: Mon & alternate Sun 9-7 GENERAL: 40 dealers with variety of stock.

**A H Baldwin & Sons Ltd**, 11 Adelphi Terrace, WC2N 6BJ TEL: 930 6879 FAX: 930 9450 PARKING: ASSNS: BADA, BNTA, Intl Assn of Professional Numismatists OPEN: Mon-Fri 9-5 MIN: £1 MAX: £50,000 PERIOD: 17-20th century SPECIALIST: Classical, medieval & later coins, medals & accessories. No ultra-modern OTHER INFO: Fifth generation family business.

**Bell Book & Radmall,** 4 Cecil Court, WC2N 4HE TEL: 240 2161 FAX: 379 1062 ASSN: ABA PARKING: Difficult OPEN: Mon-Fri 10-5.30, Sat 11-4 MIN: £10 MAX: £10,000 PERIOD: 19th-20th century SPECIALIST: First editions of 19th & 20th century English & American literature.

**Ann Creed Books Ltd**, 22 Cecil Court, WC2N 4HE TEL: 836 7757 FAX: 240 1439 PARKING:

Difficult OPEN: Mon-Sat 10.30-18.30 MIN: £5 MAX: £3,000+ PERIOD: 19th-20th century SPECIALIST: Only out-of-print & rare books on fine & applied art including 20th century design and avante-garde OTHER INFO: Cecil Court is a quaint byway of old fashioned bookshops unique to London.

**Pearl Cross Ltd**, 35 St Martin's Court, St Martin's Lane, WC2N 4AL TEL: 836 2814 FAX: 240 2733 PARKING: Medium OPEN: 9.30-4.45 MIN: £50 MAX: £5000 PERIOD: 19th-20th century SPECIALIST: Jewellery, silver wrist & pocket watches GENERAL: Good clocks & objets d'art.

**Stanley Gibbons Ltd**, 399 Strand, WC2R 0LX TEL: 836 8444 FAX: 836 7342 ASSNS: Philatelic Traders Society PARKING: Difficult OPEN: Mon-Fri 8.30-6, Sat 10-4 MIN: 30p MAX: £50,000+ PERIOD: 19th-20th century SPECIALIST: Rare stamps, postal history from UK & British Commonwealth GENERAL: 3 million+ stamps from Abu Dhabi to Zimbabwe, widest range of albums, catalogues, accessories, books.

**Grosvenor Prints**, 28 Shelton Street, Covent Garden, WC2H 9HP TEL: 836 1979 FAX: 379 6695 PARKING: Medium OPEN: Mon-Fri 10-6, Sat 11-4 MIN: £10 MAX: £2000 PERIOD: 18th-19th century SPECIALIST: Portraits, UK & foreign topography, sporting, dogs, decorative, most trades, natural history etc OTHER INFO: Covent Garden Market, best Italian restaurant in London, Neal St.

**S & H Jewell Ltd,** 26 Parker Street, WC2B 5PH TEL: 405 8520 ASSNS: Guild of Master Craftsmen PARKING: Medium OPEN: 9-5.30 MIN: £50 MAX: £5000 PERIOD: 19th-20th century GENERAL: Good quality traditional English furniture OTHER INFO: Once one amongst several, we are now the last surviving furniture dealer in this area, and have been here since 1848.

**The London Silver Vaults,** Chancery Lane, WC2A 1QS TEL: 242 3844 OPEN: Mon-Fri 9-5.30, Sat 9-12.30 MIN: £10 SPECIALIST: Variety of shops selling silver & jewellery in many styles & periods OTHER INFO: Members of Europe's Royal Families and the world's glitterati pass through the Vaults' doors. Its traffic-less undergound 'shopping streets' provide relaxing conditions for browsing & choosing at leisure with expert advice on hand.

**Avril Noble,** 2 Southampton Street, WC2E 7HA TEL: 240 1970 OPEN: Mon-Sat 10-6 MIN: £5 MAX: £1000 PERIOD: 16th-19th century SPECIALIST: Antique maps & views GENERAL: Worldwide maps, Englsh countries, London, Ireland, Scotland, Wales. Botanical prints.

**Henry Pordes Books Ltd**, 58-60 Charing Cross Road, WC2H 0BB TEL: 836 9031 FAX: 886 2201 PARKING: Difficult OPEN: Mon-Sat 10-7 MIN: £1 MAX: £1200+ PERIOD: 17th-20th century SPECIALIST: Judaica, art, literature GENERAL: Daily changing stock on every conceivable subject, antiquarian & new remainders OTHER INFO: Chinatown nearby for best Chinese food.

**Spatz,** 48 Monmouth Street, WC2 TEL: 379 0703 PARKING: Medium OPEN: 11.30-6.30 MIN: £6 MAX: £150 PERIOD: 19th-20th century SPECIALIST: 1940s & 50s clothing, Victorian bed & table linen.

**Stage Door Prints**, 1 Cecil Court, St Martin's Lane, WC2N 4EZ TEL: 240 1683 PARKING: Difficult OPEN: Mon-Fri 11-6, Sat 11.30-6 MIN: £1 MAX: £1,250 PERIOD: 18th-20th century SPECIALIST: Opera, ballet, music & theatre prints & signed photos. Victorian Valentine cards, greetings cards & scraps GENERAL: Prints & maps on most subjects, small antiques, performing arts book room.

**Storey's Ltd,** 3 Cecil Court, WC2 4EZ TEL & FAX: 836 3777 ASSNS: Fine Art Guild PARKING: Medium OPEN: Mon-Sat 10-6 MIN: £2.50 MAX: £1500 PERIOD: 18th-19th century SPECIALIST: Antiquarian prints OTHER INFO: Cecil Court contains 22 antiquarian book & print dealers.

**Tooley Adams & Co Ltd,** 13 Cecil Court, WC2N 4EZ TEL: 240 4406 FAX: 240 8058 ASSNS: ABA PARKING: Difficult OPEN: 9-5 MIN: £1 MAX: £10,000 PERIOD: 1477-1890 SPECIALIST: Maps, atlases, reference books OTHER INFO: Mozart once lived in Cecil Court.

**Trafalgar Square Collectors Centre**, 7 Whitcomb Street, Trafalgar Square, WC2H 7HA TEL: 930 1979 FAX: 930 1152 ASSNS: OMRS PARKING: Easy OPEN: 10.30-5 MIN: £1 MAX: £5000 PERIOD: 19th-20th century SPECIALIST: Military medals & coins GENERAL: Militaria, banknotes, badges, bonds, miniature medals.

**Zeno, The Greek Bookshop**, 6 Denmark Street, WC2H 8LP TEL & FAX: 836 2522 ASSNS: ABA PARKING: Difficult OPEN: Mon-Fri 9.30-6, Sat 9.30-5 MIN: £1 MAX: £2000+ PERIOD: 18th-20th century SPECIALIST: Antiquarian & modern books GENERAL: Cyprus, Greece, Middle East, Balkans, Byzantium history & travel etc.

# Fulham

The Manor of **Fulham** was owned by the Bishops of London from the 8th century. The area supported a number of small settlements like Fulham Town and Parson's Green which were not united until the great development of London in the 19th century. The Bishop's official residence, until 1973, was **Fulham Palace**. The existing building dates from the 15th century and stands on the site of a Roman settlement and nowadays houses a museum.

**Fulham Road**, which runs from the **Brompton Road** to **Fulham Palace Road**, dates from the 15th century and was a major coaching route to Portsmouth and the south west.

## ANTIQUE DEALERS

### LONDON SW3 (0171)

**Tony Bunzl**, 344 Kings Road TEL: 352 3697 PARKING: Easy OPEN: Mon-Fri 10-5.30 MIN: £100 MAX: £20,000 SPECIALIST: European vernacular furniture 1600-1900.

**OLD CHURCH GALLERIES**
**320 KINGS ROAD, CHELSEA, SW3 5UH TEL: 351 4649 FAX: 351 4449 ASSNS: FATG PARKING: EASY OPEN: MON-SAT 10-6 MIN: £5 MAX: £5000 PERIOD: 17TH-19TH CENTURY SPECIALIST: ANTIQUE MAPS & ENGRAVINGS, LONDON GENERAL: BOTANICAL, NATURAL HISTORY, TOPOGRAPHY, ARCHITECTURAL, SPORTING PRINTS, FRAMING SERVICE OTHER INFO: SITUATED IN THE HEART OF CHELSEA AMONGST BEAUTIFUL DESIGNER SHOPS. MANY RESTAURANTS & ANTIQUE MARKETS.**

### LONDON SW6 (0171)

**Alasdair Brown Antiques**, 560 Kings Road, SW6 2DZ TEL: 736 8077 FAX: 736 3625 PARKING: Medium OPEN: Mon-Fri 10-6, Sat 10-5 MIN: £250 MAX: £20,000 PERIOD: 18th-19th century SPECIALIST: Furniture, Regency Arts & Crafts GENERAL: Lighting, decorative items.

**Barclay-Samson Ltd**, 39 Inglethorpe Street, SW6 6NS TEL: 381 4341 FAX: 610 0434 PARKING: Easy OPEN: By appt MIN: £100 MAX: £10,000 SPECIALIST: 19th & 20th century lithographic posters.

**Robert Barley Antiques**, 48 Fulham High Street, SW6 3LQ TEL: 736 4429 PARKING: Easy OPEN: Mon-Fri 9.30-5.30, Sat 10-1 MIN: £20 MAX: £20,000 SPECIALIST: Unusual & beautiful objects & pictures 500 BC-1940.

**Benchmark**, 287 Lillie Road, Fulham TEL: 610 2050 FAX: 610 2050 PARKING: Easy OPEN: 10-5 & by appt MIN: £100 MAX: £20,000 PERIOD: 19th-20th century SPECIALIST: Architect designed furniture GENERAL: Gothic revival, aesthetic, Art & Crafts, signed & designed furniture OTHER INFO: In established antiques area.

**Big Ben Clocks**, 5 Broxholme House, New Kings Road, SW6 4AA TEL: 731 0072 FAX: 384 1957 PARKING: Medium OPEN: By appt MIN: £150 MAX: £8000 PERIOD: 18th-19th century SPECIALIST: Longcase clocks from country 30 hours to fine London walnut & mahogany clocks OTHER INFO: Long established business in prime antiques area.

**Bookham Galleries,** 164 Wandsworth Bridge Road, SW6 TEL: 736 5125 PARKING: Medium OPEN: 10-5.30 MIN: £50 MAX: £5000 OPEN: 17th-19th century SPECIALIST: Furniture.

**John Clay Antiques,** 263 New Kings Road, SW6 4RB TEL: 731 5677 PARKING: Medium OPEN: 9-6 MIN: £10 MAX: £5000 PERIOD: 18th-19th century SPECIALIST: Furniture GENERAL: Decorative smalls, boxes, mirrors, clocks, objects.

**Fergus Cochrane & Leigh Warren,** 570 Kings Road, SW6 2DY TEL: 736 9166 FAX: 297 2508 PARKING: Easy OPEN: 10-5 MIN: £100 MAX: £5000 PERIOD: 18th-20th century SPECIALIST: Lighting, mirrors & decorative furniture.

**Decorative Living,** 55 New Kings Road, London SW6 4SX TEL: 736 5623 PARKING: Easy OPEN: 10.30-5.30 MIN: £10 MAX: £2500 PERIOD: 18th-20th century SPECIALIST: Colonial, French, country furniture OTHER INFO: We do not take credit cards & there is a good fruit & vegetable shop around the corner.

**Judy Greenwood Antiques,** 657 Fulham Road, SW6 5PY TEL: 736 6037 FAX: 736 1941 PARK-

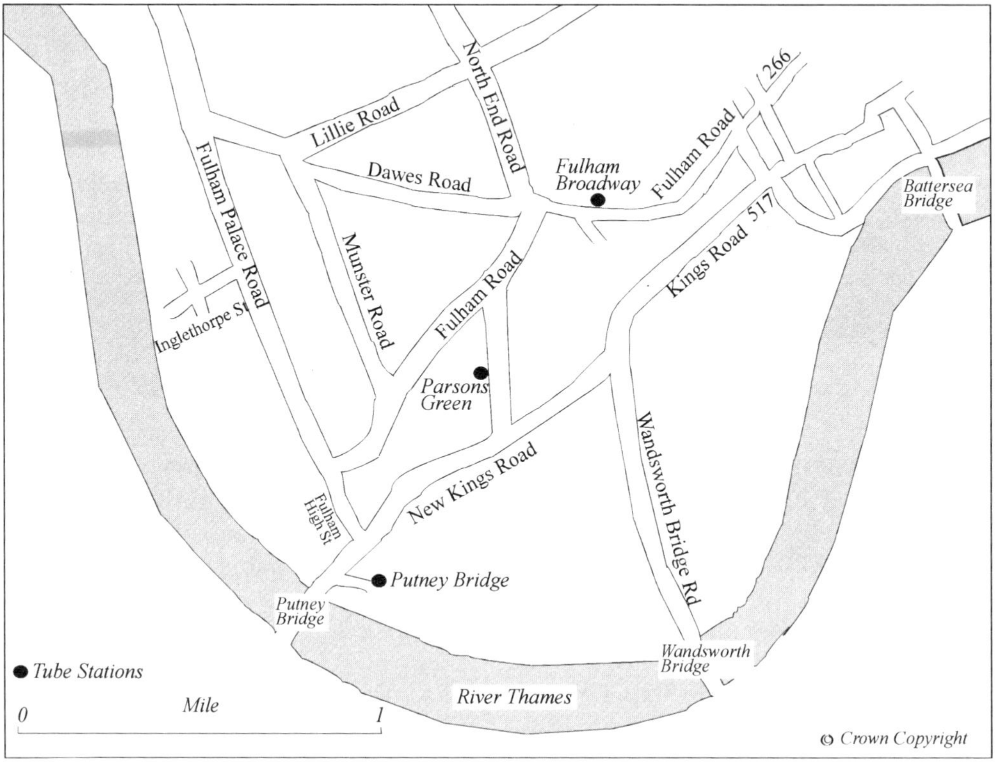


ING: Medium OPEN: Mon-Sat 10-5.30 MIN: £5 MAX: £2500 PERIOD: 19th-20th century SPECIALIST: Quilts, decorative furniture.

**Gregory, Bottley & Lloyd,** 13 Seagrave Road, SW6 1RP TEL: 381 5522 FAX: 381 5512 PARKING: Medium OPEN: Mon-Fri 9.30-5, Sat 9.30-2 MIN: £1 MAX: £5000 GENERAL: Fossils, crystals, minerals, antique mineralogical instruments & books.

**Nicholas Harris Gallery**, 564 Kings Road, SW6 2DY TEL: 371 9711 FAX: 371 9537 ASSNS: BADA, LAPADA PARKING: Medium OPEN: Mon-Fri 11-6, Sat by appt only MIN: £250+ PERIOD: 19th-20th century SPECIALIST: Aesthetic, arts & crafts, Art Deco silver GENERAL: English, American & Oriental silver. Ceramics & decorative art 1860-1960.

**Simon Horn Furniture Ltd**, 117-121 Wands-worth Bridge Road TEL: 736 3522 FAX: 736 3522 ASSNS: IDDA (corporate member) PARKING: Easy OPEN: 9.30-5.30 MIN: £120 MAX: £6000 PERIOD: 18th-20th century SPECIALIST: French classical & antique wooden beds of any size. English traditional or French provincial.

**Fairfax Fireplaces & Antiques**, 568 Kings Road, SW6 2DY TEL: (0249) 652030 FAX: Same PARKING: Easy OPEN: 10-5 MIN: £20 MAX: £2000 PERIOD: 18th-20th century SPECIALIST: Fireplaces & architectural GENERAL: Antique fixtures for restoring houses and advice on listed buildings.

**P L James**, 681 Fulham road, SW6 5PZ TEL: 736 0183 PARKING: Medium OPEN: 8-5 SPECIALIST: 18th & 19th century furniture of lacquer & painted furniture, mirrors etc Restoration of same.

**Eric King,** 11 Crondace Road, SW6 4BB TEL & FAX: 731 2554 PARKING: Easy OPEN: By appt MIN: £50 MAX: £10,000 PERIOD: 18th-20th century GENERAL: 18th & 19th century furniture & objects of quality OTHER INFO: Excellent transport facilities & restaurants. I have been exhibiting in June & Nov at Olympia for many years.

**King's Court Galleries**, 951-953 Fulham Road, SW6 TEL: 610 6939 PARKING: Medium OPEN: 9.30-5.30 MIN: £8 MAX: £2500 PERIOD: 17th-19th century SPECIALIST: Antique prints & maps GENERAL: Decorative & sporting prints.

**Lewin Antiques,** 638 Fulham Road, SW6 5RT & 82D Portobello Road, W11 2QD TEL: 731 1616 & 229 2023 FAX: (01734) 664826 PARKING: Easy OPEN: 10.30-5.30 PERIOD: 19th-20th century

SPECIALIST: Dutch colonial furniture, textiles & watercolours.

**Lunn Antiques Ltd**, 86 New Kings Road, Parsons green, SW6 4LU TEL: 736 4638 FAX: 371 7113 PARKING: Medium OPEN: Mon-Sat 10-6 PERIOD: 17th-20th century SPECIALIST: London's largest stock of antique lace GENERAL: Linen sheets & pillowcases, table linen, nightdresses.

**Magpies**, 152 Wandsworth Bridge Road. Fulham, SW6 2UH TEL: 736 3738 PARKING: Easy OPEN: Mon-Sat 10-5.30 MIN: £1 MAX: £200 PERIOD: 19th-20th century GENERAL: Antiques & bric-a-brac, kitchenalia, cutlery, etc.

**Michael Marriot Ltd**, 588 Fulham Road, SW6 5NT TEL: 736 3110 PARKING: Easy OPEN: Mon-Fri 10-5.30, Sat 10-1 & by appt MIN: £50 MAX: £20,000 PERIOD: 18th-19th century SPECIALIST: English furniture & antiquarian decorative prints.

**David Martin-Taylor Antiques**, 558 King's Road, SW6 2DZ TEL: 731 4135 FAX: 371 0029 ASSNS: LAPADA PARKING: Easy (at rear) OPEN: Mon-Fri 9.30-5.30 & by appt MIN: £20 MAX: £7,000 PERIOD: 18th-19th century GENERAL: Mainly 19th century English & Continental furniture, screens, mirrors, decorative objects & wicker furniture.

**Sylvia Napier**, 554 Kings Road, SW6 2DZ TEL & FAX: 371 5881 PARKING: Own carpark OPEN: 10-6 MIN: £50 MAX: £18,000 PERIOD: 17th-20th century SPECIALIST: Chandeliers GENERAL: Decorative.

**Old Pine & Painted Furniture**, 594 Kings Road, SW6 2DX TEL: 736 5999 PARKING: Medium OPEN: Mon-Sat 10-5.30 MIN: £75 MAX: £3500 PERIOD: 19th century SPECIALIST: Pine & painted furniture.

**Paul Orssich**, 117 Munster Road, SW6 6DH TEL: 736 3869 FAX: 371 9886 ASSNS: PBFA PARKING: Easy OPEN: Mon-Fri 9.30-6 & by appt MIN: £10 MAX: £5000 PERIOD: 17th-20th century SPECIALIST: Old & rare books, Spain & Hispanic studies GENERAL: Old maps worldwide, Art Deco illustrations 1915-1935.

**M Pauw**, 606 Kings Road, SW6 2DX TEL: 731 4072 FAX: 731 7356 PARKING: Easy OPEN: Mon-Sat 9-6 MIN: £200 MAX: £10,000 PERIOD: 18th-19th century SPECIALIST: Good Continental & English furniture, objects & light fixtures.

**Peter Place Antiques,** 636 Kings Road, SW6 2DU

TEL: 736 9945 FAX: 736 9164 PARKING: Easy OPEN: Mon-Sat 9-5.30 MIN: £20 MAX: £2000 PERIOD: 17th-20th century SPECIALIST: Architectural & decorative items.

**Rogers & Co,** 604 Fulham Road, SW6 5RP TEL: 731 8504 FAX: 610 6040 ASSNS: LAPADA PARKING: Easy OPEN: 10-6 MIN: £5 MAX: £10,000 PERIOD: 17th-20th century SPECIALIST: Fine furniture GENERAL: Antiques, decorative items, fabrics, wallpapers, interior design service, curtains, upholstery OTHER INFO: Close to Parsons Green tube station, many interesting shops in the area.

**John Spink**, 14 Darlan Road, Fulham, SW6 5BT TEL: 731 8292 FAX: 731 6955 PARKING: Easy OPEN: By appt please MIN: £500 MAX: £50,000 SPECIALIST: Fine quality British watercolours 1720-1920 all in top condition.

**Trowbridge Gallery**, 555 Kings Road, SW6 2EB TEL: 371 8733 FAX: 371 8138 ASSNS: LAPADA PARKING: Easy OPEN: 9.30-5.30 MIN: £30 MAX: £3000 PERIOD: 17th-18th century SPECIALIST: Decorative antique prints & handmade frames GENERAL: Botanical, natural history, architecture & our wonderful reproduction range.

**Tulissio de Beaumont**, 283 Lillie Road, SW6 TEL: 385 0156 ASSNS: LAPADA PARKING: Easy OPEN: Mon-Sat 10-6 MIN: £20 MAX: £5000 PERIOD: 17th-20th century SPECIALIST: Period lighting GENERAL: Furniture, scupture, pictures & decorative antiques.

## LONDON SW10 (0171)

**Chalow UK Ltd**, The Plaza, 535 Kings Road TEL: 351 0008 FAX: 351 0003 ASSNS: LAPADA PARKING: Easy OPEN: Mon-Sat 9-5 MIN: £100 MAX: £7500 PERIOD: 18th-19th century GENERAL: European country & decorative, handmade furniture.

**Collins & Hastie Ltd,** 5 Park Walk, SW10 0AJ TEL: 351 4292 PARKING: Easy OPEN: Mon-Fri 10-6 Sat 11-4 MIN: £1000 MAX: £30,000 PERIOD: 19th century SPECIALIST: Animals GENERAL: Sporting, country scenes.

**Jonathan Cooper**, Park Wall Gallery, 20 Park Walk, SW10 0AQ TEL: 351 0410 PARKING: Medium OPEN: Mon-Fri 10-6.30 MIN: £250 MAX: £250,000 PERIOD: 20th century GENERAL: Modern British & European OTHER INFO: Good restaurants in Park Walk.

**Hares Antiques**, 498 Kings Road, SW10 0LE TEL: 351 1442 ASSNS: CADA PARKING: Medium OPEN: Mon-Sat 10-5.30 MIN: £100 MAX: £70,000 PERIOD: 18th-19th century SPECIALIST: Period dining tables & chairs, upholstery GENERAL: Wide selection. restoration & re-upholstery.

**Ian G Hastie,** 5 Park Walk, SW10 0AJ TEL: 351 6820 FAX: 351 7929 ASSNS: BADA PARKING: Medium OPEN: Mon-Fri 10-6, Sat 11-4 MIN: £200 MAX: £30,000 PERIOD: 18th-19th century GENERAL: Furniture & works of art.

**Simon Hatchwell Antiques,** 533 Kings Road at the Furniture Cave, SW10 0TZ TEL: 351 2344 & 351 3520 FAX: 351 3520 PARKING: Easy OPEN: 11-6 MIN: £50 MAX: £10,000 PERIOD: 19th century SPECIALIST: Biedermeier GENERAL: English & Continental furniture, clocks, barometers, paintings.

**Langford's Marine Antiques,** The Plaza, 535 Kings Road, SW10 0SZ TEL: 351 4881 FAX: 352 0762 ASSNS: LAPADA PARKING: Easy MIN: £100 MAX: £40/50,000 PERIOD: 19th-20th century SPECIALIST: Ships models, antique nautical items, sextants, globes, chronometers, etc.

**Stephen Long**, Albion House, 348 Fulham Road, SW10 9UH TEL: 352 8226 PARKING: Easy OPEN: Mon-Fri 9-1, 2.15-5.30, most Sats 10-12.30 MIN: £5 MAX: £1000 PERIOD: 18th-19th century GENERAL: English pottery, glass, papier mache, tole, fabrics, painted furniture.

**McVeigh & Charpentier**, 498 Kings Road TEL: 351 1442 PARKING: Easy OPEN: 10-5.30 MIN: £300 MAX: £5000 PERIOD: 18th-19th century SPECIALIST: Continental furniture GENERAL: Objets d'art, mirrors, beds, garden statuary, ironwork.

**HW Poulter & Son**, 279 Fulham Road, SW10 9PZ TEL: 352 7268 FAX: 351 0984 PARKING: Easy OPEN: Mon-Fri 9-5, Sat 10-1 MIN: £250 MAX: £50,000 PERIOD: 18th-19th century SPECIALIST: Marble, stone, wood chimney pieces GENERAL: Fenders, firegrates, fire irons, chandeliers OTHER INFO: Marble restoration .

**Whiteway & Waldron Ltd,** 305 Munster Road, SW6 6BJ TEL & FAX: 381 3195 PARKING: Mon-Fri 10-6, Sat 11-4 MAX: £7000 PERIOD: 19th century SPECIALIST: Ecclesiastical, church items only.

**Harriet Wynter Ltd**, 50 Redcliffe Road, SW10 9NJ TEL: 352 6494 FAX: 252 9312 ASSNS: BADA PARKING: Medium OPEN: By appt only MIN: £15 MAX: £50,000 PERIOD: 17th-early 19th century SPECIALIST: Early scientific instruments GENERAL: Antique decorative items, early furniture, paintings & sculpture.

# Hampstead

There is evidence of settlements in **Hampstead** in prehistoric times. Two barrows have been found in the area, one on **Primrose Hill** which has been flattened, and another on **Parliament Hill**. During medieval times the area belonged to the church and, still being forest, was used for hunting. The trees were mostly cut down for rebuilding London after the Great Fire in 1666. In the early 18th century Hampstead became fashionable for its health giving spring water and people flocked to the **Heath** to take the water. It was at this time that development really started.

During the 19th and 20th centuries Hampstead has rapidly expanded although retaining much of its village character, it has remained a highly sought-after place to live.

Kenwood House, in **Hampstead Lane**, was originally built in 1616 although it was largely rebuilt just eighty years later. In the second half of the 18th century much of the house was remodelled by Robert Adam. Now the late 17th century building lies behind an 18th century facade. The house contains the Iveagh Bequest of Old Master and British Paintings which includes works by Rembrandt, Vermeer, Hals, Gainsborough, Turner and Reynolds. There is also a fine collection of neo-classical furniture.

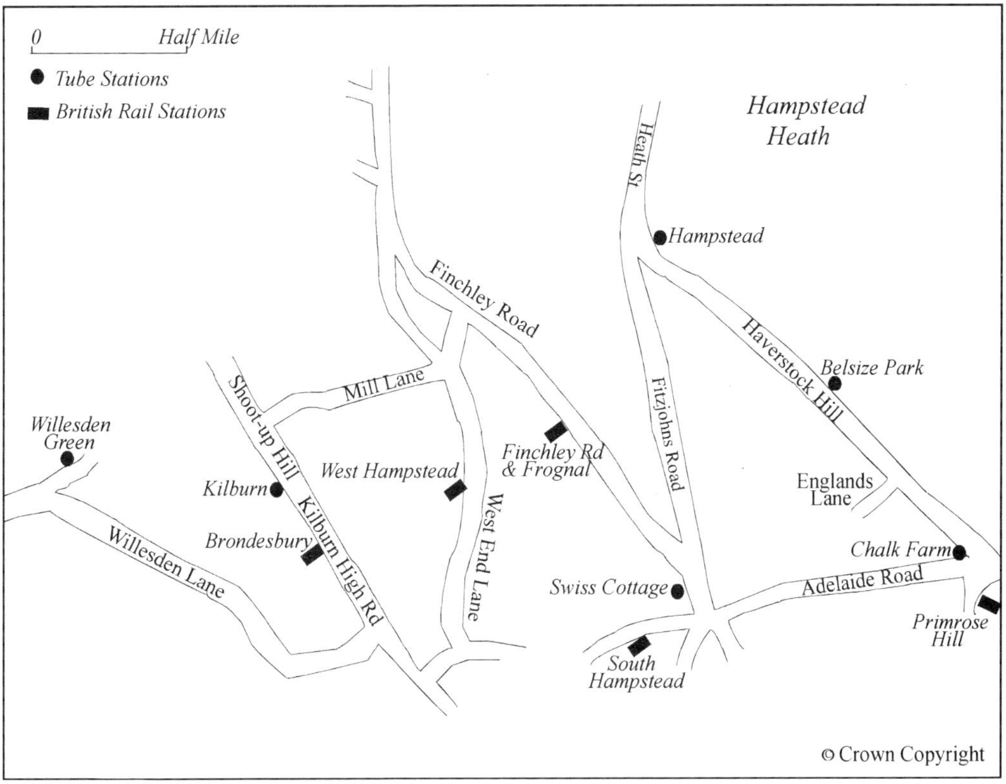




## ANTIQUE DEALERS

## LONDON NW3 (0171)

**Dolphin Coins**, 2c Englands Lane, Hampstead, NW3 4TG TEL: 722 4116 FAX: 483 2000 ASSNS: BNTA PARKING: Easy OPEN: 9-5, Sat by appt MIN: £5 MAX: £7500 PERIOD: 25 AD-1937 SPECIALIST: World coins GENERAL: British coins.

**John Denham Gallery**, 50 Mill Lane, West Hampstead, NW6 1NJ TEL: 794 2635 PARKING: Easy OPEN: 10-5, Sun 11-5, Sat, Mon PM only MIN: £20 MAX: £5000 PERIOD: 17th-20th century SPECIALIST: Paintings, watercolours, drawings, etc. Restoration & framings service.

**S Farrelly**, 152 Fleet Road, Hampstead, NW3 2QX TEL: 485 2089 PARKING: Medium OPEN: 10-5 MIN: £2 MAX: £4000 PERIOD: 18th-20th century GENERAL: General antiques OTHER INFO: Hampstead Heath, Kenwood House near, John Keats' House.

## LONDON NW6 (0171)

**Gallery Kaleidoscope**, 66 Willesden Lane, Kilburn, NW6 7SX TEL: 328 5833 PARKING: Easy OPEN: Mon-Sat 10-6 MIN: £20 MAX: £2000 PERIOD: 19th-20th century GENERAL: Paintings, sculpture, ceramics OTHER INFO: Lots of local junk shops.

**Scope Antiques**, 64 Willesden Lane, Kilburn, NW6 7SX TEL: 328 5833 PARKING: Easy OPEN: 10-6 MIN: £20 MAX: £2,000 PERIOD: 19th century GENERAL: Furniture, glass, pottery, decorative items OTHER INFO: Good bargain-finding area.

# Mayfair and St James's

**Mayfair** is the area bounded by **Oxford Street, Regent Street, Park Lane** and **Piccadilly**. It is so named because, from the late 17th century until the mid 18th century, there was a fair held here every year during the first two weeks of May. Development had started as early as the 1660s near the present day **Piccadilly Circus** and spread north and west until almost the whole the area was built up in less than a hundred years. The streets reflect the names of the great estate holders who had owned the land. The Grosvenor Estate still owns much of the freehold. From the first, Mayfair was a very fashionable place to live and has remained so.

**Grosvenor Square** has probably always been the place with the greatest social *cachet* in Mayfair and the enormous rents have ensured that only the wealthiest people can afford to live there. Consequently it has never suffered a decline. The American Embassy, completed in 1961, stands on the west side of the Square.

Building along **Piccadilly**, although an ancient route to the west, only began in the early 17th century. One of the first shops gave the street its name. Robert Baker sold picadils or ruffs hence Piccadilly. During the late 17th and early 18th centuries famous residents of the area included the Duke of Wellington, Lady Hamilton (Nelson's mistress) and her husband, and Lord Byron. The Ritz Hotel is sited on the south side of Piccadilly, next to **Green Park**. Synonymous with luxury, the hotel was completed in 1906 to the specifications of César Ritz, a Swiss hotelier.

**Piccadilly Circus** was constructed in 1819 and was intended to be as elegant as **Regent Street** but alterations in the late 19th century changed the original layout. The statue of Eros in the centre was erected in 1893 to commemorate the work done by Lord Shaftesbury and was meant to represent the Angel of Christian Charity not Eros.

**Regent Street**, designed by John Nash, was built to connect Regent's Park to Carlton House, home of the Prince Regent. It was also hoped that the new street would relieve traffic problems at **Charing Cross** and in the **Strand**. Quite quickly Regent Street became most fashionable and the shops catered for high society customers. By the beginning of the 20th century, however,they had started to cater more for the affluent middle classes. Regent Street has remained one of London's premier shopping areas.

St James's Palace was originally built by Henry VIII on the site of a hospital. It became the monarch's principal London residence after Whitehall Palace was destroyed by fire in 1698. In 1809 a large part of St James's Palace was also burnt down but rebuilding was completed by 1814. It was George IV who was the instigator of the move to Buckingham Palace. He had lived at Carlton House after a row with his father, then the king. After his accession to the throne he thought Carlton House not grand enough for a reigning monarch so he commissioned Nash to design a palace on the site of Buckingham House. Parliament, with great reluctance, authorised a budget of £200,000 to repair and improve Buckingham House. However, the King was determined to have a grand palace and, although the shell of the old house and some of the floorplan was retained, it was to be much bigger and more expensive to complete. King George IV died before it was finished as did his successor, William IV. Queen Victoria was the first monarch to live there. Its eventual cost was £700,000.

## London — Mayfair & St James's

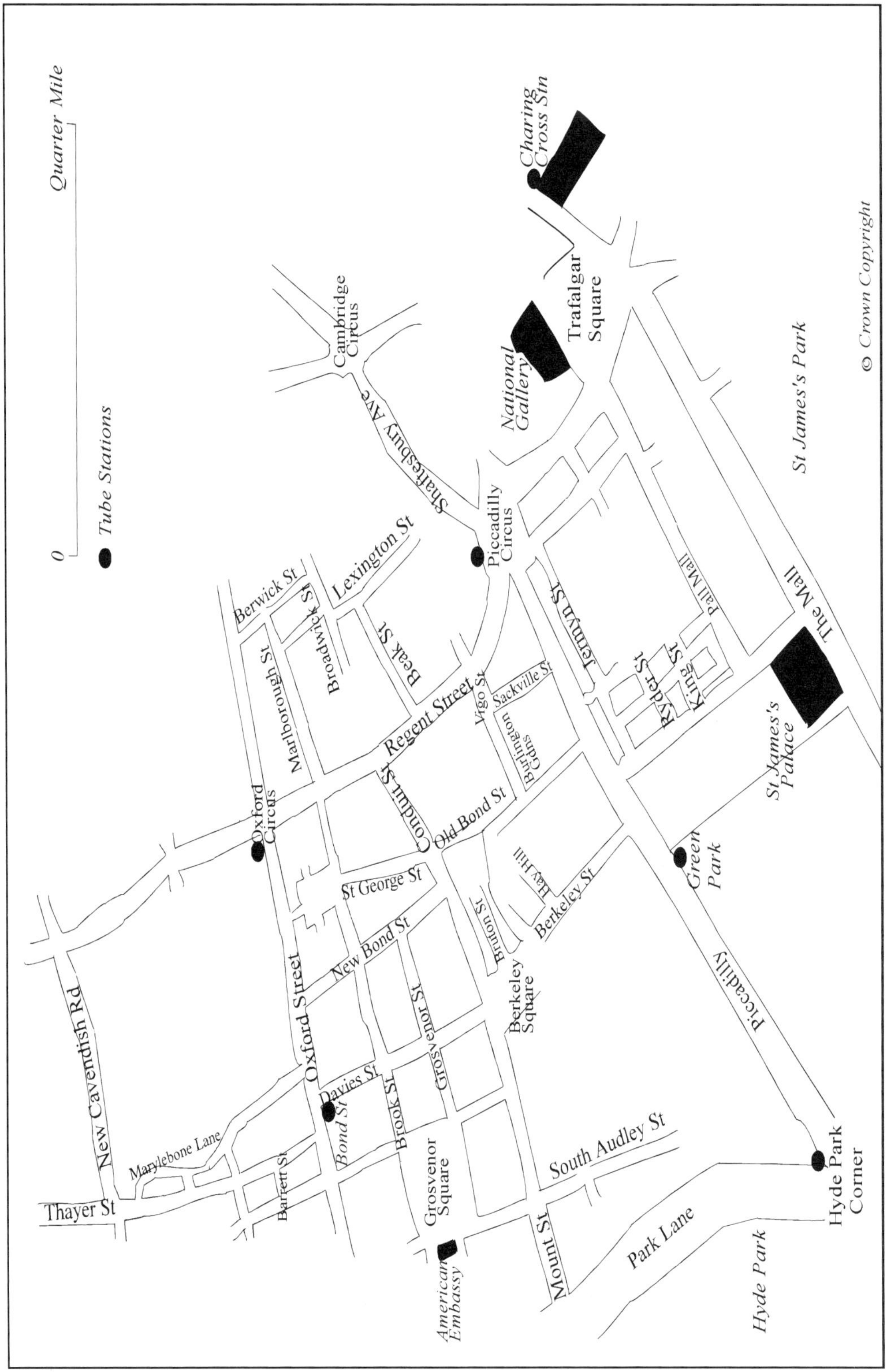

# ANTIQUE DEALERS

## LONDON SW1 (0171)

**Verner Amell Ltd**, 4 Ryder Street, St James's, SW1Y 6QB TEL: 925 2759 FAX: 321 0210 ASSNS: SLAD PARKING: Difficult OPEN: Weekdays 10-5.30 MIN: £10,000 MAX: £1.5 million SPECIALIST: 17th century Dutch, Flemish, Italian paintings GENERAL: 19th century Scandinavian paintings.

**The Armoury of St James's**, 17 Piccadilly Arcade, SW1Y 6NH TEL: 493 5082 FAX: 499 4422 ASSNS: OMRS PARKING: Medium OPEN: Mon-Fri 9.30-5.30, Sat 11-4.30 MIN: £5 PERIOD: 18th-20th century SPECIALIST: Military & civil medals of the world GENERAL: Militaria, handpainted military figurines & toy soldiers OTHER INFO: At the centre of everything.

**JH Bourdon-Smith Ltd**, 24 Mason's Yard, Duke Street, St James's, SW1Y 6BU TEL: 839 4714 FAX: 839 3951 ASSNS: BADA PARKING: Medium/difficult OPEN: Mon-Fri 9.30-6 MIN: £20 MAX: £50,000 SPECIALIST: Early Georgian to Victorian silver OTHER INFO: Excellent shopping area, Fortnum & Mason's, Christie's auction house etc.

**Paolo Brisigotti,** 44 Duke Street, St James's, SW1Y 6DD TEL: 839 4441 FAX: 976 1663 PARKING: Medium OPEN: 9.30-5.30 PERIOD: 17th century SPECIALIST: Old Master paintings.

**Simon Dickinson Ltd,** 58 Jermyn Street, SW1Y 6LX TEL: 493 0340 FAX: 493 0796 PARKING: Difficult OPEN: 9-5.30 MIN: £2000 MAX: £2 million+ GENERAL: Old & modern master paintings from 15th to 20th century.

**Faustus Ancient Art & Jewellery,** Dukes Court, 32 Duke Street, St James's, SW1Y 6DF TEL: 930 1864 FAX: 930 1628 PARKING: Medium OPEN: By appt SPECIALIST: Gold jewellery, circa 2000BC.

**Thomas Heneage Art Books**, 42 Duke Street, St James's, SW1Y 6DJ TEL & FAX: 930 9223 PARKING: Medium OPEN: Mon-Fri 10-6 MIN: £5 SPECIALIST: Art reference books GENERAL: Reference books for fine & decorative arts worldwide in or out of print OTHER INFO: Between Fortnum & Mason's & Christie's.

**Iconastas,** 5 Piccadilly Arcade, SW1 TEL: 629 1433 FAX: 408 2015 PARKING: Difficult OPEN: Mon-Fri 10-6, Sat 2-5 MIN: £10 MAX: £10,000 PERIOD: 1400-1930 SPECIALIST: Russian icons GENERAL: Russian antiques & Faberge'.

**Hugh Johnson Shop,** 68 St James's Court, SW1A 1PH TEL: 491 4912 FAX: 493 0602 OPEN: Mon-Fri 9.30-5.30 MIN: £5 MAX: £5000 SPECIALIST: Antique & modern wine accessories OTHER INFO: Everything for the wine connoisseur except the wine.

**Longmire**, 12 Bury Street, St James's SWI TEL: 930 8720 PARKING: Medium OPEN: Mon-Fri 10-5, Sats in Nov/Dec MIN: £190 MAX: £15,000 PERIOD: 19th-20th century SPECIALIST: World's largest collection of cufflinks GENERAL: Custom Victorian ladies jewellery.

**MacConnal-Mason Gallery**, 14 Duke Street, St James's SW1Y 6DBTEL: 839 7693 FAX: 839 6797 PARKING: Easy OPEN: 9-6 MIN: £2,000 PERIOD: 18th-20th century.

**Mall Galleries/Federation of British Artists**, The Mall TEL: 930 6844 FAX: 839 7830 PARKING: Easy but expensive! OPEN: Mon-Sat 10-5 MIN: £100 MAX: £5000 PERIOD: 20th century SPECIALIST: Contemporary art (mainly traditional styles), paintings, sculpture etc OTHER INFO: Housed in a Nash house, close to Trafalgar Sq & Buckingham Palace.

**Peter Nahum at the Leicester Galleries,** 5 Ryder Street, SW1Y 6PY TEL: 930 6059 FAX: 930 4678 ASSNS: LAPADA, Art & Antique Dealers Assn PARKING: Medium OPEN: 9-5.30 MIN: £500 MAX: £500,000+ PERIOD: 18th-20th century SPECIALIST: Pre-Raphaelites, symbolists, modern British GENERAL: Paintings, drawings & sculpture.

**Polak Gallery Ltd**, 21 King Street, St James's, SW1Y 6QY TEL: 839 2871 FAX: 930 3467 ASSNS: BADA PARKING: Difficult OPEN: Mon-Fri 9.30-5.30 MIN: £1000 MAX: £60,000 PERIOD: 19th-20th century GENERAL: English & European oils & watercolours OTHER INFO: Opposite Christie's.

**St George's Gallery/Zwemmer**, 8 Duke Street, St James's, SW1Y 6BN TEL: 930 0935/4930 FAX: 930 3534 PARKING: Difficult OPEN: 10-6 MIN: £5 MAX: £25,000 PERIOD: 20th century SPECIALIST: Fine & decorative art books GENERAL: New & out-of-print books OTHER INFO: Worldwide mail order available. 100 yds from Royal Academy of Art. In heart of central London's antique world.

**Johnny Van Haeften Ltd**, 13 Duke Street, St James's, SW1Y 6DB TEL: 930 3062 FAX: 839 6303 ASSNS: BADA, SLAD, TEFAF PARKING: Medium OPEN: Mon-Fri 10-6 & by appt MIN: £5000 MAX: £2 million PERIOD: 17th century SPECIALIST: Dutch & Flemish Old Master paintings only.

**Rupert Wace Ancient Art Ltd**, 107 Jermyn Street, SW1Y 6EE TEL: 495 1623 FAX: 930 7310 ASSNS: ADA PARKING: Difficult OPEN: 10-5 MIN: £100 MAX: £15,000+ PERIOD: Up to 1000 AD SPECIALIST: Antiquities: Egyptian, classical, Near Eastern & European.

**The Woollahra Trading Co,** 6 Bury Street, SW1Y 6AB TEL: 839 9252 PARKING: Medium OPEN: Mon-Fri 10-5.30 MIN: £200 MAX: £50,000 PERIOD: 17th-18th century SPECIALIST: !8th century English & continental porcelain, 17th-18th century European paintings OTHER INFO: We are also located in Australia at 160 Queen St, Sydney 2025, Tel & Fax 02-362 3144.

## LONDON W1A (0171)

**Astarte Gallery**, Britannia Hotel, Grosvenor Square, W1A 3AN TEL: 409 1875 FAX: 409 1875 ASSNS: ADA PARKING: Own carpark OPEN: Mon-Fri 10-5 & by appt MIN: £5 MAX: £10,000 PERIOD: BC to 6th century AD SPECIALIST: Ancient Egypt, Rome, Greece items GENERAL: Coins ancient & modern OTHER INFO: On the site where the despatch to the King & Prime Minister arrived from Wellington announcing his victory at Waterloo.

**JAL Franks Ltd,** 7 New Oxford Street, WC1A 1BA TEL: 405 0274 FAX: 430 1259 ASSNS: PTS PARKING: Difficult OPEN: Mon-Fri 10.30-5.15 PERIOD: 18th-20th century SPECIALIST: Atlases & maps, airmail philately, stamps, postcards.

**SJ Phillips Ltd,** 139 New Bond Street, W1A 3DL TEL: 629 6261 FAX: 495 6180 ASSNS: BADA PARKING: Difficult OPEN: Mon-Fri 10-5 MIN: £50 MAX: £1,000,000 PERIOD: 16th-20th century SPECIALIST: English & Continental silver & jewellery GENERAL: Boxes, miniatures, objects.

**The Scripophily Shop,** Britannia Hotel, Grosvenor Square, W1A 3AN TEL: 495 0580 FAX: 495 0565 PARKING: Medium OPEN: Mon-Fri 10-5 MIN: £5 MAX: £1000 PERIOD: 19th-20th century SPECIALIST: Original old financial papers, bonds & shares.

## LONDON W1M (0171)

**Blunderbuss Antiques**, 29 Thayer Street, W1M 5LJ TEL: 486 2444 PARKING: Medium OPEN: 9.30-4.30 MIN: £1 PERIOD: 17th-20th century SPECIALIST: Antique arms, armour & militaria.

**The Button Queen**, 19 Marylebone Lane, W1M 5FF TEL: 935 1505 ASSNS: British Button Society PARKING: Medium OPEN: Mon-Fri 10-6, Sat 10-1.30 PERIOD: Some 18th, 19th-20th century SPECIALIST: Buttons, old & antique GENERAL: Modern buttons OTHER INFO: Wheelchair access.

**Brian Fielden**, 3 New Cavendish Street, W1M 7RP TEL: 935 6912 PARKING: Medium OPEN: Mon-Fri 9.30-1, 2-5.30, Sat 9.30-1 MIN: £500 MAX: £20,000 PERIOD: 18th-19th century SPECIALIST: English period furniture OTHER INFO: 200 yds to Wallace Collection.

**E Joseph Booksellers**, 1 Vere Street, W1M 9HQ TEL: 493 8353 PARKING: 629 2759 ASSNS: ABA, BADA OPEN: Mon-Fri 9.30-5.30 MIN: £50 MAX: £40,000 PERIOD: 17th-20th century GENERAL: Antiquarian books, fine bindings, library sets, childrens illustrated.

**David Richards & Sons**, 12 New Cavendish Street TEL: 935 3206/0322 FAX: 224 4423 ASSNS: LAPADA PARKING: Medium OPEN: 9.30-5.30 & by appt MIN: £25 MAX: £5000 PERIOD: 18th-20th century SPECIALIST: Old Sheffield plate, Victorian plate.

**Venners Antiques**, 7 New Cavendish Street, W1M 7RP TEL: 935 0184 PARKING: Meters OPEN: Tues-Fri 10.15-4.15, Sat 10-1 MIN: £10 MAX: £10,000 PERIOD: 18th-19th century SPECIALIST: English pottery & porcelain.

**Wilkins & Wilkins**, 1 Barrett Street, W1M 6DN TEL: 935 9613 FAX: 935 5720 PARKING: Medium OPEN: 10-5 MIN: £500 MAX: £10,000 PERIOD: 17th-18th century SPECIALIST: British decorative paintings & portraits.

## LONDON W1R (0171)

**Andrew Edmunds**, 44 Lexington Street, W1R 3LH TEL: 437 8594 FAX: 439 2551 PARKING: Difficult OPEN: Mon-Fri 10-6 MIN: £85 MAX: £2000 PERIOD: 18th-19th century SPECIALIST: English caricatures GENERAL: Prints OTHER INFO: Excellent restaurant next door.

**Gallery Zadah Ltd,** 29 Conduit Street, W1R 9TA TEL: 493 2622 FAX: 629 6682 PARKING: Medium OPEN: 9.30-6 PERIOD: 17th-20th century GENERAL: Oriental & European carpets, rugs, tapestries & textiles.

**Liberty plc**, Antiques & Fine Art Dept, Regent Street, W1R 6AH TEL: 734 1234, FAX: 734 8323 PARKING: Medium OPEN: Mon-Sat 9.30-6, Thurs till 7.30 MIN: £30 MAX: £10,000 PERIOD: 19th-20th century SPECIALIST: Furniture & metalware 1860-1920 including Arts & Crafts movement, with pieces by Liberty & Co, Heal's etc.

**Sheppard & Cooper Ltd**, 11 St George Street, W1R 9DF TEL: 629 6489 FAX: 495 2905 PARKING: Difficult OPEN: Weekdays 10-6 MIN: £70+ SPECIALIST: Ancient & antique glass.

## LONDON W1V (0171)

**J & A Beare Ltd**, 7 Broadwick Street, W1V 1FJ TEL: 437 1449 FAX: 439 4520 ASSNS: Int Society of Violin & Bow Makers, BADA PARKING: Difficult OPEN: Mon-Fri 9-12.15, 1.30-5 PERIOD: 17th-20th century SPECIALIST: Musical instruments of the violin family & their accessories only.

**MacConnal-Mason Gallery**, 15 Burlington Arcade, Piccadilly, W1V 9AB TEL: 839 7693 FAX: 839 6797 PARKING: Easy OPEN: 9-6 MIN: £2000 PERIOD: 18th-20th century.

**Michael Rose**, 3 Burlington Arcade, Piccadilly, W1V 9AB TEL: 493 0714 FAX: 491 1051 NAG PARKING Medium OPEN: 9.30-5.45 MIN: £50 PERIOD: 19th-20th century SPECIALIST: Period & antique jewellery.

**W Sitch & Co Ltd**, 48 Berwick Street, W1V 4JD TEL: 437 3776 PARKING: Medium OPEN: Mon-Fri 9-5.30, Sat 9-1 PERIOD: 19th-20th century GENERAL: Late Victorian & Edwardian lighting, chandeliers, wall brackets, floor standards etc.

## LONDON W1X (0171)

**Asprey**, 165-169 New Bond Street, W1Y 0AR TEL: 493 6767 FAX: 491 0384 ASSNS: BADA PARKING: Medium OPEN: Mon-Fri 9-5.30, Sat 9-1 MIN: £60 MAX: £600,000 PERIOD: 17th-18th century SPECIALIST: Furniture, silver, clocks, glass, Fabergé.

**Raymond Bernadout**, 18 Grosvenor Street, Mayfair, 355 4531 ASSNS: BADA TEL: 355 4531 PARKING: Easy OPEN: 9-5 MIN: £2000 MAX: £100,000 PERIOD: 17th-20th century SPECIALIST: Quality not quantity, antique decorative carpets, rugs, tapestries, textiles OTHER INFO: Restoration, cleaning, valuations.

**Burlington Gallery Ltd**, 10 Burlington Gardens, W1X 1LG TEL: 734 9228 FAX: 494 3770 PARKING: Difficult OPEN: Mon-Fri 9.30-5.3-, Sat 10-5 MIN: £30 MAX: £12,000 PERIOD: 18th-19th century SPECIALIST: Sporting prints, Cecil Aldin & other antique prints, Some watercolours especially Hugh Cushing OTHER INFO: Museum of Mankind next door, celebrated Columbian café.

**Burlington Paintings Ltd**, 12 Burlington Gardens, W1X 1LG TEL: 734 9984 FAX: 494 3770 ASSNS: BADA PARKING: Difficult OPEN: Mon-Fri 9.30-5.30, Sat 10-5 not bank holiday weekends MIN: £500 MAX: £50,000 PERIOD: 19th-20th century GENERAL: British & European oils.

**Connaught Brown,** 2 Albemarle Street, W1X 3HF TEL: 408 0362 FAX: 495 3137 PARKING: Difficult OPEN: Mon-Fri 10-6, Sat 10-12.30 MIN: £300 MAX: £120,000+ PERIOD: 19th-20th century SPECIALIST: Impressionist, contemporary & modern artists GENERAL: Calder, Chagall, Dubeffet, Dufy, Hockney, Holsor, Matisse, Miro, Moore, Picasso, Pissaro, Warhol, Wesselmann.

**Ermitage Ltd**, 14 Hay Hill, W1X 7LJ TEL: 499 5459 FAX: 499 5459 PARKING: Medium OPEN: Mon-Fri 10-5 & by appt MIN: £100 MAX: £100,000 PERIOD: 17th-20th century SPECIALIST: Fabergé, Russian works of art, silver.

**Frost & Reed Fine Art**, 16 Old Bond Street, W1X 3DB TEL: 629 2457 FAX: 499 0299 ASSNS: BADA, SLAD PARKING: Medium OPEN: Mon-Fri 9-5.30 MIN: £500 MAX: £350,000 SPECIALIST: 20th century artists: Dawson, Dyf, Penny, Sir A.J.Munnings, St Clair Davis, P. Smith GENERAL: 19th & 20th century British & European, especially sporting paintings & impressionists/post impressionist watercolours & drawings.

**Deborah Gage (Works of Art) Ltd**, 38 Old Bond Street, W1X 3AE TEL: 493 3249 FAX: 495 1352 ASSNS: Bond Street Assn PARKING: Difficult OPEN: Mon-Fri 9.30-5.30 MIN: £2000 MAX: £100,000 SPECIALIST: 17th-18th century European decorative arts & paintings, 19th century & modern British paintings.

**Christopher Gibbs Ltd,** 8 Vigo Street, W1X 1LG TEL: 439 4557 FAX: 287 9961 PARKING: Medium OPEN: 9.30-5.30 MIN: £20 MAX: £500,000 PERIOD: Ancient to 20th century

SPECIALIST: English furniture GENERAL: A wide range of unusual decorative items including paintings & sculpture.

**Robert Hall,** 15c Clifford Street, W1X 1RF TEL: 734 4008 FAX: 734 4408 ASSNS: BADA PARKING: Medium OPEN: 10-5.30 MIN: £800 MAX: £5000 PERIOD: 18th-19th century SPECIALIST: Chinese snuff bottles GENERAL: Chinese art.

**Hancocks & Co**, 1 Burlington Gardens W1X 2HP TEL: 493 8904 FAX: 493 8905 ASSNS: BADA PARKING: Easy OPEN: 9.30-5.30 MIN: £50 MAX: £250,000 PERIOD: 17th-20th century SPECIALIST: Jewellery & silver OTHER INFO: Opposite Burlington Arcade.

**Harvey & Gore**, 4 Burlington Gardens, Old Bond Street, W1X 1LH TEL: 493 2714 FAX: 493 0324 ASSNS: BADA PARKING: Medium OPEN: 9.30-5 MIN: £250 MAX: £50,000 PERIOD: 18th-20th century SPECIALIST: Fine jewellery & silver.

**WR Harvey & Co (Antiques) Ltd**, 5 Old Bond Street, W1X 3TH TEL: 499 8385, 495 0209 ASSNS: BADA PARKING: Medium OPEN: Mon-Sat 10-5.30 MIN: £250 MAX: £250,000 SPECIALIST: Fine English furniture 1675-1830 GENERAL: Furniture, clocks, barometers, engravings, pictures, mirrors, objet d'art OTHER INFO: Ideally set in centre of Mayfair between Sotheby's & Christie's.

**Brian HaughtonAntiques,** 3B Burlington Gardens, W1X 1LE TEL: 734 5491 FAX: 494 4604 PARKING: Medium OPEN: 10-5.30 MIN: £500 MAX: £150,000 PERIOD: 18th-19th century SPECIALIST: English & Continental porcelain & pottery.

**John Jaffa (Antiques) Ltd**, 13 Royal Arcade, 28 Old Bond Street, W1X 3HD TEL: 499 4228 FAX: 499 4228 PARKING: Medium OPEN: Mon-Fri 10-5.30 MIN: £50 MAX: £20,000 PERIOD: 18th-19th century SPECIALIST: English & Continental enamels, gold snuff boxes GENERAL: Objets de vertu, fine silver OTHER INFO: Opposite Brown's Hotel on Albermarle Street.

**Kennedy Carpets**, 9a Vigo Street, W1X 1AL TEL: 439 8873 FAX: 437 1201 ASSNS: LAPADA PARKING: Medium OPEN: Mon-Fri 9.30-6 MIN: £250 MAX: £150,000 PERIOD: 19th-20th century SPECIALIST: Decorative carpets GENERAL: Antique & collectable carpets, kilims, rugs OTHER INFO: Les Madeleines Brasserie opposite.

**Meltons**, 27 Bruton Place, W1X 7AB TEL: 629 3612 FAX: 495 3196 PARKING: Easy OPEN: 9-5.30 by appt MIN: £100 MAX: £15,000 PERIOD: 19th century SPECIALIST: Unusual, decorative GENERAL: Smalls, porcelain, terracotta OTHER INFO: Opposite excellent Guinea Grill.

**David Messum Fine Art Ltd,** 8 Cork Street, W1X 1PB TEL: 437 5545 FAX: 734 7018 PARKING: Difficult OPEN: 10-5.30 MIN: £250 MAX: £100,000 PERIOD: 19th-20th century SPECIALIST: British impressionist paintings GENERAL: Paintings.

**Ronald Phillips Ltd,** 26 Bruton Street, W1X 8LH TEL: 493 2341 FAX: 495 0843 ASSNS: BADA PARKING: Medium OPEN: 9.15-5.15 PERIOD: 18th-19th century SPECIALIST: Furniture.

**Portal Gallery**, 16a Grafton Street/Bond Street, W1X 3LF TEL: 493 0706 FAX: 629 3506 PARKING: Medium OPEN: Mon-Fri 10-5.30, Sat 10-1 MIN: £50 MAX: £2000 PERIOD: 17th-19th century SPECIALIST: Idiosynchratic objects GENERAL: Victorian fly catchers & optical testing instruments to biscuit tins, assortment of Vestas, money boxes, treen OTHER INFO: Selection of objet tatzkas.

**The Sladmore Gallery,** 32 Bruton Place, Berkeley Square, W1X 7AA TEL: 499 0365 FAX: 409 1381 ASSNS: SLAD PARKING: Easy OPEN: 10-6 MIN: £1000 PERIOD: 18th-20th century SPECIALIST: Rembrandt, Bugatti GENERAL: Fine 19th & 20th century bronze sculpture OTHER INFO: One of London's hidden delights, tucked away in a mews just off Berkeley Square next to the famous Guinea pub.

**Stephen Somerville Ltd,** 14 Old Bond Street, W1X 3DB TEL: 493 8363 ASSNS: SLAD PARKING: Difficult OPEN: Mon-Fri 10-5 PERIOD: 18th-20th century SPECIALIST: English paintings, drawings, watercolours, prints, Old Master works.

**Henry Sotheran Ltd**, 2-5 Sackville Street, Piccadilly, W1X 2DP TEL: 439 6151 ASSNS: ABA, ILAB, PBFA PARKING: Medium OPEN: Mon-Fri 9.30-6, Sat 10-4 MIN: £5 MAX: £25,000 PERIOD: 17th-20th century SPECIALIST: Antiquarian books, prints, library furniture OTHER INFO: In heart of Mayfair's prestigious shopping area, close all Bond Street's fine antique dealers.

**M Turpin,** 27 Bruton Street, W1X 7BD TEL: 493 3275 FAX: 408 1869 ASSNS: LAPADA PARKING: Mon-Fri 10-6 or by appt MIN: £300 MAX: £385,000 PERIOD: 17th-19th century SPECIALIST: English furniture, mirrors, objets d'art.

**Williams & Son,** 2 Grafton Street, W1X 3LB TEL:

493 5751 FAX: 409 7363 PARKING: Medium OPEN: Mon-Fri 10-6 PERIOD: 19th-20th century GENERAL: European & British paintings.

## LONDON W1Y (0171)

**Gregg Baker Oriental Art**, 34 Brook Street, W1Y 1YA TEL: 629 7926 FAX: 495 3872 ASSNS: BADA, LAPADA PARKING: Medium OPEN: Mon-Fri 10-6 & by appt MIN: £500 MAX: £100.000 PERIOD: 17th-19th century SPECIALIST: Japanese & Chinese works of art, paper screens, bronzes & carvings in many materials.

**Konrad O Bernheimer Ltd**, 1 Mount Street, W1Y 5AA TEL: 495 7028 FAX: 495 7027 ASSNS: BADA, CINOA, SLAD PARKING: Medium OPEN: By appt only PERIOD: 17th-18th century SPECIALIST: Old Master paintings, Continental furniture, Oriental ceramics.

**N Bloom & Son (1912) Ltd,** The Bond Street Antiques Centre, 124 New Bond Street, W1Y 9AE TEL: 629 5060 FAX: 493 2528 ASSNS: LAPADA PARKING: Mon-Fri 10-5.30, Sat 10.30-4.30 MIN: £100 MAX: £30,000 PERIOD: 19th-20th century SPECIALIST: Jewellery GENERAL: Small items of furniture, paintings, decorative items, silver (small stocks) OTHER INFO: Myself: one of BBC Antiques Roadshow.

**Bond Street Antiques Centre**, 124 New Bond Street, W1Y 9AE TEL: 351 5353 FAX: 351 5350 PARKING: Easy OPEN: Mon-Fri 10-5.45, Sats seasonally MIN: £40 MAX: £100,000 PERIOD: 18th-20th century SPECIALIST: Jewellery & silver GENERAL: Watches, porcelain, glass, Oriental antiques, & paintings OTHER INFO: Tubes: Bond Street & Green Park.

**Colefax & Fowler,** 39 Brook Street, W1Y 2JE TEL: 493 2231 FAX: 355 4037 PARKING: Medium OPEN: Mon-Fri 9.30-1, 2-5.30 GENERAL: Decorative antiques.

**Charles Ede Ltd,** 20 Brook Street, W1Y 1AD TEL: 493 4944 FAX: 491 2548 ASSNS: IADAA, CINOA PARKING: Medium OPEN: Tues-Fri 12.30-4.30 & by appt MIN: £50 MAX: £100,000 GENERAL: Greek, Roman, Egyptian & Near Eastern antiquities 5000 BC-600 AD OTHER INFO: Claridges 50 yards.

**Grays Antique Market**, 58 Davies Street, W1Y 1LB TEL: 629 7034 FAX: 493 9344 PARKING: Difficult OPEN: Mon-Fri 10-6 MIN: £1 MAX: £30,000 PERIOD: 17th-20th century SPECIALIST: Antique jewellery, medical instruments, commemorative china, prints, silver, Oriental GENERAL: Clocks, watches, furniture, glass, lace, majolica, militaria, sporting collectables OTHER INFO: Basement café. Heart of West End shopping area & close to Philips, Sotheby's.

**Grays in the Mews**, 1-7 Davies Mews, W1Y 1AR TEL: 629 7034 FAX: 493 9344 PARKING: Difficult OPEN: Mon-Fri 10-6 MIN: £1 MAX: £30,000 PERIOD: 17th-20th century SPECIALIST: Toys, ancient art, antiquities, jewellery, collectables, clocks & watches, glass, Oriental ceramics, Persian art.

**Hadji Baba Ancient Art**, 34a Davies Street, W1Y 1LD TEL: 499 9363 FAX: 493 5504 ASSNS: ADA, IADA PARKING: Medium OPEN: 9.30-6 MIN: £100 MAX: thousands PERIOD: 3000BC-1914AD SPECIALIST: Antiquities of pre-Islamic & Islamic periods: ancient Egyptian, Persian, Roman, Greek OTHER INFO: Parallel to Bond Street & close to Claridges Hotel.

**Halcyon Days,** 14 Brook Street, W1Y 1AA TEL: 629 8811 FAX: 409 0280 ASSNS: BADA PARKING: Medium OPEN: Mon-Fri 9.15-5.30, Sat 9.30-5.30 MIN: £100 MAX: On request PERIOD: 18th-19th century SPECIALIST: Enamels, treen GENERAL: Papier mache, tole, peinte, objects of vertu, small unusual Georgian furniture.

**Howard Antiques**, 8 Davies Street, Berkeley Square TEL: 629 2628 PARKING: Easy OPEN: 10-6 MIN: £250 PERIOD: 18th-19th century SPECIALIST: English & Continental furniture GENERAL: Period ornaments, vases, candlesticks, chandeliers, objets d'art etc OTHER INFO: Between Claridges and Connaught hotels.

**Robin Kennedy**, 29 New Bond Street, WIY 9HD TEL: 4081238 FAX: 491 1662 PARKING: Medium OPEN: Mon-Fri 10-6 MIN: £50 MAX: £5,000 PERIOD: 18th-20th century SPECIALIST: Fine Japanese prints OTHER INFO: 30 yds from Sotheby's.

**Mayfair Carpets Gallery Ltd**, 41 & 47 New Bond Street, W1Y 0HB TEL: 493 0126 FAX: 408 2496 PARKING: Easy OPEN: 9.30-6 MIN: £59 MAX: £250,000 PERIOD: 19th-20th century SPECIALIST: Very rare antique Persian & Turkish silk & wool carpets & rugs.

**Mayfair Gallery**, 36 Davies Street, W1Y 1LG TEL: 491 3435 FAX: 491 3437 PARKING: Medium OPEN: 10-6 MIN: £500 MAX: £10,000 PERIOD: 19th-20th century SPECIALIST: French porcelain & furniture GENERAL: Antiques & decorative arts.

**Mayfair Gallery**, 37 South Audley Street, W1Y 5DH TEL: 491 3436 FAX: 491 3437 PARKING: Medium OPEN: 10-6 MIN: £500 MAX: £10,000 PERIOD: 19th-20th century SPECIALIST: French porcelain & furniture GENERAL: Antiques & decorative arts.

**John Mitchell & Son,** 160 New Bond Street, W1Y 9PA TEL: 493 7567 FAX: 493 5537 ASSNS: BADA, SLAD PARKING: Medium OPEN: Mon-Fri 9.30-5.30, Sat by appt MIN: £500 MAX: £1,000,000+ PERIOD: 17th-19th century SPECIALIST: Flower paintings GENERAL: Old Master paintings, drawings & watercolours, 17th century Dutch, 18th century English, 19th century French OTHER INFO: Gallery on 1st floor, family owned firm established 1931.

**The O'Shea Gallery**, 120 Mount Street, W1Y 5HB TEL: 629 1122 FAX: 629 1116 ASSNS: ABA, BADA CINOA PARKING: Medium OPEN: Mon-Fri 9.30-6 Sat 9.30-1 MIN: £5 MAX: £5000 PERIOD: 16th-19th century GENERAL: Worldwide maps & topographical prints, decorative prints, sporting, marine, botanical, natural history, architecture, caricature etc OTHER INFO: We exhibit at major antiques fairs in London & New York.

**The Oriental Art Gallery,** 4 Davies Street, W1Y 1LJ TEL: 499 7009 FAX: 409 0122 ASSNS: BADA PARKING: Easy OPEN: 9.30-6 PERIOD: 2000BC-1916AD SPECIALIST: Oriental art GENERAL: Chinese & Japanese ceramics, jades, hardstones, ivory, bronze, enamels, jewellery, etc.

**Nicholas S Pitcher Oriental Art**, 1st Floor, 29 New Bond Street, W1Y 9HD TEL: 499 6621 FAX: 491 1662 PARKING: Medium OPEN: 10-5 & by appt (advisable to ring anyway) MIN: £100 MAX: £10,000 PERIOD: 17th-18th century and much earlier SPECIALIST: Early Chinese pottery & porcelain GENERAL: Chinese & Japanese works of art OTHER INFO: Buys at auction & in Far East.

**Jonathan Potter Ltd**, 125 New Bond Street, W1Y 9AF TEL: 491 3520 FAX: 491 9754 ASSNS: ABA, BADA, LAPADA PARKING: Medium OPEN: Weekdays 10-6 & by appt MIN: £50 MAX: £10,000 PERIOD: 15th-19th century SPECIALIST: Original antique British & worldwide maps.

**Jonathan Robinson**, 1st Floor, 29 New Bond Street, W1Y 9HD TEL: 493 0592 FAX: 491 1662 PARKING: Medium OPEN: 10-5 MIN: £40 MAX: £10,000 PERIOD: 17th-20th century and much earlier SPECIALIST: Chinese porcelain GENERAL: Oriental works of art OTHER INFO: 4 doors from Sotheby's. On 1st floor so ring bell.

**Toynbee-Clarke Interiors Ltd**, 95 Mount Street, W1Y 5HG TEL: 499 4472/3 FAX: 495 1204 PARKING: Meters OPEN: Mon-Fri 9.30-5.30 MIN: £1000 MAX: £100,000 PERIOD: 18th-early 19th century SPECIALIST: Chinese export wallpaper GENERAL: Decorative Continental furniture, works of art & paintings OTHER INFO: Between Grosvenor & Connaught hotels, opposite Scotts restaurant.

**Linda Wrigglesworth**, Ground Floor, 34 Brook St, W1Y 1YA TEL: 408 0177 FAX: 491 9812 ASSNS: LAPADA PARKING: Meters, NCP OPEN: 10-6 or by appt MIN: £500 MAX: £15,000 PERIOD: 15th-19th century SPECIALIST: Chinese & Japanese Imperial court costume & textiles OTHER INFO: We work with museums & private collectors worldwide. Author of *Imperial Wardrobes.*

# Portobello Road W11 to Church Street NW8

**Portobello Road** is named for the farm to which it once led. The world famous market started in the 1870s and its traders were mostly gypsies dealing in horses and herbs. Although the character of the market changed over the years, it only became a centre for antiques in 1948 when the Caledonian Road market closed. There are antique shops here open all week but the principal trading day is Saturday when antique dealers from all over the country come to buy and sell.

**Notting Hill Gate** was a site of sand and gravel extraction from the 17th to 19th centuries and there was just a small settlement around this activity. Much of the surrounding land was countryside. Development started in the mid 19th century and the area was to prove one of contrasts between fine houses and terrible slums.

**Edgware Road**, lying to the east, follows the route of the Roman road of Watling Street. Starting at **Marble Arch** it runs north east to **St John's Wood** where it changes its name to **Maida Vale**. St John's Wood got its name because, between the 14th and 16th centuries, it was owned by the Knights of St John of Jerusalem. As the name suggests, during that time it was mostly forested and only in the time of Cromwell were the trees were felled. During the next 300 years the area retained a rural charm, although there was some small scale development. As in so many other London villages, it was the railways that changed the character of St John's Wood. Many of the charming houses and squares that had been erected were demolished to make way for tracks and large scale development followed. However, in many places, a charming and gracious atmosphere is still retained.

## ANTIQUE DEALERS

### LONDON W2 (0171)

**Bayswater Books,** 27A Craven Terrace, Lancaster Gate, W2 3EL TEL: 402 7398 PARKING: Easy OPEN: 11-7 or later MIN: 50p MAX: £1000 PERIOD: 19th-20th century SPECIALIST: Stereoscopic & other photographica GENERAL: Books, comics, maps, prints OTHER INFO: If the Serpentine kept flowing north out of Hyde Park it would flood my shop.

**John Bonham, Murray Feely Fine Art**, 46 Porchester Road, W2 6ET TEL: 221 7208 FAX: 589 0655 PARKING: Easy OPEN: 10.30-5.30 or by appt MIN: £100+ MAX: £50,000 PERIOD: 18th-20th century SPECIALIST: British & Continental surrealism.

**Ruby Buckle Antique Fireplaces**, 18 Chepstow Corner, Pembridge Villas, W2 4XE TEL: 229 8843 PARKING: Medium OPEN: 10-6 PERIOD: 19th century GENERAL: Pine, marble & stone fireplaces.

**Hosain's Books & Antiques**, 25 Connaught Street, W2 2AJ TEL & FAX: 262 7900 PARKING: Medium OPEN: Mon-Fri 11-5, Sat by appt MIN: £15 MAX: £3000 PERIOD: 17th-20th century SPECIALIST: Rare books, prints of India & Middle East GENERAL: Antique & second hand books on India, Central Asia & Middle East OTHER INFO: Shop is located off Edgware Road, near to Marble Arch.

**William Mansell,** 24 Connaught Street, W2 2AF TEL: 723 4154 PARKING: Easy OPEN: Mon-Fri 9-6, Sat 10-1 MIN: £20 MAX: £2000 PERIOD: 19th-20th century SPECIALIST: Silver & plate GENERAL: Silver & gold jewellery, watches.

**Mark Gallery**, 9 Porchester Place, Marble Arch, W2 2BS TEL: 262 4906 FAX: 224 9416 ASSNS: BADA, CINOA PARKING: Easy OPEN: Mon-Fri 10-1, Sat 11-1 MIN: £25 PERIOD: 19th-20th century SPECIALIST: 16th-19th century Russian icons GENERAL: Modern & contemporary French school lithographs, etchings, etc OTHER INFO: In the immediate vicinity there are 3 Italian restaurants, 1 French, 1 Persian & Indian plus 2 sandwich bars & a delicatessen.

### LONDON W8 (0171)

**Valerie Arieta**, 97b Kensington Church Street, W8 7LN TEL: 243 1074 PARKING: Medium OPEN: 10.30-5.30 MIN: £20 MAX: £8000 PERIOD: 19th century SPECIALIST: North American Indian & Eskimo art GENERAL: Folk art, curiosities.

**Garry Atkins**, 107 Kensington Church Street, W8 7LN TEL: 727 8737 FAX: 792 9010 PARKING:

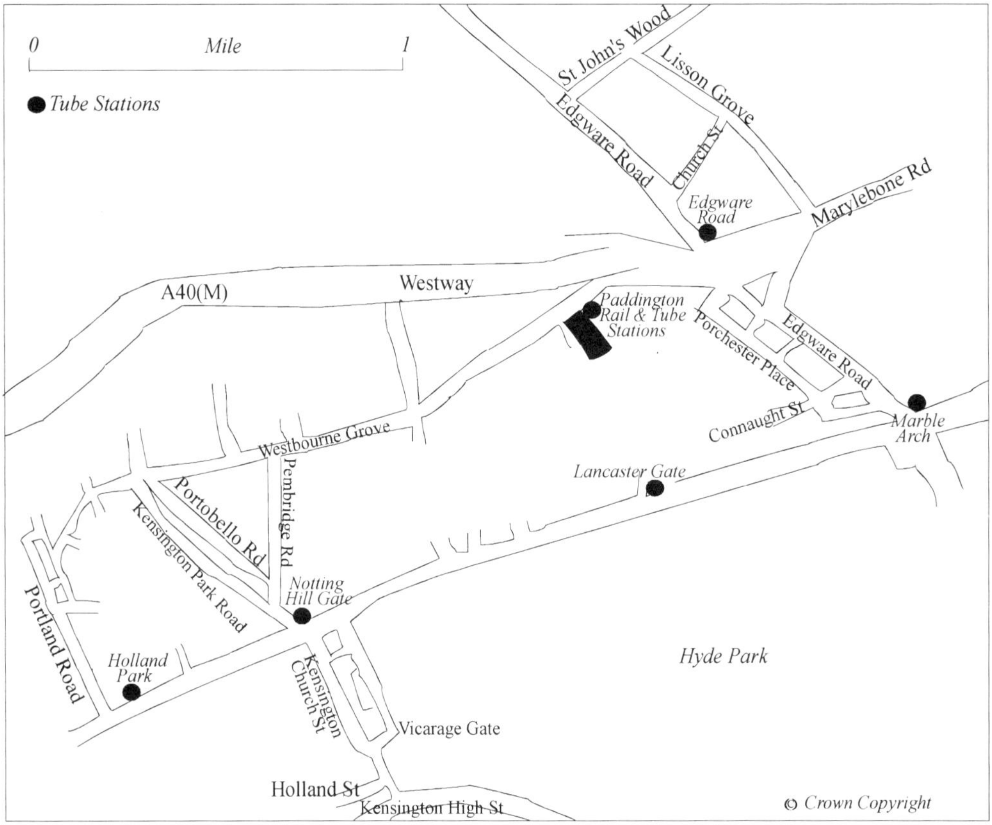


Medium OPEN: 10-5.30 MIN: £100 MAX: £10,000 PERIOD: 17th-18th century SPECIALIST: English & continental pottery.

**Eddy Bardawil Antiques**, 106 Kensington Church Street, W8 7LN TEL: 221 3967 FAX: 221 5124 ASSNS: BADA PARKING: Easy OPEN: Mon-Fri 9.30-5.30, Sat 10-1 MIN: £500 MAX: £25,000 PERIOD: 18th-early 19th century GENERAL: Furniture & works of art.

**Baumkotter Gallery**, 63a Kensington Church Street, W8 4BA TEL: 937 5171 FAX: 938 2312 ASSNS: LAPADA PARKING: Easy OPEN: Mon-Fri 9.30-6 MIN: £300 MAX: £60,000 PERIOD: half 17th, 10% 18th & 40% 19th century SPECIALIST: Oil paintings.

**David Brower Antiques**, 113 Kensington Church Street, W8 7LN TEL: 221 4155 FAX: 221 6211 PARKING: Medium OPEN: Mon-Fri 10-6 MIN: £200 MAX: £10,000 PERIOD: 19th century SPECIALIST: Continental, Oriental, English porcelain & bronzes.

**Lucy B Campbell,** 123 Kensington Church Street, W8 7LP TEL: 727 2205 FAX: 229 4352 ASSNS: BADA PARKING: Medium OPEN: Mon-Fri 10-6, Sat 10-4 MIN: £20 MAX: £2500+ PERIOD: 17th-20th century SPECIALIST: Antiquarian prints, naive artists.

**Belinda Coote,** 29 Holland Street, W8 4NA TEL: 937 3924 FAX: 376 1027 PARKING: Difficult OPEN: 10-6 MIN: £15 MAX: £2000 PERIOD: 20th century SPECIALIST: Tapestry wall hangings GENERAL: Tapestry cushions, fabrics.

**H W Deutsch**, 111 Kensington Church Street, W8 7LN TEL: 727 5984 ASSNS: LAPADA PARKING: Medium OPEN: Mon, Thurs, Fri PERIOD: 18th-19th century SPECIALIST: Silver GENERAL: Porcelain, objets d'art.

**Graham & Oxley (Antiques) Ltd**, 101 Kensington Church Street, W8 7LN TEL: 229 1850 FAX: 792 3348 ASSNS: BADA PARKING: Medium OPEN: 10-5.30 MIN: £100 MAX: £25,000 PERIOD: 18th-19th century SPECIALIST: English porcelain & engravings GENERAL: Decorative accessories.

**Robert Hales Antiques Ltd**, 131 Kensington Church Street, W8 7LP TEL & FAX: 229 3887 PARKING: Medium OPEN: Tues-Fri 9.30-5.30

MIN: £100 MAX: £50,000+ PERIOD: 17-19th century and earlier SPECIALIST: Oriental, Islamic, tribal arms & armour.

**Robert Harmon Antiques,** 140-142 Kensington Church Street, W8 4BN TEL: 221 6790 & (01525) 402322 ASSNS: BADA, LAPADA PARKING: Difficult OPEN: 10-6 MIN: £200 MAX: £50,000 PERIOD: 18th century SPECIALIST: Tea caddies, works of art GENERAL: 18th & 19th century pine furniture.

**Jeanette Hayhurst Fine Glass**, 32a Kensington Church Street, W8 4HQ TEL: 938 1539 PARKING: Medium OPEN: Mon-Fri 10-5, Sats 12-5 MIN: £10 MAX: £5,000 SPECIALIST: 18th-20th century glass, contemporary art glass.

**D Holmes Antiques,** 47c Earls Court Road (in Abingdon Villas), W8 6EE TEL: 937 6961 & (01208) 880254 PARKING: Medium OPEN: Fri 2-6, Sat 10-5 MIN: £50 MAX: £3/4000 PERIOD: 18th-19th century SPECIALIST: Mahogany furniture GENERAL: Good restored domestic furniture OTHER INFO: 100yds from the famous pub, The Scarsdale, Edwardes Sq.

**Hope & Glory**, 131a Kensington Church Street, W8 7LP TEL: 727 8424 PARKING: Medium OPEN: Mon-Sat 10-5 MIN: £5 MAX: £1000 PERIOD: 19th-20th century SPECIALIST: Royal commemorative ceramics & other items.

**Jonathan Horne Antiques Ltd,** 66c Kensington Church Street, W8 4BY TEL: 221 5658 FAX: 792 3090 PARKING: Medium OPEN: Mon-Fri 9.30-5.30 MIN: £45 MAX: £30,000 PERIOD: Medieval to early 19th century SPECIALIST: Early English pottery & works of art.

**Valerie Howard,** 2 Campden Street, W8 7EP TEL: 792 9702 ASSNS: LAPADA PARKING: Medium OPEN: Mon-Fri 10-5.30, Sat 10-4 MIN: £50 MAX: £15,000 PERIOD: 18th-20th century SPECIALIST: Mason's Ironstone china, services a speciality. French faience especially from Quimper.

**Iona Antiques**, P.O.Box 285, W8 6HZ TEL: 602 1193 FAX: 371 2843 ASSNS: BADA PARKING: Medium OPEN: Anytime by appt MIN: £1000 MAX: £20,000 SPECIALIST: 19th century paintings of animals.

**Japanese Gallery**, 66d Kensington Church Street, W8 4BY TEL: 229 2934 PARKING: Medium OPEN: 10-6 MIN: £5 MAX: £10,000 PERIOD: 19th-20th century SPECIALIST: Japanese woodcut prints GENERAL: Japanese arts, screens & furniture OTHER INFO: Free authentifications, on the spot framing.

**John Jesse**, 160 Kensington Church Street, W8 4BN TEL: 229 0312 FAX: 229 4732 PARKING: Easy OPEN: 10-6 MIN: £50+ PERIOD: 1880-1980 SPECIALIST: Art Nouveau, Deco objets, furniture GENERAL: Silver, glass, jewellery, lamps, paintings, ceramics & posters OTHER INFO: Near one of London's best restaurants, Kensington Place.

**Peter Kemp Antiques**, 170 Kensington Church Street, W8 4BN TEL & FAX: 229 2988 PARKING: Difficult OPEN: 10-5 or by appt MIN: £200 MAX: £200,000 PERIOD: 17th-18th century SPECIALIST: Oriental & Continental porcelain & works of art.

**Kensington Church Street Antiques Centre,** 58-60 Kensington Church Street, W8 4DB TEL: 937 4600 FAX: 937 3460 PARKING: Mon-Sat 10-6 PERIOD: 17th-20th century SPECIALIST: Arts & Crafts, Galle, Lalique & Loetz glass, jewellery, vintage fashion, furniture, pottery & porcelain, etc.

**Kensington Fine Arts**, 46 Kensington Church Street, W8 4BY TEL: 937 5317 PARKING: Medium OPEN: 10-5.30 MIN: £600 MAX: unlimited PERIOD: 17th-19th century SPECIALIST: Large decorative paintings.

**Lev Antiques**, 97a Kensington Church Street, W8 7LN TEL: 727 9248 PARKING: Medium OPEN: 10.30-5.30 MIN: £5 MAX: £500 PERIOD: 18th-20th century SPECIALIST: Jewellery, silver GENERAL: Paintings, curios.

**Little Winchester Gallery**, 36a Kensington Church Street, W8 4BX TEL: 937 8444 PARKING: Easy OPEN: 10-6 MIN: £500 MAX: £25,000 SPECIALIST: French 19th-20th GENERAL: Dutch 19th century, English primitives.

**London Curiosity Shop**, 66e Kensington Church Street, W8 4BY TEL: 792 2166 PARKING: Easy OPEN: Mon-Sat 10-6 MIN: £6 MAX: £6000 PERIOD: 19th-20th century SPECIALIST: Dolls (bisque head) GENERAL: Porcelain figurines, cups & saucers, prints of London.

**E & H Manners**, 66a Kensington Church Street, W8 4BY TEL: 229 5516 FAX: 229 5516 PARKING: Medium OPEN: Mon-Fri 10-5.30 MIN: £100 MAX: £20,000 PERIOD: 18th century SPECIALIST: European porcelain.

**Michael Coins**, 6 Hillgate Street, W8 7SR TEL: 727 1518 PARKING: Medium OPEN: Mon-Fri 10-

5 PERIOD: 17th-20th century GENERAL: Coins, banknotes, stamps etc.

**Roderick Antiques - Clocks**, 23 Vicarage Gate (junction Kensington Church Street), W8 4AA TEL: 937 8517 FAX: 937 8517 ASSNS: LAPADA PARKING: Medium OPEN: 10-5 MIN: £200 MAX: £5000 PERIOD: 18th-19th century SPECIALIST: 200+ longcase, carriage, bracket, skeleton & decorative clocks OTHER INFO: All stock fully restored & guaranteed. Export arranged.

**Brian Rolleston Antiques,** 104A Kensington Church Street, W8 4BU TEL & FAX: 229 5892 ASSNS: BADA PARKING: Medium OPEN: 10-1, 2.30-5.30 MIN: £1500 MAX: £50,000 PERIOD: 18th century SPECIALIST: Furniture.

**Santos,** 1 Campden Street, W8 7EP TEL: 727 4872 FAX: 229 4801 PARKING: Medium OPEN: Mon-Fri 10-1, 2-6 PERIOD: 17th-18th century SPECIALIST: Chinese export porcelain.

**M & D Seligmann,** 37 Kensington Church Street, W8 4LL TEL: 937 4044 FAX: 483 0480 ASSNS: BADA PARKING: Medium OPEN: Mon-Fri 10.30-5.30 Sat 11-4 PERIOD: 17th-19th century GENERAL: Country furniture, treen, early English pottery & objets d'art.

**Jean Sewell (Antiques) Ltd,** 3 Campden Street, W8 7EP TEL: 727 3122 ASSNS: BADA PARKING: Difficult OPEN: Mon-Fri 10-5.30, Sat 10-5 MIN: £1 MAX: £8000 PERIOD: 19th century SPECIALIST: English pottery, porcelain & ironstone.

**Constance Stobo,** 31 Holland Street, W8 4NA TEL: 937 6282 PARKING: Medium open; Mon-Fri 11-5, Sat 10-2 MIN: £80 MAX: £3500 PERIOD: 18th-19th century SPECIALIST: English Lustreware, Staffordshire animals.

**Stockspring Antiques**, 114 Kensington Church Street, W8 4BH TEL: 727 7995 FAX: 727 7995 ASSNS: LAPADA PARKING: Medium OPEN: Mon-Fri 10-5.30, Sat 10-1 MIN: £5 MAX: £5,000 PERIOD: 18th century SPECIALIST: English porcelain figures, Liverpool porcelain, pre 1830 English porcelain, Oriental porcelain GENERAL: World's main antique porcelain street.

**Pamela Teignmouth & Son**, 108 Kensington Church Street, W8 4BH TEL: 229 1602 FAX: 229 1602 PARKING: Medium-meters OPEN: 10-6 MIN: £30 MAX: £10,000 PERIOD: 18th-19th century SPECIALIST: Decorative furniture GENERAL: English & Continental furniture & decorative objects.

**Mary Wise & Grosvenor Antiques Ltd**, 27 Holland Street TEL: 937 8649 PARKING: Medium OPEN: Mon-Fri 9.30-5.30 MIN: £100 MAX: £5000 PERIOD: 18th-19th century SPECIALIST: Chinese watercolours GENERAL: Bronzes, porcelain, works of art.

## LONDON W11 (0171)

**Arbras Gallery**, 292 Westbourne Grove, W11 2PS TEL: 226 5221 FAX: 226 5221 ASSNS: PADA PARKING: Difficult OPEN: Fri 10-4, Sat 7-4.30 & by appt MIN: £20 MAX: £5000 PERIOD: 19th-20th century SPECIALIST: Silver, decorative arts GENERAL: Fine antique boxes, objects, pictures, prints, books OTHER INFO: On site Britain's largest wholesaler of modern silver photograph frames.

**P R Barham Antiques**, 111 Portobello Road, W11 2QB TEL: 727 3397 FAX: 243 1719 ASSNS: LAPADA PARKING: Easy OPEN: Mon-Sat 9-5 MIN: £50+ MAX: £15,000 PERIOD: 18th-20th century SPECIALIST: Fine Victorian furniture & clocks GENERAL: Good Continental furniture, French, Dutch, paintings & decorative items.

**Barham Antiques**, 83 Portobello Road, W11 2QB TEL & FAX: 727 3845 PARKING: Easy OPEN: 10-5 MIN: £10 MAX: £6000 PERIOD: 19th century SPECIALIST: Boxes, inkwells, glass, tea caddies, Victoriana.

**Sophia Blanchard Antiques,** 107 Portobello Road, W11 TEL: 229 5577 ASSNS: PADA PARKING: Medium OPEN: Sat 7.30-3 MIN: £5 MAX: £5000 PERIOD: 17th-20th century SPECIALIST: Needlework samplers, decorative clocks, snuff boxes, smalls GENERAL: Ceramics, treen.

**Books & Things**, at Arbras Gallery, 292 Westbourne Grove, W11 2PS TEL: 370 5593 FAX: 370 5593 ASSNS: ABA, PBFA PARKING: Difficult OPEN: Sat only 7-4 MIN: £5 MAX: £2000 PERIOD: 19th-20th century SPECIALIST: Posters & photography GENERAL: Books: childrens illustrated, decorative art, modern 1st editions.

**F E A Briggs/Wellington Antiques**, 73 Ledbury Road, W11 2AG TEL: 727 0909 PARKING: Medium OPEN: 8.30-5.30 MIN: £150+ MAX: £6,000 PERIOD: 19th century SPECIALIST: Mainly Victorian but some 18th and Edwardian furniture OTHER INFO: Warehouse & 2 shops. Interesting new pub, Beach Blanket Babylon.

**Butchoff Antiques**, 229 & 233 Westbourne Grove, W11 2SE TEL: 221 8174 FAX: 792 8923 ASSNS: LAPADA PARKING: Medium OPEN: Mon-Fri 10-6, Sat 10-4 MIN: £1000 MAX: £30,000 PERIOD: 17th-19th century SPECIALIST: English & Continental furniture.

**Caelt Gallery,** 182 Westbourne Grove, W11 2RH TEL: 229 9309 FAX: 727 8746 PARKING: Easy OPEN: 9.30-6 MIN: £100 MAX: £1000 PERIOD: 19th-20th century SPECIALIST: Soviet Realism & Impressionism GENERAL: 6000 oils from all periods, trade prices OTHER INFO: Supplying the trade for 25 years. Pubs, good restaurants & Portobello Road nearby.

**Jack Casimir Ltd**, 23 Pembridge Road, W11 3HG TEL: 727 8643 ASSNS: BADA, LAPADA PARKING: Medium OPEN: Mon-Sat 9.30-5.30 & by appt SPECIALIST: 16th-19th century brass, copper & pewter OTHER INFO: Fourth generation family business.

**Chanticleer Antiques,** Crown Arcade, 119 Portobello Road, W11 TEL & FAX: 385 0919 ASSNS: LAPADA, Fan Circle PARKING: Medium OPEN: Sat only 9.30-5, at home by appt MIN: £100 MAX: £2000 PERIOD: 18th-early 20th century GENERAL: Ivory, tortoiseshell, chess sets, European & Oriental works of art, miniatures.

**Cohen & Pearce,** 84 Portobello Road, W11 2QP TEL: 229 9458 FAX: 229 9653 ASSNS: BADA, PADA PARKING: Easy OPEN: Fri 10-4, Sat 8-4 & by appt MIN: £30 MAX: £100,000 PERIOD: 4th century BC to 18th century SPECIALIST: Chinese export porcelain GENERAL: Oriental pottery, porcelain & works of art.

**Sheila Cook Textiles**, 184 Westbourne Grove, W11 2RH TEL: 792 8001 PARKING: Medium OPEN: Tues-Sat 10-6 MIN: £1 MAX: £5000 PERIOD: 18th-20th century SPECIALIST: Textiles GENERAL: Decorative antiques.

**John Dale Antiques**, 87 Portobello Road, W11 2QB TEL: 727 1304 ASSNS: PADA PARKING: Difficult on Sats OPEN: Mon-Fri 10-4, Sat 7-5 MIN: £5 MAX: £1500 PERIOD: 17th-20th century SPECIALIST: Cameras, toys, antiquities, old books & prints, stained glass GENERAL: Furniture & furnishings.

**Peter Delehar & His Three Sisters**, 146 Portobello Road, W11 2DZ TEL: (081) 866 8659 PARKING: Difficult OPEN: Sat 9-4 MIN: £50 MAX: £5,000 PERIOD: 15th-20th century SPECIALIST: Scientific & medical instruments GENERAL: Fine bijouterie, textiles, objects, ephemera, costume jewellery OTHER INFO: Organizer of world's largest scientific & instrument fair.

**The Facade**, 196 Westbourne Grove, W11 2RH TEL: 727 2159 PARKING: Medium OPEN: Tues-Sat 10.30-5 MIN: £1 MAX: £5000 PERIOD: 19th-20th century SPECIALIST: French lighting & decorative furniture.

**Fleur de Lys Gallery**, 227a Westbourne Grove, W11 2SE TEL: 727 8595 PARKING: Easy OPEN: Mon-Sat 10.30-5 MIN: £1000 MAX: £5000 PERIOD: 19th century SPECIALIST: All decorative oil paintings of Dutch, English, European schools.

**J Freeman**, 85a Portobello Road, W11 2QB TEL: 221 5076 FAX: 221 5329 PARKING: Medium OPEN: 9-5 MIN: £5 MAX: £3000 PERIOD: 19th-20th century SPECIALIST: Silver + plate, canteens of cutlery.

**Garrick Coleman Antiques**, Stand II, Van's Arcade, 105 Portobello Road, W11 2QR TEL: 937 5524 FAX: 937 5530 PARKING: Difficult OPEN: Sat 8-2 & by appt MIN: £50 MAX: £5000 PERIOD: 17th-19th century SPECIALIST: Fine chess sets & boards, glass paperweights, works of art & decorative arts.

**Patricia Harbottle**, Stand 16, Geoffrey Van's Arcade, 107 Portobello Road, W11 2QB TEL: 731 1972 FAX: 731 3663 ASSNS: PADA PARKING: Difficult OPEN: Sat 6.45-3 MIN: £5 MAX: £1500 PERIOD: 18th-19th century SPECIALIST: Wine-related antiques.

**Hirst Antiques**, 59 Pembridge Road, W11 3HN TEL: 727 9364 PARKING: Difficult OPEN: 10-6 MIN: £2 MAX: £10,000 PERIOD: 17th-20th century SPECIALIST: Fourposter & half tester beds GENERAL: Sculpture, bronzes, decorative items.

**Jones Antique Lighting**, 194 Westbourne Grove, W11 2RH TEL & FAX: 229 6866 PARKING: Medium OPEN: 6 days 9.30-6 PERIOD: 1860-1960 SPECIALIST: Lighting—Victorian, Arts & Crafts, Art Deco & Nouveau, many signed pieces, no reproduction.

**Peter Kennedy**, 1st Floor, 305 Westbourne Grove, W11 2QA TEL: 243 1416 FAX: 243 2271 ASSNS: ABA PARKING: Easy OPEN: By appt MIN: £10 MAX: £2000 PERIOD: 17th-19th century SPECIALIST: Prints & books (illustrated only).

**Kleanthous Antiques Ltd**, Stouts Antiques Market, 144 Portobello Road, W11 2DZ TEL: 727 3649 FAX: (0181) 980 1199, (01923) 897618 ASSNS: LAPADA, PADA PARKING: Difficult OPEN: Sat 6.30-4 PERIOD: 18th-20th century SPECIALIST: Vintage wrist & pocket watches (Rolex, Cartier etc), Georgian, Victorian, Art Nouveau/Deco jewellery, silver, clocks, objets de vertu OTHER INFO: Guarantees with all purchases.

**Daniel Mankowitz**, 208a Westbourne Grove, W11 2RH TEL: 229 9270 FAX: 229 4687 PARKING: Easy OPEN: 10-6 MIN: £50+ MAX: £15,000 PERIOD: 17th-18th century SPECIALIST: Early & unusual furniture, sculptures, paintings, textiles, & decoratives.

**Robin Martin Antiques**, 44 Ledbury Road TEL: 727 1301 PARKING: Easy OPEN: 10-5.30 MIN: £200 MAX: £15,000 PERIOD: 17th-19th century GENERAL: English & Continental furniture, works of art.

**Mayflower Antiques,** 117 Portobello Road, W11 TEL: 727 0381 FAX: (01255) 504079 ASSNS: PADA PARKING: Medium OPEN: Sat 7-5 MIN: £10 MAX: £10,000 PERIOD: 19th century SPECIALIST: Mechanical music, clocks, scientific instruments & collectors' items.

**Mercury Antiques**, 1 Ladbroke Road, W11 3PA TEL: 727 5106 ASSNS: BADA PARKING: Medium OPEN: Mon-Sat 10-5.30 PERIOD: 18th-early 19th century SPECIALIST: English porcelain & pottery, Delft & glass.

**E & A Di Michele,** 36 Ledbury Road, W11 2AB TEL & FAX: 229 1823 PARKING: Medium PERIOD: 17th-19th century GENERAL: Continental & general stock.

**Terence Morse & Son Ltd,** 237 Westbourne Grove, W11 2SB TEL: 229 9320 & 229 4059 PARKING: Medium OPEN: Mon-Fri 10-6, Sat 11-2 PERIOD: 18th-19th century SPECIALIST: Quality furniture.

**Myriad Antiques**, 131 Portland Road, Holland Park Avenue TEL: 229 1709 Parking Easy OPEN: Mon-Sat 11-6 MIN: £5 MAX: £1,500 PERIOD: 18th-20th century SPECIALIST: Decorative unusual items including garden furniture, kitchen, bathrooms, beds OTHER INFO: 2 amusing & delectable restaurants.

**Old Father Time Clock Centre,** 101 Portobello Road, W11 2BQ TEL & FAX: 546 6299 PARKING: Fri easy, Sat difficult OPEN: Fri 9-2, Sat 6-4 or by appt MIN: £25 MAX: £10,000 PERIOD: 18th-20th century SPECIALIST: Clocks, all types OTHER INFO: The landmark of the premises is a large teapot outside.

**Peter Petrou**, 195 Westbourne Grove, W11 2SB TEL: 229 9575 FAX: 229 9575 PARKING: Medium OPEN: 10-6 MIN: £100 MAX: £50,000 PERIOD: 17th-20th century SPECIALIST: Vienna bronzes, Blue John, sculpture GENERAL: Works of art, Oriental & European bronzes, antiquities, ethnographica, good decorative items.

**ES Philips & Sons,** 99 Portobello Road, W11 2QB TEL: 229 2113 FAX: 229 1963 ASSNS: Guild of Master Craftsmen PARKING: Medium MIN: £20 MAX: £3000 PERIOD: 19th century SPECIALIST: Stained glass & ecclsiastical regalia.

**Portobello Antique Co,** 133 Portobello Road, W11 2DY TEL: 221 0344 FAX: 365 0746 PARKING: Medium OPEN: Fri 10-4, Sat 8-5 or by appt MIN: £3.50 MAX: £2500 PERIOD: 19th-20th century SPECIALIST: Silver plate cutlery & giftware GENERAL: Table lamps, small furniture OTHER INFO: We are one of the original shops in Portobello Road, established 1950.

**Rogers Antiques Gallery**, 65 Portobello Road TEL: 351 5353 FAX: 351 5350 PARKING: Medium OPEN: Sat 7-4 MIN: £5 MAX: £5,000 PERIOD: 18th-20th century GENERAL: Good jewellery & silver OTHER INFO: Since 1974 first & longest Portobello Road gallery with own café serving quality homemade food.

**Silver Fox Gallery,** 121 Portobello Road, W11 2DY TEL & FAX: 243 8027 ASSNS: PADA PARKING: Easy OPEN: Sat 6-3 MIN: £50 MAX: £500+ PERIOD: 17th-20th century SPECIALIST: Jewellery GENERAL: Seals, pocket & wrist watches OTHER INFO: We are a specialist trade gallery for antique jewellery. There are 21 dealers under one roof.

**Louis Stanton**, 299-301 Westbourne Grove, W11 2QA TEL: 727 9336 FAX: 727 5424 ASSNS: BADA, CINOA PARKING: Easy OPEN: 6 days 10-5.30 MIN: £100 MAX: £20,000 SPECIALIST: Early oak furniture 1550-1700 GENERAL: Objects pre1840 OTHER INFO: Wonderful restaurants.

**Stern Art Dealers**, 46 Ledbury Road, W11 2HB TEL & FAX: 229 6187 ASSNS: LAPADA PARKING: Easy OPEN: 10-6 MIN: £300 MAX: £7000 SPECIALIST: Paintings by Pissaro family GENERAL: 19th century & early 20th century British & post-impressionist.

**Themes & Variations**, 231 Westbourne Grove,

W11 2SE TEL: 727 5531 FAX: 221 6378 OPEN: 10-1, 2-6 SPECIALIST: Exclusive Fornasetti furniture, 1940-70's furniture, Murano glass & Italian ceramics 1950-60's, contemporary designers.

**Graham Walpole**, 187 Westbourne Grove, W11 2RS TEL: 229 0267 ASSNS: LAPADA PARKING: Medium OPEN: Mon-Sat 10-5.30 MIN: £50 MAX: £10,000 PERIOD: 18th-19th century GENERAL: Austrian bronzes, folk & maritime art, small furniture, decorative antiques.

**Wynard Wilkinson Antique Silver**, 165-169 Portobello Road TEL: 229 0539 FAX:L 229 3506 PARKING: Medium OPEN: Sat 7-3.30 MIN: £5 MAX: £50,000 PERIOD: 17th-20th century SPECIALIST: Collectors silver, colonial & provincial GENERAL: Table silver + plate OTHER INFO: Green painted stall, T.F. Wilkinson always wears green baize apron.

## LONDON NW8 (0171)

**Alfies Antique Market**, 13-25 Church Street, NW8 8DT TEL: 723 6066 FAX: 724 0999 PARKING: Easy OPEN: 10-6 MIN: £5 MAX: £5,000 PERIOD: 18th-20th century GENERAL: Whole spectrum of antiques & collectables OTHER INFO: 200 dealers with 370 stands, England's largest covered antique market with rooftop restaurant.

**Beverley**, 30 Church Street, Marylebone, NW8 8EP TEL: 262 1576 PARKING: Medium OPEN: Mon-Thurs 11-7, Fri-Sat 9.30-7 MIN: £5 MAX:£7000 PERIOD: 19th-20th century SPECIALIST: Clarice Cliff, Suzie Cooper, Art Deco GENERAL: 1850-1950 ceramics, metals, glass OTHER INFO: 10 mins walk from Baker Street Station, Madame Tussauds & Planetarium.

**Dodo,** F073 Alfies, Church Street, NW8 (& 286 Westbourne Grove, W11 on Sats 7-4) TEL: 706 1545 & 229 3132 evenings PARKING: Medium OPEN: Tues-Fri 10.30-5.30 MIN: 50p MAX: £750 PERIOD: 19th-20th century SPECIALIST: Advertising, posters, labels, etc GENERAL: Biscuit & sweet tins, signs, showcards.

**J Nicholas Drummond**, 6 St Johns Wood Road, NW8 8RE TEL: 286 6452 FAX: 286 6452 PARKING: Medium OPEN: By appt MIN: £200 MAX: £40,000 PERIOD: 19th-20th century SPECIALIST: Continental, American, British oils GENERAL: 19th century paintings supplied to the trade, decorators, hotels etc.



**Patricia Harvey Antiques**, 42 Church Street, NW8 8EP TEL:262 8989 FAX: 262 9090 PARKING: Easy OPEN: Mon-Fri 10-6, Sat 12-5 MIN: £50 MAX: £5,000 PERIOD: 17th-20th century SPECIALIST: Decorator's accessories, textiles, beautiful and unusual items GENERAL: Primitive watercolours, paintings, decorative furniture OTHER INFO: Established antiques area, 3 cafés.

**Just Desks,** 20 Church Street, NW8 8EP TEL: 723 7976 FAX: 402 6416 ASSNS: LAPADA PARKING: Medium OPEN: Mon-Sat 9.30-5.30 MIN: £500 MAX: £4000 PERIOD: 19th-20th century SPECIALIST: Pedestal desks GENERAL: Desks

**Lenson-Smith**, 11 Church Street, Lisson Grove, NW8 8EE TEL: 724 7763 PARKING: Medium OPEN: 10-5 MIN: £50 MAX: £5,000 PERIOD: 19th-20th century SPECIALIST: Animalia GENERAL: Decorative, interesting items.

**The Studio,** 18 Church Street, NW8 8EP TEL: 258 0763 OPEN: Mon-Fri 10-6 MIN: £10 MAX: £10,000 PERIOD: 19th-20th century SPECIALIST: Arts & Crafts, Gothic, Art Deco particularly architect & designer furniture.

# North Kent

*The statue of Sir Winston Churchill at Westerham*

This tour starts in the south east outer suburbs of Greater London, wending its way through the lovely villages of Mid Kent before passing through the industrial landscape of North Kent along the Thames Estuary.

After first stopping in pleasant suburban **Beckenham,** the route goes, via **Sundridge**, to **Chislehurst** which, in spite of being on the edge of the metropolis, still retains the appearance of a rural village. It is famous for its underground chalk galleries, the Chislehurst Caves, and for the association with Napoleon III and the Empress Eugenie who lived at Camden House. A memorial to their son, who died in in the British war against the Zulus, stands on the large wooded common. Next is the town of **Farnborough** (not to be confused with Farnborough , Hampshire) Proceeding onwards the tour reaches **Biggin Hill,** closely associated with aviation particularly during the Second World War when it was used as a Battle of Britain airfield. It is now a business and flying club airport with a very big airshow, usually every May.

Further south, **Westerham** is next, boasting numerous antique shops. General Wolfe was born here in 1727 in Quebec House and lived there for his first eleven years. Wolfe was famous for his defeat of the French in Canada but was killed on the Heights of Abraham at the very moment of his victory. Quebec House is now owned by the National Trust and has been restored to its 17th century appearance.

Chartwell, two miles south of Westerham, was the home of Sir Winston Churchill, Britain's great war-time leader. Owned by the National Trust, the views from the house across the Kentish countryside are lovely. There are six doors from the house into the garden, perhaps indicating its importance to the

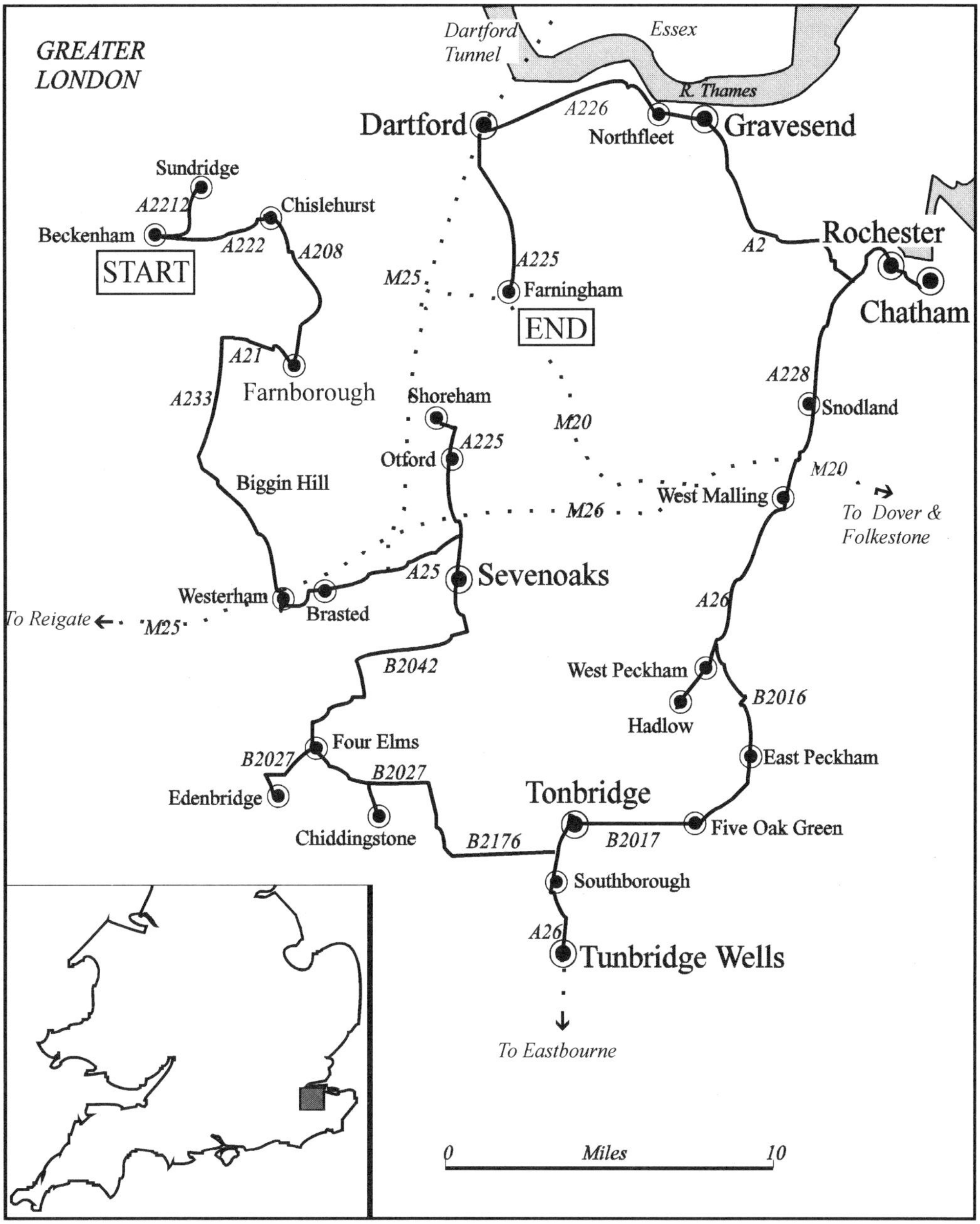
GREATER LONDON
Dartford Tunnel
Essex
R. Thames
Dartford
A226
Northfleet
Gravesend
Sundridge
A2212
Chislehurst
Beckenham
A222
A208
START
A225
M25
Farningham
END
A2
Rochester
Chatham
A21
A233
Farnborough
Shoreham
A228
Snodland
M20
A225
Otford
Biggin Hill
M20
West Malling
To Dover & Folkestone
M26
A25
Sevenoaks
Westerham
Brasted
To Reigate
M25
A26
B2042
West Peckham
B2016
Hadlow
Four Elms
East Peckham
B2027
B2027
Edenbridge
Tonbridge
Chiddingstone
Five Oak Green
B2176
B2017
Southborough
A26
Tunbridge Wells
To Eastbourne
0
Miles
10

residents of Chartwell. There are many reminders of Sir Winston. His paintings hang on the walls, the stand-up desk where he wrote his books is still here as are his medals, uniforms and the family photographs. A most poignant reminder of one of his favourite spots is the garden chair standing by the pond where he used to sit to feed the fish. **Brasted,** just east, is also choc-a-bloc with antiques shops.

After the villages of **Otford** and **Shoreham** the tour comes to **Sevenoaks** whose most notable place of interest is Knole, a 15th century mansion set in a most beautiful park of 1000 acres. The house was built by Thomas Bourchier, Archbishop of Canterbury, and remained the property of the Archbishops until Thomas Cranmer was forced to give it to Henry VIII. Given to Thomas Sackville by Elizabeth I, his family, first the Earls then the Dukes of Dorset, have lived there ever since. Knole's wonderful treasure house of furnishings can be attributed to the sixth Earl who was Lord Chamberlain to William III and as such was entitled to take any discarded furnishings from the royal palaces.

Four and a half miles east of Sevenoaks, off the A25, stands Ightham Mote, one of the most complete medieval moated manor houses in the country. A National Trust property, this 14th century house standing in a wooded valley, has half-timbered upper storeys and steeply pitched gables. Alterations made through the centuries do not detract from its appearance as local stone was used and the changes were in keeping with the style of the house.

Moving south, through **Four Elms** village, the town of **Edenbridge** stands close to Hever Castle, a 13th century double-moated castle, the childhood home of Anne Boleyn, Henry VIII's tragic queen. At the beginning of this century the American millionaire, William Waldorf Astor, bought the castle. He spent three years restoring it and filling it with treasures. Now there are exhibitions on the Astors and Anne Boleyn as well as a regimental museum.

A much later castle may be seen at **Chiddingstone**. Mostly dating from the 18th and 19th centuries, nevertheless it does incorporate a 17th century manor. It contains wonderful collections of Egyptian antiquities, Japanese swords and armour, lacquerware, Stuart and Jacobite memorabilia as well as fine furniture and paintings.

Detouring along the A26, **Southborough** is followed by **Tunbridge Wells**. Perhaps seen now as the epitome of suburban gentility, it was a fashionable spa in the 17th century. The area of the Pantiles takes its name from the large roofing tiles that were laid as a pavement.

The next stop, ancient **Tonbridge**, has only the ruins of its castle. The Saxons had a fortress here and later a castle was built on the same mound. Now only the 13th century gatehouse remains although an 18th century mansion was built alongside.

Between **Five Oak Green** and **East Peckham**, is the famous brewery, Whitbread's Hop Farm. Despite the map, **Hadlow** can also be reached following country lanes a mile west of East Peckham. **West Peckham** is much smaller but has a really nice village green and an unusually interesting church, probably dating back before William The Conqueror with evidence of work throughout the next 800 years. **West Malling**, next, is a market town with the remains of a Norman castle and abbey.

Approaching the Thames Estuary via **Snodland** and **Cuxton,** (just south of the M2), neighbouring **Rochester** was a Roman town, situated where Watling Street crosses the River Medway. It has a medieval castle following the lines of the earlier Roman fortress which, because of the extreme strategic importance of the site, was one of the first to be constructed. Rochester's cathedral attracted enough pilgrims for present day visitors to see the steps worn down by their feet. Henry VIII first met Anne of Cleves, The Flanders Mare, at the Old Hall. She was one of his luckier wives—she was only divorced. Lovers of Charles Dickens, who lived at Gads Hill from 1857 to 1870, will find interest in Rochester as it was a setting in *Great Expectations*. At Eastgate House, in the High Street, there is the Charles Dickens Centre which recreates Victorian life for the visitor.

Tthe tour now crosses the Medway to come to **Chatham** with its famous naval shipyard. In the Chatham Historic Dockyard there are 47 Scheduled Ancient Monuments, mainly from the 18th century. This is said to form the most complete surviving early to mid 18th century dockyard in the country. It was from here that the Victory, Nelson's ship at Trafalgar, was launched in 1765. The Dockyard contains eight galleries covering 400 years of shipbuilding history. The award winning 'Wooden Walls' display recreates the building of a wooden warship in the mid 18th century. The Royal Engineers Museum displays examples of military engineering starting with an assault bridge built by Julius Caesar. General Gordon of Khartoum, the most renowned Royal Engineer, is commemorated here. The Medway Heritage Centre tells the story of the Medway from the earliest times.

Now heading towards London again, **Gravesend** is partly famous for the association with Pocahontas, the American Indian who saved the life of John Smith in Virginia. She is buried in the churchyard of St George's Church and also has a statue. Not a mile upriver is **Northfleet** and then, 6 miles closer to London is the **Dartford** conurbation once a Roman crossing point for the River Darent and the site of a Roman station. The town contains one of the few existing Georgian galleried inns in the country, the Bull Hotel. The M25 crosses into Essex at this point via the Dartford Tunnel. The last stop is **Farningham**, just south of the M20 on the A225. Many unusual plants can be seen at the nearby Wood Nature Reserve.

## ANTIQUE DEALERS

### BECKENHAM (0181)

**Norman Witham**, 2 High Street TEL: 650 9096 PARKING: Medium OPEN: Fri-Sat or by appt MIN: £5 MAX: £500 PERIOD: 18th-20th century SPECIALIST: English small china & glass GENERAL: Good old English china teaware OTHER INFO: 20 mins from London's Victoria.

### SUNDRIDGE (01959)

**Sundridge Gallery**, 9 Church Road, TN14 6DT TEL: 564104 PARKING: Own carpark OPEN: 10-5.30 & by appt MIN: £80 MAX: £15,000 PERIOD: 19th-20th century SPECIALIST: Watercolours, some oils GENERAL: Some period rugs OTHER INFO: Close to Brasted village, Ide Hill & Emmetts.

**Colin Wilson Antiques**, 103 Main Road, TN14 6EQ TEL: 562043 PARKING: Medium OPEN: 10-5 MIN: £200 MAX: £2000 PERIOD: 19th century SPECIALIST: Mahogany furniture GENERAL: Chests, tables, bookcases, sets of chairs, single armchairs OTHER INFO: Chartwell, Ightham Mote.

### CHISLEHURST (0181)

**Michael Sim**, 1 Royal Parade, BR7 5PG TEL: 467 7040 FAX: 467 4352 PARKING: Easy OPEN: 7 days 9-6 MIN: £250 MAX: £50,000 PERIOD: 18th-19th century SPECIALIST: Clocks, barometers, globes, scientific instruments, miniatures GENERAL: Georgian & Regency furniture OTHER INFO: Chislehurst Caves are 22 miles long and many say better than Cheddar or Derbyshire.

### FARNBOROUGH (01689)

**Farnborough (Kent) Antiques**, 10 Church Road, BR6 7DB TEL: 851834, ASSNS: BADA PARKING: Easy OPEN: Sats 9.30-5.30 & by appt MIN: £250 MAX: £5000 PERIOD: 16th-18th century SPECIALIST: Oak furniture & wood carvings GENERAL: OTHER INFO: Close to Kent countryside: Knole, Chartwell, Westerham & Brasted.

### BIGGIN HILL (01959)

**Antiques & Country Pine International**, Leaves Green Trading Company, Unit 4, Concorde Business Centre, The Airport, TN16 3YN TEL: 540449 FAX: 540448 PARKING: Own carpark OPEN: Mon-Sat 10-5 MIN: £5 MAX: £500 PERIOD: 18th-20th century SPECIALIST: Full range of pieces made from antique timbers GENERAL: Antique & reproduction country pine furniture from all over UK & Europe, wholesale/retail. Containers packed for overseas OTHER INFO: World famous WWII Battle of Britain airfield, 4 miles from Winston Churchill's home at Chartwell.

### WESTERHAM (01959)

**Apollo Galleries**, 19-21 Market Square, TN16 1AN TEL: 562200 ASSNS: LAPADA PARKING: Medium OPEN: Mon-Sat 9.30-5.30 MIN: £20 MAX: £12,500 PERIOD: 18th-early 20th century (mainly 19th) SPECIALIST: Victorian oils & bronzes GENERAL: Clocks, water-colours, furniture, porcelain, silver, pottery, glass boxes, objets d'art OTHER INFO: King's Arm Hotel, Chartwell, Honours Mill restaurant in centre Edenbridge (expensive but superb!).

**Castle Antiques Centre**, 1 London Road, TEL: 562492 PARKING: Medium OPEN: Mon-Sat10-5 MIN: £1 MAX: £500 PERIOD: 19th-20th century SPECIALIST: Linen GENERAL: Silver plate, books, postcards, small furniture, country bygones,

(8 dealers) OTHER INFO: Centre of tourist area, Penshurst Place, Hever Castle, Knole House, Quebec House, Chartwell. Good hotels, 50 local antique shops, 6 antiques centres.

**Anthony Hook Antiques**, 3 The Green, TN16 1AT TEL: 562161 PARKING: Medium OPEN: 9-5.30 MIN: £100 MAX: £10,000 PERIOD: 18th-20th century GENERAL: Furniture.

**Marks Antiques,** 5 The Green, TN16 1AS TEL & FAX: 562017 PARKING: Easy OPEN: Mon-Sat 9.30-5.30 MIN: £50 MAX: £15,000 PERIOD: 18th-19th century SPECIALIST: Fine Georgian furniture GENERAL: English furniture.

**Hugh McNair Antiques**, Fullers Hill TEL: 562970 PARKING: Medium OPEN: Mon-Sat 10-5 MIN: £5 MAX: £1,000 PERIOD: 18th-19th century SPECIALIST: Small silverware GENERAL: Furniture, music boxes OTHER INFO: Centre of very popular, busy tourist & antiques area but well worth stopping. 2 large carparks on outskirts of town.

**Mistral Galleries**, 12 Market Square, TN16 1AW TEL: 564477 FAX: 61417 PARKING: Easy OPEN: Mon-Sat 9.30-5.30 MIN: £500 MAX: £50,000 PERIOD: 18th-19th century SPECIALIST: Victorian oil paintings & watercolours GENERAL: Fine quality period English & continental furniture, porcelain, silver, bronzes.

**Old Hall Antiques**, 24 Market Square, TN16 1AR TEL: 563114 ASSNS: LAPADA PARKING: Easy MIN: £30 MAX: £10,000+ PERIOD: 17th-19th century SPECIALIST: Early oak furniture GENERAL: Brass, copper, pewter, Delft carvings.

**Regal Antiques,** 2 Market Square, TN16 1AW TEL & FAX: 561778 PARKING: Medium OPEN: Tues-Sat 10-5 MIN: £15 MAX: £2000 PERIOD: 18th-20th century SPECIALIST: Vintage watches, portrait miniatures GENERAL: Jewellery.

**Sargeants Antiques,** 21 The Green, TN16 1AX TEL: 562130 PARKING: Medium OPEN: 9-5.30 SPECIALIST: Glass, chandeliers, decanters, lustres GENERAL: Bronze, ormolu OTHER INFO: We also clean & restore chandeliers.

**Taylor-Smith Antiques**, 4 The Grange, High Street, TN16 1AH TEL: 563100 FAX: 561561 ASSNS: LAPADA PARKING: Own carpark OPEN: Mon, Tues, Thurs-Sat 10-5 MIN: £50 MAX: £15,000 PERIOD: 17th-19th century SPECIALIST: Items relating to Sir Winston Churchill, furniture, Lalique, Gallé and Art Deco.

**Taylor-Smith Books,** 2 High Street, TN16 1RE TEL & FAX: 561561 PARKING: Own carpark OPEN: Tues-Sat, 10-5, Sun 2.30-5 MIN: £1 MAX: £5000 PERIOD: 18th-20th century SPECIALIST: Winston Churchill (3000 items) GENERAL: Large stock of history, biography, local history, etc. OTHER INFO: Only Winston Churchill specialist in the UK, opened in 1792, one of the oldest bookshops in the country.

**BRASTED (01959)**

**The Attic (Sevenoaks) Ltd**., The Village House, TN16 1HU TEL: 563507 ASSNS: ABA PARKING: Own carpark STOCK: 18th-20th century.

**Courtyard Antiques**, High Street TEL: 564483 PARKING: Own carpark OPEN: Mon-Sat 10-5.30 MIN: £20 MAX: £3000 PERIOD: 19th-20th century SPECIALIST: Large Victorian wind-out tables, jewellery, silver GENERAL: Furniture, porcelain OTHER INFO: Near Chartwell, Knole Park & Sevenoaks.

**Darenth Antiques,** 5 High Street, TN16 1JJ TEL: 565911 PARKING: Easy OPEN: 10-5.30 MIN: £20 MAX: £3500 PERIOD: 18th-19th century GENERAL: Furniture, silver, watercolours.

**Peter Dyke**, Kentish House, High Street, TN16 1RJ TEL: 565020 OPEN: 9.30-5 PARKING: Easy OPEN: 9.30-5 MIN: £250 MAX: £10,000 PERIOD: 18th-19th century SPECIALIST: Library & dining room furniture GENERAL: Georgian, some Victorian furniture, mainly early 19th century items, some paintings OTHER INFO: In centre of village next to popular tearooms

**Roy Massingham Antiques**, The Old Coach House, High Street TEL: 562408 ASSNS: LAPADA PARKING: Good OPEN: Mon-Sat 9.30-5.30 MIN: £150 MAX: £15,000 PERIOD: 18th-19th century SPECIALIST: Furniture GENERAL: Pictures and decorative furniture.

**Old Bakery Antiques**, High Street, TN16 1JA TEL: 562994 PARKING: Easy OPEN: 9.30-5.30 MIN: £200 MAX: £2500 PERIOD: 18th-19th century SPECIALIST: Pine & country furniture OTHER INFO: Kent's premier antique village, 18+ shops.

**The Old Manor House**, The Green, TN16 1JL TEL: 562536 PARKING: Easy OPEN: 10-5.30 MIN: £1 MAX: £4000 PERIOD: 18th-20th century SPECIALIST: Mantel, regulator, longcase clocks GENERAL: Barometers, small furniture, mirrors, lights, copperware, boxes OTHER INFO: Old Manor House built in 1592. Visitors should not be put off by signs saying 'For security reasons -

please ring' it shows we have good stock.

**Southdown House Antiques**, High Street, TN16 1JE Tel: 563522 PARKING: Own carpark OPEN: Mon-Sat 9.30-5.30 not Bank Hols MAX: £5000 PERIOD: 18th-early 20th century GENERAL: Furniture, pictures, porcelain, metalware, textiles.

**Dinah Stoodley**, High Street, TN16 1JE TEL: 563616 PARKING: Own carpark OPEN: Mon-Sat 9.30-5.30 PERIOD: 17th-18th century MIN: £50 MAX: £10,000 SPECIALIST: Period oak & country furniture, English ceramics.

**TilingsAntiques**, High Street TEL: 564735 PARKING: Easy OPEN: Mon-Sat 10-5 MIN: £10 MAX: £2000 PERIOD: 17th-19th century GENERAL: Furniture, porcelain, decorative items, needlework.

**Village Antique Centre,** 4 The High Street, TN16 1HR TEL: 564545 PARKING: Own carpark OPEN: Mon-Sat 10-5.30 MIN: £10 MAX: £12,000 PERIOD: 17th-20th century SPECIALIST: Silver, jewellery GENERAL: Furniture, general antiques.

## OTFORD (01959)

**Gossips Antiques,** 11A High Street TEL: 524322 PARKING: Easy OPEN: Tues, Thurs-Sat 10-5.30 Wed & Sun 12-5 MIN: £1 MAX: £500 PERIOD: 19th-20th century SPECIALIST: China & glass GENERAL: Furniture.

## SHOREHAM (01959)

**The Porcelain Collector**, High Street, TN14 7TD TEL: 23416 PARKING: Easy OPEN: By appt MIN: £50 MAX: £2,000 PERIOD: 19th-20th century SPECIALIST: Worcester porcelain from founding of original companies to present day, Lambeth wares GENERAL: English & Continental porcelain figures up to Art Deco period, modern porcelain & bronze limited editions, particularly military subjects OTHER INFO: Specialist in porcelain restoration. In unspoilt River Darenth valley.

## SEVENOAKS (01732)

**Amherst Antiques**, 23 London Road, Riverhead TN13 2BU TEL: 455047 PARKING: Difficult OPEN: Mon, Tues, Thurs-Sat 9.30-5 MIN: £10 MAX: £4000 PERIOD: 18th-20th century SPECIALIST: Tunbridgeware, 19th century European ceramics GENERAL: Small furniture, silver, coloured glass, prints OTHER INFO: Shop on main A25. Good buying route through Brasted & Westerham. Chartwell, Hever Castle, Penshurst Place, Ightham Mote & Knole House all nearby.

**TheAntiques Centre**, 120 London Road, Tubs Hill, TN13 1BA TEL: 452104 PARKING: Easy OPEN: 10-1, 2-4.30, but Weds & Sat 10-1 & by appt (ring doorbell-resident) MIN: £5 MAX: £5000 PERIOD: 17th-19th century GENERAL: Furniture in mahogany, oak, decorative items, silver, porcelain, brass, copper. Reference books on antiques. OTHER INFO: Close to station, London 25 mins.

**Atropos Antiques,** 21 St John's Hill, TN13 3NX TEL: 454179 PARKING: Easy OPEN: 10-5.30, closed Wed MIN: £5 MAX: £10,000 PERIOD: 18th-19th century SPECIALIST: Antique barometers GENERAL: Natural history items, collectables, decorative, curious, mysterious & unusual items.

**Bradbourne Gallery**, 4 St John's Hill,TN13 3NP TEL & FAX: 460756 PARKING: Easy OPEN: Mon-Fri 9.30-5, Sats 9-1 MIN: £1 MAX: £1000+ PERIOD: 18th-20th century GENERAL: Furniture, silver, copper, brass, jewellery, china, kicthenalia, bygones OTHER INFO: Interior design service.

**Chandlers Antiques & Fine Upholstery**, 4b St John's Hill, TN13 3NX TEL: 743680 PARKING: Easy OPEN: Mon-Fri 9.30-5, Sat 9.30-1 MIN: £20 MAX: £2500 PERIOD: 18th-20th century SPECIALIST: Furniture GENERAL: Ceramics, glass.

**Mandarin Gallery**, 32 London Road, Riverhead, TN13 2DE TEL: 457399 PARKING: Easy OPEN: Mon, Tues, Thurs-Sat 9.30-5 MIN: £150 MAX: £3,500 PERIOD: 18th-20th century SPECIALIST: Chinese hardwood furniture GENERAL: Porcelain, paintings, ivories OTHER INFO: Donnington Manor Hotel.

**Peppercorns Antique & Crafts Centre,** 57-59 High Street, TN13 1JF TEL: 740329 PARKING: Medium OPEN: Mon-Sat 10-5.30, Sun 10-4 MIN: 50p MAX: £2000 PERIOD: 18th-20th century GENERAL: Furniture, china, jewellery, collectables, metalware, etc OTHER INFO: 50 dealers on 2 floor, wheelchair access on ground floor.

**Roundabout Antiques,** 28a London Road, Riverhead TN13 2DE TEL: 741873 PARKING: Fairly easy OPEN: 9.30-5, closed Wed & Sun MIN: 50p MAX: £1000 PERIOD: 19th-20th century GENERAL: Furniture, china, metalware, silver, etc.

**Sheldon Ward Antiques**, 57 St Johns Hill, TN13 3NY TEL: 455311 PARKING: Medium OPEN: Tues, Thurs 10-5, Fri 2-5, Sat 10-1 MIN: £10 MAX:

£1,200 PERIOD: 19th-20th century GENERAL STOCK: Furniture & mixed bric-a-brac OTHER INFO: Penshurst Place, Knole House, Hever Castle & 6 others within 10 miles.

## FOUR ELMS (01732)

**Treasures**, The Crossroads TEL: 700363 PARKING: Easy OPEN: Mon-Sat 10-5.30, Sun 2-5.30 MIN: 50p MAX: £400 PERIOD: 18th-20th century GENERAL: 9 dealers with quality silver, jewellery, porcelain, linen, small furniture.

## EDENBRIDGE (01892)

**Chevertons of Edenbridge Ltd**, 67-71 High Street, TN8 5AL TEL: 863196, 863358 FAX: 864298 ASSNS: LAPADA PARKING: Own carpark OPEN: Mon-Sat 9-5.30 MIN: £250 MAX: £25,000 PERIOD: 17th-19th century SPECIALIST: English & Continental furniture in 20 showrooms.

## CHIDDINGSTONE (01892)

**Barbara Lane Antiques**, Tudor Cottages, TN8 7AH TEL: 870577 PARKING: Own carpark OPEN: Daily (as much as possible) 12 noon-5 winter, 10.30-5.30 summer PERIOD: 18th-19th century GENERAL: Furniture, glass, ceramics, brass, bric-a-brac.

## SOUTHBOROUGH (01892)

**Henry Baines**, 14 Church Road, TN4 0RX TEL: 532099 ASSNS: LAPADA PARKING: Easy OPEN: Normally Mon-Fri 9.30-5, Sat 10-4.30 but phone first MIN: £50 MAX: £15,000 PERIOD: 17th-19th century SPECIALIST: Early English & Continental oak & country furniture especially sets chairs GENERAL: We import French farm tables.

## TUNBRIDGE WELLS (01892)

**Aaron Antiques,** 77 St John's Road, TN4 9TT TEL: 517644 PARKING: Easy OPEN: Mon-Sat 9-5 GENERAL: Clocks, china, furniture, paintings, prints, silver, plate, metalware, coins & medals.

**Amadeus Antiques**, 32 Mount Ephraim TEL: 544406 PARKING: Own carpark OPEN: 9.30-5 MIN: £10 MAX: £5,000 PERIOD: 19th-20th century SPECIALIST: Unusual interesting furniture GENERAL: China, bric-a-brac, lighting OTHER INFO: Town centre a short walk.

**Annexe Antiques**, 33 The Pantiles, TN2 5TE TEL: 547213 PARKING: Medium OPEN: Mon, Tues, Thurs-Sat 9.30-5 MIN: £5 MAX: £2000 PERIOD: 17th-20th century SPECIALIST: Weapons, books, prints, games, Staffordshire, silver & porcelain.

**Baskerville Books,** 13 Nevill Street, Frant Road TEL: 526776 PARKING: Easy OPEN: 10-5 MIN: £1 MAX: £1000 PERIOD: 18th-20th century SPECIALIST: Antiquarian & secondhand books, also antiques & decorative items at sensible prices.

**Nicholas Bowlby**, 9 Castle Street, TN1 1XJ TEL & FAX: 510880 PARKING: Medium OPEN: Tues, Thurs-Sat 10-5 MIN: £50 MAX: £25,000 century SPECIALIST: Early 19th-early 20th century watercolours GENERAL: Paintings OTHER INFO: In town's prettiest street close to Pantiles.

**Chapel Place Antiques**, 9 Chapel Place, TN1 1YQ TEL: 546561 PARKING: Medium OPEN: Mon-Sat 9-6 MIN: £1 MAX: £3000+ PERIOD: 19th-20th century SPECIALIST: English silver, photo frames, candlesticks etc GENERAL: Antique & new jewellery, glass, brass, copper, silver plate etc OTHER INFO: Pantiles area & Chapel Place is old & quite charming.

**Clare Gallery**, 21 High Street, TN1 1UT TEL: 538717 FAX: (01323) 412900 PARKING: Medium OPEN: Mon-Sat 9.30-5.30 MIN: £5 MAX: £20,000 PERIOD: 19th-20th century SPECIALIST: Paintings GENERAL: Ceramics, glass & Chinese furniture OTHER INFO: Near the Central Railway Station & the famous Pantiles.

**Corn Exchange Antiques,** 64 The Pantiles, TN2 5TN TEL: 539652 PARKING: Medium OPEN: 9.30-5 MIN: £10 MAX: £4000 GENERAL: Furniture, clocks, silver, porcelain, antiquarian books, prints, collectables.

**County Antiques**, 94 High Street TEL: 530767 PARKING: Medium OPEN: Mon-Sat 10-5 MIN: £10 MAX: £2500 PERIOD: 18th-20th century GENERAL: Oak, mahogany, chairs, silver plate.

**Cowden Antiques**, 24 Mount Ephraim Road, TN1 1ED TEL: 520752 ASSNS: LAPADA PARKING: Medium OPEN: 10-5 MIN: £50 MAX: £5000 PERIOD: 17th-19th century GENERAL: Curtains, period oak, mahogany & decorative items.

**Franca Antiques**, 2-4 Castle Street TEL: 525779 PARKING: Medium OPEN: 10.30-5.30 MIN: £5 MAX: £1500 PERIOD: 19th-20th century GENERAL: Prints, postal history, furniture, china, glass, jewellery, silver.

**Graham Gallery**, 1 Castle Street, TN1 1XJ TEL: 526695 PARKING: Medium OPEN: Tues, Thurs-

Sat 10.30-5 MIN: £100 MAX: £4500 PERIOD: 19th-20th century SPECIALIST: Watercolours & modern British paintings OTHER INFO: Castle Street (off High Street), is village area & centre for specialist shopping.

**Hadlow Antiques**, No.1 The Pantiles TEL: 529858 PARKING: Medium OPEN: Mon, Tues, Thurs, Fri 10-1 & 2-5. Wed, Sat 10-1 PERIOD: 17th-20th century SPECIALIST: Clocks, watches, instruments, dolls, automata, mechanical music.

**Linden Park Antiques**, 7 Union Square, The Pantiles, TN4 8HE TEL: 538615 PARKING: Easy OPEN: Mon-Sat 10-5.30 MIN: £10+ MAX: £5000 PERIOD: 19th-20th century SPECIALIST: Extending tables, Victorian dining room furniture GENERAL: Furniture, porcelain, prints, brass, copper OTHER INFO: In the historic colonnaded shopping area, The Pantiles, which grew around the Chalybeate Spa Spring in 18th century.

**Howard Neville Antiques,** 21 The Pantiles TEL: 511461 PARKING: Easy OPEN: Mon-Sat 10-6 MIN: £200 PERIOD: 16th-18th century SPECIALIST: European works of art & furniture.

**Pantiles Spa Antiques**, 4-6 Union House, The Pantiles, TN4 8HE TEL: 541377 FAX: (01435) 862748 PARKING: Easy OPEN: Mon-Sat 9.30-5 MIN: £30 MAX: £20,000 PERIOD: 17th-19th century SPECIALIST: Dolls GENERAL: Wide variety furniture includes dining tables, silver, porcelain, jewellery in spacious showroom in room settings.

**Rare Chairs**, 37 Quarry Road TEL: 521783 PARKING: Easy OPEN: 10-5.30 MIN: £150 MAX: £2500 PERIOD: 18th-19th century SPECIALIST: Bottom back chairs GENERAL: Furniture OTHER INFO: Restoration & high class upholstery.

**Patricia Russell Antiques**, 43 Mount Ephraim, TN4 8AA TEL: 523719 PARKING: Medium OPEN: 10-5.30 MIN: £20 MAX: £800 PERIOD: 18th-19th century GENERAL: Jewellery, silver, paintings, small furniture, china OTHER INFO: Spa, Royal Wells hotels, Thackerays's restaurant.

**John Thompson**, 27 The Pantiles TEL: 547215 PARKING: Medium OPEN: 9.30-1, 2-5.30 MIN: £100 MAX: £5000 PERIOD: 18th-20th century GENERAL: Furniture, paintings, decorative items.

**Tunbridge Wells Antique Centre**, 12 Union Square, The Pantiles TEL: 533708 PARKING: Easy OPEN: Mon-Sat 9.30-5 MIN: £1 MAX: £5000 PERIOD: 18th-20th century SPECIALIST: Staffordshire figures, linen & lace, jewellery GENERAL: 24 dealers in 2500 sq ft showing furniture, silver, pottery, pine, pictures etc OTHER INFO: 3 antique centres and 7 antique shops in The Pantiles.

**Up Country**, The Old Corn Stores, 68 St.Johns Road, TN4 9PE TEL: 523341 FAX: 530382 PARKING: Own carpark OPEN: Mon-Sat 9-5.30 MIN: £20 MAX: £5000 PERIOD: 19th-20th century SPECIALIST: Period, pine & fruitwood furniture GENERAL: Country furniture & decorative artefacts OTHER INFO: 4000 sq ft in 5 showrooms. Courier service. Shipping services with parent company. Packing & restorations.

## TONBRIDGE (01732)

**Barden House Antiques**, 1-3 Priory Street, TN9 2AP TEL: 350142 PARKING: Easy OPEN: Mon-Sat 10-5, Sun by appt MIN: £1 MAX: £500 usually PERIOD: 19th-20th century SPECIALIST: Watercolours GENERAL: 6 dealers with furniture, china, glass, prints, oil paintings, jewellery, linen & lace, postcards, silver, copper & brass. OTHER INFO: Small market town with castle & large recreation ground surrounded by River Medway.

**Derek Roberts Antiques**, 25 Shipbourne Road, TN10 3DN TEL: 358986 FAX: 771842 ASSNS: BADA, CINOA PARKING: Easy OPEN: Mon-Sat 9.30-5.30 or by appt MIN: £1000 clocks MAX: £100,000 (clocks) PERIOD: 17th-19th century SPECIALIST: Probably UK's widest range of fully restored antique clocks, music boxes etc OTHER INFO: Penshurst Place, Hever & Leeds castles, Chartwell (Churchill's home) & Knowle.

## FIVE OAK GREEN (01892)

**Lafayette Antiques**, The Barn, Mill House, Badsell Road, TN12 6QU TEL: 832802 PARKING: Own carpark OPEN: Mon, Wed, Fri, Sat 11-5 MIN: £10+ MAX: £1000+ PERIOD: 19th-20th century GENERAL: General antiques OTHER INFO: Whitbread Hop Farm.

## EAST PECKHAM (01622)

**Desmond & Amanda North**, The Orchard, Hale Street, TN12 5JB TEL: 871353 PARKING: Easy OPEN: Anytime by appt MIN: £80 MAX: £3500 PERIOD: 19th-20th century SPECIALIST: Cushions, tablemats, coasters made from old rugs GENERAL: Old & antique persian & other Oriental rugs, carpets, runners, hangings, cushions OTHER INFO: Nothing new or contemporary. People come here to buy things that don't look bought. Suggestions made.

## WEST PECKHAM (01732)

**Persian Rug Gallery**, Vines Farm, Matthews Lane, ME18 5JS TEL & FAX: 850228 PARKING: Own carpark OPEN: 9-6 MIN: £20 MAX: £10,000 PERIOD: 19th-20th century SPECIALIST: 200+ rugs & carpets etc. Repairs & hand cleaning.

## HADLOW (01732)

**The Pedlars Pack**, The Square, TN11 0DA TEL: 851296 PARKING: Easy OPEN: Tues, Thurs-Sat 10-5.30 MIN: £3 MAX: £800 PERIOD: 17th-20th century SPECIALIST: Old oak, copper, brass, pewter GENERAL: Mahogany, china, glass, silver plate, jewellery, pottery, walnut, prints OTHER INFO:

Hadlow Folly, St Mary's Church (1000 years old).

## WEST MALLING (01732)

**Andrew Smith Antiques**, 89 High Street, ME19 6NA TEL: 843087 National Pawnbrokers Assn PARKING: Easy OPEN: 9.30-5.30 MIN: £20 MAX: £3000 PERIOD: 19th-20th century SPECIALIST: Secondhand gold jewellery GENERAL: Some antique jewellery.

## SNODLAND (01634)

**Aaron Antiques,** 90 High Street, ME6 5AL TEL: 241748 PARKING: Easy PERIOD: 17th-20th century GENERAL: Clocks, china, furniture, paintings, prints, silver, plate, metalware, coins & medals.

## CUXTON (01634)

**Country Pine Antiques Co**, Upper Bush Farm, Upper Bush, ME2 1HQ TEL: 296929 FAX: 296393 PARKING: Own carpark OPEN: Mon-Fri 8.30-6, Sat 9-5, Sun 10-2 MIN: £100 MAX: £1800 PERIOD: 18th-20th century SPECIALIST: Pine.

## ROCHESTER (01634)

**Francis Iles**, Rutland House, La Providence TEL: 843081 PARKING: Medium OPEN: Mon-Sat 9.30-5.30 MIN: £120 MAX: £10,000 PERIOD: Contemporary SPECIALIST: Pictures - Rowland Hilde, Clive, Madgwick, Kenneth Denton etc GENERAL: All mediums, traditional style OTHER INFO: Dickens interest, 10th century castle & cathedral.

**Deo Juvante Antiques,** 43 High Street, ME1 1LN TEL: 843750 PARKING: Easy OPEN: 10-5, closed Wed MIN: £2.50 MAX: £2000 PERIOD: 19th-20th century GENERAL: China glass, furniture, clocks, paintings, jewellery.

**Memories Antique Centre**, 128 High Street, ME1 1JT TEL: 811044 PARKING: Easy OPEN: Mon-Sat 9-5 MIN: £2 MAX: £400 PERIOD: 19th-20th century GENERAL: Small antiques, bric a brac, china, linen OTHER INFO: 14 dealers on 4 floors.

## CHATHAM (01634)

**Antiquities**, The Chaplain's House, Chatham Historic Dockyard, ME1 2HY TEL: 818866 FAX: 818877 PARKING: Easy OPEN: 10-4 MIN: £50 MAX: £15,000 PERIOD: 18th-20th century GENERAL: Chandeliers, wall lights, specialist bulbs, flexes, wax electric candles OTHER INFO: Sited in a living museum.

## GRAVESEND (01474)

**Manor Antiques,** 9 Manor Road TEL: 356050 PARKING: Medium OPEN: Mon-Sat 10-5, closed Wed pm MIN: £1 MAX: £500 PERIOD: 19th-20th century GENERAL: Jewellery, furniture, glass, general OTHER INFO: Opposite what is probably the cheapest Thai restaurant around, at lunchtime all you can eat for £3.50.

## NORTHFLEET (01474)

**Northfleet Hill Antiques**, 36 The Hill, DA11 9EX TEL: 321521 PARKING: Easy OPEN: Tues, Fri, Sat 9.30-5 MIN: £2 MAX: £800 PERIOD: 19th-20th century GENERAL: Furniture, collectables & decorative items OTHER INFO: This building was the home, from 1849 to 1891, of Samuel Honeycombe, great grandfather of Gordon Honeycombe, writer & broadcaster. Close to 3 pubs and the Heritage Restaurant

## .DARTFORD (01322)

**Dartford Antiques,** 27 East Hill TEL: 291350 PARKING: Easy OPEN: 10-4.30 MIN: £1 MAX: £500 PERIOD: 19th-20th century GENERAL: Very general, some very collectable pieces.

**Peppercorns Antique & Craft Centre,** 3 Orchard Street, DA1 2DH TEL: 220187 PARKING: Easy OPEN: Mon-Sat 9.30-5.30 MIN: 50p MAX: £2000 PERIOD: 19th-20th century GENERAL: Furniture, general antiques, collectables OTHER INFO: 30 dealers, good wheelchair access.

## FARNINGHAM (01322)

**Peter T Beasley,** Forge Yard, High Street, DA4 0DB TEL: 862453 PARKING: Own carpark OPEN: 9-6, closed Tues MIN: £50 MAX: £4000 PERIOD: 17th-18th century SPECIALIST: Early oak GENERAL: Mahogany furniture OTHER INFO: In a pleasant village bypassed by the A20 road.

# East Kent

This tour of East Kent provides scenic and historic contrasts: small villages, genteel seaside towns and the more extrovert resort of Margate, the busy ferry ports of Folkestone and Dover, and, above all there is Canterbury, a regional and religious centre for centuries. The chalk cliffs of the region's coast epitomize for many the picture of England.

The first call is at the picturesque village of **Teynham**, a fruit growing centre since the days of Henry VIII, then the route moves on to the market town of **Faversham**. Once a flourishing port the town contains many buildings of note. At the Fleur de Lys Heritage Centre in Preston Street there are audio-visual displays covering a 1000 years of the town's history and giving information on its 400 listed buildings. Housed in an old inn, an infamous murder was plotted there in 1540. Thomas Arden was murdered by his wife and this later became the subject of the play *Arden of Faversham.* **Boughton-under-Blean** village is mile east of the M2/A2/A299 junction.

Turning towards the Thames estuary is the resort of **Whitstable**, famous for its oysters. The Whitstable to Canterbury railway line was the first passenger line in the country and the town has one of the oldest railway bridges, built in 1834. Moving inland, **Canterbury** was a Roman administrative centre although there had been a settlement here since prehistoric times. The present city walls follow those originally built by the Romans, even the gates correspond to the Roman ones. In AD597 St Augustine landed in Kent and built a priory on the site of the present cathedral precincts. He also built an abbey outside the city walls where he was buried as were other early archbishops. This abbey was torn down in the reign of Henry VIII during the Dissolution of the Monasteries and now only the ruins may be seen.

The Cathedral is the city's major attraction. There has been one on the site since Saxon times and it has long been the main church of English Christians. The Archbishops of Canterbury were usually extremely powerful and often counsellors to kings. The stories attached to it are many. Amongst the most famous is the murder in December 1170 ofThomas à Becket, Archbishop of Canterbury. Becket had long been a favourite of Henry II but then they quarrelled over the legal privileges of the clergy. Four of Henry's knights, thinking the King wanted Becket dead, came to the Cathedral and murdered him there. It could be said that the final victory belonged to Thomas à Becket because he was made a saint in 1173 and his tomb became a principal place of pilgrimage. King Henry II himself visited and, as a penance, was scourged by the monks in front of the tomb.

The beauty of the Cathedral is well-known and the points of interest too numerous to mention. A visit to the Tourist Information Centre and possibly the Cathedral bookshop is essential to appreciate it. The city itself is very attractive with its crooked streets and timber framed houses projecting over the pavements. One notable feature is King's School which has a unique exterior Norman staircase. There are also long stretches of the city walls left standing. Numerous museums exist, amongst the most interesting are the Canterbury Centre, St. Alphege Lane, which is in a converted medieval church, Canterbury Heritage Museum, Stour Street, again housed in a medieval building, the Roman Mosaic in Butchery Lane, and The West Gate, a museum of arms and armour housed in a 14th century gatehouse.

South of the city, on the A257, stand the pretty villages of **Littlebourne** and then **Wingham,** which has a 15th century inn, the Red Lion, typical of many of the half-timbered houses in the village. Also notable is the 600 year old church with its green copper spire and timbered arcade.

Heading to the coast, **Birchington** is a quiet seaside resort where the grave of Dante Gabriel Rossetti may be seen in the churchyard. Quex House, a Georgian mansion in the town, is also well worth a visit. Altered during Victorian times, the house is very much a tribute to Major Percy Powell-Cotton who was born in 1866 and died in 1940. During his numerous visits to Africa, Major Powell-Cotton assembled one of the finest collections of African ethnography in the world. He also created great dioramas using some 500 African and Asian animals. Addition-

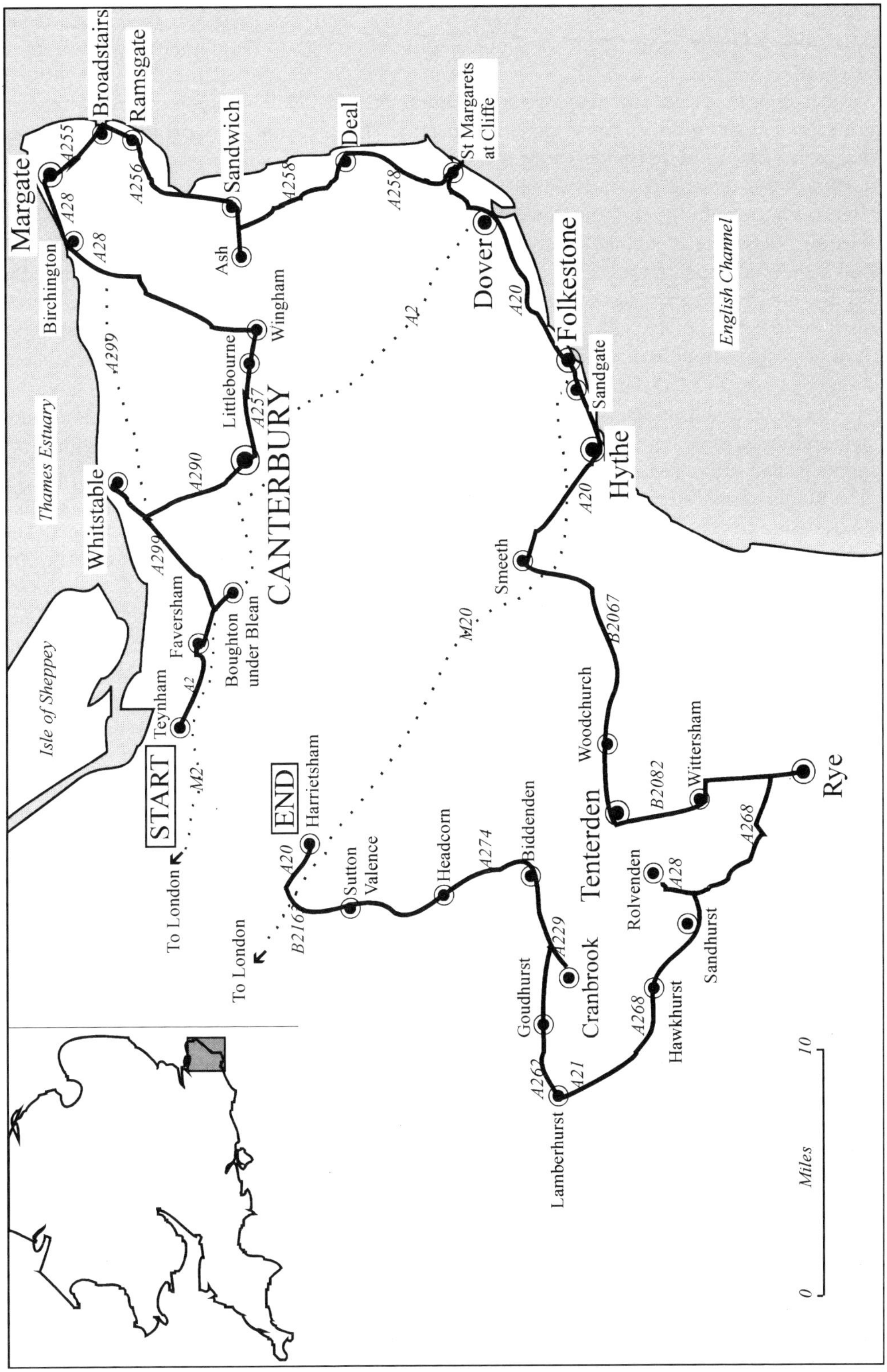
Margate
A255
Broadstairs
Ramsgate
A256
A28
A28
Birchington
Sandwich
A258
Ash
Deal
A258
St Margarets
at Cliffe
Dover
A2
Wingham
Littlebourne
A257
A299
Thames Estuary
Whitstable
A290
CANTERBURY
A299
Faversham
Boughton
under Blean
A2
Teynham
Isle of Sheppey
START
M2
To London
Folkestone
English Channel
A20
Sandgate
Hythe
A20
Smeeth
M20
B2067
END
Harrietsham
A20
To London
B216
Sutton
Valence
Headcorn
A274
Biddenden
Woodchurch
Wittersham
B2082
Tenterden
Rye
A268
Rolvenden
A28
Sandhurst
A229
Cranbrook
Goudhurst
A268
Hawkhurst
A262
A21
Lamberhurst
Miles
0
10

ally, the Major gathered a unique collection of Chinese Imperial porcelain as well as a good collection of English and Continental porcelain now housed in the adjoining purpose-built museum.

Further along the coast, **Margate** was once an important port but nowadays is principally known as a seaside resort with all the attractions expected. The next stop, **Broadstairs**, has a strong Dickensian flavour. Here Dickens wrote *David Copperfield* in a house he rented for the summer and which was the original Bleak House. Part of the building is now a Dickens Museum and in Victoria Place stands the Dickens House Museum with rooms furnished in the appropriate style.

Nearby **Ramsgate** is another seaside resort and port. Its fine sands guaranteed its popularity with visitors although there are also other attractions. The East Kent Maritime Museum has displays on local history and shipwrecks. Along the coast, **Sandwich**, one of the Cinque Ports, is a truly delightful place with many medieval buildings. Some of the more notable being the Customs House, a medieval timber building with a later brick skin, St. Clement's Church whose tower dates back to 1100 and the Guildhall dating from 1579. The finest of Sandwich's timbered houses can be found in Strand Street constructed on reclaimed land. One of the most memorable features is the Barbican, built in 1539 as a defensive work but later used as a toll house for the bridge and still in use as late as 1978.

The Roman ruin of Richborough Castle, to the west of Sandwich, has walls up to 25 feet high still standing on three sides and dates from the last days of Roman occupation of Britain. The castle was built as a defence against Saxon marauders. In the centre lies the foundation of a triumphal arch built in AD85 to celebrate the Roman invasion of Britain.

One mile west of Sandwich lies **Ash**. The tour then continues to **Deal** with its many Georgian houses, castle and pebble beach. Ships may be seen passing relatively closely because the treacherous Goodwin Sands lie only 5 miles offshore. Deal Castle was built by Henry VIII as part of the South Coast defence against a French invasion. At the time its rounded surface to deflect cannon balls was a revolution in castle design. By the end of the 16th century, some fifty years after its construction, Deal Castle was falling into disrepair. During the Civil War it was initially held for Parliament until the people of Kent rebelled against Parliamentary rule and marched on London. This rebellion was largely abortive as there was no popular support for it outside the area but the rebels did take the castle. Parliamentary forces laid siege and eventually the rebels surrendered. After that the castle saw little action until a German bomb fell on it in the Second World War and destroyed a bastion.

Further south, the appropriately named **St Margaret's-at-Cliffe** is situated on cliffs that rise to 400 feet above the sea. The village has a notable late Norman church where early ship carvings may be seen in the nave. The neighbouring town of **Dover** is, of course, famous for its white cliffs, immortalised in the Second World War song by Dame Vera Lynn which became a symbol of home for the servicemen and women overseas. Once the Roman walled city of *Dubris,* the town's history goes back to ancient times. Dover Castle was built on the site of an Iron Age fort. The present castle dates from the 12th century with later additions and modifications. During the Civil War the castle was held for Parliament so was not slighted. It was in the 18th century that it suffered the most damage and extensive improvements were made. Most of the towers were reduced in height, the southern barbican and associated towers were removed entirely as was the eastern curtain wall. The keep was strengthened to withstand heavy artillery. A Roman lighthouse, the Pharos, lies to the south east of the keep and closeby stands the Saxon church of St Mary de Castro. Separated from France by only 21 miles of the English Channel, Dover has been the main crossing point to the Continent. Captain Matthew Webb, the first man to swim the Channel in 1875, is commemorated in a statue on the promenade as is Charles Rolls who flew to France and back in a single journey in 1910.

Next is **Folkestone** which was heavily bombed during the Second World War. It has a wide grassy promenade, The Leas, along the clifftop and many attractive wooded walks down to the beach. Rosemary bushes are planted along the road running from The Leas to the harbour in remembrance of the many soldiers who marched down this road to embark on troopships but who never returned. The adjoining seaside town of **Sandgate** has a good pebble bathing beach and a reconstructed 16th century castle. Just north is the Eurotunnel Exhibition Centre and just west of Sandgate is **Hythe,** also well known as a holiday resort and the terminus for the narrow gauge Romney, Hythe and Dymchurch Railway.

Then, via the villages of **Smeeth** and **Woodchurch**, the tour moves on to **Tenterden** which once held Cinque Port rights. For theatre lovers, there is Smallhythe Place which houses the Ellen Terry Memorial Museum with momentoes of the famous actresses, Dame Ellen Terry and Mrs Siddons amongst others. In nearby Sissinghurst there is a literary connection at Sissinghurst Castle, once the home of writers, Harold Nicolson and his wife Vita Sackville-West. When they took it over in 1930 it was virtually derelict. Over the next ten years they restored the Tudor buildings and made a beautiful garden from the former wilderness. After first visiting **Wittersham** the route follows the A268 to arrive in the charming and pretty Cinque Port of **Rye**, full of half-timbered and Georgian buildings. Even in the time of Henry James, the American novelist, it was a tourist attraction. He lived in Lamb House from 1897 to 1914 where he wrote *The Ambassadors* and *The Golden Bowl.* The Mayor of Rye between the First and Second World Wars was another novelist, E.F. Benson, famous for his Mapp and Lucia novels, and he lived in the very same house which now belongs to the National Trust. The town is very well-endowed with pubs, reputedly seventeen in all, quite a lot for a small town. Also worth mentioning is the museum in the Ypres Tower.

**Rolvenden**, with its Booth Historic Vehicle Collection in the High Street, is next and then **Sandhurst**, followed by **Hawkhurst**. 8 miles north west, **Lamberhurst** is famous for its vineyards and wine-making. Nearby are several attractions. One is Owl House Gardens, 13 acres of beautiful gardens surrounding a 16th century smuggler's cottage. There are lawns, oaks, elm, birch, rhododendrums, azaleas and camellias and an informal sunken water garden. From there the road passes Scotney Castle, once a moated 14th century castle now with only the curtain wall and one of the towers remaining but set in lovely, romantic gardens. Three miles east, the village of **Goudhurst** is notable for its Culpepper monuments and brasses and for Finchcocks, a fine 18th century house in beautiful gardens and parkland. Finchcocks also has a fine collection of historical keyboard instruments most of which are restored to concert condition.

Next, **Cranbrook**, is sited on a hill above the Kentish Weald and has many charming features. The Elizabethan Old Cloth Hall is one of the many fine, historic buildings in the town. The church is also of interest with a porch dating from 1291.

The tour then visits **Biddenden** before heading north to **Headcorn**, once closely associated with weaving as shown by its 15th century Cloth Hall, and **Sutton Valence** where the man who introduced round arm bowling into cricket, John Willes, is buried. The last stop is the village of **Harrietsham** with its 18th century almshouses. Close by is the spectacular Leeds Castle which for centuries was a royal castle and given to the wives of the kings of England.

## ANTIQUE DEALERS

### TEYNHAM (01795)

**Jackson-Grant Antiques**, The Old Chapel, 133 London Road, ME9 9QJ TEL: 522027 FAX: (01634) 727064 PARKING: Easy OPEN: Mon-Sat 10-5, Sun 1-5 (resident) MIN £1 MAX: £5000+ PERIOD: 17th-early 20th century SPECIALIST: Early coffers when available GENERAL: 3500 sq ft of antiques (no repro), porcelain, jewellery, silver etc, good trade call OTHER INFO: First place in England to grow cherries. Tearooms opposite.

### FAVERSHAM (01795)

**Periwinkle Press,** 119 West Street, ME13 7SB TEL: 533086 ASSNS: FATG PARKING: Easy OPEN: 9.30-5 MIN: £1 MAX: £500 PERIOD: 18th-20th century SPECIALIST: Prints, engravings, maps GENERAL: Second hand books.

**Squires Antiques**, 3 Jacob Yard, Preston Street, ME13 TEL: 531503 FAX: 59160 PARKING: Easy OPEN: Mon-Tues, Fri-Sat 10-5 MIN: £1 MAX: £3000 PERIOD: 17th-20th century GENERAL: Wide variety of everything OTHER INFO: Ancient buildings in historic town, local museum, sailing barges on The Creek.

### BOUGHTON-UNDER-BLEAN (01227)

**Jean Collyer**, 194 The Street, ME13 9AL TEL: 751454 PARKING: Own carpark OPEN: 10-5 Tue, Fri & Sat, or by appt MIN: £2 MAX: £1000 PERIOD: 18th-19th century SPECIALIST: Porcelain & glass GENERAL: Some silver, lace & furniture OTHER INFO: Plenty of old buildings, pubs, and excellent Garden House restaurant opposite.

### WHITSTABLE (01227)

**Tankerton Antiques**, 136 Tankerton Road, CT5 2AN TEL: 266490 PARKING: Medium OPEN: Tues 10-4, Wed 10-1, Thurs-Sat 10-5 MIN: £1 MAX: £2000 PERIOD: 18th-20th century SPECIALIST: 10,000+ postcards GENERAL: English china, glass, furniture & collectables OTHER INFO: Excellent for birdwatching (Swale Estuary) and watersports

### CANTERBURY (01227)

**Antique & Design**, Unit 14, Graham Bell House, Roper Close, CT1 2RD TEL: 762871 FAX: 762871 PARKING: Own carpark OPEN: Mon-Fri 9-5, Sat 10-2 or by appt MIN: £5 MAX: £2500 PERIOD: 18th-20th century SPECIALIST: Antique pine furniture GENERAL: Shipping furniture, some reproduction, i.e.shelves & tables OTHER INFO: Stock of 1,300+ pieces in 10,000 sq ft.

**BURGATE ANTIQUES**
**10C BURGATE, CT1 2HG TEL: 456500 PARKING: EASY OPEN: MON-SAT 10-5 MIN: £2 MAX: £2000 PERIOD: 18TH-20TH CENTURY SPECIALIST: PERIOD FURNITURE, PORCELAIN, SILVER GENERAL: JEWELLERY, CLOCKS, ART DECO, MILITARIA, LEAD SOLDIERS, OLD PRINTS, BOOKS, WATERCOLOURS. EGYPTIAN ANTIQUITIES OTHER INFO: ANTIQUES CENTRE WITH 12 DEALERS ON 2 FLOORS BACKING ONTO CATHEDRAL GROUNDS.**

**The Canterbury Bookshop,** 37 Northgate, CT1 1BL TEL: 464773 FAX: 780073 ASSNS: PBFA PARKING: Easy OPEN: 10-5 MIN: 50p MAX: £1000 PERIOD: 19th-20th century SPECIALIST: Children's, Kent topography GENERAL: We cover most subjects.

**The Chaucer Bookshop**, 6 Beer Cart Lane, CT1 2NY TEL: 453912 ASSNS: ABA, PFBA PARKING: Medium OPEN: Mon-Sat 10-5 MIN: £1 MAX: £500 PERIOD: 17th-20th century GENERAL: Good general stock, books and prints OTHER INFO: 4 mins walk S.W. of Cathedral, inside City walls.

**Roger Clark,** 1 The Borough, CT1 2DR TEL: 455664 PARKING: Medium OPEN: 10.30-5 MIN: £12 MAX: £1150 PERIOD: 18th-20th century SPECIALIST: Restored clocks GENERAL: Smalls of all kinds OTHER INFO: Public house opposite, good food at good prices.

**Coach House Antiques,** 2A Duck Lane, St Radigunds, Northgate, CT1 2AE TEL: 463117 PARKING: Easy OPEN: 10-4 MIN: 50p MAX: £500 PERIOD: 19th-20th century GENERAL: Small pieces, antiquarian & secondhand books, ephemera.

**Nan Leith's "Brocanterbury"**, Curios, 68 Stour Street, CT1 2NZ TEL: 454519 PARKING: Easy OPEN: 12-6pm & anytime by appt (resident) MIN: £2 MAX: £75 PERIOD: late 19th-20th century SPECIALIST: Pressed & art glass GENERAL: Collectables & books, prints OTHER INFO: Brocante North European word for such stock. Situated on small street a few mins walk from Post Office.

**Parker-Williams Antiques**, 22 Palace Street TEL: 768341 ASSNS: LAPADA PARKING: Good OPEN: Mon-Sat 10-1, 2-6 MIN: £10 MAX: £10,000 PERIOD: 17-19th century SPECIALIST: Good quality furniture, clocks, porcelain GENERAL: Silver, bronzes, copper, brass, watercolours & oils, OTHER INFO: Good selection of antique shops.

**Michael Pearson Antiques**, 2 The Borough, CT1 2DR TEL: 459939 PARKING: Good OPEN: Mon-Sat 10-6, Thurs AM only PERIOD: 17th-early 19th century SPECIALIST: Woodcarvings GENERAL: Early oak & walnut country furniture OTHER INFO: UK's second most visited city after London.

**Pine & Things Ltd**, Oast Interiors, Wincheap Road TEL: 470283 FAX: 470283 PARKING: Own carpark OPEN: Mon-Sat 9-5.30, Sun 10-4 MIN: £5 MAX: £1000 PERIOD: 19th-20th century SPECIALIST: Repro & antique pine furniture OTHER INFO: Hop Poles pub next door.

**Saracen's Lantern**, 8-9 The Borough, CT1 2DR TEL: 451968 PARKING: Easy OPEN: 9-4 MIN: £1 MAX: £2500 PERIOD: 18th-20th century GENERAL: Pottery, porcelain, silver, furniture, paintings, prints, postcards, books.

**Stablegate Antiques**, 19 The Borough, CT1 2DR TEL: 764086 PARKING: Easy OPEN: 10-5.30 closed Mon MIN: £10 MAX: £4000 PERIOD: 19th-20th century SPECIALIST: Dining tables, chairs, sideboards, etc GENERAL: Jewellery, dolls, pictures, glass, furniture (some larger pieces) OTHER INFO: Good food & specialist shops in street.

**The Victorian Fireplace,** Thanet House, 82 Broad Street, CT1 2LU TEL: 767723 FAX: 767743 PARKING: Easy OPEN: 10-5.30 MIN: £40 MAX: £8000 PERIOD: !8th-20th century SPECIALIST: Fireplaces.

## LITTLEBOURNE (01227)

**Jimmy Warren Antiques**, Cedar Lodge, 28 the Hill, CT3 1TA TEL: 721510 FAX: 722431 PARKING: Own carpark OPEN: 7 days 9-6 MIN: £10 MAX: £4000 PERIOD: 18th-19th century SPECIALIST: Decorative & country furniture GENERAL: Furniture, antiques OTHER INFO: Also garden ornaments in landscaped gardens.

## WINGHAM (01227)

**Bridge Antiques**, 97 High Street, CT3 1DE TEL: 720445 PARKING: Own carpark OPEN: Thurs-Sat 9-5 or by appt MAX: £10,000 PERIOD: 18-20th century SPECIALIST: Fine period furniture, porcelain, dolls GENERAL: Shipping goods OTHER INFO: Excellent restaurant opposite. Good golf locally. Own cottage for letting in lovely riverside garden.

**Chairs & Things,** Victoria House, 30 High Street, CT3 1AB TEL: 720309 PARKING: Easy OPEN: Mon-Sat 9-5.30, closed Wed pm PERIOD: 19th-20th century GENERAL: Antiques, lighting, pine, mahogany, etc, a real Aladdin's Cave OTHER INFO: Gary Glitter, Joanna Lumley amongst previous customers, the rich & famous, poor & humble all visit!

**Lloyd's Bookshop**, 27 High Street, CT3 1AW TEL: 720774 ASSNS: ABA PARKING: Easy OPEN: Mon-Sat 9.30-1, 2.15-5 MIN: £1 MAX: £600 PERIOD: 17th-20th century SPECIALIST: Early children's books GENERAL: All subjects including prints, watercolours & music OTHER INFO: Beautiful Kentish village dating from 13th century.

**Silvesters Antiques**, 33 High Street, CT3 1AB TEL: 720278, (0843) 41524 ASSNS: LAPADA PARKING: Own small carpark MIN: £20 MAX: £1,000 PERIOD: 18th-20th century GENERAL: Period and decorative furniture & objects OTHER INFO: Wingham dates from 1200.

## BIRCHINGTON (01843)

**John Chawner Antiques**, 36 Station Approach, CT7 9RD TEL: 843309 PARKING: Own carpark OPEN: 10.30-12.30, 1.30-5, closed Tues MIN: £5 MAX: £5000 PERIOD: 18th-20th century SPECIALIST: Clocks & barometers GENERAL: Repairs, restorations, valuations.

## MARGATE (01843)

**RG Scott Furniture Mart**, Bath Place, Grotto Hill, CT9 2BU TEL: 220653 ASSNS: FSB PARKING: Medium OPEN: 9.30-1, 2-5 MIN: £1 MAX: £2000 SPECIALIST: Refinishing goods GENERAL: Large quantity, on 3 floors, of all types antiques & s/h furniture OTHER INFO: Upholstery, French polishing, cabinet-making, restorations on site.

## BROADSTAIRS (01843)

**Broadstairs Antiques & Collectables**, 49 Belvedere Road, CT10 1PF TEL: 861965 PARKING: Easy OPEN: Summer 10-5, Winter 10-4.30 MIN: £1 MAX: £1000 PERIOD: 19th-20th century SPECIALIST: Victorian teaplates, lace & linen GENERAL: Small furniture, pretty china, cutlery-all pre 1940 OTHER INFO: Pretty harbour & safe sandy beaches. Dickens Festival in June - we all dress in Dickensian dress and parade in Town. Events throughout week, all welcome. Folk Week every August, Admiral Dundonald Hotel 4 doors away, coffee & light snacks in The Coffee House, Charlotte Street.

## RAMSGATE (01843)

**De Tavener Antiques**, 24 Addington Street TEL: 582213 ASSNS: GMC, HA PARKING: Easy OPEN: Mon-Sat 9.30-5.30, Wed AM only SPECIALIST: Clocks, barometers GENERAL: Bric-a-brac.

**Granny's Attic,** 2 Addington Street, CT11 9JL TEL: 588955 day, 596288 eve PARKING: Easy OPEN: Mon-Sat 10-5 MIN: £1 MAX: £1000 PERIOD: 19th-20th century GENERAL: 1500 sq ft of furniture, clocks, pictures, linen, lighting, etc. OTHER INFO: Delivery arranged worldwide.

## SANDWICH (01304)

**Hythe Galleries,** 47A Strand Street, CT13 9DS TEL: 614971 PARKING: Medium OPEN: 10-5 MIN: £10 MAX: £1000 PERIOD: 18th-20th century GENERAL: Jewellery, porcelain, silver, furniture, objets d'art.

**Noah's Ark Antique Centre**, 5 King Street, CT13 9BT TEL: 611144 PARKING: Medium OPEN: Mon, Tues, Thurs-Sat 10-4 MIN: £2 MAX: £400 PERIOD: 18th-19th century SPECIALIST: Staffordshire figures, fairings GENERAL: Porcelain, pottery, silver + plate, glass, oils, watercolours and prints.

**Pillory Gate Wharf Antiques,** 38 Strand Street, CT13 9EU TEL: 614460 PARKING: Own carpark OPEN: 7 days 10-5 GENERAL: Furniture, china, clocks, Staffordshire, silver, paintings, prints, jewellery.

**James Porter Antiques**, 5-5a Potter Street, CT13 9DR TEL: 612218 PARKING: Medium OPEN: Mon-Sat 10-5 (ring bell if closed) MIN: £30 MAX: £850 PERIOD: 19th century OTHER INFO: Bell Hotel (parking on riverbank).

**Roses,** 60 King Street, CT13 6BT TEL: 615303 FAX: 851228 PARKING: Easy OPEN: 9.30-5.30 PERIOD: 18th-20th century GENERAL: Furniture, ceramics, silver, jewellery, paintings, books, collectables, linen, lace OTHER INFO: Interior of shop remains a grocers shop, original grocer's bike, scales, etc.

**Sandwich Fine Books,** 13 Strand Street, CT13 9DX TEL & FAX: 620300 ASSNS: ABA, PBFA PARKING: Easy OPEN: 10.30-4.30 MIN: £5 MAX: £5000 PERIOD: 17th-19th century SPECIALIST: Leather bound antiquarian books OTHER INFO: Shop dates from 1230.

**Nancy Wilson Antiques,** Monken Quay, Strand Street, CT13 9HP TEL: 612345 PARKING: Mon-Sat 11-5 MIN: £150 MAX: £4000 PERIOD: 18th-19th century SPECIALIST: Clocks GENERAL: Furniture OTHER INFO: The shop is 17th century wine vault.

## ASH (01304)

**Henry's of Ash,** 51 The Street, CT3 2EN TEL: 812600 PARKING: Easy OPEN: 10-12.15, 2-5 except Wed MIN: £1 MAX: £500 PERIOD: 19th-20th century GENERAL: Victoriana, Art Deco.

## DEAL (01304)

**The Print Room,** 96A Beach Street, CT14 6JE TEL: 368904 PARKING: Medium OPEN: 10-1, 2.30-5.30, closed Thurs, some winter months closed Tues & Wed. Phone for appt MIN: £1 MAX: £300 PERIOD: 17th-20th century SPECIALIST: Local topographical antiquarian prints GENERAL: Antiquarian prints & maps, a few Victorian watercolours, contemporary watercolours & prints OTHER INFO: A very pretty & largely ignored small town mostly dating from 17th & 18th century.

**Quill Antiques**, 12 Alfred Square TEL: 375958 PARKING: Easy OPEN: Varies MIN: 50p MAX: £500 PERIOD: 18th-20th century SPECIALIST: Postcards GENERAL: Ceramics, bric-a-brac, small furniture, silver.

**Serendipity,** 168 High Street, CT14 6BB TEL: 366536 PARKING: Easy OPEN: Mon-Wed, Fri 10-12.30, 2-4.30, Sat 9-5 MIN: 50p MAX: £500 PERIOD: 18th-20th century SPECIALIST: Staffordshire portrait figures & animals GENERAL: General antiques OTHER INFO: Excellent pub grub & B&Bs.

## ST MARGARET'S BAY (01304)

**Alexandra's Antiques**, 1-3 The Droveway, CT15 6DH TEL: 853102 FAX: 853306 PARKING: Own carpark OPEN: 10-4 MIN: £5 MAX: £1500 PERIOD: 19th-20th century GENERAL: Victorian watercolours, silver + plate, furniture, jewellery, bric-a-brac.

## DOVER (01304)

**Stuff,** 87 London Road, CT17 0SH TEL: 215405

PARKING: Medium OPEN: 9.30-5.30, closed Wed & Sun MIN: 10p MAX: £300+ PERIOD: 18th-20th century SPECIALIST: Everything inc bikes, records, household items, etc.

## FOLKESTONE (01303)

**Alan Lord Antiques**, 71 Tontine Street, CT20 1JR TEL: 253674 (24 hr) PARKING: Easy OPEN: Mon-Fri 9-1 & 2-5, Sat 10-1 MIN: £5 MAX: £5000 PERIOD: 18th-19th century SPECIALIST: Furniture GENERAL: China, some shipping goods OTHER INFO: Ferry to France from the port here and the shop is up from harbour. Plenty of good B&Bs and hotels.

**G & DI Marrin & Sons**, 149 Sandgate Road, CT20 2DA TEL: 253016 FAX: 850956 ASSNS: ABA, PFBA PARKING: Easy OPEN: Mon-Sat 9.30-5.30 (winter closed lunchtime) MIN: £1 MAX: £5,000 PERIOD: 18th-20th century SPECIALIST: Books on First World War, prints & maps GENERAL: Kentish topography and general fine books.

## SANDGATE (01303)

**Beaubush House Antiques**, 95 High Street, CT20 3BY TEL: 249099 ASSNS: LAPADA PARKING: Medium OPEN: Mon-Sat 9.30-5.30 MIN: £150 MAX: £4,000 PERIOD: 18th-19th century SPECIALIST: Pottery & porcelain GENERAL: Furniture, jewellery, collectables & textiles OTHER INFO: Sandgate Hotel.

**Christopher Buck Antiques**, 56-60 High Street, CT20 3AP TEL: 221229 FAX (01795) 533155 ASSNS: BADA, LAPADA PARKING: Easy OPEN: 10-5.30, closed Wed & Sun MIN: £200 MAX: £20,000 PERIOD: 18th-19th century SPECIALIST: Quality English furniture OTHER INFO: 20+ shops in one High Street.

**Dench Antiques**, Cromwell House, 32 High Street, CT20 3AP TEL & FAX: 240824 PARKING: Medium OPEN: 9-6 MIN: £300 MAX: £25,000 PERIOD: 17th-19th century SPECIALIST: Decorative & Continental furniture-oak & objets d'art GENERAL: Architectural statues OTHER INFO: 5 star Imperial Hotel, Hythe, La Bouge Bistro ideal for lunch nearby.

**Michael W Fitch Antiques**, 99 High Street, CT20 3BY TEL: 249600 FAX: 249600 ASSNS: LAPADA PARKING: Own carpark OPEN: Mon-Sat 10-5.30 MIN: £150 MAX: £10,000 PERIOD: 18th-19th century SPECIALIST: Dining & library furniture GENERAL: Furniture, clocks OTHER INFO: Warehouse with antiques for trade buyers, Channel Tunnel/M20 5 mins.

**Freeman & Lloyd**, 44 High Street, CT20 3AP TEL: 248986 ASSNS: BADA, LAPADA PARKING: Easy OPEN: Tues, Thurs-Sat 10-5.30 MIN: £150 MAX: £50,000 PERIOD: 18th-early 19th century SPECIALIST: English period furniture GENERAL: Tea caddies, clocks, bronzes, pictures OTHER INFO: Approx 20 other antique shops in Sandgate.

**David Gilbert Antiques,** 30 High Street, CT20 3AP TEL: 850491 PARKING: Easy OPEN: 9.30-5 PERIOD: 18th-20th century SPECIALIST: Arts & crafts GENERAL: Good quality useful clean furniture & decorative items.

**Jonathan Greenwall Antiques**, Sandgate Antiques Centre, 61-63 High Street, CT20 3AH TEL: 248987 ASSNS: LAPADA PARKING: Easy OPEN: Seven days 9.30-5.30 MIN: £5 MAX: £10,000 PERIOD: 17th-20th century SPECIALIST: Furniture, jewellery, pictures GENERAL: General antiques OTHER INFO: Port Lympne Zoo, 2 golf courses, large seaside funfair, huge Sunday market.

**Hole in the Wall Antiques,** 30b High Street, CT20 3AP TEL: 240725 PARKING: Medium OPEN: 9.15-6 MIN: £10 MAX: £2000 PERIOD: 19th-20th century SPECIALIST: Furniture GENERAL: Smalls, silver plate, Deco.

**Robin Homewood Antiques**, 59a High Street, CT20 3AH TEL: 249466 PARKING: Medium OPEN: Mon-Sat 9.30-5.30 PERIOD: 18th-20th century GENERAL: General antiques OTHER INFO: Romney, Hythe and Dymchurch Railway.

**Hyron Antiques**, 86 High Street, CT20 3BY TEL: 240698 PARKING: Medium OPEN: Mon-Sat 9.30-5.30 MIN: £1 MAX: £750 PERIOD: 19th-20th century GENERAL: Victorian, Edwardian furniture, bric-a-brac OTHER INFO: Sandgate Castle, Euro Tunnel Exhibition & entrance. Seafront B&B's.

**David Lancefield Antiques**
**53 Sandgate High Street, CT20 3AH TEL: 850149 ASSNS: LAPADA PARKING: Own carpark OPEN: Mon-Sat 10-6 Sun 11-5 MIN: £5 MAX: £10,000 PERIOD: 18th-19th century SPECIALIST: Large stock of all antiques, silver & plate, furniture, ceramics, prints, metalware, etc on two floors.**

**Annette Mobbs Antiques,** 53 High Street, CT20 3AH TEL: 850149 PARKING: Easy OPEN: Mon-Sat 10-6 Sun & Bank Holidays 11-5 MIN: £5 MAX:

£5000 PERIOD: 18th-20th century SPECIALIST: Prints, silverplate GENERAL: Walnut & mahogany furniture, wrought iron furniture, jewellery.

**Nordens,** 43 High Street, CT20 3AH TEL: 248443 PARKING: Easy OPEN: 10-5.30 MIN: 10p MAX: £2000 PERIOD: 18th-20th century GENERAL: Furniture, china, glass, silver, bric a brac.

**Old English Pine,** 100 High Street, CT20 3BY TEL: 248560 PARKING: Medium OPEN: 10-6 MIN: 50p MAX: £1800 PERIOD: 18th-20th century GENERAL: Pine furniture, objets d'art, bric a brac, architectural antiques.

**Palm House Antiques** 13-15 High Street, CT20 3BD TEL: 850696 PARKING: Easy OPEN: Mon-Sat 9.30-5.30, Suns 11-5 MIN: £5 MAX: £5000 PERIOD: 18th-20th century GENERAL: 12 dealers with wide varied stock OTHER INFO: Seaside village, 16th century castle. 35 dealers in one street.

**J T Rutherford & Son,** 55 High Street TEL: 249515 PARKING: Easy OPEN: 8.30-6 MIN: £3 MAX: £8000 PERIOD: 17th-19th century SPECIALIST: Weapons, furniture.

**Sandgate Antiques Centre,** 61-63 High Street, CT20 3AH TEL: 248987 PARKING: Easy MIN: £5 MAX: £10,000 PERIOD: 17th-20th century SPECIALIST: General antiques, furniture.

## HYTHE (01303)

**Den of Antiquity,** 35 Dymchurch Road, CT21 6JE TEL: 267162 PARKING: Easy OPEN: 9-5 PERIOD: 19th-20th century SPECIALIST: Jewellery & Staffordshire GENERAL: Wide range of interesting stock OTHER INFO: We have largest exisitng piece of Staffordshire and a live macaw.

**Owlets,** 99 High Street, CT21 6JE TEL: 230333 PARKING: Easy OPEN: 9-5.30 MIN: £15 MAX: £5000 PERIOD: 19th-20th century SPECIALIST: Jewellery & silver GENERAL: Pottery & porcelain, paintings, small furniture, stone carvings, etc.

**Samovar Antiques,** 158 High Street, CT21 5JR TEL: 264239 PARKING: Own carpark OPEN: Mon-Sat 9.30-5 MIN: £5 MAX: £1000+ PERIOD: 18th-20th century SPECIALIST: Oriental carpet & rugs GENERAL: Antiques, furniture, silver etc.

## SMEETH (01303)

**Richard Moate Antiques,** Wentworth, Plain Road, TN25 6QN TEL & FAX: 813241 PARKING: Own carpark OPEN: By appt (anytime) MIN: £3 MAX: £1000 PERIOD: 18th-20th century SPECIALIST: English & European pine.

## WOODCHURCH (01233)

**Treasures,** 1-3 The Green, TN26 3PE TEL: 860249 PARKING: Easy OPEN: 10-5.30, closed Thurs MIN: £1 MAX: £700 PERIOD: 19th-20th century SPECIALIST: Stripped antique pine GENERAL: Some other darkwood furniture, china, linen, kitchenalia & collectables OTHER INFO: Situated by delightful village green, cricket etc in summer.

## TENTERDEN (01580)

**John McMaster,** 5 Sayers Square, Sayers Lane, TN30 6BW TEL: 762941 ASSNS: BADA PARKING: Easy OPEN: Mon-Sat 9-5.30 MIN: £10 MAX: £10,000 PERIOD: 18th-19th century SPECIALIST: Georgian furniture, engravings GENERAL: Large stock quality silver + plate, porcelain, glass OTHER INFO: Sissinghurst, Bodiam, steam railway.

**Sparks Antiques,** 4 Manor Row, High Street, TN30 6HP TEL: 766696 PARKING: Own carpark OPEN: Mon-Sat 9-5.30 MIN: £100 MAX: £10,000 PERIOD: 17th-19th century SPECIALIST: English & Continental furniture GENERAL: Paintings, works of art, decorative & collectors items. OTHER INFO: Shop size, 2500 sq ft. This is a pretty market town with 8-10 antiques shops & good restaurants.

**The Weald Antiques Gallery,** 106 High Street, TN30 6HT TEL: 762939 PARKING: Easy OPEN: Mon-Fri 10-5, Sat 10-5.30 MIN: £5 MAX: £5000 PERIOD: 18th-19th century SPECIALIST: Dolls, teddies, samplers, jewellery, Tunbridge ware, prints, pictures, silver, ceramics GENERAL: Interior decorative pieces including furniture.

## WITTERSHAM (01797)

**Old Corner House,** 6 Poplar Road, TN30 7PG TEL: 270236 PARKING: Easy OPEN: 10-5, closed Friday MIN: £20 MAX: £5000 PERIOD: 17th-19th century SPECIALIST: Early English ceramics especially Blue & White, samplers, carvings, English watercolours GENERAL: Country furniture OTHER INFO: Several good pubs nearby for lunch or Rye teashops.

## RYE (01797)

**Bragge & Sons,** Landgate House, TN31 7LH TEL: 223358 PARKING: Easy OPEN: 9-5, closed Tues pm PERIOD: 18th century SPECIALIST: English & Continental furniture.

**Herbert Gasson,** The Lion Galleries, Lion Street,

TN31 7LB TEL: 222208 PARKING: Medium OPEN: 9-5.30 MIN: £60 MAX: £5000 PERIOD: 17th-19th century SPECIALIST: Early oak & country furniture GENERAL: Pre 1850 furniture, copper & brass OTHER INFO: Jeake's House Hotel, The Bistro, Landgate, the church & Rye's cobbled streets.

**Landgate Antiques**, 22 Landgate, TN31 7LP TEL: 224746 FAX: 225143 ASSNS: LAPADA PARKING: Medium OPEN: Usually seven days 9-5.30 MIN: £20 MAX: £6500 PERIOD: 19th century GENERAL: Decorative items

**Ann Lingard**, 18-22 Rope Walk, TN31 7NA TEL: 223486 FAX: 224700 ASSNS: LAPADA PARKING: Own carpark OPEN: Mon-Sat 9-5.30 & by appt MIN: £1 MAX: £2,000 PERIOD: 19th-20th century SPECIALIST: Antique pine furniture. Kitchen shop GENERAL: Complementary antique accessories, china, glass, copper, brass box & wooden objects, etc (no reproductions). Trade warehouse nearby, shippers welcome OTHER INFO: Ancient Cinque Port town. Small population 4000.

**The Mint Arcade**, 71 The Mint, TN31 7EW TEL: 225952 PARKING: Easy OPEN: 7 days 10-5 MIN: £1 MAX: £100 PERIOD: 19th-20th century SPECIALIST: Original cigarette cards, handmade wooden picture frames, old dolls & teddys, handpainted soldiers & old jewellery OTHER INFO: Come and see Napoleon Viner at work, painting soldiers. He will always stop for a chat about his idol, Napoleon Bonaparte.

**Rye Antiques**, 93 High Street, TN31 7JN TEL: 222257 PARKING: Easy OPEN: 9.30-5.30 MIN: £5 MAX: £500 PERIOD: 18th-20th century SPECIALIST: Cameo jewellery GENERAL: Silver, copper, brassware, small oak, pewter, jewellery, some glassware & porcelain OTHER INFO: Whole town is an antique gem with wealth of antique shops.

## ROLVENDEN (01580)

**Falstaff Antiques**, 63-67 High Street, TN17 4LP TEL: 241234 PARKING: Easy OPEN: Mon-Sat 9-6 MIN: £1 MAX: £500 PERIOD: 19th-20th century GENERAL: Antiques & reproductions OTHER INFO: Motor Museum also at this site.

**Kent Cottage Antiques**, 39 High Street, TN17 4LP TEL: 241719 PARKING: Easy OPEN: 9.30-4 MIN: £50 MAX: £2000 PERIOD: 18th-20th century SPECIALIST: Scent bottles GENERAL: Porcelain, silver, small furniture OTHER INFO: Motor Museum, Hole Park Gardens, Great Maytham Hall.



**JD & RM Walters**, 10 Regent Street, TN17 4PE TEL: 241563 ASSNS: GMC PARKING: Easy OPEN: 8-6 PERIOD: 18th-19th century SPECIALIST: Antique furniture restorers & makers of period copies up to circa 1830. OTHER INFO: Close to Tenterden, Kent's most picturesque town.

## SANDHURST (01580)

**Forge Antiques & Restorations**, Rye Road, TN18 5JG TEL: 850665, 850308 PARKING: Own carpark OPEN: Variable, phone first MIN: £1 MAX: £3000 PERIOD: 19th-20th century SPECIALIST: Tunbridgeware, rosewood tables, work tables, bookcases, chairs, porcelain, tea services, glass OTHER INFO: Also furniture repair workshops.

## HAWKHURST (01580)

**Septimus Quayles Emporium,** Ockley Road, TN18 4NG TEL: 752222 PARKING: Own carpark OPEN: Mon-Sat 9.30-5, except Wed 9.30-1 MIN: £1.50 MAX: £200 PERIOD: 19th-20th century GENERAL: Copper, brass, linen, china, silverplate.

## LAMBERHURST (01892)

**The China Locker**, Bedwyn Cottage, The Slade, TN3 8HN TEL: 890555 PARKING: Own carpark OPEN: Anytime MIN: £5 MAX: £45 PERIOD: 19th century GENERAL: 18th-19th century prints

OTHER INFO: Scotney Castle, Bewl Reservoir.

## GOUDHURST (01580)

**Foxhole Antiques,** High Street TEL: 212025 PARKING: Easy OPEN: Tues-Sat 10-4 SPECIALIST: Antique pine & country furniture.

**Old Saddlers Antiques**, Church Road, TN17 1BH TEL: 211458 PARKING: Easy OPEN: Mon, Wed-Sat 9.30-12, 2.30-5.30 MIN: £5 MAX: £500+ PERIOD: 18th-20th century SPECIALIST: Heavy horse brasses & decorations GENERAL: Blue & White transferware, brass, copper, wrought iron. Victorian & Georgian jewellery, pewter OTHER INFO: One of the prettiest villages with wonderful views over the High Weald of Kent, 12th century church, lovely old inns.

## CRANBROOK (01580)

**Cranbrook Antiques**, 15 High Street TEL: 712173 PARKING: Easy OPEN: Mon-Sat 10-5 MIN: £1 MAX: £1000 PERIOD: 18th-20th century GENERAL: 6 dealers selling furniture, porcelain, pottery, toys, jewellery, silver, pictures & prints, etc OTHER INFO: Famous 14th century weaving town with many historic buildings and a working windmill.

**Cranbrook Gallery,** 21b Stone Street, TN17 3HE TEL: 713021 ASSNS: FATG PARKING: Easy OPEN: Tues-Fri 9-5, Sat 9-4 MIN: £8 MAX: £1,000 SPECIALIST: Prints, maps, watercolours OTHER INFO: Near Sissinghurst Castle. Town museum with working windmill.

**The Old Bakery Antiques**, St David's Bridge, TN17 3HN TEL: 713103 FAX: 712407 ASSN: BADA, LAPADA PARKING: Easy OPEN: Mon-Sat 9.30-5 Weds AM only or by appt MIN: £50 MAX: £20,000 PERIOD: 17th-18th century SPECIALIST English oak & walnut furniture, some metalware OTHER INFO: Pretty Wealdon town close to Sissinghurst Castle, approach from London via A21, A262, nearest BR station Staplehurst.

**Swan Antiques**, Stone Street, TN17 3HP TEL: 712720 PARKING: Own carpark OPEN: Mon, Tues, Thurs-Sat 9.30-5.30 MIN: £10 MAX: £5,000 PERIOD: 18th-19th century SPECIALIST: Country furniture, folk art GENERAL: Early painted & primitive furniture.

**The Wooden Chair,** Waterloo Road, TN17 3JR TEL: 713671 PARKING: Easy OPEN: 9.30-5.30 MIN: 50p MAX: £2000 OTHER INFO: In an old bakery.

## BIDDENDEN (01580)

**Harriet Ann Sleigh Beds,** Standen Farm, TN27 8JT TEL: 291220 PARKING: Own carpark OPEN: Mon-Sat 9.30-5.30 MIN: £250 MAX: £1500 PERIOD: 19th century SPECIALIST: Pine European beds GENERAL: Other pine from Eastern Europe & Scandinavia OTHER INFO: Lots of good local B&Bs, good local pubs.

**Two Maids Antiques,** 6 High Street, TN27 8AH TEL & FAX: 291807 PARKING: Easy OPEN: 10-5.30 MIN: £5 MAX: £2000 PERIOD: 17th-19th century SPECIALIST: Gilding & picture framing GENERAL: Inglenook metalwork, lace bobbins, picture frames, carvings, treen, miniature & small furniture OTHER INFO: Biddenden is dominated by Siamese twins born in 1100, joined at the shoulder & hips, they lived in this state for 34 years & left money to the poor of the village. The charity is still active to this day.

## HEADCORN (01622)

**Penny Lampard**, 31-33 High Street, TN27 9NE TEL: 890682 PARKING: Easy OPEN: 10-5.30 MIN: £25 MAX: £1500 PERIOD: 19th century SPECIALIST: Pine furniture GENERAL: Dark wood & giftware OTHER INFO: Coffee shop in Victorian style on premises.

## SUTTON VALENCE (01622)

**Sutton Valence Antiques**, North Street, ME17 4AP (Warehouse at Manston) TEL: 843333, FAX: 692593 ASSNS: LAPADA PARKING: Own carpark OPEN: Mon-Sat 10-5, Sun 11-4 MIN: £10 MAX: £5000 PERIOD: 17th-20th century GENERAL: Large mixed stock OTHER INFO: 3 miles from Leeds Castle & M20.

## HARRIETSHAM (01622)

**Judith Peppitt**, Chegworth Manor Farm, Chegworth Road, ME17 1DD TEL: 859313 PARKING: Own carpark OPEN: Anytime by appt MIN: £20 MAX: £2000 PERIOD: 18th-20th century SPECIALIST: British watercolours OTHER INFO: Superb Leeds Castle. Great Danes Hotel.

# Croydon to East Grinstead

This tour commences in the startlingly modern commercial suburb of Croydon and proceeds through leafy, pleasant Surrey towns and villages, many showing evidence of ancient origins, until reaching East Grinstead, the final place on the route.

Seeing modern **Croydon**, it is almost impossible for the visitor to guess at its historic past. Situated on the Roman road between London and Portsmouth, from Norman times the area was owned by the Archbishops of Canterbury. The Archbishops' 14th century manor house still exists and is now used as a school. With the coming of the railways the population increased rapidly throughout the 19th century. Croydon Airport was built in 1915 and Amy Johnson started her record breaking flight to Australia here. During the Second World War the town was heavily bombed which led to extensive rebuilding and the construction of the modern town centre seen today.

The route continues through **Sutton** and **Carshalton,** the centre of which is now a conservation area. Carshalton, mentioned in the Domesday Book, owed its prosperity in times past to its position on the banks of the River Wandle and the many industries associatd with water such as paper-making and calico bleaching. At both Carshalton and **Wallington,** the next call, lavender and mint were grown and processed. Wallington was only a hamlet with a local manor until the coming of the railway in 1867 after which it grew quickly. Further on, the tour reaches **Coulsdon**, where the first recorded game of cricket using three stumps and 2 bails was played in 1766, and **Kenley**, the site of an airfield used in both World Wars for the defence of London.

Turning south-west, the tour reaches first **Tadworth** and then **Dorking**, a town with many attractive antique shops. This is an ancient town situated on the Roman road of Stane Street. In the High Street there are many fine 17th century, Georgian and Victorian buildings. Just one mile north of the town, on the A24, stands Box Hill, a striking landmark rising 400 feet above the River Mole. It is a beautiful area with the gentle rounded features of a chalk escarpment and crowned with beechwoods. The summit gives breath-taking views over the surrounding countryside and it is a popular place for day trips from London.

East on the A25, **Bletchworth** follows and then to linked towns of **Reigate** and **Redhill**, the latter having an unusual museum: the Royal Earlswood Hospital Museum dealing, unsurprisingly, with medical history. From here there is a detour along the A23 to visit **Merstham** before continuing eastward to **Bletchingley** with its broad main street containing several interesting timbered and tile-hung buildings. The town has a particularly fine church; the Norman tower was built in the 11th century and the remainder of the building is mostly 15th century.

Next is **Oxted** and then **Limpsfield,** where the composer, Frederick Delius, is buried in the churchyard. The tour doubles back slightly and then turns south 8 miles to **Lingfield** where there is a famous racecourse. The last town, **East Grinstead**, appears as a typical commuter sprawl but in the High Street it retains the layout and many of the buildings of a medieval market town. There are 14th, 15th and 16th century half-timbered houses A major feature of the town, the Sackville College (not an educational college but rather almhouses), was built by the the Earl of Dorset, Thomas Sackville, and was completed in 1619. One of the wardens was the Rev. John Mason Neale who ran the college from 1846 until his death twenty years later. He wrote the hymns Good King Wenceslas and Jerusalem the Golden.

East Grinstead is renowned in the field of medicine for the revolutionary plastic surgery work done at the Queen Victoria Hospital by Sir Archibald McIndoe. He started in the hospital at the beginning of the Second World War and continued there until his death in 1960. He is particularly famous for his work on severely burned airmen whose special club, The Guinea Pigs, is still centred on the Queen Victoria.

## Croydon to East Grinstead

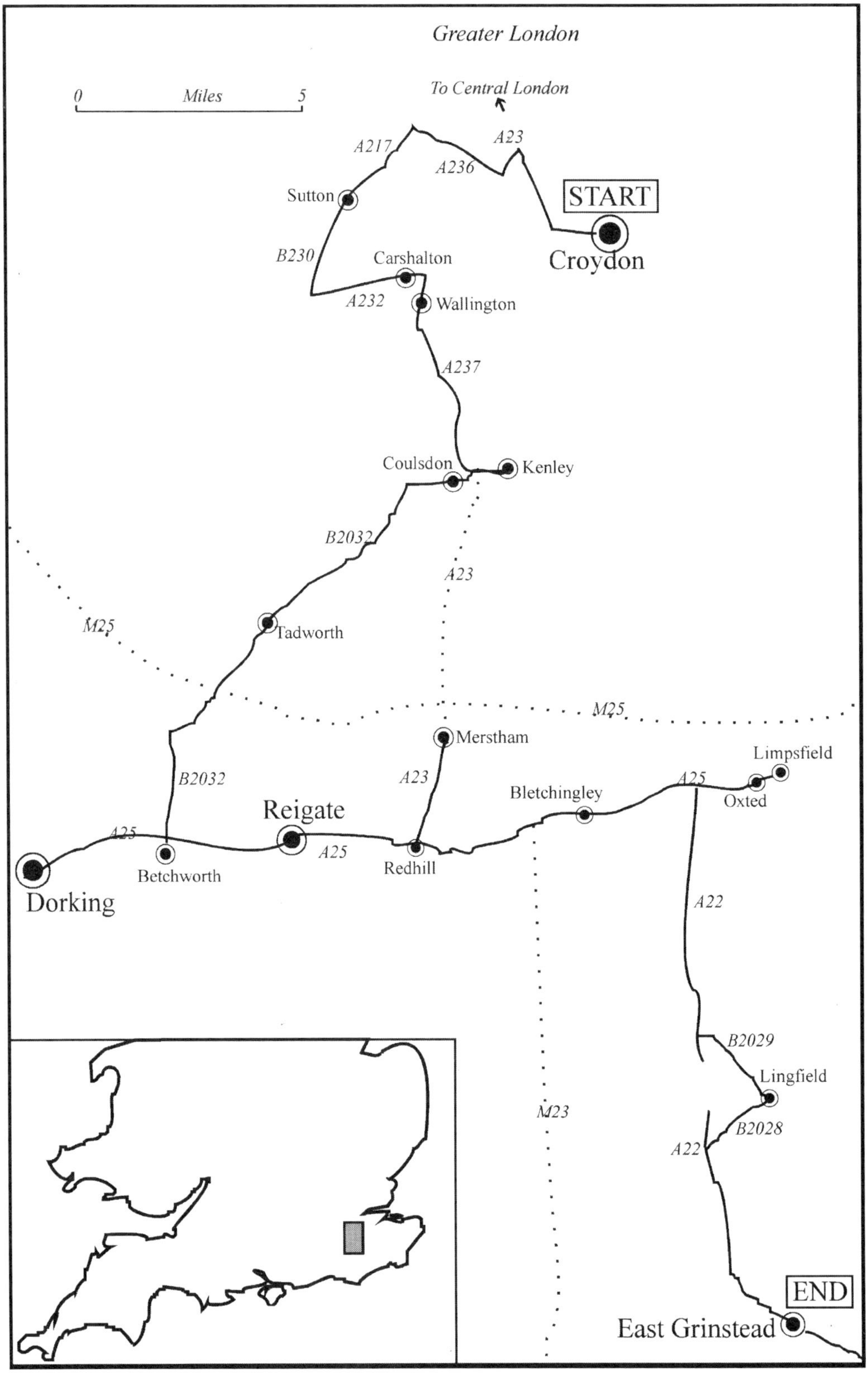

## ANTIQUE DEALERS

### CROYDON (0181)

**Oscar Dahling Antiques,** 87 Cherry Orchard Road TEL: 681 8090 PARKING: Medium OPEN: 10.30-6 PERIOD: 18th-20th century GENERAL: Furniture, glass, Art Deco, jewellery, linen, costume.

**GE Griffin**, 43a Brighton Road, South Croydon, CR2 6EB TEL: 688 3130 PARKING: Easy OPEN: 8-5 MIN: £10 MAX: £10,000 PERIOD: 19th-20th century SPECIALIST: Furniture GENERAL: General antiques.

**Collectors Corner**, 43 Brighton Road, South Croydon, CR0 6EB TEL: 680 7511 PARKING: Medium OPEN: Tues, Thurs-Sat 9.30-4.30 MIN: £5 MAX: £10,000 PERIOD: 19th-20th century SPECIALIST: Dinky, die cast toys, old dolls, teddies GENERAL: Ephemera, furniture, collectables.

**Trengrove**, 46 South End, CR0 1DP TEL: 688 2155 PARKING: Medium OPEN: 9.30-4, closed Wed MIN: £5 MAX: £5000 PERIOD: 19th-20th century GENERAL: Wide range, bit of everything.

### SUTTON (0181)

**David Aldous-Cook,** PO Box 413, SM3 8SZ TEL & FAX: 642 4842 SPECIALIST: Reference books on antiques and collectables OTHER INFO: We attend major antique fairs and a postal service is available.

**Westmead Antiques,** 82 Westmead Road, SM1 4HY TEL & FAX: 643 1133 PARKING: Easy OPEN: 10-6 MIN: £5 MAX: £2000 PERIOD: 19th-20th century SPECIALIST: English & Continental pine GENERAL: Furniture.

### CARSHALTON (0181)

**McDonald Antiques**, 376 Carshalton Road, TEL: 669 7402 ASSNS: BAFRA PARKING: Medium OPEN: Mon-Sat 10.30-6 MIN: £2 MAX: £500 PERIOD: 19th-20th century GENERAL: Furniture, general smalls, collectors junk.

### WALLINGTON (0181)

**Manor Antiques**, 75a Manor Road TEL: 669 5970 PARKING: Easy OPEN: Mon, Tues, Thurs-Sat 10.30-5 MIN: £1 MAX: £500 PERIOD: 19th-20th century GENERAL: General antiques.

### COULSDON (0181)

**VICTORIA ANTIQUES CENTRE**
**147 BRIGHTON ROAD, CR5 2NJ TEL: 763 9650 PARKING: EASY OPEN: MON-SAT 9.30-5.30, SUN 11-5 MIN: £5 MAX: £2000 PERIOD: 18TH-20TH CENTURY, DATE-LINE 1940 SPECIALIST: LIGHTING, WOODWORKING TOOLS, GRAMO-PHONES GENERAL: GLASS, CHINA, BRASS, COPPER, PRINTS, SMALL FURNITURE OTHER INFO: CONVENIENTLY SITUATED ON A23, LONDON TO BRIGHTON ROAD, 3 MINS FROM M25, JUNCTION 7.**

### KENLEY (0181)

**Michael Addison Antiques**, 28-30 Godstone Road, CR8 5JE TEL: 668 6714 PARKING: Easy OPEN: 10-5, closed Mon MIN: £100 MAX: £2,000 PERIOD: 18th-20th century GENERAL: Victorian, Georgian & Edwardian furniture OTHER INFO Selsdon Park Hotel.

## TADWORTH (01737)

**Ian Caldwell**, 9a The Green, Dorking Road, KT20 5SQ TEL: 813969 ASSNS: LAPADA PARKING: Easy OPEN: 10-5 MIN: £1 MAX: £10,000 PERIOD: 17th-19th century SPECIALIST: Georgian town furniture GENERAL: Furniture, prints, watercolours, oils, porcelain, etc.

**Showcase,** 24 Cross Road, KT20 5SR TEL: 814219 PARKING: Easy OPEN: 10-5.30 except Wed MIN: £2 MAX: £700 PERIOD: 19th-20th century SPECIALIST: Pine GENERAL: Furniture, made to measure, paint finishes OTHER INFO: Plenty of country pubs & picturesque villages nearby.

## DORKING (01306)

**Howard Blay Antiques,** 56 West Street, RH4 1BS TEL: 743398 PARKING: Easy OPEN: 10-5 MAX: £10,000 PERIOD: 17th-18th century GENERAL: Pre 1800 walnut mahogany & oak furniture.

**Tom Burton & Rod Johnston**, Dorking Antiques Centre, 17-18 West Street, RH4 1BS TEL: 740915 PARKING: Easy OPEN: Mon-Sat 10-5.30 MIN: £50 MAX: £500 PERIOD: 19th century SPECIALIST: Ceramics, mainly British Ironstone and Blue & White GENERAL: Victoriana including desk sets, small Victorian & Edwardian furniture.

**J & M Coombes,** 44 West Street, RH4 1BU TEL: 885479 PARKING: Medium OPEN: 6 days 9-5 MIN: £100 MAX: £3500 PERIOD: 19th-20th century SPECIALIST: Chests of drawers GENERAL: 300 pieces furniture, mostly restored.

**Dorking Antique Centre**, 17-18 West Street TEL: 740915 PARKING: Easy OPEN: Mon-Sat 10-5.30 MIN: £25 MAX: £6000 PERIOD: 18th-20th century SPECIALIST: Furniture GENERAL: Wide selection of clocks, paintings & porcelain OTHER INFO: Two 18th century pubs in street.

**DORKING DESK SHOP**
**41 WEST STREET, RH4 1BU. TEL: 883327 FAX: 875363 ASSNS: LAPADA, DADA PARKING: MEDIUM OPEN: MON-FRI 8-5.30, SAT 10.30-1, 2-5 MIN: £3 MAX: £30,000 PERIOD: 18TH-19TH CENTURY SPECIALIST: ALL TYPES OF DESKS INCLUDING 30 PARTNERS GENERAL: ANTIQUE WRITING FURNITURE, BUREAUX BOOKCASES ROLLTYPES, CHAIRS, TABLES, SECRETAIRES.**

**The Dorking Emporium**, 1a West Street TEL: 876646 PARKING: Easy OPEN: Mon-Fri 10-5, Sat 10-5.30 MIN: £1 MAX: £4,000 PERIOD: 18th-20th century SPECIALIST: Georgian & Edwardian mahogany furniture GENERAL: Antique Centre, good variety of antiques, collectables, pictures, books, Art Deco OTHER INFO: Coffee shop providing homemade light lunches. Dorking is a centre for antiques having 3 antique centres & innumerable antique shops.

**Hampshires of Dorking**, 51-52 West Street, RH5 4LB TEL: 887076 FAX: 881029 PARKING: Own carpark OPEN: Mon-Sat 9.30-5.30 MIN: £300 MAX: £50,000 PERIOD: Late 17th-early19th century SPECIALIST: Fine Georgian, 16th-early 19th century satinwood, mahogany, walnut, some oak, rosewood OTHER INFO: Burford Bridge Hotel, Fountain Garden, Chinese restaurant, Box Hill etc.

**HARMAN'S ANTIQUES**
**19 WEST STREET, RH4 1QH TEL: 743330 FAX: 742593 PARKING: EASY OPEN: MON-SAT 10-5 MIN: £700 MAX: £15,000 PERIOD: 17TH-19TH CENTURY SPECIALIST: DINING TABLES & CHAIRS ALWAYS IN STOCK GENERAL: LINEN PRESSES, TALL BOYS, CHESTS, MIRRORS, DESKS, WARDROBES.**

**Hebeco**, 47 West Street, RH4 1BU TEL: 875396 PARKING: Easy OPEN: 10.30-5 MIN: £10 MAX: £3000+ PERIOD: 18th-20th century SPECIALIST: Silver & plate, glass, pewter, blue & white transfer printed wares OTHER INFO: Situated in a street occupied primarily by antique dealers..

**John Lang Antiques**, Kings Head Court, 11 High Street, RH14 1AR TEL: 882203 PARKING: Easy OPEN: Mon, Tues, Thurs-Sat 9-5 MIN: £25 MAX: £1500 PERIOD: 18th century SPECIALIST: Country furniture, oak GENERAL: Coffers, chess, brass, copper, decorators items OTHER INFO: 32 antiques shops and 5 antiques centres.

**King's Court Galleries**, 54 West Street TEL: 881757 OPEN: 9.30-5.30 PARKING: Easy OPEN: 9.30-5.30 MIN: £8 MAX: £2500 PERIOD: 17th-19th century SPECIALIST: Antique prints & maps GENERAL: Decorative & sporting prints limited editions.

**Mayfair Antiques,** 43 West Street TEL: 885007 FAX: 742636 PARKING: Easy OPEN: 9-5 MIN: £250 MAX: £5500 PERIOD: 18th-19th century GENERAL: Furniture OTHER INFO: Dorking has a good variety of restaurants & most pubs have food at realistic prices.

**Denis Murphy Period Furniture,** 62A West Street, RH4 1BS TEL: 743661 PARKING: Medium OPEN: 9.30-5.30, closed Wed MIN: £100 MAX: £2500 PERIOD: 18th-19th century GENERAL: Good quality mixed selection, boxes to bureaux, selected 18th century pieces.

**Norfolk House Galleries,** 48 West Street, RH4 1BU TEL: 881028 PARKING: Easy OPEN: 10-5 MIN: £100 MAX: £10,000 PERIOD: 17th-19th century SPECIALIST: Dining tables & sets of chairs GENERAL: Furniture OTHER INFO: Excellent B&B at Fairdene Guest House.

**Oriental Carpets & Decorative Arts**, 37 West Street, RH4 1BU TEL: 876370 FAX: (01483) 202983 PARKING: Medium OPEN: 10-5, closed Wed MIN: £150 PERIOD: 19th-20th century SPECIALIST: Oriental carpets & rugs, antique & semi-antique OTHER INFO: Valuation, repair & cleaning. Beautiful countryside, good hotels & an orgy of restaurants.

**Pilgrims Antique Centre,** 7 West Street, RH4 1BL TEL: 815028 PARKING: Easy OPEN: 6 days 10-5.30 MIN: £5 MAX: £2000 PERIOD: 18th-20th century GENERAL: China, furniture, paintings, brass, copper, curios.

**Elaine Saunderson Antiques,** 18-18a Church Street TEL: 881231 PARKING: Easy OPEN: 10-5.30 & by appt (resident) MIN: £50 MAX: £10,000 PERIOD: 18th-early 19th century SPECIALIST: Furniture.

**Patrick Thomas-Antique Clocks,** 62A West Street, RH4 1BS TEL: 743661 PARKING: Easy OPEN: Mon-Sat 9.30-5.30, closed Wed MIN: £10 MAX: £5000 PERIOD: 18th-20th century GENERAL: Wide selection of all types of clocks.

**Thorpe & Foster Ltd**, 50 West Street, RH4 1BU TEL: 887076 FAX: 881029 PARKING: Own carpark OPEN: 9.30-5.30 MIN: £3 MAX: £50,000 PERIOD: 17th-19th century SPECIALIST: Furniture, satinwood, mahogany, rosewood, walnut..

**Victoria & Edward Antiques Centre**, 61 West Street TEL: 889645 PARKING: Easy OPEN: Mon-Sat 9.30-5.30 MIN: £2 MAX: £4,000 PERIOD: 18th-20th century GENERAL: Wide range of scintillating antiques.

**Pauline Watson Antique Jewellery**, Old King's Head Court (by pump corner), RH14 1AR TEL: 885452 ASSNS: NAG registered valuer, Fellow of Gemmological Assn of GB PARKING: Easy OPEN: Mon-Sat 9.30-5. MIN: £25 MAX: £5,000 PERIOD: 18th-19th & some 20th century SPECIALIST: Seals, Victorian jewellery GENERAL: Antique jewellery & some silver

**West Street Antiques**, 63 West Street, RH4 1BS TEL: 883487 PARKING: Easy OPEN: 9.30-5.30 MIN: £20 MAX: £10,000 PERIOD: 18th-19th century SPECIALIST: Arms & armour, fishing tackle GENERAL: Furniture.

**Patrick Worth**, 11 West Street TEL: 884484 ASSNS: BADA PARKING: Easy MIN: £850 MAX: £15,000 PERIOD: 18th-19th century SPECIALIST: 18th century & Regency, also decorative items OTHER INFO: Fine old market town with Tudor & Georgian buildings, West Street is given over to antique shops.

## BETCHWORTH (01737)

**Dorking Desk Shop,** Stoney Croft Farm, Reigate Road, RH3 7EY TEL: 845215 ASSNS: LAPADA, DADA PARKING: Own carpark OPEN: Mon-Fri 8-5.30 MIN: £50 MAX: £40,000 PERIOD: 18th-19th century SPECIALIST: Large bookcases, dining tables, sets of chairs GENERAL: Oak & country furniture, study & library furniture.

## REIGATE (01737)

**Bourne Gallery**, 31-33 Lesbourne Road, RH2 7JS TEL: 241614 ASSNS: LAPADA PARKING: Easy OPEN: Tues-Sat 10-5 MIN: £100 MAX: £10,000 PERIOD: 19th-20th century SPECIALIST: Fine paintings GENERAL: European oils & watercolours OTHER INFO: 23,000 pictures sold in 23 years to collectors, dealers & corporations.

**Heath Antiques**, 15 Flanchford Road, RH2 8AB TEL: 244230 PARKING: Easy OPEN: Mon-Fri 10-6, Sats & Suns 2-5, prefer prior appt MIN: £2 MAX: £1500 PERIOD: 18th-20th century SPECIALIST: Small furniture, porcelain GENERAL: Silver, porcelain, country artefacts, furniture OTHER INFO: Shop is on Reigate Heath, just off A25 Dorking Rd.

**Bertram Noller (Reigate)**, 14A London Road, RH2 9HY TEL: 242548 PARKING: Easy OPEN: Mon, Thurs & Sat 9.30-1 & 2-5.30 MIN: £1 MAX: £500 PERIOD: 19th-20th century SPECIALIST: Fireplace equipment, including brass fenders & fire grates GENERAL: Metalware, silver, lamps, small furniture & curios OTHER INFO: Shop backs onto

castle moat, mound & caves under castle.
**Reigate Galleries,** 45A Bell Street, RH2 7AQ TEL: 246055 ASSNS: PBFA PARKING: Easy OPEN: 9-5.30, closed Wed pm MIN: 50p MAX: £3000 PERIOD: 19th-20th century SPECIALIST: Travel & illustrated books GENERAL: All subjects.

## REDHILL (01737)

**FG Lawrence & Sons**, 89 Brighton Road, RH1 6PS TEL: 764196 & 764197 PARKING: Own carpark OPEN: Mon-Fri 9-1, 2-5, Sats 9-1 MIN: £50 MAX: £5000 PERIOD: 17th-20th century SPECIALIST: Georgian, Victorian, Edwardian furniture OTHER INFO: Warehouse at rear.

## MERSTHAM (01737)

**Merstham Village Antiques Centre,** 3 High Street, RH1 3BA TEL: 643012 OPEN: 10.30-5, closed Wed PERIOD: 18th-20th century GENERAL: Furniture, decorative items, glass, china, textiles, kitchenalia.
**The Old Smithy**, 7 High Street, RH1 3BA TEL: 642306 PARKING: Own carpark OPEN: 10-5.30 MIN: £1 MAX: £3000 PERIOD: 17th-20th century SPECIALIST: Lighting, glassware GENERAL: Furniture, collectables, pictures, prints OTHER INFO: 2 more shops here.
**Village Pine,** 6 High Street, RH1 3BA OPEN: 10.30-5, closed Wed PERIOD: 19th-20th century SPECIALIST: Antique pine furniture OTHER INFO: Small high street with 4 antique shops.

## BLETCHINGLEY (01883)

**The Cider House Galleries Ltd.**, Norfolk House, 80 High Street, RH1 4AA TEL: 742198 FAX: 744014 PARKING: Own carpark OPEN: Mon-Fri 9.30-5.30. Sats 10-1 MIN: £250 MAX: £40,000 PERIOD: 17th-20th century SPECIALIST : 19th century Victorian GENERAL: 600+ oils in stock OTHER INFO: Village has 9 antique shops.
**Post House Antiques**, High Street, RH1 4PE TEL: 743317 PARKING: Easy OPEN: Mon-Fri 10-5, Sats 9.30-4 or by appt MIN: £10 MAX: £1500 PERIOD: 18th-20th century SPECIALIST: Antique restored lighting GENERAL: Wood, metal, decorative etc in 6 showrooms.

## OXTED (01883)

**Antiques & Interiors**, 64 Station Road East TEL: 712806 PARKING: Easy OPEN: Mon-Sat 9.30-5.30 MIN: £5 MAX: £2000 PERIOD: 19th-20th century GENERAL: Wide range of antiques, interior design OTHER INFO: Coffee shop on site, good lunches.
**Antiques Centre,** 80-84 Station Road East, RH8 0PG TEL: 712806 PARKING: Easy (free public carpark to rear) OPEN: 9.30-5.30 MIN: £1 MAX: £3000 PERIOD: 17th-20th century SPECIALIST: Silver GENERAL: Furniture, ceramics, metalware, jewellery, pictures, books OTHER INFO: 15 dealers over 2 floors. There is an interior design section & a coffee shop on site serving good lunches.
**Treasures**, 151 Station Road East TEL: 713301 PARKING: Medium OPEN: Mon-Sat 10-5 MIN: £1 MAX: £500 PERIOD: 19th century GENERAL: 12 dealers offering porcelain, clocks, silver, jewellery, small furniture, pictures, collectables etc.

## LIMPSFIELD (01883)

**The Lace Place,** Briars Cross, Limpsfield Chart, RH8 0SY TEL: 722358 PARKING: Own carpark OPEN: Tues 10-4 or by appt MIN: 50p MAX: £300 PERIOD: 19th-20th century SPECIALIST: Lace, linen & embroideries GENERAL: Interesting & useful textiles OTHER INFO: The premises are converted stables attached to our house.
**Limpsfield Watercolours**, High Street TEL: 717010 PARKING: Easy OPEN: Tues 11-3, Thurs, Fri 10-2, Sat 10-3 MIN: £7 MAX: £5000 PERIOD: 19th-20th century SPECIALIST: Victorian, Edwardian watercolours GENERAL: Contemporary artists, antiquarian prints, Harley Davidson pens, jewellery inc. 'mood' jewellery (changes colour with your mood - frivolous fun) OTHER INFO: Old Lodge restaurant opposite.

## LINGFIELD (01342)

**IOU, Interesting Old & Unusual,** Paris House, 52-56 High Street TEL: 836565 PARKING: Easy OPEN: Mon-Sat 9.30-5 MIN: £2 MAX: £1500 PERIOD: 19th-20th century GENERAL: Furniture, pictures, collectors' items OTHER INFO: Light hearted approach (IOU), dance band, jazz played (sometimes too loud), can be changed to customer's choice on request. Lingfield Racecourse, good local restaurants.

## EAST GRINSTEAD (01342)

**Antique Atlas Gallery,** 31A High Street, RH19 3AF TEL: 315813 FAX: 318058 PARKING: Medium OPEN: Wed-Sat 10-5 MIN: £5 upwards

PERIOD: 16th-19th century SPECIALIST: Americana GENERAL: Maps, charts, plans & views of all parts of the world, some decorative prints.

**The Antique Print Shop**, 11 Middle Row, High Street, RH19 3AX TEL: 410501 FAX: 410795 PARKING: Easy OPEN: Mon-Sat 9.30-6 MIN: £10 MAX: £5000 PERIOD: 15th-19th century SPECIALIST: Rare 15th, 16th century maps GENERAL: Wide selection of antique maps & prints covering many subjects. Decorative prints.

**Keith Atkinson Antiques**, Moorhawes Farm, Sandhawes Hill, Dormansland RH19 3NR TEL: 870765 FAX: 870767 PARKING: Own carpark OPEN: Mon-Fri 9-6, weekends by appt MIN: £20 MAX: £10,000 PERIOD: 19th-20th century GENERAL: Georgian, Victorian, Edwardian & shipping furniture. OTHER INFO: Gravetye Manor, Hever Castle.

# East Sussex

This tour passes through beautiful quiet villages, busy market towns and popular seaside resorts of East Sussex. It starts in **Mayfield** which has a number of picturesque old houses, especially the attractively timbered medieval Middle House and continues on to **Wadhurst,** once a centre of iron smelting as shown by the thirty iron gravestones in the local churchyard. **Ticehurst** is next. A few miles south west of **Hurst Green**,where the Rother and Dudwell rivers meet, is Etchingham. The 14th century church of St Mary & St Nicholas has the oldest dated brass in Sussex. The nearby Haremere Hall, 17th century manor house has a panelled great hall with good carvings and an unusual rug collection. Two miles further on is the charming village of **Burwash**. Here too iron smelting was an important industry in past centuries and the oldest iron gravestone in Sussex may be found in the Burwash churchyard. Burwash was the home of Rudyard Kipling who lived in the 17th century house, Batemans, from 1902 to 1936 and also used the area as a setting in *Puck of Pook's Hill.*

**Sedlescombe** has a restored 15th century Queen's Head Inn, a gabled roof covering an old pump on the village green and an Anglo-Saxon treasure trove disinterred some 130 years ago after reportedly being buried by King Harold's paymaster soon after 1066. The route then reaches **Hastings**, a Cinque Port and an important harbour in Saxon times. William the Conquerer landed a few miles away at Pevensey Bay and went to Hastings where he built a fortress. The ruins of the later Hastings Castle can still be seen on the site of that Norman fortress. William then marched to Battle to fight the Saxons where he defeated King Harold. As a thanksgiving for his victory William built Battle Abbey and placed the high altar on the spot where Harold died. Now little survives but there is a newly restored 14th century gatehouse in which an exhibition displays the history of the abbey.

The Hastings Embroidery, an interesting modern achievement displayed in the Town Hall, is nearly 250 feet long and was made in 1966 to commemorate the 900th anniversary of the Battle of Hastings. It consists of over eighty events from British history including the murder of Becket right up to the 1953 conquest of Everest. Also on display are items of maritime history. Another fascinating museum is the award winning Shipwreck Heritage Centre in Rock-a-Nore Road. The major exhibits here are from three local wrecks, a warship from 1690, a Dutch ship dated 1749 and a Danish ship of 1861. This is the only museum in Britain licensed and equipped with radar to monitor shipping in the English Channel. It also has a direct link to satellites for weather forecasting.

Now turning west along the coast the tour passes through ever so slightly oldfashioned (or genteel **St Leonards** and then **Bexhill** where one can always venture a toe in the briny as it is a seaside resort with good sandy beaches. **Pevensey** was where William the Conqueror landed. The castle here dates from the 4th century AD. It was one of the forts built all along the coast from Hampshire to Norfolk as defences against the Saxons. Unlike some other forts of the period, Pevensey did not fall into disuse after the departure of the Romans and in fact the Normans built a castle on the site. During the Middle Ages Pevensey Castle saw considerable action. It was held by the rebel Bishop of Bayeaux, Odo, against the king in 1088 and had to be retaken by siege. Some 15 years later it was used by another rebel, the Count of Mortain, in a revolt against Henry I which resulted in that family losing Pevensey. Its troubled history continued until the 15th century in spite of the fact that by then it was in a sad state of disrepair with contemporary reports of walls falling down and the keep being in a ruinous condition. It was only in 1587, when England was threatened by the Spanish Armada, that the castle was repaired as part of the coastal defences but after this it was once again left to decay. The castle's last service was during the Second World War when once again invasion threatened. The castle had 'pill-boxes' (gun emplacements) built on some of the Roman walls and bastions and the medieval towers were adapted for the accommodation of troops. These alterations were all camouflaged

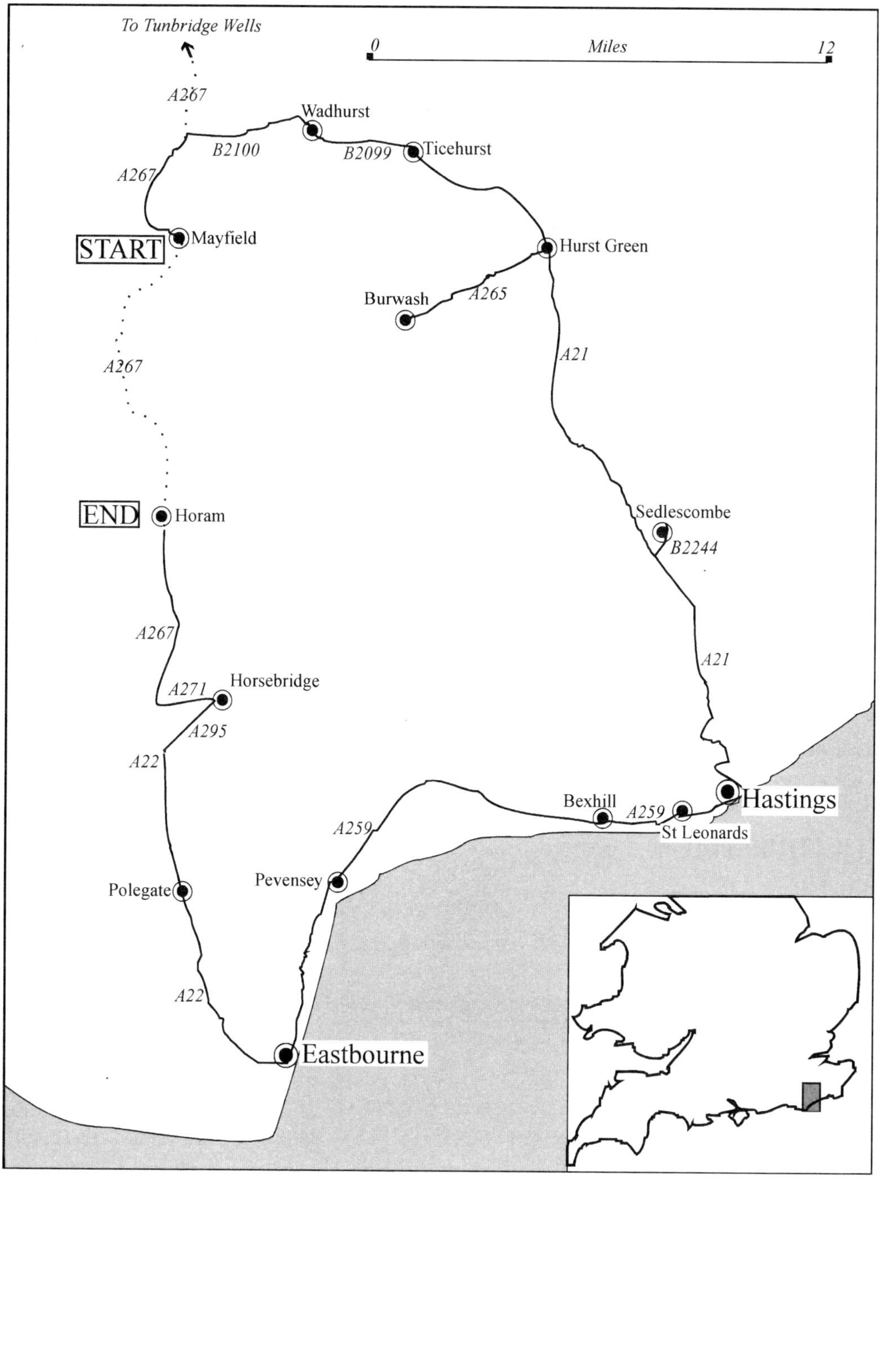
To Tunbridge Wells
0
Miles
12
A267
Wadhurst
B2100
B2099
Ticehurst
A267
START
Mayfield
Hurst Green
Burwash
A265
A267
A21
END
Horam
Sedlescombe
B2244
A267
A21
A271
Horsebridge
A295
A22
Bexhill
A259
Hastings
St Leonards
A259
Pevensey
Polegate
A22
Eastbourne

to blend into the rest of the castle.

The next stop is **Eastbourne**, seen by many as the epitome of the genteel 19th century seaside resort with its elegant parades and gardens. For those interested in seeing how the town looked in Victorian times the Towner Art Gallery & Local History Museum has a display of watercolours of Eastbourne in the 1850s. The Museum covers the area from prehistoric to Edwardian times and is housed in a Georgian manor house.

Now turning north, **Polegate** has an nearby urban windmill. **Horsebridge** is on the north-east corner of Hailsham. The tour ends at **Horam** with its lovely nature trail.

## ANTIQUE DEALERS

### MAYFIELD (01435)

**Gravener Antiques**, High Street, TN20 6AA TEL: 873389 PARKING: Easy OPEN: Mon-Fri 9-5.30, Sat 9-1 MIN: £100 MAX: £5000 PERIOD: 18th-19th century SPECIALIST: Furniture OTHER INFO: Picturesque village steeped in history.

### WADHURST (01892)

**Park View Antiques**, Durgates High Street, TN5 6DE TEL: 783630 PARKING: Easy OPEN: 10-5 MIN: £5 MAX: £1000 PERIOD: 18th-20th century SPECIALIST: Country furniture & artifacts GENERAL: Native wood furniture, pine, oak etc, cast iron, kitchenalia, lighting OTHER INFO: Scotney Castle, Bewl Water, Bartley Mill, Lamberhurst vineyards.

### TICEHURST (01580)

**Croft House Antiques,** 36 High Street, TN5 7AS TEL: 201455 PARKING: Easy OPEN: 9-1, 2-5 MIN: £100 MAX: £3000 PERIOD: 17th-19th century SPECIALIST: Furniture GENERAL: Treen, metalware, glass, engravings, watercolours.

### HURST GREEN (01580)

**Pigeon House Antiques**, 52 London Road, TN19 7PN TEL: 860474 ASSNS: LAPADA PARKING: Own carpark OPEN: 9am-10pm MIN: £50 MAX: £15,000 PERIOD: 18th-19th century SPECIALIST: Mirrors, chandeliers, furniture, decorative items.

### BURWASH (01435)

**Michael Walsh**, Chaunt House, High Street TEL: 882221 PARKING: Easy OPEN: 10-5.30, closed Mon MAX: £1000 PERIOD: 19th-20th century SPECIALIST: Clocks, watches, barometers OTHER INFO: 1993 Best Kept Village award, tearooms etc.

### SEDLESCOMBE (01424)

**Claire Kinloch**, Bulmer House, The Green, TN33 0QA TEL: 870364 PARKING: Easy OPEN: Wed-Sat 10-5 MIN: £1 MAX: £1000 PERIOD: 19th-20th century SPECIALIST: Dolls, original dolls clothing, teddies, toys GENERAL: Antique children's & baby clothes, quilts.

### HASTINGS (01424)

**Courthouse Antiques,** 17 Courthouse Street, Old Town, TN34 3AU TEL: 882009 PARKING: Own carpark OPEN: 10-4.30, except Wed & Fri 10-2, closed Sun MIN: £25 MAX: £850 PERIOD: 18th-20th century SPECIALIST: Furniture, light fittings GENERAL: Bric a brac.

**Howes Bookshop,** Trinity Hall, Braybrook Terrace, TN34 1HQ TEL: 423437 ASSNS: ABA PARKING: Own carpark MIN: £1 MAX: £5000 PERIOD: 17th-20th century SPECIALIST: Antiquarian & scholarly books in arts & humanities.

**Nakota Curios**, 12 Courthouse Street, Old Town, TN35 5PB TEL: 438900 PARKING: Medium OPEN: Mon, Tues, Thurs-Sat 10.30-1, 2.30-5 MIN: £1 MAX: £300 PERIOD: 19th-20th century GENERAL: Occasional ethnographical items, jewellery, paintings, glass, small furniture, textiles, country items, china OTHER INFO: The old town of Hastings with its fishing quarter, 16th-18th century buildings & streets, is unique and worth visiting in its own right.

### ST LEONARDS-ON-SEA (01424)

**Aarquebus Antiques**, 37-46 Norman Road, TN38

0EJ TEL: 433267 ASSNS: LAPADA PARKING: Easy OPEN: 9-1, 2-5.30 MIN: £50 MAX: £5000 PERIOD: 17th-19th century SPECIALIST: Period furniture GENERAL: Porcelain, glass, pictures, bric-a-brac.

**Banner Antiques**, 56 Norman Road, TN40 1BN TEL: 420050 PARKING: Medium OPEN:10-5, closed Weds MIN: £10 MAX: £1500 PERIOD: 19th-20th century SPECIALIST: Royal Worcester porcelain, Blue & White transfer ware. GENERAL: Furniture, porcelain, treen & watercolours OTHER INFO: Cinque Port hotel & Cooden Resort Hotel, site of Battle of Hastings in 1066.

**The Book Jungle**, 24 North Street, TN38 0EXTEL: 421187 PARKING: Medium OPEN: 10-5, closed Weds & Sun MIN: £1 MAX: £100 PERIOD: 19th-20th century GENERAL: Secondhand books only.

**Gensing Antiques,** 70 Norman Road, TN38 0EJ TEL: 424145 PARKING: Easy OPEN: 10.30-1, 2.15-5 MIN: £5 MAX: £5000 PERIOD: 17th-20th century SPECIALIST: Early Chinese furniture GENERAL: Furniture, paintings, porcelain, Oriental items OTHER INFO: 20+ dealers & 2 antique centre in Norman Road. Well worth a call.

**Hastings Antique Centre**, 59-61 Norman Road, TN38 0EG TEL: 428561 PARKING: Easy OPEN: Mon-Sat 9-5.30 MIN: £5 MAX: £3000 PERIOD: 19th-20th century SPECIALIST: Sporting goods, clocks, jewellery GENERAL: Furniture, pine, paintings, porcelain, gold, silver, watches, textiles, Victoriana, architectural items OTHER INFO: Historic, excellent tourist centre, museums, numerous antique shops.

**Helgato Antiques**, 121 Bohemia Road (A21), TN37 6RL TEL: 423049 PARKING: Medium OPEN: By appt MIN: £3 MAX: £500 PERIOD: 18th-19th century GENERAL: Porcelain, glass, objets d'art & vertu, prints, maps pre 1890, books.

**John Lang Antiques**, 65 Norman Road, TN38 0EG TEL: 714848 PARKING: Medium OPEN: Mon-Fri 10-5, Sat 10-1 MIN: £2 MAX: £1500 PERIOD: 18th-19th century GENERAL: Georgian, Victorian & shipping furniture, smalls, house clearance items OTHER INFO: Historical area with caves and castle. 21 other antique shops + 1 centre close.

**Monarch Antiques**, 6 Grand Parade TEL: 445841 FAX: 434338 PARKING: Medium OPEN: Mon-Fri 9-5, or by appt MIN: £10 MAX: £3000 PERIOD: 19th-20th century GENERAL: Victoriana & shipping goods.

**JOHN YORKE ANTIQUES FILSHAM FARM HOUSE, HARLEY SHUTE ROAD, TN38 8BY TEL: 433109 FAX: 461061 PARKING: OWN CARPARK OPEN: 9-5 OR BY APPT MIN: £25 MAX: £2000 PERIOD: 17TH-20TH CENTURY SPECIALIST: OLD CARVED OR PANELLED OAK FURNITURE GENERAL: LARGE STOCK OF ANTIQUES, FURNITURE & SHIPPING GOODS OTHER INFO: THIS IS A 17TH CENTURY SUSSEX FARMHOUSE AND IS ON THE AA SELECT LIST FOR BED & BREAKFAST.**

## BEXHILL-ON-SEA (01424)

**Bexhill Antique Centre**, TEL: 830554 OPEN: By appt OTHER INFO: Not run as an antiques centre but houses 3 floors of furniture

**Bexhill Antique Exporters**, 56 Turkey Road TEL: 225103, 210182 FAX: 731430 PARKING: Own carpark OPEN: Mon-Fri 8-5.30 MIN: £50 MAX: £5000 PERIOD: 18th-20th century OTHER INFO: One of the largest exporters in the southeast.

## PEVENSEY BAY (01323)

**The Old Mint House**, High Street, BN24 5LF TEL & FAX: 762337 ASSNS: LAPADA PARKING: Easy OPEN: Mon-Sat 8.45-5.30 MIN: £5 MAX: £20,000 PERIOD: 18th-20th century SPECIALIST: Furniture GENERAL: Clocks, china, metalware, barometers, etc OTHER INFO: Large 33 showroom shop & 20,000 sq ft warehouse nearby, container service available.

## EASTBOURNE (01323)

**Bell Antiques**, 47 South Street TEL: 641339 PARKING: Medium OPEN: 9.30-4.45 MIN: £5 MAX: £500 PERIOD: 18th-20th century GENERAL: Pottery, porcelain, furniture, lace, dolls, pictures.

**Bygones**, 24 Willingdon Road, Old Town TEL: 737537 PARKING: Medium OPEN: Mon, Tues, Thurs & Sat 10.30-5 MIN: £1 MAX: £200 PERIOD: 19th-20th century SPECIALIST: Vintage clothing 1920's to early 1950's GENERAL: Accessories, jewellery, linen OTHER INFO: Lovely seafront leading to Beachy Head. Old Town has many antique shops.

**Camilla's Bookshop**, 57 Grove Road, BN21 4TX TEL: 736001 PARKING: Easy OPEN: Mon-Sat 10-6 MIN: 5p MAX: £1000 PERIOD: 17th-20th century SPECIALIST: 500,000 books, aviation, crafts, miitary, transport GENERAL: 3 large floors, 1/2 million books, 2000 WWII books OTHER INFO: Great pizza restaurant next door, 2 other large secondhand bookshops within 5 mins walk.

**John Cowderoy Antiques**, 42 South Street TEL: 720058 FAX: 410163 ASSNS: LAPADA, GMC PARKING: Easy OPEN: Mon-Sat 9.30-5, closed Wed pm PERIOD: 18th-20th century SPECIALIST: Musical boxes, clocks, barometers GENERAL: Furniture, pianos, china & glass, display cabinets OTHER INFO: Daily demonstrations of mechanical music free of charge. Clean beaches & famous carpet gardens 1 mile from shop.

**John Day of Eastbourne FineArt**, 9 Meads Street, BN20 7QY TEL: 725634 PARKING: Easy OPEN: 10-4 MIN: £100 MAX: £10,000 SPECIALIST: Victorian oils & watercolours, East Anglian paintings. Restoration on site GENERAL: 1800-1930's English & Continental paintings.

**Eastbourne Antique Market**, 80 Seaside, BN22 7QP TEL: 720128 PARKING: Easy OPEN: Mon-Fri 10-5.30, Sat 10-5 PERIOD: 18th-20th century GENERAL: 40 stalls antiques & collectables.

**James Ludby Antiques,** 25 Ocklynge Road, BN21 1PY TEL: 732073 PARKING: Easy OPEN: Mornings, anytime by appt MIN: £5 MAX: £500 PERIOD: 18th century-1930 GENERAL: Furniture, china, glass, brass, unusual interesting items.

**Timothy Partridge Antiques**, 46 Ocklynge Road, BN21 1PP TEL: 638731 PARKING: Easy OPEN: Mon-Fri 10-5, Sat 10-1 MIN: £10 MAX: £300 PERIOD: 19-20th century SPECIALIST: Furniture GENERAL: General antiques.

**Pharaohs Antique Centre**, 28 South Street TEL: 738655 PARKING: Medium OPEN: Mon-Sat 10-5 MIN: £1 MAX: £1200 PERIOD: 19th-20th century GENERAL: Pine, furniture, kitchenalia, light fittings, some medical items, drawing instruments, lace, linen, brassware OTHER INFO: Town is winner of 'South East in Bloom'. Lots of tennis events during season & air event during summer.

**Raymond Smith**, 30 South Street TEL: 734128 ASSNS: ABA PARKING: Medium OPEN: Mon. Tues, Thurs-Sat 9-5.30 MIN: £1 MAX: £1000 PERIOD: 17th-20th century SPECIALIST: Theology GENERAL: Most subjects.

**Stewart Gallery**, 25 Grove Road, BN21 4TT TEL: 729588 PARKING: Medium OPEN: Mon-Sat 9-5.30 MIN: £10 MAX: £20,000 PERIOD: 19th-20th century SPECIALIST: Paintings GENERAL: Porcelain, glass, Chinese furniture OTHER INFO: 100+ restaurants, all nationalities.

**Lloyd Williams Antiques**, Anglo-American Warehouse, 2A Beach Road, BN22 7EX TEL: 648661 FAX: 648658 PARKING: Easy OPEN: Mon-Sat 9.30-5 or by appt MIN: £30 MAX: £3000 PERIOD: 19th-20th century SPECIALIST: Good oak GENERAL: 2000+ pieces shipping furniture.

## POLEGATE (01323)

**Graham Price Antiques Ltd**, Unit 4, Chaucer Industrial Estate, BN26 6JD TEL: 487167 FAX: 483904 PARKING: Own carpark OPEN: Mon-Fri 9-6 & by appt MIN: £10 MAX: £5000 PERIOD: 18th-20th century SPECIALIST: Larger items of furniture suitable for commercial use GENERAL: English, Continental furniture & decorative items with a country base.

## HORSEBRIDGE (01323)

**Horsebridge Antiques**, 1 North Street, BN27 4DJ TEL: 844414 PARKING: Own carpark OPEN: Mon-Sat 10-5 MIN: £10 MAX: £1000 PERIOD: 18th-20th century GENERAL: Country items, collectables OTHER INFO: Good food opposite.

## HORAM (01435)

**John Botting Antiques**, Winstan House, High Street, TN21 0ER TEL & FAX: 813553, mobile: (0385) 393389 PARKING: Own carpark OPEN: Mon-Sat 9-5.30, by appt & by chance MIN: £2 MAX: £3000 PERIOD: 19th-20th century SPECIALIST: French imported direct GENERAL: Victorian furniture plus some Georgian & Edwardian, also stripped pine & bric a brac OTHER INFO: Other shops in the area. Trade welcome. Close to Merrydown Cider factory.

# Sussex: Countryside and Coast

Sussex is a county of busy towns, pretty villages and popular seaside resorts. This tour visits one of the most famous of all English holiday towns, Brighton, it also passes through some much less familiar places.

First **Uckfield,** this town is the site of the beautiful Sheffield Park Garden on the A275, with cascading lakes and a host of lovely and unusual plants.The famous Bluebell Railway is also here, operating vintage steam trains to Horsted Keynes in Sussex.

The route turns westward via **Lindfield,** considered one of Sussex's loveliest villages with many old house and then to the large market town of **Haywards Heath**. Its Muster Green was the scene of a Civil War battle when 200 Royalists were killed, Just to the west, **Cuckfield**, is a growing town based on a 13th century village retaining many of the old buildings. One of the county's great gardens, Nymans Garden, stands about three miles north, containing rare collections of plants and trees from all over the world including azaleas, rhododendrons, magnolias and roses. High Beeches Gardens is closeby. These are twenty acres of landscaped woodland, water gardens and a wildflower meadow all containing beautiful plants.

Moving on, **Ditchling** contains many 16th century houses including one that Henry VIII gave to Anne of Cleves, a wife that escaped with her head. Ditchling Beacon, at over 800 feet one of the highest points in Sussex, lies to the south and to the north there is Ditchling Gibbet where a peddler was executed after being convicted of triple murder in 1734.

The next stop is **Lewes**, situated on a gap in the South Downs through which flows the River Ouse. The town has a history going back at least to Saxon times. King Alfred established a fort here and later the Norman, William de Warenne, Earl of Surrey and Sussex and son-in-law of William the Conqueror, built a castle on two artificial mounds made of large lumps of quarried chalk. This castle saw little action until 1264 when Simon de Montfort fought and defeated Henry III just outside Lewes. Soon after two towers were added to the keep and in the 14th century a barbican was built. However, it was then ignored as being of little military significance and by the early 17th century was gradually demolished for the building material. A local merchant then leased it and converted the keep into a summer house so saving the remainder. Remains of the walls and barbican can still be seen.

Anne of Cleves also had a house in Lewes given to her by Henry when he divorced her. Built at the beginning of the 16th century with additions made later in the century, it is now used as a folk museum and houses the Every Collection of ironwork, including spits, ladles, stewpans, embossed firebacks, and chimney-cranes. The museum also displays furniture, local crafts and prisoner-of-war art made by Russian prisoners from the Crimea.

The twisting High Street contains many buildings of interest: houses that are flint-faced, Georgian, timber-framed, stucco, tile-clad. At the top of the High Street stands the Norman church of St Anne's, the oldest church in Lewes. Immediately to the south is Southover High Street where St John's Church now houses the remains of William de Warenne and his wife, Gundrada. This church was originally the guesthouse of the Priory of St Pancras, founded by William and Gundrada. Apart from the guesthouse, the priory was destroyed in the Dissolution of the Monasteries and only a few walls and foundations can be seen.

Two notable houses stand a mile apart on the Eastbourne to Lewes road: Firle Place and Glynde Place. The first was originally a Tudor mansion but much altered in the 18th century. It now has an important collection of European and British paintings. The house has been the home of the Gage family since the 15th century and contains items relating to General Gage, Commander of the British Forces in the American War of Independence. Glynde Place is a lovely 16th century house built around a courtyard. It has an interesting collection of pictures, bronzes and historical documents.

Just a mile south of Lewes is **Iford** village, after which the route heads for the coast and the

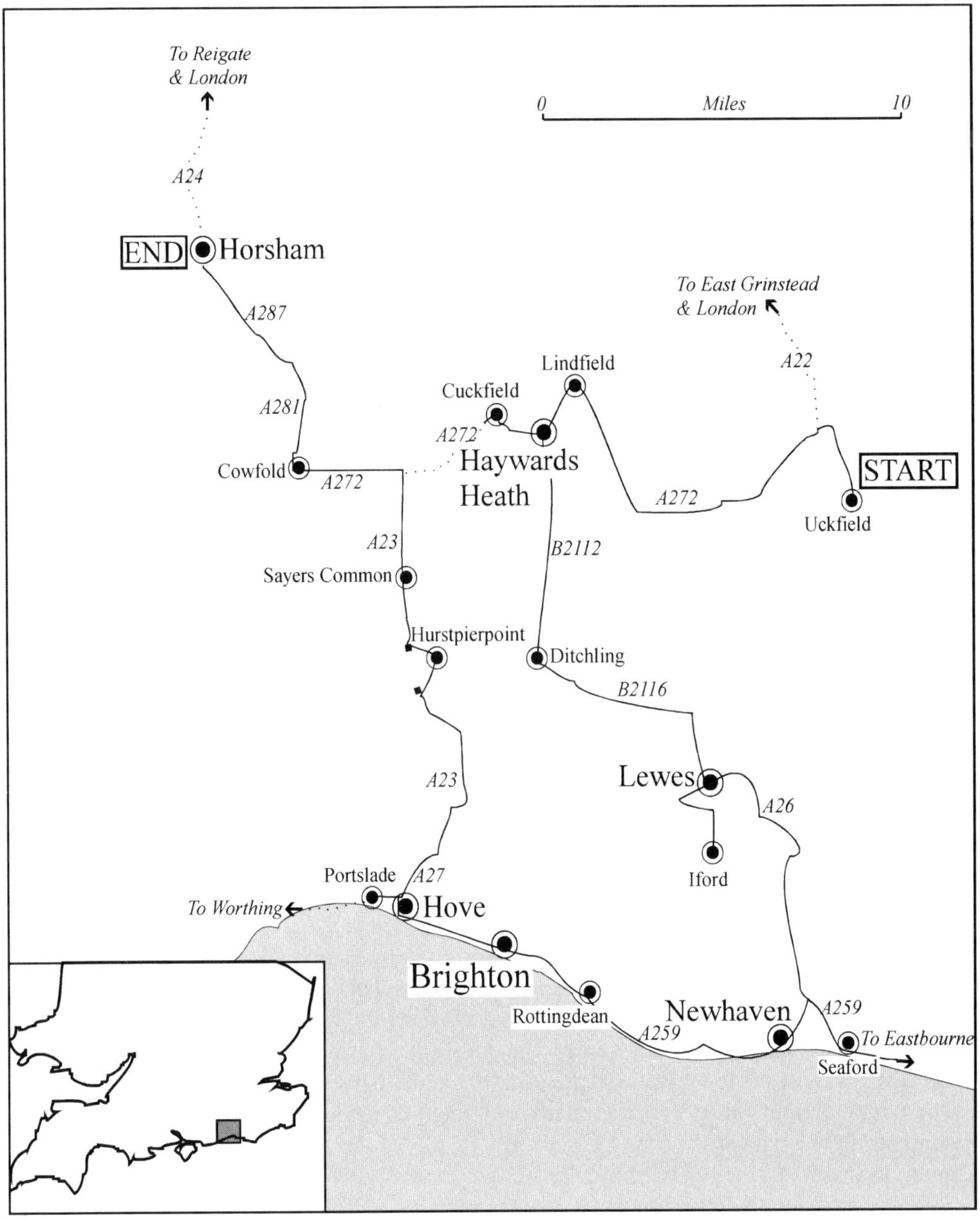


resort of **Seaford,** with a shingle beach, the beautiful Cuckmere Valley and good view of the Seven Sister cliffs. **Newhaven** is a cross-Channel ferry port although at one time the ferries were threatened with closure. **Rottingdean** is where Rudyard Kipling lived and several miles away is the world famous Roedean school for girls. It is also on the eastern outskirts of **Brighton**, the most famous of the Sussex seaside resorts. Originally called Brighthelmstone, Brighton's pre-eminence is due to the Prince Regent who first visited the small fishing village in 1783. Here he built the Royal Pavilion which was first constructed to a much more conventional design. Later alterations gave it the flamboyance and startling Oriental flavour which has made it such an enduring landmark and symbol of the town. However unthinkable Brighton without the Royal Pavilion might seem this almost happened. During the reign of Queen

Victoria the Pavilion was left to decay and was nearly demolished in 1850. Saved only by the residents of Brighton raising £50,000 , over the years it has been restored to a former splendour and the original contents returned.

The Lanes are another quaint, much visited feature, particularly for the antiques enthusiast. This is an area of narrow alleys and tiny squares, some of which are the remains of old Brighthelmstone rebuilt in the 17th century after part of the original village had been washed away by the sea.

The adjoining town of **Hove** has an excellent museum: The British Engineerium in Nevill Road. This is a working steam museum in the restored Goldstone Pumping Station. It has an Eastons and Anderson beam engine from 1876 and many other full size engines and hundreds of models. The museum recounts the story of the development of the many different uses of steam power. Restoration projects from all over the world are undertaken.

After first visiting **Portslade**, which is not a port, instead lying 1 mile inland, the route turns north to **Hurstpierpoint** where a visit to the Elizabethan mansion of Danny Park is recommended. **Sayers Common** and **Cowfold** are next. Near Cowfold is St Hugh's monastery with a really tall spire. The village is also pretty. The last town on the tour is **Horsham** which has been a borough and market town since the 13th century. A notable feature is the Causeway, a quiet street lined with timber-framed and Georgian houses leading down to the 13th century church. At the top is the 16th century Causeway House, now a museum with exhibits ranging from prehistory to bicycles. Five miles away at the junction of the A279 and A281 is Leonardslee Gardens. A most beautiful place set in a valley with six lake,.there are wonderful displays of camellias, magnolias, rhododendrons and azaleas. Bonsai are also shown.

## ANTIQUE DEALERS

### UCKFIELD (01825)

**Barnes Gallery**, 8 Church Street, TN22 1BJ TEL: 762066 PARKING: Easy OPEN: Tues-Sat 10-1, 2-5 MIN: £100 MAX: £5000 PERIOD: 19th century SPECIALIST: Watercolour scenes of rural England GENERAL: Watercolours, oil paintings & drawings OTHER INFO: Horsted Place Hotel associated with East Sussex National Golf club, caters particularly for overseas clients.

**IR Deverall**, Duval House, The Glen, Cambridge Way, TN22 2AB TEL: 762474 PARKING: Own carpark OPEN: By appt PERIOD: 17th century SPECIALIST: Antique maps GENERAL: Colour-me service.

**Georgian House Antiques**, 222 High Street, TN22 1RE TEL & FAX: 765074 PARKING: Medium OPEN: Mon-Sat 10-6 MIN: £50 MAX: £4000 PERIOD: 17th-19th century SPECIALIST: English domestic oak & country furniture & related decorative objects GENERAL: Furniture, decorative items.

**Ringles Cross Antiques**, Ringles Cross, TN22 1HF TEL: 762909 PARKING: Own carpark OPEN: Mon-Sat 9-6. Resident MIN: £50 MAX: £5000 PERIOD: 17th-18th century SPECIALIST: English furniture made from indigenous woods, walnut, oak, fruitwoods, accessories. Some Oriental furniture OTHER INFO: Buxted Park Country Hotel 1 mile, East Sussex National Golf Club 3 miles, Bluebell Railway 10 miles.

### LINDFIELD (01444)

**Hinsdale Antiques**, 75 High Street, RH16 2HN TEL: 483200 FAX: 484736 PARKING: Medium OPEN: 10-5 MIN: £5 MAX: £5000 PERIOD: 18th-20th century SPECIALIST: Dolls, teddy bears GENERAL: Good quality general antiques, furniture, silver, porcelain, etc..

### HAYWARDS HEATH (01444)

**David Burkinshaw**, Sugworth Farmhouse, Borde Hill Lane, RH16 1XP TEL: 459747 PARKING: Own carpark OPEN: 9-5 MIN: £2000 MAX: £45,000 PERIOD: 18th-19th century SPECIALIST: Antique pedestal & partner's desks (restored).

### CUCKFIELD (01444)

**David Foord-Brown Antiques**, High Street TEL: 414418 ASSNS: LAPADA PARKING: Own carpark OPEN: Mon-Sat 10-5 PERIOD: 18-19th century SPECIALIST: Furniture GENERAL: Porcelain, glass.

**Richard Usher Antiques**, 23 South Street, RH17 5LB TEL: 451699 PARKING: Medium OPEN: 10-5.30, Wed & Sat AM only MIN: £5 MAX: £2000 PERIOD: 17th-19th century GENERAL: Furniture, decorative items OTHER INFO: Attractive village, Ockenden Manor Hotel in walking distance.

## DITCHLING (01273)

**Chichester House Antiques,** High Street, BN6 8SY TEL: 846615 PARKING: Easy OPEN: Tues-Sat 10.30-5, Sun 2-5 MIN: £30 MAX: £3000 PERIOD: 17th-18th century SPECIALIST: Oak & country furniture GENERAL: Some Georgian mahogany OTHER INFO: Beautiful downland village, full of artists, writers & musicians.

**Dycheling Antiques**, 34 High Street (shop) & 12 Lewes Road (showroom), BN6 8TA TEL: 842929 PARKING: Easy OPEN: 10.30-5.30, closed Wed & Sun MIN: £20 MAX: £5000 PERIOD: 18th-19th century SPECIALIST: Dining chairs & finder service GENERAL: Furniture OTHER INFO: Historic village with many famous artists, past & present. Craft & picture galleries, museum, country park, 13th century church.

**Nona Shaw Antiques**, 4, 8 West Street, BN6 8TS TEL: 843290, 327398 PARKING: Easy OPEN: Mon-Tues, Fri-Sat 11-5 MIN: £5 MAX: £500 PERIOD: 18th-19th century GENERAL: General antiques, cottage furniture.

## LEWES (01273)

**Bow Windows Book Shop,** 128 High Street, BN7 1XL TEL & FAX: 480780 ASSNS: ABA, PBFA PARKING: Medium OPEN: Mon-Sat 9-5 MIN: £1 MAX: £1000 PERIOD: 17th-20th century SPECIALIST: Fine books GENERAL: Natural history, literature, Japan, fine bindings & sets OTHER INFO: Castle & museum 2 mins walk from shop.

**Charleston Antiques**, 14 Lansdown Place TEL: 477916 PARKING: Medium OPEN: Tues-Sat 10-5 MIN: £150 MAX: £1500 PERIOD: Late 18th-20th century SPECIALIST: Arts & Crafts furniture/ inlaid mahogany GENERAL: English furniture.

**Cliffe Antiques Centre**, 47 Cliffe High Street, BN7 2AN TEL: 473266 PARKING: Own carpark OPEN: Mon-Sat 9.30-5 GENERAL Collectables, Victoriana, paintings, prints, furniture, china, jewellery etc OTHER INFO: Interesting castle, Anne of Cleves Museum. Ancient county town situated on river.

**Cliffe Gallery Antiques**, 39 Cliffe High Street, BN7 2AN TEL: 471877 ASSNS: CADO PARKING: Easy OPEN: 9-5 MIN: £3 MAX: £2700 PERIOD: 18th-20th century GENERAL: Pine, mahogany, oak, kitchenalia, luggage, fishing, pictures.

**Coombe House Antiques**, 121 Malling Street, BN7 2RJ TEL: 473862 FAX: 479645 ASSNS: BADA CINOA LAPADA PARKING: Own carpark OPEN: Mon-Fri 9.30-6 & by appt PERIOD: 18th-19th century SPECIALIST: English furniture & decorative items GENERAL: Works of art, clocks, paintings, garden items OTHER INFO: On A26 south of Horsted Place. Country House Hotel. London 1 hr, Brighton 15 mins.

**AJ Cumming**, 84 High Street, BN7 1XN TEL: 472319 FAX: 486364 ASSNS: ABA PARKING: Medium OPEN: Mon-Fri 10-5, Sat 10-5.30 PERIOD: 19th-20th century SPECIALIST: Antiquarian books OTHER INFO: Shelleys & White Hart Hotel. 3 bookshops.

**HP Dennison & Son**, 22 High Street, BN7 2LN TEL: 480655 PARKING: Medium OPEN: Mon-Tues, Thurs-Sat 9-4.30 MIN: £120 MAX: £2,500 PERIOD: 19th-20th century GENERAL: Furniture.

**The Drawing Room,** 53 High Street, BN7 1XE TEL: 478560 PARKING: Medium MIN: £5 MAX: £4000 PERIOD: 19th-20th century GENERAL: Objets d'art, paintings, small furniture.

**Felix Gallery**, 2 Sun Street, BN7 2QB TEL: 472668 PARKING: Medium OPEN: Mon-Sat 10-6 MIN: £10 MAX: £2000 PERIOD: 18th-20th century SPECIALIST: "Cats in Art" & collectables only GENERAL: Paintings, prints, pottery, bronzes, pewter, porcelain, bronze, silver, objets d'art OTHER INFO: 11th century castle, Norman & Roman ruins. Prize-winning Tourist Information Centre.

**The Fifteenth Century Bookshop**, 99-100 High Street, BN7 1XH TEL: 474160 FAX: 477488 PARKING: Easy OPEN: Mon-Sat 10-5.30 MIN: £1 MAX: £1,000 PERIOD: 17th-20th century SPECIALIST: Collectable childrens/illustrated books GENERAL: Secondhand & antiquarian books on all subjects. Our shop is an original 15th century building, (oldest in town).

**Foundry Lane Antiques Centre**, 15 Cliffe High Street, BN7 2AH TEL: 475361 PARKING: Easy OPEN: Tues-Sat 10-5 MIN: £2 MAX: £1,000 PERIOD: 19th-20th century SPECIALIST: Arts & Crafts, Nouveau, Deco, Victorian GENERAL: General antiques.

**Lewes Antiques Centre**, 20 Cliffe High Street, BN7 1AH TEL: 476148 PARKING: Medium OPEN: Mon-Sat 9.30-5, Sun 12-4 MIN: £1 MAX: £950 PERIOD: 19th century GENERAL: Antiques.
**Pastorale Antiques**, 15 Malling Street TEL: 473259 FAX: 473259 PARKING: Easy OPEN: Mon-Sat 10-5.30 & by appt PERIOD: 18th-19th century SPECIALIST: 8000 sq ft warehouse of pine & European country furniture, mahogany & decoratives.
**Pine Furniture**, 6 Station Street TEL: 474842 PARKING: Own carpark OPEN: 9-5, Wed & Sat 9-1 MIN: £100 MAX: £2500 PERIOD: 19th century SPECIALIST: Pine, longcase pine clocks GENERAL: Furniture.
**Trevor Antiques and Works of Art**, Trevor House, 110 High Street, BN7 1XY TEL: 471975 ASSNS: BADA PARKING: Own carpark OPEN: Mon-Sat 9-6 but appt advisable MIN: £5000 MAX: £250,000 PERIOD: Late 17th-early 19th century SPECIALIST: Furniture & works of art

## IFORD (01273)

**John Bird Antiques**, Norton House, BN7 3EJ TEL: 483366 PARKING: Own carpark OPEN: 24 hrs by appt MIN: £10 MAX: £5000 PERIOD: 17th-20th century SPECIALIST: Lacquer & pai nted furniture GENERAL: English furniture in oak, pine, fruitwood & mahogany. Accessories & garden antiques OTHER INFO: Why not visit Virginia Woolf's Monks House at Rodmell & Charleston Farmhouse, country retreat of the Bloomsbury set..

## SEAFORD (01323)

**JR Clocks,** The Old House, High Street, BN25 1PD TEL: 892091 PARKING: Easy OPEN: Mon-Sat 9-5 MIN: £50 MAX: £3000 PERIOD: 17th-20th century SPECIALIST: Clocks.
**The Old House,** 15-17 High Street, BN25 1PD TEL: 893795 FAX: 894474 PARKING: Easy OPEN: Mon-Sat 9-5, closed Wed pm MIN: £1 MAX: £3000 PERIOD: 19th-20th century GENERAL: Furniture, china, glass, silver & plate, brassware, books.
**Steyne House Antiques**, Steyne House, 35 Steyne Road, BN25 1HT TEL: 895088 PARKING: Easy OPEN: Tues-Fri 10.30-5, Sat 10.30-4 MIN: £20 MAX: £800+ PERIOD: Some 18th, mostly 19th century SPECIALIST: Victorian, Staffordshire figures GENERAL: English pottery & porcelain, also Continental & Oriental.

## NEWHAVEN (01273)

**Newhaven Flea Market**, 28 Southway, BN9 LA TEL: 517207, 516065 PARKING: Own arpark OPEN: Seven days 10-5.30 MIN: £1 AX: £500 PERIOD: 19th-20th century GENERAL INFO: Bric-a-brac & furniture.
**Leonard Russell**, 21 Kings Avenue, Denton, N9 0NB TEL: 515153 ASSNS: BADA PARKING: Easy OPEN: By appt only MIN: £350 MAX: £2,500 PERIOD: 18th-early 19th century SPECIALIST: Early English pottery figures 1700-1835 GENERAL: Animals, toby jugs, busts, plaques, from factories of Whieldon, Ralph Wood, Enoch Wood, Sherratt, Marked Walton, Salt.

## ROTTINGDEAN (01273)

**Trade Wind**, Little Crescent, BN2 7GF TEL: 301177 PARKING: Own carpark OPEN: By appt only MIN: £60+ MAX: £900+ PERIOD: 17th-19th century SPECIALIST: Wide selection wine labels GENERAL: Small furniture, English porcelain, coloured glass, other choice items OTHER INFO: Rottingdean noted for Rudyard Kipling.

## BRIGHTON (01273)

**Art Deco Etc**, 73 Upper Gloucester Road, BN1 3LQ TEL: 329268 ASSNS: ATA PARKING: Easy MIN: £1 MAX: £2000 PERIOD: 19th-20th century SPECIALIST: Art Deco, Art Nouveau, Arts & Crafts, 1950's, pottery, glass, furniture, lighting, mirrors, pictures, collectables.
**Ashton's**, 1-3 Clyde Road, Preston Circus, BN1 4NN TEL: 605253 PARKING: Medium OPEN: Mon-Fri 9.30-5.30, Wed AM only, Sat 10-4 MIN: £1 MAX: £2500 PERIOD: 19th-20th century GENERAL: 4 showrooms of stock from modern repro to Victorian, antique & shipping furniture.
**Attic Antiques**, 23 Ship Street TEL: 326378 PARKING: Medium OPEN: Mon-Fri 11-1, 2.30-5 MIN: £25 MAX: £4000 PERIOD: 18th-19th century SPECIALIST: Imari & Oriental porcelain GENERAL: Furniture, paintings, clocks, bronze.
**H Balchin**, 18-19 Castle Street, BN1 2HD PARKING: Medium OPEN: 9.30-1, 2.30-5.30, Thurs/Sat AM only PERIOD: 18th-19th century SPECIALIST: Furniture GENERAL: China, glass.
**Bears & Friends**, 41 Meeting House Lane, BN1 1HB TEL: 208940 FAX: 202736 PARKING: Medium OPEN: Mon-Fri 9-5.30, Sat 9-6, Sun 10-6

MIN: £1 MAX: £5000 PERIOD: 20th century SPECIALIST: Old & new teddy bears GENERAL: Old dolls & bear-related items, furniture & pictures OTHER INFO: Our Museum of Childhood & Juvenalia has just opened on 2 floors with enchanting scenes & includes a resident ghost.

**Brighton Antique Wholesalers**, 39 Upper Gardner Street, BN1 4AN TEL: 695457 PARKING: Easy OPEN: Mon-Sat 9-5.30 MIN: £5 MAX: £10,000 PERIOD: 17th-20th century GENERAL: Basic shipping to fine period & Victorian.

**Brighton Flea Market**, 31a Upper St James's Street, BN1 2JN TEL: 624006 PARKING: Medium OPEN: Seven days 9.30-5.30 MIN: £1 MAX: £1000 PERIOD: 19th-20th century GENERAL: Bric-a-brac & furniture.

**Mary Brown,** 42 Surrey Street, BN1 3PB TEL: 721160 OPEN: Mon-Sat 10.30-5.30 MIN: £3 MAX: £65 PERIOD: 19th-20th century SPECIALIST: Period clothes GENERAL: Linen, lace, jewellery.

**Sheila Cashin**, 40 Upper North Street, BN1 3FH TEL: 326619 PARKING: Medium OPEN: Mon-Sat 10-5 MIN: £10 MAX: £2000 PERIOD: 19th century SPECIALIST: Well restored Victorian bamboo GENERAL: Lacquer & painted pine furniture, papier maché & decorative mirrors OTHER INFO: Situated in a street of 12 antique shops with a range from brown furniture to decorative & Art Deco.

**Classic Automobilia & Regalia Specialists, (CARS)**, 4-4a Chapel Terrace, Kemp Town, BN2 1HU (wholesale warehouse) TEL: 601960 FAX: 623846 & Prinny's Gallery, 3-7 Meeting House Lane, BN1 1HB TEL: 204554 (retail shop) ASSNS: Pedal Car Collectors Club PARKING: Own carpark (Kemp Town) OPEN: 10-6 MIN: £50+ MAX: £5000 PERIOD: 20th century SPECIALIST: Automobilia, car mascots, car badges, memorabilia, motoring nostalgia. Restoration of old pedal cars.

**Alan Fitchett Antiques**, 5-5a Upper Gardner Street, BN1 4AN TEL & FAX: 600894 PARKING: Easy OPEN: Mon-Fri 9-5.30 MIN: £50 MAX: £10,000 PERIOD: 17th-20th century SPECIALIST: Victorian walnut, marquetry, inlaid & Continental furniture, Georgian to shipping.

**Gallery 39,** 39 Upper North Street, BN1 3FH TEL: 772060 PARKING: Easy OPEN: Mon-Fri 9.30-5.30 MIN: £30 MAX: £2000 PEROD: 19th century SPECIALIST: Decorative furniture GENERAL: Furniture, mirrors, lamps, candlesticks, glass, porcelain OTHER INFO: This 100 yard section of Upper North Street boasts the oldest established grouping of 12 trade shops in Brighton. Also 2 good pubs, excellent bistro and a fish & chip shop.

**Paul Goble Jewellers**, 44 Meeting House Lane, The Lanes, BN1 1HB TEL: 202801 FAX: 202736 ASSNS: NAG, N.A.Pawnbrokers PARKING: Medium OPEN: Mon-Sat 9-5.30, Sun 10-5.30 MIN: £5 MAX: £25,000 PERIOD: 17th-20th century SPECIALIST: Jewellery, silver GENERAL: Pictures & prints, old dolls & bears OTHER INFO: 100yds from Museum of Childhood & Juvenalia.

**Hallmarks**, 4 Union Street, BN1 1HA TEL: 725477 PARKING: Medium OPEN: Mon-Sat 9-5 MIN: £15 MAX: £3000 PERIOD: 19th-20th century SPECIALIST: Collectable items, scent bottles, vinaigrettes GENERAL: Solid silver & plate. Table items, new silver photo frames & old jewellery.

**M & D Hawkins**, 27 Meeting House Lane, The Lanes TEL: 321357 ASSNS: LAPADA PARKING: Medium OPEN: Mon-Sat 9-5.30 MIN: £2 MAX: £4500 PERIOD 17th-20th century SPECIALIST: Antique weapons, militaria, armour, cannon GENERAL: All antiques , silver, bronzes etc with strong emphasis on military & maritime armour. Swords from 1300AD OTHER INFO: Hospitality Inn, Grand, Metropole, London 50 mins by train.

**House of Antiques**, 17 Prince Albert Street, BN1 1HF TEL: 327680 ASSNS: LAPADA PARKING: Difficult OPEN: Mon-Sat 10-5 MIN: £150 MAX: £15,000 PERIOD: 18th-20th century GENERAL: Jewellery & silver.

**Hynford Antiques**, 143 Edward Street, BN2 2JG TEL: 679936 PARKING: Medium OPEN: Tues, Thurs, Sat 10.30-4, Wed AM only or by appt MIN: £1 MAX: £250 PERIOD: 19th-20th century SPECIALIST: Brighton prints & ephemera. Far Eastern prints, Oriental collectables GENERAL: Ephemera, collectables, bygones & small furniture.

**JH Jewellery**, Hallmarks, 4 Union Street, The Lanes, BN1 1HA TEL: 725477 PARKING: Medium OPEN: Mon-Sat 9-5 MIN: £70 MAX: £3500 PERIOD: 19th-20th century SPECIALIST: Engagement gem-set rings GENERAL: Antique jewellery, wedding bands.

**Leoframes**, 70 North Road, BN1 1YD TEL: 695862 PARKING: Medium OPEN: Mon-Sat 9-5.30 MIN: £3 MAX: £600 PERIOD: 18th-19th century SPECIALIST: Brighton GENERAL: Prints of sport, topography, botanical, hunting, fashion, maps, all pre 1920 OTHER INFO: Situated in the 'North Laine' area, 5 mins from sea.

**Patrick Moorhead Antiques,** 22B Ship Street TEL: 326062 & 774227 PARKING: Medium OPEN: 10-5.30 MIN: £20 MAX: £5000+ SPECIALIST: Oriental & English furniture GENERAL: Glass, silver, pictures, bronzes, metalware.

**Oasis Antiques,** 39 Kensington Gardens, BN1 4AL TEL: 683885 PARKING: Easy OPEN: Mon-Sat 10-5.30 MIN: £1 MAX: £5000 PERIOD: 17th-20th century SPECIALIST: Lighting, decorative arts GENERAL: Art Nouveau & Deco, Arts & Crafts, furniture, glass, bronze, European & Oriental period clothes, modern one-off items to encourage an interest in plain design.

**Odin Antiques,** 43 Preston Street, BN1 2HP TEL: 732738 PARKING: Medium OPEN: Mon-Fri 10-5, Sat 10-4 MIN: £15 MAX: £5000 PERIOD: 18th-20th century SPECIALIST: Telescopes & maritime items GENERAL: Furniture, brass, copper OTHER INFO: Preston Street is full of restaurants, has reasonable B&Bs & underground parking next door in Regency Square, 1 min walk. Top class hotels minutes away on the seafront.

**Brian & Colin Page,** 18 Regent Arcade, East Street, BN1 1HR TEL: 609310 FAX: 609310 ASSNS: ABA PARKING: Medium OPEN: Mon-Sat 10-5.30 MIN: £2 MAX: £5000 PERIOD: 17th-20th century & earlier SPECIALIST: Japanese & Chinese works of art, antiquarian & rare books GENERAL: British & European decorative arts, historic cameras & scientific instruments OTHER INFO: Oriental porcelain from 10th century. Next to Town Hall, close to Lanes.

**Colin Page Antiquarian Books,** 36 Duke Street, BN1 1AG TEL: 325954 FAX: 746246 ASSNS: ABA PARKING: Difficult OPEN: Mon-Sat 10-5.30 MIN: £1 MAX: £10,000 PERIOD: 17th-20th century SPECIALIST: Colour plate books, leather bindings GENERAL: 10,000+ quality books.

**Dermot & Jill Palmer Antiques,** 7-8 Union Street, The Lanes, BN1 1HA TEL: 328669 FAX: 777641 PARKING: Medium OPEN: Mon-Sat 9-6 MIN: £5 MAX: £5000 PERIOD: 18th-20th century GENERAL: Mainly 19th century English & French furniture & objects., garden urns, stone & statuary, garden furniture OTHER INFO: The shop is on 3 floors, triple its original 1969 size.

**B Ponting Antiques,** 53 Upper North Street TEL: 329409 PARKING: Medium OPEN: Mon-Sat 9.30-5.30 MIN: £100 MAX: £6,000 PERIOD: 18th-20th century SPECIALIST: English furniture.

**Prinnys Antique Gallery,** 3 Meeting House Lane, BN1 1HB TEL: 204554 PARKING: Medium OPEN: Mon-Sat 9.30-5 MIN: £5 MAX: £5000 PERIOD: 18th-20th century SPECIALIST: Art Deco & Nouveau GENERAL: Maps, silver, jewellery, clocks, watches, ivory, prints, porcelain, paintings, amber etc OTHER INFO: Cafe on site in this 18th century building, reputedly with ghost.

**Pyramid,** 9a Kensington Gardens, BN1 4AL TEL: 607991 PARKING: Medium OPEN: Mon-Fri 10-5.30, Sat 9.30-6 MIN: £1 MAX: £500 PERIOD: 20th century SPECIALIST: Art Deco to 1950s GENERAL: Period lighting, old telephones, mirrors, radios, 'lava' lamps, collectables.

**Recollections,** 1a Sydney Street, BN1 4EN TEL: 681517 PARKING: Medium OPEN: Mon-Sat 10.30-5 MIN: £1 MAX: £500 PERIOD: 19th-20th century SPECIALIST: Fenders & fire furniture GENERAL: Brass, copper, ironwork on small scale, studio pottery, small collectables OTHER INFO: Close to station & Royal Pavilion. Sat morning street market around corner.

**Tapsell Antiques,** 159 Middle Street, BN1 1AL TEL: 328341 ASSNS: LAPADA PARKING: Own small carpark OPEN: Mon-Sat 9-5.30 MIN: £5 MAX: £40,000 PERIOD: 18th-19th century SPECIALIST: Chinese Blue & White and Japanese porcelains GENERAL: Clocks, European furniture and porcelain OTHER INFO: Large stock. Trade calls out of hours and collection from station.

**Timewarp,** 6 Sydney Street, BN1 4EN TEL: 607527 PARKING: Medium OPEN: 10.30-6 MIN: £2 MAX: £800 PERIOD: 20th century SPECIALIST: Deco lighting, Victorian oil lamps, stylised items 1930s to 1960s.

**Graham Webb,** 59A Ship Street, BN1 1AE TEL & FAX: 321803 PARKING: Difficult OPEN: Tues-Fri 10-5, Sat 10-1.30 MIN: £650 MAX: £19,000 PERIOD: 19th century SPECIALIST: Musical boxes & mechanical music.

**The Witch Ball,** 48 Meeting House Lane, BN1 1HB TEL: 326618 FAX: 329127 PARKING: Medium OPEN: 10.30-6 MIN: £1 MAX: £2000 PERIOD: 17th-19th century SPECIALIST: Antiquarian maps & prints.

**E & B White,** 43-47 Upper North Street, BN1 3FH TEL: 328706 PARKING: Difficult OPEN: Mon-Fri 9.30-4.30, Sat 9.30-1 MIN: £50 MAX: £3000

PERIOD: 18th-19th century SPECIALIST: Country oak GENERAL: Oak furniture.

## HOVE (01273)

**Michael Norman Antiques Ltd**, Palmeira House, 82 Western Road, BN3 1JB TEL: 326712, 329253 FAX: 206556 ASSNS: BADA PARKING: Own carpark OPEN: Mon-Sat 9.30-1, 2-5.30 MIN: £500 MAX: £50,000 PERIOD: 17th-19th century SPECIALIST: English furniture GENERAL: General antiques.

**Clive Rogers Oriental Rugs,** 22 Brunswick Road, BN3 1DG TEL: 738257 FAX: 738687 PARKING: Difficult OPEN: By appt MIN: £30 PERIOD: 16th-19th century SPECIALIST: Tribal rugs, textiles GENERAL: Oriental carpets.

**Sussex Commemorative Ware Centre**, 88 Western Road, BN3 1JB TEL: 773911 FAX: 747866 PARKING: Easy OPEN: Mon-Fri 9-12, Sat 9-12 & 2-3.30 & by appt MIN: £1 MAX: £1500 PERIOD: 19th-20th century SPECIALIST: Commemoratives, British & foreign royalty, military, political, also royalty postcards OTHER INFO: Royal Pavilion, Brighton which has the Willett Collection of early commemoratives.

**Yellow Lantern Antiques Ltd**, 34 & 34b Holland Road, BN3 1JL TEL: 771572, 455476 ASSNS: LAPADA PARKING: Easy OPEN: Mon-Sat 9-1, 2.15-5.30 MIN: £50 MAX: £7500 PERIOD: 18th-19th century SPECIALIST: Regency furniture, French clocks, ormolu & bronzes GENERAL: Furniture, paintings, chandeliers, fine art & porcelain OTHER INFO: Dudley Hotel, Richards restaurant.

## PORTSLADE (01273)

**Peter Semus Crafting Antiques**, The Warehouse, Gladstone Road, BN41 1LJ TEL: 420154 FAX: 430355 PARKING: Own carpark OPEN: 8-5 MIN: £1 MAX: £2000 PERIOD: 19th-20th century GENERAL: 1920's furniture, conversions from old wood, restoration OTHER INFO: Container packing own stock/nationwide service.

**J Powell (Hove) Ltd**, 120 Wellington Road, BN41 1DN TEL: 411599 FAX: 421591 ASSNS: LAPADA PARKING: Medium OPEN: Mon-Sat 7.30-5.30 MIN: £50 MAX: £3000 PERIOD: 18th-20th century SPECIALIST: English furniture & clocks. OTHER INFO: Topps Hotel.

## HURSTPIERPOINT (01273)

**Julian Antiques**, 124 High Street, BN6 9PX TEL: 832145 ASSNS: LAPADA PARKING: Own carpark OPEN: Mon-Fri 9-6, closed 1-2 MIN: £100 MAX: £3000 PERIOD: 19th century SPECIALIST: French mirrors & fireplaces, other French items.

**Samuel Orr Clocks**, 36 High Street, BN6 9RS TEL: 832081 PARKING: Own carpark OPEN: Tues-Sat 10-5.30 MIN: £200 MAX: £15,000 PERIOD: 18th-19th century SPECIALIST: Longcase, bracket Vienna wall & carriage clocks.

## SAYERS COMMON (01273)

**Recollect Studios**, The Old School, London Road, BN6 9HX TEL: 833314 ASSNS: UKIC PARKING: Own carpark OPEN: Tues-Fri 10-5, Sat 10-2 MIN: £1 MAX: £200 PERIOD: 19th-20th century SPECIALIST: Dolls, dolls houses, miniatures, dolls Repairs OTHER INFO: Mail order catalogue £2 (overseas £4.50).

## COWFOLD (01403)

**The Squire's Pantry Pine & Antiques,** Station Road, RH13 8DA TEL: 864869 & 864586 FAX: 865283 PARKING: Easy OPEN: Mon-Sat 10-1, 2-5 PERIOD: 19th-20th century SPECIALIST: Pine.

## HORSHAM (01403)

**LE Lampard & Sons**, 23-31 Springfield Road, RH12 2PW TEL: 64332, 54012 PARKING: Medium OPEN: Mon-Sat 8-1, 2-5.30 MIN: £5 MAX: £5000 PERIOD: 18th-19th century GENERAL: Period oak & mahogany furniture OTHER INFO: Kings Head Hotel.

# West Surrey

Staying mostly inside the M25, this tour concentrates on the south-west suburbs of London. These are prosperous and pretty towns and villages, many with long histories and interesting associations.

**Kew**, the first stop, is world famous for the Royal Botanic Gardens begun in 1759 and covering 300 acres, six of which are under glass. The new Princess of Wales Conservatory includes 10 different types of climate from steamy jungle to arid desert. The collections of plants, shrubs and trees are superb both indoors and out.

Moving on, there is evidence of settlement at **Isleworth,** situated on the Thames, from earliest times and the area is mentioned in the Domesday Book under the name of the Manor of Gristlesworde. The magnificent Syon House stands on the site of an earlier monastery. The present house was started in the late 16th century by Edward Seymour, Duke of Somerset. He was executed and the estate was given to John Dudley, Duke of Northumberland and father of Lady Jane Grey. He was also executed after his daugher's nine day reign as queen. Queen Elizabeth I gave the estate to Henry Percy, Earl of Northumberland and it has stayed in that family ever since. In the 17th century Inigo Jones was brought in to improve and alter the property but it is the work on the interior a century later by Robert Adams that nowadays sets the house apart. The striking Great Conservatory, said to have been the model for the Crystal Palace used for the Great Exhibition in 1850, was built in the 19th century.

Nearby **Twickenham**, now largely a residential suburb of London, has some Georgian houses in Syon Row and Montpelier Row. The modern church of All Hallows, built in 1940, incorporates a Wren tower which once stood in the City of London and was re-erected here. Continuing on, **Richmond**, now a part of Greater London still retains a character of its own. Situated on the River Thames it contains many Georgian and Queen Anne buildings. One of the town's most notable features is Richmond Park which covers over 2000 acres. Herds of deer still roam the park at will.

**Hampton Hill** & then **Hampton** are the next calls, The major attraction in this area is the world-famous palace of Hampton Court, a magnificent building, set in beautiful and extensive gardens, and built by Cardinal Wolsey who was compelled to make a gift of it to Henry VIII in 1520. Five of Henry's wives lived here and it continued as a royal residence until 1760. **Kingston-on-Thames**, next, has a number of historic and noteworthy buildings. There is also the Coronation Stone near the Guildhall, said to have been used for crowning Saxon kings. From Kingston the route carries on to **East Molesey** which is full of antique shops and then **Thames Ditton**. .

Continuing, the route passes through **Shepperton**, where so many British films have been made, to the Thames-side town of **Chertsey**. A number of old buildings still exist here amongst which is the 18th century Curfew House. It is said a man destined to be executed when curfew was sounded was saved because his lover hung on the clapper of the bell to prevent it being rung. Next come the towns of **Weybridge** and then **Byfleet,** close to world-famous, pre-war Brooklands banked racing circuit.**Cobham**, 4 miles east, is where the remains of a Bronze Age settlement and Roman pottery have been found. From here the route crosses the M25 to visit the mainly 19th century **East Horsley** village and then **Great Bookham** where the church is of particular interest. Built in the 11th century, remains of contemporary frescoes may be seen on the north wall.

Turning back across the M25 again, **Ashtead** is next with its 18th century Ashstead Park, followed by **Epsom**, synonymous with racing. The racecourse stands a mile and a half from the town and it is the venue for the great classic races, the Derby and the Oaks. The town was well-known in the 18th century for its medicinal springs from which we get the name Epsom Salts. The final destination is **Wimbledon**, known throughout the world as the home of tennis. At the time of the Domesday Book, Wimbledon was part of the manor of Mortlake but it was in the

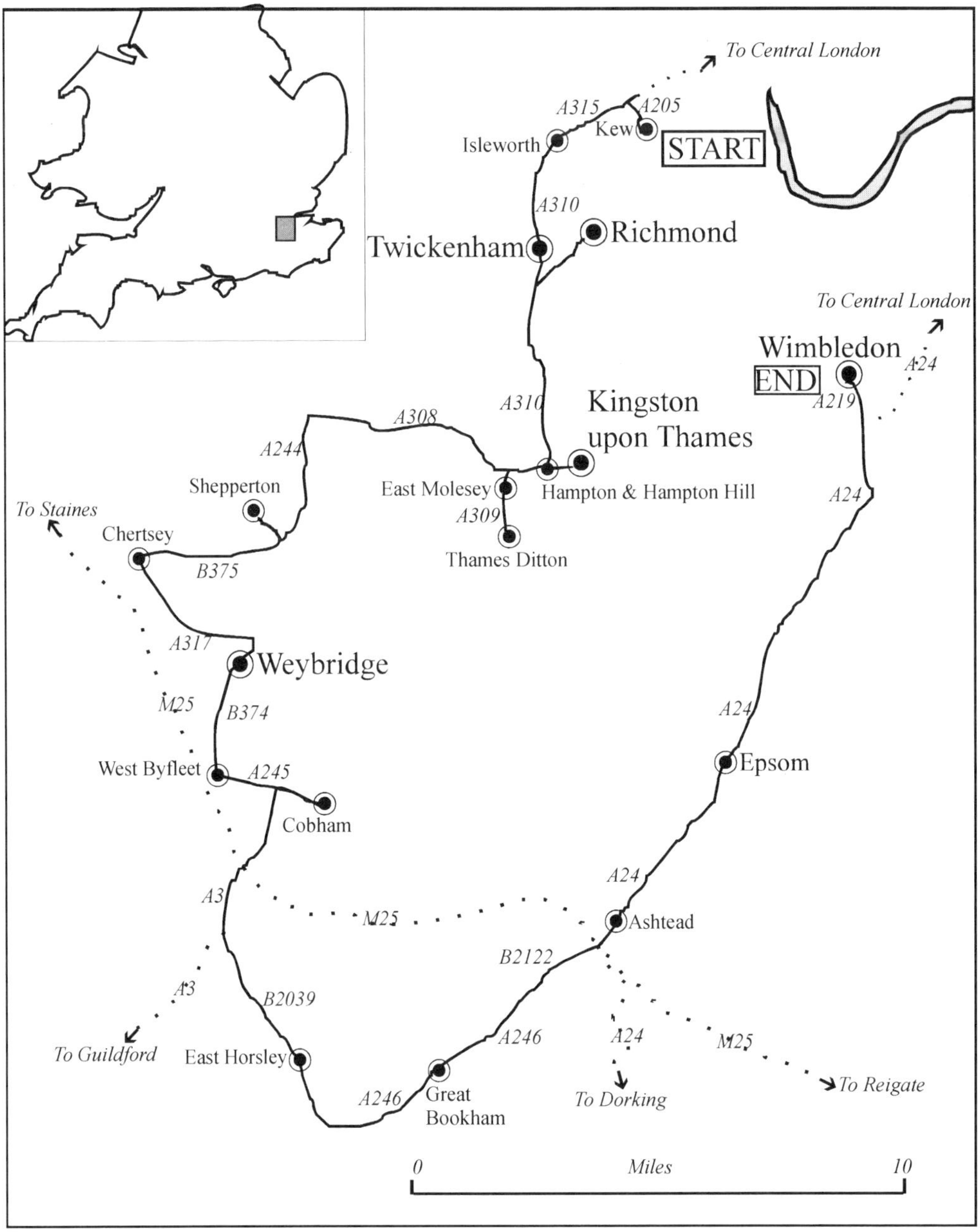


Middle Ages that the village started to grow. The Rose and Crown, in the High Street, dates from the mid 17th century and Eagle House from 1613. In 1838 Wimbledon was one of the first south London villages to get a railway station although the great residential expansion took place in the last quarter of the 19th century. Wimbledon Common, covering about 1100 acres and still completely unenclosed, has two man-made attractions. The first is a restored windmill. The original was built in the 17th century but the present one was constructed in 1817. The other is Southside House built in the 17th century by Robert Pennington. He built the house for his family as a refuge from the Plague after his young son died of it. Still owned by the same family, much of the original furnishings remain as well as portraits by Van Dyke and Hogarth. There are royal connections as Anne Boleyn's sister married into the family and there is an exhibition of the tragic queen's personal possessions. A display of gifts to John Pennington may also be seen. He helped aristocrats escape from the guillotine during the French Revolution. Amongst these items is a pearl necklace, said to have fallen from the neck of Marie Antoinette when she was beheaded.

## ANTIQUE DEALERS

### KEW (0181)

**Lloyds of Kew**, 9 Mortlake Terrace, Kew TW9 3DT TEL: 940 2512 PARKING: Easy OPEN: Mon-Tues, Thurs-Fri 10-4, Sat 10-5.30 MIN: £1 MAX: £2500 PERIOD: 20th century SPECIALIST: Large stock gardening/ botanical books-world's most comprehensive GENERAL: Small stock on most subjects with emphasis on natural history, travel & history.

**Dennis Woodman Oriental Carpets**, 105 North Road, TW9 4HJ TEL: 878 8182 PARKING: Easy OPEN: Tues-Sat 10-6 & by appt MAX: £5000 PERIOD: 19th-20th century GENERAL: Oriental kilims & textiles.

### ISLEWORTH (0181)

**Crowther of Syon Lodge**, Busch Corner, London Road, TW7 5BH TEL: 560 7978 FAX: 568 7572 PARKING: Own carpark OPEN: Mon-Fri 9-5, Sat, Sun 11-4.30 MIN: £500 MAX: £80,000+ PERIOD: 17th-19th century SPECIALIST: Antique panelling & manufacture of period style, quality 18th century chimneypieces GENERAL: Statues, urns, fountains, seats, temples OTHER INFO: Syon Lodge was designed by Robert Adam in 1776.

### TWICKENHAM (0181)

**Alberts & Golden Oldies,** 113 London Road, TW1 1EE TEL: 891 3067 FAX: 744 3133 PARKING: Medium OPEN: Tues-Fri 10-6, Sat 10-4 MIN: 40p MAX: £3000 PERIOD: 20th century SPECIALIST: World's largest stock of cigarette cards, film memorabilia GENERAL: UK comics, lead figures, ephemera OTHER INFO: Catalogue available £1.

**Anthony C Hall (Bookseller)**, 30 Staines Road, TW2 5AH TEL: 898 2638 ASSNS: ABA, PBFA PARKING: Easy OPEN: Mon-Fri 9-5.30, Weds 9-1 MIN: £1 MAX: £2000 PERIOD: 17th-20th century SPECIALIST: Russian & East European studies, Middle East, Asia, Africa social & industrial history GENERAL: Also medium general stock.

**Marble Hill Gallery,** 70-72 Richmond Road, TW1 3BE TEL: 892 1488 FAX: 891 6591 PARKING: Easy OPEN: 10-5 MIN: £50 MAX: £10,000 PERIOD: 19th-20th century SPECIALIST: Victorian watercolours GENERAL: Louis XV & XVI style French marble mantels.

**Phelps Ltd**, 133-135 St Margarets Road, East Twickenham, TW1 1RG TEL: 892 1778 FAX: 892 3661 ASSNS: LAPADA PARKING: Easy OPEN: Mon-Sat 9-5.30 MIN: £150 MAX: £6000 PERIOD: 18th-20th century GENERAL: 6000 sq ft mostly furniture & mirrors OTHER INFO: Excellent coffee & sandwiches opposite.

### RICHMOND (0181)

**Antiques Arcade**, 22 Richmond Hill, TW10 6QX TEL: 940 2035 PARKING: Medium OPEN: Thurs, Sat 10-5 & by appt MIN: £120 MAX: £4000 PERIOD: 18th-20th century SPECIALIST: Fine porcelain, Staffordshire figures, fine smallish furniture, childrens' furniture, objets d'arts, samplers, gift pieces, some copper, brass & glass.

**The Antique Mart**, 72-74 Hill Rise, TW10 6UB TEL: 940 6942 PARKING: Medium OPEN: 10-1, 3-6 PERIOD: 18th-19th century SPECIALIST: English & French furniture.

**Mollie Evans Antiques**, 82 Hill Rise, TW10 6UB TEL: 948 0182 PARKING: Medium OPEN: Thurs, Sat 10-5.30, Sun 2.30-5.30 & by appt MIN: £25 MAX: £4000 PERIOD: 17th-20th century SPECIALIST: 18th-19th century sculptures, paintings, drawings GENERAL: Country & decorative furniture, unusual objets d'art from all periods.

**Peter & Debbie Gooday**, 20 Richmond Hill, TW10 6QX TEL: 940 8652 PARKING: Easy OPEN: Sat 11-5.30, Sun 2-5.30 & by appt MIN: £20 MAX: £8000 PERIOD: 19th-20th century SPECIALIST: 1880-1940 Arts & Crafts GENERAL: Art Nouveau, Art Deco & tribal art.

**Hill Rise Antiques**, 26 Hill Rise, TW10 6UA TEL: 332 2941 (24 hrs) ASSNS: LAPADA PARKING: Own carpark OPEN: Mon, Tues, Thurs-Sat 10.30-5.30, Sun 2.30-5.30 or by appt MIN: £30 MAX: £10,000 PERIOD: 18th-19th century SPECIAL-

IST: English mahogany furniture GENERAL: Accessories, glassware, silver + plate, clocks, mirrors.

**Hortons**, 2 Paved Court, The Green, TW9 1LZ, TEL: 332 1775 ASSNS: LAPADA, Gemmological Assn of GB PARKING: Medium OPEN: Mon-Tues, Thurs-Sat 10-5 MIN: £50 MAX: £5000+ PERIOD: 19th-20th century SPECIAL-IST: Jewellery GENERAL: Silver + plate.

**Robin Kennedy,** PO Box 265, TW9 1UB TEL: 940 5346 FAX: 940 0614 OPEN: By appt MIN: £50 MAX: £5000 PERIOD: 18th-20th century SPECIALIST: Japanese prints.

**F & T Lawson Antiques**, 13 Hill Rise, TW10 6UQ TEL: 940 0461 PARKING: Medium OPEN: 10.30-5.30, closed Wed & Sun MIN: £10 MAX: £3000 PERIOD: 18th-20th century SPECIALIST: Furniture GENERAL: Ceramics, paintings, brass, prints of local views OTHER INFO: Only shop on river side of Hill Rise. Superb & very well known Siamese on prowl - cat that is.

**MARRYAT**

**88 SHEEN ROAD, TW9 1UF TEL: 332 0262 FAX: 332 0256 PARKING: EASY OPEN: MON-SAT 10-5.30, SUN BY APPT MIN: £1 MAX: £8000 PERIOD: 18TH-20TH CENTURY SPECIALIST: EARLY ENGLISH CERAMICS & VICTORIAN WATERCOLOURS GENERAL: VICTORIAN OILS, WATERCOLOURS & PRINTS, QUALITY FURNITURE, SILVER, GLASS, DOULTON, JEWELLERY, DECORATIVE OBJECTS. OTHER INFO: SELECTED AT 'FRIENDLIEST ANTIQUES SHOP' BY *BBC HOMES & ANTIQUES* MAGAZINE. SIX LINKED SHOWROOMS.**

**Piano Nobile Fine Paintings**, 26 Richmond Hill, TW10 6QX TEL & FAX: 940 2435 PARKING: Medium OPEN: Tues-Sat 10-6 MIN: £350 MAX: £100,000 PERIOD: 1860-1960 SPECIALIST: Modern paintings & sculpture GENERAL: Quality paintings & sculpture for the private & corporate collector OTHER INFO: Richmond Hill offers the finest view of the Thames in London, depicted by so many great painters.

**Richmond Antiques Traders**, 28-32 Hill Rise, TW10 6UA TEL: 948 4638 PARKING: Medium OPEN: Mon,Tues, Thurs-Sat 11-5.30, Sun 2-5.30 MIN: £5 MAX: £5000 PERIOD: 19th-20th century GENERAL: More than 20 small dealers offering a wide variety of items from small collectables to quality furniture & clocks.

**Roderic Antiques**, 84 Hill Rise, TW10 6UB TEL & FAX: 332 6766 PARKING: Medium OPEN: Mon-Tues, Thurs-Sat 10-5.30, Sun 2-5.30 MIN: £100 MAX: £10,000 PERIOD: 18th-19th century SPECIALIST: Satinwood & ebony colonial furniture GENERAL: Furniture.

## TWICKENHAM (0181)

**Alberts & Golden Oldies,** 113 London Road, TW1 1EE TEL: 891 3067 FAX: 744 3133 PARKING: Medium OPEN: Tues-Fri 10-6, Sat 10-4 MIN: 40p MAX: £3000 PERIOD: 20th century SPECIALIST: World's largest stock of cigarette cards, film memorabilia GENERAL: UK comics, lead figures, ephemera OTHER INFO: Catalogue available £1.

**Anthony C Hall (Bookseller)**, 30 Staines Road, TW2 5AH TEL: 898 2638 ASSNS: ABA, PBFA PARKING: Easy OPEN: Mon-Fri 9-5.30, Weds 9-1 MIN: £1 MAX: £2000 PERIOD: 17th-20th century SPECIALIST: Russian & East European studies, Middle East, Asia, Africa social & industrial history GENERAL: Also medium general stock.

**Marble Hill Gallery,** 70-72 Richmond Road, TW1 3BE TEL: 892 1488 FAX: 891 6591 PARKING: Easy OPEN: 10-5 MIN: £50 MAX: £10,000 PERIOD: 19th-20th century SPECIALIST: Victorian watercolours GENERAL: Louis XV & XVI style French marble mantels.

**Phelps Ltd**, 133-135 St Margarets Road, East Twickenham, TW1 1RG TEL: 892 1778 FAX: 892 3661 ASSNS: LAPADA PARKING: Easy OPEN: Mon-Sat 9-5.30 MIN: £150 MAX: £6000 PERIOD: 18th-20th century GENERAL: 6000 sq ft mostly furniture & mirrors OTHER INFO: Excellent coffee & sandwiches opposite.

## KINGSTON-UPON-THAMES (0181)

**Classic Automobilia & Regalia Specialists, (CARS)**, 2 Applemarket, Eden Street, KT1 1JE TEL: (01273) 601960 FAX: (01273) 623846 ASSNS: Pedal Car Collectors Club PARKING: Own carpark OPEN: 10-6 MIN: £50+ MAX: £5000 PERIOD: 20th century SPECIALIST: Automobilia, car mascots, car badges, memorabilia, motoring nostalgia. Restoration of old pedal cars from pre/ post war periods.

**Cockrell Antiques**, 278 Ewell Road, Surbiton, KT6 7AG TEL: 390 8290 PARKING: Easy OPEN:

Thurs-Sat 9-6 & by appt MIN: £20 MAX: £5000 PERIOD: 18th-20th century SPECIALIST: Furniture GENERAL: Silver plate, porcelain, pictures.

## EAST MOLESEY (0181)

**Abbott Antiques**, 75 Bridge Road, KT8 9HH TEL: 941 6398 PARKING: Easy OPEN: Mon-Sat 10-5 MIN: £50 MAX: £8000 PERIOD: 18th-20th century SPECIALIST: Clocks.

**Antix,** 8 Bridge Street, KY8 9LX TEL: 224 0734 PARKING: Easy OPEN: Sat, Sun 11-6 MIN: £5 MAX: £500 PERIOD: 18th century SPECIALIST: Decoupage, gifts, parchment flowers GENERAL: Antiques, French, pine & painted furniture OTHER INFO: The best Indian restaurant, The Palace Tandoori, is a few doors away.

**BS Antiques**, 39 Bridge Road TEL: 941 1812 PARKING: Easy OPEN: Mon-Sat 10-5, closed Wed MIN: £100 MAX: £3500 PERIOD: 18th-19th century SPECIALIST: Old clocks, barometers, horological books. Repairs & restoration OTHER INFO: Close to Hampton Court Palace, good pubs & restaurants nearby.

**Court Gallery**, 16 Bridge Road, KT8 2HA TEL: 941 2212 PARKING: Medium OPEN: Tues-Sat 8.30-4.30 MIN: £20 MAX: £2000 PERIOD: 18th-20th century SPECIALIST: Oils GENERAL: Watercolours, engravings. Restoration & framing.

**Hampton Court Antiques**, 75 Bridge Road, KT8 9HH TEL: 941 6398 PARKING: Easy OPEN: Mon-Sat 10-5 MIN: £5 MAX: £2000 PERIOD: 19th-20th century GENERAL: General antiques.

**Hampton Court Emporium**, 52-54 Bridge Road, KT8 9HA TEL: 941 9032 PARKING: Easy OPEN: Mon-Sat 9.30-5.30, Sun 10-5 PERIOD: 19th-20th century GENERAL: Furniture, paintings, silver, jewellery, mirrors, books, clocks, metalware etc.

**Howard Hope - Gramophones & Phonographs**, 21 Bridge Road, KT8 9EU TEL: 941 2472 FAX: 398 7630 PARKING: Easy OPEN: Fri & Sat 10-5 MIN: £80+ MAX: £10,000 PERIOD: 19th-20th century SPECIALIST: Gramophones, phonographs, paper-rolls, musical boxes, organs, typewriters, sewing machines & other Victorian and later mechanical & musical items.



**Jillings Antiques**
**Hampton Court Emporium, 52-54 Bridge Road, KT8 9HA TEL: 941 9608 PARKING: Medium OPEN: Tues-Sat 10-5 MIN: £100 MAX: £4500 PERIOD: 18th-19th century SPECIALIST: Clocks & barometers GENERAL: Some Georgian furniture, scientific instruments, small crystal chandeliers OTHER INFO: Across the road from Hampton Court Palace & opposite station. The building has more general antiques, crafts & excellent coffee shop.**

**Nicholas Antiques**, 31 Bridge Road, KT8 9ER TEL: 979 0354 PARKING: Easy OPEN: Mon-Sat 9.30-5.30 MIN: £5 MAX: £5000 PERIOD: 18th-20th century SPECIALIST: Furniture & decorative items & gilt mirrors.

**Sovereign Antiques Centre**, 53 Bridge Road TEL: 783 0595 PARKING: Medium OPEN: Mon-Sat 10-5 MIN: £1 MAX: £1000 PERIOD: 19th-20th century GENERAL: General antiques.

## THAMES DITTON (0181)

**David Curzon Gallery**, 1 High Street, KT7 0SD TEL: 398 7860 PARKING: Easy OPEN: Wed-Sat 10-6 MIN: £30 MAX: £5000 PERIOD: 19th-20th century GENERAL: Landscape, marine, figurative, architectural subjects.

**Clifford & Roger Dade**, Boldre House, Weston Green, KT7 0JP TEL: 398 6293 ASSNS: LAPADA PARKING: Own carpark OPEN: Mon-Sat 9-6 (resident) MIN: £300 MAX: £6000 PERIOD: 18th-19th century SPECIALIST: Georgian mahogany furniture GENERAL: Period furniture & objects.

**Fern Cottage Antiques**, 28-30 High Street, KT7 0RY. TEL: 398 2281 PARKING: Medium OPEN: Mon-Sat 10-5.30 MIN: 50p MAX: £2000 PERIOD: 19th-20th century SPECIALIST: Art Deco GENERAL: General antiques.

## SHEPPERTON (01932)

**Crown Antiques**, Russell Road, TW17 9WF TEL: 247709, 242803 PARKING: Easy OPEN: Wed-Sat 10-5, Sun 11-4 MIN: £30 MAX: £12,000 PERIOD: 17th-19th century SPECIALIST: Quality furniture GENERAL: Mirrors, lamps, silver, porcelain, boxes etc OTHER INFO: Old Church Square on river.

**Ricketts & Co Antiques**, Church Square, TW17 8JN TEL: 243571 PARKING: Easy OPEN: 9-5 MIN: £40 MAX: £2000 PERIOD: 18th-19th century SPECIALIST: Metalwork GENERAL: Brass, copper mainly for fireplaces, some furniture.

## CHERTSEY (01932)

**Mister Gun Antiques**, 96 Guildford Street, KT16 9AD TEL: 566323 PARKING: Easy OPEN: Tues-Sat 10-5.30 MIN: £50 MAX: £2000 PERIOD: 19th-20th century GENERAL: General antiques, dolls & teddies.

**Chertsey Antiques**, Windsor Street, KT16 8AS TEL: 782453 PARKING: Medium OPEN: Mon, Tues, Thurs-Sat 10-5.15 MIN: £5 MAX: £1500 PERIOD: 17th-20th century SPECIALIST: Silver & antique jewellery GENERAL: Small furniture, unusual objets d'art, small gifts & china, books.

**Surrey Antiques Centre**, 10 Windsor Street, TEL: 563313 PARKING: Medium OPEN: Mon-Sat 10-5 MIN: £1 MAX: £650 PERIOD: 17th-20th century SPECIALIST: Mainly Victorian, Edwardian furniture & china GENERAL: Silver, books, pictures, general goods.

## WEYBRIDGE (01932)

**The Clock Shop**, 64 Church Street, KT13 8DL TEL: 840407, 855503 PARKING: Easy OPEN: Mon-Sat 9.30-6 MIN: £300+ MAX: £15,000+ PERIOD: 17th-19th century SPECIALIST: Clocks & barometers OTHER INFO: The Ship Hotel.

**Church House Antiques**
**42 Church Street, KT13 8DP TEL: 842190 ASSNS: LAPADA PARKING: Medium OPEN: Thurs-Sat 10-5.30 & by appt MIN: £30 MAX: £6000 PERIOD: 17th-20th century SPECIALIST: Decorative items, jewellery GENERAL: Wide range & decorative OTHER INFO: Attractive 16th-18th century building, there are references to curios being sold here in the reign of Charles II. Possibly the oldest antique shop?**

**Edward Cross Gallery,** 128 Oatlands Drive, KT13 9HL TEL: 851093 PARKING: Easy OPEN: Fri 10-4, Sat 10-12.30 or by appt MIN: £150 MAX: £15,000 PERIOD: 18th-20th century GENERAL: Paintings & drawings, also animal bronzes.

**Not Just Silver**, 16 York Rd, KT13 9DT TEL: 842468 FAX: 830054 PARKING: Easy OPEN: Mon-Sat 9.30-5.30 MIN: £3.50 MAX: £5000 PERIOD: 18th-20th century SPECIALIST: Silver GENERAL: Porcelain, glass & furniture.

**Weybridge Antiques,** 43 Church Street, The Quadrant, KT13 8XD TEL & FAX: 852503 PARKING: Own carpark OPEN: 9.45-5.30 MIN: £20 MAX: £5000 PERIOD: 18th-20th century SPECIALIST: Furniture, dining tables GENERAL: Silver, paintings, watercolours, glass objects.

## WEST BYFLEET (01932)

**Academy Billiard Company,** 5 Camphill Industrial Estate, KT14 6EW TEL: 352067 FAX: 353904 PARKING: Own carpark OPEN: Anytime by appt MIN: £20 MAX: £25,000 PERIOD: 19th-20th century SPECIALIST: Billiard, snooker & pool tables, accessories, associated lighting, pictures, etc.

## COBHAM (01932)

**Cobham Galleries**, 65 Portsmouth Road, KT11 1JQ TEL: 867909, (0860) 544578 ASSNS: LAPADA PARKING: Own driveway or free parking across the street at the Dumont Exchange Restaurant OPEN:Tues-Sat 10-5, Sun 11-5 MIN: £20 MAX: £10,000 PERIOD: 18th-19th century SPECIALIST: Dining tables & chairs, oils & watercolours GENERAL: 6 showrooms of Georgian to Victorian furniture OTHER INFO: Dining table finder service. Showrooms extensively renovated in cottage dating from 18th century.

## EAST HORSLEY (01483)

**AE Gould & Sons (Antiques) Ltd**, Old Rectory Cottage, Ockham Road South, KT24 6QJ TEL: 283747 PARKING: Own carpark OPEN: Mon-Fri 9.30-5 MIN: £50 MAX: £5000 PERIOD: 18th-20th century SPECIALIST: Barometers GENERAL: English furniture in mahogany & walnut.

## GREAT BOOKHAM (01372)

**Roger A Davis**, 19 Dorking Road, KT23 4PU TEL: 457655, 453167 ASSNS: BHI, AHS, BWCMG PARKING: Easy OPEN: Tues, Thurs, Sat 9.30-5.30 MIN: £50 MAX: £5000 PERIOD: 18th-19th century SPECIALIST: Clocks, barometers, telescopes, Ironstone ware.

## ASHTEAD (01372)

**Bumbles**, 90 The Street, KT21 1AW TEL: 276219 PARKING: Easy OPEN: Mon-Sat 9.30-5.30 MIN: £1 MAX: £2500 PERIOD: 19th-20th century SPECIALIST: Clocks, barometers, oil lamps, furniture GENERAL: Local prints, porcelain, glass, metalware, silver, plate etc. Restoration services.

**Memory Lane Antiques**, 102 The Street, KT21 1AW TEL: 273436 PARKING: Easy OPEN: Mon-Tues, Thurs-Sat 10-4 MIN: £5 MAX: £3000 GENERAL: General antiques.

## EPSOM (01372)

**Fogg Antiques**, 75 South Street, KT18 7P TEL: 726931 PARKING: Medium OPEN: Mon-Fri 9-5.30, Sat 10-6 MIN: £10 MAX: £900 PERIOD: 19th-20th century SPECIALIST: Antique & old pine GENERAL: Pine.

## WIMBLEDON, LONDON SW19 (0181)

**Adams Room Antiques & Interiors**, 18-20 Ridgeway, Wimbledon Village TEL: 946 4733, 946 7047 FAX: 946 4858 ASSNS: LAPADA GMC PARKING: Own carpark OPEN: Mon-Sat 9-5 MIN: £100 MAX: £15,000 PERIOD: 17th-19th century SPECIALIST: Fine English walnut, rosewood, mahogany GENERAL: French & decorative furniture & objects.

**Allegras Lighthouse Antiques**, 75-77 Ridge-way, Wimbledon Village, SW19 4ST TEL: 946 2050 FAX: 944 6338 ASSNS: LAPADA, Antique & Decorative Lighting Assn PARKING: Easy OPEN: Mon-Sat 12-5.30 MIN: £100 MAX: £3,000 PERIOD: 19th-20th century SPECIALIST: Lights, mirrors GENERAL: Furniture, jewellery, gifts.

**Chelsea Bric a Brac Shop Ltd,** 16 Hartfield Road, SW19 3RA TEL: 946 6894 OPEN: 10-5, closed Wed MIN: £5 MAX: £3000 PERIOD: 19th-20th century GENERAL: Victorian & Edwardian furniture, old pine & items of china & glass.

**Clunes Antiques**, 9 West Place, Wimbledon Common, SW19 4UH TEL: 946 1643 PARKING: Easy OPEN: Tues-Sat 10-4.30 MIN: £1 MAX: £140 PERIOD: 19th-20th century SPECIALIST: Staffordshire figures GENERAL: Ephemera.

**Mark J West**, 39B High Street, Wimbledon Village, SW19 5BY TEL & FAX: 946 2811 ASSNS: BADA PARKING: Easy OPEN: Mon-Sat 10-5.30 MIN: £5 MAX: £5000 PERIOD: 17th-19th century SPECIALIST: English & Continental glass GENERAL: London's largest stock of antique glass.

# West Sussex and Surrey

In spite of the proximity of this area to London, the villages have a timeless air and remain largely unspoilt whilst the seaside resorts are quieter and more sedate than Brighton, just a few miles along the coast. The long history of settlement in the region is evident in places like Chichester.

The tour starts in **Hindhead,** a beautiful spot, particularly by Waggoners' Wells, and **Haslemere**, with many old buildings in the centre and nestling under the 800 foot Blackdown another beautiful area. **Petworth**, next, is quite charming with many 16th and 17th century edifices. The great house dominates Petworth especially as its boundary walls extend into the town. The lords of the manor, the Percys, first came here in the 12th century. In 1682 Elizabeth Percy married the Earl of Somerset who built Petworth House, demolishing houses and diverting streets in the process. The house and grounds are now owned by the National Trust. Some of it is used as an art gallery with pictures and sculptures ranging from Van Dyck to Turner. Portraits of the former owners, the Percys can also be seen. There is a portrait of the seventh Earl of Northumberland, Thomas Percy, who was beheaded for his support of Mary, Queen of Scots. Another unfortunate Percy was the ninth Earl who was implicated in the Gunpowder Plot and was imprisoned in the Tower of London for sixteen years. He was only released after payment of £11,000, an enormous amount then.

Moving on, **Midhurst** has Georgian and half-timbered buildings. The Spread Eagle is particularly interesting. It is a large coaching inn whose sign is reputed to date from 1430. The main attraction in Midhurst is Cowdray Park. Cowdray was a mansion started in the late 15th century by Sir David Owen, said to be the son of Owen Glendower. He had financial difficulties so he sold the house to Sir William Fitzwilliam in 1529 who completed it. The mansion passed to his half-brother, Sir Anthony Browne, who was cursed by a monk because he was granted Battle Abbey at the Dissolution of the Monasteries. The curse was that Sir Anthony's line would end by fire and by water. In 1793 his descendent drowned in the Laufenburg Falls on the Rhine and in the same year Cowdray caught fire and was reduced to ruins. Today, most of the gatehouse still stands as does enough of the shell of the building to give a good idea of its former splendour.

Following the A286 via **Cocking**, the route arrives in **Chichester**, the social and administrative centre for western Sussex since Roman times. The street pattern, four main streets within a walled enclosure, remains that of a typical Roman town although now, of course, it has been much amplified. The cathedral was started in the late 11th century and completed in 1123 although altered and enlarged considerably since then. The spire collapsed in 1861 but was rebuilt between 1865-67. The cathedral has long been a patron of the arts and there are many modern features in the cathedral testifying to the continuation of this tradition, e.g. the tapestry behind the high altar from 1966, the pulpit of concrete and cast aluminium, a Graham Sutherland painting in the St. Mary Magdalene Chapel and a window by Chagall in the retrochoir. The city contains many fine buildings and consists of a harmonious mixture of Georgian brick and medieval stone.The city is also home to the Chichester Festival which runs from May to September each year.

Continuing the tour, **Birdham** and **Hunston** are next, followed by **Bognor Regis**. A quiet and sedate seaside resort, it earned its title 'Regis' because George V convalesced here in 1928. Turning inland, the route comes to **Arundel.** The town pre-dates the Norman Conquest although it is the Norman castle, built by Roger de Montgomery, which dominates Arundel. The inner gateway dates from the 11th century, the keep from the 12th century and the outer barbican was built in the 13th century by the Fitzalan family. The Fitzalans retained the castle until the mid-16th century when it went to Thomas Howard, Duke of Norfolk. Dukes of Norfolk have lived there since, apart from during the Civil War. In 1643 the castle was besieged by Roundheads who captured and occupied it until 1649. The damage caused then was not fully

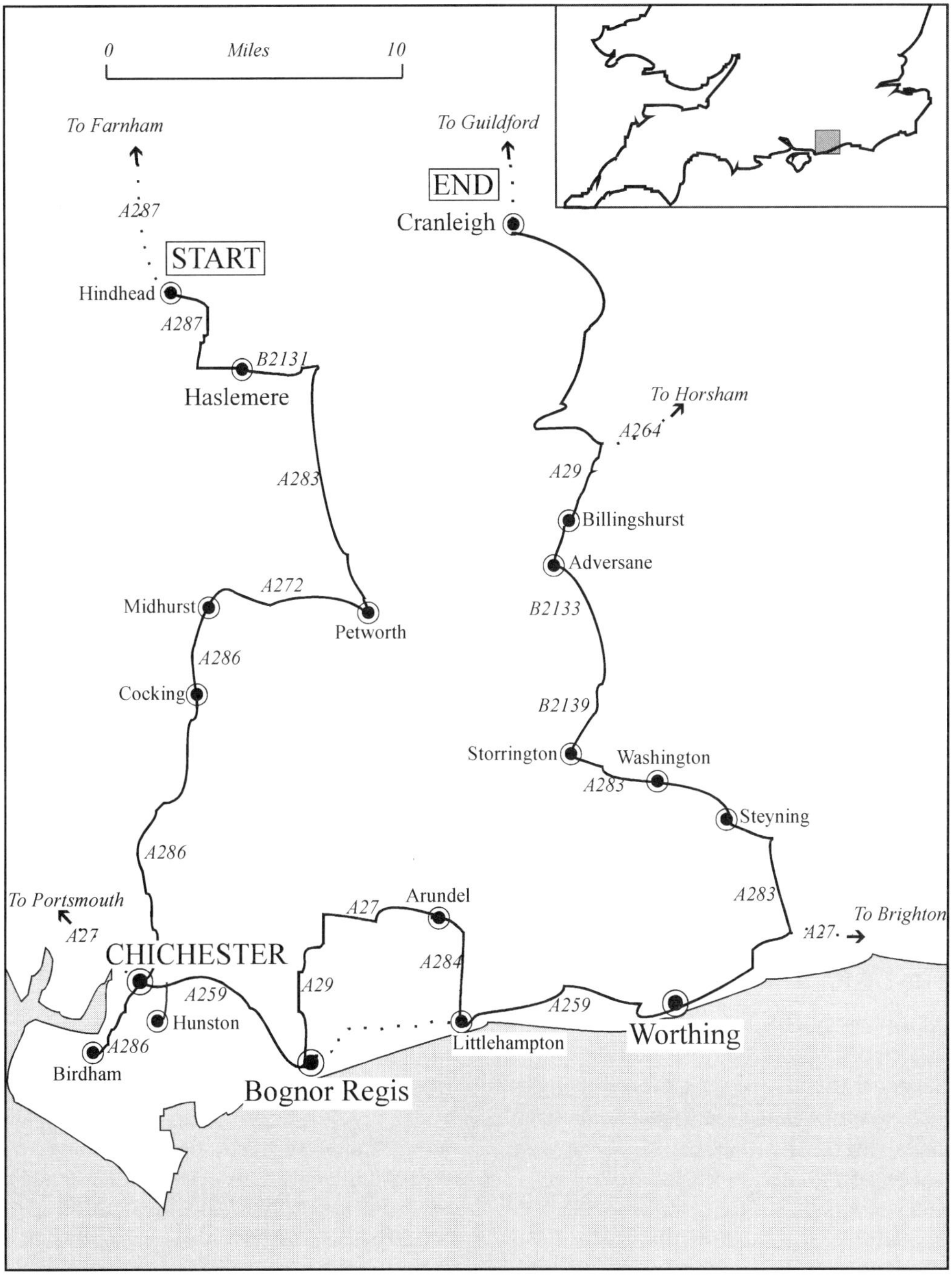


repaired until the 1890s. The castle is now open to the public and contains fine collections of furniture and paintings.

The following destination, **Littlehampton**, is now a seaside resort with pleasant sandy beaches although once an important port and royal dockyard for King Henry VIII. From here the tour moves on to **Worthing**. Royalty made the town fashionable and changed it from small fishing village to stylish resort. The Prince Regent's sister, Princess Amelia, visited the village in 1798 and the differences in character between the Prince and Princess are reflected in the differences between the dashing atmosphere of Brighton and the altogether quieter and more refined Worthing. In 1894 Oscar Wilde wrote *The Importance of Being Earnest* here and the town itself has a small part in the play. As a baby, the hero was found in a handbag and was given the surname Worthing because the man who found him had a first class ticket to Worthing in his pocket at the time.

Unfortunately in the 1850s there was an outbreak of cholera and in the 1890s a typhoid epidemic which, not unnaturally, started a decline in the town's popularity. It was only between the two World Wars that the underlying public health problems were finally solved and this brought about an expansion. Worthing possesses an excellent museum, a section being devoted to Victorian dolls, toys and games and a costume gallery with clothes from the 18th century to modern times. The prehistoric site of Cissbury Ring, three miles north of Worthing on the A24, has been the site of human of activity since Neolithic times. It was a flint mine with shafts descending to a depth of 40 feet and galleries extending along the seams of flint. An Iron Age fort was constructed there in about 250BC, covering an area of about 65 acres. This was abandoned before the arrival of the Romans although again fortified towards the end of Roman occupation, probably against the Saxons.

The old town of **Steyning** is charming with a number of historic buildings. The nearby village of Bramber contains a house said to be the best example of timber framing in Sussex. St Mary's House and Gardens was built by William Waynflete, Bishop of Winchester and founder of Magdalen College, Oxford. The house is renowned for its fine panelled rooms and collections of English furniture, ceramics, manuscripts and dolls.

Moving on, the route arrives in **Washington** and then **Storrington,** with nearby wonderful Parham Park and mansion from the Elizabethan times. **Adversane** and **Billingshurst** are next Finally **Cranleigh,** only 10 miles from the M25, unusually has Canadian maple along the High Street that were planted by Canadian soldiers during World War 1.

## ANTIQUE DEALERS

### HINDHEAD (01428)

**Albany Antiques**, 8-10 London Road, GU26 6AF TEL: 605528 PARKING: Medium OPEN: Mon-Sat 9.30-6 MIN: £10 MAX: £3000 PERIOD: 18th-19th century SPECIALIST: Furniture GENERAL: Brass, china & bric-a-brac etc.

**MJ Bowdery**, 12 London Road, GU26 6AF TEL: 606376, mobile 0374 821444 ASSNS: BADA PARKING: Own carpark OPEN: Mon-Sat 9-1 PERIOD: 18th-early 19th century GENERAL: English & Continental furniture OTHER INFO: Area of oustanding natural beauty, mostly NT.

**Second Hand Rose**, Bramshott Chase (A3), GU26 6DB TEL: 604880 PARKING: Easy OPEN: Mon-Sat 10-5.30 MIN: £10 MAX: £1500 PERIOD: 18th-20th century GENERAL: Georgian, Victorian, Edwardian & 20th century furniture. Pictures, mirrors & metalware OTHER INFO: Good ale & pub grub at the Prince of Wales. Also Hammer Hotel alongside The Devil's Punchbowl.

### HASLEMERE (01428)

**Bow Antiques Ltd**, 6 Petworth Road TEL: 652886 PARKING: Easy OPEN: Mon, Tues, Thurs, Fri 9.30-5, Sat 10-5 MIN: £5 MAX: £3500 PERIOD: 18th-20th century GENERAL: Georgian, Victorian, Edwardian furniture & early 20th century prints.

**Surrey Clocks Centre**, 3 Lower Street, GU27 2NY TEL & FAX: 651313 ASSNS: Antique Clock & Barometer Restoration PARKING: Easy OPEN: 9-5, Wed & Sat 9-1 MIN: £300 MAX: £6000 PERIOD: 18th-19th century SPECIALIST: 200 clocks & barometers.

**Woods Wharf Antiques Market**, 56 High Street, GU27 2LA TEL: 642125 FAX: 725045 PARKING:

Easy OPEN: 9.30-5 MIN: £5 MAX: £900 PERIOD: 19th-20th century GENERAL: General antiques OTHER INFO: Georgian Hotel with good food opposite.

## PETWORTH (01798)

**Masid Amini-Persian Carpet Gallery,** Church House, Church Street, GU28 0AD TEL: 343344 FAX: 342673 ASSNS: LAPADA, PADA PARKING: Easy OPEN: Mon-Sat 9-5 MIN: £100 MAX: £10,000 PERIOD: 18th-20th century SPECIALIST: Persian & Oriental rugs GENERAL: New tribal rugs, kilims, soumacs, carpets, runners.

**Angel Antiques,** Church Street, GU28 0AD TEL: 343306 FAX: 422665 ASSNS: PADA PARKING: Easy OPEN: 10-5.30 MIN: £20 MAX: £6000 PERIOD: 17th-19th century SPECIALIST: Country furniture GENERAL: Blue & white, brass, Staffordshire OTHER INFO: Our shop is located opposite Petworth House with its priceless art collection including Turners.

**The Bacchus Gallery**, Lombard Street, GU28 0AG TEL: 342844 FAX: 342634 OPEN: Mon-Sat 10-1, 2.30-5 MIN: £10 MAX: £5000 PERIOD: 18th-20th century SPECIALIST: Wine related artefacts GENERAL: Glass, books, silver, prints, corkscrews, bin labels, etc (drink related only) OTHER INFO: Goodwood House & Goodwood Races. Welldiggers pub for good food known locally as Testicle Ted's.

**Baskerville Antiques**, Saddler House, Saddlers Row, GU28 0AN TEL: 342067 FAX: 343956 ASSNS: BADA PARKING: Easy OPEN: Mon-Sat 9.30-6 PERIOD: 18th-20th century SPECIALIST: Clocks & barometers GENERAL: Furniture & paintings OTHER INFO: 20th century stock paintings only. Town carpark adjoins our premises. Clock & barometer restoration.

**Lesley Bragge**, Fairfield House, High Street, GU28 0AU TEL: 342324 ASSNS: LAPADA, PADA PARKING: Easy OPEN: Mon-Sat 10-5 MIN: £50 MAX: £5000 PERIOD: 18th-19th century SPECIALIST: Furniture, lighting GENERAL: Silver, prints, porcelain, mainly decorative OTHER INFO: Petworth House.

**Julian Du Cros,** 1 Pound Street, GU28 0DX TEL: 342071 ASSNS: PADA PARKING: Easy OPEN: Mon-Sat 10-5.30 PERIOD: 1660-1900 SPECIALIST: Oak & mahogany English furniture, metalware, Staffordshire pottery GENERAL: Boxes, treen.

**Richard Gardner Antiques,** Millhouse, Market Square, GU28 0AN TEL: 343411 PARKING: Easy OPEN: 7 days 10-5.30 MIN: £20 MAX: £6000 PERIOD: 18th-19th century SPECIALIST: Victorian Staffordshire GENERAL: Furniture, prints, silver, glass, pottery & porcelain.

**Granville Antiques**, High Street, GU28 0AU TEL: 343250 ASSNS: BADA CINOA PARKING: Easy OPEN: Normally Mon-Sat 10-5 but appt advisable MIN: £100 MAX: £10,000 PERIOD: 18th-19th century GENERAL: English & Continental furniture (mainly pre 1840) & selected accessories.

**The Green Man Antiques**, Middle Street, GU28 0BE, TEL: 343080 PARKING: Easy OPEN: Tues-Sat 10-5.30 MIN: £10 MAX: £1000 PERIOD: 17th-20th century SPECIALIST: Old kilims, nomadic & village GENERAL: Country furniture & objects, from UK, Europe & Asia Minor. Naive, rustic & primitive OTHER INFO: I'm a nomadic antique dealer finding & bringing back my purchases however I can!

**Humphry Antiques**

**North Street, GU28 0DD TEL: 343053 ASSNS: BADA, PADA PARKING: Own carpark OPEN: 10-5.30 MIN: £100 MAX: £8000 PERIOD: 17th-18th century SPECIALIST: Early oak furniture, wood carvings, tapestries & objets d'art 14th-18th century OTHER INFO: Petworth with over 20 antique shops & galleries is the centre for antiques in the south and a beautiful medieval market town.**

**John G Morris Ltd**, Market Square, GU28 0AH TEL: 42305 ASSNS: BADA, CINOA PARKING: Easy OPEN: Mon, Tues, Thurs-Sat 9.45-5.30, Weds 9.45-1 MIN: £7 MAX: £25,000 PERIOD: 18th-19th century SPECIALIST: English furniture & associated items.

**Petworth Antique Market**, East Street, GU28 0AB TEL: 342073 PARKING: Own carpark OPEN: Mon-Sat 10-5.30 PERIOD: 17th-20th century SPECIALIST: Antique market with wide range of stock & prices.

**Red Lion Antiques**, New Street, GU28 0AS TEL: 344485 FAX: 342367 ASSNS: PAADA PARKING: Medium OPEN: 10-5.30 MIN: £50 MAX: £10,000 PERIOD: 17th-19th century SPECIALIST: Oak furniture GENERAL: Antiques for the country home.

**Stewart Antiques,** High Street, GU28 0AU TEL:

342136 PARKING: Easy OPEN: 10-5 MIN: £1 MAX: £2000 PERIOD: 19th century SPECIALIST: Victorian stripped pine GENERAL: Pine furniture & kitchenalia.

**JC Tutt Antiques**, Angel Street, GU28 0BQ TEL: 343221 ASSNS: PAADA PARKING: Easy OPEN: Mon-Sat 10-5 MIN: £30 MAX: £8000 PERIOD: 18th-19th century SPECIALIST: Mahogany GENERAL: Furniture, smalls, china.

**TG Wilkinson Antiques Ltd**, Lombard Street, GU28 0AG TEL: 344443 ASSNS: BADA PARKING: Easy OPEN: Mon-Sat 10-5.30 MIN: £50 MAX: £20,000 PERIOD: 17th-18th century SPECIALIST: English & Continental furniture GENERAL: Pictures, decorative items, mirrors etc.

## MIDHURST (01798)

**Eagle House Antiques,** Market Square, GU29 9NJ TEL: 812718 PARKING: Easy OPEN: Mon-Sat 9.30-5 MIN: £1 MAX: £2000 PERIOD: 19th century GENERAL: Small furniture, porcelain, silver, metalware, etc OTHER INFO: Situated in 16th century part of town with 2 good quality hotels, many places to eat.

**Foord Antiques**, P.O. Box 14, GU29 0BS TEL: 867351 ASSNS: LAPADA PARKING: Own carpark OPEN: By appt MIN: £25 MAX: £10,000 PERIOD: 18th-early 19th century SPECIALIST: Furniture & boxes GENERAL: Treen, metal & decorative items.

**West Street Antiques & Presents,** West Street TEL: 815232 OPEN: 9.30-1, 2-4.30, closed Wed pm PERIOD: 19th-20th century OTHER INFO: Within a stones throw of famous Spread Eagle Hotel.

## COCKING (01730)

**The Victorian Brass Bedstead Company,** Hoe Copse, GU29 0HL TEL: 812287 PARKING: Own carpark OPEN: Flexible, 7 days by appt MIN: £275 MAX: £2500 PERIOD: 19th century SPECIALIST: 4 poster bedsteads, iron, brass, brass & iron bedsteads.

## CHICHESTER (01243)

**The Delightful Muddle,** 82 Fishbourne Road West, PO19 3JL PARKING: Easy OPEN: Tues-Sat 10-5 MIN: £1 MAX: £100 PERIOD: 19th-20th century GENERAL: Glass, old lace, linen, period clothing, bric a brac OTHER INFO: Near Fishbourne Roman palace & Bosham where King Canute's 8 year old daughter is buried in the church.

**Gems Antiques**, 39 West Street, PO19 1RP TEL: 786173 PARKING: Easy OPEN: Mon-Sat 10-1, 2-5.30 MIN: £5 MAX: £2000 PERIOD: 18th-19th century SPECIALIST: Staffordshire figures GENERAL: Furniture, glass, china OTHER INFO: Close to harbour & cathedral. Next door to messy antique emporium!

**Peter Hancock**, 40-41 West Street, PO19 1RP TEL: 786173 FAX: 778865 PARKING: Easy OPEN: Mon-Sat 10-1, 2-5.30 MIN: £1 MAX: £2500 PERIOD: 18th-20th century SPECIALIST: Furniture, silver, scientific instruments, books plus wide selection of general antiques OTHER INFO: Good pub, Indian restaurant & Trust House Forte in same street. Next door to a pretty antique shop.

**Heritage Antiques**, 77d St Pancras, PO19 4LS TEL: 783796 PARKING: Easy OPEN: Mon-Sat 9-5.30 MIN: £3 MAX: £1500 PERIOD: 18th-20th century GENERAL: Antique & older style furniture & other interesting items OTHER INFO: Goodwood House & Park, Fishbourne Roman Villa, Weald & Downland Open Air Museum.

**St Pancras Antiques**, 150 St Pancras, PO19 1SH TEL: 787645 PARKING: Easy OPEN: 9.30-5 MIN: £10 MAX: £3000 PERIOD: 17th-19th century SPECIALIST: Arms & armour, furniture, fine porcelain, medals, early militaria OTHER INFO: Shop is 16th-17th century. Festival Theatre.

## BIRDHAM (01243)

**Birdham Antiques,** The Old Bird & Ham, Main Road, PO20 7HS TEL: 511341 PARKING: Own carpark OPEN: Mon-Sat 9-5, Sun by appt MIN: £20 MAX: £2500 PERIOD: 17th-19th century GENERAL: Country furniture, treen, metalwork & pottery OTHER INFO: Excellent pub, The Lamb.

## HUNSTON (01243)

**Antiques, J & M Riley,** Frensham House, PO20 5NX. TEL: 782660 PARKING: Easy OPEN: 9.30-5.30 by appt MIN: £200 MAX: £5000 PERIOD: 18th-19th century SPECIALIST: Furniture GENERAL: Oils, copper, mirrors OTHER INFO: Spotted Cow pub & restaurant, Hunston Mill, 'Hunston Canal' painted by Turner, in the Tate.

## BOGNOR REGIS (01243)

**Gough Bros Art Shop & Gallery**, 71 High Street, PO21 1RZ TEL: 823773 ASSNS: FATG PARK-

ING: Easy OPEN: Mon-Sat 9-5, Wed AM only MIN: £50 MAX: £950 PERIOD: 19th-20th century GENERAL: Watercolours, oils, drawings, miniatures, cartoons, OTHER INFO: Shop tucked away behind The Unicorn off the High Street towards seafront. We also sell art materials & are framers & picture restorers.

## ARUNDEL (01903)

**Armstrong-Davis Gallery**, The Square, BN18 9AB TEL: 882752 PARKING: Own carpark OPEN: Mon-Sat 10-6 PERIOD: 17th-20th century SPECIALIST: International sculpture, bronzes, fountains, statuary etc OTHER INFO: Arundel Castle, Wildfowl Trust, Norfolk Arms Hotel.

**Baynton-Williams**, 37a High Street, BN18 9AG TEL & FAX: 883588 PARKING: Easy OPEN: Mon-Sat 10-6 MIN: £5 MAX: £5000 PERIOD: 17th-19th century SPECIALIST: Maps & prints OTHER INFO: Arundel Castle, very attractive town, many dealers in 'small' antiques, beautiful surrounding country

**Richard Davidson Antiques**, Romsey House, 51 Maltravers Street BN18 9BQ TEL: 883141 FAX: 883914 ASSNS: BADA PARKING: Medium OPEN: By appt MIN: £200 MAX: £25,000 SPECIALIST: Late 18th-early 19th century furniture GENERAL: Paintings, decorative items.

**Pat Golding**, 6 Castle Mews, Tarrant Street TEL: 883980 PARKING: Easy OPEN: Mon-Sat 10-1, 2-5 MIN: £5 MAX: £1000 PERIOD: 18th-20th century GENERAL: Ceramics, pottery, glass OTHER INFO: Arundel Castle & Cathedral closeby. Wild Fowl Trust 1 mile.

**Serendipity Antiques**, 27 Tarrant Street, BN18 9DG TEL: 882047 PARKING: Medium OPEN: Mon-Sat 10-1, 2-5.30 MIN: £5 MAX: £650+ PERIOD: 17th-19th century SPECIALIST: Early maps & engravings GENERAL: Some etchings, watercolours & oils.

**Spencer Swaffer**, 30 High Street, BN18 9AB TEL: 882132 FAX: 884564 ASSNS: LAPADA PARKING: Easy OPEN: 9-6, but appts welcome anytime MIN: £10 MAX: £15,000 PERIOD: 17th-20th century SPECIALIST: Decorative antiques GENERAL: English china, glass, wide stock of accessories, pine, bamboo, English furniture OTHER INFO: In top 5 of England's leading decorative antique dealers.

**Stuart Thompson**, 39 Tarrant Street, BN18 9DG TEL: 883796 FAX: 884491 PARKING: Medium OPEN: 8.30-5.30 MIN: £5 MAX: £1000+ PERIOD: 17th-20th century SPECIALIST: Walking sticks & canes GENERAL: Walking stick stands OTHER INFO: Arundel is a maze of antique shops & pubs.

**Treasure House Antiques & Saturday Market**, 31 High Street, BN18 9AG TEL: 883101 PARKING: Easy OPEN: All Sats, daily in summer, variable in winter PERIOD: 19th-20th century GENERAL: Wide range of mainly smalls, veritable treasure trove OTHER INFO: Opposite Toy & Military Museum & Arundel Teddy Bears. Beside Swan Hotel.

**Whitehouse Antique Interiors,** 4 Tarrant Square, Tarrant Street, BN18 9DE TEL: 882443 PARKING: Easy OPEN: Daily 10-4.30 PERIOD: Mixed GENERAL: A mixture of traditional styles & varying periods.

## LITTLEHAMPTON (01903)

**The Round Pond**, Faux Cottage, 4a Selborne Road, BN17 5NN TEL: 714261 PARKING: Easy OPEN: By appt MIN: £50 MAX: £3500 PERIOD: 19th-20th century SPECIALIST: Vintage model pond yachts & model boats.

## WORTHING (01903)

**Cheriton Antiques,** 21 New Broadway, Tarring Road, BN11 4HP TEL: 235463 & 0850 224280 ASSNS: LAPADA PARKING: Medium OPEN: Thurs-Sat 9.30-5.30 MIN: £250 MAX: £5000 PERIOD: 18th-19th century GENERAL: General antiques & 20th century lighting.

**Geoffrey Godden**, c/o 19a Crescent Road, BN11 1RL TEL: 235958 ASSNS: BADA PARKING: Own carpark OPEN: By appt only SPECIALIST: Ceramic consultant only.

**Rathbone Law**, 7-9 The Arcade TEL: 200274 ASSNS: NAS PARKING: Medium OPEN: Mon, Tues, Thurs-Sat 10-5 MIN: £50 PERIOD: 19th-20th century SPECIALIST: Diamond merchants, largest & most varied stock of emerald set rings in Sussex GENERAL: Teddybears, dolls, antiques jewellery, silver, porcelain, glass OTHER INFO: Character sea-side town with beautifully cultivated bowling parks, old style cinema & lively provincial theatre nestled between shingle beaches & the rolling South Downs.

**Steyne Antique Galleries**, 29 Brighton Road, BN11

3EF TEL: 200079 PARKING: Medium OPEN: Tues, Thurs-Sun 9.30-5.30, Weds 9.30-1 MIN: £5 MAX: £2500 PERIOD: 18th-20th century SPECIALIST: Walnut, rosewood & mahogany furniture GENERAL: General antiques

**Robert Warner & Sons Ltd**, 1-13 South Farm Road TEL: 232710 FAX: 217515 PARKING: Own carpark OPEN: 9.3-5, Wed AM only PERIOD: 19th-20th century GENERAL: 30,000 sq ft shipping furniture, bric-a-brac OTHER INFO: Warehouse adjacent Orme Road.

**Wilsons Antiques**, 57-59 Broadwater Road, BN14 8AH TEL: 202059 ASSNS: LAPADA PARKING: Own carpark OPEN: Mon-Sat 10-5 MIN: £10 MAX: £15,000 PERIOD: 18th-20th century SPECIALIST: English furniture & fine art including, Edwardian furniture, oils & watercolours OTHER INFO: Main A24, 500 yds south of Broadwater Church, 7 showrooms.

## STEYNING (01903)

**David Fileman Antiques**, Squirrels, Bayards, Horsham Road, BN44 3AA TEL: 813229 PARKING: Own carpark OPEN: Any time MIN: £50 MAX: £20,000 SPECIALIST: 18th-19th century glass, chandeliers, table lights, wall lights, lustres. table glass, collectors glass, French paperweights. Restoration of above OTHER INFO: Brambe Castle, old house, cottages.

## WASHINGTON (01903)

**Chanctonbury Antiques**, Clematis Cottage, School Lane, RH20 4AP TEL: 892233 PARKING: Easy OPEN: By appt MIN: £3 MAX: £500 PERIOD: 18th-19th century SPECIALIST: English pottery & porcelain GENERAL: Needlework, small interesting items, treen, small furniture OTHER INFO: Good pub lunch next door.

## STORRINGTON (01903)

**Stable Antiques,** 46 West Street, RH20 4EE TEL: 740555 FAX: 740441 PARKING: Easy OPEN: 7 days 10-6 MIN: 50p MAX: £2500 PERIOD: 17th-20th century GENERAL: Antiques, furniture, bric a brac OTHER INFO: Numerous stall holders on 2 floors. The premises are more than 200 years old and were the stables for adjoining house. Many of the original features have been retained along with mangers, cobbled floors & central courtyard.

## ADVERSANE (01403)

**Bradley Antiques & Orchard Market**, The Little Shop, Old House Antique Centre, RH14 9TT TEL: 782186 PARKING: Own carpark OPEN: 7 days 10-6 MIN: £15 MAX: £2000 PERIOD: 18th-20th century SPECIALIST: Gramophones, pestles & mortars GENERAL: Furniture, metalware OTHER INFO: 30 dealers, tearooms & lunches on site. 1 mile from Sotheby's at Summer Place.

## BILLINGSHURST (01403)

**Tom Burton & Rod Johnston**, Great Grooms Antique Centre, Parbrook TEL: 786202 PARKING: Own carpark OPEN: Seven days 9.30-5.30 MIN: £50 MAX: £500 PERIOD: 19th century SPECIALIST: Ceramics, mainly ironstone, Blue & White pottery and some porcelain.

**Great Grooms Antique Centre**, Great Grooms, Parbrook, RH14 9EU TEL: 786202 PARKING: Own carpark OPEN: 9.30-5.30 except Thurs 9.30-8 & Sun 10.30-4.30 MIN: £4 MAX: £10,000 PERIOD: 18th-20th century SPECIALIST: Variety of specialist dealers in English & Continental furniture, pictures, silver, plate, pottery, porcelain, jewellery, treen, etc OTHER INFO: 1 mile from Sotheby's at Summers Place, Billingshurst, opposite The Gables restaurant.

**Wakelin & Linfield**, P.O.Box 48, RH14 0YZ TEL: 700004 FAX: 700004 ASSNS: BADA, LAPADA PARKING: Own carpark OPEN: By appt MIN: £500 MAX: £50,000 PERIOD: 17th-19th century SPECIALIST: English & Continental furniture and decorative accessories from 15th-19th centuries.

## CRANLEIGH (01483)

**Barbara Rubenstein Fine Art**, Smithwood House, Smithwood Common, GU6 8QY TEL: 267969 FAX: 267575 PARKING: Own carpark OPEN: By appt MIN: £250 MAX: £5000 PERIOD: 19th-20th century GENERAL: Watercolours & oils OTHER INFO: Stock housed in a Georgian house amid beautiful countryside.

## South-Western Home Counties

Starting in Surrey, then continuing through Hampshire and Berkshire, this tour passes through market towns, pretty villages and the ultra modern town of Basingstoke.

**Woking**, the first stop, is situated on the disused Basingstoke Canal. Old Woking, once a market town, has several notable houses in the high street including the 17th century manor house. Next, **Ripley** is a village with many half-timbered houses and was on the coaching route to Portsmouth. The Royal Horticultural Society's Garden of Wisley lies a mile north east. 250 acres of gardens provide a feast for the eyes in all seasons. Detouring to the lovely **Shere** and then **Abinger Hammer** which lies in wooded country, the name comes from earlier local blacksmiths. The effigy of one hangs out high over the A25 for all to see. The next stop is busy **Guildford**. Standing on an ancient route crossing the River Wey, it has been important since early times. The town prospered in the 16th century because of the local weaving industry. The High Street has a variety of architecture, gabled overhung, timber-framed, Georgian and Victorian. Abbot's Hospital, an almshouse founded in 1619, has a brick entrance tower with corner turrets in the Tudor style, leading to a courtyard. The newly-restored Guildford House, in the High Street, dates from 1660 and contains a fine carved staircase, plaster ceilings and wrought-iron window fittings.

The route continues to **Bramley** and then **Godalming**. A market town set in a valley formed by River Wey, Godalming grew mainly along the route through the valley. In the early Middle Ages it was important as the centre of a large manor and parish with the town receiving a charter for a market in 1300. During the 16th century weaving became an important industry in the area and Godalming became the chief textile town in Surrey. A local attraction is the Pepperpot, a former town hall, built in 1814 and which now houses a local museum.

There is an unusual National Trust property in this area: the River Wey and Godalming Navigation which extends for nearly 20 miles from Godalming to the River Thames. From 1635 to 1653 Sir Richard Weston, the builder and original owner of the nearby mansion of Sutton Place, supervised the canalisation of the River Wey. He constructed 15 miles of navigation consisting of building 12 locks and digging ten miles of canal. In 1760 it was extended upstream by four miles to Godalming. The navigation was used principally to transport timber and other agricultural produce. The opening of the railways brought about a decline and it is now used for recreation.

**Badshot Lea** is really right on the southern edge of the military town of **Aldershot** which was only a quiet hamlet surrounded by heathland until the mid 19th century. Now much of the British Army is based here and army life is the main theme of several museums. **Farnborough**, (Hampshire), just to the north has been home to the Royal Aircraft Establishment since 1906 and the internationally known Farnborough Air Festival. **Farnham** has many well-preserved Tudor and Georgian buildings and the 12th century castle was built by Henry of Blois, Bishop of Winchester. The town led a relatively peaceful existence until action in the Civil War. Nearby **Odiham** also had a castle one mile west but little remains of this early 13th century edifice that was besieged by the French in 1216. The town itself contains predominantly Georgian buildings although there are some earlier examples. The George Inn dates from 1540 and the priory is 15th to 17th century. In the churchyard of the 14th century church stands a pest house, a reminder of the Great Plague of 1665.

**Basingstoke** gives the overwhelming impression of a modern commercial and industrial city. However, there are some remnants here of a very old settlement. The Church of St. Michael and All Angels has parts dating from the 12th, 15th and 16th centuries. Its 16th century stained glass came from the 13th century Chapel of the Holy Ghost, the remains of which may be seen near the railway station. Basing House, 2 miles out, was once the largest private house in England and owned by William Paulet, first Marquess of Winchester, Tudor Lord Treasurer of England under three monarchs. Its destruction came during the Civil War when after a two year siege by Parliamentary forces, it finally fell to Oliver Cromwell himself. Now the ruins cover approximately 10 acres. There are Norman earthworks, remains of Tudor kitchens and various of other structures including a 300 foot long tunnel.

**Oakley** village is just east and then, enroute to **Halfway,** the A339 passes Greenham Common Airbase,

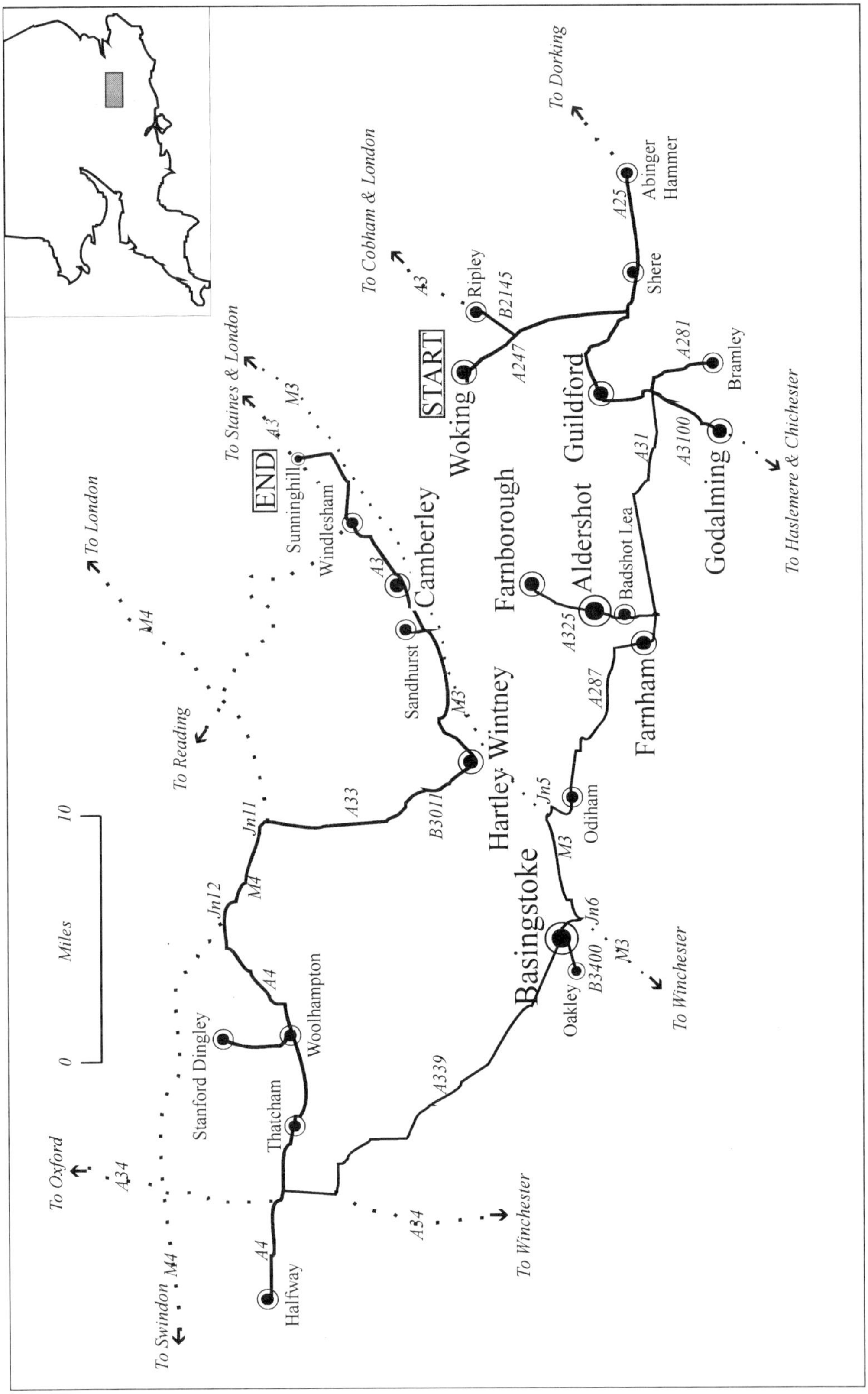
START
Woking
Ripley
B2145
A247
A3
To Cobham & London
Guildford
Shere
Abinger Hammer
A25
To Dorking
A281
Bramley
A3100
Godalming
To Haslemere & Chichester
A31
Farnborough
Aldershot
Badshot Lea
A325
Farnham
A287
Camberley
Windlesham
Sunninghill
END
To Staines & London
M3
Sandhurst
Hartley Wintney
Jn5
Odiham
M3
Basingstoke
Jn6
B3400
Oakley
To Winchester
B3011
A33
Jn11
M4
Jn12
A4
Woolhampton
Stanford Dingley
Thatcham
A339
A34
To Winchester
A34
To Oxford
A4
Halfway
M4
To Swindon
To Reading
To London
Miles
0
10

now inactive. However during the 1980's it was anything but as the U.S.A.F were said to have sited Cruise missiles there. Protesters, almost exclusively women after the first few days, laid seige to the base for years even after the missiles were removed. **Thatcham** in the Kennet valley is truly ancient since remains of settlements from 5000BC have been found. Here may be seen a 14th century chapel, converted into a school in 1707, and a church with a Norman doorway and a pinnacled tower from the 15th century. **Woolhampton** lies two miles east and then, due north on country lanes via Chapel Row, is **Stanford Dingley**. If time permits a visit to Englefield House, two miles east of Chapel Row gives spectacular views. There is also a deer park and seven acres of woodland plus a water garden

18 miles south east, **Hartley Wintney** is set amidst nice heathland and at one time its business and club airfield, Blackbushe, had been proposed for development as London's second airport. Nearby the 18th century West Green House is lovely and once was owned by General Hawley. Possibly George I's unacknowledge son, he became known as The Hangman for his brutal repressions after the 1745 rebellion. **Sandhurst** has the National Army Museum, and the world famous Royal Military Academy.

This tour finishes heading back to London with visits to three towns all on and around the A30: **Camberley, Windlesham** and then **Sunninghill**, five miles short of the M25/M3 interchange.

# ANTIQUE DEALERS

## WOKING (01483)

**Chattels Antiques**, 156 High Street, Old Woking TEL: 771310 PARKING: Own carpark OPEN: Mon-Fri 9-5 MIN: £10 MAX: £10,000 PERIOD: 18th-19th century SPECIALIST: Longcase clocks, barometers GENERAL: 19th century furniture OTHER INFO: 30 years experience in the restoration of the 17th century clock case.

**Wych House Antiques**, Wych Hill, GU22 0EV TEL: 764636 PARKING: Easy OPEN: 9-6 MIN: £5 MAX: £5,000 PERIOD: 18th-20th century SPECIALIST: Georgian & Victorian furniture.

## RIPLEY (01483)

**Antique Tea Pot,** The Old Poste, High Street, GU23 6AQ TEL: 224078 & 223674 PARKING: Easy OPEN: 10-5, closed Sun, Mon & Wed pm MIN: £10 MAX: £1000 PERIOD: 19th century SPECIALIST: Victorian stipped pine GENERAL: Copper, brass, farm implements, kitchenalia, etc.

**Baker's,** 42 Arnold Road, GU21 5JU TEL: 767425 PARKING: Easy OPEN: Wed-Sat 9-5 GENERAL: General antiques.

**Cedar House Gallery**
**GU23 6AE TEL: 211221 PARKING: Easy OPEN: 7 days ring bell (resident) MIN: £50 MAX: £20,000 PERIOD: 19th (mainly) & early 20th century SPECIALIST: Decorative oils & large oils GENERAL: 19th century oils & watercolours of fine quality OTHER INFO: Cedar House was a coaching inn in the 17th century (built 1580). Ripley was the first stopping place on the London - Portsmouth coaching run. Attractive 18th-19th century village, good pubs & walks. Near Grade I 19th century landscape garden of Painshill, short drive to Watts Gallery.**

**J Hartley Antiques Ltd**, 186 High Street, GU23 6BB TEL: 224318 ASSNS: LAPADA PARKING: Easy OPEN: Mon-Fri 8.45-5.45, Sat 9.45-4.45 MIN: £100 MAX: £3500 PERIOD: 18th-19th century GENERAL: English mahogany furniture, some walnut, oak etc OTHER INFO: Possibly England's largest remaining unenclosed village green. Lord Nelson & Lady Hamilton frequented the nearby Talbot Hotel. Pastimes was a watering stop for long distance stage coaches.

**Manor House Antiques**, High Street, GU23 6AF TEL: 225350 PARKING: Easy OPEN: Mon, Tues, Thurs-Sat 10-5.30, Weds 10-1 MIN: £2 MAX: £10,000 PERIOD: 17th-19th century SPECIALIST: Early oak, brass, copper GENERAL: Oak, walnut, mahogany, rosewood, British and Continental metalware, clocks.

**Ripley Antiques**, 67 High Street, GU23 6AN TEL: 224981 FAX: 224333 ASSNS: LAPADA PARKING: Easy OPEN: 9.30-5.30 MIN: £50 MAX: £10,000 PERIOD: 18th-19th century SPECIALIST: English & Continental furniture, decorative items, chandeliers, mirrors etc.

**Sage Antiques & Interiors**, High Street, GU23 6BB TEL: 224396 FAX: 211996 PARKING: Easy OPEN: Mon-Sat 9.30-5.30 MIN: £100 MAX: £10,000 PERIOD: 17th-19th century GENERAL: Period furniture pre-1830, mahogany, walnut, oak, country furniture, oil paintings, silver + plate, china OTHER INFO: 5 other quality antique shops with large showrooms.

**Anthony Welling Antiques**, Broadway Barn, High Street, GU23 6AQ TEL: 225384 ASSNS: BADA PARKING: Easy OPEN: Mon-Sat 9.30-1, 2-5.30 MIN: £500 MAX: £6000 SPECIALIST: Period oak & country furniture 1600-1830, metals pre 1840 OTHER INFO: 5 village pubs & 3 Egon Ronay recommended restaurants.

## SHERE (01483)

**Shere Antique Centre**, Middle Street, GU5 9HF TEL: 202846 PARKING: Easy OPEN: Mon-Sat 10-5, Sun 11-5 MIN: £10 PERIOD: 18th-19th century GENERAL: Showrooms on 2 floors, 12 dealers in china, silver, furniture. Dateline 1930s OTHER INFO: 16th century building with a ghost.

**Yesterday's Pine**, Gomshall Lane, GU5 9HE TEL: 203198 PARKING: Easy OPEN: Mon-Sat 9-5 MIN: £35 MAX: £1500 PERIOD: 19th century SPECIALIST: Victorian pine OTHER INFO: Next to excellent B&B & restaurant.

## ABINGER HAMMER (01306)

**Abinger Bazaar (Junk Antiques)**, Guildford Road TEL: 730756 PARKING: Own carpark OPEN: Thurs, Sat, Sun 11.30-5.30 MIN: £1 MAX: £300 PERIOD: 19th-20th century SPECIALIST: Fireplaces & grates plus accessories GENERAL: China, glass, brass, silver + plate, bric-a-brac OTHER INFO: Next to Frog Island vegetarian restaurant.

## GUILDFORD (01483)

**The Antique Centre**, 22 Haydon Place TEL: 67817 PARKING: Easy OPEN: Tues, Thurs, Fri 10-4, Sat 10-4.30 MIN: £1 PERIOD: 17th-20th century SPECIALIST: 7 separate shops dealing in silver, jewellery, glass, pottery, lace, oriental Devonware & collectables OTHER INFO: Cathedral, historic High Street, castle & gardens.

**Denning Antiques**, 1 Chapel Street, GU4 8AD TEL: 39595 PARKING: Easy OPEN: 10-5 MIN: £5 MAX: £1000 PERIOD: 19th-20th century SPECIALIST: Silver, jewellery GENERAL: Lace, linen, collectables OTHER INFO: Close to High Street in fascinating side street.

**Horological Workshops,** 204 Worplesdon Road, GU2 6UY TEL: 586496 ASSNS: BADA PARKING: Own carpark OPEN: Mon-Fri 8.30-5.30, Sat 9-12.30 MIN: £500 MAX: No limit SPECIALIST: Clocks of all types, eg longcase, bracket, skeleton, marine chronometers, Vienna regulators, etc.

**Charles W Traylen**, Castle House, 49-50 Quarry Street, GU1 3UA TEL: 572424 FAX: 450048 ASSNS: ABA PARKING: Difficult OPEN: Tues-Sat 9-1 & 2-5 MIN: £1 MAX: £10,000 PERIOD: 17th-20th century SPECIALIST: Fine books & bound sets.

## BRAMLEY (01483)

**Drummonds of Bramley Architectural Antiques Ltd**, Birtley Farm, GU5 0LA TEL: 898766 Fax: 894393 PARKING: Own carpark OPEN: Mon-Fri 9-6, Sat 9.30-5, Sun 10-5 MIN: £10 MAX: £50,000 PERIOD: 17th-19th century SPECIALIST: Architectural antiques, antique garden statuary & furniture GENERAL: Fully restored period bathrooms & many materials for restoration.

**Memories Antiques**, High Street, GU5 0HB TEL: 892205 PARKING: Easy OPEN: Mon-Sat 10-5 MIN: £1+ PERIOD: 18th-20th century GENERAL: 6 dealers with furniture, silver, brass, copper, glass, china, lace, old pine, kitchenalia, bygones, collectables OTHER INFO: Good trade call.

## GODALMING (01483)

**Cry For The Moon**, 31 High Street, GU7 1AU

TEL: 426201 FAX: 860117 PARKING: Easy OPEN: Mon-Sat 9.30-5.30 MIN: £50 MAX: £10,000 PERIOD: 19th-20th century SPECIALIST: Jewellery & silver GENERAL: Objets d'art, paintings, watches.

**Heath-Bullock**, 8 Meadrow, GU7 3HN TEL: 422562 FAX: 426077 ASSNS: BADA PARKING: Own carpark OPEN: Mon-Sat 10-1, 2-4 MIN: £500 MAX: £10,000 PERIOD: 18th-19th century GENERAL: English & Continental furniture 1650-1903 OTHER INFO: Godalming Museum, Inn-on-the-Lake Hotel, General Oglethorpe (founder of the State of Georgia) lived here.

**Ivelet Books Ltd**, Church Street Bookshop, 26 Church Street, GU7 1EW TEL: 418878 FAX: 418656 ASSNS: PBFA PARKING: Medium OPEN: Mon-Sat 10.30-5.30 MIN: £1 MAX: £3000 PERIOD: 18th-20th century SPECIALIST: Books on architecture & interiors, gardening, natural history, topography OTHER INFO: The heart of Lutyens/Jekull country (Munstead Wood nearby), a few miles from RHS gardens, Wisley.

**The Olde Curiosity Shoppe**, 99 High Street, GU7 1AQ TEL: 415889 PARKING: Easy OPEN: Mon-Sat 10-5 MIN: £1 MAX: £300 PERIOD: 19th-20th century GENERAL: China, silver, plate, jewellery.

## BADSHOT LEA (01252)

**Casque-Gauntlet Militaria,** 55-59 Badshot Lea Road, GU9 9LP TEL: 20745 PARKING: Medium OPEN: 10-5.30 MIN: 50p MAX: £2600 SPECIALIST: Militaria from 15th century to modern day.

## ALDERSHOT (01252)

**House of Christian**, 5 Vale Road, Ash Vale, GU12 5HH TEL: 314478 PARKING: Medium OPEN: Mon-Sat 10-5.30 MIN: £5 MAX: £1500 PERIOD: 19th-20th century SPECIALIST: Pine furniture GENERAL: Old, new & made up pine furniture. Occasionally old mahogany & oak furniture, small pine items. Brass, china, copper etc.

## FARNBOROUGH (01252)

**Martin & Parke**, 97 Lynchford Road TEL: 515311 PARKING: Easy OPEN: Mon-Fri 9-5, Sat 9-4 MIN: £5 MAX: £1000 PERIOD: 18th-20th century GENERAL: Shipping goods, Edwardian, Victorian, period.

**The Trading Post,** Opp. The Depot, Solartron Road, GU14 7QL TEL: 372737 FAX: 372717 PARKING: Own carpark OPEN: Mon-Sat 10-6, Sun 10-4 MIN: £5 MAX: £400 PERIOD: 19th-20th century OTHER INFO: Antiques & crafts centre & specialist retail shopping, coffee shop housed in converted 18,000 sq ft warehouse.

## FARNHAM (01252)

**Annies Antiques**, 1 Ridgeway Parade, Frensham Road (A287) TEL: 713447 & 723217 PARKING: Own carpark area OPEN: Mon-Sat 9.30-5.30, Fri 10.30 start, & by appt MIN: £1 MAX: £3000 PERIOD: 19th-20th century GENERAL: General antiques OTHER INFO: A browsing disorganised shop, never know what you may find under a table or in the cellar.

**Bourne Mill Antiques**, 39-43 Guildford Road, GU9 9PY TEL: 716663 PARKING: Own carpark OPEN: Seven days 10-5 MIN: £1 MAX: £3000 PERIOD: 18th-20th century GENERAL: Bric-a-brac, pine, antique furniture, garden stock, tea rooms, tapestries, lights, books OTHER INFO: Bush Hotel, Bishops Table, Farnham Castle, all in town centre.

**Childhood Memories**, 27a South Street, GU9 7QU TEL: 724475 PARKING: Own carpark OPEN: Mon-Sat 9.30-5 MIN: £5 MAX: £2000 PERIOD: 19th-20th century SPECIALIST: Antique teddy bears, dolls, toys, games.

**Farnham Antique Centre**, 27 South Street, GU9 7QU TEL: 724475 PARKING: Own carpark OPEN: Mon-Sat 9.30-5 MIN: £5 MAX: £2000 PERIOD: 18th-20th century SPECIALIST: Clocks, silver, furniture, porcelain, jewellery.

**The Packhorse Antique Centre,** Tongham Road, Runfold GU10 1PQ TEL: 783863 FAX: 783876 PARKING: Own carpark OPEN: 7 days 10.30-5.30 GENERAL: General antiques OTHER INFO: Restaurant, WCs, listed buildings, 20,000 sq ft.

**Karel Weijand**, Lion & Lamb Courtyard, GU9 7LL TEL: 726215 ASSNS: LAPADA PARKING: Own carpark OPEN: Mon-Sat 9.30-5.30 MIN: £45 MAX: £30,000+ PERIOD: 19th-20th century SPECIALIST: Antique & decorative GENERAL: Oriental carpets & rugs OTHER INFO: The largest selection of oriental carpets outside London.

## ODIHAM (01256)

**Monaltrie Antiques,** 76 High Street, RG25 1LN TEL & FAX: 702660 PARKING: Easy OPEN: Tues, Thurs, Fri 10-12.30, 2.30-4, Wed & Sat 10-12.30 MIN: £50 PERIOD: 19th century SPECIAL-

IST: Small furniture, brass & copper GENERAL: Silver, general antiques.

**Odiham Gallery**, 78 High Street TEL: 703415 PARKING: Easy OPEN: Mon-Sat 9.30-5.30 MIN: £100 PERIOD: 19th-20th century SPECIALIST: Room sized decorative carpets GENERAL: Antique rugs, carpets, kilims & runners OTHER INFO: Good restaurant opposite - La Foret (French).

## BASINGSTOKE (01256)

**Squirrel Collectors Centre**, 9a New Street, RG21 1DF TEL: 464885 PARKING: Medium OPEN: Mon-Sat 10-5.30 Wide price range PERIOD: 19th-20th century SPECIALIST: Antique & modern silver, gold & silver jewellery GENERAL: Small antiques, books, old postcards, dolls houses furniture, prints, dolls, toy cars, collectables OTHER INFO: Basingstoke mainly pedestrianised with good facilities, New Concert Hall, theatre etc.

## OAKLEY (01256)

**EH Hutchins**, 48 Pardown, RG23 7DZ TEL: 780494 PARKING: Own carpark OPEN: Mon-Sat 8-5 MIN: £30 MAX: £1000 PERIOD: 18th-19th century GENERAL: All types of furniture.

## HALFWAY (01488)

**Walker & Walker**, Halfway Manor TEL & FAX: 658693 ASSNS: TVADA PARKING: Easy OPEN: By appt MIN: £100 MAX: £100,000 PERIOD: 18th-19th century SPECIALIST: Fine barometers OTHER INFO: Restoration undertaken.

## THATCHAM (01635)

**Richard Kimbell Ltd**, Country Gardens, Turnpike Road, RG13 3AN TEL: 874822 FAX: 874388 PARKING: Own carpark OPEN: Seven days 9-6 MIN: £1 MAX: £3,000 PERIOD: 19th century SPECIALIST: Antique & reproduction pine country furniture and crafts.

## WOOLHAMPTON (01734)

**The Old Bakery Antiques**, RG7 5RE TEL: 712116 PARKING: Easy OPEN: Tues, Thurs-Sat 9-5.30 MIN: £10 MAX: £600 PERIOD: 18th-20th century SPECIALIST: Furniture GENERAL: Country items & collectables.

## STANFORD DINGLEY (01734)

**Eliot Antiques**, RG7 6LX TEL: 744649, 744346 PARKING: Easy OPEN: Mon-Sat 10.30-1 or by appt PERIOD: 18th-19th century SPECIALIST: 18th century English enamel boxes GENERAL: Porcelain OTHER INFO: Royal Oak, Yattendon, hotel & good food 2 miles from shop.

## HARTLEY WINTNEY (01252)

**Nicholas Abbott**, High Street, RG27 0RF TEL: 842365 PARKING: Easy OPEN: Mon-Sat 9.30-5.30 MIN: £50 MAX: £10,000 PERIOD: 17th-19th century SPECIALIST: English furniture 1600-1830 GENERAL: Furniture OTHER INFO: Stratfield Saye (House of Duke of Wellington) 5 miles. The Vyne (17th century country house) 10 miles.

**Airedale Antiques**, c/o Deva Antiques, High Street. TEL: 843538 FAX: 842946 PARKING: Easy OPEN: Mon-Sat 9-5.30 MIN: £10 MAX: £6000 PERIOD: 17th-19th century SPECIALIST: Country furniture GENERAL: Furniture, treen, metalware.

**Andersons,** High Street, RG27 8NY TEL: 845499 ASSNS: LAPADA PARKING: Own carpark OPEN: Mon-Sat 10-5 MIN: £100 MAX: £15,000 PERIOD: 18th-19th century GENERAL: Period & decorative furniture & accessories.

**Antique House**, 22 High Street, RG27 8NY TEL: 844499 FAX 844499 PARKING: Easy OPEN: Mon-Sat 9.30-6 or by appt MIN: £50 MAX: £5000 PERIOD: 18th-20th century SPECIALIST: Dining room & library furniture GENERAL: Mainly Georgian mahogany, rosewood & walnut & some Edwardian inlaid furniture OTHER INFO: The Lamb (hotel & restaurant), Stilton Dish & The Shoulder of Mutton , The Cricketers.

**Cedar Antiques Ltd**, High Street, RG27 8HL TEL: 843252 FAX: 845235 ASSNS: LAPADA PARKING: Easy opposite OPEN: Mon-Sat 9-5 MIN: £25 MAX: £15,000 PERIOD: 17th-19th century SPECIALIST: French provincial country furniture & accessories. Non-period decorative furnishings but in the country style GENERAL: Large stock of good English 18th century country furniture.

**Brian Clisby Antique Clocks**, Andwell Antiques, The Row TEL: 716436 PARKING: Own carpark OPEN: Mon-Sat 9.30-5.30 MIN: £300 MAX: £15,000 PERIOD: 18th-19th century SPECIALIST: Longcase clocks GENERAL: Antique clocks & barometers.

**Deva Antiques**, The Corner House, High Street, RG27 8NY TEL:843538, 843656 FAX: 842946

PARKING: Easy OPEN: Mon-Sat 9-5.30 MIN: £50 MAX: £6000 PERIOD: 18th-19th century GENERAL: Mahogany & walnut furniture OTHER INFO: Winchfield station 2 miles, collection arranged.

**Colin Harris Antiques**, at Deva, High Street TEL: 843538, home (0734)732580 PARKING: Easy OPEN: Mon-Sat 9-5.30 MIN: £50 MAX: £5000 PERIOD: 18th-19th century GENERAL: Victorian & Georgian quality furniture.

**Just The Thing**, High Street, RG27 8NS TEL: 843393 PARKING: Easy OPEN: Mon-Sat 9-5 MIN: £5 MAX: £2000 PERIOD: 18th-20th century SPECIALIST: Art Deco, pine & country OTHER INFO: Large choice of antique shops, pubs & restaurants in village.

**David Lazarus Antiques**, High Street, RG27 8NS TEL: 842272 OPEN: Mon-Sat 10-5.30 PERIOD: 17th-19th century GENERAL: Period antique furniture & objets d'art.

**AW Porter & Son**, High Street, RG27 8NY TEL: 842676 FAX: 842064 ASSNS: BHI, NAG PARKING: Easy OPEN: Mon-Sat 9-5.30 MIN: £20 MAX: £5000 PERIOD: 18th-20th century SPECIALIST: Clocks, silver, jewellery.

**Sheila Revell Antiques,** at Deva Antique, High Street, RG27 8NY TEL: 843538 PARKING: Own carpark OPEN: Mon-Sat 9-5.30 PERIOD: 17th-20th century SPECIALIST: Unusual collectors' items. GENERAL: Small furniture & decorative items OTHER INFO: Attractive village with oak studded Common, also cricket green with one of the oldest playing clubs in England.

## SANDHURST (01252)

**Berkshire Metal Finishers Ltd**, Swan Lane Trading Estate, GU17 8DD TEL: 873475 FAX: 875434 PARKING: Easy OPEN: 8.30-1, 2-6 PERIOD: 20th century GENERAL: Metalware.

## CAMBERLEY (01276)

**The Pedlar**, 231 London Road, GU15 3EY TEL: 64750 PARKING: Own carpark OPEN: 10-5, closed Wed PERIOD: 19th-20th century GENERAL: General antiques.

## WINDLESHAM (01344)

**Country Antiques**, at Country Garden Centre, London Road, GU20 6LL TEL: 873404 PARKING: Own carpark OPEN: Mon-Tues, Thurs-Sun 10-5 MIN: £5 MAX: £1500 GENERAL: General antiques OTHER INFO: 20 dealers selling wide range mainly furniture in a garden centre.

**Richard Kimbell Ltd**, Country Gardens, London Road, GU20 6LL PARKING: Own carpark OPEN: Seven days 9-6 MIN: £1 MAX: £3000 PERIOD: 19th century SPECIALIST: Antique & reproduction pine GENERAL: Country furniture & crafts.

## SUNNINGHILL (01344)

**Antiques of Ascot**, 3c High Street, SL5 9NQ TEL: 872282 PARKING: Easy OPEN: Mon-Sat 10-4.45 MIN: £1 MAX: £2500 PERIOD: 19th-20th century GENERAL: Pine, mahogany, oak & walnut furniture, bric a brac.

# Hampshire

This tour of Hampshire visits cities and towns, like Winchester, that are rich in the history of the country, its wars, religion and politics. The route also travels through the historic and ecologically vital area of the New Forest.

First to **Alresford** on the River Alre. Divided by the river into Old and New Alresford, this was a medieval wool town and still has some attractive Georgian houses in Broad Street. Graves of French prisoners-of-war from the Napoleonic Wars may be seen in the churchyard.

Next, **Winchester**, the county town of Hampshire, stands on the River Itchen amidst the rolling chalk downs. The Romans built their town of *Venta Belgarum*, later to become Winchester, alongside a prehistoric settlement. The city walls and High Street still follow those ancient lines. Decline came after the Romans left, but with the emergence of the kingdom of Wessex it became of first importance as its capital.

The see of Winchester was wealthy and the bishops powerful. Its Bishop Henry of Blois, who built Wolvesey Castle, was involved in the Civil War between King Stephen and the Empress Matilda when much of Winchester was burnt including the royal palace. The Domesday Book was compiled at Wolvesey Castle and it also contained the royal treasury until the end of the 12th century. Now all that remains of the castle is Henry III's Great Hall, probably the finest aisled medieval hall in England.

Winchester Cathedral, the second longest in Europe, was started in 1079 using stone from the Isle of Wight and shows early Norman and perpendicular work. It has many notable features:14th century carved stalls, a restored 15th century reredos, the oldest iron grill in England, coffers containing the bones of Saxon & Danish kings. The tombs of Izaak Walton, Jane Austen and King William Rufus, killed in the New Forest, can be found there. Hooks still in the cathedral pillars once held decorations for the wedding of Queen Mary Tudor and Philip of Spain in 1554.

Winchester contains many other fine and historic buildings and in parts of the city these still conform to the Saxon street pattern. Superb examples of medieval and later architecture can be found in the cathedral close, notably the Deanery, where Charles II stayed for a time, and which is partly 14th century and Cheyne Court with three timber-framed gables rising above the ground floor.

The tour continues via **Twyford, Morestead,** and then **Upham**, all almost equidistant from the well known Marwell Zoological Park at Hensting village. **Eastleigh,** Southampton's airport, and also where the very first Spitfire flew in the mid 1930's, owes much of its recent activities to the adjoining great marshalling railway yards. The market town of **Romsey** is next. Here an abbey, very likely one of Europe's finest Norman buildings, was founded in the early 10th century and enlarged in the 12th century. Lord Mountbatten of Burma is buried in the south transept. His home, Broadlands, is nearby and well worth a visit. Queen Elizabetth II and Prince Philip, and later the Prince and Princess of Wales, spent part of their honeymoons here. This splendid mid-Georgian mansion is set alongside the River Test, famous for its game fishing, in a park landscaped by Capability Brown. In the 19th century it was the home of Lord Palmerston, the great Victorian Prime Minister. The Mountbatten Exhibition, in the stable building, celebrates Lord Mountbatten's life and achievements. The house, with its collections of pictures, sculpture, furniture, porcelain, is also open to the public.

At the most westerly edge of this trip is **Fordingbridge** on the River Avon. Nearby Breamore House is worth a call. This Elizabethan manor house is set in parkland with good collections of paintings, tapestries, furniture and porcelain. 6 miles south stands the market town of **Ringwood**, where reputedly, the Duke of Monmouth, pretender to the English throne, sheltered in a house in the High Street after the Battle of Sedgemoor. He was later caught and executed in London.

The route now moves on to the New Forest, the largest area of lowland common land in Britain and with a history as a legal forest going back to Norman times. There is a suggestion that areas of

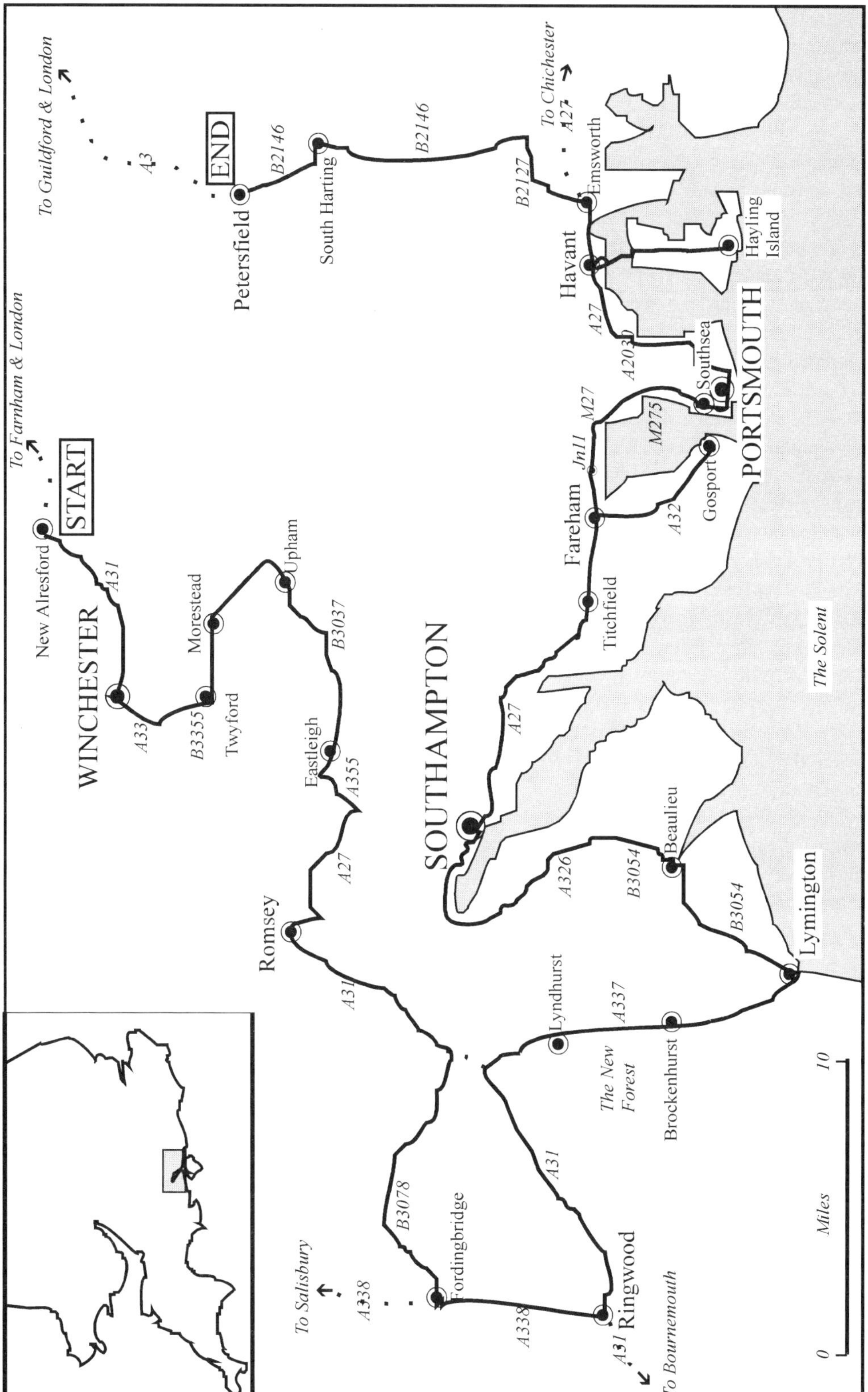

To Guildford & London
A3
END
Petersfield
B2146
South Harting
B2146
To Chichester
A27
B2127
Emsworth
Havant
Hayling Island
A27
A2030
PORTSMOUTH
Southsea
M27
M275
Jn11
Fareham
Gosport
A32
Titchfield
To Farnham & London
START
New Alresford
A31
WINCHESTER
A33
B3355
Twyford
Morestead
Upham
B3037
Eastleigh
A355
SOUTHAMPTON
A27
The Solent
Romsey
A27
A31
A326
Beaulieu
B3054
B3054
Lymington
Lyndhurst
A337
Brockenhurst
The New Forest
A31
B3078
Fordingbridge
Ringwood
To Salisbury
A338
A338
A31
To Bournemouth
Miles
0
10

the New Forest were part of the primeval forest once covering most of Britain after the last Ice Age. The Normans gave legal status to the forest which was an area, not necessarily wooded, in which animals were protected by special law, i.e. forest law, aimed at preserving game for hunting by the king or his licensees. Special courts administered forest law and this is the origin of the Court of Verderers still based in Lyndhurst. There were severe penalties attached to poaching. At first a man convicted of killing a deer could be put to death or blinded but later the penalties were changed to fines. Because part of the affect of forest law meant that the land could not be used for arable farming, local people were given various common rights, for example the right to grazing. Properties in the New Forest still have their ancient common rights attached to them and it is these that allow the famous New Forest ponies to graze freely.

Gradually, though, the New Forest's role as a royal hunting ground declined, although herds of deer still roam the Forest today. Oak for building the navy's ships became important. This started the still-continuing trend to commercial tree plantations. Because of the Forest's unique ecostructure there are strict rules on the planting of trees and their felling, for example, clear felling of a whole area is not allowed. However, there are still areas that have not been commercially planted, amongst which are the Ancient and Ornamental Woodlands.

Nowadays the New Forest is of paramount importance for recreation and conservation. It has an unusual range of ecosystems from dry heathland to valley bogs and it contains several kinds of lowland habitat that are rare or endangered elsewhere; this is why its preservation is essential.

The Forest is extremely popular as a tourist destination and visitors can find plenty of well-maintained carparks and campsites as well as opportunities for golf, fishing and riding. Because there are few public roads through the Forest it is quite easy to enjoy the countryside without the noise and pollution found in other beauty spots. Also, the carparks, as a matter of policy, are sited close to attractions such as water, picnic areas or forest walks. As many people do not move far from their cars it is quite possible to be free of other tourists after even a relatively short walk.

The next destination, **Lyndhurst**, was the administrative centre of the New Forest and is still home to the Verderers Court, the New Forest District Council and the Forestry Commission offices. A legacy of forest law can be seen in the Tudor stirrup, kept in the Verderers' Hall, used to decide whether a dog was a threat to the king's deer. If a dog was too big to pass through the stirrup its claws were maimed so that it could no longer hunt effectively. Next door is the Queen's House, built in 1563 and a former royal hunting lodge. Another celebrated local attraction is the grave of Alice Liddell, the original Alice in Wonderland.

Continuing south, **Brockenhurst** is a most attractive New Forest village. There is a memorial in the local churchyard to Brusher Mills who was responible for killing 3180 adders. Arriving now at the coast, **Lymington**, dates from the end of the 12th century and was founded by William de Redvers, Earl of Devon and Lord of the Isle of Wight. Throughout the Middle Ages Lymington was an important market town with a good import and export trade. Its wide High Street is typical of a market street with ample space for stalls. Even today an open market is held every Saturday.

Turning inland, **Beaulieu**, stands at the head of the Beaulieu River and was the site of a Cistercian Abbey founded in 1204 on land granted by King John. The abbey church was torn down during the Dissolution of the Monasteries in 1538 and the abbey gatehouse is now incorporated into Palace House, the home of Lord Montagu of Beaulieu, and built in 1870. The estate includes the National Motor Museum with over 250 vintage and historic cars on display including Donald Campbell's Bluebird. There is scarcely a trace now of the busy American wartime airbase.

Downstream from Beaulieu stands Bucklers Hard comprising of two rows of 18th century houses. Incredibly this tiny village was once the centre of a thriving ship building industry supplying men-of-war for the navy in the war against Napoleon. In the village there is a Maritime Museum which includes a display of how Bucklers Hard looked then. The Museum also has reconstructions of rooms in the the New Inn in 1793 and some of the village houses have also been restored to their original state so that the homes of an 18th century labourer, shipwright and master shipbuilder may be experienced.

The next call is **Southampton**, an important port for nearly two thousand years. Armies have embarked for invasions and foreign troops have landed here for raids on Britain. The Romans had a port here, William the Conqueror used it for ships arriving from Normandy, Richard I left from Southampton to go on his crusades, the French sacked the town in 1338 and Edward III embarked from here to win the Battle of Crécy. More recently, during the First and Second World Wars millions of troops left the port to go into battle. Southampton was also the major port for transatlantic liners like the Queen Elizabeth and the Queen Mary.

*HMS Victory, Portsmouth.*
*By courtesy of Portsmouth City Council*

Reminders of the medieval town can be seen in the town walls and their towers. Only one section of the wall itself survives, in Western Esplanade. The towers have all survived: Polymond, Catchcold, Wind Whistle and God's House Tower stood at the four corners of the walls. God's House Tower, on the Town Quay, is now a museum of local archaeology. Other museums are housed in the 14th century Wool House, a maritime museum, and the Tudor House, a 16th century mansion with overhanging gables, half-timbered walls and mullioned windows standing in St Michael's Square.

The tour then goes south east to pretty, history-packed, **Titchfield** and its closeby 13th century Abbey. Surprisingly this small town was once seaport until a wall was built across the River Meon, in the 18th century, draining the marshes. Take your time in Titchfield. **Fareham,** however, is a port and at the end of a small creek. **Gosport** , next, has many naval connections, particularly being noted for the naval hospital and its submarine base. A passenger ferry connects it to **Portsmouth.** This city was built around a natural harbour in the 12th century by John de Gisors, lord of the manor of Titchfield. After he rebelled against Richard I, Portsmouth was taken over by the king who made it a royal borough. Although not as important as Southampton as a port, troops fighting France embarked here and consequently the French sacked the town several times.

Henry VIII built a dry dock and also a castle at **Southsea** as part of the coastal defences. Parliamentary troops captured it during the Civil War and in the reign of Charles II it was used as a prison. Much of the castle was destroyed by an accidental explosion in 1760. Reconstructed in the 19th century, today it serves as a museum of Portsmouth's defensive history.

Portsmouth started to become important as a naval dockyard in the reign of Charles I and continued to expand in the 18th century. During the Napoleonic Wars, however, the dockyard became prominent. Nelson's ship, HMS Victory, is berthed in a dock dating from that time with contemporary buildings nearby. The oldest of these, the Royal Naval Academy, dates from 1732. The remains of the Mary Rose, the Tudor ship which was raised from Portsmouth harbour, are also on display here.

One of Portsmouth famous sons was Isambard Kingdom Brunel, born here in 1806. He worked with Sir Samuel Bentham (brother of the philosopher, Jeremy Bentham) and another engineer, Henry Maudslay in Portsmouth Dockyard. They designed machinery for making pulley blocks. These took the strain of ropes in rigging and were extremely important. The machinery they designed was steam-driven and is said to have been the first mass-produced components of this type in the world.

Some of the old town of Portsmouth still survives in spite of being heavily bombed during the Second World War. These bombsites have been rebuilt but the old street pattern still persists.

The tour now moves off the mainland on to **Hayling Island,** a holiday resort covering only four square miles. It is connected to the mainland by a bridge and the island has good sandy beaches, fishing and sailing. Next, **Havant**, as the junction of numerous trackways and Roman roads, has been the site of a settlement since earliest times.

On the way to the final destination it is well worth exploring the smaller country roads because there is extremely beautiful countryside and pretty villages. Examples are the next two stops, **Emsworth** and **South Harting**, where the writer, Anthony Trollope, lived for a while. The last stop on this tour is the handsome market town of **Petersfield** with its splendid Georgian buildings.

## ANTIQUE DEALERS

### ALRESFORD (01962)

**Alresford Antiques**, 49 West Street, SO24 9AB TEL: 735959 PARKING: Medium OPEN: Fri-Sat 10-5 or by appt other days MIN: £1 MAX: £500 PERIOD: 18th-20th century GENERAL: Small unusual items, china, glass, treen, toys, all sorts OTHER INFO: Watercress steam railway, B&B in Cheriton's Flowerpots (has own brewery).

**Artemesia**, 16 West Street, SO24 9AT TEL: 732277 ASSNS: LAPADA PARKING: Easy OPEN: Mon-Sat 9.30-1, 2-5 MIN: £10 MAX: £3500 PERIOD: 17th-19th century SPECIALIST: Oriental porcelain & works of art GENERAL: English furniture, ceramics & works of art OTHER INFO: 1st century AD to 1908 Chinese from the Han to the Qing. Good food at 2 hotels & several pubs, all close.

**Evans & Evans**, 40 West Street, SO24 9AU TEL: 732170 ASSNS: LAPADA PARKING: Medium OPEN: Fri & Sat 9-1, 2-5 or by appt MIN: £400 MAX: £30,000 PERIOD: 17th-20th century SPECIALIST: English & French clocks, barometers GENERAL: Musical boxes, secondhand wristwatches OTHER INFO: Unspoilt 18th century market town.

**Jonathan Shirley Antiques & Restoration,** Bell House Interiors, 26 West Street, SO24 9AX TEL: 732211 PARKING: Medium OPEN: 6 days 9.30-5 MIN: £150 MAX: £5000 PERIOD: 18th-19th century GENERAL: French & English furniture OTHER INFO: Beautiful Georgian town with good hotels & restaurants, also the base for the Watercress Steam Railway.

**Studio Bookshop & Gallery**, 17 Broad Street, SO24 9AW TEL: 732188 ASSNS: FATG ABA PARKING: Medium OPEN: Mon-Sat 9-5 MAX: £3000 PERIOD: 18th-20th century SPECIALIST: Antiquarian & old books GENERAL: Includes India & Far East, topographical prints, Victorian & later watercolours OTHER INFO: Mary Russell Mitford was born here, in same road.

### WINCHESTER (01962)

**Bell Fine Art**, 67b Parchment Street, SO23 8AT TEL: 860439 ASSNS: FATG PARKING: Own carpark OPEN: Mon-Sat 9.30-5.30 MIN: £10 MAX: £5000 PERIOD: 19th-20th century SPECIALIST: British watercolour & drawings OTHER INFO: Longest cathedral in Europe only 5 mins, opposite 3 star Royal Hotel.

**Henry March Gilbert**, 19 The Square, SO23 9EY TEL: 852832 ASSNS: ABA PARKING: Medium OPEN: Mon-Sat 9-5.30 MIN: £1 MAX: £1,000 PERIOD: 19th-20th century SPECIALIST: English Literature including library sets GENERAL: Interesting range of secondhand & rare books OTHER INFO: Located in cul-de-sac 200 yds NW of cathedral, many good pubs near, also other antique shops.

**Gerald Marsh Antique Clocks Ltd**, 32a The Square, SO23 9EX ASSNS: BADA, BHI, Clockmakers Company TEL: 844443 FAX: (0869) 40087 PARKING: Medium OPEN: Mon-Sat 9.30-5 MIN: £20 MAX: £100,000 PERIOD: 17th-20th century SPECIALIST: Fine early English clocks GENERAL: Clocks, watches & antique & new barometers. New watch stands. Full repair & restoration workshop OTHER INFO: Hotels: Wessex, Royal. Wyckham Arms pub.

**Printed Page**, 2-3 Bridge Street, SO23 9BH TEL: 854072 FAX: 862995 ASSNS: FATG PARKING: Medium OPEN: Tues-Sat 9.30-5.30 MIN: £5 MAX: £750 PERIOD: 19th-20th century SPECIALIST: Antique maps & prints GENERAL: Modern prints & cards, picture framing OTHER INFO: Adjacent to very good Cricketers pub, Youth Hostel & pizza restaurant.

**Mary Roofe Antiques**, 1 Stonemasons' Court, Parchment Street, SO23 8AT TEL: 840613 ASSNS: LAPADA PARKING: Medium OPEN: Tues-Sat 10-5 MIN: £20 MAX: £2000 PERIOD: 18th-19th century SPECIALIST: Boxes GENERAL: Country furniture, treen OTHER INFO: Ancient capital of England, cathedral, Winchester College.

**Samuel Spencers Antiques & Decorative Arts Emporium**, 39 Jewry Street TEL: 867014 PARKING: Easy OPEN: Mon-Sat 10-5.30 MIN: £1 PERIOD: 17th-20th century GENERAL: All types of antiques & decorative items in 31 individual units OTHER INFO: Interior designer available. The Great Hall with King Arthur's Round Table.

**Thompson Antiques,** 20a Jewry Street TEL: 866633 FAX: 864173 PARKING: Easy OPEN: Mon-Sat 9.30-5 MIN: £5 MAX: £10,000 PERIOD: 18th-20th century SPECIALIST: Long tables, large furniture GENERAL: Furniture & smalls.

**Webb Fine Art**, 38 Jewry Street, SO23 8RY TEL: 842273 FAX: 842246 ASSNS: GMC PARKING: Own carpark OPEN: Mon-Fri 9-5, Sat 9.30-4 PERIOD: 19th century SPECIALIST: Victorian oils GENERAL: Over 300 oil paintings always in stock.

## TWYFORD (01962)

**Twyford Antiques**, High Street, SO21 1WH TEL: 713484 PARKING: Medium OPEN: Mon-Sat 9.30-5.30 MIN: £250 MAX: £3000 PERIOD: 18th-19th century SPECIALIST: Clocks & decorative items GENERAL: Good quality, well-restored furniture OTHER INFO: Picturesque village short walk to famous Water Meadows. 2 antique shops, 3 good pubs. Close to other shops with varying stock.

## MORESTEAD (01962)

**The Pine Cellars**, Burgess Farm, SO21 1LZ TEL: 777546 ASSNS: GMC PARKING: Own carpark OPEN: Mon-Sat 9-5 MIN: £5 MAX: £5000 PERIOD: 17th-19th century SPECIALIST: Individual pieces of antique pine GENERAL: 20,000 sq ft stocked with antique pine (many photos in Miller's 1994 guide) OTHER INFO: Shipping worldwide available, also B&B at the farmhouse.

## UPHAM (01489)

**Susanna Fisher**, Spencer, SO32 1JD TEL: 860291 FAX: 860638 PARKING: Own carpark OPEN: By appt only MIN: £50 MAX: £5.000 PERIOD: 17th-19th century SPECIALIST: Navigational charts & related books.

## EASTLEIGH (01703)

**Tappers Antiques**, 186 Southampton Road, SO5 5QW TEL: 643105 PARKING: Easy OPEN: Mon-Sat 10-5 MIN: £2 MAX: £2000 PERIOD: 18th-19th century GENERAL: Postcards, furniture, china, glass chimneypots - anything & everything OTHER INFO: Large shop, a museum in itself. Handy for M27

## ROMSEY (01794)

**Bell Antiques**, 8 Bell Street, SO51 8GA TEL: 514719 ASSNS: GA PARKING: Easy OPEN: Mon-Sat 9.30-5.30, closed Wed pm in winter MIN: £1 MAX: £6000 PERIOD: 19th-20th century SPECIALIST: Jewellery GENERAL: China, glassware, small silver, small furniture, pictures, prints OTHER INFO: Piaf's Bar & Restaurant, good French bar & bistro, La Parisienne.

**Cambridge Antiques & Medal Centre**, 5 Bell Street, SO51 8GY TEL: 523089, 512069 FAX: 830332 ASSNS: LAPADA, OMRS PARKING: Medium OPEN: Mon-Sat 8.30-5.30 MIN: £20 MAX: £5000 PERIOD: 19th-20th century SPECIALIST: Medals (worldwide customer service) GENERAL: China, silver, glass, jewellery, oriental, Moorcroft OTHER INFO: Quaint market town with individual shops & friendly people. Well worth a visit.

**Eddison Antiques,** 5 Plaza Parade, Winchester Road, SO51 8JA TEL: 512 061 PARKING: Own carpark OPEN: Closed Sun & Mon MIN: £1 MAX: £1000 PERIOD: 18th-early 20th century GENERAL: Copper, brass, darkwood & pine furniture, English china, general antiques OTHER INFO: My wife runs an English Tourist Board commended B&B in a village a couple of miles away.

## FORDINGBRIDGE (01425)

**Quatrefoil**, Burgate, SP6 1LX TEL: 653309 PARKING: Own carpark OPEN: Resident, anytime MIN: £30 MAX: £10,000 PERIOD: 17th-18th century SPECIALIST: Oak, English & Continental furniture. Medieval & Renaissance carvings & sculpture, antiquities & classical coins.

## RINGWOOD (01425)

**Barbara Davies Antiques**, 30a Christchurch Road, BH24 1.. TEL: (0860) 690744 shop, (0202) 872260 home PARKING: Easy OPEN: Tues 10-1, Wed & Fri 10-3 MIN: £1 MAX: £250 PERIOD: 18th-20th century SPECIALIST: Porcelain GENERAL: Smalls and small furniture

**Millers Antiques**, Netherbrook House, 86 Christchurch Road, BH24 1DR. Tel: 472062 FAX: 472727 ASSNS: LAPADA PARKING: Own carpark OPEN: Mon-Fri 9-5.30, Sat 10-4 MIN: £25 MAX: £3,500 PERIOD 18th-19th century SPECIALIST: Large stocks of English & Continental furniture with emphasis on the country look. Quimper & majolica GENERAL: Furniture, gilt, treen, faience & metalware OTHER INFO: Near prize-winning Chewton Glen Hotel (New Milton), Tyrell's Ford Hotel (3 star, reasonable).

**The Pine Company**, 104 Christchurch Road TEL: 476705 FAX: 480467 PARKING: Own carpark OPEN:Mon-Sat 9-6 MIN: £5 MAX: £2500 PERIOD: 18th-19th century SPECIALIST: Pine, leading importer of antique Chinese furniture.

**Glen Robinson Interiors & Antiques**, 82 Christchurch Road, BH24 1DR TEL: 480450 PARKING: Easy OPEN: Mon-Sat 10-5 PERIOD: 18th-19th century SPECIALIST: Decorative pieces and objects GENERAL: Small pieces of furniture.

## LYNDHURST (01703)

**Peter Humphries**, 6 High Street, SO43 7BD TEL: 282754 PARKING: Easy OPEN: Mon-Sat 9.30-5 GENERAL: 2nd hand various OTHER INFO: Mad Hatter tearoom, Bow Windows restaurant.

**Lita Kaye of Lyndhurst**, 13 The High Street TEL: 282337 PARKING: Easy OPEN: Mon-Sat 9.30-5 MIN: £150 MAX: £15,000 PERIOD: 18-19th century GENERAL: Upmarket furniture, decorative porcelain, clocks OTHER INFO: New Forest Visitors Centre, Lyndhurst Church burial place of Alice Hargreaves (Alice in Wonderland).

## BROCKENHURST (01590)

**Bazaar**, Lyndhurst Road, SO42 7RH TEL: 624044 OPEN: 7days 9.30-5.30 SPECIALIST: Old pine, basketry, furniture, bric a brac, linen.

**Squirrels**, Lyndhurst Road, SO42 7RL TEL: 622433 PARKING: Easy OPEN: Wed-Sun 10-5 MIN: 50p MAX: £595 PERIOD: 19th-20th century SPECIALIST: Stripped pine & pretty china.

## LYMINGTON (01590)

**Corfield Antiques Ltd**, 120 High Street, SO41 9AQ TEL: 673532 FAX: 678855 ASSNS: BADA PARKING: Medium OPEN: Mon-Sat 9.15-5.30 MIN: £50 MAX: £10,000 PERIOD: 18th-19th century SPECIALIST: Coalport porcelain, English furniture GENERAL: Pictures & silver, porcelain OTHER INFO: Corfields have been in the charming Georgian town of Lymington for 30 years. Market day Saturday.

**Hughes & Smeeth Ltd**, 1 Gosport Street, SO41 9BG TEL: 676324 ASSNS: ABA PFBA PARKING: Medium OPEN: Mon-Sat 9.30-5 PERIOD: 18th-20th century SPECIALIST: Books on sailing, natural history & topography GENERAL: Old & secondhand books, topographical prints & British county maps.

**The Lymington Antique Centre**, 76 High Street, SO41 9AL TEL: 670934 PARKING: Medium OPEN: Mon-Fri 10-5, Sat 9-5 PERIOD: 19th-20th century SPECIALIST: Furniture, postcards, books GENERAL: Oil lamps, jewellery, silver frames, pictures, collectables.

**Barry Papworth**, 28 St.Thomas Street, SO41 9NE TEL: 676422 PARKING: Easy OPEN: Mon-Sat 9-5 MIN: £5 MAX: £10,000 PERIOD: 18th-20th century SPECIALIST: Antique silver, jewellery GENERAL: All small to medium size jewellery, silver OTHER INFO: Pretty town, best hotel: Stanwell House Hotel.

**Robert Perera Fine Art**, 19 St Thomas Street,

SO41 9NB TEL: 678230 FAX: 678230 PARKING: Easy OPEN: Mon-Fri 10-5, Sat 9-5.30 MIN: £50 MAX: £7500 PERIOD: 19th-20th century SPECIALIST: Marine paintings including work by Norman Wilkinson CBE GENERAL: Over 200 paintings, watercolours & etchings. Also studio pottery & Worcester porcelain.

**Treasure Trove,** 1a Captains Row, SO419RP TEL: 673974 PARKING: Difficult OPEN: Mon-Sat 10-4 MIN: £2 MAX:1,000 PERIOD: 18th, 20th century GENERAL: Bric-a-brac, curios and antiques.

**Triangle Books**, Lymington Antiques Centre, 76 High Street, SO41 9ZK TEL: 670934 ASSNS: PBFA PARKING: Easy OPEN: Mon-Fri 10-5, Sat 9-5 MIN: £1 MAX: £250 PERIOD: 19th-20th century SPECIALIST: Art, antiques, cookery, horse racing, topography GENERAL: 2500 good quality books + ephemera, prints & sheet music.

## BEAULIEU (01590)

**Beaulieu Fine Arts**, The Malt House, High Street, SO42 7YA TEL: 612089 PARKING: Easy OPEN: Mon-Sat 9.30-5.15 MIN: £5 MAX: £7000 PERIOD: 18th-20th century SPECIALIST: Marine watercolours GENERAL: Wide range of paintings, prints & contemporary works in five gallery rooms.

## SOUTHAMPTON (01703)

**Highfield Antiques**, 33 Highfield Lane TEL: 324101 PARKING: Own carpark OPEN: Mon-Sat 10-5.30 MIN: £5 MAX: £800 PERIOD: 18th-early 20th century SPECIALIST: Furniture GENERAL: Antiques OTHER INFO: Close to university & Moat House Hotel.

**Henry March Gilbert**, 2½ Portland Street, SO14 7EB TEL: 226420 ASSNS: ABA PARKING: Medium OPEN: Mon-Sat 8.30-5 MIN: 50p MAX: £500 PERIOD: 19th-20th century SPECIALIST: English Literature (including library sets) GENERAL: Interesting range of books.

**L Moody**, 70 Bedford Place, SO15 2DS TEL: 333720 PARKING: Easy OPEN: 9-5 PERIOD: 17th-20th century GENERAL: Furniture.

**Old Curiosity Shop & Morris Gallery**, 280 Shirley Road, Shirley, S01 3HL TEL: 774772 PARKING: Own carpark OPEN: Mon-Sat 9-6 MIN: £1 MAX: £3000 PERIOD: 19th-20th century SPECIALIST: Furniture, marine art & artefacts GENERAL: Curios, paintings, china, bronzes, silver, militaria etc.

## TITCHFIELD (01329)

**Alexanders,** 13 South Street, PO14 4DL TEL: 315962 PARKING: Easy OPEN: Tues-Sat 10-5 MIN: £10 MAX: £1500 PERIOD: 19th-20th century SPECIALIST: Art Nouveau & Deco GENERAL: Objects, glass & furniture.

**Gaylords Antiques**, The Old School, 75 West Street, PO14 4DG TEL: 843402 PARKING: Own carpark OPEN: Mon-Sat 9-5.30 MIN: £150 MAX: £5000 PERIOD: 18th-20th century GENERAL: Furniture & clocks, 19th century fully restored and in fine order OTHER INFO: We are retail warehouse in historic village 2 mins from M27.

**Robin Howard Antiques**, 6-8 South Street, PO14 4DJ TEL: 842794 PARKING: Easy OPEN: Mon-Sat 9.30-5.30 MIN: £10 MAX: £500 PERIOD: 18th-20th century SPECIALIST:Antique & modern silver & jewellery.

**Titchfield Antiques Ltd**, 13-15 South Street, PO4 4DL TEL: 845968 PARKING: Easy OPEN: MIN: £10 MAX: £1000 PERIOD: 19th-20th century SPECIALIST: Art nouveau & art deco GENERAL: Silver, small furniture OTHER INFO: Historic village with abbey & church where the earls of Southampton are embalmed in honey. Adjoining original 1930's teashop & gardens complete with furniture & fittings.

## FAREHAM (01329)

**The Elizabethan Antiques**, 58 High Street, PO16 7BG TEL: 234964 PARKING: Easy OPEN: 10-4 MIN: £5 MAX: £1000 PERIOD: 19th-20th century GENERAL: Furniture, silver, pictures, jewellery, china, glass etc OTHER INFO: Shop is a listed building & in the street is a conservation aera.

## GOSPORT (01705)

**Joys Dolls House**, Peter Pan's Bazaar, 105-107 Forton Road, PO12 4TQ TEL: 524254 PARKING: Easy OPEN: Thurs-Sat 10-5 MIN: £5 MAX: £1000 PERIOD: 18th-19th century SPECIALIST: Victorian dolls GENERAL: Dolls house miniatures & miniature bronzes.

**Peter Pan's Bazaar**, 105 Forton Road, PO12 4TQ TEL: 524254 PARKING: Easy OPEN: Thurs-Sat 10.15-5 MIN: £1 MAX: £2000 PERIOD: 19th-20th SPECIALIST: Vintage cameras GENERAL: Photographic collectors items.

## PORTSMOUTH/SOUTHSEA (01705)

**Affordable Antiques**, 89 Albert Road, Southsea, PO5 2SG TEL: 293344 PARKING: Easy OPEN: Mon-Fri 10-3, Sat 9.30-5 MIN: £5 MAX: £3500 PERIOD: 19th-20th century SPECIALIST: Victorian, Edwardian & 1930's furniture.

**A Fleming (Southsea) Ltd**, The Clock Tower, Castle Road, Southsea, PO5 3DE TEL: 822934 FAX: 293501 ASSNS: BADA PARKING: Easy OPEN: Mon-Fri 8.30-5, Sat 8.30-1 MIN: £5 MAX: £5000+ PERIOD: 18th-20th century GENERAL: Furniture, china, silverplate, nautical & misc.

**Oldfield Gallery**, 76 Elm Grove, PO5 1LN TEL & FAX: 838042 ASSNS: PFBA, IMCOS PARKING: Medium OPEN: Mon-Sat 10-5 MIN: £5 MAX: £3000 PERIOD: 17th-19th century SPECIALIST: Antique maps, prints, sea charts.

**Pretty Chairs**, 189-191 Highland Road TEL: 731411 PARKING: Easy OPEN: Mon-Sat 10-4.30 MIN: £75 MAX: £1500 PERIOD: 19th-20th century SPECIALIST:Pretty furniture GENERAL: Continental chairs, tables, desks, sofas, bedroom furniture OTHER INFO: Hilton, Queens hotel.

**Times Past**, 141 Highland Road, Southsea, PO4 9EY TEL: 822701, (0831) 418488 FAX: 822701 PARKING: Medium OPEN: Mon-Sat 10-4 MIN: £1 MAX: £2000 PERIOD: 19th-20th century GENERAL: Antiques & shipping goods OTHER INFO: Seagull Restaurant, Rosies Winebar (live jazz. at weekends), Walsingham Guest House.

**Wessex Medical Antiques**, 77 Carmarthen Avenue, PO6 2AG TEL: 376518 FAX: 201479 PARKING: Easy OPEN: By appt MIN: £200 MAX: £6000 PERIOD: 18th-19th century SPECIALIST: Medical microscopes. Also 1st-2nd century Roman items.

## HAVANT (01705)

**Trentham Gallery**, 40 North Street TEL: 484935 PARKING: Own carpark OPEN: Mon-Sat 10-5 MIN: £5 MAX: £2000 PERIOD: 18th-20th century GENERAL: Maps, prints, glass, blue & white pottery, small furniture, books, paintings, collectors items OTHER INFO: On Chichester harbour.

## HAYLING ISLAND (01705)

**J Morton Lee**, Cedar House, Bacon Lane, PO11 0DN TEL: 464444 ASSN: BADA PARKING: Own carpark OPEN: By appt MIN: £50 MAX: £10,000 PERIOD: 18th-20th century SPECIALIST: Marine watercolours GENERAL: 18th-20th century watercolours OTHER INFO: Fair exhibitions - World of Watercolours (Jan), Harrogate (Feb), NEC Birmingham (Aug), Buxton (May), Olympia (June), Northern (Sept), Surrey (Oct), Kensington (Nov). Also own Spring & Summer exhibitions in Emsworth (Mar) & Chichester (Sept).

## EMSWORTH (01243)

**Tiffins Antiques**

**12 Queen Street, PO10 7BL TEL: 372497 FAX: 378498 PARKING: Medium OPEN: 10-5, not Wed or Sun MIN: £2/3 MAX: £1000 PERIOD: 18th-20th century (Georgian & Edwardian) SPECIALIST: Oil lamps & clocks GENERAL: Furniture & small items of interest.**

## SOUTH HARTING (01730)

**Julia Holmes Antique Maps & Prints**, South Gardens Cottage, GU31 5QJ TEL: 825040 ASSNS: FATG PARKING: Own carpark OPEN: Strictly by appt MIN: £10 MAX: £1000 PERIOD: 17th-20th century GENERAL: Antique maps & views of the British Isles 1575-1850. Old & new prints of sporting & country life, especially horses and dogs 1750-1940 OTHER INFO: B&B possible in our 16th century thatched cottage. Excellent pubs.

## PETERSFIELD (01730)

**Cull Antiques**, 62 Station Road, GU32 3ES TEL: 263670 ASSNS: LAPADA PARKING: Medium OPEN: Mon-Sat 10-1, 2-5 MIN: £200 MAX: £5000 PERIOD: 18th-19th century GENERAL: Mahogany furniture & accessories only OTHER INFO: Harrow Inn, best pub winner. Gilbert White's house (Selborne), Jane Austen's Chawton Uppark House (Harting). Between Petworth & Winchester, airports & London 1 hour, ferries ° hour.

**The Petersfield Bookshop**, 16a Chapel Street, GU32 3DS TEL: 263438 FAX: 269426 ASSNS: ABA BADA PBFA PARKING: Easy OPEN: Mon-Sat 9-5.30 MIN: £1 MAX: £9000 PERIOD: 17th-20th century SPECIALIST: Early angling books, natural history, travel & topography.

# West Berkshire to North Wiltshire

This tour visits the beautiful countryside of West Berkshire and North Wiltshire. With good motorway connections, it is easily accessible but many of the villages and market towns retain an ageless unspoilt air.

The first stop,**Great Shefford** village is on the River Lambourn, just 2 miles north of the M4 Jn14. Next, **Hungerford**, is built on the old Roman road to Bath and is a mecca for antique dealers and collectors because of the wide range of antique shops and centres. In the 18th and 19th centuries the town was on the major coach road between London and Bath and so had many inns. Today only one survives, The Bear, used by William of Orange and King James II in 1668 for holding a meeting to discuss the future of the monarchy.

Many of the buildings date from the 17th and 18th centuries and line the elegant High Street. It is also a centre for anglers because, apart from the Kennet and Avon Canal which cuts through the town, Hungerford also has the Rivers Kennet and Dunn, famous for trout.

Three miles west stands the unspoilt Tudor manor, Littlecote House. It has a complete Cromwellian chapel, stark in its simplicity, and a collection of Cromwellian arms and armour from the local Parliamentary force. There is a Roman villa in the grounds where visitors can see the restored Orpheus Mosaic, said to be the largest coloured Roman mosaic in the country.

Two miles north west, **Ramsbury** is a small village on the River Kennet containing Jacobean and Georgian buildings and an early English church which displays some ancient sculptured stones.

The route proceeds to ancient **Marlborough** with one of the widest high streets in the country and many historic buildings ranging from Tudor to Victorian. In the grounds of the 19th century Marlborough College, a prehistoric barrow on which the Normans built a castle was often used by the monarch when hunting in the nearby Savernake Forest. Here King John was married and Henry III summoned Parliament. Edward VI, son of Henry VIII and Jane Seymour, gave the castle to his mother's family and later the diarists, Samuel Pepys and John Evelyn, both stayed here. In the 18th century the castle was used as an inn on the coach road between London and Bath. Finally it became the centre of the public school, Marlborough College.

After first visiting **Milton Lilbourne**, the next call is **Swindon**. This large town has been closely associated with railways and The Great Western Railway Museum in Faringdon Road is fascinating with exhibits ranging from locomotives through to posters and tickets. Also in Faringdon Road is the Railway Village Museum which is an original Great Western Railway Company village restored to its turn of the century appearance. The Museum and Art Gallery in Bath Road displays items of local historical and archeological interest.

After first visiting **Minety** and **Brinkworth**, the tour crosses the motorway at Jn16, south to **Wootton Basset**. It contains some fine Georgian buildings and a half timbered town hall built on stone pillars in 1700 by the Earl of Rochester. Stocks, a ducking stool and a small wooden fire-engine may be seen inside.

**Cherhill**, next, has two nice stories attached. A white horse, dating from 1780, was cut into the hillside above the village by a Dr Alsop from Calne. The story goes that he stood more than a mile away from the site and shouted instructions through a megaphone to his workmen. The finished work can be seen for about 40 miles. The other tale concerns a group of thieves, called the Cherhill Gang, who used to strip naked before attacking to make it harder to identify them.

Nearby **Calne**, of great antiquity, originally prospered as a weaving centre but when this declined it turned to curing bacon with the Harris Bacon factory. This developed because droves of Irish pigs passed regularly on their way from Bristol to London. Unfortunately, this factory has now closed but is still commemorated by a bronze pig near the shopping mall. The town also has a fine coaching inn. The 18th century Bowood House and Gardens, landscaped

# West Berkshire to North Wiltshire

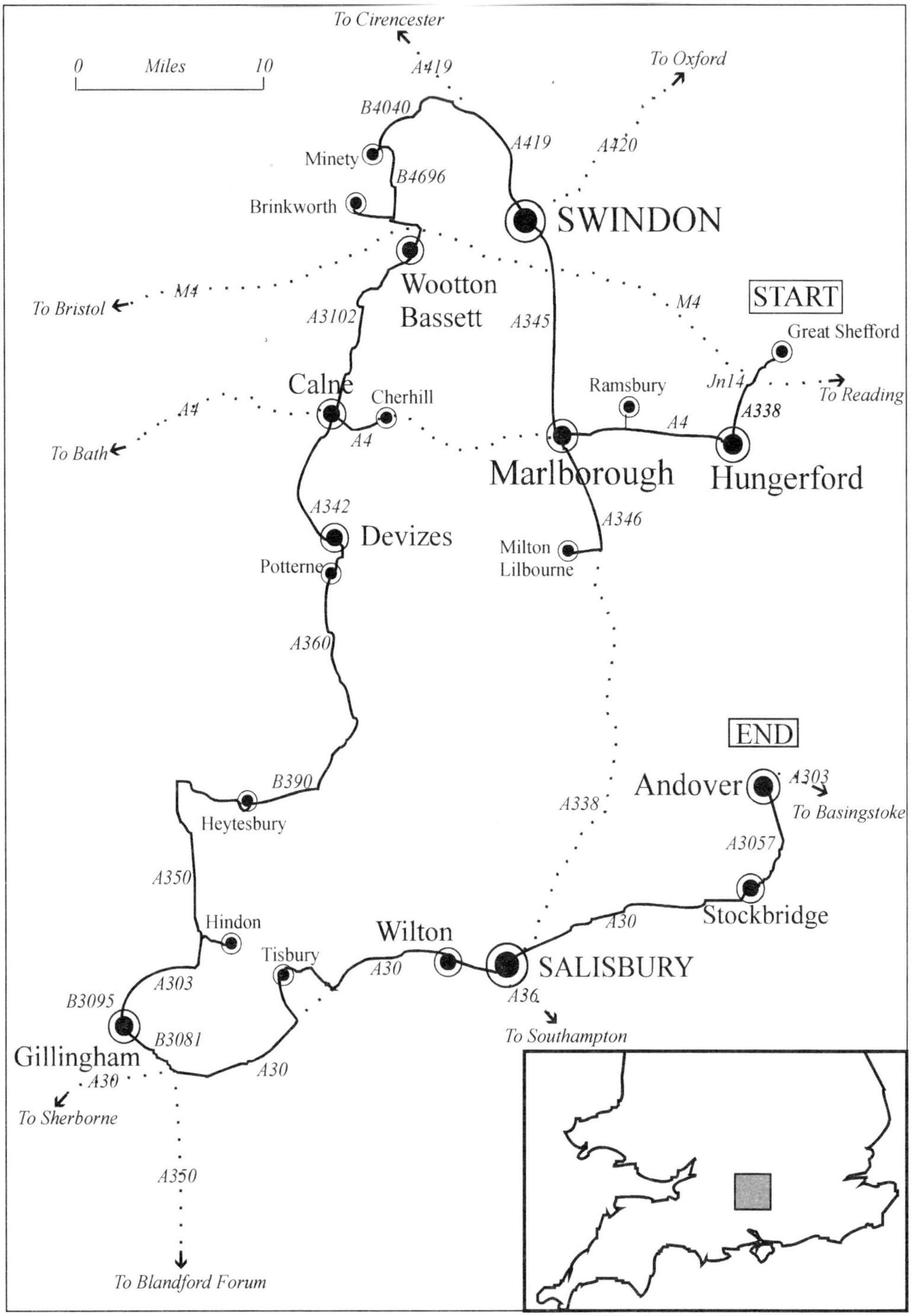

*Thatching in Wiltshire*

by Capability Brown, stands closeby. The house has fine collections of silver, porcelain, paintings and Victoriana.

The next call is the market town of **Devizes**, surrounded by rich farming country. The first fortifications here were pre-Norman earthworks although a castle was constructed in the reign of Henry I. During the Civil War it was besieged by Parliamentary troops and it eventually surrendered and was slighted. The present building was constructed in the 19th century. The Devizes Museum in Long Street has an important collection of local antiquities including finds from Wiltshire Neolithic, Bronze, and Iron Age sites. There are many good Georgian buildings and a 16th century timbered house can be seen in St John's Alley. The Kennet and Avon Canal, passing near the town, rises with the aid of 29 locks and connects London and Bristol. The town has a museum in Couch Lane devoted to telling the story of the canal.

After calling at delightful **Potterne** village, next comes **Heytesbury**, in the Wylye Valley, with its many old buildings, some dating from the 15th century. First stopping in **Hindon,** the tour then briefly crosses into Dorset to visit **Gillingham** on the River Stour before returning to Wiltshire and the small village of **Tisbury** in the Nadder Valley. One mile north east is a truly large (200ft long) tithe barn called Place House dating from the 13th century.

Ten miles east is the village of **Wilton** with one of the most famous stately homes in Southern England, Wilton House. The home of the Earls of Pembroke, this house was rebuilt in the mid 17th century to a design by Inigo Jones after a fire had destroyed the earlier building. The Cube Room and the Double Cube Room are said to be the most perfectly proportioned rooms in the country. It contains a superb collection of paintings and other works of art. A family of influence and power, it was the eighth Earl of Pembroke who introduced carpet weaving to the area. Later the half-brother of the twelfth Earl, Sidney Herbert, was Secretary of War during the Crimean War and was instrumental in enabling Florence Nightingale and her nurses to go to the Crimea. Her portrait can be seen in Wilton House.

Moving on, the sight of **Salisbury** Cathedral with its famous spire soaring to the heavens is the first glimpse that most people have approaching this city. A quintessential English scene, it has been painted by, amongst others, Constable, and engraved by Whistler. The first cathedral was on the nearby hill of Old Sarum, a cold, windy and unfriendly place but which had seen the earliest settlement because it was a good defensive position at 240 feet above the River Avon. There is evidence of human habitation going back to the Iron Age, continuing through the Roman occupation and then to the Saxons with, finally, the Normans building a castle and a cathedral side by side on the hill.

In the 13th century the clerics decided they had had enough of this miserable, windy, waterless hill and moved down to the valley and the townspeople followed them. In just 40 years the magnificent cathedral that we know today was built. The foundation stones were laid in 1220 by Bishop Richard Poore who later became Bishop of Durham where he continued his interest in great cathedral building. The world-famous 400 foot spire was added to Salisbury Cathedral in the 14th century but to prevent probable collapse, in the 15th century, strainer arches had to be built to support its weight.

Amongst the treasures and items of interest in the Cathedral, the famous dialless clock in the bell tower dates from the 14th century and is one of the oldest clocks in the country. The Cathedral also has an original copy of Magna Carta, one of only four surviving copies. The cathedral close is reputed to be one of the finest in England and contains buildings ranging from the 14th to 18th centuries. Here in the close Anthony Trollope conceived the idea for his Barchester series of novels.

The fact that Salisbury was a new town built on a green field site, albeit seven centuries ago, can be seen from the regular grid pattern of streets rather than the more usual haphazard jumble seen in cities that have grown gradually through the centuries. Historic buildings from the 14th century onwards still survive in the city today, including many of the inns.

A visit to this area would not be complete without seeing Stonehenge, perhaps the most famous prehistoric site in Europe. Considered to be some 5000 years old, the exact purpose of this incredible monument is still unclear. Its construction points to a considerable effort with some of the stones weighing up to 50 tons each and with 80 stones being brought from the Preseli Mountains in South Wales, well over 200 miles. Imagine the problems involved in such a journey. Stonehenge illustrates the sophistication of the culture in those distant times. Not only was there the organisation, and also the resources to manage a scheme of this scale, but those prehistoric builders aligned the stone avenue with sunrise on Midsummer's Day.

Taking the A30, one of the many Roman roads in the area, the next town is **Stockbridge** on the River Test with its unusally wide High Street, followed by the final destination, **Andover**, now a busy modern town but a place with a long history as shown by the coaching inns and traces of Iron Age encampments on hills nearby.

## ANTIQUE DEALERS

### GREAT SHEFFORD (01488)

**Ivy House Antiques,** Wantage Road, RG16 7DA TEL: 648549 PARKING: Medium MIN: £1 MAX: £1000 PERIOD: 18th-20th century SPECIALIST: Country furniture & collectables GENERAL: Kitchenalia, collectors items, pine, Victoriana. OTHER INFO: Shop is in a thatched, beamed cottage. Location A338, M4, Jn 14 only 2 miles away.

### HUNGERFORD (01488)

**Ashley Antiques**, Hungerford Arcade TEL: (0672) 20481(ANS) PARKING: Easy OPEN: Mon-Sat 9.30-5.30, Sun 10-6 MIN: £5 MAX: £1500 PERIOD: 17th-20th century GENERAL: General antiques OTHER INFO: Apart from Arcade, over 20 shops a walk away. Hotels: Three Swans, Bear.

**Below Stairs**, 103 High Street, RG17 0NB TEL: 682317 PARKING: Easy OPEN: Seven days 10-6 MIN: £10 MAX: £2-3000 PERIOD: 19th century SPECIALIST: Kitchen antiques, bedroom furniture, lighting, decorative garden items, taxidermy, interior fittings, interesting collectables OTHER INFO: No modern or repro, emphasis on good English items.

**Sir William Bentley Billiards**, Standen Manor Farm, RG17 0RB TEL: 681711 FAX: 685197 PARKING: Own carpark OPEN: Anytime by appt PERIOD: 18th-20th century SPECIALIST: Largest stock of billiard tables in Europe. GENERAL: Dining/boardroom tables.

**The Fire Place (Hungerford) Ltd**, The Old Fire Station, Charnham Street, RG17 0EP TEL: 683420 PARKING: Easy OPEN: Mon-Sat 10-1, 2.15-5 MIN: £10 MAX: £2000 PERIOD: 19th-20th century SPECIALIST: Fireplace furnishings especially fenders GENERAL: Paintings.

**Garden Art,** Bath Road, RG17 0HE TEL: 681881 FAX: 681882 PARKING: Own carpark OPEN: Mon-Sat 10-6, Sun 12-6 MIN: £10 MAX: £10,000 PERIOD: 19th century SPECIALIST: Gates & statuary GENERAL: Garden pieces OTHER INFO: 1.2 acres of big beautiful & bizarre madness!

**Robert & Georgina Hastie**, 35a High Street, RG17 0NF TEL: 682873, (0860) 641560 ASSNS: LAPADA PARKING: Easy OPEN: Mon-Sat 9.30-5 (closed August) MIN: £40 MAX: £5000 PERIOD: 18th-20th century GENERAL: Furniture & objects.

**The Hungerford Pine Company,** 14-15 Charnham Street, RG17 0ES TEL: 686935 FAX: 686936 PARKING: Own carpark OPEN: Mon-Sat 9.30-5.30, Sun 11-5.30 MIN: £30 MAX: £2000 PERIOD: 18th-19th century SPECIALIST: Unusual Continental & English stripped pine of all sorts, even the occasional stripped pine washing machine!

**Roger King Antiques**, 111 High Street, RG17 0NB TEL: 682256 PARKING: Easy OPEN: Mon-Sat 9.30-5 MIN: £50 MAX: £2000 PERIOD: 19th century GENERAL: Georgian & Victorian furniture.

**Medalcrest Ltd**, 29-30 Charnham Street TEL: 684157 PARKING: Easy OPEN: Mon-Sat 9.30-5 MIN: £200 MAX: £10,000 PERIOD: 17th-19th century SPECIALIST: Clocks & barometers GENERAL: Georgian furniture & country oak OTHER INFO: The Bear Hotel, Behind the Green Door, The John of Gaunt, Dundas Arms.

**The Old Malthouse**, 15 Bridge Street, RG17 0EG TEL & FAX: 682209 ASSNS: BADA, CINOA PARKING: Easy OPEN: Mon-Sat 10-5.30 MIN: £25 MAX: £25,000 PERIOD: 18th-19th century SPECIALIST: Walnut furniture GENERAL: Furniture, mirrors, barometers, general antiques OTHER INFO: Interesting town with ancient rites handed down from John of Gaunt.

**Riverside Antiques Ltd**, Charnham Street, RG17 0EP TEL: 682314 PARKING: Own carpark OPEN: Mon-Sat 10-5.30 MIN: £50 MAX: £5000 PERIOD: 18th-20th century SPECIALIST: Georgian mahogany OTHER INFO: All items carefully restored.

**Styles Silver**, 12 Bridge Street, RG17 0EH TEL: 683922 ASSNS: LAPADA PARKING: Easy OPEN: Mon-Sat 9.30-5.30 (closed school holidays) MIN: £5 MAX: £5000 PERIOD: 18th-20th century SPECIALIST: Silver of all periods OTHER INFO: On receipt of SAE will send out leaflet *Guide to Antiques in Hungerford* listing dealers.

## RAMSBURY (01672)

**Heraldry Today**, Parliament Piece, Back Lane, SN8 2QH TEL: 29617 FAX: 20183 ASSNS: ABA PARKING: Own carpark OPEN: Mon-Fri 9-4.30 MIN: £3 MAX: £6000 PERIOD: 17th-20th century SPECIALIST: Heraldic & genealogical books in all languages, also peerage, family history, biography, history, topography and reference.

**Inglenook Antiques,** 59 High Street, SN8 2QN TEL: 20261 PARKING: Easy OPEN: 10-5, closed Mon & Wed MIN: £1 MAX: £2000 PERIOD: 18th-19th century SPECIALIST: 40 oil lamps always in stock GENERAL: Chandeliers & parts, longcase & wall clocks, metalware.

## MARLBOROUGH (01672)

**The Antique & Book Collector,** Katharine House, The Parade, SN8 1NE TEL: 514040 ASSNS: PBFA PARKING: Easy OPEN: Mon-Sat 9.45-5.30 MIN: £10 MAX: £2000 PERIOD: 18th-20th century (antiquities 1500 BC-500 AD) SPECIALIST: Modern British pictures, Roman glass & other antiquities GENERAL: General antiques, books.

**Cavendish House Antiques Centre,** 138 High Street, SN8 1HN TEL: 511875 PARKING: Easy OPEN: 7 days 10-5 GENERAL: General antiques.

**Cross Keys Jewellers**, 21a High Street, Hilliers Yard, SN8 lLW TEL: 516260 ASSNS: IJL PARKING: Easy OPEN: Mon-Sat 9.30-5.30 MIN: £1 MAX: £3000 PERIOD: 20th century SPECIALIST: Antique (mainly rings & amber) jewellery GENERAL: Jewellery & watches OTHER INFO: In main carpark entrance near Polly Tearooms.

**Knicknackertorium**, Loncraines, 4 London Road, SN8 1PH TEL: 513593 PARKING: Easy OPEN: Thurs-Sat 9-6.30 MIN: £1 MAX: £1000 PERIOD: 18th-20th century SPECIALIST: Glasses, pictures GENERAL: General antiques.

**The Marlborough Parade Antique Centre**, The Parade, SN8 1NE TEL: 515331 PARKING: Medium OPEN: Seven days 10-5 MAX: £5000 PERIOD: 18th-20th century GENERAL: Very high quality stock, we have 50+ dealers covering almost everything OTHER INFO: We are frequently told by the public and trade that we have the best antique centre in Britain.

**Military Parade Bookshop,** The Parade, SN8 1NE TEL: 515470 FAX: (01980) 630150 PARKING: Easy OPEN: Mon-Sat 10-5 MIN: 50p MAX: £300 PERIOD: pre 17th-20th century SPECIALIST: Napoleonic, First World War, manuals, military, all periods, approx 6000 titles.

**Principia Fine Art**, 5 London Road, SN8 1PH TEL: 512072 FAX: 511551 PARKING: Easy OPEN: Mon-Sat 9.30-5.30 PERIOD: 2000 BC to 19th century GENERAL: Collectables including pottery, fabrics, objets de vertu, scientific & decorative.

**Annmarie Turner Antiques**, 22 Salisbury Road, SN8 4AD TEL: 515396 PARKING: Own carpark OPEN: Mon-Sat 10-6 or by appt (resident so ring side door bell) MIN: £5 MAX: £1500 PERIOD: 18th-19th century SPECIALIST: Welsh items GENERAL: Country furniture, decorative & unusual items OTHER INFO: We usually give a plant or 2nd hand book to anyone spending £25 or more.

## MILTON LILBOURNE (01672)

**Rupert Gentle Antiques,** The Manor House, SN9 5LQ TEL: 63344 FAX: 64136 ASSNS: BADA PARKING: Own carpark OPEN: Mon-Sat 9-6 or by appt MIN: £50 MAX: £10,000 PERIOD: 17th-19th century SPECIALIST: English & Continental domestic metalwork GENERAL: Furniture, needlework & accessories.

## SWINDON (01793)

**Allan Smith Antique Clocks**, Amity Cottage, 162 Beechcroft Road, Upper Stratton, SN2 6QE TEL: 822977 PARKING: Own carpark OPEN: Anytime by appt MIN: £995 MAX: £7950 PERIOD: 17th-19th century SPECIALIST: Longcase clocks usually 30+ in stock GENERAL: Bracket, lantern, fusee dial, weight driven Vienna. Barometers OTHER INFO: 100 yards from Baker Arms pub.

**Antiques & All Pine**, 11 Newport Street, SN1 3DX TEL: 520259 PARKING: Easy OPEN: Mon 10-4, Tues, Thurs-Sat 10-5.30 MIN: £3 MAX: £1000 PERIOD: 20th century SPECIALIST: Pine country furniture GENERAL: General antiques & special size mattresses for old pine beds.

**Marlborough Bookshop & Sporting Gallery**, Unit 22, Cheney Manor, SN2 2PJ TEL: 421458 FAX: 421640 PARKING: Own carpark OPEN: Mon-Fri 9-4.30 MIN: £10 MAX: £5000 PERIOD: 19th-20th century SPECIALIST: We are country's biggest dealers in equestrian prints and watercolours.

**Victoria Bookshop,** 30 Wood Street, Old Town, SN1 4AB TEL: 527364 ASSNS: Booksellers Assn PARKING: Easy OPEN: 9-5.30 MIN: 50p MAX: £50 PERIOD: 19th-20th century GENERAL: New & secondhand books, old postcards, ephemera OTHER INFO: The Old Town was the original Swindon before Brunel's Great Western Railway.

## MINETY (01666)

**Sambourne House Antiques**, Sambourne House, SN16 9RQ TEL & FAX: 860288 PARKING: Own carpark OPEN: Mon-Sat 8.30-5.30 MIN: £2 MAX: £3000 PERIOD: 19th-20th century SPECIALIST: Antique pine, kitchens & furniture made from reclaimed pine OTHER INFO: Recommend the Smoking Dog pub, Malmesbury, & Wild Duck, Ewen - supplied both with tables & chairs.

## BRINKWORTH (01666)

**North Wilts Exporters**, Farm Hill House, SN15 5AJ TEL: 510876 PARKING: Own carpark OPEN: Mon-Sat 9-5 or by appt MIN: £1 MAX: £5000 PERIOD: 19th-20th century SPECIALIST: Pine, antiques & shipping goods.

## WOOTTON BASSETT (01793)

**Tubbjoys Antiques Market**, 118 High Street, SN4 7AY TEL: 849499 PARKING: Own carpark OPEN: Seven days 10-5 MIN: £5 MAX: £1000 PERIOD: 19th-20th century GENERAL: 15 units. General antiques OTHER INFO: Good coffee shop in market, B&B in town (out of hours opening).

## CALNE (01249)

**Calne Antiques**, 2a London Road TEL: 816311 PARKING: Own carpark OPEN: Seven days 10-5 or by appt MIN: £l0 MAX: £2000 PERIOD: 19th-20th century GENERAL: Stripped pine, mahogany, satinwalnut, oak. Smalls 1800-1950 OTHER INFO: Largest selection of furniture in the area priced £100-500. Help given for local accommodation & visits.

**Sophie Dupre & Clive Farahar**, XIV The Green, SN11 8DQ TEL & FAX: 821121 ASSNS: ABA, ILAB PARKING: Own carpark OPEN: By appt MIN: £5 MAX: £5000 PERIOD: 17th-20th century SPECIALIST: Autograph letters & manuscripts, rare books on voyages & travels.

## CHERHILL (01249)

**PA OXLEY ANTIQUES CLOCKS THE OLD RECTORY, SN11 8UX TEL: 816227 FAX: 821285 ASSNS: LAPADA PARKING: OWN CARPARK MIN: £300 MAX: £30,000 PERIOD: 17TH-19TH CENTURY SPECIALIST: ANTIQUE CLOCKS & BAROMETERS GENERAL: OVER 40 RESTORED QUALITY LONGCASE CLOCKS. GUARANTEED AND DELIVERED UK OTHER INFO: EXCELLENT TOURIST AREA, AVEBURY STONE CIRCLE 3 MILES.**

## DEVIZES (01380)

**The Antiquary,** 10 Northgate Street, SN10 1JL TEL: 722018 PARKING: Easy OPEN: Erratic hours, best by appt PERIOD: 17th-19th century SPECIALIST: Oak, metalware, pottery, primitive paintings.

**Cross Keys Jewellers**, The Ginnel, The Market Place, SN10 1HN TEL: 726293 ASSNS: IJL PARKING: Easy OPEN: Mon-Sat 9.30-5.30 MIN: £1 MAX: £3000 PERIOD: 20th century SPECIALIST: Antique (mainly rings & amber) jewellery GENERAL: Jewellery & watches.

**McElleavey Antiques & Interiors,** Rear of 4 Northgate Street, SN10 1JL TEL: 728572 PARKING: Easy MIN: £5 MAX: £5000 PERIOD: 16th-late 19th century GENERAL: English & Continental furniture, faience, metalware, small decorative items, garden statuary.

**Margaret Mead Antiques,** 17 Northgate Street, SN10 1JT TEL: 721060 PARKING: Easy OPEN: Tues, Thurs-Sat 10-5 GENERAL: Furniture, brass, collectables.

**St Marys Chapel Antiques,** Northgate Street, TEL: 721399 PARKING: Own carpark OPEN: Wed-Sat 10-6 or by appt MIN: £10 MAX: £8000 PERIOD: 18th-19th century GENERAL: 6000 sq ft: furniture, some smalls.

## POTTERNE (01380)

**The Antique Gallery**, 17 High Street, SN10 5NA TEL: 728007 PARKING: Easy OPEN: Fri-Sat 10-5 & by appt PERIOD: 17th-19th century SPECIALIST: Looking glasses, antique picture frames GENERAL: Furniture, architectural items, decorative antiques.

## HEYTESBURY (01985)

**Edmond Fellowes Antiques,** 69 High Street, BA12 0EB TEL: 212727 (Shop), 841001 (Home) FAX: 846042 ASSNS: LAPADA PARKING: Easy OPEN: By appt only MIN: £50 MAX: £10,000 PERIOD: 18th-early 19th century SPECIALIST: Georgian & Regency small furniture, sporting prints & caricatures, porcelain & decorative items of the period OTHER INFO: While most of my business is done at fairs, I am very pleased to show stock by appt. Heytesbury has a super pub, the Angel, which serves excellent food & has rooms.

## HINDON (01747)

**Monkton Galleries**, High Street, SP3 6DR TEL: 820235 PARKING: Own carpark OPEN: Mon-Sat 9-5.30, closed Wed MIN: £25 MAX: £10,000 PERIOD: 17th-18th century SPECIALIST: Early oak & country furniture & metalwork GENERAL: Pottery, treen & other decorative items OTHER INFO: Opp.country hotel & restaurant: The Lamb.

## GILLINGHAM (01747)

**Talisman**, The Old Brewery, Wyke, SP8 4NW TEL: 824423 FAX: 823544 ASSNS: LAPADA PARKING: Easy OPEN: Mon-Fri 9-6, Sat 10-5 MIN: £5 MAX: £50,000 PERIOD: 17th-20th century GENERAL: English & Continental furniture, mirrors, paintings, garden furniture & statuary, decorative & unusual objects.

## TISBURY (01747)

**Edward Marnier Antiques**, 17 High Street, SP3 6HF TEL: 870213 PARKING: Easy OPEN: Mon-Sat 10-5.30 MIN: £4 MAX: £4000 PERIOD: 17th-20th century SPECIALIST: Old rugs, carpets GENERAL: Furniture, pictures, mirrors & interesting decorative objects OTHER INFO: Howards House Hotel, Teffont. BR Station, Wardour Castle, Stourhead House, Fonthill Abbey.

**Carol Pearson Antiques**, 2-3 High Street, SP3 6PS TEL: 871165 PARKING: Easy OPEN: Mon-Sat 10-5, Wed & Sun by appt MIN: £15 MAX: £15,000 PERIOD: 18th-19th century SPECIALIST: Oil paintings & furniture GENERAL: Porcelain, oils & watercolours OTHER INFO: Ancient Dower House for meals & accommodation.

## WILTON (01722)

**Ian J Brook Antiques & Fine Art**, 26 North Street, SP2 OHJ TEL: 743392 PARKING: Own carpark OPEN: Mon-Sat 8.45-6 MIN: £10 MAX: £5000 PERIOD: 18th-19th century SPECIALIST: Fine oil paintings & watercolours. Fine mahogany & oak furniture & small items.

**Earle**, 47 North Street, SP2 0HE TEL: 743284 PARKING: Easy OPEN: Mon, Tues, Thurs-Sat 9-5 PERIOD: 20th century GENERAL: Small furniture & china.

**Hingstons of Wilton**, 36 North Street, SP2 0HJ TEL: 742263 FAX: 812143 PARKING: Own carpark OPEN: Mon-Fri 9-5.30, Sat 9.30-1.30 MIN: £10 MAX: £3750 PERIOD: 19th-20th century SPECIALIST: Furniture, mahogany, walnut, oak.

**Pamela Lynch**, 18 West Street, SP2 0DF TEL: 744113 PARKING: Easy (Market Square) OPEN: Mon-Sat 10-5 but resident MIN: £48 MAX: £2000 PERIOD: 18th-19th century SPECIALIST: Enamel boxes, needlework pictures & watercolours GENERAL: Furniture & some porcelain OTHER INFO: Carpet factory due to Huguenot refugees, church & hotel: The Pembroke Arms.

## SALISBURY (01722)

**John Amos Antiques**, 7a St. John Street, SP1 2SB TEL: 330888 PARKING: Medium OPEN: Mon, Tues, Thur, Fri 9.30-1.30, 2.30-5, Sat 9.30-1.30 MAX: £400 PERIOD: 19th-20th century GENERAL: Mainly porcelain & china with small furniture & some brass, copper, glass & silver.

**Antique & Collectors Market**, 37 Catherine Street, SP1 2DH TEL: 326033 PARKING: Easy OPEN: Mon-Sat 9-5.30 MIN: £1 MAX: £500 PERIOD: 19th-20th century SPECIALIST: Silver, plate, old toys GENERAL: All type antiques & collectables OTHER INFO: 3 floors & 20 dealers.

**DM Beach,** 52 High Street, SP1 2PG TEL: 333801 FAX: 333720 ASSNS: ABA PARKING: Easy OPEN: Mon-Sat 9-5.30 PERIOD: 16th-20th century SPECIALIST: Rare books GENERAL: Second hand & antiquarian books, prints, maps, watercolours, oils OTHER INFO: Main shop built before 1341,, established 63 years.

**Derek Boston,** 223 Wilton Road, SP2 7JY TEL: 322682 PARKING: Easy OPEN: 10-5.30 MIN: £50 MAX: £25,000 PERIOD: 18th-19th century SPECIALIST: Fine rare articles of museum interest GENERAL: Inlaid & marquetry furniture.

**Robert Bradley Antiques**, 71 Brown Street, SP1 2BA TEL: 333677 PARKING: Easy OPEN: Mon-Fri 9.30-5.30 MIN: £200 MAX: £50,000 PERIOD: 17th-18th century GENERAL: English furniture & related objects.

**Ronald Carr**, 6 St. Francis Road, SP1 3QS TEL: 328892 FAX: 328593 PARKING: Easy OPEN: Anytime by appt MIN: £5 MAX: £1000 PERIOD: 19th-20th century SPECIALIST: Modern British etchings 1850-1940 GENERAL: Wood-engravings & woodcuts OTHER INFO: Pleasant countryside, Cathedral, interesting city with many good English pubs for meals.

**Castle Galleries**, 81 Castle Street, SP1 3SP TEL: 333734 PARKING: Easy OPEN: Tues, Thurs, Fri 9-5, Sat 9-2 PERIOD: 18th-20th century SPECIALIST: Coins, medals GENERAL: Gold, silver, jewellery, objets d'art OTHER INFO: Come & 'medal' with Castle Galleries!

**John & Judith Head,** The Barn Book Supply, 88 Crane Street, SP1 2QD TEL: 327767 FAX: 339888 ASSNS: ABA PARKING: Medium OPEN: Mon-Sat 9.30-5 PERIOD: 17th-20th century SPECIALIST: Books on angling, shooting, horses GENERAL: Books on field sports with small stock of mixed subjects.

**Edward Hurst Antiques,** Stirling House, Paynes Hill, SP1 2BN TEL: 320595 PARKING: Easy OPEN: Mon-Fri 9.30-5.30, Sat by appt PERIOD: 1650-1820 SPECIALIST: Country house furniture & decorative items.

**The Jerram Gallery**, 7 St John Street, SP1 2SB TEL: 412310 PARKING: Easy OPEN: Mon-Fri 9.30-5.30, Sat 10-4 MIN: £100 MAX: £15,000 PERIOD: 1850-1950 & contemporary artists SPECIALIST: Figurative etchings, watercolours, oils & sculpture.

**Micawber's**, 53 Fisherton Street, SP2 7SU TEL: 337822 PARKING: Easy OPEN: Mon, Tues, Thurs-Sat 9.30-5 MIN: £1 MAX: £700 PERIOD: 19th-20th century SPECIALIST: Jewellery, clothes, military, prints GENERAL: General antiques OTHER INFO: Market 4 floors.

**AJ Romain & Sons,** The Old House, 11 North Street, SP2 0HA TEL: 743350 PARKING: Easy OPEN: 9-5.30, closed Wed pm PERIOD: 17th-19th century SPECIALIST: Oak GENERAL: Mahogany, walnut, brass, china, bronze.

**Chris Wadge Clocks**, 142 Fisherton Street, SP2 7QT TEL: 334467 FAX: 334467 PARKING: Medium OPEN: Tues-Sat 9-1, 2-5 MIN: £1 MAX: £2500 PERIOD: 19th-20th century SPECIALIST: 400 day clocks GENERAL: Clocks: longcase, Vienna regulators, carriage plus barometers OTHER INFO: New clocks & barometers also. 10 mins from Tourist Advice Centre, bus station, 5 mins from Cathedral, 2 mins from railway station.

## STOCKBRIDGE (01264)

**George Hoffman**, At The Sign of The Black Cat, High Street, SO20 6EY TEL: 810570 PARKING: Easy OPEN: Mon-Sat 9.30-5.30 MIN: £1 MAX: £2500 PERIOD: 17th-20th century SPECIALIST: Furniture GENERAL: Brass, pewter, lamps etc - no jewels or silver OTHER INFO: River walks plenty of ducks and fish, Pleasant street.

**Stockbridge Antiques**, High Street, SO20 6EX TEL: 810829 ASSNS: LAPADA PARKING: Easy OPEN: 9.30-5 MIN: £10 MAX: £9000 PERIOD: 18th century SPECIALIST: Georgian glass/silver GENERAL: Mahogany furniture, interesting gilts, early Victorian porcelain OTHER INFO: Something for all tastes. Very small historic town. Centre of trout fishing on River Test. Good restaurants, beautiful walks, Danebury Hill Fort. Halfway between Winchester & Salisbury. Wide main street.

## ANDOVER (01264)

**Parker Fine Art Ltd,** Finkley House, Finkley, SP11 6AE TEL: 352412 FAX: 358241 PARKING: Own carpark OPEN: By appt MIN: £200 MAX: £100,000 PERIOD: 17th-20th century.

# Dorset

Dorset is the county of Thomas Hardy and many of the places have strong associations with the writer. The countryside ranges from rolling farmland to uncultivated heaths. Much of the county is extremely beautiful and unspoilt.

The starting point is **Wimborne Minster.** The town's outstanding feature is the Minster with its two towers and walls of red sandstone and pale limestone. There has been a church on this site since AD 713 when a nunnery was built. The present church dates from Norman times although it was enlarged in the 13th and 15th centuries. Amongst the many interesting features are a 14th century astronomical clock showing the sun and moon orbiting the earth, a fine chained library and a 17th century sundial which used to be on a gable but was blown down and relocated below the west tower.

The town also has an award-winning museum with the tongue-twisting name of the Priest's House Museum of East Dorset Life and Garden. Situated in the High Street, it is set in a beautiful walled garden and features a working Victorian kitchen, where cooking demonstations are given, a stationer's and an ironmonger's shops of the same period.

Stopping then in **Charlton Marshall**, the tour continues to **Blandford Forum** which, despite its name, was not a Roman town. A devastating fire in 1731 destroyed much of the town, two nearby villages and caused the death of 74 people so most of the buildings date from the 18th century. There is a memorial outside the church of St Peter and St Paul in the form of a portico once housing a pump. On it is inscribed "in remembrance of God's dreadful visitation by fire."

The next call is **Sturminster Newton**, Thomas Hardy's 'Stourcastle' and where he wrote *Return of the Native*. The town is reputed to hold England's largest calf market although the old Market Place has been partly built upon. Well worth a visit, Sturminster Newton Mill is set on a weir on the River Stour. There is a record of a mill on this site since the Domesday Book although the present building dates from the 17th century with later additions. Restoration was carried out in 1981 and it is open to the public. The mill is worked so visitors can see grain processed into flour and animal feed.

Further west, **Sherborne** is a pleasant country town on the River Yeo. The buildings are mainly Georgian, Regency and Victorian. Its main attraction is St Aldhelms Abbey with its wonderful 15th century fan vaulting and Gothic monument to the Digby family. It also contains all the 35 available colours (flags) of the Dorsetshire Regiment. Nearby there are 15th century almshouses and the Conduit, a roofed house where monks shaved their heads and washed.

Bishop Aldhelm built the church and famous school in the 8th century and two of King Alfred's brothers were buried here. It is said that King Alfred was educated at the school for a time. The town has two castles. Sir Walter Raleigh, the Elizabethan explorer and writer who ended on the scaffold, was given the 12th century castle by Elizabeth I. He then built a new one a few hundred yards away from the old castle on the site of a former hunting lodge. Legend has it that while Sir Walter was sitting in the grounds of his castle a servant found him smoking. Thinking his master was on fire he threw a bucket of water over him.

In the early 17th century Sir Walter's castle was enlarged by its new owner, Sir John Digby and in the 18th century Capability Brown laid out the grounds. During the Civil War the old castle was involved in two sieges, the second of which saw fierce fighting. When Parliamentary forces finally took it, the castle was rendered undefendable. Some ruins still remain.

The pretty villageof **Trent** seems very sheltered. Charles II was hidden for a fortnight in a manor house near the church immediately after the 1651 Battle of Worcester. **Melbury Osmond,** lies 10 miles south, via Yeovil and the next call is at **Beaminster.** Set in a designated area of outstanding natural beauty, the town retains many of its older buildings. Much was rebuilt in the 18th century after a fire although it still has the beautiful 15th century church of St Mary. The story goes that victims of Judge Jeffreys' 'Bloody Assizes' were hung from this church

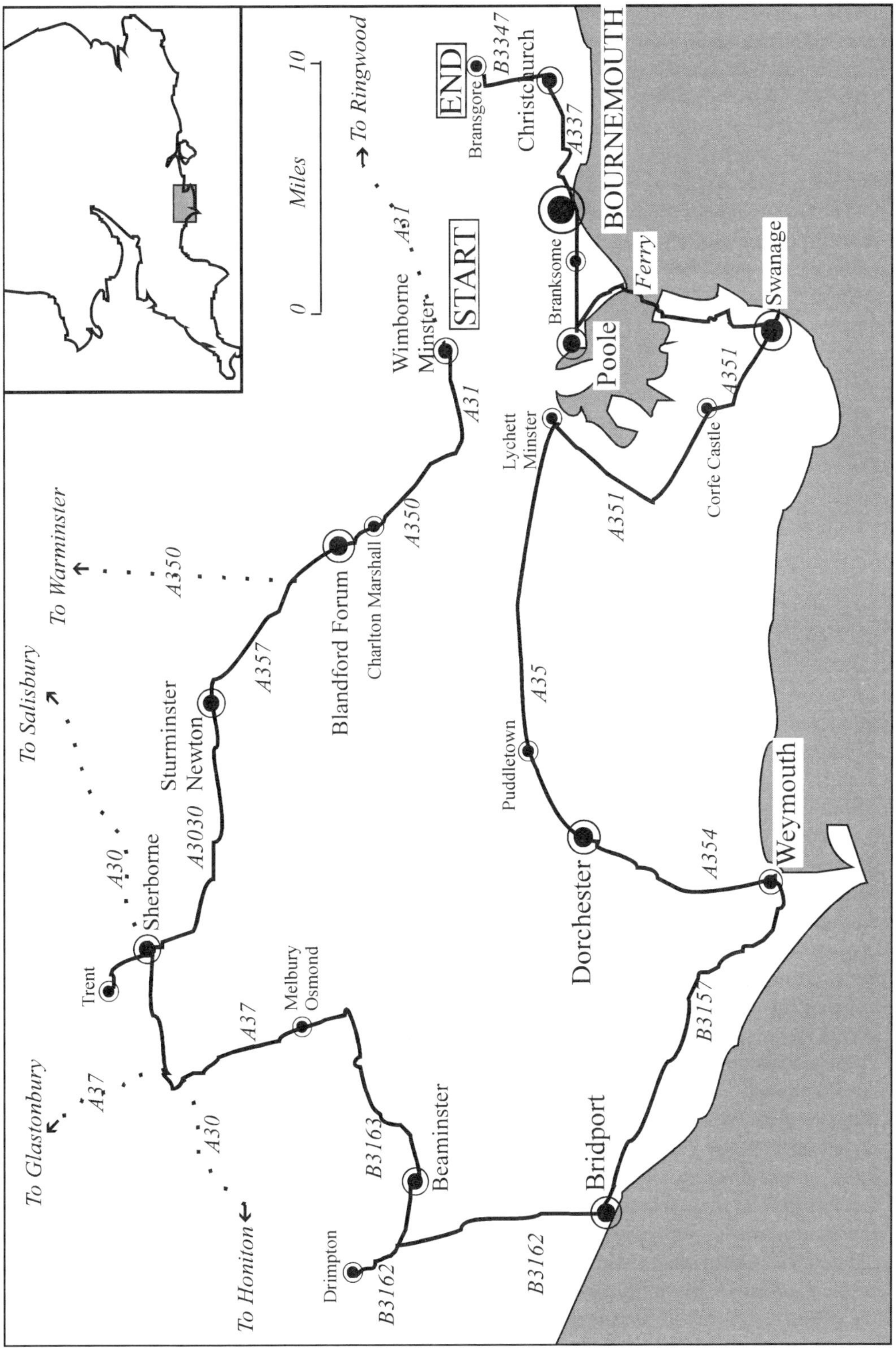
START
END
Wimborne Minster
A31
To Ringwood
Miles
0
10
Bransgore
B3347
Christchurch
A337
BOURNEMOUTH
Branksome
Ferry
Poole
Swanage
A351
Corfe Castle
Lychett Minster
A351
To Warminster
A350
Blandford Forum
Charlton Marshall
A350
To Salisbury
A357
Sturminster Newton
A3030
A30
Sherborne
Trent
Melbury Osmond
A37
To Glastonbury
A37
A30
To Honiton
Beaminster
B3163
Drimpton
B3162
B3162
Bridport
B3157
Dorchester
Puddletown
A35
A354
Weymouth

tower. Close to the town there are two large houses of note: Mapperton and Parnham. Mapperton is a Tudor manor set in lovely terraced gardens. The restored manor at Parnham is, instead, Elizabethan and surrounded by gardens designed by Inigo Jones.

The tour then visits **Drimpton** before turning for the coast and **Bridport.** Called Port Bredy by Thomas Hardy, the principal industry of rope and net-making, important here for 750 years, has had an effect on the streets. They are unusually wide and were once used to lay out new rope and nets. There are many fine Georgian buildings including the town hall.

The route continues along the line of the coast to **Weymouth,** also with fine Georgian buildings. A port and holiday resort, the town has royal connections. King George III once lived in Gloucester House, now a hotel, and there is a statue of him in the town.

Turning inland, **Dorchester** is a very ancient settlement and once the Roman town of *Durnovaria*. The remains of a Roman villa have been found in Colliton Park behind the Council Offices and Maumbury Rings, formerly a henge or stone circle, was converted by the Romans into an amphitheatre where gladiators fought for the gratification of the crowd.

Judge Jeffreys held his Bloody Assize here in 1685. Out of 300 prisoners who were tried, 292 were sentenced to death and 74 hung within the city walls. Almost 150 years later, in 1839, Dorchester was associated with another infamous trial, that of the Tolpuddle Martyrs. They combined to demand a wage increase but because unions and fraternities were illegal they were sentenced to transportation. The Old Shire Hall, where they were put on trial, is now the Tolpuddle Memorial.

Perhaps the most famous and finest earth fortress in Europe, Maiden Castle, stands 2 miles south-west of Dorchester and really, must be seen. Stone Age remains have been found here although now there is no visible trace of these earliest settlers. However, Iron Age inhabitants vastly expanded the settlement. Covering some 120 acres, it could accommodate perhaps some 5000 people. Using a simple ditch and bank system, the complexity grew as time went on. More banks were added to the original fortifications and it is suggested that these prevented attackers coming close enough to effectively use a sling. There were two gates which, by the 1st century AD, were reinforced with limestone blocks.

With the Roman invasion of Britain, inevitably Maiden Castle had to be subdued. Under the command of Vespasian (later to be Emperor), the 2nd Augustan Legion attacked the fortification under cover of darkness. Their aim was to break through the more lightly defended Eastern Gate. First it was bombarded by *ballistae* (powerful crossbow devices mounted on frames), then the legion moved in and fought from rampart to rampart until the fortress fell. Archeologists have found skeletons bearing the marks of that battle: one had an arrowhead from the *ballistae* embedded in the vertebra and others show signs of sword cuts. Although the Romans allowed the settlement to continue after the castle had been rendered defenceless, it was abandoned by about 70 AD.

Next is **Puddletown,** lying on the edge of open heathland, the Egdon Heath of Thomas Hardy's novels. It has a fine perpendicular church with the west gallery supported on pillars. One of the finest medieval houses in England, Athelhampton, is situated about a mile east. Built in 1485 on the site of King Athelstan's palace, it is set in 10 acres and the house contains heraldic glass, linenfold panelling and a good collection of furniture. Nearby Dawnay House is also notable. Said by Sir John Betjeman to be the amongst his favourite Dorsetshire houses, although Georgian it is built in the Queen Anne style with collections of antiques, antiquities and oriental art.

15 miles east is **Lytchett Minster** and then the route turns south to Wareham, a town standing within earthworks, and probably Saxon in origin being built as a defence against Viking raiders. Large parts still remain and the north west section is called 'Bloody Bank' because of the executions carried out there after the Monmouth Rebellion. The town is quartered by East, West, South and North Streets which meet in the centre. The church of St Paul dates in parts from the 11th century and a memorial to Lawrence of Arabia is inside. Lady St Mary's Church

contains the coffin of Edward the Martyr and an unusual six sided lead font.

The A351 then heads for **Corfe Castle**, a fortification that covers more than three acres. This Norman castle's finest hour came under the command of a woman during the Civil War. In 1643 it was besieged by Parliamentary forces but Lady Banks resisted. The besiegers made great endeavours to subdue the determined forces inside including bringing up heavy guns, some of which were mounted on a church tower in the village and lead from the roof was melted to make bullets. Another battery of guns was positioned on the west side of the castle. In spite of the bombardment Lady Banks and the garrison still held out. Finally the Parliamentary forces withdrew and the castle was left in peace for three years. Then Lady Banks went to London and the Parliamentary forces again attacked but this time the castle was betrayed and fell to the attackers. Two-thirds of the castle was blown up by the victorious army but about 60 feet of the keep is still intact.

*Corfe Castle*

**Swanage**, was once the centre of the Purbeck stone industry which was used to decorate many English cathedrals. Now it is a popular seaside resort with sandy bathing beaches and the nearby Durlston Country Park which includes the cliffs of Durlston Head. Two of the town's attractions have been transplanted from London. Wellington Clocktower near the pier once stood at the end of London Bridge and was moved here in 1867. The facade of the Town Hall was formerly the front of the Mercers' Hall in Cheapside.

Using the ferry, the tour continues to **Poole,** a town with a long history going back to at least the 13th century when it was developed on the north side of a natural harbour. It became a thriving port and in the 17th and 18th century specialised in trading with Newfoundland. The 19th century church of St James illustrates this trade with its Newfoundland pine pillars. The town has houses of historic note: almshouses built in the reign of Henry V, the Guildhall from 1761 (now a museum) and the house of Sir Peter Thompson, in Market Close, built in 1746. The Customs House, on the Quay, was originally a late 18th century building but was rebuilt in 1813 after a fire.

The town has several museums: the Guildhall Museum showing aspects of Poole through the ages, the Old Lifeboat House on East Quay, the Royal National Lifeboat Museum on West Quay, Scaplen's Court Museum housed in a 15th century building and concentrating on domestic history, Waterfront in the High Street, mostly devoted to the town's maritime past although there is also a reconstruction of a Victorian street.

Poole harbour, enclosed by the peninsulas of Studland and Sandbanks, is one of the largest natural harbours in the world and for centuries has been a safe haven for sailors. There are five islands within the harbour, the largest of which is Brownsea, the site of Lord Baden-Powell's first camp for 20 boys in 1907, a pre-curser to the Scout movement which he founded. The northern part is a nature reserve where red squirrels, now extinct throughout much of Britain, may be found. Brownsea can be visited by ferry from either Poole Quay or Sandbanks.

After a visit to **Branksome, Bournemouth** is next. A relative upstart in this ancient and historic area, the first house was built in 1810 on the site of the present Royal Exeter Hotel. The long sandy beaches and pleasant wooded chines have guaranteed the town's success as a holiday resort. There are two fine museums to visit: the Russell-Cotes Art Gallery and Museum, housed in a Victorian mansion on East Cliff and the Shelley Rooms Museum in Boscombe in the former home of Percy Bysshe Shelley's son.

By contrast, **Christchurch,** at the meeting of the Rivers Stour and Avon, has a history going back at least to Saxon times when it was called Twyneham. Although some of the town has been modernised, evidence of the ancient past can still be seen. First and foremost is the magnificent church which gives the town its present name. At 311 feet in length, this is the longest parish church in England. Standing on the site of a 7th century church, building started in 1094 as part of Christchurch Priory. An interesting feature is the Miraculous Beam protruding through an arch in the south choir. This timber was cut a foot too short but during the night the beam was lengthened and put in place, according to legend, by Jesus Christ, hence the name Christchurch was given to the church.

Just to the north stand the ruins of Christchurch Castle, built in the 12th century and originally owned by the de Redvers family, Earls of Devon. Some of its owners met unfortunate ends: in 1541 the Countess of Salisbury was beheaded in the Tower of London and the Lord Protector, Edward Duke of Somerset, was executed in 1552. During the Civil War the castle was held for the King but was captured by Parliamentary forces in 1645. Five years later an order was made by Parliament for it to be demolished. Now all that remains are two walls of the Norman keep. However, a large part of the nearby Constable's House, dating from 1160, still stands. It is said that King Edward VI paid several visits to the house.

This tour ends in the small, picturesque village of **Bransgore.**

## ANTIQUE DEALERS

### WIMBORNE MINSTER (01202)

**Antiqua Tat Antiques,** Antiqua Tat House, Hanham Road, BH21 1AS TEL: 887496 FAX: 888424 ASSNS: LAPADA PARKING: Own carpark OPEN: Mon-Sat 9-5 £500 MAX: £30-40,000 PERIOD: 18th-19th century GENERAL: Furniture, dining tables & chairs, chests of drawers etc OTHER INFO: Good restaurant above showrooms.

**Barnes House Antiques**, 11a West Row TEL: 886275 PARKING: Easy OPEN: Mon-Sat 10-4.30 MIN: £5 MAX: £5000+ PERIOD: 17th-20th century GENERAL: Period oak and mahogany furniture, porcelain, silver, glass OTHER INFO: Kings Head Hotel, Priest's House Museum.

**Victoriana**, 3 Leigh Road TEL: 886739 PARKING: Easy OPEN: Tues, Thur, Sat 10-1, 2.30-4 MIN: £12 MAX: £300 PERIOD: 19th-20th century GENERAL: Silver, jewellery, glass, brass, china & small antiques OTHER INFO: Kingston Lacey House (NT), Good restaurants, Trust House.

**Terry White Antiques,** 13A Mill Lane TEL: 888958 PARKING: Easy OPEN: 10-1.30 MIN: £1 MAX: £1000 PERIOD: 18th-20th century SPECIALIST: Commemoratives, china, etc GENERAL: Small furniture.

### CHARLTON MARSHALL (01258)

**Zona Dawson Antiques**, The Old Club House, 2 The Close, DT11 9PA TEL: 453146 PARKING: Easy OPEN: Tues-Sat 10-5, Sun by appt (Closed June & closed September) MIN: £50 MAX: £2500

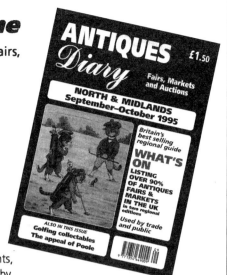

PERIOD: 18th-19th century GENERAL: Mahogany, oak, walnut furniture (mainly small) OTHER INFO: Diagonally opposite to Charlton Inn, on the corner of the main A350.

## BLANDFORD FORUM (01258)

**A & D Antiques**, 21 East Street, TEL: 455643 PARKING: Easy OPEN: Tues, Thurs-Sat 10-5, Wed 10-1 MIN: £10 MAX: £5000 PERIOD: 18th-20th century SPECIALIST: 18th century drinking glasses to Lalique, silver + plate.

**Ancient & Modern Bookshop**, 84 Salisbury Street DT11 7QE TEL: 455276 PARKING: Medium OPEN: Mon, Tues, Thurs-Sat 9.30-12.30, 1.30-5 MIN: £1 MAX: £500 PERIOD: 18th-20th century GENERAL: Books, antiques.

## STURMINSTER NEWTON (01258)

**Branksome Antiques**, Toll House, Bagber Lane, Bagber, DT10 2HS TEL: 472296 PARKING: Own carpark OPEN: By appt MIN: £20 MAX: £3000 PERIOD: 18th-20th century GENERAL: Georgian & Victorian furniture, general shipping goods OTHER INFO: Facilities for packing containers.

**Market Cross Antiques,** 2 Old Market Cross, DT10 1AN TEL: 473612 PARKING: Easy OPEN: Mon-Sat 10-5 PERIOD: 18th-20th century GENERAL: All varieties in complete price range OTHER INFO: Market day Monday.

**Quarter Jack Antiques**, Bridge Street, DT10 1BZ TEL: 472558 PARKING: Medium OPEN: Mon-Sat 9.5.30 MIN: £1 MAX: £1500 PERIOD: 18th-19th century SPECIALIST: Glass, walking sticks, corkscrews, brasses GENERAL: Furniture, pictures OTHER INFO: Monday Market.

**Tom Tribe & Son**, Bridge Street, DT10 1BZ TEL: 472311 PARKING: Easy OPEN: Mon-Fri 9-1, 2-5, Sat 9-1 MIN: Eng. longcase £1500 MAX: £8000 PERIOD: 18th-19th century SPECIALIST: English longcase clocks (20-30 always in stock) GENERAL: French carriage & mantel clocks, English bracket clocks. Mercurial barometers OTHER INFO: Working mill, town museum & our shop which has many horological items displayed but not for sale. Plumber Manor Hotel, high class food & accommodation. Swan Hotel.

## SHERBORNE (01935)

**Abbas Antiques**, 17 Newlands, DT9 3JG TEL: 0963-371019 PARKING: Easy OPEN: Mon-Sat 9.30-5 MIN: £5 MAX: £2000 PERIOD: 19th century GENERAL: Antiques.

**Antiques of Sherborne**, 1 The Green, DT9 5HZ TEL: 816549 PARKING: Easy OPEN: Mon-Sat 10-5 £2 MAX: £5000 PERIOD: 19th century SPECIALIST: Upholstery, beds, linen GENERAL: Furniture, decorative items OTHER INFO: Good display of early porcelain in Sherborne Castle.

**Dodge & Son**, 28-33 Cheap Street, DT9 3PU TEL: 815151 FAX: 816902 ASSNS: LAPADA PARKING: Own carpark OPEN: Mon-Sat 9-5.30 MIN: £10 MAX: £10,000 PERIOD: 18th-19th century SPECIALIST: Dining tables & chairs GENERAL: Furniture & pictures.

**Steven Ferdinando**, The Swan Gallery, 51 Cheap Street, DT9 3AX TEL: 814465 PARKING: Easy OPEN: Mon-Sat 9.30-5 (Weds halfday) MIN: £5 MAX: £2000 PERIOD: 19th-20th century SPECIALIST: Antiquarian books GENERAL: Old & out of print books. Maps, prints, watercolours.

**Fox & Co,** Long Street, DT9 3BS TEL: 816566 PARKING: Easy OPEN: Mon-Sat 10-5, closed Wed MAX: £2000 PERIOD: 17th-19th century SPECIALIST: Coins, militaria, antiquities GENERAL: Ethnographica, ephemera, country pottery, ceramics, pewter, etc.

**Greystoke Antiques**, Swan Yard, Cheap Street, DT9 3AX TEL: 812833 PARKING: Easy OPEN: Mon, Tues, Thurs-Sat 10-4.30 MIN: £5 MAX: £5000 PERIOD: 18th-20th century GENERAL: Silver OTHER INFO: Next to Old Market carpark.

**Heygate Browne**, South Street, DT9 3NG TEL: 815487 PARKING: Own carpark OPEN: Mon-Sat 10-5 £20 MAX: £10,000 PERIOD: 18th-19th century GENERAL: General antiques.

**The Nook Antiques**, South Street, DT9 3LX TEL: 813987 PARKING: Easy OPEN: Thurs-Sat 10-5 MIN: £5 MAX: £1100 PERIOD: 19th-20th century GENERAL: General antiques OTHER INFO: Half Moon Hotel, ex coaching stage. Free parking.

**The Swan Gallery**, 51 Cheap Street, DT9 3AX TEL: 814465 FAX: 01308 868195 PARKING: Easy OPEN: Mon-Sat 9.30-5, (Wed halfday) MIN: £10 MAX: £2500 PERIOD: 18th-20th century SPECIALIST: Victorian watercolours GENERAL: Maps, prints. Antiquarian & out of print books.

**Henry Willis,** 38 Cheap Street, DT9 3PX TEL: 816828 FAX: 816829 PARKING: Easy OPEN: 10-5 MIN: £20 MAX: £5000 SPECIALIST: English silver spoons pre 1700 GENERAL: Silver & plate.

## TRENT (01935)

**Old Barn Antiques**, Flamberts Trent, DT9 4SS TEL: 850648 PARKING: Own carpark OPEN: By appt MIN: £200 MAX: £10,000 PERIOD: 18th-19th century GENERAL: Mahogany furniture.

## MELBURY OSMOND (01935)

**Hardy Country**, Holt Mill Farm, DT2 OLX TEL: 873361 PARKING: Own carpark OPEN: Mon-Sat 9-4 MIN: £20 MAX: £1500 PERIOD: 19th-20th century SPECIALIST: Antique pine GENERAL: Old country furniture.

## BEAMINSTER (01308)

**Beaminster Antiques**, 4 Church Street, DT8 3AZ TEL: 862591 PARKING: Easy OPEN: Mon-Sat 10-4.30 MIN: £20 MAX: £1000 PERIOD: 18th-20th century SPECIALIST: Silver, sewing implements GENERAL: Porcelain, general collectors pieces OTHER INFO: A small shop packed with curiosity pieces.

**Good Hope Antiques**, 2 Hogshill Street, DT8 3AE TEL: 862119 PARKING: Easy OPEN: Mon, Thurs-Sat 9.30-5 PERIOD: 18th-19th century SPECIALIST: Longcase, bracket & wall clocks. Barometers GENERAL: Furniture.

## DRIMPTON (01308)

**Drimpton Antiques**, The Old Barn, Netherhay, DT8 3RH TEL: 867597 PARKING: Own carpark OPEN: Mon-Sat MIN: £2 MAX: £1500 PERIOD: 17th-20th century SPECIALIST: Samplers, oak furniture GENERAL: Bric a brac, pictures, garden items, china, silver plate OTHER INFO: 3 milking parlours of junk & bric a brac, 1 barn of antiques.

## BRIDPORT (01308)

**Pic's Bookshop**, 11 South Street, DT6 3NR TEL: 425689 PARKING: Easy OPEN: 9-4.30 MIN: £1 MAX: £200+ PERIOD: 18th-20th century GENERAL: Rare & general stock of secondhand books, 50 classifications. Reference libray to Dorset.

**Tudor House Antiques**, 88 East Street, DT6 3LL TEL: 427200 PARKING: Easy ASSNS: LAPADA OPEN: Mon-Sat 9-5.30 MIN: £10 MAX: £3000 PERIOD: 17th-19th century GENERAL: Furniture. Some oils, porcelain, silver, clocks etc.

**Westdale Antiques**, 18A St Michael's Trading Estate, DT6 3RR & Bridport Antique Centre, West Allington TEL: 427271 & 425885 PARKING: Medium OPEN: Mon-Sat 9-5 PERIOD: 19th century GENERAL: Taxidermy, lace, linen, jewellery.



## WEYMOUTH (01305)

**Books Afloat**, 66 Park Street, DT4 7DE TEL: 779774 PARKING: Easy OPEN: Mon-Sat 9.30-5.30 MIN: £1 MAX: £650 PERIOD: 19th-20th century SPECIALIST: Naval & maritime books, nautical hardware & ephemera GENERAL: Out of print books on all subjects, diecast toys, prints, pictures

**Nautical Antique Centre**, Old Harbour Passage, 3a Hope Square, DT4 8TR TEL: 777838, home 783180 PARKING: Easy OPEN: Tues-Sat 10-5.30 or by appt MIN: £1 MAX: £850 PERIOD: 19th-20th century SPECIALIST: All nautical, ships models, clocks, bells, lights, old chandlery, telescopes, etc. OTHER INFO: Opp. Brewers Quay Timewalk & Museum complex with full facilities.

**Park Antiquities,** 37 Park Street, DT4 7DF TEL: 787666 PARKING: Easy OPEN: 10-5, not Wed MIN: £1 MAX: £600 PERIOD: 19th -20th century OTHER INFO: Our clients crawl under tables to find the long lost items now really worth their price.

## DORCHESTER (01305)

**Box of Porcelain**, 51d Icen Way, DT1 1EW TEL: 250856 PARKING: Medium OPEN: Mon-Fri 10-4, Sat 10-5 MIN: £1 MAX: £2000 PERIOD: 19th-20th century SPECIALIST: Beswick, Doulton GENERAL: Quality porcelain: Worcester, Coalport, Derby etc OTHER INFO: Collectors finder service

## PUDDLETOWN (01305)

**The Antique Map & Bookshop**, DT2 8RU TEL: 846633 FAX: 848992 ASSNS: ABA PBFA PARKING: Medium OPEN: Mon-Sat 9-5 MIN: £1 MAX: £2,000 PERIOD: 17th-20th century SPECIALIST: Thomas Hardy/Dorset material, local antique maps & prints GENERAL: OTHER INFO: Various subjects such as illustrated books, English literature & Modern Firsts, UK & foreign travel etc.

## LYTCHETT MINSTER (01202)

**The Old Button Shop Antiques**, Dorchester Road, BH16 6JF TEL: 622169 PARKING: Own carpark OPEN: Tues-Fri 2-5, Sat 11-1 or by appt MIN: 50p MAX: £500 PERIOD: 17th-20th century SPECIALIST: Dorset buttons, antique buttons GENERAL: Antiques & curios OTHER INFO: The only place in the world where Dorset buttons can be bought at any time (in small numbers). These buttons are sometimes available at auctions etc but most come from this collection. Shop dates from 17th century & is connected with the 300 year old Dorset button industry. The shop is on the main street between 2 famous pubs, The Bakers Arms & St Peters Finger, good food at both.

## CORFE CASTLE (01929)

**Memory Lane,** 18A East Street, TEL: 480006 PARKING: Medium OPEN: Mon, Wed, Fri 2-5, Sat 10.30-5 PERIOD: 18th-20th century SPECIALIST: Worcester, Coalport GENERAL: Victorian furniture, china.

**Georgina Ryder Textiles**, Rempstone Hall, BH20 6LD TEL & FAX: 480382 ASSNS: LAPADA PARKING: Own carpark OPEN: By appt MIN: £250 MAX: £15,000 PERIOD: 17th-19th century SPECIALIST: Textiles & 18th & 19th century painted French furniture, tapestries & decorative items OTHER INFO: Heart of Hardys beautiful historic Dorset, next to Corfe Castle.

## SWANAGE (01929)

**Georgian Gems**, 28 High Street, BH19 2NU TEL: 424697 FAX: 426200 ASSNS: NAG, GA PARKING: Medium OPEN: Mon-sat 9.30-1, 2.30-5 (Thurs halfday winter only) or by appt MIN: £2 MAX: £5000 PERIOD: 18th-20th century SPECIALIST: Antique jewellery & silver OTHER INFO: We are the smallest jewellers in UK in the smallest shop, a 16th century building.

**Reference Works**, 12 Commercial Road, BH19 1DF TEL: 424423 FAX: 422597 PARKING: Medium OPEN: By appt MIN: £2 MAX: £600 PERIOD: 18th-20th century SPECIALIST: Reference books on antique pottery & porcelain of all countries. New & out of print. Small range of porcelain OTHER INFO: Steam railway, art galleries, The Galley, award-winning restaurant.

## POOLE (01202)

**Capricorn**, 15 Parr Street, Ashley Cross, Lower Parkstone TEL: 429712 PARKING: Easy OPEN: Mon, Tues, Thurs, Fri 9.30-4 £5 MAX: £500 PERIOD: 19th-20th century SPECIALIST: Porcelain & silver GENERAL: Small furniture, glass.

**DJ Jewellery**, 166-168 Ashley Road, Parkstone, BH14 9BY TEL: 745148 PARKING: Easy OPEN: Mon-Sat 9-5.30 MIN: £5 MAX: £2000 PERIOD: 19th-20th century SPECIALIST: Antique & modern jewellery, small silver, clocks & china OTHER INFO: We are between Poole & Bournemouth with both towns having ample hotels, restaurants and entertainment.

**Wiffen's Antiques & Furnishings**, 95-101 Bournemouth Road, Parkstone, BH14 0ER TEL: 736567 FAX: 717305 PARKING: Own carpark OPEN: Mon-Sat 9-5.30 MIN: £35 MAX: £15,000 PERIOD: 17th-20th century GENERAL: General antiques, statuary, architectural, garden pieces & replicas OTHER INFO: Dorset gives you the seaside & countryside. Lots of antiques & pleasure.

**Christopher Williams (Antiquarian Bookseller),** 19 Morrison Avenue, Parkstone, BH12 4AD TEL: 743157 ASSNS: PBFA PARKING: Easy OPEN: Anytime by appt MIN: £2 MAX: £1000 PERIOD: 19th-20th century SPECIALIST: Books on antiques, art, cookery GENERAL: Lacemaking & local history.

## BRANKSOME (01202)

**Allens (Branksome) Ltd**, 447-449 Poole Road, BH12 1DH TEL: 763724 FAX: 763724 PARKING: Medium OPEN: Mon-Sat 9-5.30 MIN: £20 MAX: £7500 PERIOD: 19th-20th century GENERAL: Clean good quality Victorian, Edwardian & 1920's OTHER INFO: Main road between Bournemouth & Poole

**Branksome Antiques**, 370 Poole Road, BH12 1AW TEL: 763324 PARKING: Medium OPEN: Mon, Tues, Thurs, Fri 10-4.30 £20 MAX: £10,000 PERIOD: 18th-20th century SPECIALIST: Marine & scientific instruments GENERAL: Georgian & Victorian furniture, china, copper, brass, clocks.

**David Mack Antiques**, 434-437 Poole Road TEL: 760005 FAX: 765100 PARKING: Own carpark OPEN: Mon-Sat 9-5.30 £200 MAX: £7000 PERIOD: 18th-20th century SPECIALIST: Dining room furniture GENERAL: Furniture and all aspects thereof OTHER INFO: In Bournemouth/ Poole conurbation with excellent transport facilities.

## BOURNEMOUTH (01202)

**Michael Andrews Antiques**, 916 Christchurch Road, Boscombe, BH7 6DL TEL: 427615 PARKING: Medium OPEN: Mon, Tues, Thurs-Sat 10-5 £5 MAX: £2000 PERIOD: 19th-20th century GENERAL: Furniture, glass, ceramics.

**The Antique Centre**, 837-839 Christchurch Road, Boscombe East TEL: 421052 FAX: 391950 PARKING: Own carpark OPEN: Mon-Sat 9.30-5.30 £5 MAX: £2000+ PERIOD: 18th-20th century GENERAL: Silver, plate, Art Deco, collectables, furniture, pictures.

**The Antique Shop**, 646 Wimborne Road, Winton, BH9 2EH TEL: 527205 PARKING: Medium OPEN: Mon-Sat 10.15-5.15 MIN: £1 MAX: £200 PERIOD: 19th-20th century GENERAL: China, glass, silver, flatware.

**Arcade Antiques,** 6 The Arcade, Westbourne, BH4 9AY TEL: 764800 PARKING: Easy OPEN: 10-4.30 PERIOD: 18th-20th century SPECIALIST: Poole Pottery GENERAL: Wide-ranging stock of general antiques, furniture & collectables. OTHER INFO: Situated in a fine Victorian arcade in an interesting village just west of Bournemouth.

**Boscombe Militaria**, 86 Palmerston Road, Boscombe, BH7 4HU TEL: 304250 PARKING: Medium OPEN: Mon, Tues, Thurs-Sat 10-1, 2.45-5 MIN: £1 MAX: £1000 PERIOD: 19th-20th century SPECIALIST: De-activated guns, Third Reich militaria GENERAL: Any militaria from the 180's to the present day.

**Boscombe Models & Collectors Shop**, 802c Christchurch Road, Boscombe, BH7 6DD TEL: 398884 PARKING: Medium OPEN: Mon, Tues, Thurs-Sat 10-1, 2-4.30 £1 MAX: £1000 PERIOD: 19th-20th century SPECIALIST: Collectors toys OTHER INFO: Shop just off main road, 3 doors inside Somerset Road.

**Chorley-Burdett Antiques,** 828 Christchurch Road, Boscombe, BH7 6DF TEL & FAX: 423363 PARKING: Own carpark OPEN: 8.30-6 MIN: £20 MAX: £1500 PERIOD: 18th-20th century GENERAL: General antiques.

**Collectors Corner**, 63 Seabourne Road, Southbourne TEL: 420945 PARKING: Medium OPEN: Mon, Tues, Thurs-Sat 10-4.45 £3 MAX: £800 PERIOD: 19th-20th century SPECIALIST: Old advertising, Doulton goods GENERAL: General antiques, OTHER INFO: 20 antique shops within half a mile, many hotels and good eating.

**Peter Denver Antiques**, 36 Calvin Road, Winton BH9 1LN TEL: 532536 PARKING: Easy OPEN: Tues-Sat 10.30-4.30 MIN: £10 MAX: £1000 PERIOD: 19th-20th century GENERAL: Anything good quality including 1920-40's reproduction OTHER INFO: 100 yds from main shopping area.

**Richard Dunton Antiques**, 914 & 920 Christchurch Road, Boscombe, BH7 6DL TEL: 425963 FAX: 418456 PARKING: Easy OPEN: Mon-Sat 9-5.30 MIN: £5 MAX: £60,000 PERIOD: 18th-20th century GENERAL: Furniture, china, glass, metalware, paintings, photograph frames, garden urns, fountains, statues, etc.

**Lionel Geneen Ltd**, 781 Christchurch Road, Boscombe, BH7 6AW TEL: 422961 (shop) 520417 (home) ASSNS: LAPADA, BDADA PARKING: Easy OPEN: Mon-Fri 9-5 Sat 9-12 (not lunchtime) & by appt £50 MAX: £3500. PERIOD: 18th-20th century GENERAL: Decorative European & Oriental furniture, china, glass, bronzes, objects OTHER INFO: Some 20th century Art Deco.

**Hampshire Gallery**, 18 Lansdowne Road, BH1 1SD TEL: 551211 ASSNS: LAPADA PARKING: Own carpark OPEN: By appt MIN: £250 MAX: £10,000 PERIOD: 19th century to 1930 SPECIALIST: English & Continental pictures OTHER INFO: Some earlier pictures.

**Kebo Antiques**, 823 Christchurch Road, Boscombe TEL: 417052 PARKING: Medium OPEN: 10-4.30 £5 MAX: £500 PERIOD: 19th-20th century SPECIALIST: Pocket watches & jewellery GENERAL: All general antiques.

**GB Mussenden & Son,** 24 Seamoor Road, Westbourne BH14 9AB TEL: 764462 SPECIALIST: Jewellery, silver & plate.

**Geo A Payne & Son Ltd**, 742 Christchurch Road, Boscombe TEL: 394954 ASSNS: NAG PARKING: Medium OPEN: Mon-Sat 9-5.30 MIN: £10 MAX: £4000 PERIOD: 19th century GENERAL: Jewellery & silverware OTHER INFO: New jewellery & silverware.

**Pegasus Antiques,** 13 Gladstone Road West, Boscombe PARKING: Medium OPEN: 9-5 MIN: £1 MAX: £500 PERIOD: 18th-20th century GENERAL: Linen, lace, textiles, porcelain, glass, jewellery, small furniture OTHER INFO: Antique centre, 8 to 12 dealers.

**Shickell Antiques**, 869 Christchurch Road, Boscombe, BH7 6AT TEL: 418497 PARKING: Medium OPEN: Mon-Sat 9-5 MIN: £5 MAX: £2-3000 PERIOD: 17th-20th GENERAL: Furniture, porcelain, jewellery, silver items OTHER INFO: 30 other antique shops in same street, nice beaches, conference & holiday area, mild weather year round.

**Peter Stebbing**, 7 Post Office Road, BH1 1BB TEL: 552587 PARKING: Easy OPEN: Mon-Sat 9.30-5 MIN: £5 MAX: £5000 PERIOD: 18th-19th century GENERAL: Mixed - furniture, glass, porcelain, brass, copper etc OTHER INFO: Russell-Coates Museum (original house used in film *Valentino*).

**Vera Strange Antiques,** 811 Christchurch Road, Boscombe, BH7 6AP TEL: 429111 FAX: 887837 PARKING: Easy OPEN: Mon-Fri 10-5, Sat 10-1 MIN: £20 MAX: £2000 PERIOD: 18th-19th century GENERAL: Porcelain, glass, furniture.

**Mark C Taylor**, 995 Christchurch Road, BH7 6BB TEL: 429718 ASSNS: GMC PARKING: Easy OPEN: 8-6 £150 MAX: £5000 PERIOD: 19th century SPECIALIST: English longcase & dial clocks GENERAL: Antique clocks.

**The Victorian Chairman,** 883 Christchurch Road, BH7 6AU TEL: 420996 PARKING: Easy OPEN: Mon-Fri 9-5, Sat 9-3.30 MIN: £100 MAX: £3000 SPECIALIST: Chairs, settees, chaises longues, dining tables, chairs OTHER INFO: A full restoration & upholstery services.

**Victorian Parlour Antiques**, 874 Christchurch Road, BH7 6DJ TEL: 433928 PARKING: Easy OPEN: Mon-Sat 9-5.30 MIN: £1 MAX: £700 PERIOD: 19th century SPECIALIST: Stripped pine GENERAL: Victorian furniture.

**Yesterday Tackle & Books,** 42 Clingan Road, Boscombe East, BH6 5PZ TEL: 476586 PARKING: Easy OPEN: By appt Mon-Sat 9am-9pm MIN: 25p MAX: No limit SPECIALIST: Fishing books & catalogues, tackle & reels GENERAL: Stuffed & carved fish (when available), ephemera, prints. OTHER INFO: Catalogue issued occasionally, £1 (£2 overseas) refundable against order.

**York House Gallery**, York House, 32 Somerset Road, Boscombe TEL: 391034, 394275 PARKING: Own carpark OPEN: Mon-Sat 2.15-4.30 & by appt £25 MAX: £5000 PERIOD: 19th century SPECIALIST: Watercolours, oils.

## CHRISTCHURCH (O1202)

**Christchurch Carpets**, 55-57 Bargates TEL: 482712 PARKING: Own carpark OPEN: Mon-Sat 9-5.30 MIN: £30 MAX: £5000 PERIOD: 19th-20th century SPECIALIST: Persian old oriental rugs GENERAL: Rugs & carpets OTHER INFO: Part exchange welcome.

**HLB Antiques**, 139 Barrack Road, BH23 2AW TEL: 429252 PARKING: Easy OPEN: Mon-Sat 10-4 PERIOD: 19th-20th century SPECIALIST: Old postcards GENERAL: Objects of art, collectables, pocket watches.

**M & R Lankshear Antiques**, 149 Barrack Road, BH23 2AP TEL: 473091 PARKING: Own carpark (large forecourt) OPEN: Mon-Sat 9.30-5.30 PERIOD: 19th-20th century SPECIALIST: Militaria, swords, uniforms GENERAL: Furniture, clocks, pictures, china, glass, copper, walking sticks.

## BRANSGORE (01425)

**The Old Stores**, West Road, BH23 8BQ TEL: 672616 PARKING: Own carpark OPEN: Thurs & Fri 9.30-7 or by appt MIN: 10p MAX: £350 PERIOD: 19th-20th century GENERAL: General antiques & collectables. OTHER INFO: The shop is in a village on edge of the New Forest, lovely local scenery, many good local hotels & pubs.

# Bath to Crewkerne

Avon, Wiltshire and Somerset are steeped in history, from Bath with its Roman remains to the legends of Glastonbury. They are rural counties, for the most part, with gentle rolling hills and pleasant river valleys.

The tour begins in the Wiltshire village of **Castle Combe,** often described as the most beautiful village in England. It is certainly very picturesque with stone-built cottages, church and covered market set against a background of trees. Moving on via small, but pretty, **North Wraxall**, the route reaches **Bath**, a famous spa even in Roman times, then called *Aquae Sulis.* In the 18th century the town became extremely fashionable and the distinctive Regency architecture dates from this time. Probably the greatest tourist attraction is, the Pump Room. Here there are the remains of the Roman baths, remarkably complete, and the Roman Temple Precinct. Another outstanding landmark is Bath Abbey. Started in 1499 on the site of a 7th century church, there is an unusual carving on the west front of angels ascending and descending a ladder from heaven.

*Bath Abbey*

There are numerous museums; perhaps one of the most interesting to visitors is the Building of Bath Museum in The Paragon. This recounts the story of how the town grew from the 18th century onwards. On display are pattern books, tools and architectural fragments. Another fascinating museum, housed at Claverton Manor, three miles away, is the American Museum in Britain exhibiting American decorative arts from the late 17th to mid 19th centuries including furniture, paintings, glass, textiles, folk art and much more besides. In Julian Road there is quite an unusual museum: Mr Bowler's Business - Bath Industrial Heritage Centre, consisting of the entire stock of a J.B. Bowler, a Victorian brass founder, engineer and mineral water manufacturer , all displayed in authentic settings with some working machinery.

The last two museums of special note are No.1 Royal Crescent and Sally Lunn's House. The first is a Georgian townhouse in Bath's most splendid terrace, redecorated and furnished in late 18th century style. Sally Lunn's House in North Parade Passage is the oldest house in Bath with a cellar museum showing the ancient kitchen and excavations of Roman, Saxon and medieval buildings on the same site. It was here that the famous Sally Lunn bun was created. There are many other museums and the Tourist Information Centre is the place to find out more.

After stopping in **Midsomer Norton,** next is the beautiful cathedral city of **Wells** at the foot of the Mendip Hills. There were holy wells here in Saxon times and a monastery was founded in the 8th century. Near the site of the present cathedral there was probably a small Saxon church.

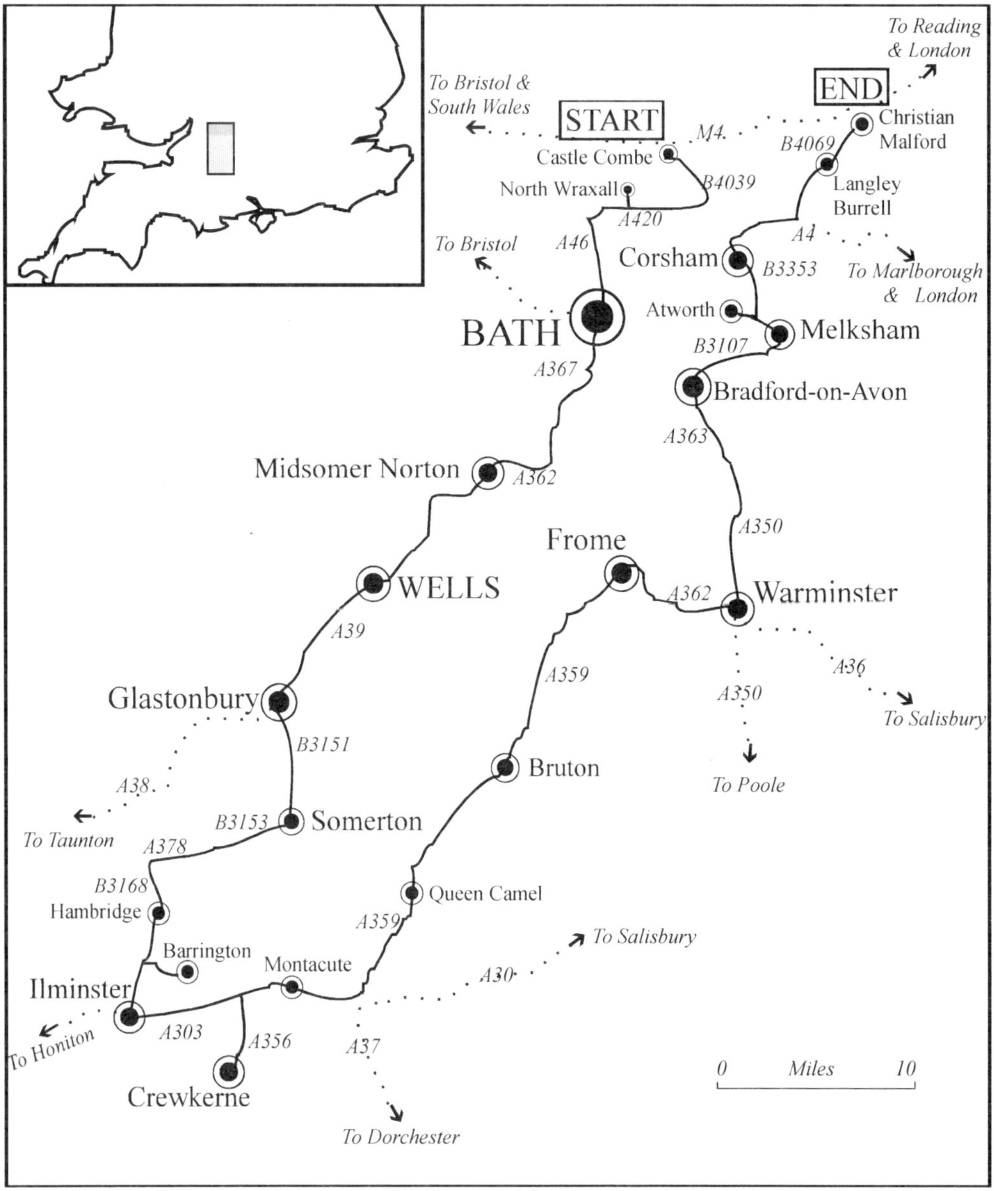


A larger Norman one, consecrated in 1148, replaced it. However, in the last quarter of that century the bishop, Reginald de Bohun, started the present cathedral. The building was continued by Bishop Jocelyn through most of the first half of the 13th century.

During this time there was a political struggle over which town should be the seat of the diocese of Bath and Wells. The monks in Bath abbey were campaigning to have the bishopric there. However, when Bath made a final attempt in the mid 13th century, the bishop of Wells was able to inform the Pope that a worthy cathedral already existed in Wells.

This wonderful cathedral has many beautiful features; amongst the most notable is the 24 hour dial clock from 1390 where the earth is shown as the centre of the universe and the sun is the hour hand. Every quarter hour knights on horseback rotate. Perhaps the greatest work in the cathedral is the West Front, designed as a sculpture gallery and housing 293 medieval statues,

*Stalagmites and stalagtites in Cheddar Caves*

two-thirds of which are life-size. This is, without doubt, a magnificent medieval cathedral. The Bishop's Palace is also quite splendid and set within a moat on which the swans ring a bell for food. Also the original holy well of St Andrew stands within the bishop's garden.

The city has a number of other places of interest including both the Archdeacon's house, Deanery, cathedral school and organist's house. There is also a fine medieval tithe barn and William Penn once preached from an upper window of the Crown Hotel.

Wells is also the ideal place from which to make a detour to visit Wookey Hole, quite close by, and Cheddar Gorge, eight miles away. Wookey Hole is a great cavern with a number of chambers carved by water in the carboniferous limestone. Through it runs part of the River Axe and there is evidence that this series of caves was inhabited between 250BC and 450BC. On the site is a museum, a papermill with an exhibition about handmade paper and another exhibition of fairground figures.

Cheddar Gorge may be reached by taking the A371 from Wells which, nearing the Gorge, changes from a gradual descent to a breathtaking plunge down to the valley floor with the cliffs rising to a height of 450 feet in places. The village of Cheddar is now very commercialised with cafes, gift shops, etc but nothing can spoil the beauty and wonder of the caves. Inhabited by Paleolithic man, 10,000 years ago, the rock formations and the effects caused by minerals colouring the rocks are quite dramatic as are the numerous stalagmites and stalagtites (tites come down, mites grow up).

Next, **Glastonbury** is a town full of legends. One of them tells the story of Joseph of Arimathea landing in Somerset with the Holy Grail and coming inland to Glastonbury. He stuck his staff in the ground while he rested and the staff took root and flowered, a sign that his travels should end and he should build a church here. Glastonbury is also a centre of Arthurian legends and is reputedly where King Arthur and Queen Guinevere are buried.

There is evidence of settlement in prehistoric times although little is known of this early

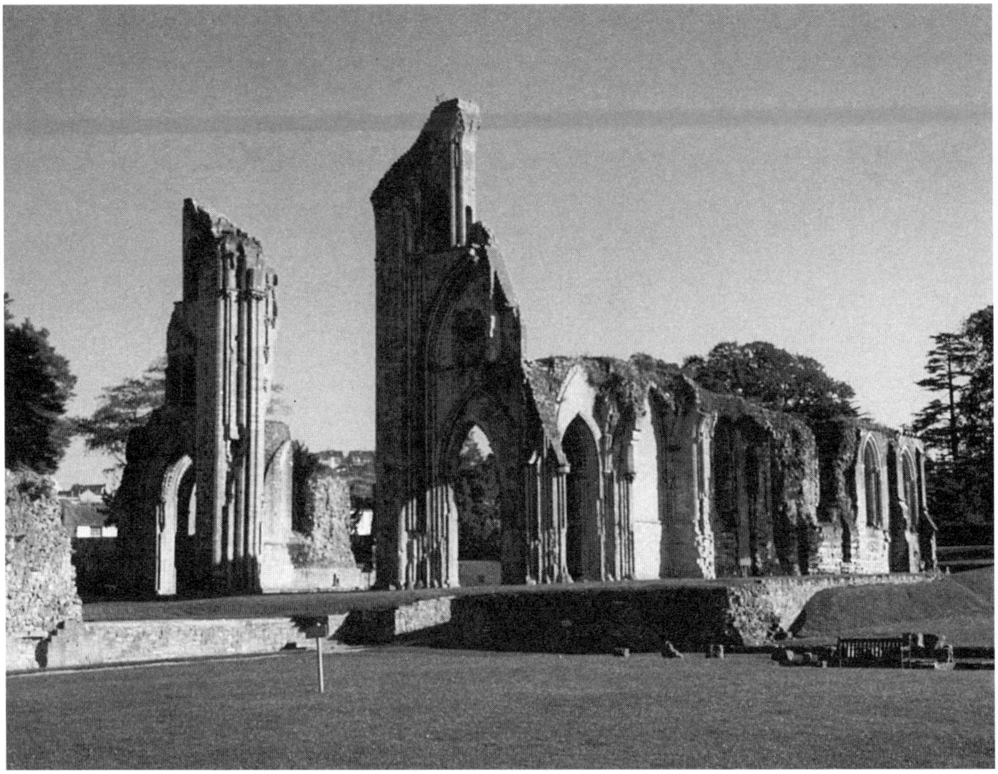

*The ruins of Glastonbury Abbey*

period. The famous abbey was probably Celtic with later Saxon additions. It was attacked by Vikings but St Dunstan, who became abbot in 943AD, repaired it and also presided over its rise to become a wealthy and influential establishment. At about this time the abbey expanded, and was still further enlarged after the Norman Conquest. This expansion continued until the Dissolution of the Monasteries which left the building in ruins. The remains of the abbey give an idea of its size and grandeur. The Abbot's Kitchen is a notable feature with the famous flowering thorn tree near by which is reputed to be from a cutting of the one planted by Joseph of Arimathea. The town has two museums: Glastonbury Lake Village in the High Street showing a collection of prehistoric antiquities and the award winning Somerset Rural Life Museum, Chilkwell Street.

Going via **Somerton** and **Hambridge**, the tour arrives in the village of **Barrington**, where the restored Tudor house, Barrington Court, stands set in its beautiful gardens. These were laid out by Gertrude Jekyll as a series of rooms. Next, **Ilminster** was once a centre for flax and lace making. It has a 15th century church with a fine perpendicular central tower and its grammar school was founded in 1586. A well known local family, the Spekes, suffered in the Monmouth Rebellion. The elder son, fighting for Monmouth, survived the Battle of Sedgemoor and managed to escape abroad afterwards. In retribution, Judge Jeffreys hanged his younger brother instead from a tree in the market place.

The ancient town of **Crewkerne**, the most southerly point on this route, was a Roman settlement then later a Saxon one when the town had a royal mint. As well as being the market town for the surrounding agricultural area, Crewkerne had a thriving sail-making industry and made sails for the ships at Trafalgar including Nelson's Victory. The 15th century church is extremely beautiful with a particularly fine west facade.

North-east, the lovely village of **Montacute** contains the magnificent Elizabethan Montacute House. Built in local Ham stone during the latter part of the 16th century, its Long Gallery, measuring 189 feet, is reputed to be the longest in England. It has fine collections of heraldic glass, tapestries, panelling, furniture and Elizabethan and Jacobean portraits. Next is the peculiarly named village of **Queen Camel** followed by **Bruton** with a fine Gothic parish church, a 16th century grammar school, a 16th century roofless dovecote and some 12th century abbey walls.

Moving onwards, the riverside market town of **Frome** retains much history as most of the town centre is a conservation area. A watercourse still runs down the centre of Cheap Street. This is another place affected by Judge Jeffreys who had twelve local men hanged. From Frome the route passes on to **Warminster,** a royal manor in the time of King Alfred. The town has many inns, survivors of the days when it was on a coach road. One of the most interesting building is probably the parish church, dating from the 14th century with a 15th century tower and some later 18th and 19th century work.

**Bradford-on-Avon**, next, is mentioned in the Domesday Book and has a history that goes back beyond the Norman Conquest. The town is built on a steep slope of the Avon valley and its streets rise in terraces on the hillside. Built of local limestone, they give the feeling of having grown in position over the centuries. The highest of the main terraces, Tory from the word Tor meaning high place, was originally 18th century weavers' cottages, many of which have been restored. Some of these cottages were first built with kitchens excavated from caves in the hillside. On a lower terrace, Middle Rank, there are late 17th century weavers' cottages, also mostly renovated. In Bradford's centre lies the medieval shopping area of The Shambles, a narrow lane joining Market Street and Silver Street.

A find of major historic interest was made in the town in the 1850s. The vicar of the parish, Canon William Jones, noticed the cruciform shape of some cottages under repair. The workmen uncovered two carved angels and this confirmed Canon Jones' suspicions that there was a forgotten Saxon church here. The chancel had been converted into a cottage and the nave into a school. Other buildings had been built against the church so that it was no longer recognisable. Only in 1870 were these adjoining buildings removed and the clear shape of the Saxon church, the most complete in the country, came to light again.

Nearby **Melksham** on the River Avon, has a history going back to before the Norman Conquest. This town also contains some fine old coaching inns from the days it was on the main coach road between London and Bath. Some of the town's oldest houses, from the 16th to 18th centuries, stand in Canon Square and adjoining Church Walk.

After visiting **Atworth** the route arrives in **Corsham**, on the southern most edge of the Cotswolds. Evidence indicates there was a settlement here in pre-Roman times and it grew through the centuries to be a thriving market town and also part of the medieval Cotswold weaving industry; weavers' cottages may be seen in the High Street. Another building of interest is the 17th century almshouses. The Elizabethan Corsham Court, built on the site of a Saxon royal manor, contains a wonderful collection of paintings and furniture and is set in a park designed by Capability Brown.

Another manor house stands between Chippenham and Corsham: Sheldon Manor. Parts of the building date from as early as 1282 with the main part rebuilt in the 17th century. Unfortunately, this house has known many different owners who allowed the house to deteriorate. Its fortunes have changed and today it contains collections of oak furniture, porcelain, paintings and Nailsea glass.

This tour finishes after first visiting the small villages of **Langley Burrell** and **Christian Malford.**

# ANTIQUE DEALERS

## CASTLE COMBE (01249)

**Combe Cottage Antiques**, SN14 7HU TEL: 782250 ASSNS: BADA PARKING: Medium OPEN: Mon-Sat 10-5.30 (closed Thursday 1-2), phone if coming any distance MIN: £20 MAX: £10,000 PERIOD: 17th-19th century but also some earlier SPECIALIST: Medieval furniture, early oak, metalware GENERAL: Country antiques.

## NORTH WRAXALL (01225)

**Delomosne & Son Ltd**, Court Close, SN14 7AD TEL: 891505 FAX: 891907 ASSNS: BADA, BABADA PARKING: Easy OPEN: Mon-Fri 9.30-5.30, Sat 9.30-1 MIN: £20 PERIOD: 17th-20th century GENERAL: 18th-19th century English & Continental glass, porcelain, chandeliers & light fittings. Some decorative items.

## BATH (01225)

**Adam Gallery**, 13 John Street, BA1 2JL TEL: 480406 ASSNS: FATG, Inst of Paper Conservators PARKING: Easy OPEN: Mon-Sat 9.30-5.30 MIN: £200 MAX: £15,000+ PERIOD: 19th-20th century SPECIALIST: Fine oils, watercolours 1880-1940, contemporary works GENERAL: Paintings and watercolours OTHER INFO: Splendid Georgian city, Bath Spa-5 star hotel.

**Alderson**, 23 Brock Street, BA1 2LW TEL: 421652 FAX: 421652 ASSNS: BADA PARKING: Easy OPEN: Mon-Sat 9.30-5.30 MIN: £25 MAX: £20,000 PERIOD: 18th-19th century SPECIALIST: English furniture and accessories.

**Antique Linens and Lace**, 11 Pulteney Bridge, BA2 4AY TEL: 465782 PARKING: Easy OPEN: Seven days 10-6 MIN: £2 MAX: £600/800 PERIOD: 19th century SPECIALIST: Christening gowns, baby bonnets, GENERAL: Bed linen, table linen, wedding veils, lace shawls etc. OTHER INFO: Situated on 1 of only 2 bridges in the world that have shops on. The other one is in Florence.

**Bartlett Street Antique Centre**, 5-10 Bartlett Street, BA1 2QZ TEL: 466689 PARKING: Medium OPEN: Mon, Tues, Thurs-Sat 9.30-5pm Weds 8-5 PERIOD: 17th-20th century SPECIALIST: Ancient Chinese art, clocks, carpets & rugs GENERAL: General antiques OTHER INFO: Centre has 65 stalls, a quality cafe. We also have a Wednesday general antique market. Manned display case area.

**Bath Antiques Market**, Guinea Lane, off Lansdown Road TEL: 337638 FAX: 445118 PARKING: Easy OPEN: Wed 6.30-2.30 MIN: £1 MAX: £5000 PERIOD: 18th-20th century GENERAL: Antiques, furniture, silver, jewellery, porcelain, china, paintings, prints, textiles etc OTHER INFO: Arrive early for best deals as primarily trade market. Café serving quality homemade food, unrestricted parking above Hedgemead Park.

**Bath Galleries**, 33 Broad Street, BA1 5LP TEL: 462946 PARKING: Easy OPEN: 10-5 MIN: £200 MAX: £5000 PERIOD: 18th-19th century SPECIALIST: Clocks, silver GENERAL: Most things before 1880.

**Bath Stamp & Coin Shop**, 12 Pulteney Bridge, BA2 4AY TEL: 463073 ASSNS: Philatelic Trade Society PARKING: Medium OPEN: Mon-Sat 9.30-5.30 MIN: £1 MAX: £200 PERIOD: Roman times to 20th century GENERAL: Stamps, coins, medals, banknotes OTHER INFO: Excellent views, sited on the world-famous Pulteney Bridge.

**George Bayntun**, 21 Manvers Street, BA1 1JW TEL: 466000 FAX: 482122 ASSNS: ABA PARKING: Own carpark OPEN: Mon-Fri 9-1, 2-5.30, Sat 9.30-1 MIN: £10 MAX: £5000 PERIOD: 17th-20th century SPECIALIST: Fine bindings, first editions of English literature OTHER INFO: Book Museum specialising in Jane Austen, Dickens & other famous authors local or visited.

**Beau Nash**, 1st floor, Union Passage, BA1 1RD TEL: 447806 FAX: 447806 PARKING: Difficult OPEN: Mon-Sat 10-5 MIN: £500 MAX: £15,000 PERIOD: 18th-early 19th century SPECIALIST: Regency and George III furniture GENERAL: Decorative objects, oil paintings OTHER INFO: Grade I listed house close to Roman Baths.

**Bladud House Antiques**, 8 Bladud Buildings, BA1 5LS TEL: 462929 PARKING: Medium OPEN: Tues, Weds, Fri 9-5 MIN: £25 MAX: £1500 PERIOD: 18th-20th century SPECIALIST: Jewellery & objects of art GENERAL: General antiques.

**Blyth Antiques**, 28 Sydney Buildings, BA2 6BZ TEL: 469766 PARKING: Easy OPEN: By appt MIN: £50 MAX: £2000 PERIOD: 18th-19th century SPECIALIST: Brass GENERAL: Treen & small furniture.

**Geoffrey Breeze**, 6 George Street, BA1 6EH TEL: 466499 FAX: 466499 ASSNS: LAPADA, BABADA PARKING: Medium MIN: £100 MAX: £10,000 PERIOD: 18th-19th century SPECIALIST: Sexy furniture.

**Bryers Antiques**, First Stall, Guildhall Market, TEL: 466352 PARKING: Difficult OPEN: Mon-Sat 9.30-5 MIN: £5 MAX: £5000 PERIOD: 18th-20th century SPECIALIST: Antique silver, Sheffield plate GENERAL: Some porcelain & glass OTHER INFO: Close to historic Bath Guildhall & Abbey.

**Carr Linford**, 10-11 Walcot Buildings, London Road, BA1 6AD TEL: 317516 PARKING: Medium OPEN: Mon-Sat 9-5 MIN: £100 MAX: £5000 PERIOD: 18th-19th century SPECIALIST: Painted & decorative furniture & objects.

**Brian & Caroline Craik Ltd**, 8 Margaret's Buildings BA1 2LP TEL: 337161 PARKING: Easy OPEN: Mon-Sat 9.30-5.30. MIN: £5 MAX: £1000 PERIOD: 19th-20th century SPECIALIST: Treen, brass, copper, glass objects GENERAL: Candlesticks, sporting objects, small objects.

**Corridor Stamp Shop**, 7a The Corridor, BA1 5AP TEL: 463368 PARKING: Medium OPEN: Tues-Sat 9.30-5 MIN: £1 PERIOD: 18th-20th century SPECIALIST: GB, Dominions, Western Europe GENERAL: Worldwide, plus albums and accessories OTHER INFO: B&B at Sherford House, Lansdown Road.

**John Croft Antiques**, 3 George Street, BA1 2EH TEL: 466211 ASSNS: LAPADA PARKING: Medium PERIOD: 18th-19th century SPECIALIST: Snuff shoes, Staffordshire GENERAL: Furniture OTHER INFO: Adjacent to good restaurants.

**Andrew Dando**, 4 Wood Street, Queen Square, BA1 2JQ TEL: 422702 ASSNS: BADA PARKING: Medium OPEN: Mon-Fri 9.30-5.30, Sat 10-1 MIN: £5 MAX: £5000 PERIOD: 18th-19th century SPECIALIST: Large stock of fine pottery & porcelain 1700-1860 GENERAL: Selection of antique prints including local topography, furniture.

**D & B Dickinson**, 22 New Bond Street, BA1 1BA TEL: 466502 ASSNS: BADA, PARKING: Easy OPEN: Mon-Fri 9.30-1, 2-5, Sat 9.30-1 MIN: £10 MAX: £5000 PERIOD: 18th-20th century SPECIALIST: Silver, old Sheffield plate, antique and secondhand jewellery OTHER INFO: 5 star Bath Spa Hotel, Museum of Costume.

**Frank Dux Antiques**, 33 Belvedere, Lansdown Road, BA1 5HR TEL: 312367 FAX: 312367 ASSNS: BBADA PARKING: Easy OPEN: Mon-Sat 10-6 MIN: £1 MAX: £5000 PERIOD: 17th-19th century SPECIALIST: Georgian glass GENERAL: Period oak and fruitwood furniture, Georgian and later glass, pewter, rugs, pictures etc OTHER INFO: Good bistro closeby.

**4 Miles Buildings,** off George Street, BA1 2QS TEL: 425486 PARKING: Medium OPEN: Wed & Sat 10-5 MIN: £10 MAX: £2500 PERIOD: 19th-20th century SPECIALIST: British fine art, popular art, naive art, country pottery.

**Paul Michael Farnham**, 27a 27b Belvedere, Lansdown, BA1 5HR TEL: 428256 PARKING: Easy OPEN: Mon-Sat 10-5.30 or by appt MIN: £20 PERIOD: 17th-20th century SPECIALIST: Beyond description OTHER INFO: Prehistoric bones.

**Simon Freeman Antiques**, 11 Walcot Buildings, London Road, BA1 6AD TEL: 317516 PARKING: Medium OPEN: Mon-Sat 9-5 MIN: £50 MAX: £5000 PERIOD: 18th-19th century GENERAL: Period & decorative furniture & objects.

**The Galleon**, 33 Monmouth Street, BA1 2AN TEL: 312330 PARKING: Easy OPEN: Tues-Sat 10-5.30 MIN: £5 MAX: £3000 PERIOD: 18th-20th century GENERAL: Collectables, jewellery, general antiques, decorative items OTHER INFO: Close to Roman Baths, Costume Museum, theatre, river trips, good restaurants & specialist shops.

**David Gibson**, 4 Wood Street, Queen Square, BA1 2JQ TEL: 446646 ASSNS: BADA, LAPADA PARKING: Easy OPEN: Anytime by appt MIN: £2500 MAX: £25,000 PERIOD: 18th century SPECIALIST: Clocks & barometers.

**Graylow & Co**, 7 Princes Building, George Street TEL: 469859 FAX: 215405 PARKING: Easy OPEN: Mon-Sat 10-5.30 MIN: £100 MAX: £8000 PERIOD: 18th-19th century SPECIALIST: Georgian furniture GENERAL: Paintings, silver, oriental items.

**George Gregory**, Manvers Street, BA1 1JW TEL: 466055 FAX: 482122 ASSNS: ABA PARKING: Own car park OPEN: 9-1, 2-5.30, Sat 9.30-1 MIN: £1 MAX: £2000 PERIOD: 18th-20th century SPECIALIST: English Literature, antique engravings, views and portraits.

**Great Western Antique Centre**, Bartlett Street, BA1 2QZ TEL: 424243 FAX: 424243 PARKING: Medium OPEN: Mon, Tues, Thurs, Fri 10-5, Sat 9.30-5.30, Weds 8.30-5, Wednesday Market 7.30-4 SPECIALIST: Buttons, linen, lace, stamps,

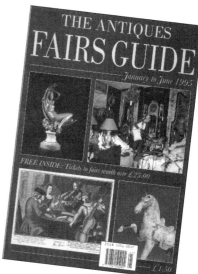

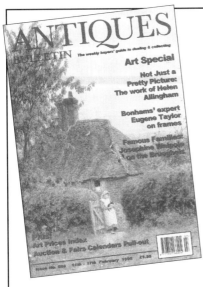

railwayiana, jewellery, paintings, prints, furniture, ceramics, coins etc OTHER INFO: 50 stalls.

**Haliden Oriental Rug Shop**, 98 Walcot Street, BA1 5BG TEL: 469240 PARKING: Easy (multi storey nearby) OPEN: Mon-Sat 10-5 MIN: £20 MAX: £2000 PERIOD: 19th & some early 20th century GENERAL: Old & antique Caucasian, Persian, Turkish, Turcoman, tribal rugs & carpets OTHER INFO: 250 yards Hilton Hotel, next to Walcot Reclamation. Cleaning, repairs, conservation, restoration.

**Helena Hood & Company,** 3 Margaret's Buildings, Brock Street, BA1 2LP TEL: 424438 PARKING: Easy OPEN: Tues-Fri 9.30-1 & 2.15-5.30, Sat 10.30-1 MIN: £40 MAX: £4000 PERIOD: 18th-19th century GENERAL: Engravings, porcelain, creamware, decorative furniture OTHER INFO: Adjacent to Royal Crescent.

**Orlando Jones,** 10B Monmouth Place, Upper Bristol Road, BA1 2AX TEL: 422750 PARKING: Medium OPEN: Mon-Sat 10-1, 2-5 MIN: £250 MAX: £2000 SPECIALIST: Brass & iron beds only.

**Ann King**, 38 Belvedere, Lansdown Road TEL: 336295 PARKING: Medium OPEN: Mon-Sat 10.30-4.30 MIN: £1 MAX: £100+ PERIOD: 17th-20th century SPECIALIST: Clothes, linen, lace, textiles, quilts, old cushions, curtains.

**Kingsley Gallery (Bath) Ltd,** 16 Margaret's Buildings, Brock Street, BA1 2LP TEL & FAX: 448432 ASSNS: BBADA PARKING: Easy OPEN: 7 days 10-5.30 GENERAL: Furniture, decorative items.

**Lansdown Antiques**, 23 Belvedere, Lansdown Road, BA1 5ED TEL: 313417 ASSNS: BBADA PARKING: Medium OPEN: Mon-Sat 9.30-6 MIN: £2 MAX: £2500 PERIOD: 17th-19th century SPECIALIST: Painted pine & country furniture, unusual & decorative items OTHER INFO: From A4/A46 junction, turn right at 3rd set of lights, 300 yds up hill on left. Edouards is an excellent bistro across the road.

**Looking Glass**, 96 Walcot Street TEL: 461969 PARKING: Own carpark OPEN: Mon-Sat 9-6 MIN: £50 MAX: £5000 PERIOD: 18th-19th century SPECIALIST: Mirrors & frames GENERAL: Replica mirrors & picture frames OTHER INFO: Somewhat disorganised shop & workshop stuffed with period & replica mirrors, frames, etc.

**Mallory of Bath**, 1-4 Bridge Street, BA2 4AP TEL: 465885 FAX: 442210 ASSNS: BADA, NAG PARKING: Medium OPEN: Mon-Sat 9.30-5.15 MIN: £10 MAX: £20,000 PERIOD: 18th-20th century SPECIALIST: Fine antique silver & jewellery GENERAL: Modern jewellery, silver, watches, china, glass & gifts OTHER INFO: Also at 5 Old Bond Street. Spa Hotel, Grove Hotel, The Francis Hotel. Wednesday Antique Market & 40 local dealers in the association.

**Paragon Antiques Market**, 3 Bladud Buildings, The Paragon TEL: 463715 PARKING: Easy OPEN: Wed 6.30-3.30 OTHER INFO: 60 stalls of antiques & collectables.

**Patterson Liddle**, 10 Margaret's Buildings, Brock Street, BA1 2LP TEL: 426722 FAX: 426722 ASSNS: ABA, PBFA PARKING: Easy OPEN: Mon-Sat 10-5.30 MIN: 50p PERIOD: 18th-19th century SPECIALIST: Antiquarian, secondhand and paperback books on art, architecture, travel, English literature, illustrated books & transport history OTHER INFO: Our buyer will visit throughout Avon, Glos, Somerset and Wilts if necessary.

**Pennard House Antiques**, 3-4 Piccadilly, London Road, BA1 6PL TEL: 313791 FAX: 448196 ASSNS: LAPADA, BABADA PARKING: Own carpark OPEN: Mon-Sat 9.30-5.30 OTHER INFO: We are 6 dealers under one roof and we are particularly geared to assisting overseas customers. MIN: £10 MAX: £5000 PERIOD: 18th-19th century SPECIALIST: French provincial fruitwood, pine furniture GENERAL: Decorative items, original paintwork OTHER INFO: Queensberry Hotel, New Moon Pub.

**Quiet Street Antiques**, 3 Quiet Street, BA1 2JS TEL: 315727 ASSNS: BABADA PARKING: Easy OPEN: Mon-Sat 10-6 MIN: £100 MAX: £5000 PERIOD: 18th-19th century SPECIALIST: Interesting boxes and caddies, good clocks, Royal Worcester porcelain GENERAL: General antiques OTHER INFO: 4 showrooms, every item priced and described. Well known on tour circuit as friendly, helpful and knowledgable. Exports arranged. Happy to listen to amusing anecdotes on any subject.

**TE Robinson Antiques,** 3A, 3 & 4 Bartlett Street, BA1 2QZ TEL: 463982 ASSNS: BADA PARKING: Medium OPEN: 10-4 MIN: £75 MAX: £7500 PERIOD: 17th-early 19th century SPECIALIST: Good period furniture & other interesting objects.

**Michael and Jo Saffell**, 3 Walcot Buildings, London Road, BA1 6AD TEL: 315857 PARKING: Medium OPEN: Mon-Fri 9.30-5 or by appt. Best phone first anyway MIN: £5 MAX: £2000

PERIOD: 19th-20th century SPECIALIST: British tins mainly, other advertising items GENERAL: Decorative and collectors items.

**Sullivan Fine Art**, Bartlett Street Antiques Centre, 5-10 Bartlett Street, BA1 2QZ TEL & FAX: 483133 PARKING: Medium OPEN: Mon-Sat 9.30-5 (Thurs by appt only) PERIOD: 18th-20th century SPECIALIST: Original oils & watercolours.

**Trim Bridge Galleries,** 2 Trim Bridge, BA1 1HD TEL: 466390 PARKING: Easy OPEN: Mon-Sat 10-5.30 MIN: £50 MAX: £5000 PERIOD: 18th-19th century SPECIALIST: Watercolours GENERAL: Some paintings & prints OTHER INFO: Oldest established gallery in Bath - 1976.

**Walcot Reclamation Ltd**. 108 Walcot Street, BA1 5BG TEL: 444404 FAX: 448163 PARKING: Own carpark OPEN: Mon-Fri 8.30-5.30, Sat 9-5 PERIOD: 17th-20th century SPECIALIST: Architectural salvage and antiques OTHER INFO: One of largest dealers in UK, two sites. Phone first for directions. Minutes from centre of Bath, accommodation guides on request.

**Glenda Wallis - Antiquarian & Secondhand Booksellers**, 6 Chapel Row, Queen Square, BA1 1HN TEL: 424677 PARKING: Easy OPEN: Mon-Sat 10-5.30 MIN: £1 MAX: £1000 PERIOD: 18th-20th century SPECIALIST: Victorian childrens, illustrated, Canadian & folklore GENERAL: Large general stock on most subjects OTHER INFO: Next door to good French bistro (The Beaujolais).

**Widcombe Antiques**, 9 Claverton Buildings, Widcombe, BA2 4LE TEL: 428767 PARKING: Own carpark OPEN: Mon-Sat 10.30-5.30 PERIOD: 18th-19th century GENERAL: Period pine & brass, dressers, tables, chests-brass & iron fenders.

## MIDSOMER NORTON (01761)

**Somervale Antiques**, 6 Radstock Road, BA3 2AJ TEL: 412686 (24 hours) ASSNS: BADA, LAPADA, CINOA, BABADA PARKING: Own carpark OPEN: By appt only MIN: £20 MAX: £5000 PERIOD: 17th-19th century SPECIALIST: English drinking glasses, decanters, cut and coloured Bristol and Nailsea glass. Bijouterie, scent bottles OTHER INFO: Coal Mining Museum nearby Sats only. Trains from Bath met by arrangement.

## WELLS (01749)

**Sadler Street Gallery,** 7a Sadler Street, BA5 2RR TEL: 670220 PARKING: Medium OPEN: Tues-Sat 10-6 MIN: £5 MAX: £250 PERIOD: 19th-20th century SPECIALIST: !9th century & contemporary watercolours GENERAL: Pictures, prints, picture framing & restoration OTHER INFO: Charming bow-windowed gallery, very near the Cathedral, the excellent Swan Hotel & the Market Place.

**Ken Holdsworth Antiques,** 72-74 St Thomas Street, BA5 2UZ TEL: 672520 PARKING : Easy OPEN Mon, Tues, Thurs-Sat 10-4 MIN: £50 MAX: £1,000 PERIOD 19th-20th century SPECIALIST: Victorian & Edwardian furniture GENERAL: Collectables

**Bernard G House,** Market Place, BA5 2RB TEL: 672607, home (01761) 221511 PARKING: Easy OPEN: Mon-Sat 9.30-5.30 MIN: £300 MAX: £12,000 PERIOD: 18th-20th century SPECIALIST: 18th century longcase clocks, Sextants, barometers microscopes, barographs, telescopes, aeronautical instruments. Repairs & restoration

**Edward G Novell,** 12 Market Place, BA5 2RB TEL: 672415 FAX: 670508 ASSNS: BADA PARKING: Easy OPEN: Mon-Sat 10-5 MIN: £300 MAX: £15,000 PERIOD: 17th-19th century SPECIALIST: Barometers, clocks, furniture, silver, jewellery, porcelain.

## GLASTONBURY (01458)

**Borough Antiques,** St Mary's Road, Meare, BA6 9SP TEL: 860701 PARKING: Easy OPEN: Mon-Sat 10-5 & by appt MIN: £10 MAX: £1000 GENERAL: Town & country furniture, decorative accessories.

## SOMERTON (01458)

**P Deering Antiques & Collectables,** West Street, TA11 7PS TEL: 274015 PARKING: Easy OPEN: 10-5 MIN: £5 MAX: £800 PERIOD: 19th century GENERAL: Pottery, porcelain, smaller furniture, glass, metalwork, pictures.

**London Cigarette Card Co Ltd**, West Street, TA11 6QP TEL: 273452 PARKING: Easy OPEN: Mon-Sat 9-1, 2-5, closed Wed & Sat pm MIN: 5p MAX: £10,000 PERIOD: 19th-20th century SPECIALIST: Over 100 million cigarette and picture cards OTHER INFO: Showroom has over 2500 different sets on display, the largest in the UK.

**Times Past,** Market Place, TA11 7NB TEL: 274393 OPEN: Mon-Sat 10-5 MIN: £2 MAX: £1500 PERIOD: 17th-20th century SPECIALIST: Linen, lace, tapestries GENERAL: Samplers, period oak,

country furniture, christening gowns, quilts, costume, pictures.
**Westville House Antiques**, Littleton, TA11 6NP TEL & FAX: 273376 PARKING: Own carpark OPEN: Mon-Sat 9-6 MIN: £100 MAX: £3000 PERIOD: 18th-19th century SPECIALIST: Pine GENERAL: Country oak, mahogany.

## HAMBRIDGE (01458)

**Chalow UK Ltd**, Hambridge Hill, TA10 0BP TEL: 252374 ASSNS: LAPADA PARKING: Own carpark OPEN: Mon-Sat 9-5 MIN: £100 MAX: £7500 PERIOD: 18th-19th century GENERAL: European country and decorative handmade furniture OTHER INFO: Touring guide available, weekend breaks may be booked.

## BARRINGTON (01460)

**Stuart Interiors (Antiques) Ltd,** Barrington Court, TA19 0NO TEL: 40349 ASSNS: LAPADA PARKING: Own carpark OPEN: Mon-Fri 9-5.30 Sat 10-5, Sun by appt MIN: £10 MAX: £16,000 PERIOD: 16th-early 18th century SPECIALIST: Early oak furniture & accessories of the period.

## ILMINSTER (01460)

**Dowlish Wake Antiques**, Dowlish Wake Village, TA19 0NY TEL: 52784 PARKING: Easy OPEN: Mon-Sat 10-1, 2.30-5.30 MIN: £1 MAX: £10,000 but average range £20-£200 SPECIALIST: Ceramics GENERAL: Mostly 19th century English & Continental porcelain and pottery, 18th century porcelain, some 17th-18th century delftware & pottery. No Art Deco or Oriental. OTHER INFO: Egon Ronay listed pub, real Somerset cider mill & museum, 13th century church with 19th century tomb and memorial to explorer John Hanning Speke, discoverer of the Nile source.. Stone-arched pack bridge over (now dry) ford. Dowlish means damp and Wake from the Plantagenet Lady Isobel Wake whose sculpted tomb is in the church.
**James Hutchison**, 5 West Street, TA19 9AA TEL: 21066 PARKING: Easy OPEN: Wed-Sat 11-5 MIN: £5 MAX: £1000 PERIOD: 19th-20th century SPECIALIST: Paintings GENERAL: Prints, frames, furniture, collectables OTHER INFO: 15th century Minster, ample hotels, B&B's, restaurants.

## CREWKERNE (01460)

**Crewkerne Furniture Emporium**, Viney Bridge, South Street, TA18 8AE TEL: 75319 FAX: 75122 PARKING: Own carpark OPEN: Mon-Sat 8.30-5.30, Sun 10-5 MIN: £1 MAX: £1000 PERIOD: 19th-20th century SPECIALIST: House clearance GENERAL: Good used furniture, shipping pieces, some antiques OTHER INFO: 6 secondhand, pine, antique shops, auction room. B&B's and hotels including vegetarian.
**Hennessy,** 42 East Street, TA18 7AG TEL & FAX: 78060 ASSNS: LAPADA PARKING: Easy OPEN: Tues, Wed, Fri, Sat 10-5 & by appt MIN: £10 MAX: £5000 PERIOD: 18th-19th century SPECIALIST: Pine GENERAL: English country & French provincial furniture & decorative items OTHER INFO: Although the shop is open 10-5, we are on the premises 6 days a week from 8-5.
**Posh Pine Ltd,** 14 East Street, TA18 7AG TEL: 75623 PARKING: Own carpark OPEN: Tues-Sat 10-5 MIN: £2.50 MAX: £1000 PERIOD: 18th-20th century SPECIALIST: Pine & country furniture, associated small items.

## MONTACUTE (01935)

**Montacute Antiques**, South Street, TA15 6XD TEL: 824786 PARKING: Medium OPEN: Daily 8.30-6.30 MIN: £10 MAX: £1000 PERIOD: 18th-19th century SPECIALIST: Oak furniture, porcelain GENERAL: Brass, copper, pewter, collectables OTHER INFO: Montacute House (NT) 100 yards.

## QUEEN CAMEL (01935)

**Steven Ferdinando,** The Old Vicarage, BA22 7NG TEL: 850210 ASSNS: PBFA PARKING: Own carpark OPEN: Anytime when at home, best to phone first MIN: £5 MAX: £500 PERIOD: 19th-20th century SPECIALIST: Dorset books GENERAL: Secondhand & antiquarian books OTHER INFO: 2 pubs in the village.

## BRUTON (01749)

**Michael Lewis Gallery**, 17 High Street, BA10 0AB TEL: 813557 PARKING: Easy OPEN: Mon-Sat 9-6 MIN: £20 PERIOD: 16th-20th century GENERAL: Maps, prints, paintings.
**MGR Exports**, Station Road, BA10 0EH TEL: 812460 FAX: 812882 PARKING: Own carpark OPEN: Mon-Fri 8.30-5.30, Sat 9-12.30 MIN: £10 MAX: £7500 PERIOD: 18th-20th century GENERAL: Victorian, Edwardian, French & Continental & general shipping goods.

## FROME (01373)

**Sutton & Sons**, 15 & 33 Vicarage Street, BA11 1PX TEL: 462062, 462526 PARKING: Good OPEN: Mon-Sat 9-5 MIN: £18 MAX: £2800 PERIOD: 18th-19th century GENERAL: English furniture OTHER INFO: Longleat 4 miles, quaint town of Frome.

## WARMINSTER (01985)

**The Antique Study,** 33 Silver Street, BA12 8PT TEL: 213451 FAX: 215415 ASSNS: LAPADA PARKING: Easy OPEN: Mon-Sat 10-1, 2-5 MIN: £100 MAX: £10,000 PERIOD: 18th-20th century SPECIALIST: Desks, bookscases with study & office accessories, oil paintings, clocks, etc.

**Bishopstrow Antiques**, 55 East Street, BA12 9BZ TEL: 212683 PARKING: Easy OPEN: Mon-Sat 10-1, 2-5.30 MIN: £3 MAX: £3000 PERIOD: 17th-20th century GENERAL: Mahogany & oak furniture, country and painted, china, small silver & decorative items.

**Choice Antiques**, 4 Silver Street, TEL: 218924 PARKING: Easy OPEN: 10-1, 2-5.30 MIN: £25 MAX: £2500 PERIOD: 18th-19th century GENERAL: Small pieces mahogany and country furniture & decorative items.

**Country Antiques,** 10 Silver Street, BA12 8PS TEL: 215916 PARKING: Easy OPEN: 10-5, closed Tues & Wed MIN: £20 MAX: £800 PERIOD: 19th century GENERAL: Small items of oak furniture & upholstered chairs.

**Emma Hurley Antiques & Textiles**, 3 Silver Street TEL: 219726 PARKING: Medium OPEN: Mon-Sat 10-5 MIN: £5 MAX: £1000 PERIOD: 19th century SPECIALIST: Textiles GENERAL: Home embellishments (mirrors, lighting, paintings, French beds OTHER INFO: Good restaurant & B&B 2 doors away.

**Isabella Antiques**, 16a Silver Street TEL: 218933 PARKING: Easy OPEN: Mon-Sat 10-5.30 MIN: £25 MAX: £5000 PERIOD: late 18th-19th century GENERAL: Mahogany (especially inlaid) furniture, gilt mirrors, boxes, small clocks OTHER INFO: 12 antique shops.

**Obelisk Antiques**, 2 Silver Street, BA12 8PS TEL: 846646 FAX: 219901 PARKING: Easy OPEN: Mon-Sat 10-1, 2-5.30 MIN: £10 MAX: £10,000 PERIOD: 18th-20th century GENERAL: Large stock English & Continental furniture, chandeliers & decorative items OTHER INFO: 18 dealers in town. Bishopstrow House Hotel, The Angel, Heytesbury (good country pub with restaurant & accommodation).

**Warminster Antique Centre,** 6 Silver Street, BA12 8PT TEL: 847269 OPEN: Mon-Sat 10-5 GENERAL: 12 antique dealers offering the widest range of antiques & collectables OTHER INFO: Restoration & valuations.

## BRADFORD-ON-AVON (01225)

**Avon Antiques**, 25-27 Market Street, BA15 1LL TEL: 862052 ASSNS: BADA PARKING: Own carpark OPEN: Mon-Sat 9.45-5.30 PERIOD: 17th-mid 19th century SPECIALIST: Furniture GENERAL: Longcase clocks, metalwork, barometers needlework OTHER INFO: Saxon church, medieval Tithe Barn, Woolley Grange Hotel (864705), Priory Steps (862230).

**Harp Antiques**, 17 Woolley Street, BA15 1AD TEL: 865770 ASSNS: LAPADA, BABADA PARKING: Medium OPEN: Mon-Sat 9-6 or by appt MIN: £50 MAX: £8000 PERIOD: 18th-19th century GENERAL: Georgian furniture (no oak), silver, bronzes, decorative pieces OTHER INFO: Small town of exceptional beauty & historic interest. 5 good antique shops.

**MacHumble Antiques**, 7-9 Woolley Street, BA15 1AD TEL: 866329 ASSNS: BADA, BABADA PARKING: Easy OPEN: Mon-Sat 9-6 MIN: £25 MAX: £6000 PERIOD: 18th-19th century SPECIALIST: Samplers, needlework, metalware GENERAL: English mahogany furniture, small pieces of excellent colour & patination OTHER INFO: One of the best small towns in England with strong historic interest. 2 BADA & 3 LAPADA members with excellent quality items, no junk or rubbish. Woolley Grange Hotel, Leigh Park Hotel

**Moxham's Antiques**, 17, 23-24 Silver Street, BA15 1JZ TEL: 862789 FAX: 867844 ASSNS: LAPADA PARKING: Own carpark OPEN: Mon-Sat 9-5.30 MIN: £300 MAX: £20,000 PERIOD: 17th-19th century SPECIALIST: Georgian furniture GENERAL: Period stock, ceramics, metalware, decorative & garden items OTHER INFO: Historic woollen town near Bath with many other dealers in the town.

## MELKSHAM (01225)

**Jaffray Antiques**, 16 The Market Place, SN12 6EX TEL: 702269 FAX: 790413 ASSNS: BABADA PARKING: Own carpark OPEN: Mon-Fri 9-5.30, Sat by appt MIN: £20 MAX: £3000 PERIOD: 17th-20th century SPECIALIST: Staffordshire & decorative items GENERAL: Large - linen presses, chests, boxes on stand. Restoration facilities available OTHER INFO: Good hotels & restaurants, courier service, transport to & from station (Chippenham).

## ATWORTH (01225)

**Peter Campbell Antiques**, 59 Bath Road, SN12 8JY TEL: 709742 PARKING: Own carpark OPEN: Mon-Wed, Fri, Sat 10-5 MIN: £10 MAX: £450 PERIOD: 19th century GENERAL: English & Continental furniture & decorative arts OTHER INFO: 2 B&B's in village & 2 other antique shops.

## CORSHAM (01249)

**Matthew Eden Antiques**, Pickwick End, SN13 0JB TEL: 713335 FAX: 713644 PARKING: Own carpark OPEN: 8am-8pm, resident MIN: £5 MAX: £5000 PERIOD: 18th-20th century SPECIALIST: Country house furniture & garden items, makers of garden furniture.

## LANGLEY BURRELL (01249)

**Fairfax Fireplaces & Antiques**, Langley Green, SN15 4LL TEL & FAX: 652030 PARKING: Own carpark OPEN: 7 days 10-5 MIN: £20 MAX: £2000 PERIOD: 18th-20th century SPECIALIST: Fireplaces & architectural items OTHER INFO: Our house dates from 12th century with 15th century additions & 19th century facade.

## CHRISTIAN MALFORD (01249)

**Harley Antiques**, The Comedy, SN15 4BS TEL: 720112 PARKING: Own carpark OPEN: Seven days 9-6 MIN: £20 MAX: £3000 PERIOD: 18th-19th century GENERAL: Largest stock of decorative accessories & unusual furniture OTHER INFO: Converted stables amid 7 acres landscaped parkland.

# Bristol to Taunton

From Bristol's busy and historic docks to the pleasant sandy beaches of the Avon and Somerset holiday resorts, this tour takes in a variety of English scenes. Away from the coast the route passes through pretty villages with stone-built cottages and thatched roofs to market towns that have retained their heritage.

Not only a busy commercial and industrial centre, but also rich in history, **Bristol** has been a port for over 800 years. First trading with Europe, it was the trade with the Americas for which Bristol is famous. Cabot Tower on Brandon Hill commemorates the expedition from Bristol to discover the mainland of America, led by John Cabot. Another reminder of Bristol's seafaring past is found in the SS Great Britain built by Isambard Kingdom Brunel and the first iron, screwdriven steamship. More of his work can be seen in part of Temple Meads railway station. He also designed the Clifton Suspension Bridge but this was only constructed after his death.

Unfortunately, much of the old centre of the city was destroyed by bombing in the Second World War but there are remnants left. The oldest working theatre in the country, the Theatre Royal dating from 1766, can be found in King Street. In the same street stands the 17th century Llandoger Trow, possibly used by pirates and the inn that is said to be the Spyglass Inn in Robert Louis Stevenson's novel *Treasure Island.*

Numerous other interesting and historic buildings exist. Perhaps one of the most important is the Cathedral, originally an abbey church dating from 1148. In the 16th century the nave was demolished to build a new one but they could not afford to proceed with the work. It was only in 1868 that construction started. Fortunately, the architect, G.E. Street, designed the nave to harmonise with the 14th century east arm of the cathedral without falling into the trap of building a 19th century pastiche.

Passing through the villages of **Clutton,** and then **West Harptree** with its nice Jacobean Gournay Manor. Another one, Tilley Manor is 17th century, full of treasures, open to the public and also sells antiques. After **Yatton,** next is **Clevedon**, at the junction of two hill ranges. This pleasant seaside resort is also in the middle of good walking country. It was the birthplace of Hartley Coleridge and the poem *In Memoriam* by Tennyson was inspired by the death of Arthur Hallam who is buried in St Andrew's Churchyard. Arthur Hallam lived at the 14th century Clevedon Court, now a National Trust property. The house incorporates a 12th century tower and 13th century hall and has important collections of Nailsea Glass and Eltonware.

**Weston-super-Mare,** on the Bristol Channel, is a popular resort with two piers, one of which is also used as a jetty and lifeboat station. It has sandy bathing beaches and the other amenities usual to a good seaside town. On the southern side of Weston Bay the peninsula of Brean Down, an outcrop of the Mendip Hills, sticks out into the sea for approximately a mile and rises to a height of about 320 feet. It has been used as a defensive position throughout the ages. There is an Iron Age fort and also a 19th century fort built as a defense against a French invasion. The Romans built a temple there too.

Next is the resort of **Burnham-on-Sea** which really began in the 19th century when a curate sank two wells to turn the area into a spa. Unfortunately the water was so unpleasant that the idea failed. Instead the town has become a popular for holidays with about seven miles of sandy beaches. The church contains a white marble altar originally carved by Grinling Gibbons for the chapel in the Palace of Whitehall.

Continuing south west, **Highbridge** was a busy port during the 18th and 19th centuries then later repaired railway engines for the Somerset and Dorset Railway. The route now turns west along the A39 to **Nether Stowey** where Samuel T. Coleridge wrote *The Ancient Mariner* at his cottage here. Near the village stands Dodington Hall, a small Tudor manor house.

The tour follows the line of the coast through the villages of **Williton** and then the delightfully localed **Timberscombe** between Croydon Hill and Dunkery Hill. **Ash Priors** is five miles

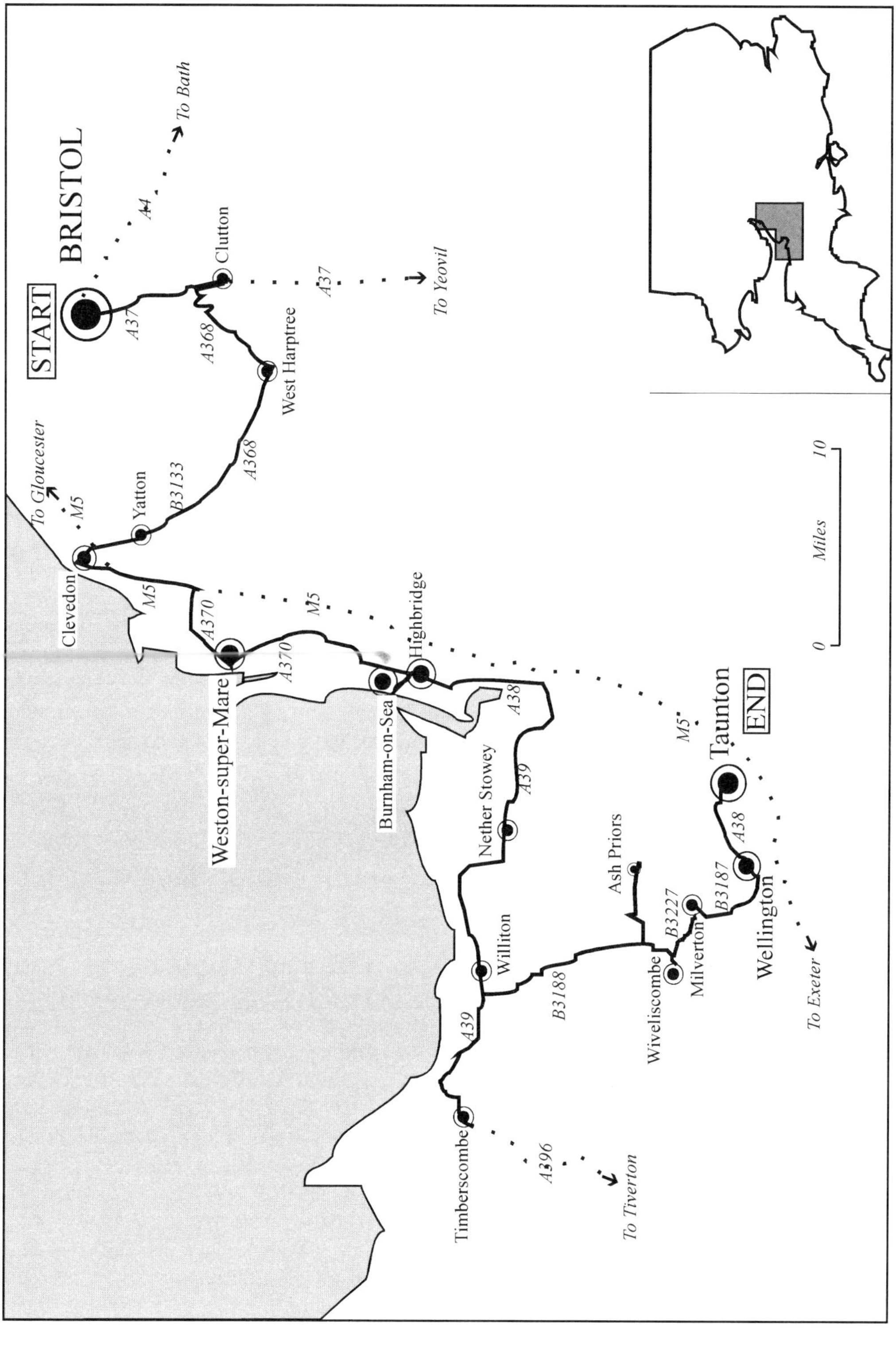
START
BRISTOL
To Bath
A4
A37
Clutton
To Yeovil
A368
West Harptree
To Gloucester
M5
Yatton
B3133
Clevedon
A370
Weston-super-Mare
Highbridge
Burnham-on-Sea
A38
Taunton
END
Nether Stowey
A39
Ash Priors
B3227
B3187
Wellington
Williton
Wiveliscombe
Milverton
B3188
To Exeter
Timberscombe
A396
To Tiverton
0
Miles
10

along a winding country road. **Wiveliscombe** and ancient **Milverton** come next before arriving in **Wellington**, the town from which the Duke of Wellington took his title. Just three miles south of the town, on the crest of the Blackdown Hills, is an obelisk erected to commemorate the Iron Duke.

The final destination is the cider making town of **Taunton** on the River Tone. Strategically placed in the centre of the river valley, it was fortified in the 8th century. Its Norman castle was built on the site of an early earthwork fortification by Henry of Blois although it has been altered considerably since then. Various parts of the castle date from as early as the 12th century with others as late as the 18th century.

To the north east, near Bridgwater, lies the battlefield of Sedgemoor. On the death of Charles II, James II, a Roman Catholic, became King. The Duke of Monmouth, illegitimate son of Charles II, and his supporters felt this was their chance to seize the throne. Monmouth had been in Holland but he sailed for England landing in Lyme Regis. There he found he had much popular support. Two of Monmouth's supporters had also landed in Scotland to rally the people there but had been caught and executed. From then on Monmouth had no chance of success. Meanwhile, royal troops under the command of John Churchill, later first Duke of Marlborough, were marching to the West Country to put down the rebellion. On 5th July 1685 battle was joined; the makeshift army stood no chance against the royal troops and was slaughtered. The Duke of Monmouth escaped for a few days before he was brought to London and executed.

Survivors from the rebel army were ruthlessly hunted down and the Lord Chief Justice, the notorious Judge Jeffreys, was sent to the West Country to deal with them. In the Great Hall of Taunton Castle in September 1685 he held his 'Bloody Assizes' in which he sentenced between 150 and 300 people to death by hanging and numerous others, possibly up to 800, to transportation and slavery in the West Indies. Reputedly, the ghost of Judge Jeffreys walks the castle on September nights.

In addition to that bloody and tragic episode in English history, Taunton contains other more peaceful reminders of the past. There are three public schools, one of which was founded in the 13th century, and a thatched leper hospital, now restored to serve as rural district offices. There is also a Tudor house in Fore Street and 17th century almshouses.

## ANTIQUE DEALERS

### BRISTOL (0117)

**Alexander Gallery Partnership**, 122 White- ladies Road, BS8 2RP TEL: 973 4692 FAX: 946 6991 ASSNS: FATG PARKING: Medium OPEN: Mon, Tues, Thurs-Sat 9-5.30, Weds 9-1 MIN: £100 MAX: £10,000 PERIOD: 19th-20th century SPECIALIST: Oils & watercolours.

**Antique Beds**, 3 Litfield Place, Clifton BS8 3LT TEL: 973 5134 FAX: 974 4450 PARKING: Own carpark OPEN: Anytime by appt MIN: £950 MAX: £5000 PERIOD: 18th-19th century SPECIALIST: Four poster beds GENERAL: Custom-made mattresses, fabrics & trimmings OTHER INFO: 100 yards from the Clifton Suspension Bridge.

**The Barometer Shop**, 2 Lower Park Row, BS1 5BJ TEL: 927 2565 ASSNS: BHI PARKING: Own carpark OPEN: Mon, Wed, Fri 10-4, Sat 10-1 MIN: £45 MAX: £8500 PERIOD: 18th-20th century SPECIALIST: Clocks, barometers GENERAL: Period furniture.

**Robin Butler**, 20 Clifton Road, BS8 1AQ TEL & FAX: 973 3017 ASSNS: BADA PARKING: Own carpark OPEN: Mon-Fri 9.30-5.30, Sat 10-3 MIN: £20 MAX: £50,000 PERIOD: 18th-19th century SPECIALIST: Furniture, wine antiques glass, silver, clocks OTHER INFO: For information or a map on how to find us, please telephone or write. Exhibitor at Bath & Olympia. Harveys Wine Museum, SS Great Britain.

**Clifton Antiques Market**, 26-28 The Mall, Clifton TEL: 973 4531, 973 4698 PARKING: Difficult OPEN: Tues-Sat 10-6 PERIOD: 19th-20th century GENERAL: Approx 30 dealers. Jewellery, silver, gold, furniture, textiles, porcelain, china, prints, pictures, linen, lace, glass, book binding, picture framing OTHER INFO: We are housed in a historic building in the heart of Georgian Clifton Village

**David Cross Fine Art**, 7 Boyces Avenue, Clifton, BS8 4AA TEL: 973 2614 ASSNS: BAG PARKING: Easy OPEN: Mon-Sat 9.30-6 MIN: £5 MAX: £50,000 PERIOD: 18th-20th century SPECIALIST: British marine, landscape, figurative, sporting, topographical GENERAL: Oils, watercolours and local prints and contemporary OTHER INFO: 100 yards to Clifton Suspension Bridge and Avon Gorge.

**Flame & Grate**, 159 Hotwells Road, Hotwells, BS8 4RY TEL: 925 2560 PARKING: Easy OPEN: Mon-Sat 9-5 MIN: £3 MAX: £8000 PERIOD: 17th-20th century SPECIALIST: Original fireplaces, marble surrounds GENERAL: All makes of original and modern fireplaces, handcarved surrounds.

**Grey-Harris & Co Ltd**, 12 Princess Victoria Street, Clifton, BS8 TEL: 973 7365 ASSNS: BADA, NAG PARKING: Medium OPEN: Mon-Sat 9.30-5.30 MIN: £50 MAX: £15,000 PERIOD: 18th-20th century SPECIALIST: Jewellery, silver OTHER INFO: One of the finest 19th century jewellers shop interiors in the provinces (restored to c. 1860).

**John Martin Antiques**, Bristol Antiques Centre, Broad Plain TEL: 929 7739 PARKING: Easy OPEN: Tues-Sat 10-4.30, Sun 12-4 MIN: £5 MAX: £3000+ PERIOD: 18th-20th century GENERAL: Clocks, furniture, oil lamps, copper and brass.

**Militaria,** 13 Lower Park Row, BS1 5BN TEL: 929 8205 PARKING: Easy MIN: 50p MAX: £3000 PERIOD: 18th-20th century SPECIALIST: Scientific instruments, shipping antiques GENERAL: Militaria & curios.

**Robert Mills Ltd**, Narroways Road, Eastville, BS2 9XB TEL: 955 6542 FAX: 955 8146 PARKING: Own carpark OPEN: Mon-Fri 9.30-5.30 MIN: £100 MAX: £50,000 PERIOD: 18th-20th century SPECIALIST: Architectural antiques for pubs & restaurants, stained glass, church interiors OTHER INFO: Trade & export only.

**No 74 Antiques & Interiors**, 74 Alma Road, Clifton, BS8 3BA TEL: 973 3821 PARKING: Medium OPEN: Mon-Sat 10.30-5.30 MIN: £50 MAX: £4000+ PERIOD: 18th-19th century SPECIALIST: Period town house furniture GENERAL: Clocks, decorative items OTHER INFO: Antique finders and interior design service, upholsterer on premises.

**Period Fireplaces**, The Old Railway Station, Station Road, Montpelier BS6 5EE TEL: 944 4449 PARKING: Own carpark OPEN: Mon-Sat 9-5 MIN: £10 MAX: £1000 PERIOD: 19th-20th century SPECIALIST: Genuine antique fireplaces OTHER INFO: The workshops are in a genuine Victorian station, trains still stop at the platform. The old waiting room is display area.

**Potters Antiques & Coins**, 60 Colston Street, BS1 5AZ TEL: 926 2551 PARKING: Medium OPEN: Mon-Sat 10.30-5 MIN: £1 MAX: £500 PERIOD: 17th-20th century SPECIALIST: Coins & antiquities GENERAL: Brass, copper,commemoratives, glass, silver OTHER INFO: Antiquities from 1500BC to 400AD. Near Christmas Steps and Red Lodge, ° mile from Museum & Art Gallery.

**Relics Pine Furniture**, 109 St Georges Road, College Green, BS1 5UW TEL & FAX: 926 8453 PARKING: Easy OPEN: Mon-Sat 10-5.30 MIN: £16 MAX: £685 PERIOD: Early 20th century SPECIALIST: Pine furniture - old and reproduction GENERAL: Large selection of mounted & unmounted picture frames & mirrors, also handpainted signboards OTHER INFO: Local pub has excellent food at low price.

**John Roberts Bookshop**, 43 Triangle West, Clifton, BS8 1ES TEL: 926 8568 PARKING:- OPEN: Mon-Sat 9.30-5.30 PERIOD: 18th-20th century GENERAL: Antiquarian and 2nd hand books.

**The Wise Owl Bookshop**, 26 Upper Maudlin Street, BS7 8EU TEL: 926 2738, after hours 924 6936 ASSNS PBFA PARKING: Medium OPEN: Mon-Sat 10.30-5.30 MIN: £3 MAX: £100 PERIOD: 19th-20th century SPECIALIST: Books on performing arts, music GENERAL: Secondhand & antiquarian books on all subjects.

## CLUTTON (01761)

**Ian McCarthy,** Arcadian Cottage, 112 Station Road, BS18 4RA TEL: 453188 PARKING: Easy OPEN: Anytime - phone first MIN: 50p MAX: £2000 PERIOD: 17th century-1920 SPECIALIST: Lighting, copper, brass GENERAL: Mostly metalware, some mechanical machinery & tools, lamp spares, restoration & repair (incl. spelter).

## WEST HARPTREE (01761)

**Tilly Manor Antiques**, Tilly Manor, BS18 6EB TEL: 221888 PARKING: Own carpark OPEN: Tues-Sat 10-5 MIN: £5 MAX: £5000 PERIOD:

18th-20th century SPECIALIST: Furniture GENERAL: Metalware, decorative collectors items OTHER INFO: Wealth of treasures in beautiful 17th century manor house 25 mins from Bath on A368

## YATTON (01934)

**Glenville Antiques**, 120 High Street. BS19 4DH TEL: 832284 ASSNS: LAPADA PARKING: Easy OPEN: Mon-Sat 10.30-1, 2.15-5 or by appt MIN: £1 MAX: £2350 PERIOD: 18th-20th century SPECIALIST: Sewing tools & other collectors' items GENERAL: General antiques.

## CLEVEDON (01275)

**John & Carol Hawley Antique Clocks**, The Orchard, Clevedon Lane, Clapton Wick, BS21 7AG TEL: 852052 ASSNS: BHI, BWCMG PARKING: Own carpark OPEN: By appt MIN: £100 MAX: £4000 PERIOD: 18th-19th century SPECIALIST: Clocks - English, longcase, fusee wall, bracket, Vienna regulators, carriage.

## WESTON-SUPER-MARE (01934)

**Sterling Books**, 43a Locking Road, BS23 3DG TEL: 625056 ASSNS: ABA, PBFA PARKING: Own carpark OPEN: Mon-Sat 9-6 MIN: 50p MAX: £2000 PERIOD: 17th-20th century SPECIALIST: Books - antiquarian, travel, topography arts & crafts GENERAL: Prints, bookbinding, restoration, picture framing.

**Tobys Antiques**, 47 Upper Church Road, BS23 2DY TEL: 623555 PARKING: Medium OPEN: Mon-Sat 9-5 PERIOD: 18th-19th century.

## BURNHAM ON SEA (01278)

**Adam Antiques,** 30 Adam Street, TA8 1PQ TEL: 783193 PARKING: Easy OPEN: 9-5 GENERAL: General antiques.

**Heape's**, 39 Victoria Street, TA8 1AN TEL: 782131 PARKING: Easy OPEN: Mon-Sat 10-4 MIN: £5 MAX: £2000 PERIOD: 19th-20th century SPECIALIST: China, silverplate GENERAL: General antiques OTHER INFO: Leaning tower parish church, lighthouse, Mitre restaurant.

## HIGHBRIDGE (01278)

**Terence Kelly Antiques**, Huntspill Court, West Huntspill, TA9 3QZ TEL: 785052 PARKING: Own carpark OPEN: By appt MIN: £10 MAX: £8000 PERIOD: 17-19th century SPECIALIST: Oak & country furniture, metalware GENERAL: Wide range including pottery, glass.

**The Treasure Chest,** 19 Alstone Lane, West Hunspill, TA9 3DS TEL: 787267 PARKING: Own carpark OPEN: Anytime by appt MIN: £10 MAX: £7000 PERIOD: 17th-20th century SPECIALIST: Musical boxes GENERAL: Furniture, glass, china, clocks, silver & plate, bronze OTHER INFO: Excellent restaurant, the White Cottage, & hotel, the Sundowner, superb sea & freshwater fishing.

## NETHER STOWEY (01278)

**House of Antiquity (Antique Books)**, 12 St Mary Street, Nether Stowey, TA5 1LJ TEL: 732426 ASSNS: PTS PARKING: Easy OPEN: Mon-Sat 9-5.30 MIN: £1 MAX: £500 PERIOD: 19th-20th century SPECIALIST: Philatelic Literature GENERAL: Fiction, non-fiction, large selection.

## WILLITON (01984)

**Edward Venn Antiques,** 52 Long Street, TA4 4QU TEL: 632631 PARKING: Own carpark OPEN: 10-4.30 PERIOD: 18th century.

## TIMBERSCOMBE (01643)

**Zwan Antiques**, TA24 7TG TEL: 841608 PARKING: Easy OPEN: Tues, Thurs, Sun 2-5 or by appt MIN: £1 MAX: £5000 PERIOD: 18th-20th century SPECIALIST: Sporting pictures and jewellery GENERAL: All sorts of small items OTHER INFO: 5 miles inland from Minehead. Close to Snowdrop Valley, 15th century church, super B&B within sight.

## ASH PRIORS (01823)

**Granary Galleries,** Court House, TA4 3NQ TEL: 432402 PARKING: Own carpark MIN: £100 MAX: £15,000 PERIOD: 17th-20th century SPECIALIST: Furniture & oil paintings GENERAL: Victorian, Edwardian, some shipping goods.

## WIVELISCOMBE (01984)

**Heads 'n' Tails**, Bournes House, Church Street, TA4 2LT TEL: 623097 FAX: 624445 PARKING: Easy OPEN: By appt MIN: £10 MAX: £5,000 PERIOD: 19th-20th century SPECIALIST: Taxidermy GENERAL: Full mount animals, including bears, birds, insects, cased fish, skulls, big game trophies.

**Stowford Antiques,** 1 Silver Street, TA4 2PA TEL & FAX: 624664 PARKING: Medium OPEN: Mon-Sat 9-5, Sat 9-12.30 MIN: 50p MAX: £300

PERIOD: 19th-20th century GENERAL: Furniture, china, bric a brac, pictures, prints.

## MILVERTON (01823)

**Milverton Antiques**, Fore Street, TA4 1JU TEL: 400597 PARKING: Easy OPEN: Mon-Sat 9.30-6 MIN: £20 MAX: £3500 PERIOD: 18th-19th century SPECIALIST: Oak & stripped pine GENERAL: China, brass & copper interesting country bygones OTHER INFO: Conservation village with fine Georgian house.

## WELLINGTON (01823)

**M & A Lewis Oriental Carpets & Rugs**, 8 North Street, TA21 8LT TEL: 667430 ASSNS: LAPADA PARKING: Easy OPEN: Tues-Fri 10-1, 2-5.30 or by appt MIN: £25 MAX: £12,000 PERIOD: 19th-20th century GENERAL: Old and antique rugs and carpets, restoration and cleaning, valuations OTHER INFO: Rummage pile £100 and under

## TAUNTON (01823)

**Staplegrove Lodge Antiques**, TEL: 331153 PARKING: Own carpark OPEN: By appt PERIOD: 17th-19th century SPECIALIST: Pratt pot lids GENERAL: Furniture, china, country items.

**Taunton Antiques Market**, 27-29 Silver Street, TA1 3DH TEL & FAX: 289327 PARKING: Easy OPEN: Mon 9-4 including Bank Holidays MIN: £1 MAX: £500 about PERIOD: 18th-20th century GENERAL: 130 dealers in West Country's largest one day market OTHER INFO: Park in Sainsbury's carpark, buy your groceries there to avoid fee - we are across the road. 2 cafés serving real food.

**Windsor House Antiques**, 35b East Reach, TA1 3ES TEL: 325012 PARKING: Easy OPEN: Mon, Thurs-Sat MIN: £2 MAX: £500 PERIOD: 19th-20th century GENERAL: All in good condition & well presented OTHER INFO: Taunton is the gateway to the West.

# South Devon

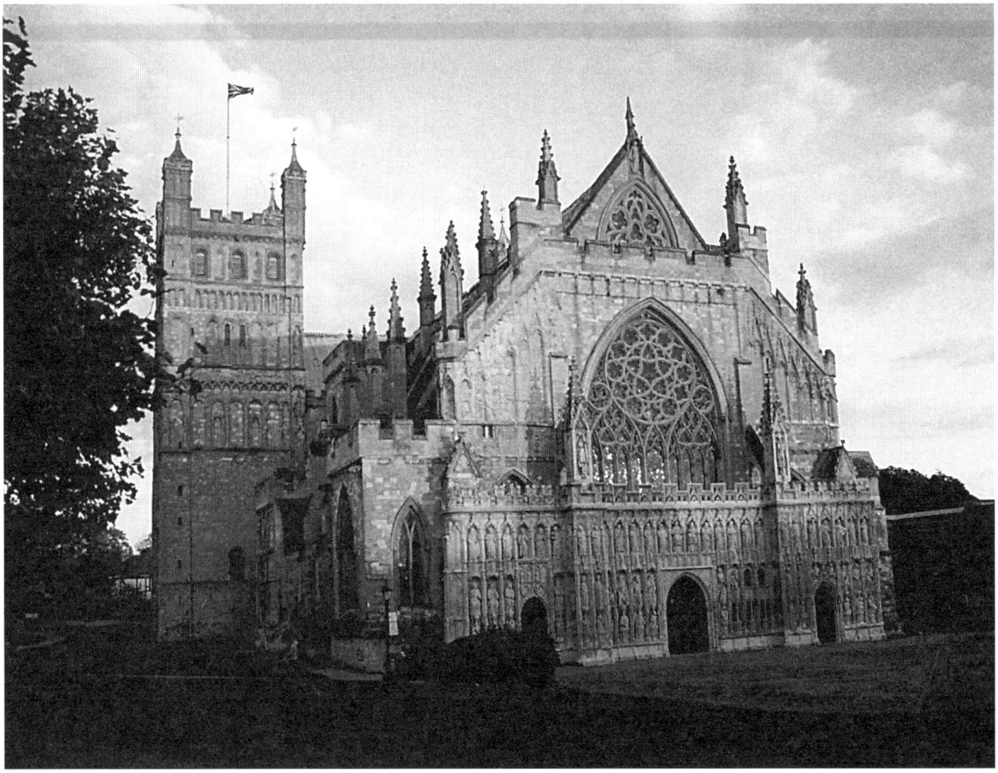

*Exeter Cathedral*

This tour moves from windswept granite moorlands to rolling hills, popular seaside resorts to picturesque villages. Prehistoric remains testify to early settlements and evidence shows that simple tin extraction was carried out 4000 years ago. Along the South Devon coast we see a much kinder milder land, popular for family holidays but move inland to Dartmoor and see the wilder, older face of Devon, unchanged for centuries but, even here, the landscape has been altered by man.

Beginning in the village of **Monkton,** the second location is **Honiton** whose long, straight main street is full of antique shops and centres. It was once on the coach road to Exeter and is best known for lace making. Because of a catastrophic fire in 1765 much of the town had to be rebuilt and so the houses are mostly Georgian. Some earlier buildings did survive however, including the 14th century Hospital of St Margaret and the early 17th century Marwood House.

**Axminster,** next, is synonymous with fine quality carpets. The manufacture of carpets here was started by Thomas Whitty in 1775 and continues to the present day, although the original factory went bankrupt in 1835. The town consists of mostly Georgian and Victorian buildings although the church has a Norman door and a Jacobean pulpit.

Moving on, **Colyton** was an important wool town in Tudor times. The lord here was Henry Courtenay who, unfortunately, came into disfavour with Henry VIII and was beheaded. The manor was then bought from the Crown by twenty local merchants and yeoman farmers under a Deed of Feoffment and to this day Colyton is still run by sixteen feoffees. Buildings of note are the Old Church House and The Great House in South Street which has a chequerboard front.

**Seaton,** situated where the River Axe runs into the sea, has developed as a seaside resort

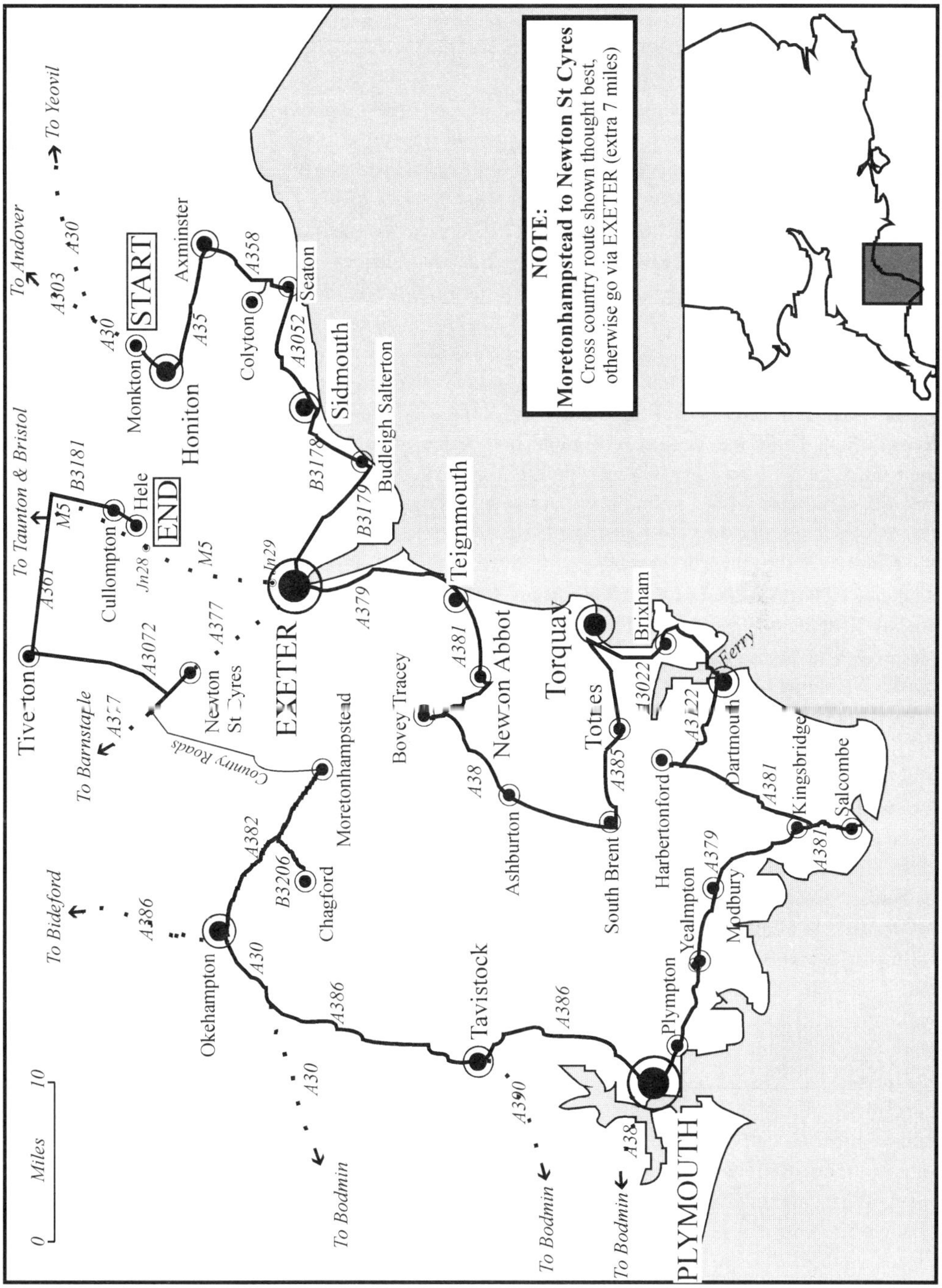
NOTE:
Moretonhampstead to Newton St Cyres
Cross country route shown thought best, otherwise go via EXETER (extra 7 miles)
START
END
EXETER
PLYMOUTH
Honiton
Monkton
Axminster
Seaton
Colyton
Sidmouth
Budleigh Salterton
Teignmouth
Torquay
Brixham
Ferry
Dartmouth
Totnes
Newton Abbot
Bovey Tracey
Ashburton
South Brent
Harbertonford
Kingsbridge
Salcombe
Modbury
Yealmpton
Plympton
Tavistock
Okehampton
Chagford
Moretonhampstead
Newton St Cyres
Tiverton
Cullompton
Hele
Jn28
Jn29
Country Roads
To Taunton & Bristol
To Andover
To Yeovil
To Barnstaple
To Bideford
To Bodmin
To Bodmin
To Bodmin
0 Miles 10
A30
A303
A35
A358
A3052
B3178
B3179
B3181
M5
A361
A3072
A377
A379
A381
A38
A385
A3022
A3122
A382
B3206
A386
A390

because it has a fine sheltered beach. Along the coast, **Sidmouth** is a small unspoilt holiday town at the mouth of the River Sid with lovely terraces of Regency houses. **Budleigh Salterton**, is at the mouth of the River Otter.

Turning inland, **Exeter** was the Roman town of *Isca Dumnoniorum* and remains of the Roman city walls may still be seen in Southernhay. Exeter has the distinction of being the last English town to hold out against the Norman invasion, only surrendering in the winter of 1068 after promises that no reprisals would be taken against the townsfolk. The city has many buildings of note including the Guildhall dating from 1330 with later alterations and additions, Wynyard's Hospital of 1436 and the restored Tudor St Nicholas' Priory. Above all there is the cathedral with its two Norman transeptal towers. Built between the 13th and 14th centuries its west front has the largest surviving collection of 14th century sculpture in Britain. Inside, reputedly, the ceiling has the longest stretch of 13th century Gothic vaulting in the world. There is also the 59 foot high Bishop's Throne and a minstrel's gallery displaying angels with musical instruments.

The route now arrives in **Teignmouth** (pronounced Tinmouth) standing at the mouth of the River Teign. There has been a settlement here since prehistoric times and its importance from then until the Middle Ages was for panning and exporting salt. Fishing also developed as an important industry in the town and boats went out from here to fish the Newfoundland Grand Banks. As fishing became less profitable the town then began to export potter's clay and granite. Nowadays it is a fairly typical seaside resort although signs of its history may still be found.

Inland, **Newton Abbot** is a typically busy English market town. Its most noteworthy features are the 14th century St Leonard's Tower and the 15th century Bradley Manor, a National Trust property. The Manor still shows many of the features, inside and outside, of a typical medieval building although there have been some 19th century alterations.

**Bovey Tracey**, next, stands on the eastern edge of Dartmoor and is now an important centre for tourists exploring the moors. The original church is said to have been built by Sir William de Tracey in 1170 to atone for his part in the murder of Thomas à Becket. This was burnt down in the early 14th century and later rebuilt.

The following stop, **Ashburton**, is an attractive small town on the River Yeo. It has some old slate hung houses, the most notable of these, in North Street, is called The House of Cards because diamonds, spades, hearts and clubs are depicted on the hanging tiles.

After first visiting the village of **South Brent**, situated on the southern edge of Dartmoor, the following town, **Totnes** on the River Dart, claims to be one of the oldest boroughs in England and it was the site of the Royal Mint during the 10th century. The line of the surrounding town walls may still be seen as well as two of the gates, one of which, the 15th century East Gate, has been restored. There are also several Elizabethan and Georgian houses as well as a picturesque Butterwalk. The two notable museums:are the Totnes Costume Museum in the High Street and the Totnes (Elizabethan) Musuem in Fore Street which is set in an Elizabethan merchant's house. Totnes Castle was built after the town surrendered to the Normans and is a good example of a motte and bailey castle. It stands on a hill overlooking the River Dart where three valleys meet. What remains of the castle is mostly 14th century although the huge mound on which it was built is Norman.

Back on the coast, the popular seaside resort of **Torquay** is famous for its mild weather and the palm trees growing along the seafront. The public gardens behind the main beach were, in the Middle Ages, part of farmland belonging to Torre Abbey. The Abbey was founded in 1196 but after the Dissolution of the Monasteries in 1539 became a private residence. It was extensively remodelled in the 18th century and contains a family chapel, furniture, paintings and works of art as well as the Dame Agatha Christie Memorial Room with many mementos of the writer who was born in Torquay. There are also ruins of the original medieval abbey and its church.

On the other side of Torbay the pretty fishing port of **Brixham** is popular with artists who can be seen painting the picturesque harbour in the summer. Although this is still a working fishing port, the town is also popular with tourists. A replica of the Golden Hind (Sir Francis Drake's ship) may be seen in the harbour. Even such a small town has had its moments of national importance. In 1688 William of Orange landed here to take the throne of England after the unacceptable James II stepped down. A statue stands on the edge of the quay to commemorate the event - often with a seagull on its head, but they have no respect for history or people. Brixham's other claim to fame is that Henry Lyte wrote the hymn *Abide with Me* in Berry Head House while he was vicar of All Saints Church.

*A cromlech (prehistoric burial chamber) on Dartmoor*

Along the coast, via the ferry at Kingswear, **Dartmouth** is closely associated with the navy for centuries, in medieval times it was used by fleets sailing for the Crusades and vessels from this port took part in the siege of Calais. Later nine ships from Dartmouth joined in the repulsion of the Spanish Armada. This importance as a naval port led to attacks which accounts for the defences - the castles of Dartmouth, Kingswear, Bearscove and Gallants Bower which were used again as defensive positions during the Second World War. In 1944 the Dart estuary was the departure point of a great fleet for the invasion of Normandy and the eventual liberation of Europe. Nowadays the Royal Naval College is most closely identified with Dartmouth and has trained many of the highest ranking naval officers this century.

After **Harbertonford,** the next stop is **Kingsbridge**, standing at the head of a deep coastal inlet and has a number of notable buildings: The Shambles, is a late 16th century arcade, Dodbrooke Church also 16th century and the Grammar School dating from 1670.

**Salcombe** stands near the mouth of the Kingsbridge estuary. A large natural harbour has brought business to the town. During the latter half of the 19th century the main trade was in citrus fruit from the Azores when the local schooners were called Salcombe fruiters. It also owned fishing fleet and nowadays is popular for yachts and other small boats. The harbour was also involved in the preparations and departures of the ships involved in the invasion of Europe during the Second World War hence the plaque in Normandy Way commemorating the D-Day landings.

**Modbury**, 10 miles north, consists of three main steep streets which converge near the Exeter Inn. With several elegant 18th century houses, the town is well known for the large number of antique shops and art galleries.

The tour passes through **Yealmpton** and then **Plympton** to arrive in **Plymouth**. This city has been an important port and navy dockyard for centuries. It was here that Sir Francis Drake is reputed to have played bowls as the Spanish Armada approached. The Pilgrim Fathers sailed from Plymouth aboard the Mayflower to settle in the New World and, more recently, Sir Francis Chichester arrived in Plymouth at the end of his round the world voyage in 1967.

Much of the centre of Plymouth has been rebuilt after wartime bombing but some of the old town still survives most notably around the harbour. The Elizabethan House in New Street is authentically furnished as an Elizabethan merchant's house and there is another Merchant's House in St Andrew's Street furnished in 16th century style.

Standing on the Rame Peninsular in Cornwall, to the west of Plymouth, is Mount Edgcumbe

House and Country Park which contains one of only three Grade 1 Historic Gardens in Cornwall. Designed 240 years ago, it contains formal gardens in Italian, French and English styles, a deer park, woodland walks and wonderful views. The house itself, owned by the Edgcumbe family for over 400 years, is a restored Tudor building now furnished and decorated in late 18th century style.

Buckland Abbey stands between Plymouth and **Tavistock** and is well worth visiting on this tour. It was a 13th century abbey which was bought by Sir Richard Grenville in the mid 16th century. It was the home of two famous seamen: Sir Richard Grenville and later Sir Francis Drake. There are many relics of Drake including the famous 'Drake's Drum'.

Tavistock, on the western fringe of Dartmoor, is a good touring centre for the surrounding beautiful country. In the late 13th century Tavistock became a Stannary town, that is a centre for the weighing and stamping of tin from the mines on Dartmoor. Although there are a few Georgian cottages by the Canal Basin, the town centre shows a more Victorian influence. In the mid-19th century the Duke of Bedford used some of his wealth to rebuild it along more spacious lines. His statue stands in the square named after him.

**Okehampton** is ideal for visitors to Dartmoor. Built between the East and West Okement Rivers, it sits just to the north of High Willhays and Yes Tor, the moor's highest points. Because of continued resistance to the invasion, the Normans built a castle here after the rebellions were ruthlessly suppressed. It was largely destroyed when an owner was executed for treason in 1538. Next comes the pretty Dartmoor town of **Chagford**, once important as a tin mining centre and standing in an area rich in prehistoric remains. Nearby **Moretonhampstead** is small but also well situated as a touring centre for Dartmoor. A group of colonnaded 17th century almshouses may be seen by the churchyard.

After first visiting **Newton St Cyres**, **Tiverton** is next. It is a charming country market town whose wealth, since the 12th century, was founded on the wool trade. Amongst the buildings of note are the Jacobean Great House, now used as council offices, St. Peter's Church founded in 1073 but greatly endowed by 15th and 16th century wool merchants, and the ruins of Tiverton Castle built in 1106. The castle has a magnificent medieval gatehouse and tower containing an important Civil War armoury, furniture, pictures, tapestry and a fine collection of clocks. The town also has the award-wining Tiverton Museum with a Railway Gallery and Lace Machine Gallery.

The penultimate stop is in **Cullompton** which once suffered badly from the heavy traffic to the West Country, but now relieved by the motorway. This was another market town that prospered through the wool trade. It was wool that paid for much of the finely decorated parish church of St Andrew. The main part of the church was built in the first half of the 15th century with later additions. The tour ends in the village of **Hele**, close to junction 28 on the M5.

# ANTIQUE DEALERS

## MONKTON (01404)

**Pugh's Antiques**, Pugh's Farm, EX14 9GH TEL: 42860 FAX: 47792 PARKING: Own carpark OPEN: Mon-Sat 9-6 MIN: £10 MAX: £1000 PERIOD: 19th-20th century SPECIALIST: Beds & furniture imported from France GENERAL: Victorian & Edwardian furniture.

## HONITON (01404)

**J Barrymore & Co**, 73-75 High Street, EX14 8PG TEL: 42244 FAX: 47071 PARKING: Easy OPEN: Mon-Sat 10-5, but Thurs by appt only. MIN: £50 MAX: £20,000 PERIOD: 18th-19th century SPECIALIST: Canteens and part sets of flatware GENERAL: Silver, plate & jewellery.

**Bramble Cross Antiques**, Exeter Road, EX14 8AL TEL: 47085 PARKING: Own carpark OPEN: Mon-Sat 10-5.30 MIN: £40 MAX: £10,000 PERIOD: 18th-20th century GENERAL: Georgian, Victorian & Edwardian furnishings. 9 showrooms.

**Roderick Butler**, Marwood House, EX14 8PY TEL: 42169 ASSNS: BADA PARKING: Own carpark OPEN: Mon-Sat 9.30-5.30, closed public holidays PERIOD: 17th, 18th & Regency 19th century SPECIALIST: Furniture, early metalwork OTHER INFO: Usually some rare, unusual or amusing items. Good food close by.

**Dairy Antiques**, Vine Passage, High Street, EX14 8NN TEL: 44876 PARKING: Medium OPEN: Thurs-Sat 10-5 or by appt MIN: £2 MAX: £750 PERIOD: 19th-20th century SPECIALIST: Country pine GENERAL: China, collectables, linen OTHER INFO: The Vine Passage is well worth a visit especially in summer. It's right in the town centre yet many call it their 'Secret Garden'.

**Alison Gosling Antiques**, Plympton House, 59 High Street TEL: 41712 PARKING: Medium OPEN: Tues, Wed, Fri, Sat mid morning to 4.30 MIN: £20 MAX: £2000 PERIOD: 18th-early 20th century SPECIALIST: Furniture GENERAL: Porcelain & decorative items.

**Fountain Antiques Centre**, 132 High Street, EX14 8JP TEL: 42074 PARKING: Medium OPEN: Mon-Sat 9.30-5.30 MIN: £1 MAX: £2000 PERIOD: 18th-20th century GENERAL: Wide range of furniture, pottery, china, books, line & lace, etc OTHER INFO: 25 dealers.

**Hermitage Antiques**, 37 High Street TEL: 44406 PARKING: Easy OPEN: 10-5 MIN: £1 MAX: £3000 PERIOD: 19th-20th century GENERAL: We are an antiques centre with a wide variety of furniture, china, glass, textiles, collectables, silver, costume jewellery, etc.

**High Street Antiques**, 62 High Street, EX14 8QR TEL: 42203 PARKING: Easy OPEN: Mon-Sat 9.30-5.30 MIN: £1 MAX: £3000 PERIOD: 18th-19th century GENERAL: Furniture, large stock of porcelain & collectables.

**Honiton Antique Centre**, Abingdon House, 136 High Street, EX14 8JP TEL: 42108, 43049 PARKING: Medium OPEN: Mon-Sat 10-5 MIN: 50p MAX: £3000 PERIOD: 18th-20th century SPECIALIST: Country items, arts & crafts GENERAL: General antiques. 20+ dealers

**Honiton Clock Clinic**, 167 High Street, EX14 8LQ TEL: 47466 PARKING: Easy OPEN: Mon-Sat 10-4 PERIOD: 17th-20th century SPECIALIST: Clocks & barometer spares, cabinet fittings, restoration material GENERAL: Clocks & barometers.

**Honiton Fine Art**, 189 High Street, EX14 8LQ TEL: 45942 PARKING: Easy OPEN: Mon-Sat 9.30-5 MIN: £300 MAX: £7000 PERIOD: 18th-19th century SPECIALIST: Old Master drawings GENERAL: English & European paintings & watercolours.

**Honiton Junction**, 159 High Street, EX14 8LJ TEL: 43436 PARKING: Easy OPEN: Mon-Sat 10-5 MIN: £1 MAX: £1000 PERIOD: 19th century SPECIALIST: Collectables GENERAL: Country pine & oak, kitchenalia, copper, brass, door & window hardware etc OTHER INFO: Honiton - the antique centre of the Southwest.

**Honiton Lace Shop**, 44 High Street, EX14 8PJ TEL: 42416 FAX: 47797 PARKING: Easy OPEN:

Mon-Sat 9.30-1, 2-5 MIN: £1 MAX: £4000 PERIOD: 17th-19th century SPECIALIST: Collectors & rare lace, textiles OTHER INFO: Museum has superb collection of Honiton lace.

**Honiton Old Bookshop**, Felix House, 51 High Street, EX14 8PW TEL: 47180 FAX: 47180 ASSNS: ABA, PBFA PARKING: Easy OPEN: Mon-Sat 10-5.30 PERIOD: Antiquarian to modern out of print GENERAL: Good quality general stock, cleanly & comfortably presented OTHER INFO: 4 other secondhand bookshops nearby, all with interesting, changing stock.

**House of Antiques**, 195 High Street, EX14 8LQ TEL: 41648 PARKING: Medium OPEN: Mon-Sat 10-6 MAX: £10,000 PERIOD: 19th-20th century SPECIALIST: Victorian & Edwardian furniture.

**LJ Huggett & Son**, Stamps Building, King Street, EX14 8AG TEL: 42403 PARKING: Own carpark OPEN: Mon-Sat 9.30-5 PERIOD:18th-19th century SPECIALIST: Period furniture.

**Kings Arms Antiques Centre**, 56 High Street TEL: 46269 PARKING: Easy OPEN: Mon-Sat 10-4.30, Thurs AM only MIN: £2 MAX: £1000 PERIOD: 18th-20th century GENERAL: 10+ dealers with comprehensive range of antiques.

**Kingsway House Antiques**, Kingsway House,3 High Street TEL: 46213 PARKING: easy OPEN: Mon-Sat 10-5.30 MIN: £20 MAX: £5000 PERIOD: 1780-1850 SPECIALIST: Large stock of clocks GENERAL: Chests of drawers, toilet mirrors, decorative items, soft furnishings etc.

**Lombard Antiques,** 14 High Street, EX14 8PU TEL: 42140 PARKING: Easy OPEN: Mon-Sat 10-5.30 PERIOD: 18th-20th century GENERAL: Mahogany, rosewood, walnut furniture, porcelain & decorative items.

**Otter Antiques**, 69 High Street, EX14 8PW TEL: 42627 PARKING: Medium OPEN: Mon-Wed, Fri, Sat 9-5. Thurs by appt MIN: £1 MAX: £1000 PERIOD: 18th-20th century SPECIALIST: Tableware GENERAL: Silver, silverplate OTHER INFO: 25 antique shops in High Street + 3 auction rooms.

**Pilgrim Antiques**, 145 High Street, EX14 8LJ TEL: 41219 FAX: 45317 PARKING: Own carpark OPEN: Mon-Sat 9-5.30 MIN: £100 MAX: £12,000 PERIOD: 17th-19th century SPECIALIST: Large stock of English & Continental furniture GENERAL: 16,000 sq ft trade warehouse, packing & shipping service.

**Polkinghorne Antiques,** Abingdon House, 136 High Street, EX14 8JP TEL & FAX: 87300 PARKING: Easy OPEN: 10-5 MIN: £50 MAX: £4000 PERIOD: 17th-20th century SPECIALIST: Period furniture & smalls OTHER INFO: Over 20 years cheerful & successful dealing.

**Stable Antiques,** Plympton House, 59 High Street, EX14 8PW TEL: 42640 PARKING: Easy OPEN: 10-4 MIN: £5 MAX: £15,000 SPECIALIST: Pine, silverplate GENERAL: General antiques, decorative items.

**Upstairs Downstairs**, 12 High Street, EX14 8PU TEL: 42140 PARKING: Easy OPEN: Mon-Sat 10-5.30 PERIOD: 18th-20th century GENERAL: General antiques.

**Wickham Antiques**, 191 High Street, EX14 8LQ TEL: 44654 PARKING: Medium OPEN: Mon-Sat 9.30-5 MIN: £100 MAX: £2000 PERIOD: 18th-19th century SPECIALIST: Georgian & Victorian furniture GENERAL: Decorative items.

**John Wignall Fine Books**, 174 High Street, EX14 8LA TEL: 43460 FAX: 47377 PARKING: Medium OPEN: 10-5.30 MIN: £8 MAX: £800 PERIOD: 18th-20th century SPECIALIST: Antiquarian & sporting books, particularly field sports OTHER INFO: 1st floor picture gallery, ceramics & antiques. Constant coffee.

**Geoffrey Woodhead Antiques**, 53 High Street, EX14 8PW TEL: 42969 PARKING: Easy OPEN: Mon-Sat 9.30-1, 2.15-5.30 MIN: £2 MAX: £5000 PERIOD: 18th-20th century GENERAL: Antiques & collectors items, antique & secondhand books.

## AXMINSTER (O1297)

**WG Potter & Son,** 1 West Street, EX13 5HS TEL: 32063 FAX: 34550 PARKING: Easy OPEN: 9-5 MIN: £50 MAX: £5000 PERIOD: 19th century SPECIALIST: Pine GENERAL: Oak & mahogany OTHER INFO: An excellent B&B is available at Fordhayes Farm, Kilmington, Devon - tel: 35002 (2 miles from Axminster).

## COLYTON (01297)

**Colyton Antiques Centre**, Dolphin Street, EX13 6NA TEL: 552339 PARKING: Own carpark OPEN: Mon-Sat 10-5 MIN: £1 MAX: £2000 PERIOD: 19th-20th century GENERAL: General antiques OTHER INFO: Colyton dating from Saxon times, a unique town with a village atmosphere. Interesting church with octagonal lantern tower.

## SEATON (01297)

**Etcetera Etc Antiques**, 12 Beer Road, EX14 2PA TEL: 21965 PARKING: Own carpark OPEN: Mon-Wed, Fri-Sat 10-1, 2-5 PERIOD: 18th-20th century GENERAL: Furniture, china, glass, brass, bric-a-brac. etc OTHER INFO: Lovely coastline walks, 18 hole links, tramway beside Axe Estuary, B&B's.

## SIDMOUTH (01395)

**Bygones**, 2 Old Fore Street, EX10 8LS TEL: 512086 PARKING: Easy OPEN: Summer 7 days 10-5, Winter Mon-Sat 10-5 closed Thurs & Sun MIN: £1 PERIOD: 18th-20th century GENERAL: Veritable cornucopia, a bit of everything.

**Devonshire House Antiques Centre**, All Saints Road TEL: 512588 PARKING: Easy OPEN: Mon-Sat 10-5; Easter to end of Sept Sun 1-5 MIN: £2 MAX: £1500 PERIOD: 18th-20th century GENERAL: Books, collectables, furniture, pictures, china, glass.

**Gainsborough House Antiques,** Libra Court, Fore Street, EX10 8AJ TEL: 514394 PARKING: Easy OPEN: Mon-Wed, Fri 9.15-1, 2.15-5, Thurs, Sat 9.15-1 MIN: 5p MAX: £500 PERIOD: 18th-20th century SPECIALIST: Militaria & medals GENERAL: Porcelain, silver, collectables OTHER INFO: Libra Court is a small attractive courtyard development housing various small businesses, close to the sea.

**Dorothy Hartnell Antiques**, 21 Fore Street TEL: 515291 PARKING: Easy in Winter OPEN: Mon-Sat 10-5, Winter Thurs halfday MIN: £1 MAX: £5000 PERIOD: 18th-20th century GENERAL: General antiques OTHER INFO: Wealth of individual shops, large & small first class hotels, winner of the Britain in Bloom Floral Town.

**Vintage Toy & Train Museum Shop**, Market Place, EX10 8LU TEL: 515124 ext 208 Assn of Indep. Museums PARKING: Easy OPEN: 31st Mar-28th Oct 10-5 MIN: £2 MAX: £500 PERIOD: 20th century SPECIALIST: Tinplate toys & trains GENERAL: Hornby Gauge 0 & Dublo, Meccano, Dinky toys, Corgis, Britains, wooden puzzles.

## BUDLEIGH SALTERTON (01395)

**Granny's Attic,** 53 High Street, EX9 6LE TEL: 443936 PARKING: Medium OPEN: 9.30-1, 2-5 MIN: £1 MAX: £4000 PERIOD: 18th-20th century GENERAL: French, English.

**New Gallery**, 9 Fore Street, EX9 6NG TEL: 443768 ASSNS: FRSA PARKING: Easy OPEN: Easter to Christmas Tues-Sat 10-1, 2-5 otherwise by appt MIN: £10 MAX: £1000 PERIOD: 19th-20th century SPECIALIST: Fine watercolours GENERAL: Oils, prints OTHER INFO: Gallery in ballroom of elegant Edwardian house set in a colourful garden.

**Wendy Cook**, Budleigh House, East Budleigh, EX9 7ED TEL: 445368 PARKING: Easy OPEN: Tues, Thur-Sun 10-5 MIN: £5 MAX: £1500 PERIOD: 18th-19th century SPECIALIST: Country furniture GENERAL: Porcelain, pottery, metalware, decorative items OTHER INFO: Opposite Sir Walter Raleigh pub. Village is his birthplace.

**David J Thorn**, 2 High Street, EX9 6LQ TEL: 442448 PARKING: Easy OPEN: Tues & Fri 10-1, 2-5, Sat 10-1 MIN: £2 MAX: £10,000 PERIOD: 17th-20th century SPECIALIST: Ceramics: English, Continental & Oriental.

## EXETER (01392)

**Exeter Rare Books**, Guildhall Shopping Centre, EX4 3HG TEL: 436021 ASSNS: ABA, PBFA PARKING: Easy OPEN: Mon-Sat 10-1, 2-5 MIN: £1 MAX: £500 PERIOD: 19th-20th century SPECIALIST: Devon & West Country topography GENERAL: Out-of-print, antiquarian & secondhand books on most subjects. Fine bindings & illustrated books OTHER INFO: In heart of city with first floor gallery of restored Georgian market building, close to cathedral, museums.

**Gold & Silver Exchange**, Eastgate House, Princesshay, EX4 3JT TEL: 217478 PARKING: Easy OPEN: Mon-Sat 9.30-3 MIN: £5 MAX: £2500 PERIOD: 19th-20th century GENERAL: Silver, antique & secondhand jewellery.

**McBains of Exeter,** Adj. Exeter Airport, EX5 2BA TEL: 366261 FAX: 365572 ASSNS: LAPADA PARKING: Own carpark OPEN: Mon-Fri 9-5.30 or by appt MIN: £50 MAX: £5000 PERIOD: 17th-19th century SPECIALIST: Furniture GENERAL: Large warehouse complex of over 45,000 sq ft.

**Micawber Antiques,** New Buildings Lane, 25-26 Gandy Street, EX4 3LS TEL: 52200 PARKING: Easy OPEN: Mon-Sat 10-5 MIN: £1 MAX: £300 PERIOD: 19th-20th century SPECIALIST: Clocks, Victorian pottery GENERAL: Oil lamps, china, costume jewellery, prints, metalware OTHER INFO: New Buildings Lane is Exeter's oldest lane situated off the High St behind C&A.

**John Nathan,** 153-154 Cowick Street, EX4 1AS TEL: 78216 PARKING: Easy OPEN: 9-1, 2-5.30, closed Weds afternoon PERIOD: 19th-20th century SPECIALIST: Silverware, Exeter silver, jewellery, clocks GENERAL: Good range of 2nd hand jewellery, new and old silver.

**Pennies**, Unit 2, Wessex Estate, Station Road, Exwick, EX4 4NZ TEL: 71928, 76532 PARKING: Own carpark OPEN: Mon-Sat 9-6 MIN: £1 MAX: £2000 PERIOD: 20th century GENERAL: General antiques OTHER INFO: 1930s, 40s & 50s and secondhand furniture.

**Quay Gallery Antiques Emporium**, 43 The Quay TEL: 213283 PARKING: Easy OPEN: 7 days 10-5 MIN: £1 MAX: £2500 PERIOD: 18th-20th century SPECIALIST: Furniture, marine items, silver + plate GENERAL: Collectables, pine, small decorative items OTHER INFO: View onto the Exeter Ship Canal, used filming *The Onedin Line*. Shop with 8 dealers is in a bonded warehouse c.1530 with excellent café below. Customs House next door.

**Strip & Wax**, Exe Street, EX4 3HD TEL: 52476 & 496688 PARKING: Own carpark MIN: £25 MAX: £800 PERIOD: 19th-20th century SPECIALIST: Period pine doors GENERAL: Furniture OTHER INFO: 30 seconds from The Mill on the Exe, pub and the Papermakers winebar.

## TEIGNMOUTH (01626)

**Charterhouse Antiques**, 1b Northumberland Place TEL: 54592 home PARKING: Easy OPEN: Tues, Wed, Fri, Sat 11-1, 2.30-4 MIN: £5 MAX: £500 PERIOD: 19th century SPECIALIST: Royal & political commemoratives GENERAL: General antiques OTHER INFO: Sometimes 18th & 20th century. Teignmouth is a picturesque holiday town & working port with clay is exported all over the world.

**The Old Passage**, 13a Bank Street, TQ14 9NN TEL: 772634 PARKING: Easy OPEN: Tues, Weds, Fri, Sat 10.30-1, 2.30-5 MIN: 50p MAX: £500 PERIOD: 19th-20th century GENERAL: Glass silver, porcelain, pottery, pictures OTHER INFO: Narrowest shop in town with eccentric opening times.

**Timepiece Antiques**, 125 Bitton Park Road, TQ14 9BZ TEL: 770275 PARKING: Medium OPEN: Tues-Sat 10-5.30 MIN: £1 MAX: £2000 PERIOD: 18th-20th century SPECIALIST: Pine and clocks GENERAL: Kitchenalia, brass, copper, brown furniture OTHER INFO: Beautiful coastline & estuary with easy access to Dartmoor, Torquay & Exeter.

## NEWTON ABBOTT (01626)

**The Attic**, 9 Union Street, TQ12 2JX TEL: 55124 PARKING: Difficult OPEN: Tues, Wed, Fri, Sat 9.15-5.30 MIN: £1 MAX: £2000 PERIOD: 18th-20th century GENERAL: Could be anything-bric-a-brac, tools, antiques, you name it I sell it.

**Newton Abbott Antiques Centre**, 55 East Street TEL: 54074 PARKING: Own carpark OPEN: Tuesdays 9-3 OTHER INFO: 45+ dealers

**Old Treasures**, 126 Queen Street TEL: 67181 PARKING: Medium OPEN: Mon-Wed, Fri, Sat 10-4 MIN: £1 MAX: £2000 PERIOD: 19th-20th century GENERAL: Antique jewellery.

## BOVEY TRACEY (01626)

**Moor Art**, 6A Station Road, TQ13 9AL TEL: 835350 PARKING: Own carpark OPEN: Mon-Sat 10-5 MIN: £20 MAX: £5000 PERIOD: 17th-20th century SPECIALIST: Period furniture, soft furnishings, decorative items, ceramics & works of art OTHER INFO: Gateway to Dartmoor, good facilities & hotels.

## ASHBURTON (01364)

**Ashburton Marbles**, Great Hall, North Street, TQ13 7QD TEL: 653189 FAX: 654075 PARKING: Own carpark OPEN: Mon-Sat 8-5 MIN: £20 MAX: £10,000 PERIOD: 18th-19th century SPECIALIST: Antique fireplaces, marble & timber GENERAL: 19th century furnishings, lighting, mirrors, garden staturary, etc.

**Moor Antiques**, 19A North Street, TQ13 7QH TEL: 653767 PARKING: Easy OPEN: Mon-Sat 10-5, Wed mornings only MIN: £20 MAX: £2500 PERIOD: 18th-19th century SPECIALIST: Furniture & clocks GENERAL: Silver, porcelain, metalware, lighting OTHER INFO: Very ancient Stannary town. Lots of Civil War history. Plenty of accommodation with good access to other areas.

## SOUTH BRENT (01364)

**Philip Andrade**, White Oxen Manor, near Rattery, TQ10 9JX TEL: 72454 FAX: 73061 ASSNS: BADA, LAPADA PARKING: Own carpark OPEN: Mon-Sat 9-5.30, Sat pm by appt MIN: £50 MAX: £10,000 SPECIALIST: English 18th-early 19th century furniture GENERAL: General stock 17th-19th century.

## TOTNES (01803)

**Cobwebs,** 19 Leechwell Street, TQ9 5SP TEL: 865711 PARKING: Easy OPEN: 10-5 except Thurs & Sun MIN: 50p MAX: £200 PERIOD: 19th-20th century SPECIALIST: 1920s/30s & old kitchenalia GENERAL: A good collection of the old and interesting OTHER INFO: Near good pubs.

**Collards Bookshop**, 4 Castle Street, TEL: Home 0548-550246 OPEN: Mon-Sat 10-5 but restricted Nov-March MAX: £200 PERIOD: 18th-20th century GENERAL: Antiquarian & out-of-print books OTHER INFO: Nestling under historic Totnes Castle. 3 other bookshops in this Elizabethan town. Keith Floyd's restaurant a few miles.

**The Magpie,** Rotherfold Square, Top of the Town, TQ9 5ST TEL: 830082 PARKING: Medium OPEN: Mon, Tues, Fri, Sat 10-5 MIN: 50p MAX: £50+ PERIOD: 19th-20th century SPECIALIST: Books, especially the West Country, antique & unusual editions GENERAL: Ephemera, coins, old & new games, playing cards, collectables OTHER INFO: Kingsbridge Inn (old with good food, dogs welcome), The Leechwell Greys Dining Room (super home made food), Dartington Hall & shops.

**Penny Farthing,** 2 Rotherfold Square, TQ9 5ST TEL: 868379 FAX: 868379 PARKING: Medium OPEN: Mon-Sat 10-5 MIN: 50p MAX: £500 PERIOD: 19th-20th century GENERAL: Collectables, Deco, furnishings china. Anything interesting & unusual. OTHER INFO: Totnes is noted for it's small, individual shops.

**James Sturges Antiques**, Past & Present, 94 High Street, TQ9 5SN TEL: 866086 PARKING: Medium OPEN: Normal MIN: £5 MAX: £5000 PERIOD: 18th-20th century GENERAL: Georgian, Victorian & Edwardian collectables etc OTHER INFO: Second oldest borough in England.

**Vine Antiques,** 93 High Street, TQ9 5PB TEL: 867391 PARKING: Medium OPEN: Tues-Fri 10.30-5, Sat 10.30-4 MIN: £5 MAX: £1000 PERIOD: 19th century SPECIALIST: Stripped pine GENERAL: General antiques OTHER INFO: We are situated on the Narrows in this historic town.

## TORQUAY (01803)

**Birbeck Gallery,** 45 Abbey Road, TQ2 5NQ TEL: 297144 FAX: 214836 PARKING: Medium OPEN: 10-5 (when there!) MIN: £2 MAX: £5000 PERIOD: 18th-20th century SPECIALIST: Paintings, Oriental works of art GENERAL: General antiques OTHER INFO: Also at Stand D1, Rogers Arcade, Portobello Rd, London

**Sheraton House Antiques,** 1 Laburnum Row, Torre, TQ2 5QX TEL: 293334 PARKING: Easy OPEN: Mornings only MIN: £50 MAX £5000 PERIOD: 18th-19th century SPECIALIST: Furniture GENERAL: Pictures, lighting, plate. Restoration, repair & conservation.

**Spencers Antiques**, 187 Higher Union Street, Torre, TQ1 4BY TEL: 296598 PARKING: Easy OPEN: Mon-Sat 10-4 MIN: c £10 MAX: £3000 PERIOD: 18th but usually 19th-20th century OTHER INFO: Central for English Riviera, Dartmoor, the beautiful South Harns & historic Totnes.

**Torre Antique Traders**, 264-266 Union Street, Torre, TQ2 5QU TEL: 292184 PARKING: Easy OPEN: Mon-Sat 10-5 MIN: £2 MAX: £2000 approx. PERIOD: 18th-20th century GENERAL: General antiques.

**G A Whiteway**, Sunsea, Teignmouth Road, Maidencombe, TQ1 4TD TEL: 329692 PARKING: Own carpark OPEN: By appt PERIOD: 18th-20th century GENERAL: Most fields except silver.

## BRIXHAM (01803)

**John Prestige Antiques**, 1-2 Greenswood Court, TQ5 9BH TEL: 856141, 853739 (home) FAX: 851649 PARKING: Own carpark OPEN: (appt advisable) Mon-Fri 8.45-6 or by appt MIN: £100 MAX: £10,000 PERIOD: 17th-19th century GENERAL: Large stock of Victorian & Edwardian furniture & some interesting smaller items OTHER INFO: One of the most beautiful fishing villages where Henry Lyte wrote *Abide with Me.*

## DARTMOUTH (01803)

**Chantry Bookshop & Gallery**, 11 Higher Street, TQ6 9RB TEL: 832796, 834208 PARKING: Medium OPEN: Mon-Sat 10.30-5 PERIOD: 17th-20th century GENERAL: Books, watercolours, sea charts, maps, town plans, prints.

## HARBERTONFORD (01803)

**Fine Pine**, Woodland Road, TQ9 7SX TEL: 732465 PARKING: Own carpark OPEN: Mon-Sat 9.30-5, Sun 11-4 MIN: £5 MAX: £1500 PERIOD: 18th-19th century SPECIALIST: Antique pine & country pine GENERAL: Furniture OTHER INFO:

Crowdy Watermill in village, Church House Inn.

## KINGSBRIDGE (01548)

**Avon House Antiques**, 13 Church Street, TQ7 1BT TEL: 853718 PARKING: Medium OPEN: Mon-Sat 10-5, closed 1-2 MAX: £3000 PERIOD: 19th-20th century GENERAL: Antiques & furniture.

## SALCOMBE (0154884)

**A-B Gallery,** 67 Fore Street, TQ8 8BU TEL: 2728 & 2764 PARKING: Easy OPEN: Normally 9am-12.45 by appt advisable MIN: 20p MAX: £5000 PERIOD: 19th-20th century GENERAL: British oils, watercolours & etchings. Many barely organised unframed originals & prints. OTHER INFO: Please avoid usual comment after examing stock, "Did you paint these?" & daily comment, "You are never open."

## MODBURY (01548)

**Context Picture Framing & Gallery,** 9 Church Street, PL21 0QN TEL: 830872 PARKING: Medium OPEN: 10-5.30 MIN: £5 MAX: £4000 PERIOD: 19th-20th century SPECIALIST: Watercolours & oils GENERAL: Prints, maps, many local landscapes, florals.

**Country Cottage Antiques**, The Old Chapel, Church Street, PL21 0QR TEL: 831079 FAX: 831081 PARKING: Medium OPEN: Mon-Sat 9-6 MIN: £15 MAX: £3500 PERIOD: 19th-20th century SPECIALIST: Country furniture.

**Fourteen A**, 14a Broad Street, PL21 0PU TEL: 830732 PARKING: Easy OPEN: Mon-Sat 10-5 MIN: £1 MAX: £300 PERIOD: 19th-20th century SPECIALIST: Antique lace & linen GENERAL: General antiques OTHER INFO: Good B&B (£14) at Little Orchard Farm.

**Welsh Dresser**, 63 Brownston Street TEL: 830317 PARKING: Easy OPEN: Mon-Sat 10-5, closed Wed pm MIN: £50 MAX: £5000 PERIOD: 17th-19th century SPECIALIST: Oak & country furniture GENERAL: Decorative china, pictures & prints.

**Wild Goose Antiques**, 34 Church Street, PL21 0QR TEL: 830715, 830238 PARKING: Easy OPEN: Tues-Sat 9.30-5 or by appt MIN: £5 MAX: £5000 PERIOD: 18th-early 20th century GENERAL: Furniture, paintings, silver, chandeliers.

**Ye Little Shoppe Antiques & Restoration**, 1a Broad Street, PL21 0PS TEL: 830732 PARKING: Easy OPEN: Mon-Sat 10-5 PERIOD: 19th-20th century SPECIALIST: Woodworking tools, book-binding implements, writing boxes, trinkets and workboxes. Oil lamps. GENERAL: Small furniture, copper, brassware, treen.

## YEALMPTON (01752)

**Torr Bridge Antiques,** Ford Road, PL8 1NA TEL: 880954 PARKING: Easy OPEN: 10-5.30, closed Mon & Wed MIN: £1 MAX: £1000 PERIOD: 18th-19th century SPECIALIST: Leatherbound books, Chinese porcelain GENERAL: Engravings, etchings, English porcelain, decorative items.

**Colin Rhodes Antiques**, 15 Fore Street, PL8 2JN TEL: 862232, 881170 ASSNS: LAPADA PARKING: Own carpark OPEN: Tues, Thurs-Sat 10-1 MIN: £40 MAX: £6000 PERIOD: 17th-19th century GENERAL: Furniture & paintings, silver, pottery + small items.

## PLYMPTON (01752)

**Alan Jones Antiques**, Applethorn Slade Farm, Sparkwell PL7 5AS TEL: 338188 PARKING: Own carpark OPEN: By appt MIN: £5 MAX: £2000 PERIOD: 17th-19th century SPECIALIST: Nautical, scientific, clocks GENERAL: Collectors, decorative.

## PLYMOUTH (01752)

**Annterior Antiques**, 22 Molesworth Road, Millbridge, PL1 5LZ TEL & FAX: 558277 PARKING: Easy OPEN: Mon-Sat 9.30-5.30 MIN: £1 MAX: £3000 PERIOD: 18th-20th century SPECIALIST: Good pine dressers GENERAL: Pine, mahogany, jewel & writing boxes OTHER INFO: Designer fabrics, wallpapers, etc.

**Antique Fireplace Centre,** 30 Molesworth Road, Stoke, PL1 5NA TEL: 559441 PARKING: Easy OPEN: 10-5 MIN: £30 MAX: £4000 PERIOD: 17th-20th century SPECIALIST: Original 18th & 19th century fireplaces & accessories.

**Barbican Antiques Centre**, 82-84 Vauxhall Street, PL4 0EX TEL: 255752 PARKING: Own carpark OPEN: Seven days 9.30-5 MIN: £1 MAX: £500 SPECIALIST: Silver & jewellery GENERAL: Porcelain, glass, furniture, coins, pictures OTHER INFO: This 18th century quayside warehouse, used as an antique centre since 1971, was used for 200 years as a store for bananas bought by clipper from the West Indies.

**Brian Taylor Antiques,** 24 Molesworth Road,

Stoke, PL1 5LZ TEL & FAX: 569061 PARKING: Easy OPEN: Fri & Sat 10-5 or by appt MIN: £5 MAX: £5000 SPECIALIST: Mechanical music, accessories, grandfather clocks, literature.

**Upstairs Downstairs**, 30 Camden Street, Greenbank TEL: 261015 PARKING: Medium OPEN: Mon-Sat 10-5 MIN: £2 PERIOD: 19th-20th century SPECIALIST: Period costume - Victorian to 1950's GENERAL: China, furniture, jewellery, lace, linen OTHER INFO: We are old fashioned curio shop hidden away in back street of Old Plymouth, phone for directions.

## TAVISTOCK (01822)

**King Street Curios**, 5 King Street, PL19 0DS TEL: 615193 PARKING: Easy OPEN: Mon-Sat 9-5 MIN: £1 MAX: £300 PERIOD: 19th-20th century SPECIALIST: Postcards & cigarette cards.

**Pendar Antiques**, 8 Drake Road, PL19 0AX TEL: 617641, 612207 PARKING: Medium OPEN: Mon-Sat 9-5 MIN: £1 MAX: £1500 PERIOD: 18-20th century SPECIALIST: Furniture GENERAL: Some china, granite troughs, bric-a-brac, mostly Victorian, Edwardian, 1920's furniture OTHER INFO: Buctor Guest House excellent B&B. Very good breakfast (I cook it).

## OKEHAMPTON (01837)

**Alan Jones Antiques,** Fatherford Antiques, EX20 1QQ TEL: 52970 FAX: 53404 PARKING: Own carpark OPEN: Mon-Fri 8.30-5.30 or by appt PERIOD: 17th-20th century GENERAL: Furniture & general antiques.

## CHAGFORD (01647)

**Mary Payton Antiques**, Old Market House, TQ13 8AB TEL: 432428 PARKING: OPEN: Tues, Thurs, Fri, Sat 10-1,2.30-5 MIN: £5 MAX: £300 PERIOD: 19th-20th century SPECIALIST: English pottery & porcelain.

## MORETONHAMPSTEAD (01647)

**Herbert Clark**, 2-4 Fore Street, TQ13 8LN TEL: 40334 PARKING: Easy OPEN: Mon-Wed, Fri, Sat 9.30-1, 2.15-5.30 MIN: £1 MAX: £200 PERIOD: 19th-20th century GENERAL: Glass & pottery, 18th century English pottery OTHER INFO: White Hart Hotel, B&B.

## NEWTON ST CYRES (01392)

**Gordon Hepworth Gallery**, Hayne Farm, EX5 5PE TEL: 851351 PARKING: Own carpark MIN: £150 MAX: £5000 PERIOD: 20th century SPECIALIST: Postwar & contemporary paintings, St Ives School and Cornish paintings with regular exhibitions in 15th century longhouse OTHER INFO: Phone for opening times, directions and gallery brochure.

## TIVERTON (01884)

**Bygone Days Antiques,** 40 Gold Street, EX16 6PY TEL: 252832 PARKING: Easy OPEN: Mon-Wed, Fri, Sat 10-5 MIN: £250 MAX: £3500 PERIOD: 18th-19th century GENERAL: Furniture, longcase clocks, soft furnishings OTHER INFO: Castle Museum, Knighthayes (NY house).

## CULLOMPTON (01884)

**Cullompton Antiques,** The Old Tannery, EX15 1DT TEL: 38476, home (0395) 279253 PARKING: Own carpark OPEN: 7 days 10-5 MIN: £1 MAX: £5000 PERIOD: 18th-20th century SPECIALIST: 6000 sq ft of country furniture & smalls.

**BA & FB Ward-Smith,** Dulford Cottage, Dulford EX15 2DX TEL: 266429 PARKING: Own carpark OPEN: 8.30 until late evening by appt MIN: £200 MAX: £2500 PERIOD: 18th-19th century SPECIALIST: French country GENERAL: English country OTHER INFO: Trade only.

## HELE (01392)

**Fagins Antiques**, Old Whiteways Cider Factory TEL: 882062 FAX: 882194 PARKING: OPEN: Mon-Fri 9.15-5, Sat 11-5 MIN: £1 MAX: £5000 PERIOD: 19th-20th century SPECIALIST: Stripped pine, mahogany, oak GENERAL: Bric-a-brac, pictures, taxidermy, architectural items. OTHER INFO: 40,000 sq ft showrooms.

# North Devon

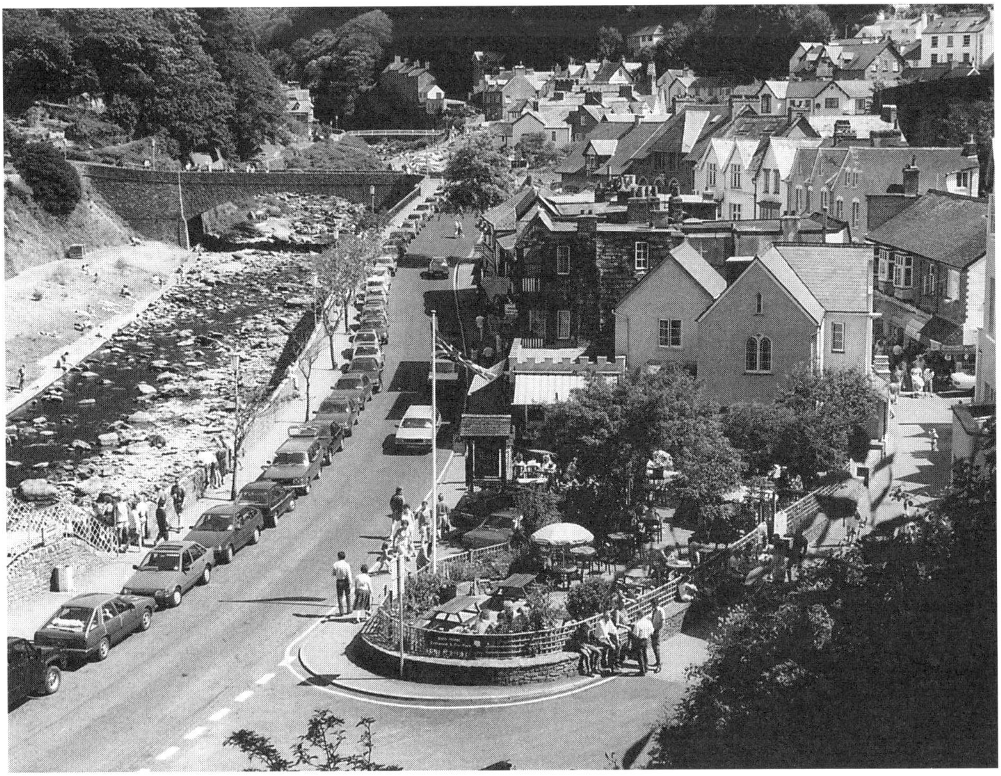

*Lowtide for the River Lyn at Lynmouth, the river that flooded to bring disaster*

North Devon is a region of high, windswept cliffs, sheltered valleys and wild moorland which gave birth to the story of Lorna Doone. There are no large cities in this area, instead small market and seaside towns and pretty villages seem designed with picture postcards in mind.

The first stop, **Bampton**, on the edge of Exmoor, plays host to the Exmoor pony fair held annually in October. In the local churchyard there are two yew trees reputed to be 500 years old. **Dulverton**, next, is actually in Somerset and is ideal for exploring Exmoor. The National Park Centre is housed here in Exmoor House, a former Victorian workhouse.

Back in Devon, **South Molton** is a centre for antiques enthusiasts with many shops. There are some Georgian houses and the Guildhall was built in 1743 with an arcaded lower storey. Going via **Hatherleigh,** although off the main tourist routes, is quite appealing, the George Hotel is medieval and there are plenty of thatched cottages. Via **Merton** and **Monkleigh,** the tour comes next to **Bideford.** Standing on the River Torridge, there is a 677 foot long, 24 arch bridge across the river in which some 15th century stonework may still be seen. The town was the main port for North Devon from 16th to 18th centuries. Now the island of Lundy may be reached by launch from here. Charles Kingsley wrote *Westward Ho!* in the Royal Hotel and there is statue of him at the park gates.

Moving on, **Braunton** is said to be the largest village in England. The church is of particular interest. Reputedly founded by St. Brannock, a 6th century Welsh missionary, legend has it that he sailed to Braunton in a stone coffin. The present building dates from the 13th century and stands on the site of the church he founded. Nearby is Braunton Burrows, a 560 acre national nature reserve.

Now to **Ilfracombe**, a simple fishing village until Victorian times when it developed into a

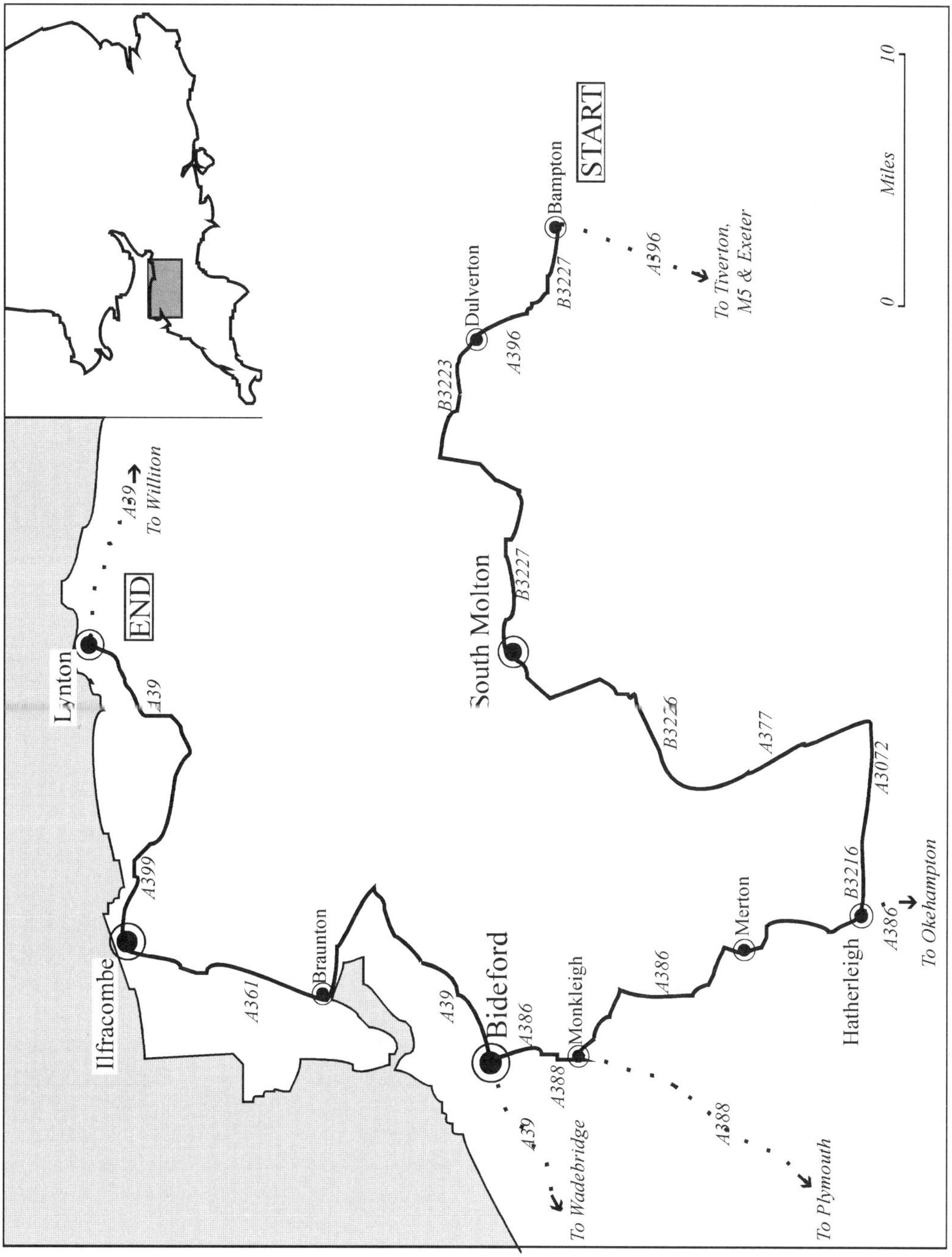
START
Bampton
B3227
A396
To Tiverton,
M5 & Exeter
Miles
0
10
Dulverton
A396
B3223
South Molton
B3227
B3226
A377
A3072
B3216
Hatherleigh
A386
To Okehampton
Merton
A386
Monkleigh
A386
A388
A388
To Plymouth
Bideford
A39
A39
To Wadebridge
Braunton
A361
Ilfracombe
A399
Lynton
A39
END
A39
To Willition

holiday resort. It is still popular and is a good centre for exploring Exmoor and North Devon. Pleasure cruisers ply between Ilfracombe and Swansea and Bristol and there are also boat trips to Lundy Island.

Continuing along the coast the route arrives finally in **Lynton**. The town is perched high on the cliffs above the small picturesque harbour town of Lynmouth and a visit to one usually includes a visit to the other. From Lynton, Lynmouth is reached either by a very steep road (1 in 4) or by a water-powered cliff railway which rises almost vertically. Both were tiny villages until the early 19th century when the poet, Shelley, stayed in Lynmouth. Later both Wordsworth and Coleridge visited. In 1952 there was a disastrous flood in Lynmouth when the East and West Lyn Rivers burst their banks and hundreds of tons of rocks were brought down by the floodwaters. A total of 34 people were killed and great damage was done. In spite of this, the original fishing village cottages alongside the harbour survived.

## ANTIQUE DEALERS

### BAMPTON (01398)

**Bampton Antiques,** 9 Castle Street, EX16 9NS TEL: 331197 PARKING: Easy OPEN: 10.30-5 MIN: £1 MAX: £1000 PERIOD: 18th-20th century SPECIALIST: Glass GENERAL: General antiques, country furniture, porcelain & glass OTHER INFO: 'Bampton in Bloom' every summer & Bampton Fair every Oct. Shop is very popular.

### DULVERTON (01398)

**Acorn Antiques**, 39 High Street, TA22 9DW TEL: 23286 PARKING: Easy OPEN: Mon-Sat 9.30-5.30 or by appt MIN: £10 MAX: £5000 PERIOD: 17th-20th century SPECIALIST: Decorative & country antiques, oil paintings & upholstery GENERAL: Furniture OTHER INFO: Information centre, country sports, good hotels, restaurants, pubs.

**Faded Elegance**, 39 High Street, TA22 9DW TEL: 23286 PARKING: Medium OPEN: Mon-Sat 9.30-5.30 MIN: £15 MAX: £5000 PERIOD: 17th-20th century SPECIALIST: Upholstered furniture.

### SOUTH MOLTON (01769)

**Architectural Antiques,** West Ley, Alswear Old Road, EX36 4LE TEL: 573342 FAX: 574363 PARKING: Own carpark OPEN: Tues-Sat 9-5 PERIOD: 19th century SPECIALIST: Original bars, back fittings & shop interiors GENERAL: Panelling, entrywayss, columns, stained glass, etc (7500 sq ft) OTHER INFO: Beautifully situated with glorious views but difficult to find.

**Bellevue House Interiors,** 103 East Street, EX36 3DF TEL: 573761 PARKING: Easy OPEN: Mon-Sat 9-5 MIN: £10 MAX: £2000 PERIOD: 19th century SPECIALIST: Fireplaces GENERAL: Architectural antiques.

**Chariot Antiques,** 1 Queen Street, EX36 3BJ TEL: 572876 FAX: 573957 PARKING: Easy OPEN: 9.30-5.30 MIN: £1800 MAX: £25,000 PERIOD: 19th-20th century SPECIALIST: Edged weapons & guns GENERAL: Furniture & porcelain.

**Cobbs Curiosity Shop,** 24 East Street, EX36 3DB TEL: 574104 PARKING: Medium OPEN: Mon-Sat 10-2 MIN: £2 MAX: £200 PERIOD: 19th-20th century GENERAL: Curios & collectables, books, ephemera etc. OTHER INFO: South Molton has the largest selection of dealers in North Devon. Market days Thurs & Sat.

**The Furniture Market**, Barnstaple Street TEL: 573401 PARKING: Easy OPEN: Mon-Sat 10-5, Wed closed pm MIN: £1 MAX: £20,000 PERIOD: 18th-20th century SPECIALIST: Pine, oak & mahogany furniture GENERAL: Shipping OTHER INFO: 2000 sq ft of large varied stock. Trade very welcome. Good restaurants.

**Memory Lane Antiques**, 100 East Street, EX36 3DF TEL: 574288 PARKING: Easy OPEN: Mon-Sat 9.30-5.30 MIN: £2 MAX: £6000 PERIOD: 18th-20th century SPECIALIST: Large stock of general antiques (4 rooms). We sell everything in good order and usable. OTHER INFO: Corndolly teashop well known.

**South Molton Antiques**, 103 East Street, EX36 3DF TEL: 573478 PARKING: Easy OPEN: Mon-Sat 9-5 MIN: £20 MAX: £3000 PERIOD: 18th-20th century SPECIALIST: Victorian & Edwardian furniture GENERAL: Furniture & shipping goods.

**Treasure Trove Antiques,** 101 East Street, EX36 3DF TEL: 574288 PARKING: Easy OPEN: Mon-Sat 9.30-5.30 MIN: £2 MAX: £6000 PERIOD: 18th-19th century SPECIALIST: Cutlery

GENERAL: Glass, pottery & porcelain, clocks, etc.
**JR Tredant**, 50-50a South Street TEL: 573006 PARKING: Medium OPEN: Mon, Tues, Thurs-Sat 10-4 MIN: £1 MAX: £3000 PERIOD: 18th-20th century GENERAL: Smalls & furniture.

## HATHERLEIGH (01837)

**Hatherleigh Antiques**, 15 Bridge Street, EX20 3HY TEL: 810159 ASSNS: BADA PARKING: Easy OPEN: Mon, Tues, Thurs-Sat 9-5 MIN: £300 MAX: £30,000+ PERIOD: 17th century SPECIALIST: Furniture & works of art OTHER INFO: My shop is in the former Manor House which is furnished and decorated circa 1610.

## MERTON (01805)

**Barometer World**, Quicksilver Barn, EX20 3DS ASSNS: BAFRA, UKIC listed TEL: 603443 FAX: 603344 PARKING: Own carpark OPEN: Mon-Sat 8-5 MIN: £50 MAX: £3000 PERIOD: 19th-20th century SPECIALIST: (recognised worldwide) Antique barometers & restoration OTHER INFO: Also housing Banfield family collection of old barometers (not for sale).

## MONKLEIGH (01237)

**Petticombe Manor Antiques,** Petticombe Manor, EX34 5JR TEL: 475605 PARKING: Own carpark OPEN: 7 days 9-6 MIN: £1 MAX: £5000 PERIOD: 19th-20th century SPECIALIST: Furniture, smalls, pictures. OTHER INFO: Restaurant in manor, morning coffee, B&B.

## BIDEFORD (01237)

**J Collins & Son**, The Studio, 63 High Street, EX39 2AN TEL: 473103 FAX: 475658 ASSNS: BADA, LAPADA PARKING: Easy OPEN: Mon-Sat 9.30-5 MIN: £30 MAX: £20,000 SPECIALIST: Georgian to Regency furniture. 19th century oil paintings and watercolours OTHER INFO: Burton Art Gallery. 3 hotels, all very good.
**The Medina Gallery,** 20 Mill Street, EX39 2JR TEL: 476483 PARKING: Medium OPEN: 9.30-5, half day Weds MIN: 50p MAX: £200 PERIOD: 19th-20th century GENERAL: Limited edition prints, antiques maps & prints, artists' materials.
**Old & New,** 25 Market Place, EX39 2DR TEL: 423535 PARKING: Medium OPEN: 10-4.30 MIN: 50p MAX: £500 PERIOD: 19th-20th century SPECIALIST: Fireplaces GENERAL: China & furniture.
**Scudders Emporium**, Bridge Street, EX39 2BU TEL: 479567, 451665 PARKING: Easy OPEN: Mon-Sat 9.30-5.30, (Suns admission 50p 10.30-4.30) MIN: £1 MAX: £1500 PERIOD: 19th century SPECIALIST: Collectables & architectural GENERAL: 6000 sq ft of browsers & dealers delights in antique, restored and revival furniture OTHER INFO: High turnover allows us to cover all periods. Shop runs as 'organised chaos' on 3 floors including "hi & lo" callers, a children friendly shop to be enjoyed. Loads of stuffed animals & museum items.

## BRAUNTON (01271)

**Eileen Cooper Antiques**, Challoners Road, EX33 2ES TEL: 813320, 816005 PARKING: Easy OPEN: Usually Tues, Thurs, Sat 10-30-1, 2-4.30, sometimes other days MIN: £1 MAX: £1000 PERIOD: 18th-20th century SPECIALIST: Fine lace, linen & textiles GENERAL: General antiques & collectables OTHER INFO: Stands beside Shell petrol station on main road to Victorian Ilfracombe. Next to popular Agricultural Inn.
**Timothy Coward Fine Silver**, Marisco, Saunton, EX33 1LG TEL: 890466 ASSNS: LAPADA PARKING: Own carpark OPEN: By appt MIN: £30 MAX: £5000 PERIOD: 17th-20th century SPECIALIST: Silver. OTHER INFO: Saunton Sands Hotel 200 yds.

## ILFRACOMBE (01271)

**Relics**, 113 High Street TEL: 865486 PARKING: Easy OPEN: Mon-Sat 9.30-5.30 MIN: £1 MAX: £500 PERIOD: 19th-20th century SPECIALIST: Pine furniture GENERAL: Small collectables, cigarette cards, china, jewellery, bottles, paperback books OTHER INFO: Old relics bought & sold but not 'her indoors' we've heard that one before!

## LYNTON (01598)

**Vendy Antiques**. 29a Lee Road, EX35 6BS TEL: 53327 PARKING: Easy OPEN: Mon-Sat 10-5 MIN: £1 MAX: £4000 PERIOD: 17th-20th century GENERAL: Antiques of all descriptions.

# Cornwall

Cornwall is a land of legend and magic. Stories of King Arthur and his knights abound, as do others dealing with giants and piskies. There are grimmer tales that tell of smugglers and wreckers, who lured ships on to rocks to steal their cargo. This is also the land where tin brought prosperity from earliest times until it became uneconomic in the 19th century. Now tourism sustains the Cornish economy. With its mild climate, picturesque villages and dramatic scenery it has much to offer.

The tour opens in **North Petherwin,** home to the Tamar Otter Park and Wild Wood, an Otter Trust conservation project. In addition to otters, wild deer, owls, wallabies and water birds may also be seen. **Camelford** and **Wadebridge** both stand on the River Camel. In Wadebridge the town's bridge was built in the 15th century, although widened twice since then. Reputedly woolpacks were used for its foundations. To the south-west, at **St Breock**, are several prehistoric sites. A number of barrows range for five miles along the hills and there are two standing stones.

To the south, **Rumford Village** is followed by **Perranporth**, famous for its beautiful sandy beaches, and **St Agnes,** at the centre of the former local tin-mining area and with several old mine-workings around it. Just south of the village, St Agnes Beacon rises to 700 feet and gives spectacular views over the area. In the 19th century nearby **Blackwater** was the birthplace of John Passmore Edward, a newspaper tycoon and philanthropist who paid for the construction of a large number of public buildings, several of which were in Cornwall and includes the Miners and Mechanics Institute in St Agnes.

**Redruth**, next, was once an important mining town. This was the home of William Murdock, an inventor, who had the first gas-lit house in Britain. About two miles south west lie the remains of prehistoric Carn Brea Castle. **Camborne** was the centre for Cornish tin-mining. The Camborne School of Mines Geological Museum and Art Gallery displays a collection of minerals and ores. At Pool, about two miles east on the A3047, is the National Trust property of Cornish Engines. The largest of the great beam engines used in tin mining still left in Cornwall stands at the East Pool and Agar Mine. This engine weighs about 52 tons and could lift 450 gallons of water a minute from a depth of 1700 feet. There are other impressive engines in the area, some used for removing water from the mines and others for men and materials. Unconnected with mining, there is another site of interest to the south-east: the Cornish Shire Horse Trust and Carriage Museum. Here shire horses are used to work the farm and there is a collection of carriages, wagons and horse-drawn farm machinery.

**Penzance,** situated at the head of Mount's Bay, is a holiday resort and port. There are Georgian and Regency buildings in Church Street, the oldest street in Penzance. The Egyptian House is also there and is a most extraordinary and striking-looking building constructed in the 1820s and now used as a National Trust shop. An excellent museum, the Trinity House National Lighthouse Centre in Wharf Road, houses the finest collection of lighthouse equipment in the world. About three miles north is Chysauster Ancient Village. It was probably settled from the Iron Age through to about the 3rd century AD and the inhabitants might have dealt in tin. Now the shape of the dwellings are still visible and some walls survive to the height of about 8 feet.

Moving to **Mousehole**, (pronounced Mouzoll). This very pretty village was once a busy fishing port with over a 1000 boats. Now, only a few trawlers are left. The nearby village of Paul has two Celtic crosses that are believed to be more than 1000 years old. Mousehole is barely eight miles east of Land's End, Britain's most south westerly point

Next, **Marazion** is a nice holiday resort with sandy beaches and an ideal spot for a sight of St. Michael's Mount, connected to it by a half mile long causeway, accessible only at lowtide. St Michael's Mount was originally built as a priory for Benedictine monks by Edward the Confessor and belonged to the Benedictine Abbey of Mont St Michel in Normandy. However, it has had a long troubled history being seized a number of times during rebellions and the Civil War. The tour continues to **Penryn** which stands in a sheltered position thereby giving it a milder climate than the surrounding area and so this Georgian town has many sub-tropical plants. The town has a long history having received a charter in 1236 and was a centre of religious learning until the Dissolution of the Monasteries in the 16th century. Standing at the

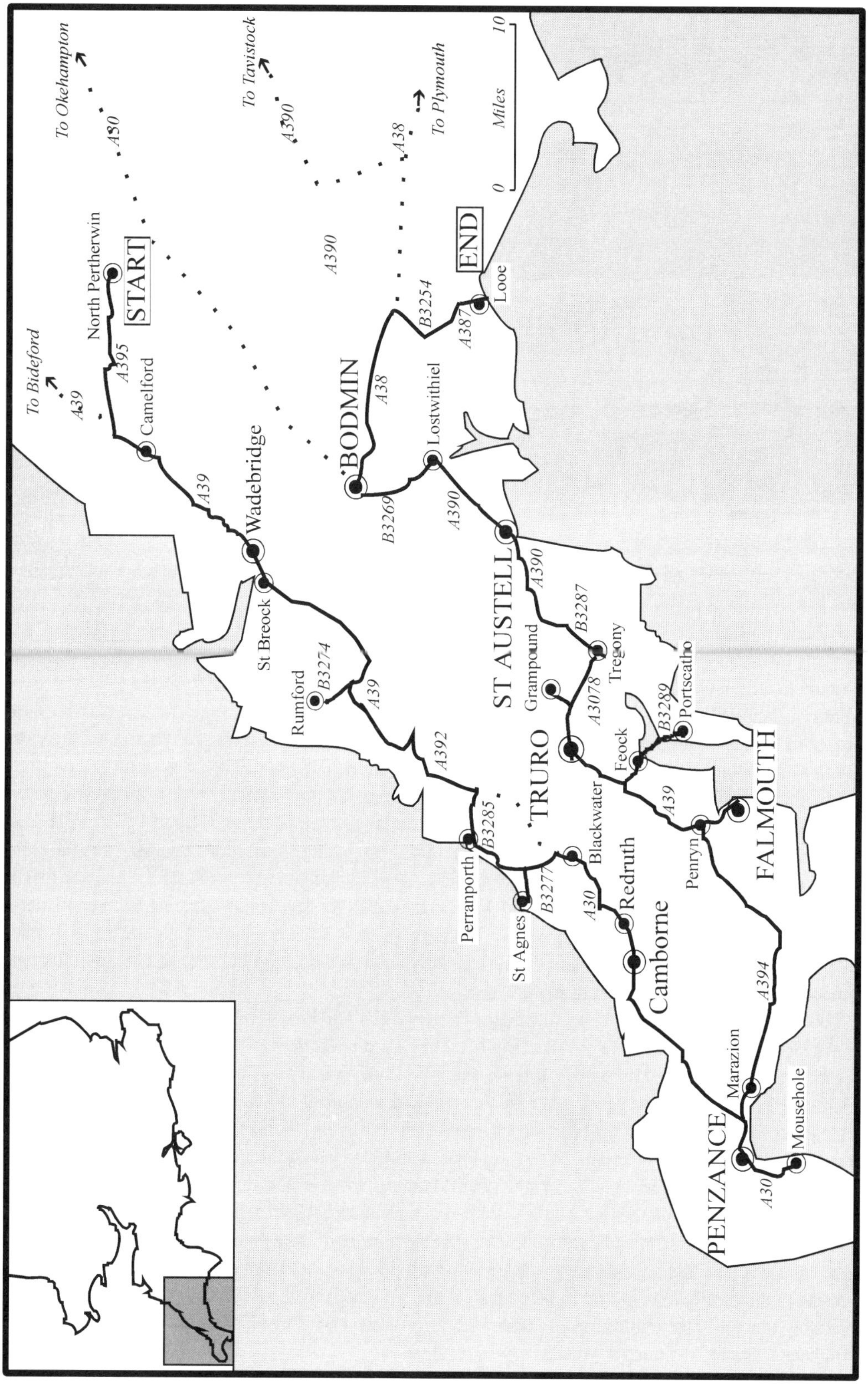

To Okehampton
To Tavistock
To Plymouth
To Bideford
A30
A390
A38
A39
0
Miles
10
START
North Pertherwin
A395
Camelford
END
Looe
A387
B3254
BODMIN
Lostwithiel
B3269
Wadebridge
St Breock
B3274
Rumford
A392
ST AUSTELL
B3287
Grampound
Tregony
A3078
Portscatho
B3289
Feock
TRURO
Blackwater
FALMOUTH
Penryn
Perranporth
B3285
St Agnes
B3277
Redruth
Camborne
A394
Marazion
Mousehole
PENZANCE

*Mousehole. By courtesy of the Cornwall Tourist Board*

head of an inlet, it was a busy port until Falmouth was developed at the mouth of the estuary.

**Falmouth**, just round the coast, combines the roles of port, marina and holiday resort. The harbour is the largest in Cornwall and handles shipping from all over the world. Overlooking the harbour, Pendennis Castle was built by Henry VIII in 1545 to guard against a French invasion. The finest hour was probably in 1646 when resisting a six month siege during the Civil War. Commanded at that time by the 70 year old Colonel Arundell, it was cut off by Parliamentary troops on the landward side and by a blockade to seaward. The siege started in March and by July things were getting so desperate that troops in the castle unsuccessfully attempted to break out to get supplies. By 17th August Colonel Arundell realised that he could hold out no longer and so surrendered. He was honoured for his bravery by being allowed to march out of the castle with the full honours of war. To the south-west lies Glendurgan Gardens, set in a valley by the Helford River. It was started in the 19th century and has a fine collection of shrubs, camellias and rhododendrons under the shelter of mature trees.

**Feock** has another beautiful Cornish garden, Trelissick Garden. From 1800 Trelissick was the home of the richest man in Cornwall, Ralph Allen Daniell. The park has a large shrub garden, woodland walks and views over the River Fal. **Portscatho**, follows and is a picturesque village popular with artists. Situated on Gerrans Bay and with good sandy beaches, there are late Georgian houses on the promenade.

Heading north-east, **Truro** sits on the convergence of the Rivers Allen and Kenwyn to form the River Truro. Made prosperous by tin, the streets are lined with Georgian and Regency houses and one, Lemon Street, is said to be the finest Georgian street in the county. However it is dominated by the cathedral, the only one in Cornwall and the first Anglican cathedral built since St. Paul's. It was started in 1879 after the diocese of Devon and Cornwall was split in two. At the time, building a cathedral in Cornwall was not an easy business. The local economy was in decline with the tin mines closing. Also Anglicanism had lost ground in the county to non-conformist faiths. In spite of this the cathedral was built in just thirty years, probably due to the determination of Bishop E.W. Benson who wanted a centre for the revival of the Anglican Catholic tradition of worship in Cornwall.

Then, via **Grampound** and **Tregony**, the route comes to **St Austell** which has now swapped the mining of tin for that of china clay, both of which have turned this once small village into a thriving market town. The past can be seen in the narrow streets and stone-built cottages. The Charlestown Shipwreck and Heritage Centre on Charlestown Harbour detail the history of the town and it also has the largest collection of shipwreck items in the country. Inland, to the north of St Austell there is an outcrop of rock 60 feet high called Roche Rock. Built into the side were the 15th century St Michael's Chapel and a hermit's cell, now both in ruins. Nearby stands the church of St Gonandus, modernised in Victorian times, but still keeping a Norman font richly carved with snakes and angels' heads.

**Lostwithiel**, on the River Fowey, was once a centre of the tin trade and capital of Cornwall. The many notable features include a medieval bridge, the 14th century Duchy House and various Georgian buildings. The 12th to 13th century Restormel Castle lies about a mile north. Mid-way between Lostwithiel and **Bodmin** is Lanhydrock, originally a 17th century house. Now owned by the National Trust, it stayed in the same family, the Robartes, from 1620 to 1953. Unfortunately a fire in 1881 destroyed all but the north wing. The house was rebuilt and remains one of the great houses of Cornwall. Four miles north west of Bodmin on the A389, stands another fine property, Pencarrow House and Garden. Set in listed gardens, this superb Georgian house contains a wonderful collection of 18th century furniture, pictures and china.

Bodmin Moor is an area of granite, rich in archeological sites including Bronze Age stone circles and huts. The highest point in Cornwall, Brown Willy in the northern part of the moor, rises to a height of 1377 feet. The inspiration for Daphne du Maurier's *Jamaica Inn* may be found on the moor at Bolventor. Bodmin itself is the only Cornish town to be recorded in the Domesday Book. Its church of St Petroc is one of the county's largest and most of it dates from the 15th century although some remnants of Norman stonework may be seen in the North Tower and the font is also Norman. The bones of St Petroc, one of the greatest of Cornish saints, are said to lie in a casket in the church.

On the channel coast the two small towns, East and West **Looe,** are joined by a bridge spanning the Looe River. For centuries it was fishing that provided the livelihood for the people but in the 19th century mining near Liskeard became important. To cater for this a quay was built in East Looe. Nowadays this trade has gone and most of the income comes from tourism.

## ANTIQUE DEALERS

### NORTH PETHERWIN (01566)

**Pine & Country Antiques,** Brockings, Petherwin Gate, PL15 8LW TEL: 785381 PARKING: Own carpark OPEN: 6 days 10-6 MIN: £5 MAX: £500 PERIOD: 19th-20th century GENERAL: Pine, mahogany, bric a brac, china OTHER INFO: There is a Post Office & exotic nursery in the same premises. Stripping & restoration service. The village contains a glass blowing business.

### CAMELFORD (01840)

**Bridge Antiques,** 1 Market Place, PL32 9PE TEL: 231701 PARKING: Easy OPEN: Mon-Sat 10-5 PERIOD: 19th-20th century SPECIALIST: Brown furniture GENERAL: Watercolours, prints, china, glass, metalware OTHER INFO: Very interesting museum of rural bygones.

### WADEBRIDGE (01208)

**Victoria Antiques,** 21 Molesworth Street PARKING: Easy OPEN: 9-5 MIN: £10 PERIOD: 17th-20th century GENERAL: Pine, walnut, mahogany furniture.

### ST BREOCK (01208)

**St Breock Gallery,** PL27 7JS TEL: 812543 FAX: 0171 243 8300 PARKING: Own carpark OPEN: Mon-Sat 10-5 MIN: £50 MAX: £4000 PERIOD: 19th-20th century SPECIALIST: Watercolours OTHER INFO: River Camel Trail, great for waterbird life.

### RUMFORD VILLAGE (01841)

**Henley House Antiques,** PL27 7SS TEL: 540322 PARKING: no restrictions OPEN: Thurs-Sat or anytime (resident) PERIOD: Mostly 19th century GENERAL: General antiques OTHER INFO: Small pretty village easily reached via St Merryn. This is a small shop but very well stocked.

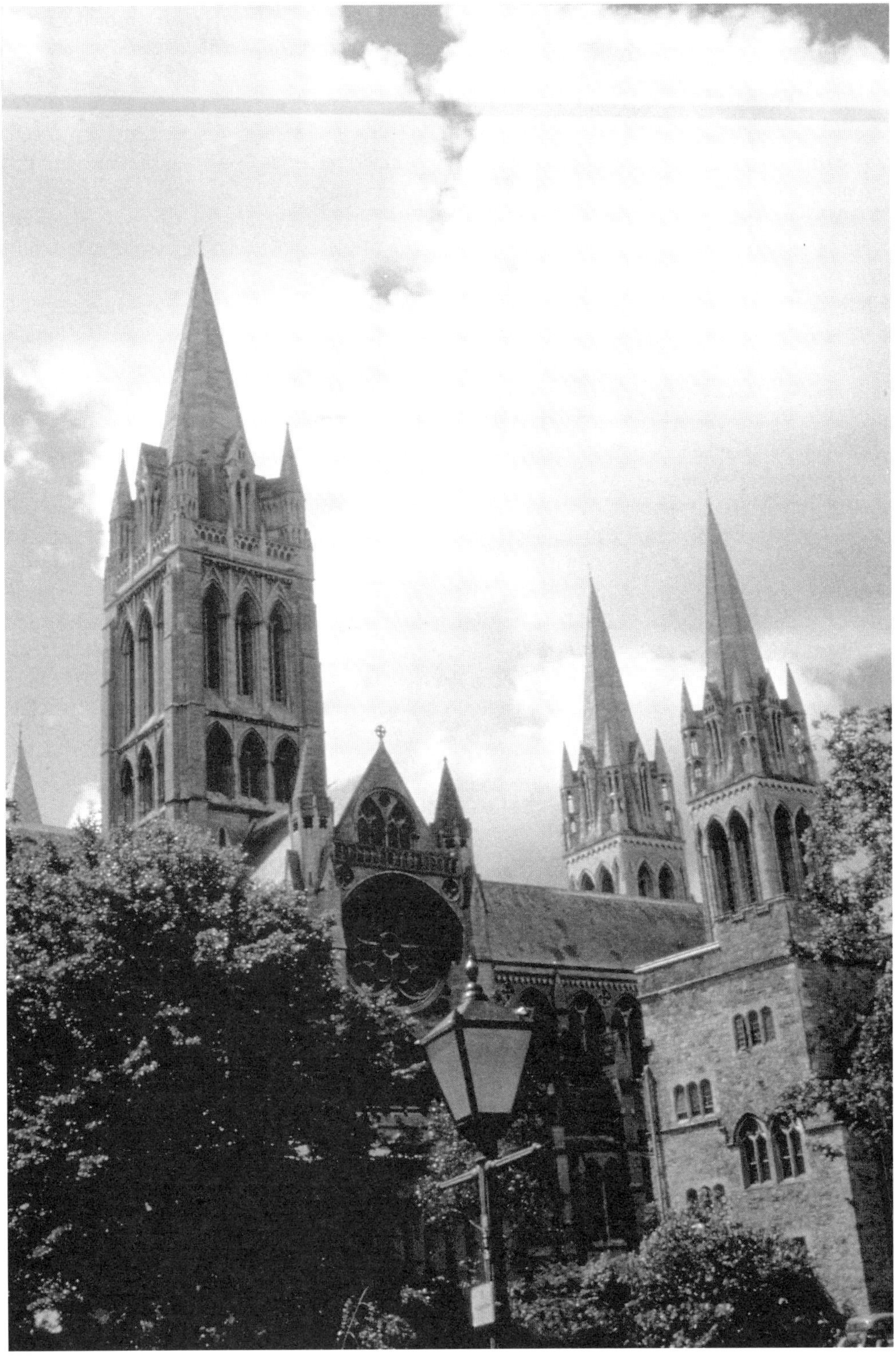

*Truro Cathedral. By courtesy of the Cornwall Tourist Board*

## PERRANPORTH (01209)

**St George's Antiques,** 33 St George's Hill, TR6 0JR TEL: 821680 PARKING: Easy OPEN: 10-5 PERIOD: 18th-19th century SPECIALIST: Small furniture, ceramics, blue & white, pictures.

## ST AGNES (01872)

**Ages Ago Antiques**, 1b Churchtown TEL: 553820 PARKING: Easy OPEN: Mon-Sat 10-1 MIN: £1 MAX: £560 GENERAL: 19th-early 20th century furniture, late 18th-19th century ceramics.

## BLACKWATER (01872)

**Blackwater Pine Antiques**, TR4 8ET TEL: 560919 FAX: 560919 ASSNS: GMC PARKING: Easy OPEN: Mon-Sat 9-6, usually Sun 2-6 PERIOD: 19th century SPECIALIST: Furniture made to order GENERAL: Original stripped pine furniture, etc OTHER INFO: Pennypots Restaurant one of best in Cornwall, several farm B&B's

## REDRUTH (01209)

**Richard Winkworth Antiques**, Station Approach TEL & FAX: 216631 PARKING: Own carpark OPEN: Mon-Sat 10-5, Sun 11-4 MIN: £2 MAX: £5000 PERIOD: 18-20th (occasionally 17th) century SPECIALIST: Furniture OTHER INFO: Containers & shipping aranged worldwide.

## CAMBORNE (01209)

**Victoria Gallery**, 28 Cross St TEL: 719268 PARKING: Easy OPEN: Mon-Wed, Fri 10-5.15, Sat 10-1 MIN: £8 MAX: £2000 PERIOD: 19th-20th century GENERAL: General antiques & books OTHER INFO: 10 minutes drive from beautiful unspoilt North Coast.

## PENZANCE (01736)

**Ken Ashbrook Antiques**, Redbrick Warehouse, Leskinnick Place TEL: 330914 PARKING: Difficult OPEN: Mon-Sat 10-1, 2.15-5 MIN: £5 MAX: £5000 PERIOD: 19th-20th century SPECIALIST: Furniture.

**Catherine and Mary**, 1-2 Old Brewery Yard, Bread Street, TR18 2SL TEL: 51053 PARKING: Easy OPEN: Mon-Sat 10-5 MIN: £1 MAX: £500 PERIOD: 19th-20th century SPECIALIST: Textiles & lace GENERAL: General antiques.

**Kitts Corner Antiques**, 51 Chapel Street TEL: 64507 (shop hours) PARKING: Easy OPEN: Mon, Tues, Thurs-Sat 10-1, 2-4.30 MIN: £1 MAX: £200 PERIOD: 19th-20th century GENERAL: General antiques, collectors & decorative items OTHER INFO: Chapel Street is the oldest street in Penzance.

**Little Jems,** 55 Chapel Street, TR18 5AE TEL: 51400 PARKING: Easy OPEN: 9.45-5.15 MIN: £3 MAX: £3000 PERIOD: 18th-20th century SPECIALIST: Opal GENERAL: Jewellery, paintings, lamps.

**The Old Posthouse,** incorporating the Bookcellar, 9 Chapel Street, TR18 4AJ TEL: 60320 10-5, 61232 after 6pm PARKING: 10-5 MIN: 20p (postcard) MAX: Variable PERIOD: 19th-20th century SPECIALIST: Secondhand & antiquarian books, pre-war picture postcards GENERAL: Small furniture, glass, china, ethnic objects OTHER INFO: Interesting museum & art gallery housing collection of Newlyn School paintings, outdoor Art Deco swimming pool, 3 week festival in June.

**Tony Sanders Penzance Gallery and Antiques**, 14 Chapel Street, TR19 4AW TEL: 68461, after hours 66620 PARKING: Easy OPEN: Mon-Sat 9-5.30 PERIOD: 19th-20th century SPECIALIST: Copper, cranberry glass, Newlyn & St Ives schools paintings, sculpture, small furniture. OTHER INFO: Turks Head, Chapel St, good pub food.

## MOUSEHOLE (01736)

**Vanity Fayre**, Commercial Road, TR19 6QG No phone PARKING: OPEN: Mon-Sat 10-1, 2-5 (outside season restricted) MIN: £1 MAX: £500 PERIOD: 18th-20th century GENERAL: Quality to bric-a-brac always changing.

## MARAZION (01736)

**Antiques**, The Shambles, Market Place, TR17 0AR TEL: 711381 PARKING: Easy OPEN: Mon-Sat 10-5.30, Sun by appt MIN: £1 MAX: £250 PERIOD: 19th-20th century GENERAL: General antiques, Staffordshire figures, glass, Art Deco & collectables.

## PENRYN (01326)

**Duchy Antiques & Leon Robertson Antiques**, 7 The Praze, TR10 8DH TEL: 372767 PARKING: Easy OPEN: Mon-Sat 10.30-5.30 (summertime) MIN: £1 MAX: £8000 PERIOD: 18th-20th century SPECIALIST: Furniture GENERAL: Paintings & china.

## FALMOUTH (01326)

**John Maggs Antiquarian Prints & Maps**, 54 Church Street TR11 3DS TEL: 313153 FAX: 313153 PARKING: Easy OPEN: Mon-Sat 10-5 PERIOD: 18th-19th century SPECIALIST: Entirely antiquarian.

## FEOCK (01872)

**Strickland & Dorling,** Come-to-Good, TR3 6QS TEL: 862394 PARKING: Easy OPEN: 10-5 MIN: £10 MAX: £1000 PERIOD: 17th-19th century SPECIALIST: Small furniture, porcelain GENERAL: Pottery, pictures, prints, silver, collectors & decorative items OTHER INFO: 40 years in the trade, small shop. Old thatched pub nearby.

## PORTSCATHO (01872)

**Curiosity Antiques**, The Square TEL: 580411 PARKING: Easy OPEN: Mon-Sat 10.30-12.30, 2.30-5.30 - but not necessarily MIN: £1 MAX: £250 SPECIALIST: Small collectables & general antiques OTHER INFO: Odd & flexible hours so please phone first if making special journey.

**Turnpike Cottage Antiques & Tearoom**, The Square, St Gerrans, TR2 5EB TEL:580853 PARKING: Easy OPEN: Tues-Sat 11-1, 3-6 but winter afternoons only MIN: £2 MAX: £1000 PERIOD: 18th-20th century GENERAL: Small antiques OTHER INFO: Also hand-made furniture & carvings, patchwork quilting & Victorian style dolls made by us on the premises. We also run a small tearoom and licensed restaurant amidst the antiques.

## TRURO (01872)

**Alan Bennett**, New Bridge House, New Bridge Street, TR1 2AA TEL: 73296 PARKING: Easy OPEN: Mon-Sat 9-5.30 MIN: £20 MAX: £20,000 PERIOD: 18th-19th century SPECIALIST: Good furniture GENERAL: General antiques.

**Pydar Antiques**, Peoples Palace off Pydar Street, TR1 2AZ TEL: 223516 FAX: (01637) 872034 PARKING: Medium OPEN: Mon-Sat 10.30-5 MIN: £5 MAX: £5000 PERIOD: 19th century SPECIALIST: Decorative soft furnishing GENERAL: Furniture, paintings, small silver OTHER INFO: Pine furniture made from reclaimed wood. Our shop is 200 years old and was the workers cottages adjacent to old tannery.

## GRAMPOUND (01726)

**Radnor House Antiques**, Radnor House, TR2 4QT TEL: 882921 PARKING: Medium OPEN: Mon-Sat 10-6 MIN: £20 MAX: £2000 PERIOD: 18th-19th century GENERAL: Furniture.

## TREGONY (01872)

**Clock Tower Antiques**, TEL: 53225 PARKING: Easy OPEN: Mon-Sat 10-6 or by appt MIN: £15 MAX: £2500 PERIOD: Early 19th-early 20th century SPECIALIST: Watercolours, Doulton stoneware GENERAL: General antiques OTHER INFO: In centre of historic medieval village with wide main street. Next to the picturesque Roseland peninsula where pretty coves, safe bathing beaches, country inns, restaurants and hotels abound.

## ST AUSTELL (01726)

**Margaret Chesterton Antiques**, 33 Pentewan Road, PL25 5BU TEL: 72926 PARKING: Own carpark OPEN: Mon-Sat 10-5 or by appt MIN: £1 MAX: £1200 PERIOD: 18th-20th century SPECIALIST: Porcelain, pottery, clocks GENERAL: Victoriana & small furniture OTHER INFO: Cliff Head Hotel (Carlyon Bay) - ° price lunches for 2, Mon-Fri.

**St Austell Antiques Centre & Radnor House Antiques**, 37-39 Truro Road, PL25 5JE TEL: 63178 FAX: (01288) 81548 PARKING: Easy OPEN: Mon-Sat 10-5 MIN: £1 MAX: £5000 PERIOD: 18th-20th century SPECIALIST: Secondhand books & records GENERAL: Antiques, collectables, decorative items, some architectural OTHER INFO: Furniture restoration service.

## LOSTWITHIEL (01208)

**John Bragg**, 35 Fore Street, PL22 0BN TEL: 872827 PARKING: Easy OPEN: Mon-Sat 10-1, 2-5, closed Weds afternoon MIN: £50 MAX: £11,000 PERIOD: 17th-19th century SPECIALIST: Furniture OTHER INFO: Fine selection of restaurants including Trewithan.

**Old Palace Antiques**, The Old Palace, Quay Street, PL22 0BS TEL: 872909 PARKING: Easy OPEN: Mon, Tues, Thurs-Sat 10-1, 2-5, Wed 10-1 MIN: £1 MAX: £600 PERIOD: 19th-20th century SPECIALIST: Mostly pine furniture GENERAL: China, brass, jewellry, postcards, collectors items.

## BODMIN (01208)

**Clocks, Art & Antiques**, 9 St Nicholas Street, PL31 1AA TEL: 74408 FAX: 74408 PARKING: Easy OPEN: Anytime by appt MIN: £5 MAX: £5000 PERIOD: 17th-20th century SPECIALIST: Clocks & good English furniture OTHER INFO: We have an idyllic cottage where customers may stay during their visit, with salmon & trout fishing.

## LOOE (01503)

**Looe Antiques,** 1 Seafront Court, East Looe Quay, PL13 1AL TEL: 265495 PARKING: Medium OPEN: Daily from 10am MIN: £1 MAX: £1000 PERIOD: All dates GENERAL: Good range of furniture, general antiques & collectors' items OTHER INFO: Tom Sawyers Tavern & the Smugglers Restaurant are highly recommended.

**Pink Cottage Antiques,** Widegates, PL13 1QL TEL: 240258 PARKING: Own carpark OPEN: Mon-Sat 9.30-5, Sun 2-4.30 MIN: £5 MAX: £2500 PERIOD: 19th & 20th century SPECIALIST: Furniture GENERAL: Brass, copper, china, glass.

**West Quay Curios**, 6 The Quay, West Looe, PL13 2BX TEL: 264411 PARKING: Easy OPEN: Mon-Sat 10-7 (Summer), 10-5 (Winter) MIN: £1 MAX: £500 PERIOD: Mostly 19th-20th century but occasionally earlier SPECIALIST: Postcards, cigarette cards, china GENERAL: General antiques & collectors items OTHER INFO: Idyllic setting right by the river and sea. Most of the pubs and restaurants are well known to me and come personally recommended.

# The Cotswolds

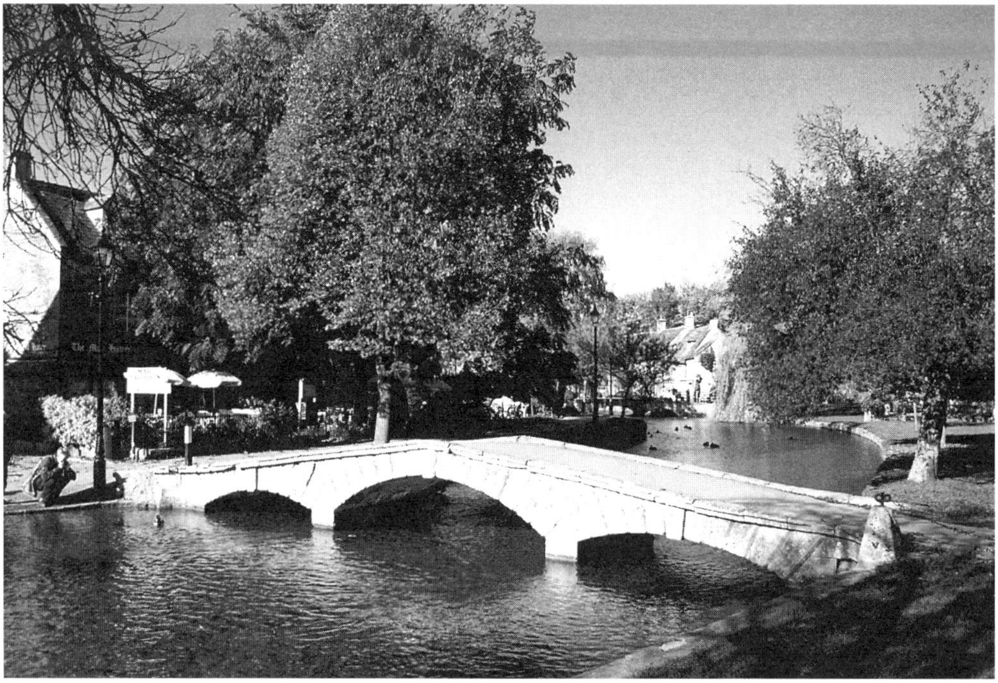

*Bourton-on-the-Water, near Stow-on-the-Wold*

The countryside in this lyrical region typifies for many the quintessential English rural scene with its sheep pastures, wooded valleys, dry stone walls and weathered Cotswold stone buildings. In the villages it is still possible to imagine life in the Middle Ages, so timeless do they seem. This is probably, also, the area outside London best known for antique shops.

The tour starts with **Woodstock**, a small town with royal connections going back to the Saxons. At the beginning of the 12th century Henry I built a residence and kept an exotic menagerie here. His grandson, Henry II, enlarged the royal manor and visited it with his mistress, the Fair Rosamund. The legendary Black Prince, eldest son of Edward III, was born at Woodstock Palace in 1330 and it stayed as a royal residence until besieged and badly damaged in the Civil War. At the beginning of the 18th century Queen Anne gave the manor and estate to John Churchill, first Duke of Marlborough, in gratitude for the victories he had won, particularly at Blenheim against the French and Bavarian armies. Not only was he given this estate, Queen Anne also promised to pay for the building of a house on the site.

The house, designed by Sir John Vanbrugh, was started in 1705. There was a series of difficulties in completing the work. Sarah, Duchess of Marlborough was the Queen's lady-in-waiting and Keeper of the Privy Purse, and these posts enabled her to keep the Queen to her promise to pay for the house. However, in 1710 she fell from favour and payments for the building work stopped and in 1712 all work also ceased. By all accounts Sarah Churchill was an extremely difficult character, albeit devoted to her husband, and she had numerous arguments with Vanbrugh who finally resigned at the end of 1716 although building had already restarted two years earlier. The Duke of Marlborough died in 1722 but Sarah continued with the work on Blenheim Palace for the remaining twenty two years of her life, seeing it as a tribute to her husband and refusing several offers of marriage.

Blenheim Palace, set in its 2500 acre park and redesigned later in the 18th century by Capa-

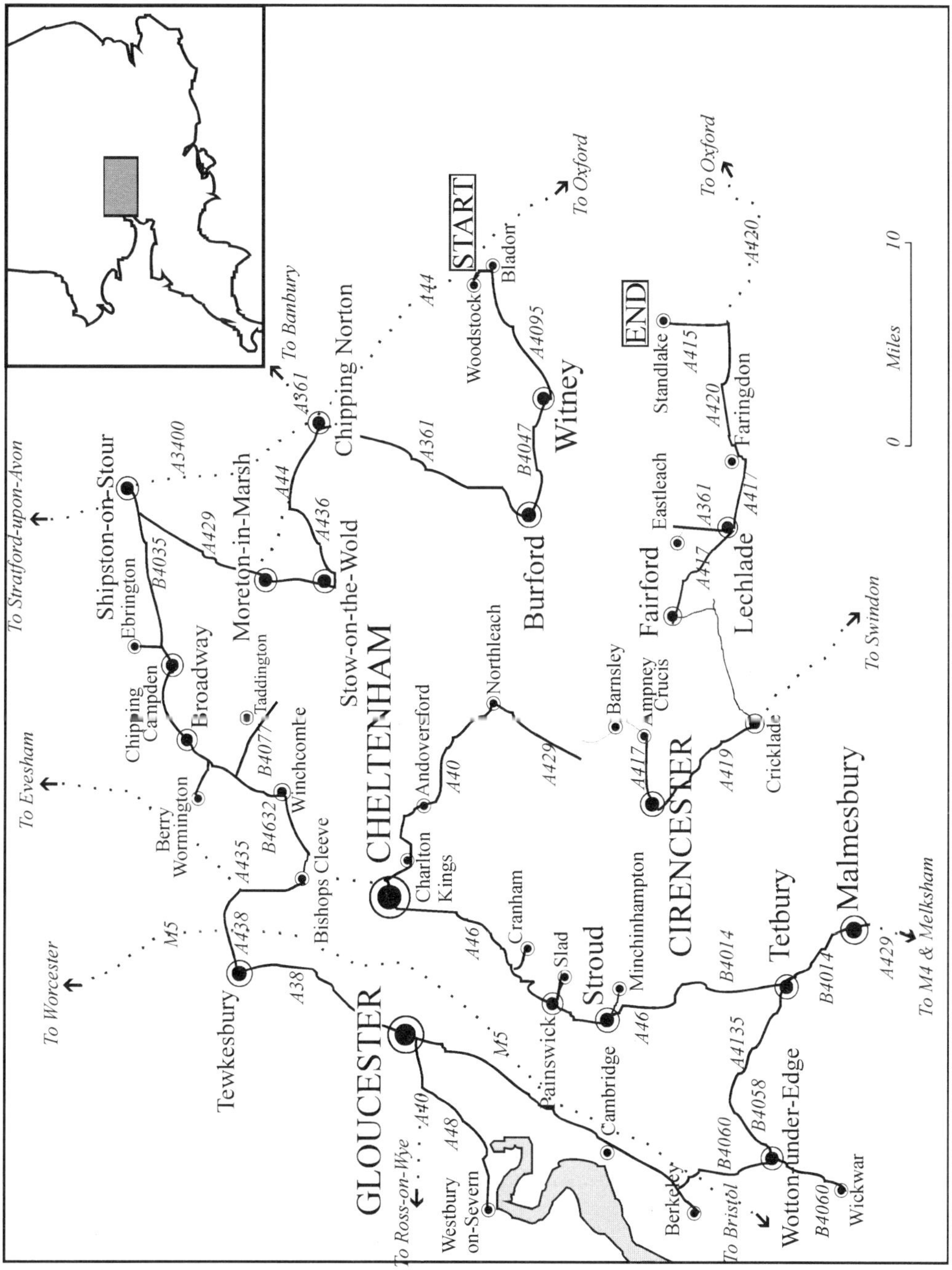
START
END
To Stratford-upon-Avon
To Evesham
To Worcester
To Banbury
To Oxford
To Oxford
To Swindon
To M4 & Melksham
To Bristol
To Ross-on-Wye
Shipston-on-Stour
Ebrington
Chipping Campden
Broadway
Moreton-in-Marsh
Taddington
Winchcombe
Berry Wormington
Bishops Cleeve
Stow-on-the-Wold
Chipping Norton
CHELTENHAM
Charlton Kings
Andoversford
Northleach
Burford
Witney
Woodstock
Bladon
Standlake
Faringdon
Eastleach
Fairford
Lechlade
Barnsley
Ampney Crucis
CIRENCESTER
Cricklade
Malmesbury
Tetbury
Minchinhampton
Stroud
Slad
Cranham
Painswick
Cambridge
GLOUCESTER
Tewkesbury
Westbury on-Severn
Berkeley
Wotton under-Edge
Wickwar
A3400
A429
B4035
A44
A436
A361
B4077
B4632
A435
A438
M5
A38
A40
A46
A429
A4095
B4047
A415
A420
A417
A4417
A419
B4014
A4135
B4058
B4060
A48
0
10
Miles

*Stow-on-the-Wold*

bility Brown, has been described as a masterpiece of Vanbrugh's work with its magnificent rooms, the most celebrated of which is the Long Library, originally designed as a picture gallery. The Battle of Blenheim is commemorated in a ceiling painting in the Great Hall and again in the Green Writing Room. There are also portraits of the forceful Sarah Churchill, possibly without whose indomitable will this glorious palace would never have been completed.

A more recent claim to fame was the birth of Sir Winston Churchill here and he proposed to his future wife, Clementine, beside the lake, in the Temple of Diana. Today there is a Churchillian exhibition and the room where he was born is open to the public.

In 1965, Sir Winston was laid to rest in nearby **Bladon**, in the churchyard of St Martin's Church, beside the grave of his father Sir Randolph. His wife, Clementine, his son and two of his daughters are also buried there.

**Witney** on the River Windrush is famous for its blankets, made there since the days of Edward III and still important today. The Cotswolds as a whole was once an important woollen textile region but declined.after the Industrial Revolution. Witney, however, had such a reputation for its blankets, with its name a guarantee of quality, that the weaving of blankets has continued to prosper. One of the notable buildings is Blanket Hall, built in 1721. Another is the 13th century church which retains the early architecture outside but the Victorian restoration inside was not sympathetic. In the Market Place there is a 17th century Butter Cross with a clock turret beneath a cupola.

The route continues to lovely **Burford**, on the River Windrush. On one of the great coaching roads and prospering accordingly, the town thrived throughout the Middle Ages as a centre for cloth, wool, saddlery and stone from local quarries. When the railways came, Burford did not get a line and so went into something of a decline; however, the boom in tourism has again brought prosperity. There are many fascinating places amongst these are the Great Almshouses founded in 1457 and, partly rebuilt in the 19th century, the 15th century Lamb Inn, the mostly 15th century Parish Church and Burford Grammar School, founded in 1577.

**Chipping Norton**, next, has one of the largest parish churches in Oxfordshire built by wealthy wool merchants who are commemorated by the brasses inside. The town is over a thousand years old and since medieval times prospered from the wool industry, particularly tweed. Nowadays, though, it is an important tourist centre for the Cotswolds and contains some ancient buildings including the Town Hall, whose windows betray Tudor origins, and almshouses in Church Street dating from 1640. A Bronze Age stone circle, the Rollright Stones, stand just three miles north.

Astride the Roman Fosse Way about 10 miles due west, **Stow-on-the-Wold** is a mecca for lovers of antiques. An ancient town with evidence of settlement going right back to the Iron Age, it is set on a hill some 700 feet above sea level at the junction of eight roads. The twice weekly markets and two annual fairs, formerly for the sale of sheep and wool, have been held here since 1107. A number of buildings are constructed in the traditional Cotswold stone. Following the Fosse Way north-east, neighbouring **Moreton-in-Marsh** has buildings in the High Street that are typical of the charming stone houses and shops one expects in this area. Of special distinction is the White Hart Royal Hotel where Charles I slept in July 1644, five years before his execution.

Now on to **Shipston-on-Stour**, lying in the Vale of the Red Horse at the edge of the Cotswolds and once the site of a thriving sheep market. The town's prosperity throughout the centuries has owed much to good transport links: first, on a coaching road, as the inns testify, then with a branch line of the tramway linking Stratford-on-Avon to Moreton-in-Marsh. Finally part of this tramway was converted into a railway line. The continued wealth has left a legacy of many fine 17th, 18th and 19th century houses.

Via the delightful **Ebrington** village, **Chipping Campden** is another largely unspoilt and very pretty town. An important wool centre as early as the mid 13th century with a weekly market and three annual fairs, importance increased over the next two centuries as trade in wool with Europe grew. Like many of the the other Cotswold wool towns, Chipping Campden's importance declined with the coming of the Industrial Revolution. However, a prosperous past has left a heritage of quite lovely buildings. Amongst these are the 14th century Grevel's House, the Woolstapler's Hall of the same period which is now used both as a museum and Tourist Information Centre, the Market Hall, built in 1627 and a row of 17th century almshouses.

**Broadway**, next, is perhaps one of the Cotswolds most visited towns. Growing prosperous in the 18th century as a staging post on the coach road from London to Worcester, it suffered some decline after the advent of the railways. However, discovered by people like William Morris and his friends, a thriving tourist trade again brought prosperity and has continued to do so since. Many of the picturesque buildings are made from mellow Cotswold stone, the 17th century coaching inn, the Lygon Arms in the centre of the High Street, is a worthy reminder of Broadway's past. A mile south east stands the late 18th century Gothic folly of Broadway Tower in Broadway Tower Country Park. At 1024 feet above sea level, this is the second highest point in the Cotswolds and a wonderful viewpoint where, on a clear day, twelve counties may be seen.

Going through **Berry Wormington** and **Taddington,** next is **Winchcombe** with its numerous historic and charming buildings including the medieval, galleried George Inn, all that is left of the great abbey and once its pilgrims' hostel. The abbey church, happily, survived the Dissolution with many notable features, amongst which are grotesque gargoyles and a magnificent altar cloth. However, remnants of the abbey still survive in Hailes Abbey Museum. On display are fragments of architecture from the ruins, 13th century roof bosses and medieval floor tiles.

To the south east is historic Sudeley Castle, largely built by Admiral Ralph Botelar in the time of Henry V. He obtained the money to build the castle by holding a French admiral to ransom, a common practice at the time. Unfortunately Botelar fell from favour and the King claimed the castle. It passed through several owners until the time of Elizabeth I when it came to Thomas

Seymour, Lord High Admiral of England and fourth husband of Catherine Parr, the wife who survived Henry VIII. She found her new husband was unfaithful so retired from London to Sudeley Castle where she gave birth to a daughter. Within a week of the birth, Catherine Parr, at the age of 36, died of puerperal fever and is buried in the castle chapel. During the Civil War, the castle was held for the King by Prince Rupert of the Rhine when besieged by Parliamentary troops. Later rendered undefendable it was left to decay. Only in the 19th century was the castle bought by a wealthy family and restored. Today, it is a popular tourist attraction with an award winning Tudor rose garden, craft workshops, and a wonderful collection of art.

Several miles west, just off the B4632, **Bishop's Cleeve** has a 14th century church containing an early 17th century carved oak musicians' gallery. **Tewkesbury**, eleven miles away, is a town of half-timbered houses and narrow alleys. The site of the decisive battle in the Wars of the Roses, the Lancastrian Prince of Wales was killed and the Yorkist Edward consolidated his claim to the throne. At the Dissolution of the Monasteries the town's magnificent abbey was saved by the townspeople. They collected enough money to buy it for the parish from the king. Its altar, dated 1239 and made from Purbeck marble, is one of England's oldest.

The route now comes to **Gloucester**, another Roman town and, for a number of years, the base for the Second Legion before leaving to subdue the Welsh tribes. Along with Lincoln, York and Colchester, Gloucester was one of the great Roman colonies, i.e. a place where veteran Roman soldiers were given grants of land to settle on when they retired. After the Roman withdrawal, like many towns, it experienced a decline. However, by the 7th century a monastery was built here, a royal palace by the 9th century and a priory, St Oswards, by the early 10th century. The town was a royal court under Edward the Confessor and William the Conqueror and here the decision was taken which led to the Domesday Book. About this time the building of the abbey church of St Peter was started, later to become the cathedral.

The grisly murder of Edward II in 1327, however, greatly benefited St Peters Church. He was buried here and, surprisingly perhaps, because he appears to have been a fairly unpleasant character, his tomb became a shrine. The benefits were that, as today, pilgrims meant an income for the place of pilgrimage. This money was poured into glorifying and extending the church now an elegant mixture of Norman and perpendicular styles, but done superbly to give a feeling of unity. Points of particular note in this beautiful cathedral are the east window, which, when made, was the largest in the world, the slender columns and the cloister where fan vaulting was used, was then a new idea.

At the Dissolution, the abbey church became a cathedral but during the reign of the Roman Catholic Mary Tudor, 'Bloody Mary' as she was called, the Bishop of Gloucester was burnt at the stake there. Elizabeth I granted the city the right to have docks which, although never rivalling nearby Bristol, were reasonably busy until the 18th century. With such a long history, there are many places to see and a visit to the Tourist Information Centre in St Michael's Tower is advisable. Amongst the museums in Gloucester are the City East Gate in Eastgate Street, the Folk Museum, Westgate Street, the National Waterways Museum and the Regiments of Gloucestershire Museum, both on the Docks.

Ten miles to the west, **Westbury-on-Severn** contains the lovely Westbury Court with its formal Dutch water-gardens and canals, all laid out in the 17th century, the earliest examples still remaining in the country. Ten miles south of Gloucester is **Cambridge** close to the late Peter Scott's Wildfowl trust at Slimbridge where a series of ornamental pools hold a superb wildfowl collection. Hides overlooking the Severn Estuary and marsh grasslands support an exceptional amount of wildfowl.

The tour briefly moves out of the Cotswolds proper to visit **Berkeley**. This is the site of still impressive 12th century castle which has been in the Berkeley family for almost 850 years. The deposed king, Edward II, was kept here as a prisoner and then murdered in an undetectable but particularly grisly manner. Later, during the Civil War, the castle was held for the king and withstood a siege by Parliamentary troops. Today it contains fine collections of pictures, tapestries, furniture, silver and porcelain. The dungeons, including Edward II's cell, medieval kitchen, the Great Hall and State Apartments are also on show.

**Wotton-under-Edge**, next, is set on the side of a hill in extremely pleasant surroundings. It has some quite charming architecture like Tolsey House with its clock and weathervane, Berkeley House with a Jacobean front, the Perry & Dawes almhouses in Church Street. Isaac Pitman, of shorthand fame, lived in one of Orchard Street's terraced houses.

After first visiting **Wickwar**, three miles away, the journey moves east to the pleasant, unspoilt, market town of **Tetbury** on the River Avon, once the local wool collecting centre. A prosperous history is reflected in the fine 17th and 18th century houses and its 17th century Market House mounted on stumpy pillars. Every Spring Bank Holiday the Tetbury Festival takes place. As part of this, young men and women form two teams in the Woolsack Race where they have to race down and then up the 1-in-4 Gumstool Hill with a 65lb sack of wool. There are also Morris dancers, a jester and stall holders dressed in medieval costume.

Neighbouring **Malmesbury** stands between two branches of the River Avon. It has a long history with the present town built on the site of a fortified Saxon town and was granted its charter by Alfred the Great in AD880. The Market Cross, standing in the centre of the town, is actually a building with a fine vaulted roof designed to shelter people from the rain. The older buildings are local stone, including the 17th century St John's Almhouse. Another notable feature is Tolsey Gate which has two cells on either side, It served as the local prison during the 18th and 19th centuries.

There is a story that an 11th century monk at Malmesbury Abbey, called Elmer, tried to fly. He made wings and fitted them to his hands and feet and then leapt off the abbey tower, thrashing wildly. He is said to have flown some 200 yards before crashing, breaking both legs and crippling himself for life. Brother Elmer's flight is commemorated in the abbey by a modern stained-glass window. The abbey was probably founded in the 7th century by St Aldhelm the first abbot. It was rebuilt in the 13th century and largely escaped destruction at the Dissolution of the Monasteries by being sold to a local wool merchant who used the buildings for weaving. Two years after acquisition, he presented the town with the abbey's nave for use as the parish church. The remains are still quite impressive, a fine, highly decorated, Norman porch and a 15th century monument to the Saxon King Athelstan, the first to rule all of England and who was probably interred here.

The next stop is **Stroud**, a centre of the Cotswolds cloth industry. Astride the River Frome, Stroud's strong advantage was its plentiful supply of clean water for washing the wool and also minerals for dyeing it. At the height of the prosperity, there were more than 150 cloth mills in the immediate area. Indeed, one mile south east is a zone known as the Golden Valley, between Chalford and Brimscombe, apparently due to the wealth brought by the weaving industry during the Middle Ages. With the coming of the Industrial Revolution and then foreign competition, weaving declined and now there are only two companies left. However, Stroud has succeeded in attracting other light industry so remains relatively prosperous. There are a number of charming buildings including the Tudor Town Hall and the Shambles, formerly selling meat but today holding a twice weekly general market. There are also several typical Cotswolds cottages preserved in Church Street. **Minchinhampton**, just a stone's throw along the A419, is a country town that has escaped being swallowed up by Stroud - just yet, and has a restored church with 14th century tower, a 17th century market hall on pillars and a famous golf course.

Nearby **Painswick** also benefited from the availability of fresh, clean water and grew prosperous as a centre for woollen and dyed cloth, reaching its peak in the 18th century. The most popular attraction is the churchyard with a mass of yew trees, mostly planted at the end of the 18th century, clipped in all imaginable shapes and forms. Some have grown and intertwined to form arches. There is a legend, difficult to check now because of the intertwining, that only ninety nine yew trees will grow here at any one time because the Devil always kills the hundredth. On the first Sunday after 18th September each year, a clipping ceremony is held in the churchyard. In this open air service children of the village, wearing flowers in their hair, hold hands to encircle the church singing a hymn. Afterwards each receives a traditional Painswick Bun and a silver coin. The churchyard holds further attractions in the form of superbly carved stone tombs.

Painswick's prosperity has left a pleasing legacy of houses, shops and inns, all built in the cream coloured stone quarried from nearby Painswick Hill. A less peaceful reminder of the past is found in the 19th century stocks put in St Mary's Street for "the punishment of those who carry on carousels to the annoyance of neighbours." Perhaps an idea that might find favour today. Half a mile away on the Gloucester road is the beautiful Painswick Rococo Garden, an 18th century six acre garden restored to its original appearance. Nearby **Slad** is famous as the home of writer Laurie Lee and the setting for his book, *Cider with Rosie.*

Slightly further north, **Cranham** is partly famous for the Great Whitcomb site of one of a line of Roman villas stretching southwest-northeast roughly along the Cotswold Edge. This one is in particularly scenic surroundings and dates probably from the 3rd century AD. Three rooms of the bath area are open but don't miss the excellent marine mosaic pavement either. A later attraction is the world-renown beautiful 300 acre Prinknash Park and Abbey (pronounced Prinage) and a smaller Bird Park with lakes containing exotic birds, tame deer, pigmy goats etc. The abbey, originally a medieval hunting lodge built around 1514, was turned into a manor house with a chapel by the last Benedictine abbot of Gloucester. In 1643 it was briefly a siege headquarters but in the 19th century, the new owner invited the Benedictines of Caldey Island to restart a monastery and work began in 1939 finishing as recently as 1972. The abbey construction gave clay and led to the idea of combining it with a pottery and viewing gallery for the delightful Prinknashware. Many visitors are made welcome.

**Cheltenham**, a once fashionable spa, is only 5 miles north east. Mineral springs were discovered in 1716 but it was transformed into a major spa by the visit of George III in 1788. Throughout the 19th century Cheltenham thrived and today, as a centre for tourism, remains prosperous. This beautiful Regency town has some fine buildings. Amongst the finest are the Montpellier Rotunda, the restored Pittville Pump Room and the two storeyed Regency Arcade of shops. The Cheltenham Music Festival, started in 1944, is another attraction. Here works by Benjamin Britten, Sir Arthur Bliss, Malcolm Arnold and many other British composers were performed for the first time. An extra feature is the steeplechase course where the Cheltenham Gold Cup race is run every March. **Charlton Kings**, once a separate village now lies in the eastern suburbs and **Andoversford** village on the A40, another three miles out.

**Northleach,** next, stands just off the A40, on the Roman Fosse Way which has brought prosperity as the fine coaching inns show. It was also a wool town and the church was endowed by wool merchants in the 15th century who are commemorated by brasses inside. The town's museum, situated in its former House of Correction, tells the story of rural Cotswold life and social history. Now the tour visits **Barnsley**. Although the 17th century Barnsley House is not open, its famous gardens are and were redesigned some 30 years ago by relatives of the present owner, who also sells antiques. A very short trip south down a country road leads to **Ampney Crucis**, the largest of three Ampney villages and the site of a beautiful church and gabled inn.

A couple of miles west, the city of **Cirencester** lies at the junction of three Roman roads: Ermin Way, Fosse Way and Akeman Street. At one time it was also the second largest Roman town in Britain. There is little to be seen of this now but the Corinium Museum in Park Street displays a very fine collection of local Roman antiquities. After the Roman withdrawal from Britain, Cirencester declined in importance although prospering again in the Middle Ages. Nowadays there are many fine and historic buildings to be seen.

The renewed prosperity of the Middle Ages is reflected in the magnificent parish church of St

John, the building of which was largely financed by wealthy local wool merchants. Built in the 15th century as part of an abbey, it escaped the ravages of the Dissolution by being turned into the town hall. It was only returned to the Church in the 18th century. The fine interior contains a painted wineglass pulpit and beautiful stained glass windows as well as brasses and monuments in the Trinity Chapel. The church's unusual three storeyed porch was built by local guilds at the beginning of the 16th century.

Three miles south west is Thames Head Bridge, once part of the Fosse Way crossing the Thames. It is close to the true source of the river at Trewsbury Mead which can be reached by footpath from the Thames Head Inn, although there is little to see apart from an inscribed stone slab.

Historic **Cricklade**, 6 miles southeast and just in Wiltshire, has many traces of Roman occupation and various excavations. The town museum can be proud of its various collections denoting the key importance of this Wessex settlement that even included a Saxon mint. Following the A417 eastward, the route arrives in **Fairford** on the River Coln. An Anglo-Saxon cemetary was found in the 19th century just to the west of the town indicating that there has been a settlement here for a considerable period of time. In the Middle Ages, home of one of the region's most prosperous wool merchants, the Thames, it was this family that built the very fine perpendicular chuch with its great tower, glorious carvings, oak beamed roof and wonderful stained glass windows, possibly done by the same craftsmen who did those in the Lady Chapel in Westminster Abbey. Fairford was once on the coach road between London and Gloucester and there are reminders of this in the historic inns. A more recent development is the American Airforce base, R.A.F. Fairford, to the south of the town which has a long runway and was also used for testing the British prototype of Concorde. This airfield, home to large air diplays every July, reputedly held the world's largest in 1995.

Further east along the A417, **Lechlade** is the limit of navigation upstream for large boats on the River Thames. The town has a fine perpendicular church with a beautiful carved door to the vestry. It has a striking slender spire and strange figures on the tower buttresses. In this churchyard the poet, Shelley, was inspired to write *Summer Evening Meditation*. Lechlade has two bridges spanning the Thames: Ha'penny Bridge, dating from the 18th century, still with its tollhouse, and the early 13th century St John's Bridge lying where the Rivers Thames and Leach meet. There is also a wealth of 17th and 18th century buildings.

Still on the A417, between Lechlade and Faringdon, stands the 18th century, 55 acre, Buscot Park. The house and estate, now a National Trust property, belonged, amongst others, to two very different and interesting characters. The first was an Australian, Robert Tertius Campbell, who, in the mid 19th century, made the estate into the most progressive farming enterprise of the time, growing mostly sugar beet. Amongst his projects was a distillery for turning the beet into alcohol and a narrow gauge railway for transporting the crop. Unfortunately, these ventures were not successful and the fortune made earlier was lost.. The second remarkable owner was Alexander Henderson, later the first Lord Faringdon, who bought Buscot Park in the late 19th century, and put together an excellent art collection to which his grandson later added even more treasures.

After detouring 4 miles north to **Eastleach**, really two joined villages, the penultimate visit is to **Faringdon** in Oxfordshire. Noted for its dairy produce and bacon, the church shows architecture ranging from trans-Norman to early English and contains historic monuments and brasses. During the Civil War the spire was lost. Faringdon has numerous charming buildings and inns including the 18th century Market Hall. **Standlake** is the final call

# ANTIQUE DEALERS

## WOODSTOCK (01993)

**Span Antiques**
**6 Market Place, OX20 1TA TEL: 811332 ASSNS: TVADA PARKING: Easy OPEN: Mon-Sat 10-5, Sun 1-5 MIN: £10 MAX: £2000 PERIOD: 18th-20th century GENERAL: 9 dealers showing furniture, silver, porcelain, glass, textiles, country bygones, Art Nouveau, Art Deco, pictures & decorative items OTHER INFO: Blenheim Palace, good hotels & restaurants make Woodstock a perfect base for touring the Cotswolds.**

**Thistle House Antiques**, 14 Market Place, OX20 1TA TEL: 811736 PARKING: Own carpark OPEN: Mon-Sat 10-6 MAX: £4000 PERIOD: 17th-19th century SPECIALIST: High class brass, desks, bureaux, chest on chests, lowboys. Mahogany & walnut OTHER INFO: The Bear & Feathers hotels have international reputation.

**Woodstock Antiques**, 11 Market Street, OX20 1SU TEL: 811494 ASSNS: LAPADA, TVADA PARKING: Easy OPEN: Tues-Sat 9.30-5.30 MIN: £50 MAX: £15,000 PERIOD: 18th-19th century SPECIALIST: Staffordshire pottery, animals GENERAL: Traditional & decorative furniture, interesting objects OTHER INFO: Author of *The A to Z of Staffordshire Dogs*.

## BLADON (01993)

**Park House Antiques**, 26 Park Street TEL: 812817 PARKING: Own carpark OPEN: Mon-Sat 9-6 MIN: £150 MAX: £10,000 GENERAL: Walnut, mahogany, satinwood, rosewood furniture 1690-1830 OTHER INFO: Sir Winston Churchills grave in churchyard opposite.

## WITNEY (0993)

**Colin Greenway Antiques**, 90 Corn Street, OX8 7BU TEL: 705026 PARKING: Easy OPEN: Mon-Sat 9-6 or by appt or chance PERIOD: 17th-20th century GENERAL: General antiques.

**Relics,** 35 Bridge Street, OX8 6DA TEL & FAX: 704611 PARKING: Easy OPEN: Mon-Sat 9-5.30 MIN: 50p MAX: £400 PERIOD: 19th-20th century SPECIALIST: Period paints for restoration, brass cabinet fittings, waxes, etc GENERAL: Pre 1930s general furniture.

**Windrush Antiques**, 107 High Street TEL: 772536 PARKING: Own carpark OPEN: Mon-Sat 10-5.30 MIN: £100 MAX: £4000 PERIOD: 17th-18th century SPECIALIST: Country furniture, mainly oak Windsor chairs, some Georgian mahogany GENERAL: Some metalware & smalls OTHER INFO: The town was a centre for blanket manufacture for 300 years.

**WITNEY ANTIQUES**
**96-100 CORN STREET, OX8 7BU TEL: 703902 FAX: 779852 ASSNS: BADA, CINOA, CADA PARKING: OWN CARPARK OPEN: MON-SAT 10-5 MIN: £200 MAX: £100,000 PERIOD: 17TH-EARLY 19TH CENTURY SPECIALIST: FINE ENGLISH & CONTINENTAL FURNITURE, CLOCKS, TEXTILES & PEWTER GENERAL: ONE OF THE FINEST STOCKS OF ANTIQUE FURNITURE & ASSOCIATED ITEMS IN THE COUNTRY. LARGE STOCK & ALL ITEMS IN FINE CONDITION OTHER INFO: WITNEY IS THE FIRST STOP OUT OF LONDON JUST OFF A40 (1-1·5 HRS). AT THE BEGINNING OF COTSWOLDS, PLENTY OF GOOD HOTELS & RESTAURANTS LOCALLY. COGGES FARM MUSEUM.**

## BURFORD (01993)

**Ashton Gower Antiques**, Burford Roundabout, Cheltenham Road, OX18 4JA TEL & FAX: 822450 ASSNS: LAPADA PARKING: Own carpark OPEN: Mon-Sat 10-5.30, Sun 2-5 MIN: £50 MAX: £5000 PERIOD: 18th-19th century SPECIALIST: English & Continental painted furniture & mirrors GENERAL: Dining tables, chairs, paintings, decorative items.

**Burford Antiques Centre,** Cheltenham Road (at the roundabout), OX8 4JA TEL: 823227 PARKING: Own carpark OPEN: 10-5.30 MIN: £20 MAX: £5000 PERIOD: 18th-20th century GENERAL: Antiques & furniture.

**The Burford Gallery**, High Street, OX18 4QA TEL: 822305 PARKING: Easy OPEN: Mon-Sat 9.30-5.30 MIN: £5 MAX: £7,000 PERIOD: 18th-20th century SPECIALIST: Watercolours.

**Jonathan Fyson Antiques**, 50-52 High Street TEL:

823204 ASSNS: CADA PARKING: Easy OPEN: Mon-Sat 9.30-5.30 MIN: £5 MAX: £5000 PERIOD: 17th-19th century GENERAL: Furniture, porcelain, glass, metalware.

**Gateway Antiques**, Cheltenham Road, Burford Roundabout, OX18 4JA TEL: 823678 FAX: 823600 ASSNS: CADA PARKING: Own carpark OPEN: Mon-Sat 10-5.30, Sun 2-5 MIN: £5 MAX: £10,000 PERIOD: 17th-20th century GENERAL: Large stock (8000sq ft covering 8 showrooms). Mainly English furniture, English pottery, metalware, arts & crafts, prints.

**Hubert's Antiques,** Burford Roundabout, Cheltenham Road, OX18 4TA TEL & FAX: 822151 ASSNS: LAPADA PARKING: Own carpark OPEN: Mon-Sat 10-5.30 MIN: £15 MAX: £10,000 GENERAL: Mahogany, walnut, oak furniture, clocks, paintings, bronzes.

**Anthony Nielsen Antiques**, 80 High Street, OX18 4QF TEL: 822014 PARKING: Easy OPEN: Mon-Sat 9.30-5.30 MIN: £50 MAX: £25,000 PERIOD: 17th-19th century SPECIALIST: English furniture, especially walnut & mahogany. Brass & copper.

**Richard Purdon Antique Carpets**, 158 High Street, OX18 4QY TEL: 823777 FAX: 823719 ASSNS: BADA, CADA PARKING: Medium OPEN: Mon-Sat 9.30-5.30 MIN: £50 MAX: £25,000 PERIOD: 18th-19th century SPECIALIST: Antique Eastern carpets OTHER INFO: Angel & Lamb hotels.

**Manfred Schotten Antiques,** 109 High Street, OX18 4RH TEL: 822302 FAX: 822055 ASSNS: CADA PARKING: Medium OPEN: 9-5.30 MIN: £10 MAX: £20,000 PERIOD: 18th-20th century SPECIALIST: Sporting items GENERAL: Furniture.

**Swan Gallery**, High Street, OX18 4RE TEL: 822244 PARKING: Easy OPEN: Mon-Sat 9.30-5.30 MIN: £100 MAX: £10,000 PERIOD: 17th-19th century GENERAL: Fine country furniture, Staffordshire figures, decorative & unusual items.

**Wren Gallery**, 4 Bear Court, High Street, OX18 4RR TEL & FAX: 823495 PARKING: Easy OPEN: Mon-Sat 10-1, 2-5 MIN: £200 MAX: £10,000 PERIOD: 19th-20th century SPECIALIST: Watercolours & drawings.

## CHIPPING NORTON (01608)

**Bugle Antiques**, 9 Horse Fair, OX7 5AL TEL: 643322 FAX: 643322 ASSNS: LAPADA PARKING: Easy OPEN: Mon-Sat 9-6 PERIOD: 18th-19th century SPECIALIST: Sets of Windsor chairs GENERAL: Dressers, tables, country furniture.

**Chipping Norton Antiques Centre**, Ivy House, 1 Middle Row, Market Square, OX7 5NH TEL: 644212 PARKING: Easy OPEN: Seven days 10-5.30 MIN: £1 MAX: £5000 PERIOD: 18th-20th century GENERAL: Metalware, treen, kitchenalia, clocks, country furniture, oak & pine, mahogany, silver, ceramics OTHER INFO: Teashop in centre.

**The Emporium**, 26 High Street, OX7 5AD TEL: 643103 PARKING: Medium OPEN: Mon-Sat 10-1, 2-5.30 MIN: £1 MAX: £100 PERIOD: 19th-20th century SPECIALIST: Postcards GENERAL: General antiques & collectables.

**Georgian House Antiques**, 21 West Street TEL: 641369 PARKING: Medium OPEN: Mon-Sat 10-5 PERIOD: 18th-19th century GENERAL: Wide variety of general antiques.

**Key Antiques,** 11 Horsefair, OX7 5AL TEL: 643777 ASSNS: BADA, CADA PARKING: Easy OPEN: 9.30-6 MIN: £10 MAX: £10,000 PERIOD: 16th-18th century SPECIALIST: Early oak, period objects including pewter, lighting, metalware, country furniture, woodcarvings.

**The Old Bakery Antiques**, 50 West Street TEL: 643441 PARKING: Medium OPEN: Mon-Sat 9-6 MIN: £5 MAX: £2000 PERIOD: 18th-19th century GENERAL: Country furniture.

**Peter Stroud Antiques**, Unit 7, Worcester Road Industrial Estate, OX7 5XW TEL: 642571 FAX: 644529 PARKING: Easy OPEN: Mon-Sat 9-5.30 MIN: £50 MAX: £10,000 PERIOD: 17th-20th century GENERAL: Furniture.

**Trada**, 21 High Street, OX7 5AD TEL: 644325 PARKING: Easy OPEN: Mon-Sat 9-5.30 MIN: £5 MAX: £500 PERIOD: 17th-18th century maps otherwise 18th-19th century SPECIALIST: Maps of English counties GENERAL: Natural history, childrens illustrations, cartoons, English topography. All steel/copper or stone engravings OTHER INFO: Small old theatre known for a friendly lively performance.

## STOW-ON-THE-WOLD (01451)

**Acorn Antiques**, Sheep Street, GL54 1AA TEL: 831519 PARKING: Easy OPEN: Mon-Sat 10-1 & 2.15-5, MIN: £5 MAX: £2000 PERIOD: 19th-20th century SPECIALIST: Staffordshire figures & animals GENERAL: Glass, pottery, small furniture.

**Baggott Church Street Ltd**, Church Street, GL54 1BB TEL: 830370 FAX: 832174 ASSNS: BADA, CADA PARKING: Easy OPEN: Mon-Sat 9.30-5.30 MIN: £50 MAX: £50,000 PERIOD: 17th-19th century SPECIALIST: English furniture GENERAL: All manner of pieces appertaining to the comforts & necessities of gentlefolk OTHER INFO: Unicorn & Grapevine hotels, Queen's Head.

**Duncan J Baggott**, Woolcomber House, Sheep Street, GL54 1AA TEL: 830662 FAX: 832174 ASSNS: LAPADA, CADA PARKING: Easy OPEN: Mon-Sat 9.30-5.30 MIN: £50 MAX: £50,000 PERIOD: 17th-19th century SPECIALIST: English furniture & paintings GENERAL: Domestic metalware, fireplace accoutrements, collectables & some garden statuary & ornaments OTHER INFO: Wyck Hill House & Fosse Manor hotels, Marsh Goose restaurant.

**Bow Cottage Antiques**, Park Street TEL: 832311 PARKING: Easy OPEN: Mon-Sat 10-5 MIN: £5 MAX: £100 PERIOD: 18th-20th century SPECIALIST: English pottery & porcelain, topographical engravings & maps & small furniture.

**Colin Brand Antiques,** Tudor House, Sheep Street, GL54 1AA TEL: 831760 ASSNS: CADA PARKING: Medium OPEN: 9-5 except Wed or Sun, anytime by appt MIN: £50 MAX: £10,000 PERIOD: 17th-20th century SPECIALIST: Clocks & porcelain GENERAL: Decorative furniture & small objects OTHER INFO: Stow is a permanent antiques fair in an original medieval setting.

**J & J Caspall Antiques**, Sheep Street, GL54 1AA TEL: 831160 PARKING: Easy OPEN: Mon-Sat 9.30-5.30 MIN: £150 MAX: £10,000 PERIOD: 17th-19th century SPECIALIST: Early lighting & carving GENERAL: Early oak metalware, early & rare domestic & decorative items OTHER INFO: Author of *Fire & Light in the Home - pre 1820.*

**Annarella Clark Antiques**

**11 Park Street, GL54 1AQ TEL: 830535 PARKING: Easy OPEN: Anytime by appt MIN: £5 MAX: £2000 PERIOD: 19th century SPECIALIST: Furniture, needlework, quilts, textiles & acessories, conservatory & garden, antique baskets OTHER INFO: Lyrical garden. Also at Durham House Antique Centre. Best B&B at 14 Park Street.**

**Christopher Clarke,** Fosse Way TEL: 830476 ASSNS: BADA, CADA, CINOA PARKING: Easy PERIOD: 17th-20th century SPECIALIST: Animals & bronzes GENERAL: English furniture, objets d'art, decorative items.

**Cotswold Galleries**, The Square, GL54 1AB TEL: 870567 FAX: 870678 ASSNS: CADA PARKING: Easy OPEN: Mon-Sat 9-1, 2-5.30 MIN: £20 MAX: £5000 PERIOD: 19th-20th century GENERAL: Original paintings (oil and watercolour) Village/ cottage scenes and traditional landscapes OTHER INFO: If you have the inclination, bring a bag of rotten tomatoes and someone to sit in the stocks.

**Country Life Antiques**, Grey House, The Square, GL54 1AF TEL & FAX: 831564 PARKING: Easy OPEN: Mon-Sat 10-5.30 & by appt MIN: £15 MAX: £5000 PERIOD: 17th-20th century SPECIALIST: Scientific intruments, pewter, brass GENERAL: Good quality mahogany, oak & pine furniture & large stock of decorative accessories.

**Durham House Antique Centre,** Sheep Street TEL: 870404 PARKING: Easy GENERAL: Furniture, books, paintings, silver, textiles, decorative items OTHER INFO: 35 dealers.

**Fosse Way Antiques**

**Ross House, The Square, GL54 1AF TEL: 830776 ASSNS: CADA PARKING: Easy OPEN: Mon-Sat 10-5 MIN: £50 MAX: £7,000 PERIOD: 18th-19th century SPECIALIST: Lots of dining chairs GENERAL: Furniture, oil paintings, decorative accessories, bronzes, Sheffield plate, mirrors, writing boxes & caddies.**

**Keith Hockin 'Antiques' Ltd**, The Square TEL: 831058 ASSNS: BADA, CADA PARKING: Medium OPEN: Mon-Sat 10-6 MIN: £50 MAX: £15,000 PERIOD: 17th-18th century SPECIALIST: Early English oak & furniture GENERAL: Brass, pewter, copper, ironwork, period objects.

**Huntington Antiques Ltd**, Church Street, GL54 1BE TEL: 830842 FAX: 832211 ASSNS: LAPADA, CADA, European Fine Art Foundation PARKING: Own carpark OPEN: Mon-Sat 9.30-5.30 MIN: £500 MAX: £100,000 PERIOD: 17th-18th century SPECIALIST: Early period furniture, works of art, tapestries GENERAL: Fine country furniture, metalware, treen, textiles OTHER INFO: Hotels and restaurants arranged locally.

**Roger Lamb Antiques & Works of Art,** 5 Church Street, GL54 1BB TEL: 831371 ASSNS: CADA PARKING: Easy OPEN: Mon-Sat 10-5 MIN: £30 MAX: £5000 PERIOD: 18th-19th century

# Durham House Antiques Centre

**Sheep Street, Stow-on-the-Wold, Gloucestershire GL54 1AA**
**Telephone: 01451 870404 After Hours: 01451 831176**

*...A Quality Antiques Centre*
*in the Heart of the Cotswolds*

Open: Mon-Sat 10am-5pm
Sunday 11am-5pm

*Professional, Well Established Trade Dealers*
*offering you a very wide selection of ...*
**Furniture ~ Art ~ Ceramics ~ Silver**
**Jewellery ~ Books ~ Collectables**

*... displayed in over 2000 square feet*
***Credit Card Facilities***

## DEALERS

**Aston Antiques** - Arts & Crafts, Victorian & decorative obects
**Judi Bland Antiques** - Toby jugs, Staffordshire, oak furniture & decorative items
**Bread and Roses** - 19th & Early 20th Century kitchen, dairy, laundry & garden objects
**Annarella Clark** - Country & painted furniture, textiles & decorative objects
**Bryan Collyer** - English pottery, Staffordshire figures, corkscrews
**Crockwell Antiques** - Longcase clocks, 18th century oak & country curniture, brass, copper & ironstone
**Paul Eisler** - 18th & early 19th century furniture & accessories, pictures & works of art
**Jane Fairfield** - Elegant silver & silverplate, Continental porcelain
**Tony & June Finnegan** - Traditional furniture, interesting home accessories & comforts
**Erna Hiscock** - Samplers, country furniture & interesting objects
**Harry Horner** - Silver & silver plated flatware & cutlery. Good selection of classic designs
**Reg & Janet Jones** - Early Worcester, fine quality blue & white transfer wares, pearlware, creamware
**Lineage Antiques** - Small silver wares, jewellery, Mauchline ware & collectables
**Audrey McConnell** - Silver & silverplate, picture frames, jewellery & some china & pottery
**Menagerie** - Animals in all mediums dating from 500BC to 1957. Viennese bronzes a speciality
**Peggy Nicholls** - Silver, silverplate, jewellery, glass & ceramics
**Peter Norden** - Period metalware, treen & pottery
**Outram Antiques** - Oak & country furniture
**Edith Prosser Antiques** - English furniture from 18th to 20th century, mirrors & period accessories
**Samarkand Galleries** - Eastern rugs & carpets; speciality - tribal rugs & trappings, valuations, restoration, cleaning, lectures
**Paper Moon Books** - Fine leather bindings, 19th & early 20th century English poetry, prose, history, etc
**Pauline Parkes** - Sewing ephemera, Mauchline ware, treen and interesting objects of merit
**Tudor Antiques** - Small period furniture from the late 18th - early 19th century. Also decorative prints
**Victoria Charles Antiques** - Interesting small furniture, quality china, glass & silverware
**Margaretha Walter-Ellis** - Small furniture & decorative objects of the 18th, 19th & 20th centuries
**Paul Wright Antiques** - Georgian & Victorian furniture, fine jewellery & silver. Jewellery restoration under taken with stones supplied and matched.
**Philippa & Paul Hughes** - Porcelain from 18th to 20th century, objets d'art

SPECIALIST: Lighting & decorative accessories, decorative small furniture.

**Little Elms Antiques**, The Square, GL54 1AF TEL: 870089 PARKING: Easy OPEN: Mon-Sat 10-5 MIN: £300 MAX: £8000 PERIOD: 17th-18th century SPECIALIST: Oak country furniture GENERAL: Dressers, tables, chairs.

**Peter Norden Antiques**, The Little House, Sheep Street, GL54 1AA TEL: 830455 PARKING: Medium OPEN: Mon-Sat 9.30-5.30 MIN: £5 MAX: £10,000 PERIOD: 17th-19th century SPECIALIST: Oak & country furniture GENERAL: Metalware, treen, arms & armour, walnut and mahogany furniture.

**No 2 Park Street Antique Centre**, 2-3 Park Street, GL54 1AQ TEL: 832311 PARKING: Easy OPEN: Mon-Sat 10-5 MIN: £5 MAX: £1500 PERIOD: 19th-20th century GENERAL: 15-20 dealers. An antique centre with 10 open stands & 10 cabinets. Wide range of porcelain, pottery, glass, furniture.

**Park House Antiques**, Park Street TEL & FAX: 830159 PARKING: Easy OPEN: Mon-Sat 10-5, please phone before making a special visit MIN: £1 MAX: £6000 PERIOD: 18th-20th century SPECIALIST: Dolls, teddies, Victorian linen & lace GENERAL: 6 showrooms. Porcelain, pottery, glass, metalware, collectables, furniture OTHER INFO: Voted 'Friendliest Antique Shop in Britain' by *BBC Homes & Antiques.*

**Antony Preston Antiques Ltd.**, The Square, GL54 1AB TEL: 831586 FAX: (0171) 581 5076 ASSNS: BADA, CINOA, LAPADA, CADA PARKING: Easy OPEN: Mon-Sat 9.30- 6 MIN: £200 MAX: £30,000 PERIOD: 17th-19th century SPECIALIST: Fine tôle-ware, ormolu, barometers GENERAL: Good English furniture & upholstery OTHER INFO: Fox Inn, Lower Oddington.

**Priests Antiques**, The Malt House, Digbeth Street, GL54 1BN TEL & FAX: 830592 PARKING: Easy OPEN: Mon-Fri 10-5, Sat 10.30-5.30 MIN: £150 MAX: £15,000 PERIOD: 17th-19th century SPECIALIST: English oak, walnut, mahogany & fruitwood furniture.

**Queen's Parade Antiques Ltd**, The Square, GL54 1AB TEL: 831586 FAX: (071) 581 5076 ASSNS: BADA, CINOA PARKING: Easy OPEN: Mon-Sat 9.30-6 MIN: £200 MAX: £15,000 PERIOD: 18th-19th century SPECIALIST: Papier maché, tôle-ware GENERAL: Period lighting, needlework, pictures, English & Continental furniture.

**Rosemary Antiques & Paper Moon Books,** 2 Park Street, GL54 1AQ TEL: 832311 PARKING: Easy OPEN: 10-5 MIN: £3 MAX: £300 PERIOD: 19th-20th century SPECIALIST: Fine leather bindings GENERAL: Bamboo items, furniture, Bibles, prayer books.

**Ruskin Antiques**, 5 Talbot Court, GL54 1DP TEL: 832254 PARKING: Easy OPEN: Mon-Sat 10-5.30, Sun 11-4 MIN: £12 MAX: £1500 PERIOD: 19th-20th century SPECIALIST: Art Deco, Art Nouveau, Arts & Crafts GENERAL: Items from any period.

**Samarkand Galleries**, 2 Brewery Yard, Sheep Street, GL54 1AA TEL: 832322 FAX: 832322 ASSNS: LAPADA, CADA PARKING: Own carpark OPEN: Mon-Sat 10-5.30 MIN: £50 MAX: £10,000 PERIOD: 19th-20th century SPECIALIST: Tribal rugs & trappings, carpets & kilims.

**Arthur Seager,** 50 Sheep Street, GL54 1AA TEL & FAX: 831605 PARKING: Own carpark OPEN: 10-5.30 MIN: £200 MAX: £15,000 PERIOD: 17th-18th century SPECIALIST: Period oak furniture, carving & objects from medieval to 18th century.

**Alison Stewart**, at Hart Villa Interiors, Sheep Street, GL54 1AA TEL: 830392 & (01608) 658744 FAX: (01608) 658085 PARKING: Easy OPEN: Erratic but officially 9.30-5 MIN: £10 MAX: £2000 PERIOD: 19th-early 20th century SPECIALIST: Painted furniture, amusing and not to be taken too seriously. Also painted pictures.

**Stow Antiques**, The Square, GL54 1AF TEL: 830377 FAX: 870018 ASSNS: LAPADA, CADA PARKING: Easy OPEN: Mon-Thurs 2-5.30, Sat 11-1, 2-5.30 MIN: £200 MAX: £24,000 PERIOD: 18th-19th century SPECIALIST: Georgian mahogany furniture, gilded mirrors GENERAL: Fine quality furniture, decorative items.

**Talbot Court Galleries**, 7 Talbot Court, GL54 1BQ TEL: 832169 ASSNS: FATG PARKING: Easy OPEN: Mon-Sat 9.30-5.30, Sun 11-5 MIN: £10 MAX: £1000 PERIOD: 17th-19th century SPECIALIST: Antiquarian engravings & maps GENERAL: English topography, botanical & sporting prints.

**Vanbrugh House Antiques**, Park Street, GL54 1AQ TEL: 830797 PARKING: Easy OPEN: Mon-Sat 10-6 MIN: £25 MAX: £10,000 PERIOD: 17th-19th century SPECIALIST: Music boxes, antique maps GENERAL: Fine furniture (pre 1830) & associated items, inc. clocks & barometers.

**Wychwood Books,** Sheep Street, GL54 1AA TEL:

831880 PARKING: Medium OPEN: Tues, Thurs-Sat 9.30-1, 2-5 MIN: 50p MAX: £500 SPECIALIST: Natural history & the countryside GENERAL: Secondhand books on most subjects, also selected antiquarian books OTHER INFO: The proprietor is an author and his Natural History books are available, signed if requested! Browsers welcome on all three floors.

## MORETON-IN-MARSH (01608)

**Astley House-Fine Art**, Astley House, High Street, GL56 0LL TEL: 650601 FAX: 651777 ASSNS: CADA PARKING: Easy OPEN: Mon, Tues, Thurs-Sat 9-5.30 MIN: £300 MAX: £20,000 PERIOD: 19th-20th century SPECIALIST: Botanical watercolours GENERAL: Oils, large decorative landscapes & portraits OTHER INFO: We have 3 galleries. Specialist framing of paintings & porcelain. Restaurants: Annies, Oxford Street & The Marsh Goose, High Street.

**Chandlers Antiques,** Chandlers Cottage, High Street, GL56 0AD TEL: 651347 PARKING: Easy OPEN: Mon-Sat 9.30-1, 2-5.30 MIN: £1 MAX: £1000 PERIOD: 18th-20th century SPECIALIST: English porcelain & glass GENERAL: Jewellery, treen, faiënce (Quimper & Rouen, etc), early Chinese pottery, smalls OTHER INFO: Good food at Marsh Goose, Black Bear. Large market Tues.

**Jon Fox Antiques,** High Street, GL56 0AD TEL: 650714 PARKING: Easy OPEN: 9.30-1, 2-5.30, closed Sun PM & Tues MIN: £10 MAX: £3000 PERIOD: 19th century SPECIALIST: Medical & pharmacy items, treen & country bygones, woodworking tools GENERAL: Furniture, decorative & country items, etc. OTHER INFO: This is a fun shop, full of interesting & unusual items, rather like the people who buy such things!

**Grimes House Antiques & Fine Art,** Grimes House, High Street, GL56 0AT TEL: 651029 PARKING: Easy OPEN: Mon-Sat 9.30-1 & 2-5, Weds 9.30-1 PERIOD: 19th century SPECIALIST: Probably the largest selection for sale anywhere of Victorian cranberry glass, collectable boxes GENERAL: Victorian furniture, glass. Accent on decorative pieces.

**Lemington House Antiques,** Oxford Street, GL56 0LA TEL & FAX: 651443 ASSNS: LAPADA PARKING: Own carpark OPEN: Mon-Sat 10-5.30 MIN: £10 MAX: £40,000 PERIOD: 17th-19th century SPECIALIST: Period walnut & mahogany furniture GENERAL: Porcelain, pewter, silver & works of art OTHER INFO: We are town's largest historic building (1430).

**London House Antiques Centre,** High Street, GL56 0AH TEL: 651084 PARKING: Easy OPEN: 7days 10-5 MIN: £5 MAX: £5000 PERIOD: 19th-20th century GENERAL: A good selection of ever changing stock, including furniture, porcelain, silver & general antiques.

**MK Nielsen,** Seaford House, High Street, GL56 0AD TEL: 650448 PARKING: Easy OPEN: Thurs-Sat 9.30-1, 2-5 MIN: £85 MAX: £8000 PERIOD: 19th-20th century SPECIALIST: English porcelain GENERAL: English furniture.

**Elizabeth Parker Antiques**, High Street, GL56 0LL TEL: 650917 PARKING: Easy OPEN: Mon-Sat 9-6 MIN: £100 MAX: £8000 PERIOD: 18th-19th century GENERAL: Quality furniture, some porcelain, copper & brass.

**Anthony Sampson Antiques**, Dale House, High Street, GL56 0AD TEL: 650763 ASSNS: BADA PARKING: Easy OPEN: Mon-Sat 9-5.30 or by appt (Resident) MIN: £50 MAX: £20,000 PERIOD: 17th-19th century SPECIALIST: Period furniture to 1830 GENERAL: Silver, paintings, porcelain, pottery, garden ornaments, decorative items.

**Southgate Gallery**, Fosse Manor Farm, GL56 9NQ TEL: 650051 PARKING: Own carpark OPEN: By appt only MIN: £500 MAX: £5000 PERIOD: 20th century GENERAL: Modern British paintings from 1920 to present day.

**Geoffrey Stead,** The Dower House, Chastleton, GL56 0SL TEL: 674364 FAX: 674533 ASSNS: BADA PARKING: BADA OPEN: By appt only PERIOD: 17th-19th century SPECIALIST: English & Continental furniture and decorative objects.

**Windsor House Antiques Centre**, High Street, GL56 0AD TEL: 650993 PARKING: Very easy OPEN: Seven days 10.30-5.30 MIN: £25 MAX: £4500 PERIOD: 17th-19th century SPECIALIST: Vintage & classic cameras GENERAL: Quality antiques of all kinds in one elegant building OTHER INFO: The quality and decor take your breath away.

## SHIPSTON-ON-STOUR (01608)

**Church Street Gallery,** 24 Church Street, CV36 4AP TEL: 662431 PARKING: Easy OPEN: 9.30-6, closed Thurs pm MIN: £5 MAX: £3000 PERIOD: 17th-20th century SPECIALIST: English watercolours GENERAL: Watercolours & oils,

maps & prints, some furniture & bric a brac.
**Fine-Lines Fine Art**, The Old Bakehouse Gallery, at The Old Rectory Lodge, West Street, CV36 4HD TEL: 662323 PARKING: Easy OPEN: Anytime by appt MIN: £300-800 MAX: £12-20,000 SPECIALIST: Quality watercolours & selected oils from 1850 to present GENERAL: 1850-1940, Still life, landscapes, good figure studies, garden subjects, marines, etc.
**The Grandfather Clock Shop,** 2 Bondgate House, West Street, CV36 4AL TEL: 662144 PARKING: Own carpark OPEN: Tues-Sat 9.30-5 MIN: £250 MAX: £4500 PERIOD: 18th century SPECIALIST: Longcase clocks GENERAL: Barometers & small clocks.
**Time in Hand**, 11 Church Street, CV36 4AP TEL & FAX: 662578 PARKING: Medium OPEN: Mon-Fri 9-1, 2-5.30, Sat 9-5 MIN: £50 MAX: £4500 PERIOD: 18th-19th century SPECIALIST: Wide range of clocks & barometers.

## EBRINGTON (01386)

**Natural Craft Taxidermy**, 21 Main Street, GL55 6NL TEL: 593231 PARKING: Easy OPEN: Anytime by appt MIN: £20 MAX: £4000 PERIOD: 19th-20th century SPECIALIST: Victorian & Edwardian taxidermy GENERAL: Antique & modern taxidermy & sporting antiques OTHER INFO: Middle of pretty N.Cotswolds village.

## CHIPPING CAMPDEN (01386)

**Campden Country Pine Antiques**, High Street, GL55 6HN TEL: 840315 FAX: 841740 PARKING: Easy OPEN: Mon-Sat 10-5 MIN: £50 MAX: £3000 PERIOD: 17th-19th century SPECIALIST: Large kitchen dressers & tables GENERAL: Good quality English antique pine, no reproductions or Continental pieces OTHER INFO: 400 year old shop in the most beautiful high street in Britain. National & international delivery service.
**Pedlars,** High Street, GL55 6AL TEL: 840680 PARKING: Medium OPEN: 10-1, 2-5 MIN: 50p MAX: £400 PERIOD: 19th-20th century GENERAL: Silver & plate, wood, metalware, china, jewellery, kitchenalia.
**School House Antiques,** High Street, GL55 6HB TEL: 841474 FAX: 841367 ASSNS: LAPADA PARKING: Own carpark OPEN: 10-5, closed Thurs Nov-April MIN: £400 MAX: £17,500 PERIOD: 18th-19th century SPECIALIST: Paintings.
**Swan Antiques**, High Street, GL55 6HB TEL: 840759 ASSNS: NAG, holder of Anderson Medal for Gemmology PARKING: Medium OPEN: Mon-Wed, Fri, Sat 9.30-5 MIN: £15 MAX: £15,000 PERIOD: 18th-19th century SPECIALIST: Silver & jewellery GENERAL: Porcelain, pictures, furniture OTHER INFO: Woolstaplers Museum, several good restaurants.

## BROADWAY (0386)

**Broadway Old Books**, The Long Room, 45 High Street, WR12 7DP TEL: 853668 ASSNS: FATG PARKING: Own carpark OPEN: Mon-Sat 9.30-5.30, Sun 11-5 MIN: £1 MAX: £5000 PERIOD: 19th century SPECIALIST: Early literature, fine bindings GENERAL: Books & engravings from 16th century, childrens' books & prints.
**Fenwick & Fisher Antiques**, 88-90 High Street, WR12 7AJ TEL: 853227, home 858502 FAX: 858504 ASSNS: CADA PARKING: Own carpark OPEN: Mon-Sat 10-6 & by appt MIN: £2 MAX: £7000 PERIOD: 17th-early 19th century SPECIALIST: Treen, pewter, samplers, boxes, lace bobbins GENERAL: Pre-Victorian furniture & accessories up to 1850 OTHER INFO: England's prettiest village, convenient for theatre at Stratford. Lygon Arms, Luigi's Backyard, Hunters Lodge etc.
**Richard Hagen Ltd**, Yew Tree House, WR12 7DT TEL: 853624, 858561 FAX: 852172 ASSNS: BADA PARKING: Easy OPEN: Mon-Sat 9.30-5.30 MIN: £550 MAX: £45,000 PERIOD: Late 19th-20th century SPECIALIST: Bronzes by James Butler RA GENERAL: British oil paintings & watercolours including contemporary artists.
**High Park Antiques Ltd**, 62 High Street, WR12 7DT TEL: 853130 PARKING: Easy OPEN: Tues-Sat 10.30-5 MIN: £50 MAX: £12,500 PERIOD: 18th-19th century GENERAL: Furniture, silver, porcelain.
**Howards of Broadway,** 27A High Street, WR12 7DP TEL: 858924 PARKING: Easy OPEN: Mon-Sat 9.30-5.30, Sun 11.30-5.30 MIN: £5 MAX: £5000 PERIOD: 18th-20th century GENERAL: Silver, jewellery & objects of vertu OTHER INFO: Shop opposite the Lygon Arms.
**HW Keil Ltd**, Tudor House, WR12 7DP TEL: 852408 PARKING: Own small carpark OPEN: Mon-Sat 9.15-12.45, 2.15-5.30 PERIOD: 17th-early 19th century SPECIALIST: Large furniture in oak, walnut & mahogany OTHER INFO: Early metal-

work, brass & copper etc, Sheffield plate. Near Lygon Arms, Buckland Manor, Dormy House hotels. Hunter's Lodge excellent retaurant.

**John Noott Fine Art**, 14 Cotswold Court, WR12 7AA TEL: 858969 FAX: 858348 ASSNS: BADA, LAPADA, CADA PARKING: Own carpark OPEN: 9.30-1, 2-5 MIN: £20 MAX: £20,000 GENERAL: Fine original paintings 17th century to contemporary.

**Olive Branch Antiques**, 80 High Street, WR12 7AJ TEL: 853831 FAX: 853440 PARKING: Own carpark front/rear OPEN: Seven days 9-5.30 MIN: £1 MAX: £3000 PERIOD: 19th-20th century SPECIALIST: Clocks OTHER INFO: Olive Branch Guest House right next door (tel: 853440).

**Withington Fine Art**, 62 High Street, WR12 7DT TEL: 853130 PARKING: Medium OPEN: Tues-Sat 10.30-5.30 MIN: £70 MAX: £10,000 PERIOD: 17th-20th century SPECIALIST: Oils & watercolours GENERAL: Jewellery.

## BERRY WORMINGTON (01242)

**Hay Loft Gallery**, WR12 7NH TEL: 621202 PARKING: Own carpark OPEN: 10-5.30 MIN: £200 MAX: £20,000 PERIOD: 19th century SPECIALIST: Victorian oils, landscapes, animal, genre GENERAL: Some watercolours. OTHER INFO: Also undertake restoration work.

## TADDINGTON (01386)

**Architectural Heritage**, Taddington Manor TEL: 584414 FAX: 584236 ASSNS: CADA PARKING: Own carpark OPEN: Mon-Fri 9.30-5.30, Sat 10.30-4.30 MIN: £250 PERIOD: 17th-20th century GENERAL: Garden statuary, fire surrounds, panelling, stained glass, bizarre items OTHER INFO: Access for helicopters which surprise the cows not to mention the rest of the hamlet.

## WINCHCOMBE (01242)

**Abbey Antiquarian Books,** The Abbey, GL54 5RA TEL: 602589 ASSNS: PBFA PARKING: Own carpark MIN: £1 MAX: £500 PERIOD: 17th-20th century SPECIALIST: Illustrated books, children's books GENERAL: Second hand hardbacked books OTHER INFO: Located in the Abbey tithe barn near to Sudeley Castle. We are a private house so please phone first.

**Muriel Lindsay**, Queen Anne House, High Street, GL54 5LJ TEL: 602319 PARKING: Medium OPEN: Mon-Sat 9.30-1, 2.15-5.15 or by appt, resident MIN: £2 MAX: £600 PERIOD: 18th-19th century SPECIALIST: Metalwork, glass, Staffordshire GENERAL: Small furniture, silver, a little porcelain.

**Prichard Antiques**, 16 High Street, GL54 5LJ TEL: 603566 ASSNS: CADA PARKING: Easy OPEN: Mon-Sat 9-5.30 & by appt PERIOD: 17th-19th century GENERAL: Period furniture & accessories, boxes, brassware, etc OTHER INFO: Sudeley Castle, Railway Museum.

## BISHOPS CLEEVE (01242)

**Cleeve Picture Framing**, Church Road TEL: 673532 ASSNS: FATG, FPPF PARKING: Medium OPEN: Mon-Fri 9-1, 2-5.30, Sat 9-1 MIN: £10 MAX: £500 PERIOD: 17th-20th century SPECIALIST: Antique prints & maps, topographical and sporting GENERAL: Original oils & watercolours, limited edition prints.

## TEWKESBURY (01684)

**FW Taylor**, 71 Church Street TEL: 295990 PARKING: Easy OPEN: Mon-Sat 9-5 MIN: £10 MAX: £3000 PERIOD: 18th-19th century GENERAL: General antiques OTHER INFO: Historic medieval town with Abbey as the centrepiece.

## GLOUCESTER (01452)

**Steve Bartrick Antique Maps & Prints,** Unit 6, Gloucester Antique Centre MIN: £2.50 MAX: £200 PERIOD: Prints & maps.

**EJ Cook & Son Antiques,** Gloucester Antique Centre MIN: £150 MAX: £15,000 SPECIALIST: Furniture.

**R Cooke & GJ Dunn,** Shop 18, Gloucester Antique Centre SPECIALIST: Cutlery GENERAL: Silver & plate, porcelain, collectables.

**Days Before Yesterday,** Unit 15, Gloucester Antique Centre TEL: 524797 MIN: £1 PERIOD: 18th-20th century SPECIALIST: Kitchenalia, pine & decor GENERAL: General antiques & collectables OTHER INFO: Family motto: Don't sit on that chair, I've just sold it.

**Gloucester Antique Centre**, 1 Severn Road TEL: 529716 FAX: 507161 PARKING: Own carpark OPEN: Mon-Sat 9.30-5, Sun 1-5 MIN: £1 MAX: £10,000 PERIOD: 18th-19th century SPECIALIST: Furniture GENERAL: Silver & print jewellery OTHER INFO: 67 dealers under one roof.

**HQ84 Military Curiosity Shop,** At the Southgate, GL1 2DX TEL: 527716 PARKING: Medium OPEN: Seven days 10-5.30 MIN: £1 MAX: £275 PERIOD: 19th-20th century SPECIALIST: Militaria of the World GENERAL: Supplier to retail, trade & film industry of reproduction uniforms, badges & medals (5000 items, lists available £1). Small antiques, brass, etc OTHER INFO: Antique Market 500 yds, plenty of eating places close. Historical docks 100 yds. 3 museums adjacent, also Gloucester Cathedral. Large indoor market close.

**M & C Stamps,** Unit 20, Gloucester Antique Centre, TEL: 522632 PARKING: Own carpark OPEN: Thurs-Mon 10-5, Sun 1-5 MIN: 2p MAX: £200 PERIOD:19th-20th century GENERAL: GB, Commonwealth, foreign stamps. GB new issue service.

**Paul Medcalf,** Unit 29 Gloucester Antique Centre, TEL: 415186 PARKING: Own carpark OPEN: Mon-Sat 9-5, Sun 1-5 MIN: £5 MAX: £2500 PERIOD: 19th-20th century GENERAL: Oils, watercolours, etchings, Japanese prints.

## WESTBURY ON SEVERN (01452)

**Pine & Country Furniture,** Landeck, Rodley TEL: 760315 PARKING: Own carpark OPEN: Seven days 9-6 MIN: £20 MAX: £1000 PERIOD: 18th-20th century GENERAL: Stripped pine & country pieces incl. kitchens from reclaimed timber OTHER INFO: Forest of Dean, Wye Valley.

## CAMBRIDGE (01453)

**Bell House Antiques**, GL2 7BD TEL: 890463 PARKING: Own carpark OPEN: Mon-Sat 10-1, 2-5 MIN: £1 MAX: £1000 PERIOD: 19th-20th century OTHER INFO: George Inn in village. Slimbridge Wildfowl Trust 2 miles.

## BERKELEY (01453)

**Berkeley Antiques Market**
**The Market Place, GL13 9BB TEL: 511032 PARKING: Own carpark OPEN: Mon-Sat 9.30-5 MIN: £5 MAX: £1000+ PERIOD: 18th-20th century SPECIALIST: Pine, oak, mahogany, brass OTHER INFO: 10 dealers with ever-changing stock, 3000 sq ft, friendly trade call.**

**Keith Gardner Antiques**, The Market Place, GL13 9PB TEL: 511032 PARKING: Own carpark OPEN: Tues-Sat 9.30-1, 2-5 MIN: £1 MAX: £1000 PERIOD: 18th-20th century GENERAL: Brass, furniture, general OTHER INFO: Berkeley Castle. 3 other antique shops here.

## WOTTON-UNDER-EDGE (01453)

**Christopher Howe,** Newark Park, Ozleworth, GL12 7PZ TEL: 842644, Mobile 0585 404730 FAX: (0171) 730 0157 PARKING: Own carpark OPEN: By appt MIN: £100 MAX: £50,000 PERIOD: 17th-19th century SPECIALIST: English country house furniture & lighting in situ OTHER INFO: Historic country house set in woodland gardens with finest views in England. A tour of other local antique shops can be arranged.

## WICKWAR (01454)

**Bell Passage Antiques**, 36-38 High Street, GL12 8NPTEL: 294251 FAX: 294251 ASSNS: LAPADA PARKING: Own carpark OPEN: Tues, Wed, Fri, Sat 9-5 MIN: £5 MAX: £10,000 PERIOD: 16th-20th century SPECIALIST: Glass & quality antiques GENERAL: English mahogany, oak, pictures, clocks. French OTHER INFO: Wickwar family of Dewares gave name to Delaware.

## TETBURY (01666)

**Antique Interiors,** 35 Long Street, GL8 8AA TEL: 504043 PARKING: Easy OPEN: Mon-Sat 9-6 MIN: £50 MAX: £3,000 PERIOD: 18th-early 19th century SPECIALIST: Papier maché & tôle tray tables GENERAL: English & French decorative furniture and accessories, mainly from the Empire & Regency periods.

**The Antiques Emporium,** The Old Chapel, Long Street, GL8 8AA TEL: 505281 PARKING: Medium OPEN: Mon-Sat 10-5, Sun 1-5 MIN: £1 MAX: £15,000 PERIOD: 17th-20th century SPECIALIST: Clocks, Staffordshire, country furniture, jewellery GENERAL: 30 dealers with ecletic & varied stock OTHER INFO: Charming 17th century wool town in the Royal Triangle.

**Art-Tique,** 18 Long Street, GL8 8AQ TEL: 503597 PARKING: Easy OPEN: Six days 9-5.30 MIN: £3 MAX: £3000 SPECIALIST: Tribal art, carpets & kelims OTHER INFO: The most unusual Central Asian shop in England.

**Ball & Claw Antiques,** 45 Long Street, GL8 8AA TEL: 502440 PARKING: Easy OPEN: 10-5 PERIOD: 17th-18th century SPECIALIST: Furniture.

**Balmuir House Antiques Ltd**, 14 Long Street, GL8 8AQ TEL: 503822 FAX: 505285 ASSNS: LAPADA PARKING: Easy OPEN: 9.30-5.30 MIN: £25 MAX: £8000 PERIOD: 19th century SPECIALIST: Edwardian & Victorian furniture GENERAL: Mirrors, paintings & decorative items OTHER INFO: Recommend the Close & Calcott Manor hotels.

**Breakspeare Antiques**, 36 & 57 Long Street, GL8 5AQ TEL: 503122 ASSNS: LAPADA, CADA PARKING: Easy OPEN: Mon-Sat 9.30-5.30, closed Thurs pm MIN: £350 MAX: £15,000 GENERAL: Early walnut 1690-1740, 18th century mahogany furniture OTHER INFO: Westonbirt Arboretum & Highgrove House are nearby. Recommend the Snooty Fox Hotel.

**J & M Bristow Antiques**, 28 Long Street, GL8 8AQ TEL: 502222 PARKING: Easy OPEN: Mon-Wed, Fri, Sat 9.30-1, 2-5.30 MIN: £85 MAX: £10,000 PERIOD: 17th-18th century SPECIALIST: Longcase, bracket & lantern clocks, barometers, furniture, metalware GENERAL: Occasional oak pieces.

**The Chest of Drawers Antiques**, 24 Long Street, GL8 8AQ TEL: 502105 PARKING: Easy OPEN: Mon-Sat 9.30-6, closed Thurs am MIN: £25 MAX: £5000 PERIOD: 17th-19th century GENERAL: English furniture, pictures, brass & other smalls OTHER INFO: Established 20 years, still sane.

**Country Homes**, 61 Long Street, GL8 8AA TEL: 502342 PARKING: Medium OPEN: Mon-Sat 9-5.30, Sun 1-5.30 MIN: £10 MAX: £2,300 PERIOD: 19th century GENERAL: Beautiful original Irish, English & German old pine furniture, restored on the premises, treen.

**Day Antiques**, 5 New Church Street, GL8 8DS TEL: 502413 Mon-Sat 9-5.30 PARKING: Easy OPEN: Mon-Sat 9-5.30 PERIOD: 17th-19th century SPECIALIST: Oak & country furniture, pottery, metalware & treen.

**The Decorator Source,** 39A Long Street, GL8 8AA TEL: 505358 PARKING: Easy MIN: £50 MAX: £5000 PERIOD: 18th-19th century SPECIALIST: French Provincial fruitwood furniture. Good call for decorators & trade buyers.

**Dolphin Antiques**, 48 Long Street, GL8 8AQ TEL: 504242 PARKING: Easy OPEN: Mon-Wed, Fri-Sat 10-5.30 MIN: £20 MAX: £2000 PERIOD: 19th century SPECIALIST: Decorative porcelain GENERAL: Small general antiques.

**Elgin House Antiques**, 1 New Church Street, GL8 8DT TEL: 504068 FAX: 503352 PARKING: Easy OPEN: Seven days 9-5.30 PERIOD: 18th-19th century SPECIALIST: Beds GENERAL: Furniture.

**Hampton Gallery**, 8 Tetbury Upton, GL8 8LP TEL: 502971 PARKING: Medium OPEN: By appt MIN: £50 MAX: £5000 PERIOD: 17th-20th century SPECIALIST: Arms & armour.

**Bobbie Middleton**, 46 Long Street, GL8 8AQ TEL: 502761, (0374)192660 FAX: (01454) 238619 PARKING: Medium OPEN: Mon, Wed-Sat 10-5 or by apt MIN: £40 MAX: £8000 PERIOD: 18th-18th century SPECIALIST: Georgian furniture and later GENERAL: country furniture, fruitwood, mahogany, decorative accessories.

**Old Mill Market Shop,** 12 Church Street, GL8 8JG TEL: 503127 PARKING: Easy OPEN: 9.30-1, 2-5.30, closed Thurs pm MIN: £1 MAX: £500 PERIOD: 19th-20th century GENERAL: Antiques, collectables, jewellery, silver, linen, books.

**Porch House Antiques**, 42 Long Street, GL8 8AQ TEL: 502687 PARKING: Medium OPEN: Mon-Sat 10-5 MIN: £2 MAX: £2000 PERIOD: 17th-20th century GENERAL: General antiques.

**Upton Lodge Galleries**, 6 Long Street, GL8 8AQ TEL: 503416 PARKING: Medium OPEN: Mon-Fri 10-6, Sat 10.30-5.30 MIN: £75 MAX: £5000 PERIOD: 20th century SPECIALIST: Early 20th century British paintings GENERAL: Contemporary paintings OTHER INFO: 18th century church & covered market.

## MALMESBURY (01666)

**Andrew Britten**, 48 High Street TEL: 823376 FAX: 825563 PARKING: Medium OPEN: Mon-Sat 9.30-5.30 MIN: £15 MAX: £1500 PERIOD: 18th-19th century GENERAL: Decorative furniture & accessories, particularly brass & boxes OTHER INFO: This is England's oldest borough (AD 880)

**Cross Hayes Antiques**, The Antique & Furniture Warehouse, 19 Bristol Street, SN16 0AY TEL: 824260 day, 822062 evening FAX: 823020 ASSNS: LAPADA PARKING: Medium OPEN: 9-5 Closed Thurs or by appt MIN: £2 MAX: £2000 PERIOD: Generally 1860-1930 SPECIALIST: Furniture GENERAL: Bric-a-brac, shipping goods.

**Dovetail Antiques**, 67-69 High Street, SN16 9AG TEL: 822191 PARKING: Medium OPEN: Mon-

Sat 10-5.30 PERIOD: 17th-19th century GENERAL: Country furniture, metalware, needlework & some mahogany furniture OTHER INFO: The Old Bell Hotel, Le Flambé restaurant.

**JP Kadwell,** Warehouse, Silver Street, SN16 9BX TEL: 823589 PARKING: Own carpark OPEN: 7 days 9-5 MIN: £1 MAX: £1500 GENERAL: Mixed, furniture OTHER INFO: Adjacent to Norman abbey.

## STROUD (01453)

**Gnome Cottage Antiques,** 55 Middle Street, GL5 1DZ TEL: 755788 FAX: 753646 PARKING: Easy OPEN: Mon-Sat 9.30-5.30 MIN: £1 MAX: £1500 PERIOD: 17th-20th century GENERAL: Wide variety of antique furniture, collectables & curios. Some militaria. Good for a rummage OTHER INFO: Good real ale pubs and pub grub nearby. Lots of alternative therapists, also collectors bookshop attached.

**Shabby Tiger Antiques**, 18 Nelson Street, GL5 2HN TEL: 759175 PARKING: Easy OPEN: Mon-Sat 10.30-5.30 MIN: £5 MAX: £1000 PERIOD: 18th-20th century GENERAL: Furniture and general antiques OTHER INFO: On good trade route between Bath & Cheltenham (A46). Painswick (Queen of the Cotswold villages) only 3 miles, Princess Anne's residence near Minchinhampton, 3 miles away. Prince Charles's (Tetbury) 12 miles.

## MINCHINHAMPTON (01453)

**MICK & FANNY WRIGHT ANTIQUES THE TRUMPET, WEST END, GL6 9JA TEL: 883027 PARKING: MEDIUM OPEN: WED-SAT 10.30-5.30 MIN: 50P MAX: £1000 PERIOD: 18TH-20TH CENTURY SPECIALIST: WATCHES GENERAL: FURNITURE, TOYS, SILVER + PLATED WARE, JEWELLERY, CHINA, GLASS, CLOCKS, METALWARE, GRAMOPHONES, MECHANICAL MUSIC, DECORATIVE ITEMS OTHER INFO: NOT A BIG SHOP SO CANNOT GUARANTEE ALL ITEMS & PERIODS AT ANY ONE TIME. OUR SHOP IS ALWAYS FULL OF RAPIDLY TURNING STOCK. GOOD LOCAL B&BS, PUBS ETC. MINCHINHAMPTON IS A LOVELY PLACE NOT MUCH VISITED.**

## PAINSWICK (01452)

**Country Living**, Cardynham House, The Cross, GL6 6XA TEL: 814006 PARKING: Medium OPEN: Mon-Sat 10.30-5 PERIOD: 19th-20th century SPECIALIST: Pine, painted furniture, china, prints GENERAL: Dummy boards, quilts, bric-a-brac OTHER INFO: Cardynham House, a Grade II listed building dating from 1489, is in centre of unspoilt village. Prinknash Abbey nearby.

**Craig Carrington Antiques**, Brook House, GL6 6SE TEL: 813248 FAX: 813539 PARKING: Own carpark OPEN: By appt MIN: £200 MAX: £50,000 PERIOD: 17th-19th century SPECIALIST: English & Continental furniture GENERAL: Fine objects, needlework, marble sculpture OTHER INFO: Painswick Hotel in village comfortable country house hotel, Oakes Restaurant 2 miles, good food.

**Painswick Antique & Craft Centre**, New Street, GL6 6XH TEL: 812431 PARKING: Medium/difficult OPEN: Mon-Fri 10-5, Sat 9.30-5.30, Sun 11-5.30 MIN: £2 MAX: £3000 PERIOD: 18th-19th century GENERAL: Porcelain, jewellery, small furniture, silver, books.

## SLAD (01453)

**Ian Hodgkins & Co Ltd**, Upper Vatch Mill, The Vatch, GL6 7JY TEL: 764270 FAX: 766716 ASSNS: ABA PARKING: Own carpark OPEN: By appt PERIOD: 19th century SPECIALIST: Pre-Raphaelites: 19th Century Literary Ladies, 1860's illustrated books, The 1890's, 19th century royalty, Victorian lady travellers OTHER INFO: Slad is the home of Laurie Lee.

## .CRANHAM (01452)

**Heather Newman Gallery**, Milidduwa, Mill Lane, GL6 6TX TEL: 812230 PARKING: Own carpark OPEN: By appt MIN: £100 MAX: £10,000 PERIOD: 18th-early 20th century SPECIALIST: Quality British watercolours & drawings.

## CHELTENHAM SPA (01242)

**Art & Antiques Cheltenham,** 17 Montpellier Walk, GL50 1SD TELL: 522939 ASSNS: LAPADA PARKING: Medium OPEN: 10-5 MIN: £5 MAX: £5000 PERIOD: 18th-19th century GENERAL: Furniture, silver, porcelain, dolls, toys, etc, anything of interest.

**Art et Maison,** Clarence Parade, GL50 3PA TEL: 222554 PARKING: Medium OPEN: Tues-Sat 10-5.30 MIN: £2.50 MAX: £2000 PERIOD: 18th-20th century GENERAL: Mahogany, pine & oak furniture, china, glass, pictures, metalware. Ideas, old & new, for house & garden.

**David Bannister FRGS**, 26 Kings Road, GL52 6BG TEL: 514287 FAX: 513890 ASSNS: AMPF, PBFA PARKING: Own carpark OPEN: By appt only MIN: £25 PERIOD: 16th-18th century SPECIALIST: Antique maps & prints only OTHER INFO: Organiser of the Bonnington Map Fair, lectures to antique clubs, valuations.

**Bed of Roses**, 12 Prestbury Road, GL52 2PW TEL: 231918 (24 hrs) PARKING: Medium OPEN: Tues-Sat 10-1, 2-5 PERIOD: 19th century SPECIALIST: Fine stripped pine.

**Butler & Co**, 111 Promenade, GL50 1NW TEL: 234439 & 522272 PARKING: Medium OPEN: Sat 10-4 PERIOD: 17th-20th century SPECIALIST: Coins & medals of all countries.

**Cheltenham Antique Market**, 54 Suffolk Road, GL50 2AQ TEL: 529812 PARKING: Medium OPEN: Mon-Sat 9.30-5.30 MIN: £1 MAX: £1000 PERIOD: 19th-20th century GENERAL: Furniture, pictures, mirrors, pine, fireplaces OTHER INFO: 25 dealers

**Cocoa**, 7 Queens Circus, Montpellier, GL50 1RX TEL: 233585 PARKING: Medium OPEN: Mon-Sat 10-5 MIN: £1 MAX: £2000 PERIOD: 18-20th century SPECIALIST: Antique lace, wedding dresses GENERAL STOCK: Costume jewellery, antique linens, christening gowns etc OTHER INFO: Very near Queens Hotel. We are set in heart of Montpellier, which is full of interesting shops.

**Government House**, 16 Suffolk Road, GL50 2AQ TEL: 255897 PARKING: Easy OPEN: Fri & Sat 10.30-6 other times by appt MIN: £10 MAX: £4000 PERIOD: 19th-20th century SPECIALIST: Vast quantities of quality antique & pre-1939 lighting & spare shades. Restoration & re-wiring.

**Greens of Montpellier**, 15 Montpellier Walk TEL: 512088 FAX: 512088 PARKING: Medium OPEN: Mon, Tues, Thurs-Sat 9-1 & 2-5 MIN: £100 MAX: £10,000 PERIOD: 18th-19th century SPECIALIST: Antique & Art Deco jewellery, silver, Oriental porcelain, glass, furniture.

**Heydens Antiques & Militaria**, 420 High Street, GL50 3JA TEL: 582466 PARKING: Medium OPEN: Mon-Sat 10-5.30 MIN: £1 MAX: £1500 PERIOD: 19th-20th century SPECIALIST: Antique weapons GENERAL: Militaria & collectables.

**David Howard 20th Century Paintings**, 42 Moorend Crescent, GL53 0EL TEL: 243379 PARKING: Easy OPEN: By appt MIN: £200 MAX: £2000 PERIOD: 19th-20th century SPECIALIST: Only fine paintings & drawings.

**HW Keil (Cheltenham) Ltd,** 129-131 Promenade, GL50 1NW TEL: 522509 ASSNS: BADA PARKING: Own parking area OPEN: Mon-Sat 9.15-12.45, 2.15-5.15 PERIOD: 17th-19th century GENERAL: Oak, mahogany, walnut, chandeliers & a little bit of glass OTHER INFO: Queens Hotel opposite, Buckland Manor a few miles.

**Kyoto House Antiques**, 14 Suffolk Road, GL50 2AQ TEL: 262549 FAX: 262549 ASSNS: BADA, Cert.in Furniture Restoring PARKING: Difficult OPEN: Mon-Sat 10-6 MIN: £5 MAX: £8,000 PERIOD: 19th century SPECIALIST: Japanese GENERAL: Japanese furniture & small items, English furniture (trade) OTHER INFO: All stock bought in Japan personally.

**Latchfords,** 215 London Road TEL: 226263 PARKING: Easy OPEN: Mon-Sat 10-5.30 MIN: £1 MAX: £1000 PERIOD: 19th-20th century

GENERAL: Stripped pine, furniture, giftware.

**The Loquens Gallery,** 3 Montpellier Avenue, GL50 1SA TEL: 254313 PARKING: Easy OPEN: 10-5 PERIOD: 18th-20th century SPECIALIST: Victorian watercolours GENERAL: Oils, watercolours, prints.

**Manor House Antiques,** 42 Suffolk Road, GL50 2AQ TEL: 232780 PARKING: Medium OPEN: Fri & Sat 10-5.30 MIN: £25 MAX: £2000 GENERAL: Furniture.

**Montpellier Clocks**, 13 Rotunda Terrace, Montpellier Street, GL50 1SW TEL: 242178 ASSNS: BADA PARKING: Easy OPEN: Mon-Sat 8.30-5.30 MIN: £100 MAX: £20,000 PERIOD: 17th-19th century SPECIALIST: Clocks & barometers only OTHER INFO: Full restoration.

**Eric Pride Oriental Rugs**, 44 Suffolk Road, GL50 2AQ TEL: 580822 & (01378) 265989 PARKING: Medium OPEN: Wed-Fri 10-6 or by appt MIN: £100 MAX: £10,000 PERIOD: 19th-20th century SPECIALIST: Caucasian tribal rugs & kilims GENERAL: Old & new Persian, Caucasian & Central Asian rugs, carpets & kilims.

**Michael Rayner Bookseller**, 11 St Luke's Road, GL53 7JQ TEL: 512806 PARKING: Own carpark for one MIN: £1 MAX: £500 PERIOD: 19th-20th century GENERAL: Wide variety of books incl topography, transport, modern firsts.

**Scott-Cooper Ltd**, 52 The Promenade, GL50 1LY TEL: 522580 ASSNS: BADA NAG PARKING: difficult OPEN: Mon-Fri 0930-1 & 2.15-5, Sat 0930-12 MIN: £35 PERIOD: 17th-20th century GENERAL: Jewellery, silver & objets d'art.

**Catherine Shinn Decorative Textiles,** 7 Suffolk Parade, GL50 2AB TEL: 574546 PARKING: Easy OPEN: Mon-Sat 10-5 MIN: £25 MAX: £2000 PERIOD: 17th-20th century SPECIALIST: Textiles, cushions & own silk trims.

**Tapestry Antiques**, 33 Suffolk Parade, GL50 2AE TEL: 512191 PARKING: Medium OPEN: Mon-Sat 10-5.30 MIN: £3 MAX: £2000 PERIOD: 19th century GENERAL: Four rooms of pine, mahogany & country furniture, mirrors, textiles, lamps, china

**The Triton Gallery**, 27 Suffolk Parade, GL50 2AE TEL: 510477 PARKING: Difficult OPEN: Mon-Sat 9-5.30 & by appt (resident) MIN: £5 MAX: £5000 PERIOD: 19th-20th century SPECIALIST: Antique mirrors, furniture, paintings GENERAL: Decorative furniture OTHER INFO: Commendation Award of Civic Society for design of garden at rear of showroom.

## CHARLTON KINGS (01242)

**Bottles & Bygones,** 96 Horsefair Street, GL53 8JS TEL: 236393 PARKING: Easy OPENL Wed-Sat 10-5 MIN: 50p MAX: £350 PERIOD: 19th-20th century SPECIALIST: Bottles, postcards, small collectables GENERAL: Doulton, china, glass, irons, tins, pot-lids, almost anything.

**Charlton Kings Antique & Craft Centre**, 199 London Road TEL: 510672 PARKING: Easy OPEN: Mon-Sat 9.30-5.30 MIN: £5 MAX: £1500 PERIOD: 19th-20th century GENERAL: Furniture, china, silverplate, mirrors, watercolours, crafts, etc.

## ANDOVERSFORD (01242)

**Julian Tatham-Losh,** Brereton House, Stow Road, GL54 4JN TEL & FAX: 820646 OPEN: 8-4 or by appt MIN: £5 MAX: £3000 PERIOD: 19th-20th century GENERAL: Majolica, blue & white, Staffordshire figures & animals, boxes, etc OTHER INFO: Trade warehouse.

## NORTHLEACH (01451)

**The Doll's House,** Market Place, GL54 3EJ TEL & FAX: 860431 ASSNS: British Toymakers Guild, MINTA, PARKING: Easy OPEN: Thurs-Sat 10-5, other days vary MIN: 20p MAX: £2000 SPECIALIST: Dolls houses & furniture OTHER INFO: Mostly new dolls houses, furniture & accessories handmade by English craftsmen. We have moved to Cotswolds after 15 years in Covent Garden.

**Keith Harding's World of Mechanical Music**, High Street, GL54 3ET TEL: 860181 FAX: 861133 ASSNS: BHI (Fellow) PARKING: Own carpark OPEN: Seven days 10-6 PERIOD: 18th-20th century SPECIALIST: Clocks & musical boxes including restoration OTHER INFO: Continuous tours of our award-winning museum..

## BARNSLEY (01285)

**Denzil Verey Antiques**, Barnsley House, GL7 5EE TEL: 740402 FAX: 740628 ASSNS: CADA PARKING: Own carpark OPEN: Mon-Fri 9.30-5.30, Sat 10.30-5.30 MIN: £5 MAX: £1500 PERIOD: 18th-19th century GENERAL: Country furniture, pine, kitchenalia, unusual & decorative items OTHER INFO: Barnsley House range of teak garden furniture & associated pieces. Award winning Barnsley House Gardens open Mon, Wed, Thurs-Sat 10-6.

## AMPNEY CRUCIS (01285)

**Jonathan Beech Antique Clocks**, Nurses Cottage, GL7 5RY TEL: 851495 ASSNS: BHI PARKING: Own carpark OPEN: Mon-Sat 9.30-5.30 & by appt MIN: £300 MAX: £5000 PERIOD: 17th-19th century SPECIALIST: Antique clocks especially pretty country longcase clocks, 30 hour & 8 day. Also bracket, Vienna and wall clocks OTHER INFO: We also sell at Tetbury Antiques Emporium. Nurses Cottage is set in a beautiful Cotswold village with 2 good pubs offering food & accommodation.

## CIRENCESTER (01285)

**At the Sign of the Herald Angel**, 19 Park Street, GL7 2BX TEL: 652972 PARKING: Medium OPEN: Mon-Sat 9-5.30 MIN: £20 MAX: £3000 PERIOD: 17th-19th century SPECIALIST: Glass, netsuke, needlework tools & workboxes GENERAL: Small works of art OTHER INFO: Corinium Museum (mainly Roman). Town was largest Roman settlement after London. Corinium Court Hotel, Gloucester Street, several good private hotels & boarding houses, also B&B.

**Walter Bull & Son Ltd**, 10 Dyer Street TEL: 653875 FAX: 641751 ASSNS: NAG PARKING: Medium OPEN: Mon-Sat 9-5 MIN: £50 MAX: £5000 PERIOD: 19th-20th century SPECIALIST: Antique silver.

**Forum Antiques**, 20 West Way, The Forum, GL7 1JA TEL: 658406 PARKING: Easy OPEN: Mon-Fri 9-5, Sat 10-5 MIN: £20 MAX: £10,000 PERIOD: 17th-19th century SPECIALIST: Oak furniture GENERAL: Oak, mahogany, walnut etc, furniture 1600-1850, some decorative items.

**Jay Gray Antiques**, Syrena House, 1 Cheltenham Road, GL7 2HS TEL: 652755 PARKING: Easy OPEN: Mon-Sat 9-6, or ring doorbell anytime MIN: £100 MAX: £10,000 PERIOD: 18th-19th century SPECIALIST: English, Sevres & Meissen porcelain GENERAL: French & Regency furniture, bronzes, French ormolu & porcelain mantel clocks, oils & watercolours, glass OTHER INFO: Wool town in heart of Cotswolds with beautiful parish church.

**Hares Antiques**, 17-19 Gosditch Street, GL7 2AG & 4 Blackjack Street (Tel: 642275) TEL: 640077 FAX: 653513 ASSNS: CADA PARKING: Easy OPEN: Mon-Sat 9.30-5.30 or by appt MIN: £100 MAX: £70,000 PERIOD: 18th-19th century SPECIALIST: Dining furniture, upholstery GENERAL: Good all round selection, restoration & upholstery service.

**AJ Ponsford Antiques**, 51-53 Dollar Street, GL7 2AS TEL: 652355 PARKING: Medium OPEN: Mon-Fri 8-5.30 MIN: £50 MAX: £15,000 PERIOD: 18th-20th century SPECIALIST: Faux books GENERAL: Oak, walnut, mahogany, rosewood furniture OTHER INFO: Restorations in own workshops. All furniture in good condition.

**Rankine Taylor Antiques**, 34 Dollar Street, GL7 2AN TEL: 652529 ASSNS: LAPADA, CADA PARKING: Own carpark OPEN: Mon-Sat 9-5.30 MIN: £15 MAX: £30,000 PERIOD: 17th-19th century, a few earlier items SPECIALIST: 17th century oak, 18th century walnut & mahogany GENERAL: Silver, glass, rare objects OTHER INFO: 7 antique shops in one street, north of the 13th century church. Stratton House Hotel, ° mile from market place on Gloucester Road, several hotels around town centre. Harry Hare's Brasserie, open all day for meals, opposite side of church.

**Silver Street Antiques & Things,** 9 Silver Street, GL7 2BJ TEL: 641600 PARKING: Difficult OPEN:

10-5.30, Fri 9-5.30 MIN: £5 MAX: £800 PERIOD: 19th & 20th century GENERAL: Ephermera, dressers. OTHER INFO: Antiques fair in Corn Hall every Fri, auctions held 3 Fridays each month.

**William H Stokes**, The Cloisters, 6-8 Dollar Street, GL7 2AJ TEL: 653907 FAX: 640214 ASSNS: BADA PARKING: Easy OPEN: Mon-Fri 9.30-5.30, Sat 9.30-4.30 MIN: £100 MAX: £20,000 PERIOD: 17th-18th century SPECIALIST: Early oak furniture, brass, textiles OTHER INFO: Harry Hare's & Tatyan Chinese restaurant.

**Waterloo Antiques**, 20 The Waterloo, GL7 2PZ TEL: 644887 PARKING: Easy OPEN: Seven days 10-5 MIN: £3 MAX: £3,000 PERIOD: 17th-20th century GENERAL: English & Continental pine. Mahogany, elm, oak, walnut country furniture, silver, porcelain & decorative pieces OTHER INFO: Our warehouse 5 min drive where further unrestored stock may be seen.

**Bernhard Weaver**, 28 Gloucester St, GL7 2DH TEL: 652055 ASSNS: CADA PARKING: Easy OPEN: Mon-Fri 9-6, Sat 9-1, MIN: £25 MAX: £20,000 PERIOD: 18th-20th century SPECIALIST: Oak & mahogany furniture GENERAL: Metamorphic/dual-purpose furniture OTHER INFO: Shipping arrangements co-ordinated.

## CRICKLADE (01793)

**Edred Gwilliam,** Candletree House, Bath Road, SN6 6AX TEL: 750241 FAX: 750359 PARKING: Own carpark OPEN: By appt MIN: £100 MAX: £10,000+ PERIOD: 17th-19th century SPECIALIST: Arms & armour.

## FAIRFORD (01285)

**Blenheim Antiques**, Market Place, GL7 4AB TEL: 712094 ASSNS: CADA PARKING: Easy OPEN: Mon-Sat 9-6 MIN: £30 MAX: £3000 PERIOD: 17th-19th century GENERAL: Town & country furniture OTHER INFO: Opposite Bull Hotel (coaching inn with trout fishing). 15th century church with medieval glass & early choir stalls.

**Cirencester Antiques**, High Street, GL7 4AB TEL: 713774 FAX: 713324 ASSNS: CADA PARKING: Own carpark OPEN: Mon-Sat 9-5.30 MIN: £50 MAX: £50,000 PERIOD: 17th-19th century SPECIALIST: Fine furniture, works of art OTHER INFO: Our sister shop, Gloucester House Antiques, close by for country antiques.

**Gloucester House Antiques Ltd**, Market Place, GL7 4AB TEL: 712790 FAX: 713324 ASSNS: CADA PARKING: Own carpark OPEN: Mon-Sat 9-5.30 MIN: £2 MAX: £16,000 PERIOD: 18th-19th century SPECIALIST: French & English country furniture GENERAL: Pottery, faïence, decorative pieces.

## LECHLADE-ON-THAMES (01367)

**Antiques Etcetera**, High Street, GL7 3AD TEL: 252567 PARKING: Medium OPEN: Mon-Wed, Fri, Sat 10-5 MIN: £5 MAX: £1500 PERIOD: 18th-19th century SPECIALIST: Good smalls GENERAL: Country effects & furniture OTHER INFO: Lechlade is last navigable point on R. Thames, and as such, is a small & busy place.

**Apsley House Antiques Centre,** Market Place, GL7 3AD TEL: 253697 PARKING: Easy OPEN: 7 days 10-5.30 MIN: £2 MAX: £3000 PERIOD: 18th-20th century GENERAL: Silver, clocks, books, metalware, pictures, furniture, etc.

**Gerard Campbell**, Maple House, Market Place, GL7 3AB TEL: 252267 PARKING: Easy OPEN: By appt only PERIOD: 18th-19th century. SPECIALIST: Biedermeier period Viennese regulators GENERAL: Clocks & paintings OTHER INFO: Lechlade is the first point of navigation on R. Thames, 50+ miles upstream from the capital.

**D'Arcy Antiques**, High Street, GL7 3AE TEL: 252471 PARKING: Easy OPEN: Mon-Sat 10.30-5 MIN: £1 MAX: £2000 PERIOD: 19th-20th century GENERAL: 1000 sq ft of furniture, glass, brass, china & furniture. Watercolours, prints also stocked.

**Greystones**, High Street, GL7 3AE TEL: 253140 PARKING: Medium OPEN: 10-5 MIN: £10 MAX: £1000 PERIOD: 19th-20th century GENERAL: Smalls, silver, plate, country furniture OTHER INFO: William Morris's Kelmscot Manor, New Inn.

**Lechlade Antiques Arcade**, 5-7 High Street TEL: 252832 PARKING: Own carpark OPEN: seven days 10-6 MIN: £1 MAX: £500 PERIOD: 19th-20th century GENERAL: Books, architectural items, collectables, furniture, kitchenalia, etc. OTHER INFO: Good restaurants, plenty of B&B, riverside walks, hotels & moorings.

**Mark A Serle Antiques & Restoration**, 6 Burford Street, GL7 3AP TEL: 253145 PARKING: Easy OPEN: Mon-Fri 9.30-5, Sat 9-1MIN: £1 MAX: £1000 PERIOD: 19th-20th century SPECIALIST: Old woodworking tools GENERAL: Militaria, brass hardware, rural implements & other collectables

OTHER INFO: I'm known as Mr Collectable & Useable.

**Swan Antiques Centre**, Burford Street, GL7 3AP TEL: 252944 PARKING: Own carpark OPEN: Mon-Sat 10.30-4.30 MIN: £2 MAX: £1000 PERIOD: 19th-20th century SPECIALIST: Doulton, Wedgewood, Staffordshire figures GENERAL: Ceramics, glass, jewellery, books, furniture, collectables OTHER INFO: Coaching Inn, The Swan, next door.

**Peter Whitby Antiques,** Ashleigh House, High Street, GL7 3AE TEL: 252347 PARKING: Medium OPEN: 10-5.30 MIN: £5 MAX: £1500 SPECIALIST: Furniture.

## EASTLEACH (01285)

**Mark Carter Antiques**, 5 Macaroni Wood, GL7 3NF PARKING: Own carpark MIN: £100 MAX: £10,000 PERIOD: 17th-18th century GENERAL: Unrestored English furniture.

## FARINGDON (01367)

**Aston Pine Antiques,** 16-18 London Street, SN7 7AA TEL: 243840 PARKING: Medium OPEN: Mon-Sat 9-5 MIN: £45 MAX: £900 PERIOD: 19th century SPECIALIST: Architectural salvage GENERAL: Victorian & Continental pine furniture OTHER INFO: Small market town with folly & cannonball still embedded in church wall.

**La Chaise Antique**, 30 London Street. SN7 7AA TEL: 240427 & mobile (0831) 205002 PARKING: Easy at rear OPEN: Mon-Sat 9.30-5.30 or by appt MIN: £50 MAX: £5000 PERIOD: Late 18th-mid 19th century SPECIALIST: Leather & fabric upholstery GENERAL: Upholstered furniture, mahogany & rosewood items

**.Faringdon Antique Centre,** 35 Marlborough Street, SN7 7JL TEL: 243650 FAX: (01451) 844447 PARKING: Easy OPEN: Tues-Sun 10-5 MIN: £1 MAX: £2000 PERIOD: 18th-20th century SPECIALIST: Funiture, clocks, lace, china, coins & decorative items OTHER INFO: The area's friendliest antiques centre with helpful dealers.

**Faringdon Gallery**, 21 London Street , SN7 7AG. TEL: 242030 PARKING: Easy OPEN: Mon-Sat 9.30-5.30 MIN: £75 MAX: £5000 PERIOD: 19th-20th century GENERAL: Quality watercolours & oils, also work by leading contemporary artists.

## STANDLAKE (0865)

**Manor Farm Antiques**, Manor Farm, OX8 7RL TEL: 300303 PARKING: Own carpark OPEN: Mon-Sat 10-6 MIN: £275 MAX: £1,500 PERIOD: 19th-20th century SPECIALIST: Victorian brass & iron bedsteads OTHER INFO: Rose Revived hotel & restaurant, New Bridge, Standlake, Harcourt Arms restaurant, Stanton Harcourt.

# Middlesex to Oxford

*Oxford*

Starting in the western suburban towns of London, this tour sees a great contrast in scenery, buildings, and human endeavour, from the rounded hills of the southern Chilterns to the great river Thames at its most scenic and civilised. Then there is the power and royalty symbolised by Windsor Castle to the quest for learning and knowledge shown by the Oxford colleges. In between there is the sheer 'Englishness' of the towns and villages on the way.

The first stops are on the edge of London. First is **Staines** where Sir Walter Raleigh stood trial, was found guilty and condemned to death. The trial took place here because London was in the grip of plague. After detouring to **Wraysbury** and **Warfield** and then **Wargrave** the route reaches **Henley-on-Thames**, a popular Thames Valley resort, famous for its regatta held first week of every July. Many Georgian and older houses exist, of particular note is the Chantry House dating back to 1400 which was formerly a school. Fawley Court is another striking building designed by Sir Christopher Wren and built in 1684. Inside the work of Grinling Gibbons can be seen and the beautiful park was designed by Capability Brown. A museum is housed in Fawley Court particularly devoted to documents of the Polish kings, historical sabres and military objects of the Polish army. There are also many classical sculptures, paintings and works of art. Since 1953 the house has been in the care of a religious community, the Congregation of Marian Fathers.

**Reading**, with **Caversham** in its conurbation, is situated on the junction of the Rivers Thames and Kennet and is a busy commercial and university town. There has been a long history, traces of which may still be found, for example, the few remains of the once-famous 13th century abbey where King Henry I was buried. This was so completely destroyed in the Dissolution that little is left apart from the restored abbey gateway. It was once a school and, in 1786, Jane Austen was a pupil. Inscribed on a stone tablet in the former chapter house was the part-song entitled *Sumer is icumen in* written by a monk in about 1240. It was also here that Edward IV made the announcement of his marriage to the hugely unpopular Elizabeth Woodville. Coming to more modern times, Oscar Wilde was imprisoned in Reading where he wrote *De Profundis*

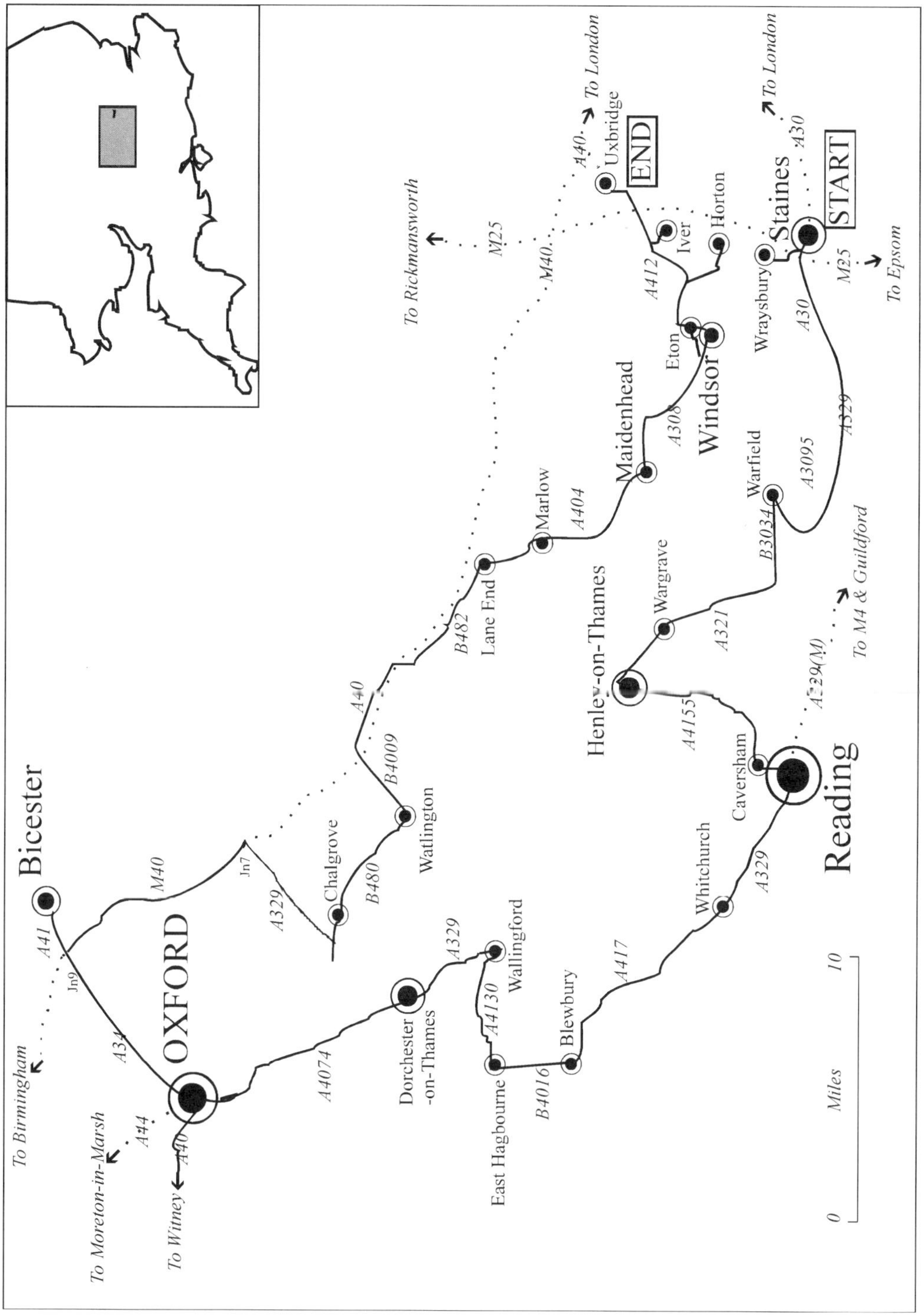
START
Staines
Wraysbury
Horton
Iver
Uxbridge
END
Eton
Windsor
Maidenhead
Marlow
Lane End
Warfield
Wargrave
Henley-on-Thames
Caversham
Reading
Whitchurch
Blewbury
East Hagbourne
Wallingford
Dorchester
-on-Thames
OXFORD
Bicester
Chalgrove
Watlington
To London
To Epsom
To Rickmansworth
To M4 & Guildford
To Birmingham
To Moreton-in-Marsh
To Witney
A30
M25
A412
A40
M40
A308
A329
A3095
B3034
A321
A329(M)
A4155
A404
B482
B4009
B480
A4074
A4130
B4016
A417
A41
A34
A44
Jn9
Jn7
Miles
0
10

and *The Ballad of Reading Gaol.*

Mapledurham House, built of red-brick in the 16th century, stands between Reading and **Whitchurch** just off the A4074. It has its original Elizabethan plaster ceilings and a magnificent oak staircase as well as a fine collection of paintings. There is also a working 15th century watermill producing flour and bran sold in the gift shop. It was the inspiration for John Galsworthy's description of a country house in *The Forsyte Saga.* The house and grounds were used in the films *The Eagle has Landed* and *Class Act.*

Now the tour arrives in **Blewbury** which contains some charming half-timbered houses and a trans-Norman to perpendicular church. Next is the village of **East Hagbourne** and then **Wallingford**, again on the banks of the Thames. This town has several notable features. There are slight remains of a castle, probably Saxon, a 17th century town hall mounted on stone pillars, and a fine bridge, with fourteen arches, crosses the river. It has two interesting churches. St Leonard's, in spite of mid 19th century alterations, still shows some Norman architectural features and St Peter's, rebuilt in 1860, has an unusual openwork spire designed by Sir Robert Taylor in 1777. There are also several notable Georgian buildings in the High Street and Thames Street. There was a Norman castle here, probably built on the site of an earlier one, now little remains after the demolition in 165.and the site is set out as gardens.

Nearby **Dorchester-on-Thames** is an ancient settlement dating back to the Bronze Age. Once a Roman station and then a Saxon town, its main claim to fame is that here Christianity was first introduced into Southern England by St Birinus. The glorious abbey dates mostly from the 12th century although there is small section that survives from an earlier Saxon church. Some of the windows contain 13th century coloured glass and there is a fine Jesse window.

Now to **Oxford**. Do visit the Tourist Information Centre immediately on arrival as it is impossible in the space available here to cover even a small part of the glories of this ancient university town.

The origins of Oxford are definitely pre-Norman with a reference to the town in the Saxon Chronicle of AD912 and it is possible that there was a prosperous settlement for some four to five hundred years before that date. Similarly, the origins of the University are unclear, although it appears likely to have sprung out of monastic schools attached to the priory. There are over thirty University Colleges, one of the earliest is New College founded by William of Wykeham in 1379 and noted for its chapel, hall and cloisters. Another early College was Queen's, founded in 1340 although much of it was rebuilt in the 18th century. University College claims to be the oldest being first endowed in 1249. One of the best known is Magdalen (pronounced Maudlen), founded in 1448. Its wonderful tower dates from the end of the 15th century.

So much is of architectural importance that it is unfair to single out particular buildings. However, amongst the most notable are the Bodleian Library, the Ashmolean Museum which, in 1683, was the first museum in Europe to be opened to the public, and the Sheldonian Theatre designed by Sir Christopher Wren.

The city is well-endowed with museums. Apart from the Ashmolean Museum of Art & Archaeology in Beaumont Street, already mentioned, the others include the Museum of the History of Science, Broad Street, the Museum of Oxford in St. Aldates, the Oxford Story also in Broad Street, the Museum of Modern Art, Pembroke Street and the Rotunda Museum of Antique Dolls' Houses in Grove House, Iffley Turn.

From Oxford 13 miles north east via the A34, is **Bicester,** (pronounced Bister), with its notable market place and medieval church. Just a few hundred yards outside (south) there is the Bicester Outlet Shopping Village complex, newly built as a 'village' with over 50 top London brands of clothing etc sell at discount prices - well worth a visit.

Next take the nearby M40 (Jn 9) south east to Jn 7 and then the A329 southwest, via Stadhampton, to the small village of **Chalgrove**. This was the scene of a Civil War battle in 1643 in which John Hampden was fatally wounded. Iit could be said that he was a catalyst in bringing about

the Civil War. His refusal to pay a King's tax, the so called Ship Money and the court case which went against him, crystallised the sense of grievance at the King's autocratic rule. John Hampden was also one of the five Members of Parliament that King Charles I sought to arrest when he went in person with his swordsmen to Parliament but the five had been warned and were not there. The outrage that this episode provoked caused Charles to withdraw from London to Hampton Court. The next time he saw London was at his trial and execution. A monument commemorates John Hampden's death in the village.

Nearby **Watlington**, at the foot of the Chiltern escarpment, contains several Georgian houses as well as the market hall which dates from 1664. The splendid viewpoint of Watlington Hill, rising to 800 feet, stands about a mile and a half south east and gives good views of the surrounding area. Continuing along the B482, **Lane End** is next and then the Thames-side town of **Marlow** which contains many charming Georgian buildings. The poet, Shelley, wrote the *Revolt of Islam* in a house in West Street and Mary Shelley wrote *Frankenstein* in the same house. The Old Parsonage and Deanery were once part of a great 14th century house and parts of the original building have survived. Moving on, the popular, pretty Thames-side town of **Maidenhead** is next. Amongst the more interesting features are a railway bridge built in 1838 by Isambard Kingdom Brunel which spans the river, 17th century almshouses and the renowned beauty spot, Boulter's Lock, a mile upriver.

The tour now comes to **Eton** and **Windsor.** Divided by the Thames, Eton has its famous school and Windsor its castle. They are connected by an 18th century bridge in Eton High Street. Eton College was founded in 1440 by Henry VI. Some of present buildings have survived from the 15th century including the kitchen, College Hall and part of the cloisters. The impressive Lupton's Tower was built in 1520. Over the centuries Eton has provided the nation with the men of power.

Windsor is dominated by its castle. There was a Saxon palace at Old Windsor but William the Conquerer decided to build a castle on top of a hill overlooking the river about two miles away. By 1086 the castle was listed in the Domesday Book. At nearby Runnymede, in June 1215,

King John put his seal to the Magna Carta. Although the barons, who had forced this on him, were principally concerned with their own interests, Magna Carta enshrined, for the first time, a citizen's rights before the law. The 39th article stated, "No free man shall be arrested or imprisoned or dispossessed or outlawed or harmed in any way save by the lawful judgement of his equals under the law of the land. Justice will not be sold to any man nor will it be refused or delayed."

The castle continued in royal use. Edward III made it his principal residence, building the Round Tower in 1348 and making alterations in other parts of the castle. As well as the residence of the Kings of England, Windsor Castle was used for keeping eminent prisoners, for example, David Bruce, King of Scotland, and John, King of France in the 14th century. During the Civil War, the castle was held by Parliament and many of its treasures were melted down.

Today some areas of the castle are open to the public: the famous State Apartments (only when the Queen is not in residence), Queen Mary's Dolls' House and the Exhibition of the Queen's Presents and Royal Carriages. St George's Chapel is a building of particular note with a magnificent perpendicular structure displaying fine fan vaulting. In the choir are the stalls and brasses of Garter Knights, and many royal tombs include those of Henry VIII, Charles I and Edward VII. Also nearby is the Albert Memorial Chapel, originally built by King Henry VII but now used to commemorate Queen Victoria's beloved Albert.

In the Home Park of Windsor Castle stands Frogmore House, also open to the public at certain times (check before visiting). Built in the latter part of the 17th century, it was the home of Queen Charlotte and Queen Victoria's mother, the Duchess of Kent. Now it has been restored and many of the original contents returned.

After leaving Windsor the tour continues through **Horton, Iver** and finally **Uxbridge.** This is a very modern looking town with ancient roots. Situated on the River Colne, only as a hamlet at the time of the Domesday Book by the 12th century it had emerged as the local market town. By the beginning of the 17th century Uxbridge was the main marketplace for the region's corn and flourmills stood alongside the river. There was a meeting held at the Treaty House here in 1645 between Royalist and Parliamentary representatives to discuss a treaty between the two factions. The building was largely rebuilt in the 18th century.

## ANTIQUE DEALERS

### STAINES (01784)

**KW Dunster Antiques**, 23 Church Street, TW18 4EN TEL: 453297 PARKING: Easy OPEN: 9-5, closed Thurs & Sun PERIOD: 19th-20th century GENERAL: Wide range of interesting antiques.

### WRAYSBURY (01784)

**Wyrardisbury Antiques,** 23 High Street, TW19 5DA TEL: 483225 PARKING: Easy OPEN: 10-5, closed Mon MIN: £75 MAX: £5000 PERIOD: 18th-19th century SPECIALIST: Clocks & clock repairs GENERAL: Small furniture, barometers.

### WARFIELD (01344)

**Moss End Antique Centre**, Moss End (A3095), RG12 6ES TEL: 861942 PARKING: Own carpark OPEN: Tues-Sun 10.30-5 MIN: £1 MAX: £5000 PERIOD: 18th-20th century SPECIALIST: Large furniture, oak mahogany & walnut GENERAL: China, silver, prints, clocks OTHER INFO: Over 6000 sq ft in 19th century barn, coffee shop with home made food, behind first class garden centre.

### WARGRAVE (01734)

**Wargrave Antiques**, 66 High Street TEL: 402914

PARKING: Easy OPEN: Wed-Sun 10-5.30 MIN: £1 MAX: £1000 PERIOD: 19th-20th century GENERAL: General antiques.

## HENLEY-ON-THAMES (01491)

**Cobwebs,** 12A Friday Street TEL: 411486 PARKING: Medium OPEN: Mon-Sat 10-6, Sun 12-5 MIN: £2 MAX: £600 PERIOD: 19th-20th century GENERAL: Small furniture, silver, tapestry, quilts.

**The Country Seat**, Huntercombe Manor Barn, RG9 5RY TEL: 641349 FAX: 641533 ASSNS: BADA, LAPADA, TVADA, CINOA PARKING: Own carpark OPEN: Mon-Sat 9-5.30 MIN: £10 MAX: £100,000 PERIOD: 17th-19th century SPECIALIST: Signed 19th century furniture, garden ornaments, furniture & statuary, panelled rooms.

**Friday Street Antique Centre,** 2 Friday Street, RG9 1AH TEL: 574104 PARKING: Easy weekdays OPEN: Mon-Sat 9.30-5.30, Sun 11-5 MIN: £1 MAX: £1,000 PERIOD: 19th-20th century GENERAL: 20 dealers selling a wide variety.

**Henley Antiques Centre**, Rotherfield Arcade, 2-4 Reading Road, RG9 1AG TEL & FAX: 411468 PARKING: Easy OPEN: Mon-Sat 9.30-6, Sun 12-6 MIN: £1 MAX: £1500 PERIOD: 17th-20th century GENERAL: Furniture, silver, porcelain, prints.

**Barry Keene Gallery**, 12 Thameside, RG9 1BH TEL: 577119 ASSNS: FATG, TVADA PARKING: Medium OPEN: Mon-Sat 9.30-5.30, Sun 10-5.30 MIN: £15 MAX: £15,000 PERIOD: 18th-20th century SPECIALIST: English watercolours GENERAL: Paintings, etchings, prints, sculpture.

**RJ Kingston Antiques**, 95 Bell Street, RG9 2BD TEL: 574535 ASSNS: BADA, TVADA PARKING: Easy OPEN: Mon-Sat 9.30-5 PERIOD: 18th-19th century SPECIALIST: Period furniture & associated antiques.

**Thames Gallery**, Thames Side, RG9 2LJ TEL: 572449 FAX: 410273 ASSNS: TVADA PARKING: Medium OPEN: Mon-Sat 10-1, 2-5 MIN: £25 MAX: £3500 PERIOD: 18th-20th century SPECIALIST: Silver & Sheffield plate.

**Thames Oriental Rug Co**, 48-56 Reading Road, RG9 1AG TEL: 574676 FAX: 577877 ASSNS: National Carpet Cleaners Assn, GMC PARKING: Own carpark OPEN: Mon-Fri 9-5, Sat 9-12.30 MIN: £15 PERIOD: 19th-20th century SPECIALIST: Antique Oriental carpets GENERAL: Modern & semi-antique rugs, needlework.

**Richard Way Bookseller,** 54 Friday Street, RG9 1AH TEL: 576663 ASSNS: ABA PARKING: Own carpark OPEN: 10-5.30 MIN: 50p MAX: £500 PERIOD: 17th-20th century SPECIALIST: River Thames & rowing GENERAL: Most subjects.

## CAVERSHAM (01734)

**The Clock Workshop**, 17 Prospect Street, RG4 8JB TEL: 470741 FAX: 474194 ASSNS: BHI, TVADA PARKING: Own carpark OPEN: Mon-Fri 9.30-5.30, Sat 10-1 MIN: £200 PERIOD: 18th-19th century SPECIALIST: English longcases GENERAL: French clocks, including carriage, bracket clocks, barometers.

## READING (01734)

**PD Leatherland Antiques**, 68 London Street, RG1 4SQ TEL: 581960 ASSNS: TVADA PARKING: Own carpark OPEN: Mon-Sat 9-5 MIN: £5 MAX: £4,500 SPECIALIST: 19th century furniture GENERAL: China & small collectables, silver + plate, furniture from 18th century to 1920 OTHER INFO: Several excellent new hotels.

**Graham Gallery**, Highwoods, Burghfield Common, RG7 3BG TEL: 832320 FAX: 831070 PARK-

ING: Own carpark OPEN: Anytime by appt MIN: £50 MAX: £2000 PERIOD: 19th-20th century GENERAL: Watercolours, oils & prints (mainly landscapes of Britain) OTHER INFO: 3 miles from M4 & 30 mins from Heathrow. Highwoods also listed in *Best B&B's in the World.*

**The Reading Emporium,** 1A Merchants Place, off Friar Street, RG1 1DT TEL: 590290 PARKING: Medium OPEN: 10.30-4.30 PERIOD: 18th-20th century GENERAL: Antiques, collectables, furniture, jewellery, etc OTHER INFO: Close to town centre, bus & train stations.

## WHITCHURCH (01734)

**Nicholas Sibley,** High Street, RG8 7EX TEL: 843286 ASSNS: TVADA PARKING: Easy OPEN: Mon-Sat 10-6 MIN: £500 MAX: £10,000 PERIOD: 18th-19th century SPECIALIST: Georgian furniture, Arts & Crafts OTHER INFO: Cross from Whitchurch to Pangbourne via historic toll bridge.

## BLEWBURY (01235)

**Blewbury Antiques**, London Road, OX11 9NX TEL: 850366 PARKING: Own carpark OPEN: 6 days 10-6, closed Tues MAX: £1000 PERIOD: 19th-20th century GENERAL: Books, antiques & collectables OTHER INFO: Old village on the edge of the Downs, thatched cottages, cob walls, 4 pubs.

## EAST HAGBOURNE (01235)

**Craig Barfoot,** Tudor House, OX11 9LR TEL: 818968 PARKING: Easy OPEN: By appt MIN: £500 MAX: £5500 PERIOD: 18th-19th century SPECIALIST: Longcase & other clocks.

**Kingholm Barn Gallery & EM Lawson & Co,** Kingsholm, OX11 9LN TEL: 818898 & 812033 ASSNS: FATG, ABA PARKING: Own carpark OPEN: 9-6 PERIOD: 17th-20th century GENERAL: Prints & picture framing, books.

## WALLINGFORD (01491)

**John Charles Antiques & Fine Art,** 20 High Street, OX10 0BP TEL: 825200 FAX: 825544 ASSNS: TVADA, LAPADA PARKING: Easy OPEN: 9.30-5.30 MIN: £50 MAX: £12,000 PERIOD: 17th-early 20th century SPECIALIST: Furniture GENERAL: Oils, watercolours, prints, clocks, chandeliers, metalware, etc.

**De Albuquerque Antiques**, 12 High Street, OX10 0BP TEL: 832322 ASSNS: TVADA PARKING: Easy OPEN: Mon-Sat 10-5 MIN: £10 MAX: £5000 PERIOD: 18th-19th century GENERAL: Furniture, paintings & objects OTHER INFO: We have one of the largest medieval castles in England.

**The Lamb Antiques Arcade**, High Street TEL: 835166 PARKING: Easy OPEN: Mon, Tues, Thurs, Fri 10-5, Wed 10-4, Sat 10-5.30 PERIOD: 17th-20th century GENERAL: 25+ shops & showcases offering furniture, porcelain, silver, jewellery, brass bedsteads, pictures, books & crafts OTHER INFO: The Lamb itself is a 16th century coaching inn.

**Lin & Chris O'Donnell Antiques**, 26 High Street, OX10 0BU TEL: 839332 PARKING: Easy OPEN: Mon-Sat 10-1, 2-5 MIN: £1 MAX: £2000 PERIOD: 18th-20th century SPECIALIST: Maps, clocks GENERAL: Silverplate & inexpensive jewellery, furniture, worldwide curios, pine, kitchenalia, rugs.

**Pennyfarthing Antiques,** 48 The Street, Crowmarsh, OX10 8EA TEL: 837470 PARKING: Easy OPEN: Mon-Sat 10-5.30 MIN: 50p MAX: £4500 PERIOD: 18th-20th century GENERAL: Furniture, porcelain, silver, kitchenalia.

**Summers Davis Antiques Ltd**, Calleva House, 6 High Street, OX10 0BP TEL: 836284 FAX: 833443 ASSNS: BADA, LAPADA, CINOA, TVADA PARKING: Own carpark (in castle gates opposite) OPEN: Mon-Fri 8.30-5.30, Sat 9-5, Sun 11-5 MIN: £25 MAX: £50,000 PERIOD: 18th-19th century SPECIALIST: English & Continental furniture, decorative items OTHER INFO: Courier service available. Wallingford could have been as important as London as the Royal Mint was here.

## DORCHESTER-ON-THAMES (01865)

**Giffengate Fine Art Ltd**, 16 High Street, OX10 7HL TEL: 340028 FAX: 341149 ASSNS: LAPADA, TVADA PARKING: Easy OPEN: Mon-Sat 9-1, 2-5 MIN: £30 MAX: £30,000 PERIOD: 17th-19th century GENERAL: English & Continental furniture, lamps, porcelain, pictures.

**Hallidays (Fine Antiques) Ltd**, The Old College, OX10 7HL TEL: 340028 FAX: 341149 ASSNS: LAPADA, TVADA PARKING: Easy OPEN: Mon-Sat 9-1, 2-5 MIN: £10 MAX: £50,000 PERIOD: 17th-19th century GENERAL: General antiques OTHER INFO: One of largest showrooms in the South. Hotels: George, White Hart.

**Shambles Antiques**, 3 High Street, OX10 7HH TEL: 341373 ASSNS: TVADA PARKING: Easy OPEN: Tues-Sun 10-5 MIN: £10 MAX: £4000

PERIOD: 18th-19th century SPECIALIST: Chairs & upholstery OTHER INFO: Directly opposite medieval abbey in an 18th century shambles.

## OXFORD (01865)

**Barclay Antiques,** 107 Windmill Road, Headington, OX3 7BT TEL: 69551 PARKING: Easy OPEN: 10-5.30 MIN: £5 MAX: £750 PERIOD: 18th-20th century SPECIALIST: Lamps GENERAL: Porcelain, glass, metalware, furniture.

**Blackwell's Rare Books**, 38 Holywell Street, OX1 3SW TEL: 792792 FAX: 248833 ASSNS: ABA PARKING: Medium OPEN: Mon-Sat 9-6 (Tues open at 9.30) MIN: £30 MAX: £10,000 PERIOD: 16th-20th century SPECIALIST: Modern Firsts & antiquarian literature, childrens books sets, private pressbook, bibliography OTHER INFO: Our main shop (48-51 Broad Street) handles general secondhand material.

**Reginald Davis (Oxford) Ltd,** 34 High Street, OX1 4AN TEL: 248347 FAX: 200915 ASSNS: BADA, NAG PARKING: Easy OPEN: 9-4.30, closed Thurs MIN: £14 PERIOD: 18th-20th century SPECIALIST: Silver.

**Christopher Legge Oriental Carpets**, 25 Oakthorpe Road, Summertown, OX2 6RU TEL: 57572 FAX: 54877 PARKING: Easy OPEN: Mon-Sat 9.30-5 MIN: £50 MAX: £7500 but most stock £275-£3500 PERIOD: 19th-20th century GENERAL: Old & antique tribal & village rugs, etc OTHER INFO: Brown's restaurant & Old Parsonage Hotel.

**Magna Gallery**, 41 High Street, OX1 4AP TEL: 245805 ASSNS: ABA PARKING: Medium OPEN: Mon-Sat 10-5.30 MIN: £5 MAX: £3000 PERIOD: 17th-19th century SPECIALIST: Oxford topography, English county maps GENERAL: Maps, topographical prints. OTHER INFO: Eastgate Hotel.

**Oxford Antiques**, 10 North Parade, OX2 6LX TEL: 512816 PARKING: Easy OPEN: Mon-Sat 10-1.30 MIN: £1 MAX: £1500 PERIOD: 18th-20th century SPECIALIST: 19th century pottery & porcelain GENERAL: Small antiques OTHER INFO: Fourth generation antique dealers. Area of Oxford where it is still possible to park. Famous Rose & Crown pub

**Oxford Architectural Antiques**, The Old Depot, Nelson Street, Jericho TEL: 53310 PARKING: Own carpark OPEN: Mon-Fri 10-4, Sat 9.30-5 PERIOD: 19th century SPECIALIST: Wide selection salvaged items GENERAL: Architectural antiques, Victorian fixtures & fittings.

**Payne & Son (Goldsmiths) Ltd**, 131 High Street, OX1 4DH TEL: 243787 FAX: 793241 ASSNS: BADA, NAG PARKING: Difficult OPEN: Mon-Sat 9-5 MIN: £50 MAX: £10,000 PERIOD: 17th-20th century SPECIALIST: Antique silver & jewellery OTHER INFO: Small family business, antique silver catalogue available free.

**Sanders of Oxford**, 104 High Street, OX1 4BW TEL: 242590 FAX: 721748 ASSNS: ABA OPEN: Mon-Fri 9-1, 2.15-5.15, Sat 9-1 MIN: £1 MAX: £2000 PERIOD: 17th-20th century GENERAL: Antique & rare prints, maps, fans & cards.

**Titles Old & Rare Books**, 15/1 Turl Street, OX1 3DQ TEL: 727928 FAX: 727928 ASSNS: ABA, PBFA OPEN: Mon-Sat 9.30-5.30 MIN: £1 MAX: £10,000 PERIOD: 17th-20th century SPECIALIST: Environment including natural history GENERAL: Travel, illustrated books, fine bindings, the arts, science & earth sciences.

## BICESTER (01869)

**Causeway Antiques**, The Causeway, OX6 7AN TEL: 248829 PARKING: Easy OPEN: Mon, Wed, Fri, Sat 10-4 MIN: £40 MAX: £750 PERIOD 19th-20th century GENERAL: China, glass, good selection of quality collectables.

## CHALGROVE (01865)

**Rupert Hitchcox Antiques**, Antique Warehouse, Warpsgrove TEL: 890241 FAX: 890241 PARKING: Own carpark OPEN: Mon-Sat 9-5, Sun 2-5 MIN: £25 MAX: £4000 PERIOD: 18th-20th century GENERAL: Furniture only, mostly oak, walnut & mahogany, all in original condition, housed in 6 barns. No smalls.

## WATLINGTON (01491)

**Cross Antiques,** 37 High Street, OX9 5PZ TEL: 612324 ASSNS: TVADA PARKING: Easy OPEN: Mon, Tues, Thurs-Sat 9-6 or by appt MIN: £20 MAX: £5000 PERIOD: 17th-19th century SPECIALIST: Furniture & decorative items, pictures, large items, etc.

**Stephen Orton Antiques**, The Antiques Warehouse, Shirburn Road, OX9 5BZ TEL: 613752 FAX: 613875 ASSNS: TVADA PARKING: Own carpark OPEN: Mon-Fri 9-5 & by appt PERIOD: 18th-19th century GENERAL: Furniture.

**Mark Shanks,** The Royal Oak, High Street, OX9 5QB TEL: 613317 FAX: 613318 ASSNS: BADA,

TVADA PARKING: Own carpark OPEN: 10-5 or by appt MIN: £100 MAX: £40,000 PERIOD: 18th-19th century SPECIALIST: Furniture, mirrors, barometers GENERAL: General antiques.

## LANE END (01494)

**Bach Antiques**, Essex House. Finings Road, HP14 3EY TEL: 882683, 881695 PARKING: Easy OPEN: Thurs & Fri 12-4, Sat 10-5 & by appt MIN: £1 MAX: £5000 PERIOD: 18th-19th century GENERAL: Furniture, pine & decorative items.

## MARLOW (01628)

**Coldstream Military Antiques**, 55a High Street, SL7 1BA TEL: 822503 Fax: 822503 OPEN: by appt only MIN: £5 MAX: £5000 PERIOD: 19th-20th century SPECIALIST: Fine original helmets, headdress, badges of the British Army OTHER INFO: Valuations.

## MAIDENHEAD (01628)

**Miscellanea**, 71 St Marks Road, SL6 2DP TEL: 23058 PARKING: Easy OPEN: Mon-Sat 10.30-5.30 MIN: £1 MAX: £2000 PERIOD: 19th-20th century GENERAL: Antique & later furniture, collectable items & books.

## WINDSOR & ETON (01753)

**Addrison,** 25 Kings Road, SL4 1AD TEL: 863780 PARKING: Medium OPEN: 11-6, sometimes longer MIN: £1 MAX: £800 PERIOD: 19th-20th century SPECIALIST: Bedroom furniture & box beds GENERAL: Pine, oak mahogany.

**Art & Antiques,** 69 High Street, Eton, SL4 6AA TEL: 855727 PARKING: Medium OPEN: 10.30-5.30 MIN: 50p MAX: £600 PERIOD: 18th-20th century SPECIALIST: Jewellery, silver, miniatures GENERAL: General antiques & collectables.

**Guy Bousfield,** 58 Thames Street, SL4 1QW TEL: 864575 ASSNS: BADA PARKING: Easy OPEN: Mon-Sat 8.30-5 MINIMUM: £300 MAXIMUM: £7,000 PERIOD: 18th century SPECIALIST: Only Georgian furniture, pre-1830 OTHER INFO: Thirty feet from Thames Bridge & opposite Wren's Old House Hotel (said to have been built by Wren).

**Claudia Casier Antiques,** 16 High Street, Eton, SL4 6LX TEL: 831039 OPEN: Mon-Sat 10-5.30, closed Wed PERIOD: 17th-20 century SPECIALIST: English & Continental furniture, porcelain.

**Cavendish Fine Arts,** 127/128 High Street, Eton SL4 6AR TEL: 860850 FAX: 833594 ASSNS: LAPADA, TVADA PARKING: Own carpark OPEN: 10.30-5pm daily except Weds afternoons MIN: £100 MAX: £25,000 PERIOD: 18th century SPECIALIST: Good English furniture, etc.

**Country Furniture**, 79 St Leonards Road, SL4 3BZ TEL: 830154 ASSNS: TVADA PARKING: Easy OPEN: Mon-Sat 9.30-6 MIN: £5 MAX: £5000 PERIOD: 18th-19th century SPECIALIST: French provincial furniture GENERAL: Farmhouse tables, painted furniture, antique beds.

**Dee's Antiques**, 89 Grove Road, SL4 1HT TEL: 865627 PARKING: Easy OPEN: Mon-Sat 10-6 MIN: £5 MAX: £1000 PERIOD: 19th century GENERAL: Furniture, pictures etc.

**Eton Antique Bookshop,** 88 High Street, Eton, SL4 6AF TEL: 855534 PARKING: Medium OPEN: Mon-Sat 10-5.30, Sun 12-5 PERIOD: 19th-20th century GENERAL: 6000 books including fine bindings & illustrated, prints & maps OTHER INFO: Book search available.

**Shirley Hayden Antiques**, 79 High Street, Eton, SL4 6AF TEL: 833085 FAX: 540203 ASSNS: TVADA PARKING: Easy OPEN: Mon-Sat 10.30-5.30 MIN: £50 MAX: £5000 PERIOD: 18th-19th century SPECIALIST: Chinoiserie boxes & decorative GENERAL: Mahogany furniture + large selection of smalls.

**Peter Martin Antiques**, 40 High Street, Eton TEL: 864901 ASSNS: TVADA PARKING: Easy OPEN: Mon-Fri 10-1 & 2-5, Sat 10-1 MIN: £50 MAX: £20,000 PERIOD: 18th-early 20th century GENERAL: 3500 sq ft of period, Victorian & later furniture OTHER INFO: Adjacent to Eton College, and in the shadow of Windsor Castle, River Thames.

**Morgan Stobbs,** 61 High Street, Eton SL4 6AA TEL: 840631 PARKING: Medium MIN: £50 MAX: £10,000 PERIOD: 1880-1930 SPECIALIST: Arts & Crafts, Art Nouveau & Deco, furniture & decorative items.

**Mostly Boxes**, 92 High Street, Eton SL4 1AF TEL: 858470 PARKING: Medium OPEN: Mon-Sat 9.30-6 MIN: £10 MAX: £1000 (average £200) PERIOD: 18th-19th century SPECIALIST: Wooden boxes: tea caddies, writing, vanity, apothecary, etc OTHER INFO: Eton High Street is a good general trade call.

**O'Connor Bros**, 59 St Leonards Road TEL: 866732 PARKING: Own carpark OPEN: Mon-Sat 8-5 PERIOD: 18th-20th century SPECIALIST: Antiques warehouse.

**Oriental Rug Gallery,** 115-116 High Street, Eton SL4 6AN TEL: 623000 FAX: 623000 PARKING: Own carpark OPEN: Mon-Sat 10-5.30 MIN: £20 MAX: £5000 PERIOD: 19th-20th century SPECIALIST: Persian Village, Tribal/Turkish GENERAL: Handmade rugs from over 14 countries OTHER INFO: Founder member of BORDA, British Oriental Rug Dealers Assn & TVADA.

**Ulla Stafford,** 41 High Street, Eton, SL4 6BD TEL: 859625 FAX: 833924 ASSNS: BADA, LAPADA, TVADA PARKING: Easy OPEN: Tues-Sat 10-5 MIN: £50 MAX: £20,000 PERIOD: 18th century SPECIALIST: European & English furniture GENERAL: Porcelain, Oriental works of art 1700-1820.

**Studio 101,** Eton High Street, SL4 6AF TEL: 863333 PARKING: Easy SPECIALIST: Furniture.

**Turks Head Antiques,** High Street, Eton, SL4 6AF TEL: 863939 PARKING: Easy OPEN: Tues-Sat 10.30-5 MIN: £5 MAX: £2,000 PERIOD: 18th-20th century SPECIALIST: Antique jewellery, silver, plate, interesting collectables.

**Woodage Antiques,** 4 High Street, Eton, SL4 6UD TEL: 863016 PARKING: Easy OPEN: 7 days MIN: £50 MAX: £9500 PERIOD: 18th-20th century GENERAL: Furniture & decorative OTHER INFO: Close to Eton College attended by Prince William.

## HORTON (01753)

**John A Pearson Antiques,** Horton Lodge, Horton Road, SL3 9NU TEL: 682136 FAX: 682136 ASSNS: BADA PARKING: Own carpark OPEN: By appt only MIN: £500 MAX: £50,000 PERIOD: 17th-early 19th century SPECIALIST: English & European furniture & works of art.

## IVER (01753)

**Yester-Year Antiques,** 12 High Street, SLO 9NG TEL: 652072 PARKING: Easy OPEN: Mon-Sat 10-6 MIN: £1 MAX: £500+ PERIOD: 18th-20th century GENERAL: China, glass, metalwork, pictures & furniture.

## UXBRIDGE (01895)

**Antiques Warehouse,** 34-36 Rockingham Road, UB8 2TZ TEL: 256963 PARKING: Own carpark OPEN: Mon-Sat 10-6 MIN: £1 MAX: £4000+ PERIOD: 19th-20th century GENERAL: Antiques.

# North-Western Home Counties

Much of this tour covers the Chiltern Hills, part of the chalk belt that stretches from Dorset through to Yorkshire. The towns and villages, surrounded by the rounded hills and beechwoods of the area, serve as dormitories for London but most have retained their ancient charm.

**Beaconsfield,** the first stop, has a wide main street, old inns, timbered cottages, and red-brick Georgian houses. In the restored 15th century church lie Edmund Burke, the 18th century writer and politician, and Edmund Waller a poet. The writer, G.K. Chesterton, lived at Top Meadow on the outskirts of the town.

After stopping first in **Penn,** next is **Amersham**. This ancient market town consists of two parts: Old Amersham and new Amersham-on-the-Hill. Old Amersham lies in the valley of the River Misborne and was once a staging post on the coach road running from London to Aylesbury. The old coaching inns of the Crown Hotel, The Griffin, the Red Lion, the Elephant and Castle, The Swan and The King's Arms are evidence of the town's past and all date back from between the 16th to the 18th centuries. The broad High Street was once a coach road and goes past the medieval market place where produce has been sold since the early 13th century when King John granted a charter. There is also an annual two-day fair, held on September 19 and 20, when the stalls and attractions stretch the length of the old town and this has also been held each year since the 13th century.

The old part contains many timbered buildings dating from the the 16th and 17th centuries. Some of these were modernised in the 18th century and given brick fronts so disguising their true age. A notable building is Shardeloes House completed in 1766 and it is an example of some of Robert Adams earliest work.

The newer Amersham-on-the-Hill developed around the railway station, built in the 1890s. Near here is the first house in Britain incorporating the ideas of the architect Le Corbusier. It is call High and Over and constructed of concrete and glass.

Now, via **Chesham** and **Great Missenden**, the tour arrives in Nearby **High Wycombe**, sited on a gap in the Chiltern Hills, is famous for the manufacture of furniture, particularly chairs. The excellent Wycombe Local History & Chair Museum at Castle House, Priory Avenue, looks at the crafts and history of the region. The town also has many notable buildings including a greatly restored 13th century church, Little Market House from 1604 but rebuilt by Robert Adam in 1761, the Guildhall dating from 1757 and the remains of the 12th century St John's Hospital.

One of High Wycombe's most famous former residents was the great British Victorian Prime Minister, Benjamin Disraeli, whose home, Hughenden Manor, stands one and half miles north. Now owned by the National Trust, Hughenden Manor holds many reminders of Disraeli and his wife, Mary Anne. They lived here from 1847 until death; Benjamin Disraeli in 1881 and his wife nine years earlier. In this house they entertained many of the great and powerful figures of the day including Queen Victoria herself. Disraeli and Lord Melbourne were the only Prime Ministers that Victoria honoured with a visit. Amongst the items of interest in the house are an autographed copy of Queen Victoria's only published work, portraits of Disraeli's parents in his study and the black-edged writing paper that he used after his wife's death. The Gallery of Friendship, lining the stairs and hall, is a collection of portraits of statesmen the Disraelis knew.

**Tetsworth**, between Jn 6 & Jn 7 of the M40 is followed by **Thame**, on the River Thames, this town has an exceptionally wide and long main street with buildings that range from medieval timber-framed to Georgian. The largely 15th century church has a 13th century chapel with fine brasses and the 16th century tomb of Lord Williams of Thame and his wife. Moving on through **Bledlow,** next is **Princes Risborough,** standing on the edge of the Chiltern escarpment. There are several picturesque old houses including the 17th century Princes Risborough Manor House which has a Jacobean staircase with an openwork balustrade cut from solid oak (open by ap-

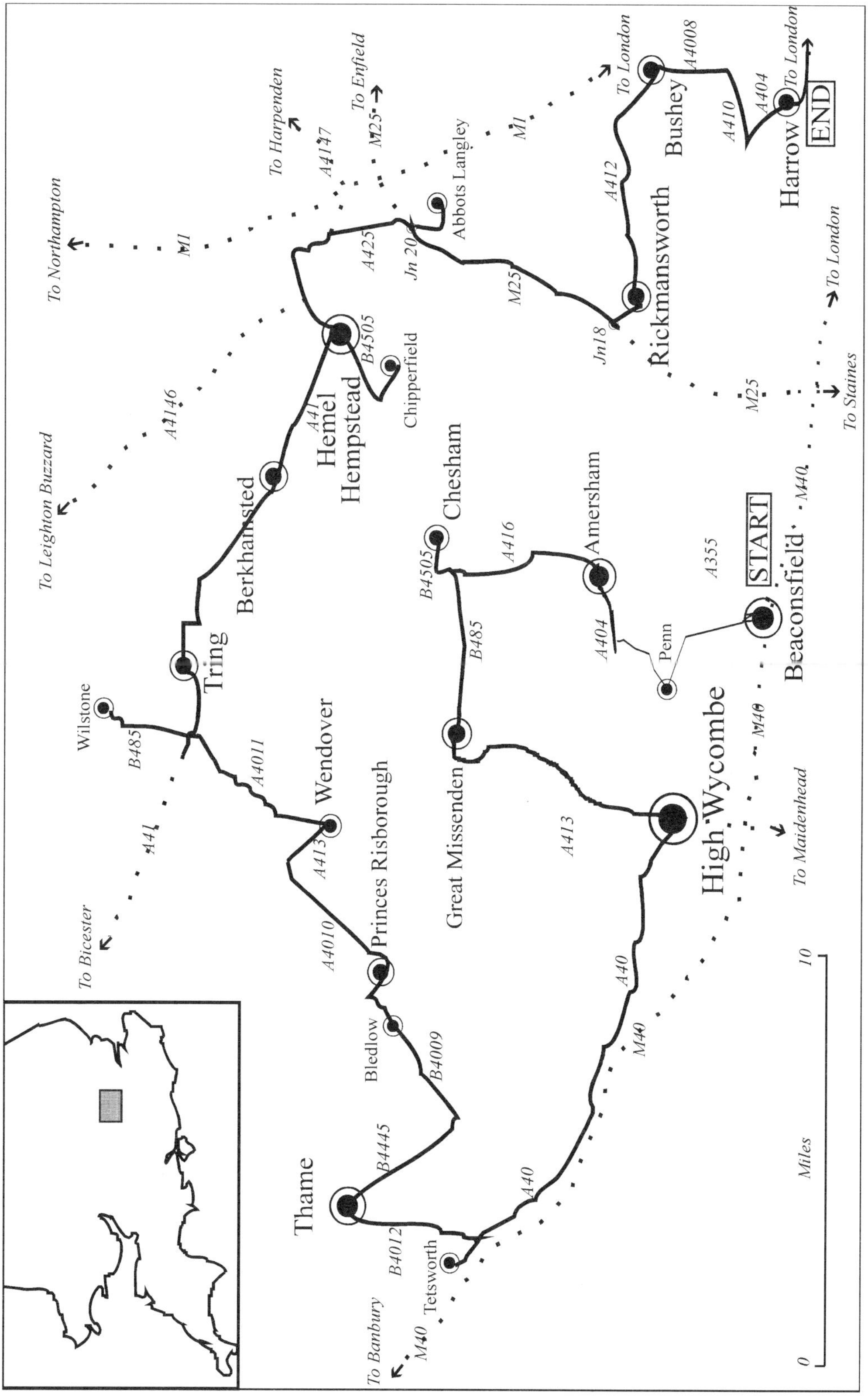
To Northampton
To Harpenden
To Enfield
To London
A4147
M25
M1
Abbots Langley
A4008
Bushey
A4404
To London
A410
Harrow
END
A412
A425
Jn 20
M25
Rickmansworth
Jn18
To London
To Staines
M25
A4146
To Leighton Buzzard
B4505
Chipperfield
Hemel Hempstead
A41
Berkhamsted
Chesham
Amersham
A416
B4505
M40
A355
START
Beaconsfield
B485
A404
Penn
Tring
Wilstone
B485
A4011
Wendover
Great Missenden
High Wycombe
M40
To Maidenhead
A41
To Bicester
A413
A413
Princes Risborough
A4010
Bledlow
B4009
A40
M40
Thame
B4445
A40
B4012
Tetsworth
To Banbury
M40
Miles
0
10

pointment only).

One mile north east is the famous Chequers, donated to the nation during the first world for use as the country home of current Prime Ministers. Three miles further is **Wendover**. Beautifully situated in the Chiltern Hills, this small town includes several Georgian and older houses and the decorated style can be seen in the local church. After **Wilstone** village lying on the Grand Union Canal, **Tring** is next. The Tring Steps are a series of six locks enabling the Grand Union Canal to rise to a height of 500 feet above sea level. Between here and Brentford, on the outskirts of London, the canal passes through 65 locks to achieve this height. The Tring Reservoirs, nearby, form a national nature reserve.

Again on the Grand Union, **Berkhamsted** is an old market town with some surviving buildings of interest. The Saxons submitted to William the Conqueror here after the Battle of Hastings. William's half-brother was given a grant of land and he started work on the castle, ruins of which may still be seen. The castle has been associated with many historic figures. Amongst previous owners have been Katherine of Aragon, Anne Boleyn, Jane Seymour and Queen Elizabeth I before she ascended the throne.

**Hemel Hempstead**, on the River Gage, was the site of a new town started in 1947. However, there has been a town here for centuries and 16th, 17th and 18th century buildings still exist in the old High Street and the parish church is mostly Norman. Moving on via **Chipperfield** and **Abbots Langley**, the route arrives in **Rickmansworth** on the River Colne. The great Palladian mansion of Moor Park stands just a mile south east. It was built in the late 17th century for the Duke of Monmouth and reconstructed in 1720 by Sir James Thornhill and Giacomo Leoni. The estate is the home of the well-known Moor Park Golf Club.

After calling at **Bushey**, the trip end in **Harrow.** Standing high on a hill, the town, with its 13th century spired church, is a notable landmark. Harrow public school is the best known feature. Founded in 1572 by John Lyon, the school has had some very famous pupils: Sir Winston Churchill, Sir Robert Peel, Lord Byron and Anthony Trollope are just a sample.

## ANTIQUE DEALERS

### BEACONSFIELD (01494)

**Buck House Antique Centre,** 47 Wycombe End, HP9 1LZ TEL: 670714 PARKING: Medium OPEN: Mon-Sat 10-5.30, Sun 12-5 MIN: £1 MAX: £5000 PERIOD: 18th-20th century GENERAL: 11 dealers carrying varied quality stock OTHER INFO: Bekonscot Model Village, good hotels & farmhouse bed & breakfast, picturesque part of the old town.

**Grosvenor House Interiors**, 51 Wycombe End, Old Town, HP9 1LX TEL: 677498 ASSNS: TVADA PARKING: Own carpark OPEN: Mon, Tues, Thurs-Sat 9.15-1, 2-5.30 MIN: £50 MAX: £8000 PERIOD: 17th-19th century SPECIALIST: Victorian upholstered furniture GENERAL: Pictures, clocks, fireplaces & porcelain.

**Norton Antiques**, 56 London End, HP9 2JH TEL: 673674 ASSNS: TVADA PARKING: Easy OPEN: Tues, Thurs-Sat 10-1, 2.15-5 MIN: £1 MAX: £5000 PERIOD: 17th-20th century SPECIALIST: Georgian mahogany furniture GENERAL: Clocks, oil & water colour paintings, woodworking tools OTHER INFO: Fine selection of coaching inns & restaurants.

**Period Furniture Showrooms**, 49 London End, HP9 2HW TEL: 674112 PARKING: Easy OPEN: Mon-Sat 9-5.30 MIN: £5 MAX: £3000 PERIOD: 18th-20th century GENERAL: General antiques.

**The Spinning Wheel**, 86 London End, HP9 2JD TEL: 673055 PARKING: Own carpark (1 space) OPEN: Mon-Sat 10-5 MIN: £5 MAX: £2500 PERIOD: 18th-19th century SPECIALIST: Glass GENERAL: Furniture & china OTHER INFO: Interesting street of 17th-19th century houses.

### PENN (01494)

**The Country Furniture Shop,** 3 Hazlemere Road, HP10 8AA TEL: 812244, mobile 0836 710912 ASSNS: LAPADA PARKING: Own carpark OPEN: Mon-Wed, Fri, Sat 9.30-1, 2-5.30, Thurs 9.30-1 MIN: £5000 SPECIALIST: Victorian dining tables & chairs GENERAL: 19th century 'brown' furniture, large stock, 500 pieces. OTHER INFO: Good local pub food, the Royal Standard of England, the oldest pub in England, just 2 miles away. Penn was the home of William Penn, one of the Pilgirm Fathers.

**Penn Barn**, By the Pond, Elm Road, HP10 8LB TEL: 815691 ASSNS: ABA PARKING: Own carpark OPEN: Mon-Sat 9.30-1, 2-5 MIN: 50p MAX: £1000 PERIOD: 19th-20th century GENERAL: Antiquarian books & pictures only OTHER INFO: Situated by the village duck pond.

## AMERSHAM (01494)

**Amersham Antiques & Collectors Centre**, 20-22 Whielden Street, Old Amersham, HP7 0NT TEL: 431282 PARKING: Difficult OPEN: Mon-Sat 9.30-5.30 MIN: £1 MAX: £1650 PERIOD: 19th-20th century SPECIALIST: Diecast model vehicles GENERAL: General antiques.

**The Cupboard Antiques,** Baileys, 80 High Street TEL: 722882 PARKING: Own carpark OPEN: 10-5, closed Fri & Sun except by appt MIN: £100 MAX: £7000 SPECIALIST: 4 showrooms filled with fine Georgian, Regency and Victorian furniture and decorative items.

**Michael Quilter Antiques**, 38 High Street TEL: 433723 PARKING: Easy OPEN: Mon-Sat 10-5 PERIOD: 19th-20th century SPECIALIST: Stripped pine GENERAL: Brass, copper.

**Partridges**, 67 High Street, Old Amersham HP7 0DT TEL: 728452 PARKING: Easy OPEN: Tues-Thurs, Sats 10.30-5, Fri 1-5 MIN: £10 MAX: £1200 PERIOD: 18th-20th century SPECIALIST: Fine porcelain GENERAL: China, glass, Sheffield plate, 18th-19th century framed engravings, mainly people, fashion prints, small furniture OTHER INFO: The Pheasant Inn, Ballinger (very good food 10 mins away), The Eton Wine Bar, Elephant & Castle, Kings Arms & The Crown-all in Amersham.

**Sundial Antiques**, 19 Whielden Street, Old Amersham HP7 0HU TEL: 727955 ASSNS: LAPADA PARKING: Medium OPEN: Mon-Sat 9.30-5.30 (closed Thurs) MIN: £5 MAX: £1500 PERIOD: 18th-20th century SPECIALIST: Metalware, horse brasses GENERAL: General antiques OTHER INFO: Local museum open weekends/bank holidays 2.30-4.30 Easter to October.

## CHESHAM (01494)

**Albert Bartram**, 177 Hivings Hill, HP5 2PN TEL: 783271 PARKING: Own carpark OPEN: By appt MIN: £50 MAX: £8000 PERIOD: 17th-19th century SPECIALIST: Pewter & metalwork OTHER INFO: Illustrated lists of antique pewter issued.

**Chess Antiques**, 85 Broad Street, HP5 2PG TEL: 783043 FAX: 791302 ASSNS: LAPADA PARKING: Own carpark OPEN: Mon-Sat 9-5 MIN: £100 PERIOD: 18th-19th century SPECIALIST: Clocks, furniture OTHER INFO: Restoration.

**Omniphil Prints Ltd**, Germains Lodge, Fullers Hill, HP5 1LR TEL: 771851 PARKING: Own carpark OPEN: Mon-Sat 9-5.30 MIN: £2 MAX: £100 PERIOD: 19th century SPECIALIST: Illustrated London News only.

**Queen Anne House Antiques**, 57 Church Street, HP5 1HY TEL: 783811 PARKING: Easy OPEN: Weds, Fri, Sat 9.30-5 & by appt MIN: £1 MAX: £2,000 PERIOD: 19th-20th century GENERAL: Quality furnishing antiques for the home, also china, glass, Persian rugs OTHER INFO: On Metropolitan Line out of London.

## GREAT MISSENDEN (01494)

**Peter Wright Antiques,** 36b High Street, HP16 0AU TEL: 891330 PARKING: Medium OPEN: 10.30-6 MIN: £5 MAX: £2500 PERIOD: 18th-20th century SPECIALIST: Barometers, clocks, small furniture GENERAL: Wide range including curios OTHER INFO: Restoration & repair service. Ballooning meet held April at nearby Black Horse inn.

## HIGH WYCOMBE (01494)

**Burrell Antiques**, Kitchener Works, Kitchener Rd TEL: 523619 ASSNS: GMC PARKING: Own carpark OPEN: Mon-Fri 8.30-5 MIN: £50 MAX: £3000 PERIOD: 19th century SPECIALIST: Victorian wind-out tables GENERAL: Furniture.

## TETSWORTH (01844)

**Tetsworth Antiques**, 42a Old Stores, High Street, OX9 7DU TEL: 281636 PARKING: Easy OPEN: Tues, Thurs-Sun 11-5 MIN: £1 MAX: £4000 PERIOD: 18th-20th century GENERAL: General antiques and some jewellery OTHER INFO: Good food & B&B at village pub next door.

**The Swan at Tetsworth Antique Centre**, 5 High Street, OX9 7AB TEL: 281777 FAX: 281770 PARKING: Own car park OPEN : Seven days 10-6 MIN: £12 MAX: £5000 PERIOD: 18th-20th century GENERAL: Large dining tables, chairs, sofas, fine bookcases, jewellery, cutlery, silver, porcelain, longcase clocks, antiquarian books, prints, garden statuary, decoratives OTHER INFO: 10,000 sq ft of historic showrooms housed in modernised medieval inn. 30 mins from Heathrow, 20 mins from Oxford.

## THAME (01844)

**Rosemary and Time**, 42 Park Street, OX9 3HR TEL: 216923 PARKING: Easy OPEN: Mon-Sat 9-6 MIN: £50 MAX: £5000 PERIOD: 18th-20th century SPECIALIST: Antique clocks of all types OTHER INFO: Spread Eagle, famous coaching inn.

## BLEDLOW (01844)

**Teatyme Antiques,** The Corner House, Chinnor Road, HP27 9QF TEL: 275220 FAX: 275220 PARKING: Own carpark OPEN: 10-5, closed Tues & Weds MIN: £3 MAX: £5000 PERIOD: 17th-20th century SPECIALIST: Early oak & artefacts GENERAL: Pine, mahogany, kitchenalia & a full restoration service. OTHER INFO: Situated in an old haunted pub opposite Lord Carrington's estate. The interior is laid out just like a house and everything for sale is priced.

## PRINCES RISBOROUGH (01844)

**Well Cottage Antiques Centre**, 20-22 Bell Street, HP17 0AD TEL: 342002 PARKING: Easy OPEN: Mon-Sat 9.30-5.30, Sun & Bank Holidays 1.30-5.30 MIN: £1 MAX: £3500 PERIOD: 18th-20th century SPECIALIST: We are a medium size antique centre with 22 dealers GENERAL: General antiques OTHER INFO: We also have a beautiful conservatory tearoom & garden.

## WENDOVER (01296)

**Antiques at...Wendover**, The Old Post Office, HP22 6DU TEL: 625335 PARKING: Own carpark OPEN: Mon-Sat 10-5.30, Sun 11-5.30 MIN: £1 MAX: £3000+ PERIOD: 18th-20th century (dateline 1930) SPECIALIST: Barometers, taps, lace & linen GENERAL: 30+ dealers in a Tudor building (pine spiral staircase & wall prints, a ghost & Hamish the Scottie dog) with very wide range of town & country items & general antiques OTHER INFO: Hamish the Scottie has been in the newspapers again. First for stealing squeaky toys from the street market, the 2nd time for turning over a new leaf and becoming store detective. He was presented to the Chief Constable of Bucks!

**Bowood Antiques**, Wendover Dean Farm, Bowood Lane (nr. Wendover), HP22 6PY TEL: 622113 FAX: 696598 PARKING: Own carpark OPEN: Mon-Sat 9-dusk (approx 5.30) MIN: £15 MAX: £10,500 PERIOD: 17th-19th century SPECIALIST: Period furniture GENERAL: Porcelain, prints, etc OTHER INFO: Shop is situated off the A413. Showrooms are in the buildings of an old farmhouse.

**Sally Turner Antiques**, Hogarth House, High Street, HP22 6DU TEL: 624402 ASSNS: LAPADA PARKING: Own carpark OPEN: Mon-Sat 10-5.30 MIN: £5 MAX: £8000 PERIOD: 17th-20th century SPECIALIST: Furniture, ceramics, decorative smalls.

**Wendover Antiques**, 1 South Street, HP22 6EF TEL: 622078 ASSNS: LAPADA PARKING: Medium (in lane opposite) OPEN: Mon-Sat 9-5.30 MIN: £25 MAX: £6000+ PERIOD: 17th-19th century SPECIALIST: Portraits, old Sheffield plate, decanters GENERAL: Furniture, pictures, silhouettes, 18th century engravings OTHER INFO: Hotels: Hartnell House, Aylesbury, The Bell (Aston Clinton).

## WILSTONE (01442)

**MICHAEL ARMSON ANTIQUES**
**34 TRING ROAD, HP23 4PB TEL: 890990 FAX: 891167 PARKING: EASY OPEN: 8-5.30, WEDS & SAT CLOSE AT 1PM MIN: £25 MAX: £10,000 PERIOD: 17TH-19TH CENTURY SPECIALIST: GEORGIAN FURNITURE GENERAL: 17TH-19TH CENTURY FURNITURE.**

## TRING (01442)

**John Bly**, 50 High Street, HP23 5AG TEL: 823030 FAX: 890237 PARKING: Easy OPEN: Mon-Sat 9-5.30 MIN: £100 MAX: £10,000 PERIOD 17th-19th century SPECIALIST: English furniture GENERAL: Old fashioned antiques.

**Country Clocks**, 3 Pendley Bridge Cottages, Tring Station, HP23 5QU TEL: 825090 PARKING: Easy OPEN: Mon-Sat 9.30-5.30, Sun 2-5 MIN: £100 MAX: £5000 PERIOD 18th-19th century SPECIALIST: Wall, mantel, carriage & longcase clocks OTHER INFO: Next to Grand Union Canal, near picturesque village of Aldbury.

**New England House Antiques,** 50 High Street, HP23 5AG TEL & FAX: 827262 PARKING: Easy

OPEN: 10-5 MIN: £10 MAX: £7000 PERIOD: 17th-19th century SPECIALIST: Furniture GENERAL: Paintings, silver, glass & decorative items OTHER INFO: Free search & find service.

## BERKHAMSTED (01442)

**Park Street Antiques,** 350 High Street, HP4 1HT TEL & FAX: 864790 ASSNS: BADA PARKING: Own carpark OPEN: Tues-Sat 9.30-5.30 MIN: £50 MAX: £40,000 PERIOD: 18-19th century GENERAL: General antiques.

## HEMEL HEMPSTEAD (01442)

**Abbey Antiques & Fine Art**, 97 High Street, Old Town, HP1 3AH TEL: 64667 ASSNS: LAPADA PARKING: Easy OPEN: Mon-Sat 9.30-5.30 , Weds halfday MIN: £5 MAX: £3,000 PERIOD 18th-20th century SPECIALIST: Jewellery, silver, water-colours GENERAL: Furniture, small antiques OTHER INFO: Valuations, repairs.

**Cherry Antiques,** 101-103 High Street, HP1 3AH TEL: 64358 PARKING: Easy OPEN: Mon-Sat 9.30-4.30, closed Wed pm MAX: £2000 PERIOD: 19th-20th century GENERAL: Furniture, shipping goods, decorative & collectors items.

## CHIPPERFIELD (01923)

**Frenches Farm Antiques**, Tower Hill, WD4 9LN TEL: 265843 PARKING: Easy OPEN: Mon-Sat 11-6 MIN: £1 MAX: £800 PERIOD: 19th-20th century GENERAL: General antiques.

## ABBOTTS LANGLEY (01923)

**Dobson"s Antiques**, 53 High Street, WD5 0AA TEL: 763186 PARKING: Easy OPEN: Mon-Sat 8.30-5.30 MIN: £1 MAX: £1000 PERIOD: 19th-early 20th century GENERAL: Pre 1914 furniture & bric-a-brac OTHER INFO: The only English pope, Pope Adrian IV born here.

## RICKMANSWORTH (01923)

**The Whitestocks Collections Ltd**, The Barn, Whitestocks Farm, Loudwater Lane, WD3 4AL TEL: 710960 FAX: 710960 ASSNS: LAPADA, BADA PARKING: Own carpark OPEN: Thurs-Sat 10-5 MIN: £15 MAX: £6,000 PERIOD: 17th-19th century SPECIALIST: Halycon Days Porcelain GENERAL: English furniture, objets d'art OTHER INFO: Lovely setting in beautiful gardens where the coffee is always hot.

## BUSHEY (0181)

**Country Life Antiques**, 33a High Street TEL & FAX: 950 8575 PARKING: Easy OPEN: Mon-Sat 9-5 MIN: £5 MAX: £2500 PERIOD 19th-20th century SPECIALIST: Antique pine from all over Europe GENERAL: Oils, watercolours, collectables etc OTHER INFO: Very interesting olde worlde shop on 3 floors. Export/shipping arranged.

## HARROW (0181)

**Kathleen Mann Antiques**

**49 High Street, HA1 3HT TEL: 422 1892 PARKING: Own carpark OPEN: Thurs-Sat 9.30-5, Sun 2-5 MIN: £3 MAX: £2000 PERIOD: 18th-20th century SPECIALIST: Harrow paintings & prints GENERAL: Furniture, textiles, ceramics, glass, metalware, etc OTHER INFO: In midst of Harrow School (tours available 7 museum open), several good restaurants, Victorian village atmosphere. I also have an antique cat museum but items not for sale.**

# North London to Hertfordshire

This area, once covered by great forests, is filled with charming towns and villages. Nowadays many of the residents commute into London but their home towns remain largely unspoilt.

The first visit is to **Edgware**, on the northern fringe of London. Situated on the Roman road of Watling Street with ancient origins, the original settlement was started in pre-Roman times about two miles north of the present site. Nowadays Edgware has a conservation area around the war memorial and the 16th century buildings there. A survivor from the great days of coaching inns, the White Hart, continues in business.

Travelling north via **Radlett,** next comes **St Albans.** Once the Roman town of *Verulamium*, the most notable feature of this city is its hilltop cathedral. Built as an abbey church by the Normans in the 11th century, Roman bricks and tiles were used in the main fabric of the building because then local materials were scarce. The abbey was wealthy and the abbots powerful. However, they were unpopular locally and at the Dissolution of the Monasteries almost all of the abbey buildings were destroyed. The church was only saved because the townspeople intended to use it as their parish church. The Lady Chapel was turned into the local grammar school. However, the upkeep of such a large building was too much and it was left to decay. By 1877 it was needed as a cathedral for the counties of Hertfordshire and Bedfordshire but was in a ruinous condition. At this point a millionaire, Lord Grimthorpe, rescued the church. He paid for the restoration of the building but insisted that everything should be done to his own designs. Much of what he did has been criticised and led to the formation of the Society for the Protection of Ancient Monuments. While it might be possible to sympathise with those people who founded the Society, one is left with the question: what would have happened to St Albans Cathedral without Lord Grimthorpe?

In the city of St Albans itself there are many fine and historic buildings. The ancient Fighting Cocks Inn is one of the oldest inns in the country and there are numerous good Georgian houses including Romeland House, one of the finest of these. Several fine churchs also survive: the perpendicular St Peter's with old glass, St Stephen's displaying an inscribed 16th century lectern and St Michael's with its monument to Francis Bacon who died here in 1626 and lived at Gorhambury House. Ruins of the old house survive near the later mansion built between 1777 and 1784. The city has some good museums. The Verulamium Museum stands on the site of the Roman settlement and there are videos of the excavations as well as displays of ordinary life in Roman Britain. Fine mosaics, including one *in situ* in the Hypocaust Annexe, are also exhibited. The St Albans Organ Museum in Camp Road has an exhibition of working mechanical music and the Museum of St Albans, Hatfield Road, displays craft and trade tools.

Passing through **Redbourn** with its Norman church and Georgian houses, the route moves to residential **Harpenden** before arriving in **Luton** in Bedfordshire. Nowadays it is difficult to guess its long history. Evidence has been found of prehistoric settlements in the area and probably there has been one here continuously ever since. Luton Hoo, just south, is a palatial mansion started in 1767. It was designed by Robert Adam and the 1500 acre park was laid out by Capability Brown. Unfortunately the house suffered a number of fires and so was redesigned in 1903. Luton Hoo is said to contain the finest private collection of works of art in the country including the work of Carl Fabergé. There is also the outstanding Russian Collection, consisting of paintings, costume and other items connected to the Russian Imperial family of the Romanovs. This collection is displayed in a Russian Orthodox consecrated chapel dedicated to the memory of the murdered Russian Tsar and his family.

On to **Hitchin**, a market town with considerable charm which was built around its market place. The streets contain Georgian and earlier houses including the 15th century Church of St Mary and the Priory built in 1770 with small parts surviving from an earlier 14th century Carmelite building. Nearby, **Baldock** has several fine Georgian buildings in the High Street.

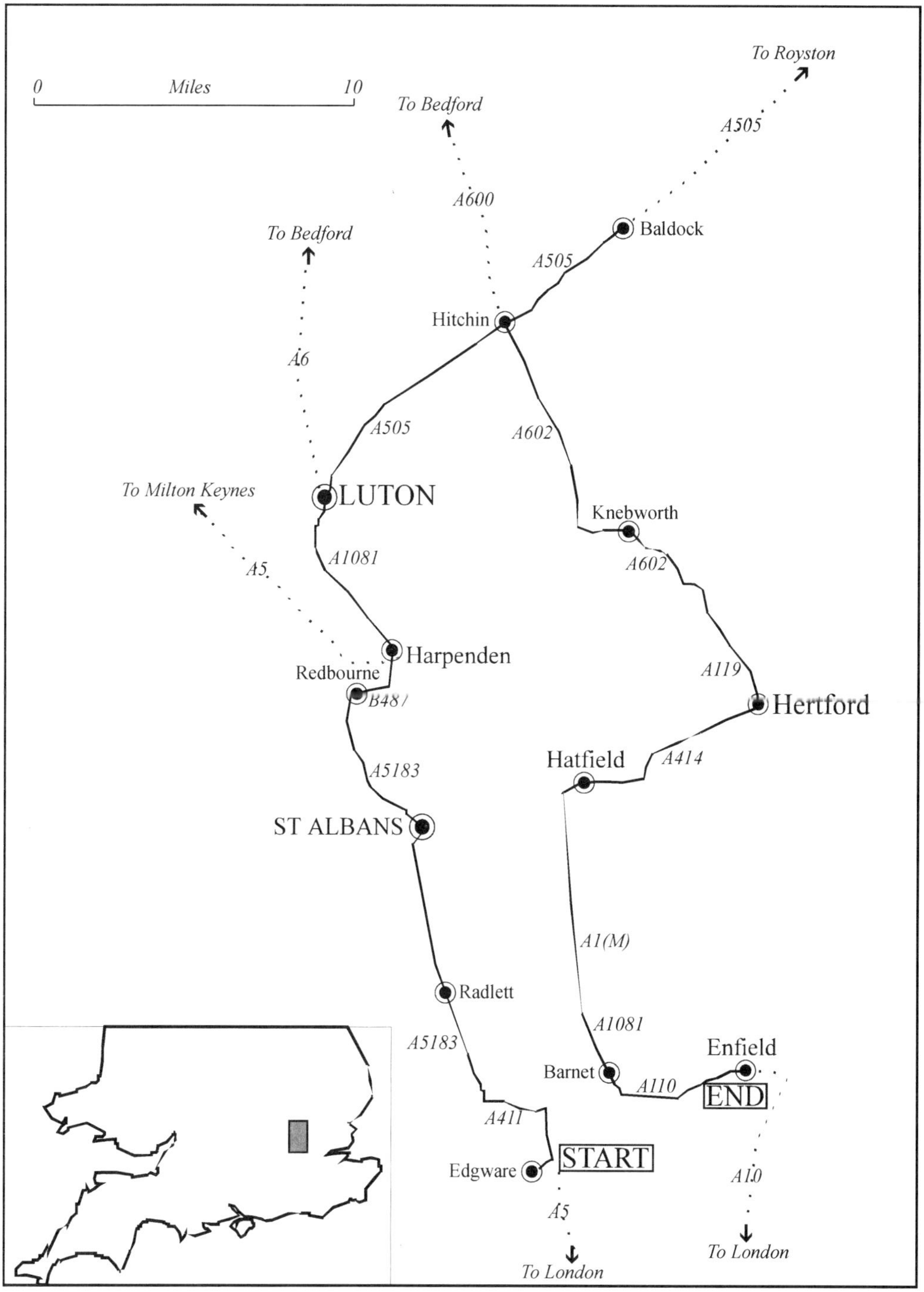
0
Miles
10
To Royston
To Bedford
A505
A600
To Bedford
Baldock
A505
Hitchin
A6
A505
A602
To Milton Keynes
LUTON
Knebworth
A5
A1081
A602
Harpenden
Redbourne
A119
B487
Hertford
Hatfield
A414
A5183
ST ALBANS
A1(M)
Radlett
A1081
A5183
Enfield
Barnet
A110
END
A411
START
Edgware
A10
A5
To London
To London

Turning south, **Knebworth** is the site of another fine country house. This has been owned by the Lyttons since 1490. It was originally a Tudor manor but was redesigned in the mid-19th century in the High Gothic style, fashionable at the time. The beautiful rooms contain portraits, furniture and a collection of manuscripts and letters. The house stands in a 250 acre park in which there are red and sika deer. Sir Edwin Lutyens designed the formal gardens surrounding the house and they include a unique Jekyll herb garden.

The route continues to **Hertford**, standing on the River Lea. The ruins of its original castle, built in the early 12th century, may still be seen. The present castle was built between 1500 and 1800. There are also a number of other fine historic buildings dating from the same period.

Following the A414 the tour passes through Hatfield where the New Town was started in 1947 and has doubled the population of the area. However Old Hatfield retains its charm and historic appearance. The palatial Hatfield House was constructed between 1607 and 1611 by Robert Cecil, first Earl of Salisbury. The Cecils have lived in the house ever since. It contains wonderful collections of rare tapestries, furniture, paintings and armour. In the grounds stands a surviving wing of the old royal palace of Hatfield where Elizabeth I spent much of her youth.

Continuing south to the edge of London, **Barnet** still retains a small town atmosphere. Situated on the Great North Road, it stands on a major route out of the capital, a fact which has contributed to its growth over the centuries. During the Wars of the Roses, the town was the site of a great battle in which the Earl of Warwick, nicknamed Kingmaker, was killed. An obelisk on Hadley Green marks the site of the battle.

The final call is on **Enfield**, another ancient settlement. For centuries a rich agricultural area, the greatest expansion came, like many places on the outskirts of London, with the the railways. Not only did the population increase but also industries moved into the area. Nearby Capel Manor is the only specialist college of horticulture and countryside studies in Greater London. The Georgian manor stands in 30 acres of gardens, many of them with specialist themes. There is also a rare breeds centre within the grounds.

## ANTIQUE DEALERS

### EDGWARE (0181)

**Edgware Antiques**, 19 Whitchurch Lane, HA8 6JZ TEL: 952 1606, 952 5924 PARKING: Easy OPEN: Thurs-Sat 10-5 or by appt MIN: £3 MAX: £1000 PERIOD: 19th-20th century GENERAL: Furniture, paintings, porcelain, silver & plate, bric-a-brac.

### RADLETT (01923)

**Hasel-Britt Ltd Antiques**, 157 Watling Street, WD7 7NQ TEL: 854477 PARKING: Medium OPEN: Mon-Sat 10-5.30 MIN: £1.50 MAX: £700 PERIOD 19th-20th century GENERAL: Stock changeable.

### ST ALBANS (01727)

**By George Antiques Centre**, 23 George Street, AL3 4DS TEL: 853032 PARKING: Medium OPEN: Mon-Fri 10-5, Sat 10-5.30 hours MIN: £2 MAX: £6000+ PERIOD: 18th-20th century GENERAL: 25+ dealers with a good range.

**The Clock Shop**, 161 Victoria Street (on City Station bridge), AL1 3TA TEL: 856633 ASSNS: BWCMG PARKING: Easy OPEN: Mon-Weds, Fri 10.30-6, Sat 10.30-4 MIN: £50 MAX: £6000 PERIOD 18th-20th century SPECIALIST: Clocks, watches, barometers. Repairs OTHER INFO: Open market Weds & Sat.

**Forget-Me-Knot Antiques,** By George Antique Centre, 23 George Street TEL: 853032 FAX: (01923) 261172 PARKING: Medium OPEN: Mon-Sat 10-5, Sun 1-5 MIN: £5 MAX: £300 PERIOD: 19th-20th century SPECIALIST: Jewellery, cufflinks, Victorian name brooches GENERAL: China, furniture, glass, collectables.

**Magic Lanterns**, By George, 23 George Street, AL3 4ES TEL: 865680, 853032 PARKING: Medium OPEN: Mon-Wed, Fri 10-5, Thurs 11-5, Sat 10-5.30, Sun 1-5 MIN: £18 MAX: £1,000+ PERIOD: 19th-20th century SPECIALIST: Over

500 antique, period & decorative light fittings: Converted gas lights, Art Nouveau & Art Deco OTHER INFO: Author of *Lamps & Lighting*. Situated in 15th century antique centre with craft arcade and restaurant. Near the Fighting Cock, one of oldest pubs in England.

**Oriental Rug Gallery Ltd**, 42 Verulam Road, AL3 4DQ TEL: 841046 FAX: 841046 PARKING: Easy OPEN: Mon-Sat 9-6, Sun 10.30-4 MIN: £40 MAX: £15,000 PERIOD 19th-20th century SPECIALIST: Carpets, rugs, kelim, old & new, from Iran, Turkey, Afghanistan, Russia OTHER INFO: 20 mins by train to London. Open Sunday.

**St Albans Antique Fair**, The Town Hall, Chequers Street TEL: 844957 PARKING: Easy OPEN: Mon-Sat 10-4 (admission 20p) 8-4 MIN: £2 MAX: £600 PERIOD 18th-19th century SPECIALIST: Records, books, 1930's jewellery Deco costume GENERAL: General antiques & collectables OTHER INFO: Town Hall is above Tourist Info Centre.

**Stuart Wharton**, 1 George Street, AL3 4EB TEL: 59489 FAX: 55474 ASSNS: NAG, FGA PARKING: Medium OPEN: Mon-Sat 9.30-6 MIN: £10 MAX: £1000 PERIOD some 18th, 19th-20th century SPECIALIST: I only have small stock of small & medium silver tableware, flatware.



## REDBOURN (01582)

**JN Antiques**, 86 High Street, AL3 7BD TEL: 793603 PARKING: Own carpark OPEN: Mon-Sat 9-6 MIN: £1 MAX: £2/3000 PERIOD 19th-20th century SPECIALIST: Furniture & china OTHER INFO: Close exit 9 of M1. Moat House, Markyate, Aubrey Park Hotel, Hempstead Rd. Coffee always on the boil, we also run Harpenden Auctions.

**Tim Wharton Antiques**, 24 High Street TEL: 794371 ASSNS: LAPADA PARKING: Easy OPEN: Tues, Wed, Fri 10-5, Sat 10-4 MIN: £10 MAX: £10,000 PERIOD 17th-19th century GENERAL: Furniture & general antiques.

## HARPENDEN (01582)

**Meg Andrews Antique Costume & Textiles**, 28 Cowper Road, AL5 5NG TEL & FAX: 460107 PARKING: Easy OPEN: Anytime by appt PERIOD: 18th-20th century SPECIALIST: Chinese costume, Arts & Crafts, paisley shawls, English costume for collectors. Archive fabrics OTHER INFO: Luton Hoo, Hatfield House, Verulamium (Roman) Museum in St Albans.

## LUTON (01582)

**Bargain Box,** 4-6a Adelaide Street, TEL: 423809 PARKING: Easy GENERAL: Antiques & general goods.

**Bernadette's Antiques,** 19a Adelaide Street TEL: 423809 GENERAL: Antiques & collectables.

**Denton Antiques,** Rear of 440 Dunstable Road, LU4 8DJ TEL: 582726 PARKING: Easy OPEN: 10.15-4 MIN: £5 MAX: £600 PERIOD: 19th-20th century GENERAL: Shipping furniture, china, brassware & assorted smalls.

## HITCHIN (01462)

**Bexfield Antiques**, 13-14 Sun Street TEL: 432641 PARKING: Medium OPEN: Mon, Tues, Thurs-Sat 9.30-5 MIN: £10 MAX: £2500 PERIOD 18th-20th century SPECIALIST: Silver GENERAL: General antiques OTHER INFO: Sun Hotel.

**Countrylife Galleries**, 41-43 Portmill Lane, SG5 1DJ TEL: 433267 PARKING: Own carpark OPEN: By appt MIN: £50 MAX: £30,000 PERIOD: 18th-19th century SPECIALIST: Garden, flower & landcape subjects.

**Hitchin Antiques Gallery,** 37 Bridge Street, SG5 2DF TEL: 434525 FAX: 441811 PARKING: Medium OPEN: Mon-Sat 10-5.30 MIN: £5 MAX: £3000 PERIOD: 18th-20th century GENERAL: No reproduction OTHER INFO: Small centre.

**Eric T Moore**, 24 Bridge Street, SG5 2DF TEL: 450497 ASSNS: ABA PARKING: Own small carpark OPEN: Mon-Sat 9.30-1, 2.15-5.30 MIN: £1 MAX: £200 PERIOD: 18th-20th century GENERAL: Books, antiquarian maps & prints.

**RJ Perry Antiques Gallery**, 38 Bridge Street, SG5 2DF TEL: 434525 FAX: 441811 PARKING: Medium OPEN: Mon-Sat 10-5.30 MIN: £5 MAX: £3000 PERIOD 18th-early 20th century GENERAL: General antiques & collectables, 8 showrooms, no reproduction OTHER INFO: Delightful market town with many period buildings. Our own dates back to 1580. Excellent selection of shops, hotels & restaurants. Market day Tuesday & Saturday. Full overseas shipping service, furniture & metal restoration.

**Phillips of Hitchin Antiques Ltd**, The Manor House, Bancroft, SG5 1JW TEL: 432067 FAX: 441368 ASSNS: BADA PARKING: Easy OPEN: Mon-Sat 9-5.30 MIN: £500 MAX: £10,000 PERIOD 18th-19th century SPECIALIST: English furniture, mainstream but also including unusual pieces: eg metamorphic, campaign, travelling furniture with makers names, library furniture etc, reference books on furniture & antiques.

**Tom Salisbury Antiques,** 9A Bridge Street, SG5 2DE TEL & FAX: 454274 PARKING: Own carpark OPEN: 10-5 MIN: £5 MAX: £2000 PERIOD: 18th-20th century GENERAL: Furniture OTHER INFO: Several dealers within 500 yards.



## BALDOCK (01462)

**Anthony Butt Antiques**, 7-9 Church Street, SG7 5AE TEL: 895272 PARKING: Easy OPEN: Tues-Sat usual hours or by appt (resident) MIN: £100 MAX: £5000 PERIOD: 17th-19th century GENERAL: Furniture & decorative objects OTHER INFO: Close to the centre of this small market town, near A1 junction.

**Howard Antique Clocks**, 33 Whitehorse Street, SG7 6QF TEL: 892385 PARKING: Own carpark OPEN: Tues-Sat 9.30-5 MIN: £150 MAX: £4,000 PERIOD 18th-20th GENERAL: Clocks: longcase, bracket, wall & carriage.

**Ralph & Bruce Moss**, 26 Whitehorse Street, SG7 6QQ TEL: 892751 PARKING: Own carpark OPEN: Mon-Sat 9-6 MIN: £15 MAX: £10,000 PERIOD 17th-20th century SPECIALIST: Musical boxes occasionally held in stock GENERAL: General antiques OTHER INFO: Historic market town with fine 12th century church.

**Graham Porter Antiques**, 31 Whitehorse Street TEL: 895351 PARKING: Easy OPEN: Mon-Sat 9-5, Sun 11-4 MIN: £5 MAX: £1500 PERIOD 18th-20th century SPECIALIST: Victorian & earlier pine GENERAL: Furniture, clean retail stock OTHER INFO: Many hotels & excellent restaurants.

## KNEBWORTH (01438)

**Hamilton & Tucker Billiard Co. Ltd.**, Park Lane TEL: 811995 FAX: 814939 ASSNS: BSAIF & Billiard Snooker Trade Assn (BSTA) PARKING: Own carpark OPEN: Mon-Fri 9-5 or by appt MIN: £250 MAX: £20,000 PERIOD 19th-20th century SPECIALIST: Billiard tables, dining tables, traditional games GENERAL: Game accessories, chairs etc OTHER INFO: Our showrooms are outside Knebworth Station.

## HERTFORD (01992)

**Beckwith & Son**, S7 St Nicholas Hall, St Andrew Street, SG14 1HZ TEL: 582079 PARKING: Easy OPEN: Mon-Sat 9-1, 2-5.30 MIN: £1 MAX: £10,000 PERIOD 17th-early 20th century SPECIALIST: Furniture & clocks GENERAL: We deal in anything old & interesing except stamps & coins. Very large varied stock OTHER INFO: Shop is very large & fascinating 15th century timbered building near centre town. Excellent B&B: Rachel Savory Tel: 01992 505897.

**Hertford Antiques,** 51 St Andrew Street, SG14 1LR TEL: 504504 FAX: 460648 PARKING: Easy OPEN: 7 days 10-5.30 MIN: £5 MAX: £5000 PERIOD: 18th-20th century GENERAL: Mahogany & country furniture, porcelain, silver, glass, jewellery, treen, etc OTHER INFO: We are an antiques centre of over 50 dealers in a 17th century building next to the church..

**Robert Horton Antiques**, 13 Castle Street, SG14 1ER TEL: 587546 ASSNS: BWCMG PARKING: Medium OPEN: Mon-Sat 9-5.30 MIN: £100 MAX: £4000 PERIOD 18th-19th century SPECIALIST: Clocks, watches, barometers GENERAL: Furniture.

## BARNET (0181)

**C Bellinger Antiques**, 91 Wood Street, EN5 4BX TEL: 449 3467 PARKING: Easy OPEN: Thurs-Sat 10-4 MIN: £20 MAX: £1000 PERIOD: 19th-20th century GENERAL: Furnitures & general antiques.

## ENFIELD (0181)

**Richard Kimbell Ltd**, Country World, Cattlegate Road, Crews Hill, EN2 9DP TEL: 364 6661 FAX: 364 5455 PARKING: Own carpark OPEN: Seven days 9-6 MIN: £1 MAX: £3000 PERIOD: 19th century SPECIALIST: Antique & reproduction pine GENERAL: Country furniture & crafts.

**La Trouvaille**, 1a Windmill Hill, EN2 6SE TEL: 367 1080 PARKING: Medium OPEN: Mon-Tues, Thurs-Sat 9.30-5.30 MIN: £5 MAX: £2000 PERIOD: Late 18th-20th century GENERAL: General antiques OTHER INFO: 1 modern & 3 antique showrooms, Unusual & exclusive gifts housed in 200 year old building overlooking attractive greens & historic Elizabethan Gentlemans Row.

# South Essex

*Paycockes, Coggeshall*

Away from London's northwest sprawling suburbs, this tour passes through the gently undulating countryside north of the Thames Estuary, taking in part of East Hertfordshire and South Essex. The sea has made numerous and often long, intricate inlets in the coastline where some of the coastal settlements were Victorian resorts for work-weary Londoners, others small river ports. The whole route is characterised by the host of quaint timbered buildings and leafy lanes.

Starting in **Chingford**, the route continues to the villages of **Abridge**, just inside the M25, and then to **Blackmore** which has a 12th-15th century restored church. Twelve miles north is **Hatfield Broad Oak** village and then the trip crosses into Hertfordshire at **Sawbridgeworth** which has some medieval to Georgian houses. The following town, **Ware** nine miles east, was a medieval centre for milling and malting. There are a number of historic buildings including the 14th to 15th century church which contains a font dating from 1400. Scott's Grotto, in Scott's Road, has been described as one of the finest grottos in the country. It was built by the Quaker, John Scott and includes a summerhouse and garden.

Still in Hertfordshire, the unspoilt **Much Hadham** has been the manor of the Bishop of London for 900 years. The Bishop's Palace is largely Jacobean and there are Elizabethan and Regency houses in the High Street. Next, **Bishops Stortford** was the birthplace of Cecil Rhodes. The house of his birth, now a Memorial Museum and Commonwealth Centre, is one of the town's interesting and historic buildings. Others include two inns, the Black Lion and the Boar's Heads. The National Trust property of Hatfield Forest lies about three miles east of Bishops Stortford and covers some 1000 acres. This is the remnants of the great Forest of Essex, a royal hunting preserve since before the Norman Conquest. **Stansted Mountfitchett**, Stansted for short, has London's third airport, but also other attractions including a windmill and toy museum.

Following the A120, **Felstead** comes next and is home to a 400 year old public school. and then

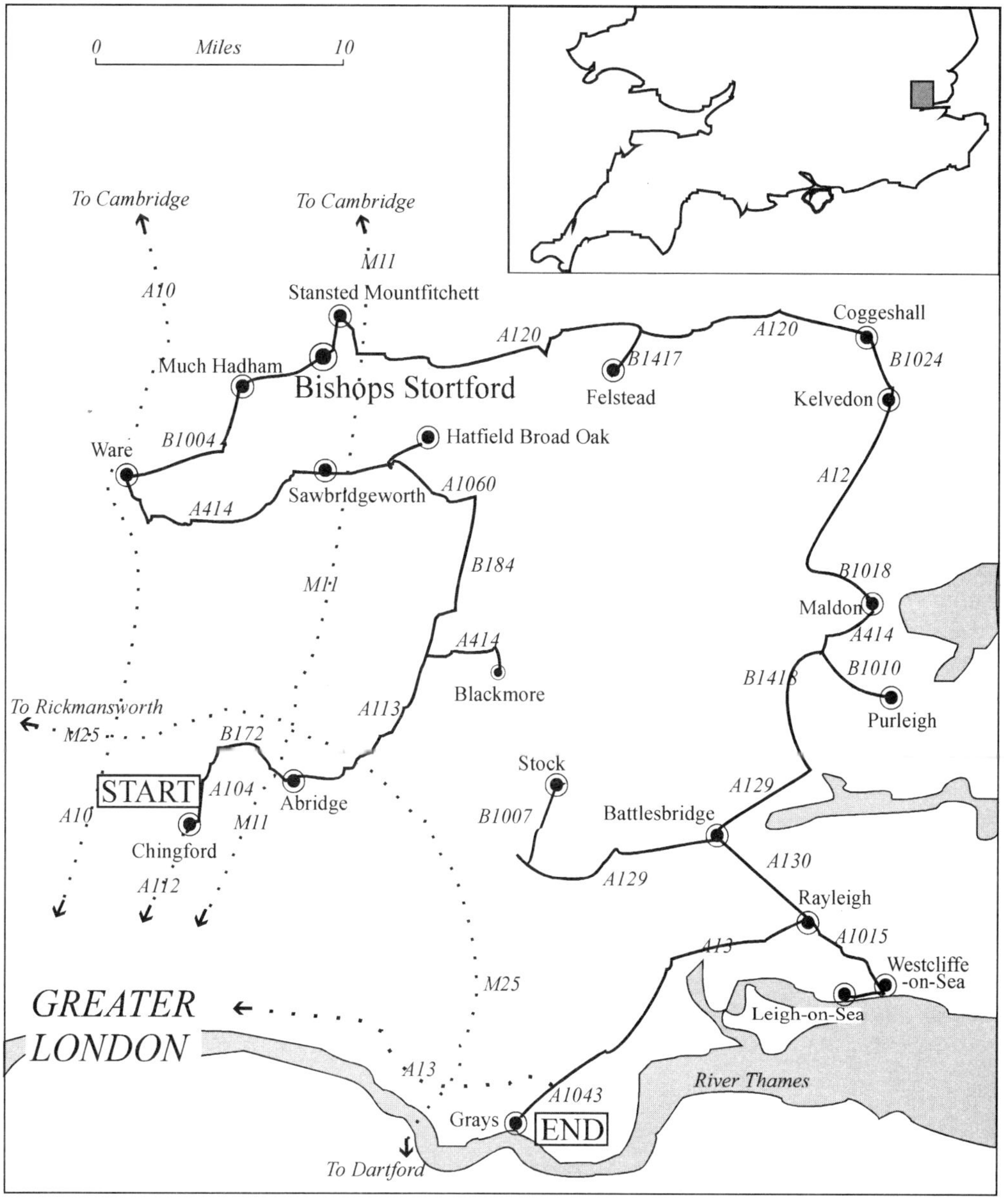


12 miles further on is the charming village of **Coggeshall**, on the River Blackwater. Noted for lacemaking and wool, the wool particularly helped make Coggeshall prosperous in medieval times. A wool merchant, John Paycockes, built the house, Paycocke's, at the beginning of the 16th century. A fine half-timbered house, with a long pink and white, brick and timber facade, an intricately carved beam runs the whole width of the front of the house just above the ground floor windows. From the latter part of the 16th century this building had a series of owners and deteriorated until, in 1890, being in such bad condition, it was sold for demolition. However, the house was saved and at the beginning of this century the Buxton family bought and restored it. In 1924 they gave the house and its garden to the National Trust.

After first visiting **Kelvedon**, the next stop is **Maldon,** on the mouth of the rivers Chelmer and

Blackwater. A very pretty town, well-known for yachting, it has a number of medieval houses in the High Street and the church has a most unusual 13th century triangular tower. Moving on, **Purleigh** has a large vineyard where visitors may buy wine after sampling the vintages. **Battlesbridge**, on the River Crouch, takes it name from a local family, the Batailles, who maintained the bridge, rather than from a more martial history. **Stock**, also reachable by country lanes, has a preserved mill. **Rayleigh** follows and then the trip reaches the coast at **Westcliff-on-Sea**, popular with holiday makers. It is, however, overshadowed in popularity by the next door neighbour, Southend, which is the epitome of a seaside town, with a pier, amusement arcades, cockle and whelk stands, fish and chip shops, etc. The adjoining town of **Leigh-on-Sea** is also a holiday resort, much quieter than Southend of course. In earlier times the inhabitants earnt their living by fishing and smuggling.

*Maldon*

The final visit is to **Grays**, on the Thames Estuary. This ancient town is now largely residential but the Thurrock Museum in the Thameside Complex has displays showing the town's long history and includes a collection of maritime exhibits.

## ANTIQUE DEALERS

### CHINGFORD (0181)

**Nicholas Salter Antiques**, 8 Station Approach, E4 7AZ TEL: 529 2938 PARKING: Own carpark OPEN: 10-5, closed Thurs MIN: £10 MAX: £2000 PERIOD: 19th-20th century GENERAL: Antiques & collectables OTHER INFO: Shop part of Victorian station that Queen Victoria visited, hunting lodge nearby. Good restaurants.

### ABRIDGE (01992)

**Revival**, Coach House, Market Place, RM4 1VA TEL: 814000 FAX: 814300 PARKING: Easy OPEN: Mon-Thurs, Sat-Sun 11-5.30 MIN: £1 MAX: £3000 PERIOD: 18th-20th century SPECIALIST: Clocks & barometers GENERAL: General antiques. Furniture restoration & upholstery

### BLACKMORE (01277)

**Haygreen Antiques**, The Farmhouse, Hay Green Lane TEL: 821275 FAX: 821275 PARKING: Own carpark OPEN: Tues-Sun 9.30-5 MIN: £100 MAX: £1500 PERIOD: 18th-19th century SPECIALIST: Pine furniture GENERAL: Victorian furniture OTHER INFO: 2000 sq ft showrooms in historic listed barns on our estate.

### HATFIELD BROAD OAK (01279)

**Tudor Antiques**, High Street, CM22 7HQ TEL:

718557 PARKING: Easy OPEN: Seven days 9.30-5.30 MIN: £1 MAX: £1000 PERIOD: 18th-20th century GENERAL: Porcelain, china, furniture (wide range). Unusual & interesting items OTHER INFO: We live opposite so easy access out of hours. Good pub/restaurant next door.

## SAWBRIDGEWORTH (01279)

**Herts & Essex Antiques Centre**, The Maltings, Station Road, CM21 9JX TEL: 722044 PARKING: Own carpark OPEN: Tues-Fri 10-5, Sat-Sun 10.30-6 MIN: £1 MAX: £2000 PERIOD: 18th-20th century GENERAL: Antiques & collectables.

## WARE (01920)

**Wareside Antiques,** SG12 7QY TEL: 469434 TEL: 469434 PARKING: Easy OPEN: By appt MIN: £5 MAX: £3000 PERIOD: 17th-19th century SPECIALIST: Furniture.

## MUCH HADHAM (01279)

**Careless Cottage Antiques**, High Street, SG10 6DA TEL: 842007 PARKING: Easy OPEN: Mon-Sat 9-5 MIN: £10 MAX: £1500 PERIOD: 18th-19th century SPECIALIST: Oak & country furniture GENERAL: China, glass, rugs, decorative items OTHER INFO: Henry Moore Sculpture Park 1 mile, Working Forge Museum.

## BISHOPS STORTFORD (01279)

**Northgate Antiques**, Northgate House, 21 Northgate End, CM23 2ET TEL: 656957 FAX: 755873 PARKING: Own carpark OPEN: Mon-Fri 9-5, Sat 9.15-3.30 MIN: £5 MAX: £3500 PERIOD 18th-20th century SPECIALIST: Oils & watercolours GENERAL: General antqiues OTHER INFO: Good hotels: Donn Hall, Watfield Heath, High Wych, Sawbridgeworth.

**The Windmill Antiquary,** 4 High Street, CM23 2LT TEL: 651587 PARKING: Easy OPEN: Sat, for appt phone 01920 821316 MIN: £100 MAX: £5000 PERIOD: 17th-18th century SPECIALIST: Clocks, mirrors, furniture.

## STANSTED MOUNTFITCHET (01279)

**Valmar Antiques**, Croft House, High Lane, CM24 8LQ TEL: 813201 FAX: 816962 ASSNS: LAPADA OPEN: By appt MIN: £100 MAX: £10,000 PERIOD: 18th-19th century SPECIALIST: Furniture, decorative furnishings.

## FELSTEAD (01371)

**Argyll House Antiques**, Station Road, CM6 3DG TEL: 820682 PARKING: Easy OPEN: Mon, Tues, Thurs-Sat 10-5 & by appt (resident) MIN: 5p MAX: £1200 PERIOD: 18th-20th century SPECIALIST: Ephemera, postcards GENERAL: General antiques, collectors items OTHER INFO: Many 12th century houses and large public school is associated with Cromwell & Lord Riche.

## COGGESHALL (01376)

**Antique Metals**, 9a East Street, CO6 1SH TEL: 562252 PARKING: Easy OPEN: Mon-Sat 9-5.30, Sun 11-5 MIN: £10 MAX: £1000 PERIOD: 18th-19th century SPECIALIST: Period & Victorian brass, copper, steel OTHER INFO: One hotel in the town, two bed & breakfast guesthouses and more nearby. Two National Trust properties in the town plus many historic buildings.

**Coggeshall Antiques**, 1 Doubleday Corner, CO6 1NY TEL: 562646 PARKING: Own carpark OPEN: 10-5 MIN: £5 MAX: £5000 PERIOD: 18th-20th century GENERAL: Decorative furniture, paintings OTHER INFO: Opposite White Hart Hotel, renowned for good food.

**Joan Jobson's Antiques**, 5a Church Street, CO6 1TU TEL: 561717 (home) PARKING: Easy Open: Mon-Sat 10-1, 2-5 closed Wed PM MIN: £1 MAX: £200-300 PERIOD: 19th-20th century GENERAL: Quality furniture, small collectables, bric-a-brac etc.

**Lindsell Chairs**, 11 Market Hill, CO6 1TS TEL & FAX: 562766 PARKING: Easy OPEN: Mon-Sat 10.30-6.30 MIN: £110 MAX: £3500 SPECIALIST: Most kinds of seating 1780-1914 GENERAL: Dining & occasional tables. Full traditional restoration (chairs, settees etc).

**Mark Marchant Antiques**, Market Square, CO6 1TS TEL: 561188 PARKING: Easy OPEN: Mon-Sat 10.30-5, Sun 2-5 MIN: £5 PERIOD: 17th-20th century SPECIALIST: Clocks GENERAL: Decorative items OTHER INFO: Market day Thursdays.

**Elkin Mathews Bookshop**, 16 Stoneham Street TEL & FAX: 561730 PARKING: Own carpark OPEN: 9.30-1, 2-4.30 closed Weds MIN: £1 MAX: £3000 PERIOD: 17th-20th century SPECIALIST: Childrens' books GENERAL: All subjects.

**Suffolk Antique Connection,** Scotland Place, Stoke by Nayland, CO6 4QG TEL: 262098 FAX: 263339 ASSNS: LAPADA PARKING: Own carpark

OPEN: By appt PERIOD: 17th-19th century GENERAL: Country furniture, tapestry, portraits & works of art.

## KELVEDON (01376)

**Colton Antiques,** Station Road, CO5 9NP TEL: 571504 PARKING: Easy OPEN: 8-6 MIN: £100 MAX: £10,000 PERIOD: 18th-19th century SPECIALIST: Furniture OTHER INFO: Antique restoration work. Adjacent to railway station.

**Kelvedon Antiques**, 90 High Street TEL: 570557 ASSNS: BADA PARKING: Easy OPEN: Mon-Sat 9.30-5.30 MIN: £20 MAX: £10,000 PERIOD: 17th-early 19th century SPECIALIST: Furniture.

**Kelvedon Art & Antiques,** 2 High Street, CO5 9AG TEL: 573065 PARKING: Own carpark OPEN: 10-5 MIN: £15 MAX: £5000 PERIOD: 18th-20th century GENERAL: Furniture, paintings.

**GT Ratcliff Ltd**, Whitebarn, Coggeshall Road & Menai House, 41 High Street, CO5 9PH TEL: 570234 FAX: 571764 PARKING: Own carpark OPEN: Menai House Mon-Sat 9-5, Whitebarn Mon-Fri 9-5, Sats by appt PERIOD: 19th-20th century SPECIALIST: Lacquer and decorative items for designers GENERAL: Large quantity of quality furniture and small collectables OTHER INFO: 45 mins from London by train.

**Millers Antiques Kelvedon**, 46 High Street, CO5 9AG TEL: 570098 FAX: 572186 ASSNS: LAPADA PARKING: Own carpark OPEN: Mon-Fri 9-5.30, Sat 10-4 MIN: £100 MAX: £20,000 PERIOD: 17th-19th century SPECIALIST: Largest showrooms in Essex stocked with furniture GENERAL: Restoration & desktop leathers service.

**Thomas Sykes Antiques**, 16 High Street, CO5 9AG TEL: 571969 FAX: 571063 ASSNS: LAPADA PARKING: Own carpark OPEN: Mon-Sat 10-5 & by appt MIN: £200 MAX: £35,000 PERIOD: 18th-19th century SPECIALIST: Georgian furniture OTHER INFO: Chambers guest house at Earls Colne. Mainline station in village.

**Templar Antiques**, 6 Peters House, High Street, CO5 9AA TEL: 572101 FAX: (0621) 818033 Templar PARKING: Own carpark OPEN: Mon, Tues, Thurs-Sat 10-5 MIN: £25 MAX: £5000 PERIOD: 18th-19th century SPECIALIST: 18th century wines decanters GENERAL: General antiques OTHER INFO: Owner's separate B&B.

**Times Past**, 110 High Street TEL: 571858 PARKING: Easy OPEN: Tues, Thurs-Sat 10-5 MIN: £2 MAX: £900 PERIOD: 19th-20th century SPECIALIST: Decorative arts 1890-1940 GENERAL: General antiques (no reproductions), many unusual items OTHER INFO: 2 mins from A12, near Messing, the ancestral home of George Bush, US ex-president.

## MALDON (01621)

**Abacus Antiques**, 105 High Street, CM9 7EP TEL: 850528 PARKING: Easy OPEN: Tues, Thurs-Sat 10-4.30 MIN: £1 MAX: £1000 PERIOD: 18th-19th century GENERAL: General antiques. No reproduction OTHER INFO: Medieval Moot Hall's 42ft long embroidery celebrating the millenium of Battle of Maldon (992 AD).

**The Antique Rooms**, 63D High Street, CM9 7EB TEL: 856985 PARKING: Easy OPEN: 10-4 MIN: £1 MAX: £500 PERIOD: 19th-20th century GENERAL: General antiques OTHER INFO: Good café opposite. Scandinavian spoken.

**Clive Beardall Antiques**, 104b High Street, CM9 7ET TEL: 857890 ASSNS: BAFRA PARKING: Own carpark OPEN: Mon-Fri 7.30-5.30, Sat 8.30-4.30 MIN: £45 MAX: £6000 PERIOD: 18th-20th century GENERAL: Quality furniture, oils, watercolours & prints OTHER INFO: Full restoration service.

## PURLEIGH (01621)

**David Lloyd Gallery**, The Studio, Turnstone (opp Bell Inn) TEL: 828093, weekends 828330 PARKING: Easy OPEN: By appt MIN: £50 MAX: £1000 PERIOD: 19th-20th century GENERAL: Watercolours, oils, etchings.

## BATTLESBRIDGE (01268)

**Battlesbridge Antiques Centre,** TEL: 769392 ASSNS: LAPADA PARKING: Own carpark OPEN: Wed-Sun MIN: £1 MAX: £3000 PERIOD: 19th-20th century SPECIALIST: Fireplaces, clocks, glass, musical boxes GENERAL: Furniture & collectables OTHER INFO: 70 dealers in 5 large interesting complexes on River Crouch.

**Battlesbridge Mills**, Chelmsford Road, SS11 8TT TEL: 570090 FAX: 768844 PARKING: Own carpark OPEN: Mon-Fri 9-5, Sat-Sun 10-2 MIN: £1 MAX: £5000 PERIOD: 19th century SPECIALIST: Stripped pine doors, Victorian fireplaces GENERAL: Cast iron baths, lamp posts, radiators, butlers sinks, pine furniture etc.

## STOCK (01277)

**Sabine Antiques**, 38 High Street TEL: 840553 PARKING: Easy OPEN: Tues-Sat 10-5.30 MIN: £50 MAX: £2000 PERIOD: 18th-19th century GENERAL: Furniture, glass, china.

## RAYLEIGH (01268)

**FG Bruschweiler (Antiques) Ltd**, 41-67 Lower Lambricks, SS6 YEN TEL: 773761, 773932 FAX: 773318 PARKING: Own carpark OPEN: Mon-Fri 8.30-5 MIN: £30 MAX: £3000 PERIOD: 18th-19th century SPECIALIST: Georgian, Victorian, Edwardian, 1920's GENERAL: Mixed furniture.

## WESTCLIFF-ON-SEA (01702)

**David & John Antiques,** 587 London Road, SS0 9PQ TEL: 339106 FAX: (01268) 560536 PARKING: Easy OPEN: 10ish-4.30ish PERIOD: 18th-20th century GENERAL: Clocks, furniture, barometers, porcelain, silver, in fact a bit of everything that is nice OTHER INFO: Opposite, The Pearl Dragon is, in my opinion, the best Chineserestaurant in the world - try the Dim Sum for lunch.

**It's About Time**, 863 London Road, SS0 9SZ TEL & FAX: 72574 PARKING: Easy OPEN: 9-5.30 closed Weds MIN: £200 MAX: £5000 PERIOD: 18th-19th century SPECIALIST: Longcase & Vienna wall clocks GENERAL: Bracket clocks, Victorian, Edwardian furniture.

## LEIGH-ON-SEA (01702)

**Antiques & Bric-a-Brac,** 86 The Broadway, SS9 1AE TEL: 72895 PARKING: Easy OPEN: 9-5 MIN: £10 MAX: £700 PERIOD: 19th -20th century SPECIALIST: Jewellery GENERAL: Silver, porcelain, collectables, small furniture.

**Castle Antiques**, 72 Broadway, SS9 1AE TEL: 75732 Mobile: 0860 477104 PARKING: Own carpark OPEN: 10-5.30, closed Weds MIN: £10 MAX: £2000 PERIOD: 18th-20th century SPECIALIST: Tribal, military, firearms/swords, pottery, Staffordshire figures, antiquities, taxidermy GENERAL: General antiques OTHER INFO: Good pubs in Leigh Old Town.

**Past & Present,** 81/83 Broardway West, SS9 2BU TEL: 79101 PARKING: Easy OPEN: 10-4.30, closed Weds & Sun GENERAL: Smalls & furniture OTHER INFO: Situated in passage opposite Public Library.

**John Stacey (Leigh-on-Sea) Ltd,** 86-90 Pall Mall, SS9 1RG TEL: 477051 FAX: 470141 PARKING: Own carpark OPEN: 9-5.30 MIN: £5 MAX: £1000 PERIOD: 18th-19th century SPECIALIST: Edwardian furniture & porcelain GENERAL: General antiques OTHER INFO: Auction rooms next door.

**Richard Wrenn Antiques,** 113-115 Broadway West, SS9 2BU TEL: 710747 PARKING: Easy OPEN: Tues, Thur, Sat 10.30-5.30, Fri 10.30-1 MIN: £50 MAX: £10,000 PERIOD: 18th-20th century GENERAL: Jewellery, silver, porcelain, furniture, textiles, metalware, etc. OTHER INFO: Very near the historic fishing village of Old Leigh.

## GRAYS (01375)

**Grays Galleries Collectors Centre**, 6 London Road, RM17 5XY TEL: 374883 PARKING: Easy OPEN: Sat only 10-5 MIN: £1 MAX: Sky's the limit PERIOD: 19th-20th century SPECIALIST: Goss & crested china, childrens' books, militaria GENERAL: Glass, various collectables, china all in 25 individually rented lockup cabinents. Furniture OTHER INFO: 5 mins from town centre & main (Fenchurch Street line) station. Another collectors shop 2 doors away.

# North Essex

Roman settlements and roads, small pretty villages and historic towns and cities, leafy lanes and picturesque thatched houses are all characteristic of this part of England.

The tour starts in **Great Bromley**, then continues on to the sedate and uncommercialised resort of **Frinton-on-Sea**. Following the coast north, **Harwich** is next. Situated on the mouths of the rivers Stour and Orwell, this has been a busy port for centuries. It was from here that Edward III set out for battle with the French in 1340, the captain of the Mayflower, Christopher Jones, was born here and nowadays it is important as a commercial and ferry port with northern Europe. Harwich Redoubt, a circular fort with a diameter of 180 feet, commands the harbour. Built as a defence against Napoleon Bonaparte and even now still having eleven guns and a museum, it is presently being restored by members of the Harwich Society.

The tour turns west through several small, picturesque villages typical of this area. Travelling on pretty minor roads, the route passes through **Manningtree**, once a busy port which was made redundant by the coming of the railways. Its other claim to fame is as the final resting place of the notorious Witchfinder General, Matthew Hopkins, buried here in 1647.

Eight miles on the A137 brings the tour to **Colchester**. This is one of the best known of English Roman towns although its history started much earlier. There is evidence of settlement from at least the 5th century BC and by the 1st century AD it was the capital of King Cunobelin, Shakespeare's Cymbeline, of the Trinovantes. After the Roman invasion in AD43 Colchester was soon taken and developed as an important centre. The town grew quickly especially as retired Roman soldiers were given grants of land and settled there. About twenty years after the invasion, Queen Boudicca (Boadicea) of the Iceni led her rebellion and in the process sacked Colchester. Many of the Roman veterans joined the fight to protect the town but to no avail. Some fled before the Iceni and took shelter inside the great temple built in honour of the Emperor Claudius. Soon this was also captured and burnt. The surviving foundations still bear the marks of the fire. The rebellion could not succeed and afterwards the Romans rebuilt Colchester, including, in the 2nd century AD, the stone walls, much of which can still be seen.

After the Roman withdrawal from Britain the fortunes of Colchester temporarily declined with repeated raids by the Saxons and Vikings. In the late 11th century the Normans built a castle on the foundations of the Claudian temple. Apart from a brief spell of military action during the barons' revolt against King John, the castle's principal role was as a prison until the Civil War when it was held for the King by two Royalists, Sir Charles Lucas and Sir George Lisle. They resisted the Parliamentary forces for some three months but in August 1648 they surrendered. The two Royalist leaders were put on trial and executed by firing squad on the 28th August 1648. There is a stone to commemorate their execution. After the Civil War the castle, like so many others, was left to decay until the 18th century when it was purchased by a Mr Charles Gray. In 1920 it was bought by Viscount Cowdray who presented it to the borough.

The castle keep is the largest surviving in the country at 151 feet by 110 feet. Originally the keep was three storeys high but today only two storeys survive. The prisoners kept here have left their mark with graffitti and carvings still be to be seen on the walls.

Colchester has several museums. The Castle Museum, housed in Colchester Castle, has a wonderful collection with particular emphasis on the Roman period. A fine collection of clocks can be found in the aptly named Clock Museum in a 16th century house in Trinity Street. There is the Natural History Museum in the High Street and Hollytrees Museum is virtually opposite with displays of toys, costume and decorative arts. Again in Trinity Street, Trinity Museum illustrates Essex rural life over the past two hundred years. Finally, the Minories Art Gallery in the High Street has exhibitions of 20th century art.

Just 6 miles south is Layer Marney Tower, built in 1520 by Lord Marney. The tallest Tudor gatehouse in Britain, from the top there are magnificent views over the surrounding country-

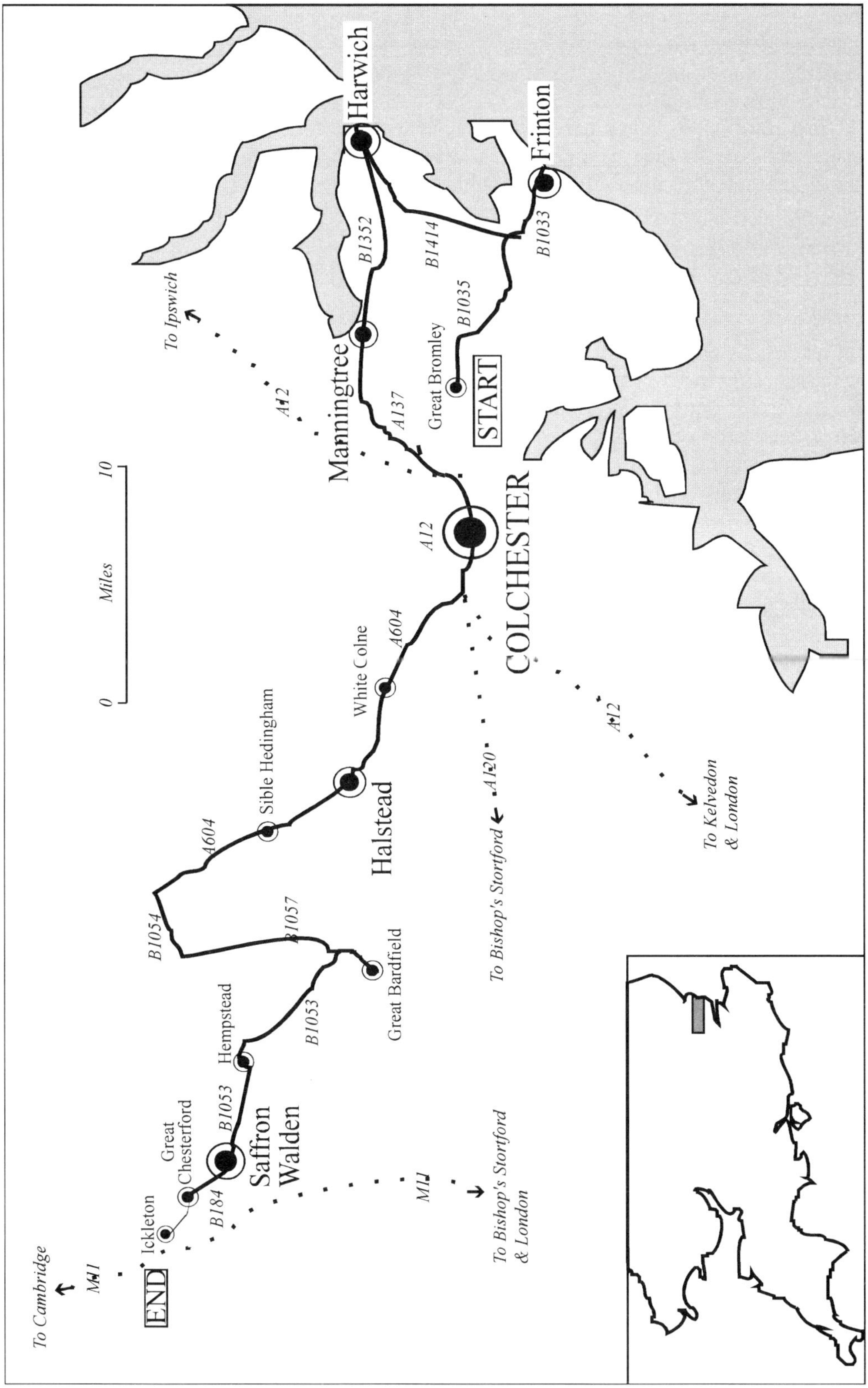
Harwich
Frinton
Manningtree
START
Great Bromley
COLCHESTER
White Colne
Sible Hedingham
Halstead
Great Bardfield
Hempstead
Great Chesterford
Saffron Walden
Ickleton
END
To Ipswich
To Bishop's Stortford
To Kelvedon & London
To Bishop's Stortford & London
To Cambridge
Miles
0
10
B1352
B1414
B1033
B1035
A137
A12
A604
A120
B1054
B1057
B1053
B184
M11

side. It is set in formal gardens with a rare breeds farm in the grounds plus a medieval barn and church with three effigy tombs of members of the Marney family. 10 miles west of Colchester is **White Colne** on the A604 and further west is **Halstead** which retains many medieval features as does **Sible Hedingham**.

**Great Bardfield's** church has an unusual stone carved rood screen. Apart from one other church in Essex, this type of screen has only been seen in Trondheim, Norway Near the B1053/B1054 junction, the village of **Hempstead** had two famous sons but with contrasting careers. One was Dick Turpin, the highwayman, who has grown into a legend over the centuries. He was born in the Bell Inn, still standing although renamed, but died on the scaffold in York. Hempstead's other famous native, William Harvey, has given birth to no legends but instead gave a great gift to medical science for he discovered the principle of blood circulation in the early 17th century.

**Saffron Walden** comes next. Although the saffron crocus is no longer grown commercially in the district, it has given Saffron Walden its name and carvings of it can be seen in many places in the area. This is not surprising as the saffron crocus brought prosperity to the region for four hundred years. Until the late 18th century this valuable plant was grown for the bright yellow dye extracted from the golden stigma of purple crocus and used to colour cloth.

The town's finest medieval building was once a malt house but now serves as a youth hostel. It is timber framed and was built around 1500. Much of its plasterwork has worn off, revealing the original window frames. In the middle of the town are the Market Square and the mid 19th century Corn Exchange which was converted in the 1970s into a library and arts centre.

On the outskirts are two of its most famous attractions: on the common the largest earth maze in England, and the mansion of Audley End. The maze, is about 40 yards in diameter but its path coils and twists for almost a mile and dates from prehistoric times. Possibly it was used in some kind of fertility ceremony to ensure a good harvest.

Audley End was started in 1603 by the first Earl of Suffolk, Lord Treasurer to James I. It was so big that it was never fully occupied or furnished. Charles II bought it in 1668 but could not afford to complete the purchase so it reverted back to the family in 1701. Because of the impossible size of the mansion, parts of it were demolished to bring it down to a more realistic scale. Still magnificent, the grounds were landscaped by Capability Brown and the interior of the house shows the work of Robert Adams.

The tour ends by visiting the Cambridgeshire villages of **Great Chesterford** and then **Ickleton** with its ancient church. Some of the interior, particularly the nave, dates from the 11th century. It also contains wall paintings, only discovered in the late 1970s, dating from the 12th century.

## ANTIQUE DEALERS

### GREAT BROMLEY (01206)

**J Dean Antiques**, Mill Farm, Harwich Road, CO7 7JQ TEL: 250485 FAX: 252040 PARKING: Own carpark OPEN: 7 days 9.30-5.30 MIN: £5 MAX: £1600 PERIOD: 19th century SPECIALIST: Original pine & country furniture OTHER INFO: Situated in a garden centre. Constable Country's Dedham Vale 5 miles, Harwich port 12 miles.

### FRINTON-ON-SEA (01255)

**Dickens Curios**, 151 Connaught Avenue TEL: 674134 PARKING: Easy OPEN: MIN: 25p MAX: £200+ PERIOD: 19th-20th century GENERAL: General antiques.

### HARWICH (01255)

**Mayflower Antiques,** 105 High Street, Dovercourt, CO12 3AP TEL & FAX: 504079 PARKING: Easy OPEN: Mon-Fri 10-5 MIN: £5 MAX: £10,000 PERIOD: 19th-20th century SEPCIALIST: Mechanical music, scientific instruments GENERAL: furniture, clocks, collectables.

### MANNINGTREE (01206)

**Antiques**, 49 High Street, CO11 1AH TEL: 346170 PARKING: Usually easy OPEN: Mon-Sat 10-1, 2-5 MIN: £5 MAX: £3500 PERIOD: Sometime 17th, 18-20th century GENERAL: 5 rooms of furniture, porcelain, silver, linens, glass.

## COLCHESTER (01206)

**S Bond & Son,** 14/15 North Hill, CO1 1DZ TEL: 572925 PARKING: Medium OPEN: 9-1, 2-5 MIN: £50 MAX: £5000 PERIOD: 18th-20th century SPECIALIST: Mahogany GENERAL: Furniture & paintings OTHER INFO: Shop premises dated about 1490, business in the family for 160 years.

**Elizabeth Cannon Antiques**, 85 Crouch Street, CO3 3EZ TEL: 575817 PARKING: Easy OPEN: Mon-Sat 9-5.30 MIN: £10 MAX: £4000 PERIOD: 18th-20th century SPECIALIST: Jewellery, silver, porcelain, glass & furniture OTHER INFO: The oldest recorded town in England. Large castle.

**Richard Iles Gallery**, 10 Northgate Street, CO1 1HA TEL: 577877 PARKING: Own carpark OPEN: Mon-Sat 9.30-4.30 MIN: £3 MAX: £1000 PERIOD: 19th century SPECIALIST: Watercolours, framing & ready-made frames GENERAL: Posters & prints & restoration.

**Mayflower Antiques,** 115 North Hill TEL: 572925, mobile 0860 843568 FAX: 504079 ASSNS: PADA PARKING: Own carpark OPEN: 9-5.30 MIN: £50 MAX: £3000 PERIOD: 19th century SPECIALIST: Victorian small furniture GENERAL: Furniture, pictures, clocks.

**Partner & Puxon** , 7 North Hill, CO1 1DZ TEL: 573317 PARKING: Medium OPEN: Mon-Sat 9-1, 2.15-5.30, Thurs AM only MIN: £5 Max: £25,000 PERIOD: 17th-19th century GENERAL: English furniture, ceramics, needlework.

**Trinity Antiques Centre**, 7 Trinity Street TEL: 577775 PARKING: Medium OPEN: 9.30-5 MIN: 50p MAX: £350 PERIOD: 18th-20th century GENERAL: China, silver, jewellery, treen, brass & copper, small furniture etc. OTHER INFO: We are in 16th century building.

## WHITE COLNE (01787)

**Fox & Pheasant Pine**, Colchester Road, CO6 2PS TEL: 223297 FAX: 224497 PARKING: Own carpark OPEN: 8-6 PERIOD: 19th century GENERAL: Antique pine OTHER INFO: In attractive complex with restaurant.

## HALSTEAD (01787)

**Antique Bed Shop**, Napier House, Head Street, CO9 2BT TEL: 477346 FAX: 478757 PARKING: Own carpark OPEN: Wed-Sat 9-6 & by appt MIN: £995 MAX: £3500 PERIOD: 19th century SPECIALIST: Most comprehensive range of antique wooden beds complete with new base & mattress. Delivery worldwide OTHER INFO: Top Indian food for miles only a stone's throw away.

**Swan Antiques,** Baythorne End, CO9 4AF TEL: 785306 PARKING: Own carpark OPEN: 7 days 9.30-6 MIN: £5 MAX: £1500 PERIOD: 18th-19th century GENERAL: Porcelain, writing boxes, caddies, pine furniture, garden items, bygones.

**Townsford Mill Antiques Centre,** The Causeway, CO9 1ET TEL: 474451 PARKING: Own carpark OPEN: Mon-Sat 10-5, Sun & Bank Hols 11-5 MIN: 50p MAX: £1000 PERIOD: 19th-20th century SPECIALIST: Furniture, porcelain, old lace, paintings, glass, silver, postcards, coins. OTHER INFO: Housed in a picturesque mill dating from 1740 with good restaurant/coffee shop with home-made food.

## SIBLE HEDINGHAM (01787)

**Hedingham Antiques**, 100 Swan Street, CO9 3HP TEL: 460360 PARKING: Easy OPEN: Mon-Sat 10-12.30, 1.30-5 or by appt MIN: £5 MAX: £2000 PERIOD: 18th-20th century SPECIALIST: Inlaid furniture GENERAL: Furniture c.1800 to Art Deco, silver & plate, 2nd hand warehouse at rear OTHER INFO: B&B here, good pubs & tearoom nearby.

**WA Pinn & Sons**, 124 Swan Street, CO9 3HP TEL: 461127 ASSNS: BADA, LAPADA PARKING: Easy OPEN: 9.30-6 MIN: £40 MAX: £10,000 PERIOD: 17th-19th century SPECIALIST: Real antiques GENERAL: Furniture & accessories.

## GREAT BARDFIELD (01371)

**Golden Sovereign**, Old Police House, High Street, CM7 4SP TEL: 810507 PARKING: Easy OPEN: Mon, Tues, Thurs 10-6, Wed, Fri-Sun 2-6 MIN: £5 MAX: £500+ PERIOD: 18th-20th century GENERAL: Mainly smalls of any material with some furniture OTHER INFO: Café, small Cottage Museum & lockup open Sat-Sun.

## HEMPSTEAD (01440)

**Michael Beaumont Antiques**, Hempstead Hall, CB10 2PR TEL: 730239 PARKING: Own carpark OPEN: 10.30-5 MIN: £40 MAX: £5000 PERIOD: 17th-20th century SPECIALIST: Furniture & rugs OTHER INFO: Excellent food at Blue Bell Pub (Dick Turpin's birthplace).

## SAFFRON WALDEN (01799)

**Bush Antiques**, 26-28 Church Street TEL: 523277 PARKING: Medium OPEN: Mon-Wed, Fri-Sat 11-4.30 MIN: £15 MAX: £1000 PERIOD: 19th century SPECIALIST: Early 19th century blue & white pottery, pink & copper lustre GENERAL: General antiques OTHER INFO: In this medieval market town full of old buildings, Bush Antiques is opposite the plasterworked Sun Inn which Cromwell used as his HQ during Civil War.

**Lankester Antiques and Books**, The Old Sun Inn, Church Street, Market Hill, CB10 1HQ TEL: 522685 PARKING: Medium OPEN: Mon-Sat 9.30-1, 2-5.30 MIN: £1 MAX: £1000 PERIOD: 18th-20th century GENERAL: General antiques, & 30,000 secondhand books OTHER INFO: Situated in 14th century Old Sun Inn, famous for its pargetting and association with Oliver Cromwell.

**Littlebury Antiques**, 58-60 Fairycroft Road, CB10 1LZ TEL: 527961 FAX: 527961 PARKING: Easy OPEN: 8.45-5.15 MIN: £100 MAX: £40,000 PERIOD: 19th century SPECIALIST: Barometers, ship models, marine antiques.

## GREAT CHESTERFORD (01799)

**C & J Mortimer & Son**, School Street, CB10 1NN TEL: 530261 PARKING: Own carpark OPEN: Thurs, Sat, Sun 2.30-5, viewing Suns & by appt MIN: £250 MAX: £25,000 PERIOD: 16th-18th century SPECIALIST: Early oak & portraits.

## ICKLETON (01799)

**Abbey Antiques**, 18 Abbey Street, CB10 1SS TEL: 530637 PARKING: Easy OPEN: Mon-Sat 10-5, Sun 2-5 MIN: £35 MAX: £2500 PERIOD: 18th-19th century SPECIALIST: 3 showrooms of furniture OTHER INFO: Excellent food 2 miles away at the Red Lion, Hinxton.

# South Suffolk

The country of Gainsborough and Constable, this area of leafy lanes and winding creeks cries out to be painted or, for those not blessed with the talent, photographed. This was a prosperous region throughout the centuries and the wealth was built upon cloth and trade with Europe. Now evidence of that prosperity may still be seen in the houses and churches of the cities, towns and villages.

The tour starts in **Sudbury**, birthplace of the painter, Thomas Gainsborough, in 1727. His house, in Gainsborough Street, is open to the public and displays a large collection of his work as well temporary exhibitions of contemporary art, particularly that of East Anglian artists.

Nearby **Long Melford**, a particularly pretty village with an impressive main street, is absolutely packed with antique shops. It still retains its medieval character with features like the timber-framed 16th century Bull Inn, a picturesque village green and an almshouse, restored in the 19th century, but founded by Sir William Cordell in 1593. There is a fine perpendicular church which includes a late 15th century chapel and stained glass from the same period. In the churchyard of the 1724 dated congregational church there is a typical crinkle-crankle (or undulating) brick wall.

The Elizabethan Melford Hall stands on the east side of the village green. This National Trust property is a magnificent creation with turrets crowned by onion domes yet still retaining a particularly English flavour. Amongst the many fascinating items is a survey of the estate done in 1580 by Sir William Cordell, owner of the Hall, with all the fields named. A later owner was the fifth Baronet, Vice Admiral Sir Hyde Parker who ran away to sea as a boy and worked his way up through the ranks to become an admiral. His son also became an admiral and their influence can be seen in the vivid paintings of naval battles lining the walls of the library. The Chinese porcelain and ivories in the house were taken by the fifth Baronet from a captured Spanish galleon in 1762.

The tour now arrives in **Lavenham**, one of the most prosperous of East Anglia's medieval wool towns. It contains over 300 listed buildings including many from the Tudor period. The church of St Peter and St Paul, with a 141 foot tall tower, stands on a hill and is one of the greatest of East Anglian 'wool' churches. The Guildhall of Corpus Christi, in the Market Place, is in the care of the National Trust. This early 16th century timber-framed building contains displays on local history and farming and includes an exhibition on the woollen cloth trade throughout the Middle Ages.

Moving on first to **Clare**, on the River Stour, with many medieval buildings and the remains of a castle, and then to **Hawkesdon**, the next visit is to **Bury St Edmunds**, county town of West Suffolk, which takes its name from the shrine of St Edmund, the last king of East Anglia, who died around 870AD. According to legend he was killed by marauding Danes who shot him full of arrows then cut off his head. His soldiers recovered his body but his head was only found by following the howls of a she-wolf who was guarding it. His shrine was a place of pilgrimage before the Normans arrived until well into the Middle Ages. The 11th century Benedictine abbey built here became one of the greatest in England and occupied about six acres of ground. Now all that is left is a splendid 14th century gateway and the 13th century Abbot's Bridge. The county of Suffolk was declared a new diocese in 1914 and Bury St Edmunds was the choice for the cathedral. The town had the fine restored church of St James, which includes a nave begun in 1438 plus a new porch, cloister, walk and chancel, to serve as the cathedral. Inside there are a thousand hassocks to represent all the parishes of Suffolk.

The city itself has some notable buildings. The 12th century Moyse's Hall, perhaps originally a Jewish merchant's house, is now a museum containing local antiquities. Amongst the many buildings of architectural interest are the 17th century town hall, remodelled by Robert Adam, the fine Unitarian Chapel, built in 1711 and Cupola House, an outstanding late 17th century town mansion. The Gershom-Parkington Memorial Collection of Clocks and Watches is in a Queen Anne house on Angel Hill. On display are timepieces from the 16th century onwards.

Detouring first to **Risby,** the route continues to **Ixworth**, a village possessing both a windmill and watermill, plus an abbey dating from Georgian times. **Woolpit** is next where the decorated and perpendicular church, St Mary's, has a double hammerbeam roof beautifully carved with angels and a splendid south

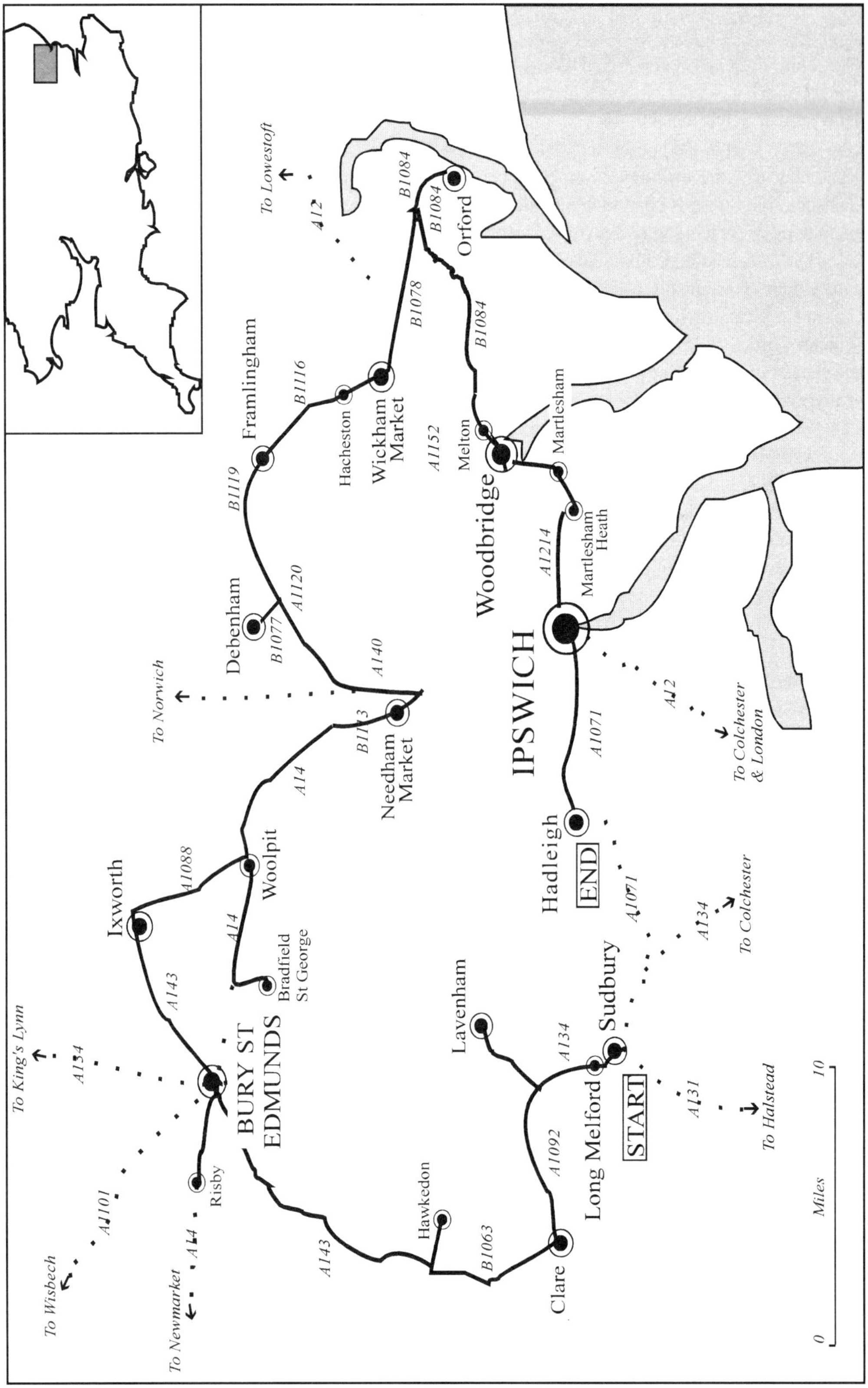

To Lowestoft
A12
B1084
Orford
B1078
Framlingham
B1116
Hacheston
Wickham Market
A1152
Melton
Martlesham
Woodbridge
Martlesham Heath
A1214
B1119
Debenham
A1120
B1077
A140
To Norwich
Needham Market
B1113
IPSWICH
A12
To Colchester & London
A1071
Hadleigh
END
A14
Ixworth
A1088
Woolpit
Bradfield St George
A143
To King's Lynn
A134
BURY ST EDMUNDS
Risby
A1101
To Wisbech
A14
To Newmarket
A143
Hawkedon
B1063
Clare
A1092
Long Melford
Lavenham
A134
Sudbury
START
A1071
A134
To Colchester
A131
To Halstead
Miles
0
10

porch and modern tower. Five miles south west is **Bradfield St George** followed by **Needham Market**, which also has an interesting church with a unique 15th century wooden hammerbeam nave roof.

Continuing, the tour comes to **Debenham.** About four miles south of the village, on the B1077 stands Helmingham Hall, built in the early 16th century and in the same family ever since. Probably one of the finest houses of its period, the original moat and drawbridges are raised and lowered daily. Set in 400 acres, it also has beautiful gardens. Nearby **Framlingham** has a 12th century castle standing just outside the town. The owners had an unfortunate habit of rebelling against the monarch of the day. In 1173, Hugh Bigod, Earl of Norfolk, rebelled against Henry II but had to surrender in 1175. Most of the castle was levelled in reprisal but Hugh Bigod's son, Roger, rebuilt it. It seems that Roger Bigod had not learnt by his father's mistakes because he rebelled against King John. He fared no better and the castle was taken by the King in 1215. In the 14th century it passed out of the possession of the Bigod family but the new owners were no luckier. In 1405 the owner, Thomas Mowbray, was beheaded by Henry IV and in 1572 yet another went to the block because Elizabth I suspected him of supporting Mary, Queen of Scots. This unlucky building was left to Pembroke College, Cambridge in 1636, later much of the inside was destroyed to make a poorhouse. Now there are extensive remains with towers, walls and chimneys still standing. The Prison Tower is the most notable as it has no outside entrance to the ground floor, the only way in is by a door on the floor above and then through a trapdoor to the lower storey.

In Framlingham itself, Mansion House on Market Hill is noteworthy, being 16th century with later additions and faced with tiles that resemble bricks. A connection with the castle's history is found in Queens Head Passage, a narrow lane at the top of Market Hill running down to Fore Street.The queen was Mary Tudor who was staying at the castle when she heard news of her succession in 1553. She later visited the town with her husband, Philip II of Spain.

The route now heads for the coast via **Hacheston** and **Wickham Market**. The quiet village of **Orford** stands on one of the area's creeks and is famous for its oysters. Because of the strength of the local lords, especially Hugh Bigod, Henry II built a castle here. Constructed in the late 12th century, the design was then revolutionary having a number of square towers built along the walls which allowed archers to defend the castle from under cover. As soon as the castle was finished a rebellion against the king broke out. One of the nobles involved was Hugh Bigod. The revolt was put down and the castle stayed in royal hands until 1336 when it was given to Robert de Ufford. Although the last section of the curtain wall collapsed in the mid 19th century, a considerable portion of the keep is still standing.

After calling at **Melton** on the outskirts of **Woodbridge**, then go into the town proper. On the River Deben and a centre for boatbuilding and sailmaking since the 14th century when they built warships here for Edward III, the town has many fine, old buildings. One of these on the Quayside, now a private house, was the Boat Inn built in 1530 and nearby is the 17th century Ferry House. Another 16th century inn has been converted to private use and is now the row of cottages at 1-5 Quayside. The most noteworthy riverside building is the weatherboarded tide mill still working until 1957 when the oak drive shaft snapped.

Seckford Hall, a fine Elizabethan mansion a mile south was the family home of Thomas Seckford, Woodbridge's great 16th century benefactor. An MP and barrister, he commissioned the first systematically surveyed maps of England. In the town the Seckford Almshouses were founded to care for thirteen poor men, although the present buildings only date from the 19th century. He also built Shire Hall on Market Hill which is heavily ornamented and has curly gables in the Dutch fashion. Seckford Hall was once connected by secret tunnel to another family home, the Abbey, just below the church. Now the Hall has been converted into an hotel and is said to be haunted by Thomas Seckford's ghost.

Going via **Martlesham** and then **Martlesham Heath**, an important wartime airfield, the route arrives in **Ipswich**, the largest town in Suffolk and at the head of the Orwell Estuary. Long a thriving port having trading links with the Continent going back over centuries, it was the birthplace of Cardinal Wolsey, Henry VIII's Lord Chancellor and favourite for many years until he was disgraced. Ipswich still has some interesting and historic buildings. Christchurch Mansion, near the centre of the town, is one of the most striking. This is a fine Tudor house set in beautiful parkland and containing superb collections of ceramics, pictures, clocks and glass as well as having rooms furnished in styles ranging from the 16th to 19th centuries.

The final stop is in the market town of **Hadleigh** with colour washed pargetted houses. Once a centre for the woollen cloth industry, it has a fine 15th century timbered Guildhall with two overhanging storeys. The church is 14th to 15th century and contains some lovely brasses.

## ANTIQUE DEALERS

### SUDBURY (01787)

**Napier House Antiques**, Church Street, CO10 6BJ TEL: 477346 FAX: 478757 PARKING: Easy OPEN: 9-5.30 MIN: £100 MAX: £3500 PERIOD: 18th-19th century SPECIALIST: Furniture OTHER INFO: Thomas Gainsborough Museum.

### LONG MELFORD (01787)

**Antique Clocks by Simon Charles**, St Mary's Court, Hall Street, CO10 9JT TEL: 880040 FAX: 375931 ASSNS: BWCMG PARKING: Easy OPEN: 10-5.30 MIN: £50 MAX: £7500 PERIOD: 17th-19th century SPECIALIST: Early English clocks GENERAL: All types of antique clocks especially lantern & longcase clocks OTHER INFO: Here there is the largest antique centre in East Anglia, many good pubs & restaurants.

**Ashley Gallery**, Belmont House, Hall Street, CO10 9JF TEL: 375434 PARKING: Easy OPEN: Mon-Sat 10-5 MIN: £100 MAX: £4000 PERIOD: 17th-20th century SPECIALIST: Paintings & watercolours GENERAL: Some china OTHER INFO: We run Alexander Lyall Antiques in same building.

**Charles Antiques,** Little St Mary's Court, Unit A, CO10 9LQ TEL: 880040 FAX: 375931 PARKING: Own carpark OPEN: Mon-Sat 10-5 MIN: £5 MAX: £3000 PERIOD: 18th-19th century SPECIALIST: Furniture, tea caddies.

**The Chater House Gallery**, Foundry House, Hall Street TEL: 379831 PARKING: Easy OPEN: Mon-Sat 10-5 MIN: £2+ MAX: £3000 PERIOD: 17th-20th century SPECIALIST: Pianos GENERAL: General antiques. At barn (2 miles away) lesser quality antiques & 2nd hand furniture etc OTHER INFO: Melford Hall, Kentwell Hall, Gainsborough's house, Sudbury. Bull Hotel, Black Lion Hotel & restaurants: Chimney, Canes.

**Sandy Cooke Antiques**, Hall Street TEL: 378265 FAX: (0284) 830935 PARKING: Own carpark OPEN: Mon, Fri-Sat 9-1, 2-5.30 MIN: £100 MAX: £30,000 PERIOD: 17th-19th century SPECIALIST: 18th century English furniture GENERAL: Furniture and smalls.

**Bruno Cooper Antiques**, Little St.Marys, CO10 9LQ TEL: 312613 PARKING: Own carpark OPEN: Mon-Sat 10-5.30 MIN: £1000 MAX: £25,000 PERIOD: 17th-18th century SPECIALIST: Fine period furniture, paintings, sculpture.

**Court Antiques**, Little St Mary's Court, CO10 9LQ TEL: 312613 FAX: (0206) 271678 PARKING: Easy OPEN: 10-5 MIN: £10 MAX: £4000 PERIOD: 18th-19th century SPECIALIST: Georgian & 19th century furniture GENERAL: General antiques.

**Alexander Lyall Antiques**, Belmont House, Hall Street, CO10 9JF. Tel 375434 PARKING: Easy OPEN: Mon-Sat 10-5 MIN: £100 MAX: £5000 SPECIALIST: Desks GENERAL: Furniture 1750-1850.

**Long Melford Antiques Centre**, Chapel Maltings TEL: 379287 PARKING: Own carpark OPEN: 9.30-5.30 MIN: £10 MAX: £10,000 PERIOD: 17th-20th century GENERAL: Period & 19th century furniture, pictures, silver, objets d'art, clocks, china, glass, lamps & accessories.

**Magpie Antiques**, Hall Street, CO10 9JT TEL: 310581 PARKING: Easy OPEN: 10.30-5, closed Mon & Wed MIN: £10 MAX: £450 PERIOD: 19th-20th century. SPECIALIST: Country pine GENERAL: China, country items, baskets.

**Patrick Marney**, The Gate House, Melford Hall, CO10 9AA TEL: 880533 PARKING: Easy OPEN: By appt MIN: £100 MAX: £10,000 PERIOD: 19th century SPECIALIST: Mercury barometers GENERAL: Aneroid & pocket aneroid barometers, scientific instruments.

**Noel Mercer Antiques**, Aurora House, Hall Street, CO10 9RJ TEL: 311882 PARKING: Easy OPEN: 10-5.30 MIN: £250 MAX: £20,000 PERIOD: 17th-18th century SPECIALIST: Early oak & walnut.

**Seabrook Antiques/Old Maltings Antique Co**, Hall Street, CO10 9JB TEL: 379638 PARKING:

Easy OPEN: 9.30-5.30 MIN: £50 MAX: £5000 PERIOD: 17th-20th century GENERAL: Oak, mahogany, walnut furniture. Decorative items.

**Oswald Simpson Antiques**, Hall Street, CO10 9JL TEL: 377523 ASSNS: BADA PARKING: Easy OPEN: Mon-Sat 10-5.30 MIN: £25 MAX: £25,000 PERIOD: 17th-19th century GENERAL: Country furniture, metalware, Staffordshire pottery.

**Suthburgh Antiques**, Red House, Hall Street, CO10 9JQ TEL & FAX: 374818 ASSNS: GMC PARKING: Own carpark OPEN: 10-5.30 but anytime by appt (resident) MIN: £20 MAX: £20,000 PERIOD: 17th-18th century SPECIALIST: 17th century oak furniture, longcase & bracket clocks & barometers. 18th century mahogany furniture GENERAL: Maps, prints, brass candlesticks, pewter, oak carved panels OTHER INFO: Sudbury is birthplace of painter, Thomas Gainsborough.

**Trident Antiques**, Hall Street, CO10 9JR TEL: 883388 Mobile: 221402 ASSNS: LAPADA PARKING: Own carpark OPEN: Mon-Sat 10-5.30 MIN: £50 MAX: £10,000 PERIOD: 17th-18th century SPECIALIST: Early English oak furniture and related objects OTHER INFO: Restoration and valuations undertaken.

**Tudor Antiques**, Little St Mary's CO10 9HY TEL: 375950, mobile 0585 768739 PARKING: Easy OPEN: Mon-Sat 9-5 MIN: £2 MAX: £3000 PERIOD: 18th-19th century SPECIALIST: Silver & plate (trading as Melford Antiques) GENERAL: General antiques, furniture & smalls OTHER INFO: Kentwell Hall does 16th century historical re-creations in summer.

**Village Clocks,** Little St Marys, CO10 9LQ TEL: 375896 FAX: (01206) 852135 ASSNS: GMC PARKING: Easy OPEN: Mon-Sat 10-5, closed Wed MIN: £50 MAX: £10,000 PERIOD: 18th-20th century SPECIALST: Clocks.

**White Hart Antique Centre,** Little St Mary's, CO10 9HX TEL & FAX: 310316 PARKING: Own carpark OPEN: 9.30-5.30, Sun 11-5 MIN: £5 MAX: £1500 PERIOD: 18th-19th century SPECIALIST: French furniture & beds GENERAL: General antiques, linens, kitchenalia OTHER INFO: Tea rooms to ponder over those difficult decisions!

## LAVENHAM (01787)

**RG Archer Bookseller,** 7 Water Street, CO10 9RW TEL: 247229 PARKING: Easy OPEN: Mon-Sat 9-5, Sun 10-5 MIN: 50p MAX: £1000 PERIOD: From early books to the latest bestseller GENERAL: Antiquarian & secondhand books OTHER INFO: Please note that we have sold out of JR Hartley's *Fly Fishing*.

**J & J Baker**, 12-14 Water Street (& 3a High Street), CO10 9RW TEL: 247610 PARKING: Easy OPEN: Mon-Sat 9-5.30 MIN: £20 MAX: £12,000 PERIOD: 17th-19th century SPECIALIST: English antiques OTHER INFO: 16th century Swan Inn (100 yds) in remarkable medieval village. Fine church & Guildhall.

## CLARE (01787)

**Clare Antique Warehouse**, The Mill, Malting Lane, CO10 8NW TEL: 278449 PARKING: Easy OPEN: Mon-Sat 9.30-5.30, Sun 1-5, most bank hols MIN: £1 MAX: £5000 PERIOD: 17th-20th century GENERAL: 50 dealers, 10,000+ sq ft. Period to shipping furniture, decorative, glass, linen, pictures, upholstered, etc.

**The Clare Collector**, 1 Nethergate Street, CO10 8NP TEL: 277909 ASSNS: LAPADA PARKING: Easy OPEN: Mon, Tues, Thurs-Sat 10-1, 2-5.30 PERIOD: 17th-19th century SPECIALIST: When possible, French provincial from Normandy. Decorative items & the unusual GENERAL: Furniture, porcelain, prints, embroideries, Oriental rugs.

**Granny's Attic,** 22 High Street, CO10 8NY PARKING: Easy OPEN: Sat 10.30-5 MIN: 50p MAX: £50 PERIOD: Victorian-1940 GENERAL: Pre-war bygones, cottage type china, etc, collectables, linen, clothing OTHER INFO: Quaint little shop with quaint holiday cottage adjoining.

**J De Haan & Son**, Market Hill, CO10 8NN TEL: 278870 FAX: 278713 PARKING: Easy OPEN: Tues, Thurs-Sat 10-5 & by appt MIN: £200 MAX: £5000 PERIOD: 18th-19th century SPECIALIST: Gilt mirrors, English 18th C. furniture, barometers.

**FD Salter Antiques**, 1-2 Church Street, CO10 8NN TEL: 277693 PARKING: Medium OPEN: Mon-Sat 9-5, Weds AM only MIN: £1 MAX: £2500 PERIOD: 18th-early 19th century GENERAL: English furniture, porcelain, glass OTHER INFO: This & several other shops used filming TV's *Lovejoy*. B&B's arranged.

## HAWKEDON (01284)

**Freya Antiques**, The Old Forge, IP29 4NN TEL: 89267 PARKING: Own carpark OPEN: Flexible or by appt MIN: £1 MAX: £1000 PERIOD: 19th century SPECIALIST: Antique pine & country furniture, upholstery GENERAL: Some glass, ceramics, kitchenalia OTHER INFO: In middle of Lovejoy country with two good hostelries nearby.

## BURY ST EDMUNDS (01284)

**Corner Shop Antiques**, 1 Guildhall Street, IP33 1PR TEL: 701007 PARKING: Medium OPEN: 10-5, closed Thurs MIN: £1 MAX: £200 PERIOD: 19th-20th century SPECIALIST: Victoriana GENERAL: Collectables OTHER INFO: Historic hub of East Anglia, ancient ruins & houses. Class winner *Britain in Bloom.*

**The Enchanted Aviary**, 'Lapwings', Rushbrooke Lane, IP33 2RS TEL: 725430 PARKING: Own carpark OPEN: By appt only MIN: £10 MAX: £1200 PERIOD: 19th-20th century SPECIALIST: Victorian cases of mounted birds, mammals, fish, also mounted butterflies in cases.

**Peppers Period Pieces**, 23 Churchgate Street TEL: 768786 FAX: 768786 PARKING: Medium OPEN: Mon-Sat 10-5.15 MIN: £2 MAX: £5000 PERIOD: 17th-early 19th century SPECIALIST: Copper, brass, iron, tin, pewter GENERAL: Furniture. No reproductions OTHER INFO: Good restaurants within 100 yards of shop in centre of town, also many hotels and guest houses only short walk.

## RISBY (01284)

**Risby Barn Antique Centre**, TEL: 811126 FAX: 811126 PARKING: Own carpark OPEN: Seven days 9-5.30 MIN: £1 MAX: £1500 PERIOD: 19th-20th century SPECIALIST: Clocks, porcelain GENERAL: Furniture, particularly oak & pine country OTHER INFO: Shared site with Garden Centre. Good local facilities.

## IXWORTH (01359)

**Ixworth Antiques**, 17 High Street, IP31 2HH TEL: 31691, (0860)902562 PARKING: Easy OPEN: Mon, Tues, Thurs-Sat 10-5 & by appt MIN: £5 MAX: £2000 PERIOD: 19th-20th century SPECIALIST: Silver plate, pine GENERAL: General antiques OTHER INFO: Good food at 17th century coaching inn opposite.

## WOOLPIT (01359)

**John Heather Antiques**, The Old Crown, Woolpit, IP30 9SA TEL: 240297 PARKING: Own carpark OPEN: 9-6 MAX: £2000 PERIOD: 17th-19th century SPECIALIST: English 18th-19th century furniture OTHER INFO: Bespoke reproduction & decorative items. Local legend of green children. Mainly 14th century church with fine woodwork.

## BRADFIELD ST GEORGE (01449)

**Denzil Grant (Suffolk Fine Arts)**, Hubbards Corner, IP30 0AQ Tel: 736576 FAX: 737679 ASSNS: LAPADA PARKING: Own carpark OPEN: Anytime though appt advisable (resident) PERIOD: 17th-19th century SPECIALIST: Oak, walnut farm tables GENERAL: English country & French provincial furniture 16th-19th century.

## NEEDHAM MARKET (01449)

**Roy Arnold**, 77 High Street, IP6 8AN TEL: 720110 FAX: 722498 PARKING: Easy OPEN: Mon-Sat 9.30-5.30 & by appt PERIOD: 17th-19th century SPECIALIST: Tools of trades and scientific instruments GENERAL: Books (antiquarian, s/hand & new) about trades and tools OTHER INFO: Englands finest example of 15th century carpentry in church roof.

**Needham Market Antiques Centre**, Old Town Hall, High Street, IP6 8AL TEL: 720773 PARKING: Easy OPEN: Mon-Sat 10-5 MIN: £1 MAX: £1500 PERIOD: 19th-20th century SPECIALIST: Jewellery GENERAL: 22+ dealers with vast range of furniture, porcelain, glass, bric-a-brac, collectables & antiques.

## DEBENHAM (01728)

**Gil Adams Antiques**, The Foresters Hall, 52 High Street, IP14 6QW TEL: 860777 FAX: 860142 PARKING: Easy OPEN: 9.30-5 PERIOD: 17th-19th century SPECIALIST: Dining tables GENERAL: Oak & mahogany furniture OTHER INFO: Ex *Lovejoy* auction house. Ancient village which won Architectural Heritage Year 1983.

## FRAMLINGHAM (01728)

**Bed Bazaar**, The Old Station, Station Road, IP13 9EE TEL: 723756 FAX: 724626 ASSNS: GMC PARKING: Own carpark OPEN: Mon-Fri 9-5, Sat 10-5, Sun 2-5 PERIOD: 19th century SPECIALIST: Mattresses & bases OTHER INFO: Over 2000 bedsteads in stock OTHER INFO: Historic market town has 12th century castle.

## HACHESTON (01728)

**Joyce Hardy Pine & Country Furniture**, The Street, IP13 0DS TEL: 746485 PARKING: Own carpark OPEN: Mon-Sat Mon-Sat 9.30-6, Sun 10-12.30 MIN: £65 MAX: £1000 PERIOD: 18th-20th century SPECIALIST: Furniture OTHER INFO: B&B's available in our large Tudor house.

## WICKHAM MARKET (01728)

**Crafers Antiques**, The Hill, IP13 0QS TEL: 747347 PARKING: Easy OPEN: 9.30-5 MIN: £1 MAX: £1500 PERIOD: 18th-early 20th century SPECIALIST: English ceramics, glass & collectables OTHER INFO: B&B all year round, beautiful Heritage coast 7 miles. Sutton Hoo, Minsmere bird sanctuary, NT heathland, Orford & Framlingham castles, plenty of rivers and boat trips.

## ORFORD (01394)

**Castle Antiques,** Market Hill, IP12 2LH TEL & FAX: 450100 PARKING: Easy OPEN: 7 days 11ish-5ish MIN: £1 MAX: £850 PERIOD: 18th-20th century GENERAL: Antiques, bric a brac, decorative goods OTHER INFO: Orford Castle, restaurants, pubs, a hotel teashop, famous oyster restaurant, etc.

## MELTON (01394)

**Melton Antiques**, Melton TEL: 386232 PARKING: Easy OPEN: Mon-Sat 9.30-5.30 MIN: £15 MAX: £600 PERIOD: 18th-20th century SPECIALIST: Decorative items, collectables, small silver GENERAL: All stock antique, sewing items, small furniture OTHER INFO: 12 miles Snape Maltings, Aldeburgh Festival.

## WOODBRIDGE (01394)

**Bagatelle**, 40 Market Hill TEL: 380204 PARKING: Easy OPEN: 10.30-5 MIN: £20 MAX: £3000 PERIOD: 18th-19th century SPECIALIST: Oriental ceramics GENERAL: English period furniture, Victorian paintings, jewellery, objets d'art.

**Simon Carter Gallery**, 23 Market Hill, IP12 4LX TEL: 382242 FAX: 388146 PARKING: Easy OPEN: Mon-Sat 9-5.30 MIN: £1 MAX: £10,000 PERIOD: 17th-20th century SPECIALIST: English oils & watercolours 1700-1950 GENERAL: Unusual furniture, decorative objects, prints, posters OTHER INFO: Cleaning, restoration & relining. Valuations. Private house atmosphere at Bassett's hotel with excellent gardens.

**David Gibbins**, 21 Market Hill, IP12 4LX TEL: 383531 FAX: 388146 ASSNS: BADA PARKING: Own carpark OPEN: Mon-Sat 9.30-5 MIN: £100 MAX: £60,000 PERIOD: 17th-18th century SPECIALIST: 18th century English furniture, English porcelain and objects OTHER INFO: Old town of narrow streets, with tide mill. Seckford Hall Hotel, Melton Grange Hotel.

**Hamilton Antiques**, 5 Church Street TEL: 387222 PARKING: Medium but public nearby OPEN: 9.30-1, 2-5.30 MIN: £60 MAX: £10,000 PERIOD: 18th-19th century OTHER INFO: Bloxsomes Restaurant, The Captain's Table (seafood).

**Anthony Hurst Antiques**, (estd 1955), 13 Church Street TEL: 382500 ASSNS: LAPADA PARKING: Own carpark OPEN: 9.30-1, 2-5.30 MIN: £60 MAX: £10,000 GENERAL: Wide range oak, mahogany, walnut furniture (1700-1900).

**Jenny Jackson Antiques**, 30 Market Hill TEL: 380667 PARKING: Easy OPEN: Mon-Wed, Sat 10.30-5 MIN: £20 PERIOD: 18th-19th century SPECIALIST: Jewellery, paintings GENERAL: Anything early, i.e. 17th-18th century & decorative OTHER INFO: Thirtlesham Hall Hotel.

**Edward Manson (Clocks)**, 8 Market Hill, IP12 4LU TEL: 380235 PARKING: Easy OPEN: 10-1, 2-5 PERIOD: 17th-19th century SPECIALIST: Clocks, barometers, scientific instruments.

**Sarah Meysey-Thompson**, 10 Church Street, IP12 1DH TEL: 382144, (0171) 727 3609 PARKING: Medium OPEN: 9.45-5, Wed AM only MIN: £15 MAX: £4000 PERIOD: 18th-20th century SPECIALIST: Curtains, textiles GENERAL: Pretty period furniture, decorative items, antique & 20th century curtains.

## MARTLESHAM (0394)

**Martlesham Antiques**, The Thatched Roadhouse, The Street, IP12 4RJ TEL: 386732 FAX: 382959 PARKING: Own carpark OPEN: Mon-Sat 10-5 MIN: £50 MAX: £20,000 PERIOD: 18th-20th century GENERAL: Mahogany, walnut, oak.

## MARTLESHAM HEATH (01473)

**John Read**, 29 Lark Rise, The Heath, IP5 7SA TEL: 624897, mobile 0860 426785 FAX: 382896 PARKING: Own carpark OPEN: Anytime but phone first MIN: £100 MAX: £4000 PERIOD: 18th-early 19th century SPECIALIST: Staffordshire figures and animals, porcelain, pottery.

## IPSWICH (0473)

**A Abbott Antiques**, 757 Woodbridge Road, IP4 4NE TEL: 728900 FAX: 728900 PARKING: Easy OPEN: Mon, Tues, Thurs-Sat 10-5 MIN: £5 MAX: £2000 PERIOD: 18th-20th century SPECIALIST: Clocks, conversation pieces GENERAL: General antiques. Reproduction OTHER INFO: You get nothing for nothing but a lot for a little in Ipswich. Try us. Near Felixstowe container-port.

**Tony Adams, Wireless & Bygones**, 175 Spring Road, IP4 5NQ TEL: 714362 PARKING: Medium OPEN: Mon, Tues, Thurs-Sat 9.30-12.30, 2.30-5 PERIOD: 19th-early 20th century SPECIALIST: Valve radios, cameras, gramophones.

**Ashley Antiques**, 20a Fore Street, IP4 IJU TEL: 251696 FAX: 233974 PARKING: Medium OPEN: Mon-Fri 9-1 & 2-5, Sats 10-4 MIN: £50 MAX: £5000 PERIOD: 18th-19th century SPECIALIST: Furniture, barometers GENERAL: Clocks, Victorian glass OTHER INFO: Christchurch Mansion Houses, some good works of art.

**Country Bygones & Antiques**, 13 St Peter's Street, IP1 1XF TEL: 253683 PARKING: Easy OPEN: Mon-Fri 10-5, most Sats 10-4 MIN: £2 MAX: £500 PERIOD: 18-19th + some early 20th century SPECIALIST: Kitchenalia, country porcelain & silver GENERAL: Decorative antiques & the unusual OTHER INFO: In Old Ipswich near Docks, 16th/17th century building, good restaurants nearby.

**Claude Cox, Old & Rare Books,** 3 Silent Street, IP1 1TF TEL & FAX: 254776 ASSNS: ABA OPEN: Mon-Sat 10-5, closed Wed PERIOD: 17th-20th century SPECIALIST: Private press, printing.

**Croydons**, 50-56 Tavern Street, IP1 3AL TEL: 256514 FAX: 231565 PARKING: Medium OPEN: Mon-Sat 9-5.30 MIN: £1 MAX: £ thousands PERIOD: 17th-20th century SPECIALIST: Diamonds GENERAL: Jewellery, giftware etc OTHER INFO: Kersey (place of interest), Ancient House, restaurants, Huntlesham Hall, Seckford Hall.

**The Edwardian Shop**, 556 Spring Road TEL: 716576, home 712890 PARKING: Own carpark OPEN: Mon-Sat 9.45-5 MIN £20 MAX: £1000 PERIOD: 19th-20th century SPECIALIST: Quality 20's, 30's shipping goods, furniture OTHER INFO: Sited caravan sleeping 6 available.

**Hyland House Antiques**, 45 Felixstowe Road, IP4 5HP TEL: 210055 PARKING: Easy OPEN: Mon-Tues, Fri-Sat 9.30-5 MIN: £1 MAX: £1250 PERIOD: 20th century SPECIALIST: 1900-1930's oak furniture GENERAL: China, copper, kitchenalia in 6 showrooms.

**Spring Antiques**, 436 Spring Road TEL: 725606 PARKING: Medium OPEN: 9.30-1, not Thurs MIN: £2 MAX: £700 PERIOD: 18th-20th century GENERAL: Metalware, plate, porcelain, jewellery.

**Thompson's Furniture**, 418 Norwich Road, IP1 4NG TEL: 747793 PARKING: Own carpark OPEN: Mon-Sat 9-5 MIN: £5 MAX: £2000 PERIOD: 19th-20th century GENERAL: Victorian & shipping goods OTHER INFO: 1 mile from town centre on main Norwich road.

## HADLEIGH (01473)

**Gordon Sutcliffe**, 105 High Street, IP7 5EJ TEL: 823464 ASSNS: BADA PARKING: Easy OPEN: Mon-Sat 9.30-5 MIN: £250 MAX: £20,000 PERIOD: 17th-18th century SPECIALIST: Furniture OTHER INFO: Many medieval towns & villages, timbered buildings & old churches. Hindlesham Hall Hotel & restaurant.

**Tara's Hall Antiques**, Victoria House, Market Place, IP7 5DL TEL: 824031 PARKING: Own carpark OPEN: 10-1, 2-5, not Weds MIN: £1 MAX: £1000 PERIOD: 19th century SPECIALIST: Textiles, jewellery GENERAL: Small silver, glass, decorative items OTHER INFO: Near lovely river walk.

# East Suffolk & Norfolk

This area of Suffolk and Norfolk is a land of windmills, fertile countryside and the ever present North Sea eroding the coastline. Here also is Britain's most easterly point at Lowestoft Ness. There are tiny villages, seemingly unchanged for centuries, and historic towns, foremost amongst these is, of course, Norwich.

Starting in Suffolk, **Snape** is famous as an international centre for music. Benjamin Britten and Peter Pears started the Aldeburgh Festival in 1948 which moved to the purpose built complex at The Maltings in Snape in 1967. Closeby, **Aldeburgh**, on the coast, is a quiet holiday resort with pebble beach. There are some Georgian houses in the main road and the Moot Hall is 16th century.

Turning north the tour passes through the villages of **Leiston,** which contains the ruins of a 14th century abbey, and **Yoxford,** just four miles from Westleton National Nature Reserve. **Peasenhall** comes next before arriving in **Blythburgh**, a busy port in the 15th century. The church has some fine carvings including a portrayal of the Seven Deadly Sins on the benches. During the Civil War Parliamentary troops used the church as a stable and the marks on the pillars where they tethered their horses may still be seen.

Back on the coast, the village of **Southwold**, at the mouth of the River Blyth, has been settled since at least Saxon times but nowadays the Dutch influence on the local architecture is a strong feature.The route continues north, via **Wrentham** and then **Kessingland**, a holiday resort with a Wildlife and Rare Breed Centre, before turning inland again to **Beccles**. This riverside town has some good Georgian houses and lovely gardens. St Michael's Church has a separate 14th century bell tower with a peal of ten bells.

Next, the village of **Bungay** is dominated by the remains of its 12th century castle. Back on the coast, **Great Yarmouth** was a busy port throughout the Middle Ages. There are many reminders of the medieval past including parts of the town walls, the narrow lanes called Rows and the 13th century Tollhouse which contains a local history museum and brass rubbing centre. The Elizabethan House Museum on South Quay, in a 16th century merchant's house, has displays of Victorian domestic life. The Maritime Museum for East Anglia in Marine Parade was once a home for shipwrecked sailors but now houses displays on herring fishing, wrecks and items associated with Lord Nelson. There is also a 144 foot tall monument to that famous sailor on South Beach Parade erected in 1819.

After first visiting **Scratby**, with its sandy beach, the tour turns inland to **Acle** and then **South Walsham** which has two churches in one churchyard. St Lawrence's was burnt down in 1827 and only the ruined tower and restored chancel remain. The other, St Mary's, is in the decorated and perpendicular style, and displays a nice two-storeyed porch. There is also a seven mile waymarked path from the village to Upton and the nearby nature reserve there.

Now the route reaches the ancient and historic city of **Norwich** with its thousand listed buildings, thirty three medieval churches and many fine modern buildings. It is the only English city on the list of European Community cities which preserve their social amenities in spite of commercial and industrial success.

At the centre lies the cathedral which is basically Norman and built in the 12th century. The two-storeyed cloister is unique and the prior's door from the cloister to the church is particularly beautiful. One treasure discovered in the 1840s is a painting of five scenes of the suffering of Christ and was probably meant for the high altar. It was the underside of a table when it was found and has been damaged in places. Norwich Cathedral was fortunate that much of its beautiful carving was out of reach of the 17th century Puritans who damaged so many lovely churches.

As one might expect, Norwich is rich in museums. Norwich Castle Museum displays natural and social history and the Royal Norfolk Regimental Museum in Castle Meadow chronicles the

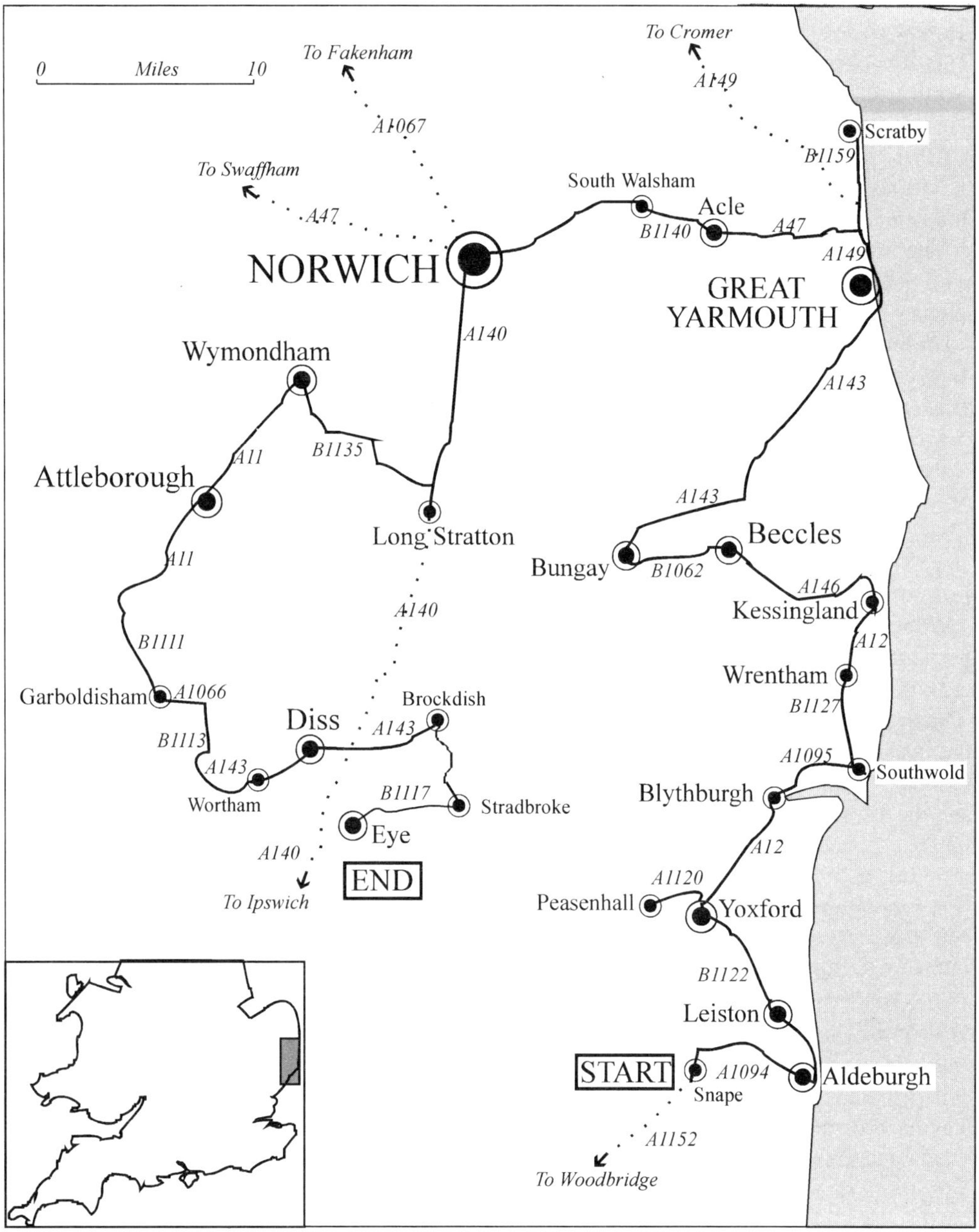
0 Miles 10
To Fakenham
A1067
To Cromer
A149
Scratby
B1159
To Swaffham
A47
South Walsham
Acle
B1140
A47
A149
NORWICH
GREAT
YARMOUTH
A140
Wymondham
A143
B1135
A11
Attleborough
Long Stratton
A143
Beccles
Bungay
B1062
A146
Kessingland
A11
A140
A12
B1111
Wrentham
B1127
Garboldisham
A1066
Brockdish
Diss
A143
B1113
A1095
Southwold
A143
Blythburgh
Wortham
B1117
Stradbroke
Eye
A12
A140
END
To Ipswich
A1120
Peasenhall
Yoxford
B1122
Leiston
START
A1094
Aldeburgh
Snape
A1152
To Woodbridge

history of this regiment and the Norfolk Yeomanry since 1685. The Sainsbury Centre for the Visual Arts, University of East Anglia, Watton Road, has many important paintings and sculptures on display including works by Picasso, Henry Moore, Giacometti and Francis Bacon. The Anderson Collection of Art Nouveau on exhibition is also here. Strangers' Hall in Charing Cross is a 14th century former merchant's house, that now displays urban domestic life from the 16th to 19th centuries.

For more information, the Tourist Information Centre is at the Guildhall in Gaol Hill where guided tours of the city start.

After Norwich **Long Stratton** is next followed by **Wymondham** (pronounced Win-dam) which has a particularly fine heritage of buildings, most built after a fire in 1615. The streets radiate from the Market Place containing an octagonal, timber market building, one of only three surviving in the country. Evidence of the devastating fire can be seen on the 15th century Green Dragon, one of the few buildings to survive, whose timbers show signs of charring. One of the most distinctive sights in the town is the church with its twin towers. This was once part of a Benedictine Priory, another casualty of the Dissolution of the Monasteries, although the church itself survives.

Nearby **Attleborough** was once famous for its turkeys and cider. The town had a yearly turkey fair after which flocks of turkeys were herded along the Great Post Road (now the A11) to be sold in London. The parish church has a Norman tower and a very fine 15th century rood screen, said to be a masterpiece of medieval carving.

The tour now visits the villages of **Garboldisham** and **Wortham** before arriving in **Diss**, John Betjeman's favourite town. It has many 16th century buildings and retains a medieval street pattern of twisting streets centred on the church. Next comes **Brockdish**, on the A143, comes next and then, via country roads, **Stradbroke** which has a decorated and perpendicular church with a lovely carved niche on the chancel wall. The final stop is in **Eye** an ancient town, granted its charter in 1205. It once had a Norman castle but it was destroyed by Parliamentary troops during the Civil War.

## ANTIQUE DEALERS

### SNAPE (01728)

**Snape Antique & Collectors Centre**, IP17 1SR TEL: 688038 PARKING: Own carpark OPEN: Summer 10-6, Winter 10-4.30 MIN: £5 PERIOD: 19th-20th century 40+ dealers GENERAL: Smalls, country & decorative textiles, linens, silver + plate, china, pictures, jewellery, OTHER INFO: Next to world famous concert hall in riverside centre.

### ALDEBURGH (01728)

**Aldeburgh Galleries**, 132 High Street, IP15 5AQ TEL: 453963 PARKING: Easy OPEN: Mon-Sat 10-5, Sun 2-4.30 MIN: £5 MAX: £450 PERIOD: 19th-20th century SPECIALIST: Contemporary studio ceramics GENERAL: General antiques

### LEISTON (01728)

**Leiston Trading Post**, 13a High Street, IP16 4EL TEL: 830081 PARKING: Easy OPEN: Mon-Sat 9.30-5, Weds AM only MIN: £1 MAX: £1000 PERIOD: 19th century SPECIALIST: Quality collectables GENERAL: Georgian-1930's furniture, china, glass & bric-a-brac OTHER INFO: On Heritage Coast, near Sizewell Power Station.

**Warren's Antiques**, 31 High Street, IP16 4EL TEL: 831414 PARKING: Own carpark OPEN: 9-1, 2-5 (closed Wed, Sat pm & Sun) MIN: £1 MAX: £1500 PERIOD: 18th-20th century SPECIALIST: Chests of drawers GENERAL: Victorian, Edwardian & 1920s oak, shipping furniture, smalls OTHER INFO: Restorers of antique & fine furniture.

### YOXFORD (01728)

**Suffolk House Antiques**, High Street, IP17 3EP TEL & FAX: 668122 PARKING: Easy OPEN: Mon-Tues, Thurs-Sat 10-1, 2.15-5.15 MIN: £20 MAX: £20,000 PERIOD: 17th-18th century SPECIALIST: Early oak & country furniture, Delft, metalware, rugs etc.

## PEASENHALL (01728)

**Peasenhall Art & Antiques Gallery**, IP17 2HJ TEL: 79224 PARKING: Easy OPEN: Seven days 9-6 MIN: £20 MAX: £2,000 PERIOD: some 18th, 19th-early 20th century SPECIALIST: Walking sticks GENERAL: Oils, watercolours, oak, mahogany & fruitwood furniture.

## BLYTHBURGH (01502)

**ET Webster Preservation in Action**, West-wood Lodge TEL: 70539 PARKING: Own carpark OPEN: 8-8 MIN: £5 MAX: £32,000 PERIOD: 15th-17th century SPECIALIST: Period oak panelling, doors, floors, fireplaces & fittings GENERAL: Complete medieval house & rooms, 30 in stock ready for reconstruction.

## SOUTHWOLD (01502)

**Emporium Antiques & Collectors Centre**, 70 High Street, IP18 6DN TEL: 723909 PARKING: Easy OPEN: Mon-Sat 10-5, Sun 12-5 MIN: £1 MAX: £3000 PERIOD: 19th-20th century GENERAL: 40 dealers selling a wide selection of antiques and collectables.

**SJ Webster-Speakman**, 52 Halesworth Road, Reydon IP18 6NR TEL: 722252 ASSNS: BADA PARKING: Own carpark OPEN: By appt MIN: £25 MAX: Around £15,000 PERIOD: 17th-19th century SPECIALIST: Animal Staffordshire, clocks GENERAL: Furniture up to 1830.

## WRENTHAM (01502)

**Wrentham Antiques Centre**, 7 High Street TEL: 675376 PARKING: Own carpark OPEN: 10-5 MIN: £1 MAX: £3000 PERIOD: 18th-20th century SPECIALIST: Art Deco, period mahogany GENERAL: Collectables OTHER INFO: Beautiful Heritage Coast. Cold easterly wind.

## KESSINGLAND (01502)

**Kessingland Antiques**, 36a High Street, NR33 7QQ TEL: 740562 PARKING: Own carpark OPEN: 6 days 10-5.30 MIN: £1 MAX: £1500 PERIOD: 18th-20th century SPECIALIST: Clocks & watches GENERAL: Everything you can think of, I stock.

## BECCLES (01502)

**Besleys Books,** 4 Blyburgate, NR34 9TA TEL: 715762 ASSNS: PBFA PARKING: Easy OPEN: 9.30-5, sometimes closed for lunch MIN: 50p MAX: £2000 PERIOD: 18th-20th century SPECIALIST: Antiquarian books on gardening, natural history, art & illustrated.

**Saltgate Antiques**, 11 Saltgate, NR34 9AN TEL: 712776 PARKING: Easy OPEN: Mon-Sat 9-5, Weds AM only MIN: £50 MAX: £4500 PERIOD: 18th-19th century GENERAL: Furniture, copper, oils, etchings OTHER INFO: Riverside Hotel 1 min.

## BUNGAY (01986)

**Black Dog Antiques**, 51 Earsham Street, NR35 1AF TEL: 895554 PARKING: Easy OPEN: 10-5 MIN: £1 MAX: £1000 PERIOD: 17th-20th century SPECIALIST: Roman pots, coins to 20th century clothes. Shop shared by 10 dealers.

**Cork Brick Antiques,** 6 Earsham Street, NR35 1AG TEL: 894873 PARKING: Easy OPEN: Tues-Sat 10.30-5.30 MIN: £1 MAX: £1000 PERIOD: 19th century SPECIALIST: Original English & European painted furniture, country & decorative.

**Country House Antiques**, 30 Earsham Street, NR35 1AQ TEL: 892875 & (01508) 558144 PARKING: Easy OPEN: 9.30-4.30 MIN: £1 MAX: £10,000 PERIOD: 17th-20th century SPECIALIST: 18th-19th century mahogany furniture GENERAL: Furniture, porcelain, china & collectables OTHER INFO: Friendly and helpful owners & staff & pub opposite. What more could the serious dealer ask for?

**Earsham Hall Pine**, Earsham Hall, NR35 2AN TEL: 894423 FAX: 895656 ASSNS: GMC PARKING: Own carpark OPEN: Mon-Fri 8-5, Sat-Sun 10-4 MIN: £1 MAX: £3000 PERIOD: 19th-20th century GENERAL: Pine, lighting, fireplaces, soft furnishings, gifts.

## GREAT YARMOUTH (01493)

**The Ferrow Family**, 6-7 Hal Quay TEL: 855391 ASSNS: LAPADA PARKING: Medium OPEN: 9-5, Thurs AM only MIN: £10 MAX: £5,000 PERIOD: 18th-20th century GENERAL: General antiques.

**Haven Gallery**, 6-7 Hall Quay TEL: 855391 PARKING: Medium OPEN: 9-5, Thurs AM only MIN: £20 MAX: £5000 PERIOD: 19th-20th century GENERAL: Oils, watercolours, prints.

## SCRATBY (01493)

**Keith Lawson LBHA, Antique Clocks,** Scratby

Garden Centre, Beach Road, NR29 3AJ TEL: 730950 FAX: 730658 PARKING: Own carpark OPEN: 7 days 2-6 MIN: £10 MAX: £15,000 PERIOD: 17th-20th century SPECIALIST: Clocks & clock related items only OTHER INFO: Parked outside you will see a Rolls Royce, reg MRTIK & a van, KITOC.

## ACLE (01603)

**Ivy House Antiques,** The Street, NR13 3BH TEL: 750682 PARKING: Easy OPEN: 9-5, closed Sun MAX: £3000 PERIOD: 18th-20th century GENERAL: Furniture, pottery & porcelain, glass, metalware, etc.

## SOUTH WALSHAM (01603)

**Leo Pratt & Son**, Old Curiosity Shop, NR13 6EA TEL: 49204 FAX: 49204 PARKING: Own carpark OPEN: 9.30-1, 2-5.30 MIN: £2 MAX: £8000+ PERIOD: 17th-20th century SPECIALIST: English furniture GENERAL: Lots of china & glass, brassware, clocks, etc, stocked in 5 warehouses OTHER INFO: South Walsham Broad (part of Norfolk Broads), excellent country club.

## NORWICH (01603)

**Allbrow & Sons**, 10 All Saints Green, NR1 3NA TEL: 622569 ASSNS: NAG PARKING: Easy OPEN: 9.30-4.15 MIN: £1 MAX: £6000 PERIOD: 18th-20th century SPECIALIST: Jewellery & silver GENERAL: Assorted china, glass, bric a brac OTHER INFO: Opposite Bonds Dept Store.

**Antiques Centre**, St. Michael at Plea, Bank Plain (nr top Elm Hill), TEL: 618989 PARKING: Medium OPEN: Mon-Sat 9.30-5 MIN: £1 MAX: £3000 PERIOD: 19th-20th century + Roman SPECIALIST: Clocks, Oriental china, lighting, linen, lace GENERAL: General antiques OTHER INFO: St. Michael at Plea is a deconsecrated medieval church. Norwich has a church for every Sunday in the year & public house for every day.

**The Bank House Gallery**, 71 Newmarket Road, NR2 2HW TEL: 633380 FAX: 633387 ASSNS: LAPADA PARKING: Own carpark OPEN: By appt MIN: £500 MAX: £50,000 PERIOD: 18th-19th century SPECIALIST: Norwich & Suffolk Schools GENERAL: Oils OTHER INFO: Norwich Castle Museum fine art collection.

**Arthur Brett & Sons Ltd**, 42 St. Giles Street TEL: 628171 FAX: 630245 ASSNS: BADA PARKING: Easy OPEN: Mon-Fri 9.30-1, 2.15-5 & by appt MIN: £200 MAX: £15,000 PERIOD: 17th-19th century SPECIALIST: English 18th century furniture GENERAL: Furniture.

**Fairhurst Gallery**, Websdales Court, Bedford Street, NR2 1AS TEL: 614214 PARKING: Medium OPEN: 10-5.30 MIN: £5 MAX: £4500 PERIOD: 18th-20th century SPECIALIST: Leaning towards nautical OTHER INFO: In centre of Norwich, restaurant next door.

**Gallery 45**, 45 St. Benedicts Street, NR2 4PG TEL: 763771 PARKING: Easy OPEN: Tues-Fri 11-3, Sat 11-4 MIN: £50 MAX: £1500 PERIOD: 20th century SPECIALIST: Modern British & Continental paintings incl. original prints & etchings & engravings OTHER INFO: Telephone home for appt 742977. Further stock available at The Coach House, Townhouse Road, Old Costessy, Norwich.

**Michael Hallam Antiques**, at St Michael at Plea Antique Centre, Redwell Street (nr London Street) TEL: 413692 PARKING: Medium OPEN: 9.30-5 MIN: £10 MAX: £1000+ PERIOD: 19th century SPECIALIST: Oriental porcelain, pottery etc GENERAL: Mainly smalls OTHER INFO: A dealer's dealer

**John Howkins Antiques**, 1 Dereham Road TEL: 627832 PARKING: Own carpark OPEN: Mon-Sat 10-5 MIN: £10 MAX: £15,000 PERIOD: 18th-20th century SPECIALIST: 18th & 19th century furniture GENERAL: Quality furniture for American, Italian, Australian, Japanese markets OTHER INFO: Packing & shipping service available. Restoration.

**Leona Levine Silver Specialist**, at Zelley The Jewellers, 35 St Giles Street, NR2 1JP TEL: 628709 ASSNS: BADA PARKING: Medium OPEN: Mon-Wed, Fri-Sat 9.15-5 MIN: £8 MAX: £1000+ PERIOD: 18th-20th century SPECIALIST: Dining table silver GENERAL: Range of silver cutlery some Sheffield plate OTHER INFO: 200 yds from Town Hall & Tourist Office which exhibits the Norwich City Silver Regalia + early silver collection.

**Mandell's Gallery**, Elm Hill, NR3 1HN TEL: 626892, 629180 FAX: 767471 ASSNS: FATG PARKING: Own carpark OPEN: Mon-Sat 9-5.30 MIN: £500 MAX: £50,000 PERIOD: 19th-20th century SPECIALIST: Norwich School GENERAL: English & Continental oil & water-colours, large stock.

**Queen of Hungary Antiques**, 49 St.Benedicts Street, NR2 4TG TEL: 625082 PARKING: Easy

OPEN: Mon-Wed, Fri, Sat 10.30-5.30 MIN: £15 MAX: £1000 PERIOD: 18th-20th century SPECIALIST: Early pine, good mahogany, brass & iron beds, ° testers GENERAL: Pine, furniture, farm tools.

**Russell-Davis,** 22-24 St Benedict's Street, NR2 4AQ TEL: 632446 PARKING: Medium OPEN: Mon-Sat 9.30-5.03 MIN: £5 MAX: £2000 PERIOD: 19th-20th century GENERAL: Art & Art Nouveau, bergere suites, upholstery, fireplaces, brass & iron beds.

**St Mary's Antique Centre,** St Mary's Church, St Mary' Plain, Duke Street, NR3 3AF TEL: 612582 PARKING: Easy OPEN: Mon-Sat 10-4.30 MIN: £1 MAX: £3000 PERIOD: 19th-20th century SPECIALIST: Toys, Dinky, trains, teddys, dolls, militaria GENERAL: China, furniture, clocks, jewellery, pine, silver, plate OTHER INFO: Housed in the last round towered Saxon church in Norwich.

**Oswald Sebley,** 20 Lower Goat Lane, NR2 1EL TEL: 626504 ASSNS: NAG PARKING: Medium OPEN: 9-5.30 MIN: £25 MAX: £4000 PERIOD: 19th-20th century SPECIALIST: Silver & jewellery.

**Second to Best,** 16 Onley Street TEL: 621653 PARKING: Easy OPEN: 10-4.30, closed Thurs MIN: 50p MAX: £500 PERIOD: 20th century GENERAL: Victoriana, china, furniture dating around 1940s onwards.

**The Tombland Bookshop,** 8 Tombland, NR3 1HF TEL: 760610 OPEN: 9.30-5 MIN: £1 MAX: £10,000 PERIOD: 17th-20th century GENERAL: Antiquarian & secondhand books OTHER INFO: Valuation service, bookbinding & repair, book finding & commission buying.

**Tooltique**, 54 Waterloo Road, NR3 1EW TEL: 414289 PARKING: Easy OPEN: Mon-Sat 9-5.30 MIN: £1 MAX: £1000 PERIOD: 18th-20th century SPECIALIST: Antique woodworking tools GENERAL: Used woodworking tools.

**Malcolm Turner,** 15 St Gile's Street, NR2 1JL TEL & FAX: 627007 PARKING: Easy OPEN: 9-5 MIN: £5 MAX: £1000 PERIOD: 19th-20th century SPECIALIST: Art Nouveau & Deco bronze figures GENERAL: Jewellery, Oriental china & porcelain OTHER INFO: A Mr Pips who died here in 1892 as a result of swallowing a packet of seeds.

## LONG STRATTON (01508)

**Old Coach House Antiques**, Ipswich Road, NR15 2TA TEL: 30942 PARKING: Easy OPEN: Tues-Sat 10-5 MIN: £5 MAX: £500 PERIOD: 19th-20th century GENERAL: Late Victorian & later mahogany, pine, oak furniture.

## WYMONDHAM (01953)

**Margaret King**, 16 Market Place, NR18 0AX TEL: 604758 PARKING: Easy OPEN: Mon-Sat 9-4.30 MIN: £20 MAX: £3000 PERIOD: 18th-19th century SPECIALIST: Victorian figures & cranberry glass, furniture GENERAL: General antiques.

**Old Bakery Antiques,** Main Street, LE14 2AG TEL: 787472 PARKING: Own carpark OPEN: 10-5.30, closed Thurs & Sun MIN: £2 MAX: £700 PERIOD: 20th century SPECIALIST: Enamel signs, kitchenalia GENERAL: Pine furniture, cottage antiques, advertising, unusual items. No repro.

**Turret House**, 27 Middleton Street, NR18 0AB TEL & FAX: 603462 ASSNS: PBFA PARKING: Easy OPEN: Normally 9-6 but appt advised (resident) MIN: £1 MAX: £2000 PERIOD: Mostly late 18th-early 20th century SPECIALIST: Antiquarian books, especially science & medicine, also antique scientific instruments GENERAL: 2nd hand & antiquarian books.

## ATTLEBOROUGH (01953)

**AE Bush & Partners**, Vineyard Antique Gallery, Leys Lane, NR17 1NE TEL: 452175 FAX: 456481 PARKING: Own carpark OPEN: Seven days 9-6 MIN: £100 MAX: £5,000 PERIOD: 17th-20th century SPECIALIST: Case furniture GENERAL: Bureau desks, writing tables etc OTHER INFO: Clients collected from airports, train & bus stations.

## GARBOLDISHAM (01953)

**Swan House Country Crafts & Tea Rooms**, Hopton Road, IP22 2RQ TEL: 818221 PARKING: Own carpark OPEN: Easter-end Sept Thurs-Sun 11-5 MIN: £1 MAX: £500 PERIOD: 20th century GENERAL: Country crafts, furniture, bric-a-brac OTHER INFO: All in 17th century characterful coaching inn.

## WORTHAM (01379)

**The Falcon Gallery,** Honeypot Farm, IP22 1PW TEL: 783312 FAX: 783293 PARKING: Easy OPEN: 7 days, any reasonable hour MIN: £150 MAX: £2000 PERIOD: 1830-1930 SPECIALIST: Oil paintings & watercolours only OTHER INFO: Beside the Gallery, we run a camping & caravan park, 5 acres of landscaped parkland overlooking a well stocked lake. Brochures available. The Farm Shop is open in summer, selling fruit, vegetables & freshly made raspberry ice cream. Junk & Disorderly is open every weekend in summer.

## DISS (01379)

**Diss Antiques**, 2-3 Market Place TEL & FAX: 642213 ASSNS: LAPADA, GMC PARKING: Easy OPEN: 9-5 MIN: £5 MAX: £6000 PERIOD: 17th-19th century SPECIALIST: Furniture, barometers GENERAL: Porcelain, silver, copper, clocks OTHER INFO: Bressingham Gardens & Steam Museum, many oak-beamed pubs.

**Raymond Norman Antiques**, 12 Market Hill TEL: 650360 PARKING: Easy OPEN: Mon-Sat 10-5 & by appt (resident) MIN: £100 MAX: £10,000 PERIOD: 18th-19th century SPECIALIST: Longcase clocks, mechanical music GENERAL: Georgian, Victorian furniture OTHER INFO: Winebar opposite. Fridays large auction.

## BROCKDISH (01379)

**Brockdish Antiques**, Commerce House, IP21 4JL TEL: 75498 PARKING: Easy OPEN: 9-5, not Wed MIN: £10 PERIOD: 19th-20th century SPECIALIST: Upholstered chairs GENERAL: Georgian, Victorian, Edwardian furniture.

## STRADBROKE (01379)

**Mary Palmer Antiques**, Cottage Farm, New Street (B1117), IP21 5JG TEL: 388100 PARKING: Easy OPEN: Seven day (resident) MIN: £1 MAX: £1000 PERIOD: 18th-19th century SPECIALIST: Glass GENERAL: Small furniture, collectables. Valuations OTHER INFO: 3 good pubs providing meals & accommodation.

**Stubcroft Period Furnishings & Restorations**, Cottage Farm, New Street (B1117), IP21 5JG TEL: 388100 PARKING: Own carpark OPEN: Seven days (resident) MIN: £50 MAX: £2500 PERIOD: 18th-19th century SPECIALIST: Oak, mahogany & country made furnishing pieces etc OTHER INFO: In 1840 Stradbroke sent 200 pauper emigrants to America.

## EYE (01379)

**Bramley Antiques,** 4 Broad Street, IP23 7AS TEL: 871386 PARKING: Easy OPEN: 9.30-5 PERIOD: 18th-early 20th century MIN: £10 MAX: £5000 SPECIALIST: English glass GENERAL: Principally furniture, some ceramics, boxes, treen & small items OTHER INFO: We are at the very centre of this ancient Suffolk town in a conservation area. The property is Grade II listed being part late 17th, early 18th century and part early Victorian.

**Corner Antiques,** 27 Castle Street, IP23 7OP TEL: 870261 PARKING: Medium OPEN: Wed-Sat 9.30-5 MIN: £5 MAX: £1500 PERIOD: 18th-20th century SPECIALIST: Jewellery, silver GENERAL: Porcelain, furniture, brass & copper.

**Laburnum Cottage Antiques,** 2 Broad Street, IP23 7AF TEL: 871386 ASSNS: LAPADA PARKING: Easy OPEN: 9.30-5 MIN: £1 MAX: £3000 PERIOD: 18th-20th century GENERAL: Linen, lace, porcelain, pottery, silver & plate, jewellery, furniture, etc.

**Raymond Norman Antiques,** Home Farm, South Green, IP23 7NV TEL: 870040 PARKING: Own carpark OPEN: Resident on premises MIN: £50 MAX: £10,000 PERIOD: 18th-19th century SPECIALIST: Clocks, especially longcase GENERAL: Georgian & Victorian furniture, mechanical music OTHER INFO: We mainly find individual items for the trade & private buyers.

**Talents,** 13 Castle Street, IP23 7AN TEL: 870888 PARKING: Easy MIN: £1 MAX: £250 PERIOD: 19th-20th century SPECIALIST: Pine furniture GENERAL: China, glass, evening clothes 1930s-1950s, ephemera OTHER INFO: Talents started as a coffee/craft shop but my own collections have taken over. Children welcome. Coffee & cakes.

**The Tartan Bow Kitchenalia & Country Curios,** 3A Castle Street, IP23 7AN TEL: 870369 PARKING: Easy OPEN: 10-4.30, closed Tues & Sun MIN: 50p MAX: £350 PERIOD: 19th-20th century SPECIALIST: Kitchenalia, old gardening implements & country related items GENERAL: Some decorative items OTHER INFO: Our shop has been featured in *House & Garden & Country Living.*

# North Norfolk

This region has some of the lowest lying and flattest land in England. It is also some of the most fertile. Along the coast there has been a continual battle against the sea with land reclamation on the one side and erosion on the other. The ports have had much trade with Holland through the centuries and many of the towns and villages show a pronounced Dutch influence in their architecture. Norfolk is a very rural county with the built-up area comprising only 5 per cent of the land. The farming, on some of the richest agricultural land in the country, is a tribute to mechanisation and the agrochemical industry. Hedges, a valuable wildlife resource, have mostly gone, as have mixed woodlands, wetlands and pastures. As a consequence much of the agricultural land resembles a prairie and waterways have been polluted by fertilisers and weedkillers. Not all is negative, however, Norfolk has some excellent nature reserves: on the Broads, on the coast and in Breckland in the south-west of the county.

The tour starts in **King's Lynn**, near the southern corner of the Wash. Standing on the Great Ouse river, its position has brought prosperity to this thriving port and market town since the Middle Ages. Called Bishop's Lynn until siezed by the king in 1536, there are many historic features. The 15th century Hanseatic Warehouse, a reminder of King's Lynn's past, is a tall, brick and timber-framed building with an overhanging upper storey and belonged to the Hanseatic League of north European merchants until the mid 18th century. Downriver the ornate Customs House, built in 1683, has a statue of Charles I over its door--this was a Royalist town during the Civil War. Between these is the Saturday Market Place, the centre in the Middle Ages, with its mostly 13th century St Margaret's Church. Closeby stands the Guildhall, built in 1421, with its striking chequered front and now containing the town hall plus the Tourist Information Centre.

Another guildhall exists, St George's, built in the early 15th century and the largest surviving guildhall in England. The size and grandeur testify to the wealth of the trade Guild of St George that built it. This building also has a chequered front and, inside, an open timber roof. Now the great hall has been converted into a theatre and stages the annual King's Lynn Festival in July.

Along the eastern side of the Wash on the A149, the village of **Heacham** comes next and then the Victorian seaside resort of **Hunstanton** with its famous striped cliffs and miles of sandy beaches. After **Brancaster Staithe**, nearby **Burnham Deepdale** and **Burnham Market** are two of seven villages in the area with Burnham in the name. In Burnham Market, the most prosperous of the seven, there is a big craft market in August. Nearby Burnham Thorpe was Lord Nelson's birthplace and the pub, named after the naval hero, is full of his memorabilia.

Still on the A149, following the line of the coast, **Wells-next-the-Sea** is appropriately named. A typical seaside resort, there are amusement arcades and souvenir shops along the seafront although some old buildings still exist including the Old Customs House in East Street. There is a good, sandy, beach and a light railway operates in summer to Walsingham. Little Walsingham, on the way to Fakenham, was a place of pilgrimage as one of Europe's great shrines where the Virgin Mary is said to have appeared. Continuing along the coast via the village of **Stiffkey** the tour comes to the now inappropriately named **Cley-next-the-Sea** (pronounced Cly to rhyme with ply) as the sea retreated leaving half a mile of marshes between it and the North Sea. Once a thriving fishing port it has suffered a decline but now is popular with holiday-makers. The salt marshes were made into a nature reserve in 1926, the first in the country. It is now said to be the best place in Britain to see rare birds.

Inland along the B1388, **Langham** is next, then **Fakenham**, an attractive market town on the River Wensum. One mile away is the Thursford Collection, with musical shows daily in the summer from nine mechanical organs and a Wurlitser cinema organ. A collection of traction and other engines is also on show. The next village, **Melton Constable**, has rare industrial interest with its locomotive works that belonged to the Midland and Great Northern Railway.

Further east is **Holt** which was destroyed by fire in 1708 but rebuilt to the medieval street

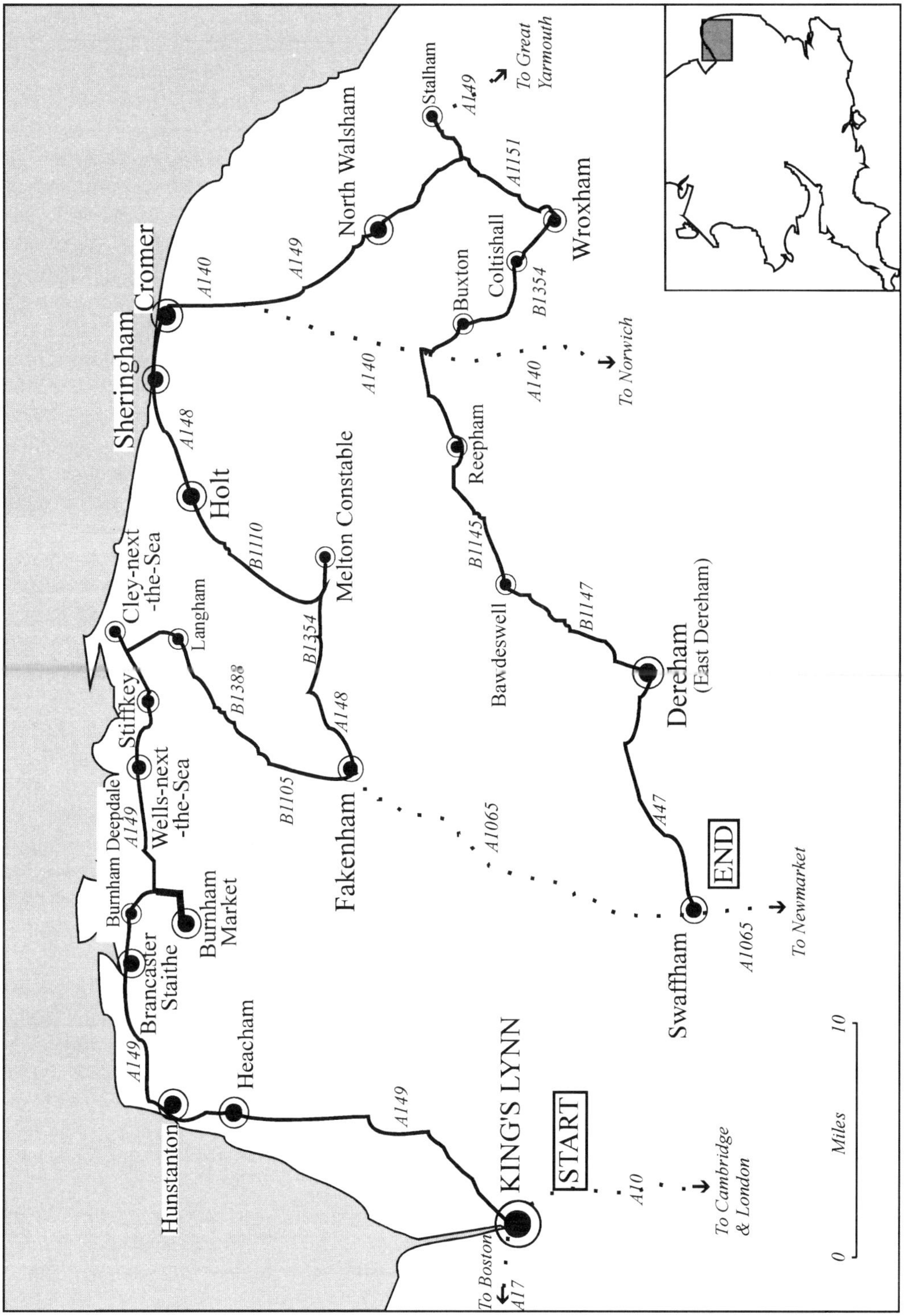
KING'S LYNN
START
Hunstanton
Heacham
Brancaster Staithe
Burnham Deepdale
Burnham Market
Wells-next -the-Sea
Stiffkey
Cley-next -the-Sea
Langham
Fakenham
Melton Constable
Holt
Sheringham
Cromer
North Walsham
Stalham
Wroxham
Coltishall
Buxton
Reepham
Bawdeswell
Dereham (East Dereham)
Swaffham
END
To Boston
A17
A10
To Cambridge & London
A149
A148
B1105
B1388
B1354
B1110
A140
A1065
A47
B1147
B1145
A1151
To Great Yarmouth
To Norwich
To Newmarket
Miles
0
10

plan. Of interest is Gresham's School, founded in 1555 by Sir William Gresham, Lord Mayor of London and also founder of the Royal Exchange. The original Tudor school building stands in the town square, though the school is now half a mile away along the Cromer road.

On the coast again, **Sheringham** was once an important fishing port with over two hundred boats operating from it. Fishing has declined in importance, although there are still a few fishing boats left. There is a good bathing beach, golf links and a carnival in August. Of note is the National Trust property of Sheringham Park, designated as a Site of Special Scientific Interest for the fulmars which nest on the cliff face. In the park are woodlands with brilliant displays of rhododendrons and azaleas and also a section of the North Norfolk coastal path.

At West Runton, between Sheringham and **Cromer**, Norfolk reaches it highest point, 340 feet (103 metres) above sea level, and the chalk that underlies most of the county comes to the surface on the beach. Cromer itself has lofty cliffs with good bathing beaches and all the attractions of a popular holiday resort. A speciality is the locally caught crabs. It also has two charming museums. The Cromer Museum, Tucker Street, is in a terrace of five Victorian fishermen's cottages. One of the cottages has been furnished as it would have been before the First World War. The museum also has exhibitions of the natural history, geology and history, including photographs of the town in Victorian and Edwardian times. The other, the Old Boathouse Lifeboat Museum on The Slipway, tells the story of the local lifeboats and the men who manned them.

Taking the A149, the tour leaves the coast and arrives in **North Walsham**. Made prosperous during the Middle Ages by the local wool trade, it continues as a centre for the surrounding countryside. Unfortunately a fire in 1600 destroyed much of the town so most of the buildings are Georgian or Victorian. **Stalham**, the next stop, on the River Ant, is a centre for the Norfolk Broads. Nearby **Wroxham** is known as the capital of the Broads and a noted yachting centre. The river bridge of 1614 was later widened, and Hoveton Little and Great Broads lie nearby. The church has a very fine late-Norman doorway and the old manor house has stepped gables. Still on the Broads, **Coltishall** is a shooting and angling centre, situated on the River Bure.

The route now passes through the villages of **Buxton** and then **Reepham** where, unbelievably, three churchs shared the same churchyard, though only a tumbledown wall still remains of one of them. **Bawdeswell** is next before coming to the market town of **East Dereham (Dereham).** Truly lovely with a host of picturesque buildings in or near the market place, this town also has something remarkable churchwise: namely the very historic St Nicholas church actually has not one but two towers. Much inside is also of good note, including a monument to William Cowper, the poet, who died here in 1800.

Finally, **Swaffham**, standing at 210 feet above sea level, has a legend about 15th century pedlar called John Chapman. He dreamt that if he went to London and stood on London Bridge he would meet a man who would make him rich, so off he went to London. After waiting on the bridge for several days a shopkeeper asked him what he was doing and when John told him the shopkeeper recounted a dream of his own. He had dreamt that a pedlar in Swaffham had found treasure beneath a tree in his garden. John hastened home and, sure enough, he did find treasure. He gave much of the money to the church to rebuild the north aisle and his generosity is recorded in the town's parish records.

In the centre of Swaffham is the Market Place with its Market Cross, given to the town by the Earl of Oxford, nephew of the writer Horace Walpole, in 1783. The cross is actually a dome held up by eight pillars with a statue on top of the cross of Ceres, Roman goddess of agriculture. A market is still held here every Saturday.

# ANTIQUE DEALERS

## KING'S LYNN (01553)

**Jubilee Antiques,** Coach House, Whin Common Road, Tottenhill, PE33 0RS TEL: 810681 PARKING: Own carpark OPEN: 7 days MIN: £20 MAX: £5000 PERIOD: 19th century SPECIALIST: Furniture.

**Norfolk Galleries**, 1 Stanley Street, Railway Road, PE30 1PF TEL: 765060 PARKING: Medium OPEN: 8.30-1, 1.30-5.30 MIN: £5,000 MAX: £20,000 PERIOD: 19th century SPECIALIST: Victorian & reconstructed period style furniture.

**Old Curiosity Shop**, 25 St. James Street, PE30 5AD TEL: 766591 PARKING: Easy OPEN: Mon, Tues, Thurs-Sat 11-5 MIN: £1 MAX: £600 PERIOD: 18th-20th century GENERAL: Antiques & collectables OTHER INFO: Ancient port, small market town, historic buildings. East Anglia's northern gateway, 2 museums, 15 miles to seaside resort.

**The Old Granary Antiques Centre**, King's Staithe Lane, (off Queen's Street), PE30 1LZ TEL: 775509 PARKING: Easy OPEN: Mon-Sat 10-5 MIN: £1 MAX: £1000 PERIOD: 19th-20th century GENERAL: General antiques OTHER INFO: An Aladdin's Cave in a 16th century granary in the historic part of town, near the Old Customs House & Hanseatic Warehouse. Area recently used by BBC's *Martin Chuzzlewit.*

## HEACHAM (01485)

**Peter Robinson**, Pear Tree House, 7 Lynn Road TEL: 570228 PARKING: Easy OPEN: Mon-Sat 9-5 MIN: £1 MAX: £5000 PERIOD: 17th-19th century SPECIALIST: English furniture GENERAL: Wide variety interesting antiques OTHER INFO: Present owner is 4th generation in the same shop, established 1880.

## HUNSTANTON (01485)

**Delawood Antiques**, 10 Westgate, PE36 5AL TEL: 532903 PARKING: Easy OPEN: Mon, Wed, Fri, Sat usually 10-5 & by appt MIN: £1 MAX: £1,000 PERIOD: 19th-20th century SPECIALIST: Jewellery, books GENERAL: Furniture & collectables, clocks, barometers OTHER INFO: High quality restoration of porcelain. Pretty Victorian seaside town famous for its red & white cliffs. PG Wodehouse wrote some of the Jeeves books in Old Hunstanton.

**RC Woodhouse (Antiquarian Horologist)**, 10 Westgate, PE36 5AL TEL: 532903 ASSNS: BHF, BWCMG, UKICHAW PARKING: Easy OPEN: Mon, Wed, Fri, Sat usually 10-5 & by appt MIN: £1 MAX: £2500 PERIOD: 19th-20th century SPECIALIST: Clocks GENERAL: Barometers, books, general antiques & collectors items OTHER INFO: Restoration of clocks, barometers & porcelain. Stable & church clocks can be undertaken locally, also some antique locks repaired & keys made to fit.

## BRANCASTER STAITHE (01485)

**Brancaster Staithe Antiques,** Coast Road TEL: 210600 OPEN: 7 days 10-5 GENERAL: Victorian furniture, pine, Art Deco, etc.

## BURNHAM DEEPDALE (01485)

**Steed-Croft Antiques,** West End Shop TEL: 210812 ASSNS: LAPADA PARKING: Easy Min: £25 MAX: £5000 PERIOD: 18th-19th century SPECIALIST: Period furniture GENERAL: Decorative antiques.

## BURNHAM MARKET (01328)

**M & A Cringle**, The Old Black Horse, PE31 8HD TEL: 738456 PARKING: Easy OPEN: Mon-Tues, Thurs-Sat 9-1, 2-5 MIN: £50 MAX: £3000 PERIOD: 18th-19th century SPECIALIST: Furniture GENERAL: Glass, decorative prints, some porcelain OTHER INFO: Listed Georgian village square, good restaurants & hotels. 4 antique shops.

**Anne Hamilton Antiques**, North Street TEL: 738187 PARKING: Easy OPEN: Mon-Sat 10-1, 2-5 MIN: £5 MAX: £4000 PERIOD: 18th-19th century SPECIALIST: English porcelain GENERAL: Small decorative items, glass, silver & furniture.

**Market House**, PE31 8HF TEL: 738475 ASSNS: BADA PARKING: Easy OPEN: Mon-Sat 9-6 MAX: £25,000 PERIOD: 18th century SPECIALIST: Period English furniture & works of art OTHER INFO: Norfolk's loveliest village & Nelson's birthplace. Excellent hotel adjacent: The Captain Sir William Hoste. Fishes restaurant.

## WELLS-NEXT-THE-SEA (01328)

**Church Street Antiques**, 2 Church Street, NR23

1JA TEL: 711698 PARKING: Easy OPEN: Tues-Sat 10-4 & by appt MIN: £1 MAX: £500 PERIOD: 19th-20th century SPECIALIST: Costume jewellery, hat pins, linen & lace, textiles GENERAL: Small furniture, collectables, china, glass etc OTHER INFO: Along coast: Heacham's Norfolk Lavender Fields, and inland: Sandringham House at Dersingham.

## STIFFKEY (01328)

**Stiffkey Antiques,** Wells Road, NR23 1AJ TEL: 830099 FAX: 830005 PARKING: Own carpark OPEN: 7 days 11-5 MIN: £5 MAX: £2500 PERIOD: 19th-20th century SPECIALIST:Original door furniture & fittings, bathroom fittings GENERAL: Furniture, items of house embellishment.

**Stiffkey Lamp Shop,** Tel: 830460 FAX: 830005 PARKING: Oan carpark OPEN: 7 days 10-5 MIN: £30 MAX: £3000 PERIOD: 19th-20th century SPECIALIST: Lighting, bronze garden statuary & fountains. OTHER INFO: Excellent pub, the Red Lion, with food. Fantastic unspoilt countryside.

## CLEY-NEXT-THE-SEA (01263)

**B & J Kerridge Antiques**, Rocket House, High Street TEL: 741154 FAX: 741154 PARKING: Medium OPEN: 10-5 MIN: £5 MAX: £2,000 PERIOD: 17th-19th century SPECIALIST: Country house items GENERAL: Period furniture OTHER INFO: Area of outstanding natural beauty. Good teashop next door.

## LANGHAM (01328)

**Sue Miller Antiques & Collectables,** The Courtyard, Langham Glass, NR25 7DG TEL: 830511 FAX: 830787 PARKING: Own carpark OPEN: 10-5 Easter to end Oct, 11-4 Nov to Easter MIN: £1 MAX: £3750 PERIOD: 18th-20th century GENERAL: Glass, china, silver, furniture OTHER INFO: In complex of 18th century farm buildings, close to Norfolk coast, factory shops, glass making, free car parking, toilets, walled garden & restaurant on site.

## FAKENHAM (01328)

**Fakenham Antique Centre**, Old Congregational Chapel, 14 Norwich Road, NR21 8AZ TEL: 862941 PARKING: Easy OPEN: Mon-Sat 10-4.30 MIN: £10 MAX: £2000 PERIOD: 18th-19th century SPECIALIST: French furniture GENERAL: General antiques.

**Lynton Clocks,** 22 Norwich Street, NR21 9AE TEL: 863666 SPECIALIST: Antique clocks of all types OTHER INFO: Quality restoration & re-enamelling including modern.

**Market Place Antiques**, 28 Upper Market, NR21 9BX TEL: 862962 PARKING: Easy OPEN: Mon-Sat 10-4.30 PERIOD: 19th-20th century SPECIALIST: Victorian jewellery GENERAL: General antiques OTHER INFO: Flea market every Thursday. Sandringham House, Congham Hall.

**Sue Rivett Bygones & Antiques,** 6 Norwich Road TEL: 860462 OPEN: 10-1, closed Wed GENERAL: Victorian furniture, porcelain, general antiques.

**Riverside Antiques Centre,** Hempton Road, NR21 7LA TEL: 863838 OPEN: 10-4.30 SPECIALIST: French & Victorian furniture, Oriental rugs, etc OTHER INFO: 5+ dealers.

## MELTON CONSTABLE (01263)

**Sharrington Antiques**, NR24 2PQ TEL: 861411 PARKING: Own carpark OPEN: Mon-Sat 9.30-5.30 MIN: £1 PERIOD: 18th-19th century SPECIALIST: Snuff boxes, treen, lace bobbins etc GENERAL: All small interesting & strange objects OTHER INFO: Holiday homes in grounds. Good pubs in Holt (4 miles). Don't go to Melton Constable - we are 4 miles west of Holt!

## HOLT (01263)

**Collector's Cabin**, 7 Cromer Road TEL: 712241 PARKING: Easy OPEN: Mon-Wed, Fri, Sat 10-1, 2-5, Thurs 10-1 MIN: £1 MAX: £50 PERIOD: 19th-20th century GENERAL: Bric-a-brac, clothes, toys, jewellery etc

**Cottage Collectables,** Fish Hill, NR25 6BD TEL: 711707 PARKING: Easy (1 hour free outside shop) OPEN: Mon-Sat 10-5 MIN: £1 MAX: £1000 PERIOD: 19th-20th century SPECIALIST: Ceramics & glass GENERAL: Antiques, collectables, gifts & furniture.

**Heathfield Antiques,** 15 Chapel Yard, NR25 6HG TEL: 711122 PARKING: Easy OPEN: 11-5, closed Thurs & Sun MIN: £2 MAX: £1500 PERIOD: 19th-20th century SPECIALIST: Antique pine GENERAL: Bric a brac, collectables.

**BJ Kerridge Antiques,** 30 High Street TEL: 712479 FAX & TEL (home): 740732 PARKING: Easy OPEN: 10-5.30 closed Thurs, Sat 11-5 MIN: £10 MAX: £3000 PERIOD: 18th-19th century SPECIALIST: Furniture GENERAL: Country house items, rugs.

**Past Caring,** 6 Chapel Yard, Albert Street NR25 6HG TEL: 713771 FAX: (01362) 683363 PARKING: Easy OPEN: 11-5, closed Thurs & Sun MIN: £1 MAX: £95 PERIOD: 19th-20th century SPECIALIST: Antique linen & period clothing GENERAL: Pre 1950s textiles, costume jewellery.

**Pretty Things,** 10-11 Chapel Yard, Albert Street, NR25 6HG TEL: 711012 PARKING: Easy OPEN: Mon-Sat 10.15-5 MIN: 25p MAX: £3000 PERIOD: 19th-20th century SPECIALIST: Collectables GENERAL: Books, linen, furniture, silver, jewellery, buttons, etc.

**Richard Scott Antiques**, 30 High Street TEL: 712479 PARKING: Medium OPEN: Mon-Wed, Fri, Sat 11-5 MIN: £5 MAX: £500 PERIOD: 18th-20th century SPECIALIST: Large stock porcelain, pottery & glass OTHER INFO: Good Georgian town close to 4 fine country house: Holkham, Houghton, 5 miles from beautiful coastline.

## SHERINGHAM (01263)

**RL Cook Antiquarian & Secondhand Books**, 12 Sycamore Grove, NR26 8PG TEL: 822050 PARKING: Own carpark OPEN: By appt MIN: £10 MAX: £500 PERIOD: 17th-20th century GENERAL: Many subjects, small stock.

**Dorothy's Antiques**, 23 Waterbank Road, NR26 8RB TEL: 822319 PARKING: Own carpark OPEN: Daily 11.15-4 PERIOD: 19th-20th century GENERAL: Small furniture, cranberry glass, Royal Worcester & other porcelain, commemoratives, collectables.

**JH Parriss**, 20 Station Road, NR26 8RE TEL: 822661 ASSNS: NAG PARKING: Easy OPEN: 9.15-1, 2.15-5.15 MIN: £50 MAX: £5000 PERIOD: 18th-20th century SPECIALIST: Silver GENERAL: Clocks, jewellery.

**Westcliffe Gallery**, 2-8 Augusta Street, NR26 8LA TEL: 824320 PARKING: Medium OPEN: Mon, Tues, Thurs-Sat 9.30-1, 2-5.30 MIN: £90 MAX: £12,000 PERIOD: 18th-20th century SPECIALIST: Ornithological paintings (period) GENERAL: Oils, watercolours, drawings & furniture (over 250 pictures always on display) OTHER INFO: Links Country Park Hotel (West Runton), Felbrigg Hall, Blickling Hall (NT).

## CROMER (01263)

**Bond Street Antiques**, 6 Bond Street, NR27 9DA TEL: 513134 ASSNS: NAG, FGA PARKING: Medium OPEN: Mon-Sat 9-1, 2-5.30 MIN: £10 MAX: £10,000 PERIOD: 18th-20th century SPECIALIST: Silver, gold & jewellery GENERAL: Jewellery, silver, porcelain OTHER INFO: End-of-Pier show, swimming complex.

**AE Seago,** 15 Church Street, NR27 9ES TEL: 512733 PARKING: Medium/difficult OPEN: Mon-Sat 9-5 MIN: £10 MAX: £1500 PERIOD: 18th-19th century GENERAL: Furniture & metals.

## NORTH WALSHAM (01692)

**Eric Bates & Sons**, Melbourne House, Bacton Road, NR28 0RA TEL: 403221 FAX: 404388 ASSNS: GMC PARKING: Own car park OPEN: Mon-Sat 8-5 MIN: £1 MAX: £10,000 PERIOD: 19th century SPECIALIST: Sets of chairs & dining tables GENERAL: Victorian furniture, 17,000 sq ft stock. Owner is known to trade as The Chairman.

## STALHAM (01692)

**Stalham Antiques Gallery**, 29 High Street, NR12 9AH TEL: 580636 FAX: 580636 ASSNS: LAPADA PARKING: Own carpark OPEN: Mon-Fri 9-1, 2-5, Sat 9-1 MIN: £50 MAX: £10,000 PERIOD: 17th-19th century SPECIALIST: Period furniture GENERAL: Brass, copper, paintings, country furniture. No repro OTHER INFO: In heart of Norfolk Broads yet 20 mins from Norwich.

## WROXHAM (01603)

**TCS Brooke**, The Grange, Norwich Road TEL: 782644 ASSNS: BADA PARKING: Own carpark OPEN: 9.15-5.30 MIN: £25 MAX: £10,000 PERIOD: 18th-19th century SPECIALIST: 18th century English porcelain GENERAL: General antiques. Valuations.

## COLTISHALL (01603)

**Liz Allport-Lomax**, TEL: 737631 ASSNS: Retired member LAPADA PARKING: Own carpark OPEN: By appt MIN: £5 MAX: £10,000 PERIOD: 19th century SPECIALIST: English porcelain, small collectables GENERAL: Silver, glass, small furniture OTHER INFO: Antique Centre + 3 shops.

**Eric Bates & Sons**, High Street, NR12 7AA TEL: 738716 FAX: 738966 ASSNS: GMC PARKING: Own carpark OPEN: Mon-Sat 8-5 MIN: £1 MAX: £10,000+ PERIOD: 18th-20th century SPECIALIST: Sets of chairs & dining tables GENERAL: Victorian furniture OTHER INFO: Owner is known in the trade as The Chairman. On Norfolk Broads, good facilities.

**Coltishall Antiques Centre,** High Street, NR12 7AA TEL: 738306 PARKING: Easy OPEN: 10-5 MIN: £5 MAX: £3000 PERIOD: 18th-20th century SPECIALIST: Militaria & Oriental GENERAL: Porcelain, glass, silver, plate, jewellery, copper, brass, furniture.

**Gwendoline Golder**, Point House, High Street, NR12 7HD TEL: 738099 PARKING: Own carpark OPEN: Mon-Sat 10-5 MIN: £5 MAX: £950 PERIOD: 19th-20th century GENERAL: Furniture, porcelain, small silver collectors items.

## BUXTON (01603)

**As Time Goes By**, Buxton Mill TEL: 278080 FAX: 278080 PARKING: Easy OPEN: Tues-Fri 9.30-5, Sat-Sun 10-4 MIN: £10 MAX: £5,000 PERIOD: 17th-20th century SPECIALIST: Antique clocks including repair & restoration.

## REEPHAM (01603)

**The Chimes**, Market Place, NR10 4JJ TEL: 870480 PARKING: Easy OPEN: 9-5 MIN: £10 MAX: £1500 PERIOD: 18th-19th century GENERAL: Furniture, writing slopes, boxes, objets d'art OTHER INFO: Reepham has the only perfect Georgian square in Broadlands. Refreshments available all day.

## BAWDESWELL (01362)

**Norfolk Polyphon Centre**, Wood Farm, NR20 4RX TEL: 88230 FAX: 88669 PARKING: Own carpark OPEN: Anytime by appt MIN: £1,000 MAX: Considerable PERIOD: 19th-early 20th century SPECIALIST: Musical boxes, mechanical organs, orchestrions etc, automata OTHER INFO: Country farmhouse near coast & Broads

## EAST DEREHAM (01362)

**Dereham Antiques,** 9 Norwich Street, NR19 1AE TEL: 693200 PARKING: Easy OPEN: 10-1, 2-5 MIN: £5 MAX: £350 PERIOD: 18th-19th century SPECIALIST: Jewellery GENERAL: Silver, glass, china, curios, furniture.

## SWAFFHAM (01760)

**A & S Pine,** 3 Theatre Street, TEL: 720841 PARKING: Easy OPEN: 9-5 MIN: £1 MAX: £400 PERIOD: 19th-20th century GENERAL: Pine & other furniture OTHER INFO: Our saleroom is situated in a converted cart shed close to the historic market place.

**Cranglegate (Antiques)**, Cranglegate, Market Place, PE37 7LE TEL: 721052 ASSNS: Antique Traders Assn PARKING: Easy OPEN: Tues, Thurs, Sat 10-5.30 (resident) MIN: £20 MAX: £500ish PERIOD: 17th-20th century SPECIALIST: Religious items, Oriental GENERAL: Small furniture, pottery & china, bronzes & sculpture.

**Swaffham Antiques Supplies**, The Old Cold Store Buildings, 7 Cley Road TEL: 721697 PARKING: Own carpark OPEN: By appt MIN: £50 MAX: £6000 PERIOD: 18th-20th century GENERAL: Furniture & shipping furniture OTHER INFO: Horse & Groom restaurant & hotel, Swaffham poultry & household effects auction on Sats.

# Cambridgeshire

*The Old Bridge at Queen's College, Cambridge*

This is a county of flat landscapes and wide vistas. The fens, once stretching from just north of Cambridge to the Wash, were once mostly marsh. Drainage started in the 17th century and has continued since and the whole area is criss-crossed by drainage canals and ditches. Apart from the beauty of the countryside, Cambridgeshire is distinguished by Cambridge university and the magnificent Ely Cathedral.

The tour starts in the Hertfordshire town of **Royston** which grew up on the junction of the Roman roads of Ermine Street and Icknield Way soon after the Norman Conquest. Now crossing into Cambridgeshire, **Duxford** has a Second World War airfield now owned by the Imperial War Museum, with the finest collection of aircraft, both civilian and military, in the country ranging from First World War aircraft right through to Concord. There is also an exhibition of other military and naval artefacts like vehicles and artillery. The route continues through the villages of **Pampisford, Little Abington, Little Shelford,** and then **Harston**. **Comberton,** on the B1046 has a church, St Mary's, with remarkable bench ends from the Middle Ages.

And then to **Cambridge**, one of the most beautiful town's in England and world famous for its University. The largest of the University Colleges is Trinity, founded by Henry VIII, and the Great Court is claimed to be the largest university court in the world. The library was built by Christopher Wren between 1679 and 1695. It contains bookcases carved by Grinling Gibbons and possesses original manuscripts by Milton, Thackeray, Tennyson, Newton and Byron.

The earlier King's College, founded in 1441 by Henry VI, is famous for its chapel and beautiful choral singing. Started in 1446, work on the chapel was halted by the Wars of the Roses and only finished in 1515. It took a further quarter of a century for Flemish craftsmen to install

# Cambridgeshire

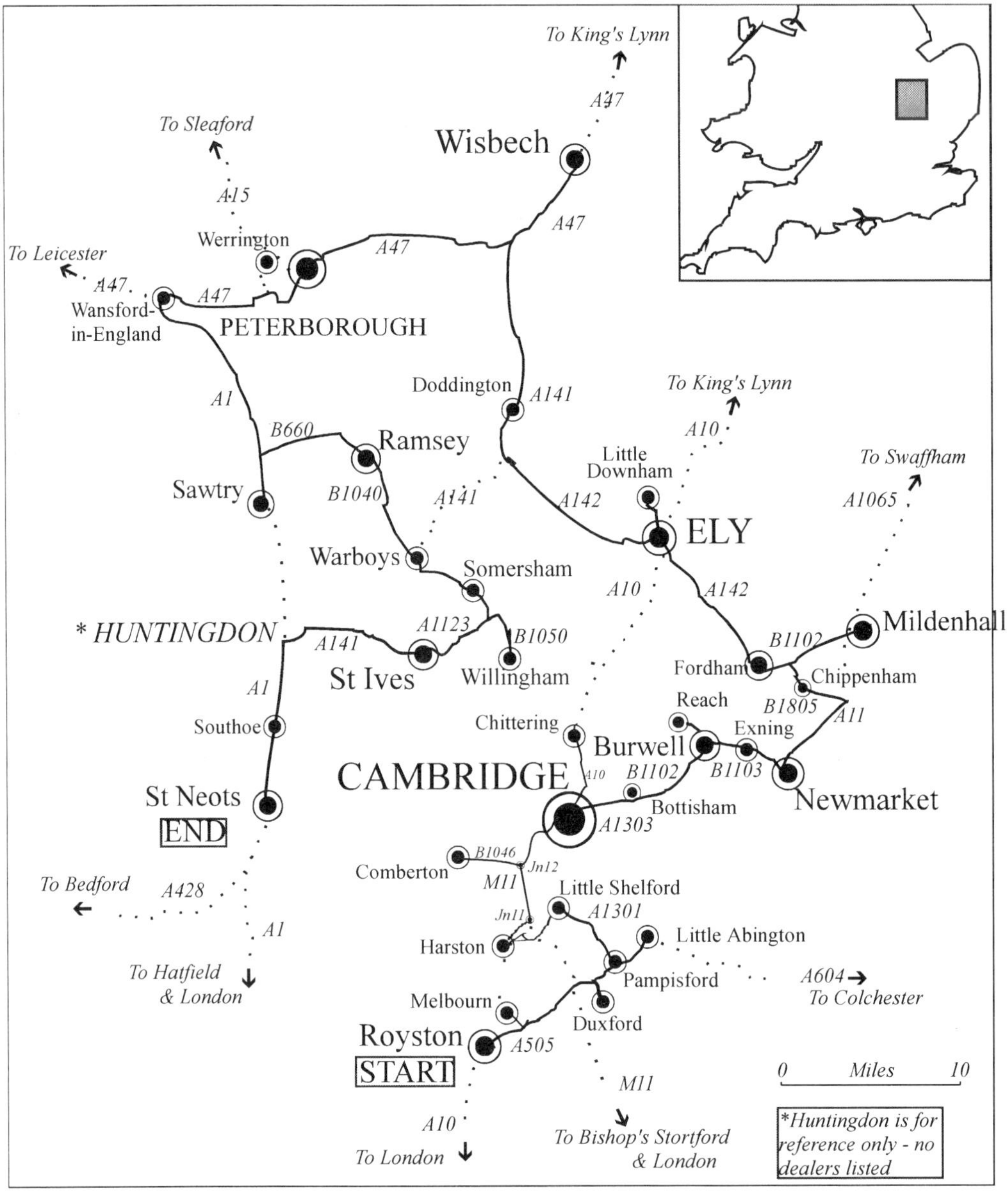

the immensely beautiful stained glass windows. The Adoration of the Magi by Rubens, the altar piece, was donated to the chapel in 1959.

Christopher Wren was involved in another of the Colleges. Pembroke College's new chapel of 1663 was built with a donation from Bishop Wren of Ely, uncle of Christopher whose design of the chapel was his first commission. This college is even earlier than King's having been founded in 1346 by the Countess of Pembroke. This is only a small taste of the University. The other Colleges are just as fascinating with wonderful stories attached and indeed whole books written about them.

Turning to the town, it is as steeped in history as the University. There is evidence of a settlement here from prehistoric times. There are several fine museums. The Fitzwilliam Museum in Trumpington Street has a picture gallery and an exhibition of antiquities, ceramics, drawings, prints and historical and medieval manuscripts. Cambridge & County Folk Museum, Castle Street, housed in the former White Horse Inn, covers the ordinary lives of the people of Cambridgeshire over the last three hundred years. The Sedgwick Museum of Geology, Downing Street, is, as its name suggests, a collection of rocks, ornamental marbles, etc and includes one million fossils. Historic scientific instruments from the 16th to 19th century can be seen at the Whipple Museum of the History of Science in Free School Lane. This is not an exhaustive list of the museums either. Cambridge is another place where it is essential for visitors to go to the Tourist Information Centre.

The next stops are in **Chittering, Bottisham** and then **Burwell,** a sprawling village whose history goes back beyond the Middle Ages. There is a sad memorial here to a major tragedy in the village. A tombstone, carved with a flaming heart, marks the grave of 82 people who died on the 8th September 1727. A travelling puppet showman had set up his theatre in a barn and people came from far and wide to see him. Although the audience was larger than the barn could comfortably hold the doors were closed. A few moments later a fire started which quickly engulfed the audience. Try as they might, the people could not escape because someone had nailed the doors shut. Later a man was accused of arson but he was acquitted at Cambridge Assizes. Nearly fifty years later, however, on his deathbed, a Fordham man confessed to starting the fire because he wanted to spite the showman.

Just east is the tiny village of **Reach**, once the Roman river port for Cambridge. It was fed by a canal from the River Cam at Upware and the quays were in use through medieval times. After first stopping in the village of **Exning**, the route crosses briefly into Suffolk to visit **Newmarket**. Closely associated with horseracing since the 17th century, the headquarters of the Jockey Club are here as is the National Stud. A National Horseracing Museum contains paintings by Stubbs and Munnings. Racing is omnipresent in and around Newmarket, from the obviously horsey types in the streets and pubs to the gallops and stables around the town. A disastrous fire in 1683 virtually destroyed the town and the only surviving building, a house in Palace Street, is said to have belonged to Nell Gwynne, mistress of Charles II.

The tour moves on to **Chippenham** and then again into Suffolk and **Mildenhall**, the site of an American Airforce base. The church has the largest porch in the county. A legacy of the Civil War may be seen in the arrowheads and shot embedded in the wood of the roof.

Back in Cambridgeshire the village of **Fordham** is next, with its famous abbey, and then the route arrives in **Ely** (pronounced eelee). According to the Venerable Bede, the town acquired its name because of the large numbers of eels caught in the fens. The magnificent cathedral dominates the surrounding Fenland and was begun, as part of a monastery, in 1083 when Ely was an island. Notable features are the octagonal lantern tower and choir stalls, both designed by Alan de Walsingham. The west front and tower, the lady chapel, the prior's door, and the chantry chapels are also of note. There is a 15th century Bishop's Palace and across the green is the Chantry, a late 17th century house. The ancient grammar school incorporates a gateway house known as Ely Porta, and the beautiful Prior Crauden's Chapel is now the school chapel.

*Ely Cathedral*

The old vicarage, once a tithe house, was the home of Oliver Cromwell and his family for ten years.

In the 11th century the surrounding area, at that time treacherous marshland, gave sanctuary to Hereward the Wake and his followers who provided the last Saxon resistance to the Norman invasion. He held out against the Normans until 1071 and was only defeated when a road was built across the marshes. His defeat signalled the end of Saxon hopes.

South of Ely lies Wicken Fen, in the care of the National Trust and one of the most important wetland reserves in Europe. The Fens once covered 2500 acres and Wicken is all that remains undrained making it a refuge for many rare species of plants, birds, butterflies and moths. The Fens have gradually been drained to provide rich agricultural land and much of this lies well below sea level because, once drained, the peat contracts. As Wicken has never been drained it now stands above the surrounding land and so water has to be pumped up to it while the boundary banks have been sealed to prevent leakage to the surrounding area.

Passing through the villages of **Little Downham** and **Doddington,** next is **Wisbech**. It is incredible to think, looking at the town now, that this was once a thriving port. 250 years ago the River Nene, on which the town stands, was navigable right into the heart of Wisbech and so trade with Holland was of considerable importance. Unfortunately, the shifting coastline of the Wash has meant that the town is now 12 miles from the coast and not accessible to ships. A legacy of its former prosperity can be found in the many fine Georgian merchants' houses situated facing the quays and river. The Dutch influence is seen in some of the architecture with Dutch gables and hipped roofs.

On the north bank of the River Nene in Wisbech stands Peckover House owned by one of the leading Quaker merchants of the town, Jonathan Peckover. He bought the house in 1777 and five years later set up a bank in partnership, with two others, in a wing of the house. The bank, Gurney, Birkbeck and Peckover merged with Barclays a century later. Although the house itself has some notable features it is the garden that is truly delightful. This has survived as a Victorian garden in which each of the plants is as important as the overall effect. It has some superb specimens: a tulip tree, redwoods, a ginkgo, a Chusan palm and a monkey puzzle tree. There is also an orangery, with three orange trees that bear fruit, and a fern house. Of interest to animal lovers is the cats' cemetery which commemorates the owners' pets.

To the west, **Peterborough** is also on the Nene. This city grew up around a medieval monastery but today few historic buildings survive. Those that do include the Knight's Gateway, the Bishop's Palace, and the west gateway which is of Norman and 14th century origin. St John's Church dates back to the 15th century and houses a painting of Charles I. The museum in Priestgate contains Roman remains and also has a costume gallery, a Victorian nursery and a period shop.

However, Peterborough's high point is the cathedral, built during the 12th century. Although some authorities do not rate the outside highly, it is agreed that inside is a wonderful example of Norman architecture. Particularly interesting are the west front, the painted nave ceiling, the nave arcades, and the fan tracery in the 15th century retrochoir. Both Catherine of Aragon, Henry VIII's first wife, and Mary, Queen of Scots were buried in the cathedral, although Mary was later moved to Westminster Abbey. There is also an 18th century picture of Robert Scarlett, the verger who buried both queens.

Just north is **Werrington** and seven miles west is the village of **Wansford-in England** with special railway workshops for the Peterborough Railway Society, who operate a seven mile stretch of track back to Peterborough in the summer and at Christmas. Unusually, the engines also include some from Europe. 13 miles south is **Sawtry**, associated with the martyr, William Sawtry, who was burnt at the stake for his beliefs in 1401. On to **Ramsey,** where there are the remains of a Benedictine Abbey founded in AD969 by St Oswald, Archbishop of York, and Ailwyn, foster-brother to King Edgar. Little remains of the abbey, only parts of the gatehouse and a small room with a mid 13th century marble tomb. Nearby **Warboys** is another village with a church of note. It has a good 13th century tower and broach spire, a Norman chancel arch, and a rare lion door knocker.

After the villages of **Somersham** and **Willingham**, whose restored church has an interesting tower and spire, the tour moves on to **St Ives**. A market town on the River Ouse, it has strong associations with Oliver Cromwell who was churchwarden here. A statue of Cromwell can be seen on Market Hill. There is a 15th century bridge with a rare restored chapel on it. A fine collection of local items can be seen in the Norris Museum.The penultimate call is on **Southoe,** finally followed by **St Neots** whose 15th century church is said to have one of the finest towers in the country.

## ANTIQUE DEALERS

### MELBOURN (01763)

**PN Hardiman**, 62 High Street, SG8 6AJ TEL: 260093 PARKING: Own carpark OPEN: Mon-Sat 9-5 MIN: £300 MAX: £4000 PERIOD: 18th-20th century GENERAL: Furniture.

### ROYSTON (01763)

**Royston Antiques**, 29 Kneesworth Street, SG8 5AB TEL: 243876 PARKING: Own carpark OPEN: Mon-Wed, Fri-Sat 09.30-5 MIN: £1 MAX: £2000 PERIOD: 19th-20th century SPECIALIST: Furniture GENERAL: General antiques & collectables OTHER INFO: Next to King James I Palace and opposite Royston Museum. Market days Wed & Sat. The medieval Cave was once used by the Knights Templar. The Bull is 17th century hotel.

### DUXFORD (01223)

**Riro D Mooney**, Mill Lane, CB2 4PS TEL: 832252 PARKING: Easy OPEN: Mon-Sat 9-7 MIN: £100 MAX: £1000 PERIOD: 19th-20th century GENERAL: Wide attractive range of quality stock.

### PAMPISFORD (01223)

**Rose Cottage Antiques,** Rose Cottage, Brewery Road, CB2 4EW TEL: 834631 PARKING: Own carpark MIN: £20 MAX: £4000 PERIOD: 18th-20th century SPECIALIST: Mainly furniture OTHER INFO: Services include cabinet making. Restoration undertaken by myself on the premises.

**Solopark Ltd,** The Old Railway Station, CB2 4HB TEL: 834663 FAX: 834780 PARKING: Own carpark PERIOD: 18th-20th century SPECIAL-

IST: Traditional building materials & architectural items OTHER INFO: 6 acre storage yard (all concreted) including a 7500sq ft showroom & display areas.

## LITTLE ABINGTON (01223)

**Abington Books**, 29 Church Lane TEL: 891645 FAX: 893724 PARKING: Easy OPEN: By appt MIN: £1 MAX: £5000+ PERIOD: 19th-20th century SPECIALIST: Books on Oriental rugs & classical tapestries.

## LITTLE SHELFORD (01223)

**Cambridge Fine Art**, Priesthouse, 33 Church Street, CB2 5HG TEL: 842866 ASSNS: LAPADA PARKING: Own carpark OPEN: Mon-Sat 10-6, Sun by appt MIN: £10 MAX: £40,000 PERIOD: 18th-20th century SPECIALIST: British & European oils 1750-1940. GENERAL: Some watercolours & a large selection of Kronheim-Baxter process prints of 1850s OTHER INFO: Large galleries in country house setting. A natural beginning or end to your tour being just off M11, 4 miles south of Cambridge.

## HARSTON (01223)

**Antique Clocks**, 1 High Street, CB2 5PX TEL: 870264 PARKING Own carpark OPEN: 9-6 MIN: £50 PERIOD: 18th-19th century SPECIALIST: All types of clocks.

## COMBERTON (01223)

**Comberton Antiques**, 5a West Street, CB3 7DS TEL: 262674 PARKING Own carpark OPEN: Fri, Sat, Mon 10-5, Sun 2-5 MIN: £5 MAX: £2000 PERIOD: 18th-19th century SPECIALIST: Victorian furniture GENERAL: Good furniture & general antiques OTHER INFO: Wimpole Hall (NT), good B&B's in village.

## CAMBRIDGE (01223)

**20th Century**, 169 Histon Road, CB4 3JD TEL: 359482 PARKING Own carpark OPEN: Tues-Fri 12-6, Sat 10-5 MIN: £5 MAX: £2000 PERIOD: 20th century SPECIALIST: Arts & Crafts, Art Nouveau, Art Deco, furniture, ceramics, lighting, jewellery, smalls.

**Jess Applin Antiques**, 8 Lensfield, CB2 1EG TEL: 315168 PARKING: Easy OPEN: Mon-Sat 9.30-5.30 MIN: £20 MAX: £10,000 PERIOD: 17th-19th century SPECIALIST: Furniture & works of art.

**John Beazor & Sons Ltd,** 78-80 Regent Street, CB2 1DP TEL: 355178 ASSNS: BADA PARKING Medium OPEN: Mon-Sat 9-5 MIN: £300 MAX: £20,000. PERIOD 18th-19th century SPECIALIST: Furniture GENERAL: Clocks, barometers, decorative items OTHER: Good hotels, 1 hour from London.

**Benet Gallery**, 19 King's Parade CB2 1SP TEL: 353783 PARKING: Very difficult OPEN: Mon-Sat 9-5 MIN: £1 MAX: £1000 PERIOD: 17th-20th century SPECIALIST: Maps & views mostly related to Cambridge and its colleges 1575-1994 OTHER INFO: Presentation pictures for retiring and visiting acadamics.

**Buckies Jewellers, Silversmiths & Valuers**, 31 Trinity Street, CB2 1TB TEL: 357910 ASSNS: NAG, LAPADA, GA PARKING Multi-storey nearby OPEN: Tues-Sat 9.45-5 MIN: £15 MAX: £15,000 PERIOD: 19th-20th century SPECIALIST: Antique, secondhand jewellery & silverware GENERAL: Distinctive new jewellery, silverware & giftware. Antique coloured glassware.

**Collector's Market**, Unit 3, Dales Brewery, Gwydir Street (off Mill Street) CB1 2LJ PARKING Easy OPEN: Mon-Sat 10-5 MIN: £1 MAX: £700 PERIOD: 19th-20th century SPECIALIST: Fireplaces, kitchenalia GENERAL: Sofa, mirrors, pictures, easy chairs etc OTHER INFO: One of 4 markets in this brewery. ° mile from colleges & universities. Garden House Hotel. Good food at The Plough pub. Excellent Midsummer House restaurant. Another 2 antique shops just outside Collectors' Market.

**Gabor Cossa Antiques**, 34 Trumpington Street, CB2 1QY TEL: 356049 PARKING: Medium OPEN: Mon-Sat 10-5.30 MIN: £5 MAX: £2000 PERIOD: 17th-19th century SPECIALIST: English & Continental Delft, early & Chinese ceramics, English glass.

**Cottage Antiques**, 16-18 Lensfield Road, CB2 1EG TEL: 316698 PARKING Medium OPEN: Mon-Sat 10-5.30 MIN: £2 MAX: £2000 PERIOD: 18th-19th century SPECIALIST: Ceramics GENERAL: Glass, copper, brass, country furniture, antiquities - Roman, British, Etruscan etc OTHER: We run a B&B 6 miles NW at Oakington.

**G David Bookseller**, 3, 4, & 16 St.Edward's Passage, CB2 3PJ TEL: 354619 FAX: 324663 ASSNS: ABA, PBFA, BA PARKING Difficult (but Lion

Yard Car Park 100yds away) OPEN: Mon-Sat 9-5 MIN: £1 MAX: £3000 PERIOD: 17th-20th century SPECIALIST: Fine antiquarian books on most books GENERAL: Secondhand books & publishers remainders on most subject.

**Gwydir Street Antiques Centre**, Units 1 & 2, Dales Brewery, Gwydir Street (off Mill Road), CB1 2LJ TEL: 356391 PARKING: Easy OPEN: Mon-Fri 10-5, Sun 11-5 MIN: £1 MAX: £500+ PERIOD: 19th-20th century GENERAL: Victorian & Edwardian furniture, sofas, mirrors, rugs & textiles.

**Hyde Park Corner Antiques**, 12 Lensfield Road, CB2 1EG TEL: 353654 PARKING Medium OPEN:Mon-Sat 10-5 MIN: £5 MAX: £1000 PERIOD: 18th- 19th century GENERAL: General antiques OTHER INFO: Three antiques shops in a row & 5 more within easy walking distance. Garden House Hotel, famous Brown's restaurant.

**Sebastian Pearson**, 3 Free School Lane, Benet Street, CB2 3QA TEL: 323999 PARKING Medium OPEN: Tues-Sat 10-5.30 MIN: £30 MAX: £4000 PERIOD: 18th -20th century SPECIALIST: 20th century British etchings GENERAL:19th-20th century oils and watercolours, 19th century prints, sporting & topographical.

**Barry Strover**, 55 Sturton Street, CB1 2QG TEL: 66302 PARKING: Easy OPEN: Chance or by appt MIN: £50 MAX: £5000 PERIOD: 18th-19th century SPECIALIST: Exclusively original painted pine, particularly dressers. Trading from warehouse for trade & public.

## CHITTERING (01223)

**Simon & Penny Rumble**, The Old School, CB5 9PW TEL: 861831 PARKING: Easy OPEN: Generally open but appt advisable PERIOD: 17th-18th century SPECIALIST: Oak & country furniture OTHER INFO: Next to good food pub.

## BOTTISHAM (01223)

**Cambridge Pine & Oak,** Hall Farm, Lode Road, CB5 9DN TEL: 811208 PARKING Own carpark OPEN:: Mon-Sat 10-5 MIN: £50 MAX: £1,200 PERIOD: 18th-20th century SPECIALIST: Pine OTHER INFO: Half mile from Anglesey Abbey.

## BURWELL (01638)

**Peter Norman Antiques**, 55 North Street, CB5 0BA TEL: 742197 ASSNS: GMC PARKING Own carpark OPEN: Mon-Sat 9-5.30 MIN: £200 MAX: £3,000 PERIOD: 17th-19th century GENERAL: Furniture, clocks, arms and Oriental rugs.

## REACH (01638)

**Reach Antiques**, Vine House (Antiques Warehouse) TEL: 741989 FAX: 743239 ASSNS: GMC, Assn. of Master Upholsters PARKING Own carpark OPEN: Mon-Fri 7.30-6, Sat 8-12 & anytime by appt MIN: £20 MAX: £3,000 PERIOD: 19th century GENERAL: Furniture for restoration. OTHER INFO: Personal collection of bygones on display. All restoration services. Good village pub & food.

## EXNING (01638)

**Derby Cottage Antiques & Collectables**, Derby Cottage, Fordham Road, CB8 7LG TEL: 578422 PARKING: Own carpark OPEN: 9-7 MIN: £1 MAX: £1,500 PERIOD: 19th-20th century SPECIALIST: Derby porcelain GENERAL: Furniture, collectables, bygones, porcelain.

## NEWMARKET (01638)

**Equus Art Gallery**, Sun Lane, CB8 8EW TEL & FAX: 560445 ASSNS: FATG PARKING: Easy OPEN: 9.30-5.30, Wed closes 1pm MIN: £200 MAX: £5000 PERIOD: 20th century SPECIALIST: Racing art GENERAL: Paintings, drawings, sculpture, prints.

**Jemima Godfrey**, 5 Rous Road, CB8 8DN TEL: 663584 PARKING: Medium OPEN: Thurs-Fri 10-1, 2-4.30 & by appt MIN: £1 MAX: £500 PERIOD: 19th-20th century SPECIALIST: Linen GENERAL: Jewellery, collectables, silverplate, postcards, bric-a-brac OTHER INFO: Racing museum, Jockey Club, Tattersalls racehorse sales, 2 courses & extensive training grounds.

## CHIPPENHAM (01638)

**Chippenham Antiques Centre,** La Hogue Farm, CB7 5PZ TEL: 751533 PARKING: Own carpark OPEN: 7 days 10-6 MIN: £1 MAX: £5000 PERIOD: 17th-20th century GENERAL: Furniture, pictures, glass, china, bric a brac, shipping goods.

## MILDENHALL (01638)

**Hunt & Clement Antiques,** 10 North Terrace TEL: 718025 PARKING: Own carpark OPEN: Mon-Sat 10-5 MIN: £1 MAX: £1000 PERIOD: 19th-20th century SPECIALIST: Antique pine, 1900-20s oak OTHER INFO: Near the US airbase.

## FORDHAM (01638)

**Phoenix Antiques**, 1 Carter Street, CB7 5NG TEL: 720363 PARKING Own carpark OPEN: Prefer by appt MIN: £5 MAX: £10,000 PERIOD: 16th-18th century SPECIALIST: Pre 1750 interiors GENERAL: General antiques OTHER INFO: Anglesea Abbey & Newmarket Racing Museum. B&B on premises (16th century 4 poster bed).

## ELY (01353)

**Mrs Mills Antiques**, 1a St Mary's Street, CB7 4ER TEL: 664268 PARKING: Easy OPEN: Mon, Wed-Sat 10-1, 2-5 MIN: £5 MAX: £1,000 PERIOD: 19th-20th century GENERAL: Porcelain, silver, jewellery OTHER INFO: Thursday is market day.
**Waterside Antiques**, The Wharf, CB7 4AU TEL: 667066 PARKING Own carpark OPEN: Mon-Sat 9.30-5.30, Sun 1-5.30 MIN: £1 MAX: £5,000 PERIOD: 17th-20th century GENERAL: Antique centre with 70 dealers offering a complete range of antiques & collectables. Some specialists OTHER INFO: We are by the waterside with cafeterias & restaurants close by.

## LITTLE DOWNHAM (01353)

**The Bishops Palace Antique Centre**, Tower Farm, Tower Road, CB6 2TD TEL: 699177 PARKING: Own carpark OPEN: Fri-Sun + bank hols 10-5.30 MIN: £5 MAX: £4100 PERIOD: 17th-20th century SPECIALIST: Pictures & prints, guns, fishing tackle, golf clubs, lace, linens, kelims, SE Asian artifacts, bronzes, swords, clocks, etc GENERAL: Furniture, smalls OTHER INFO: In medieval Bishop of Ely's Summer Palace, a beautiful, historic building in grounds of Tower Farm. Excellent B&B's, country pub: The Plough.

## DODDINGTON (01354)

**Doddington House Antiques**, 2 Benwick Road, PE15 0TG TEL: 740755 PARKING Own carpark OPEN: Mon-Sat 10-5.30 MIN: £10 MAX: £3000 PERIOD: 18th-19th century SPECIALIST: Clocks, barometers, furniture OTHER INFO: Restoration service on barometers, clocks, plus chair caning.

## WISBECH (01945)

**Peter A Crofts**, 117 High Road, Elm, PE14 0DN TEL: 584616 ASSNS: BADA, CINOA PARKING Own carpark OPEN: Mon-Fri 8-5 (pls telephone) MIN: £5 MAX: £5000 PERIOD: 18th-20th century SPECIALIST: Pottery & porcelain, silver GENERAL: Furniture, glass, Victorian jewellery OTHER INFO: We have a large warehouse beside a bungalow - NO SIGN. Good pub on corner.
**AP & MA Haylett,** Glen Royd, 393 Wisbech Road, Outwell PE14 8PG TEL: 772427 PARKING: Own carpark OPEN: 8.30-6 MIN: £1 MAX: £1500 PERIOD: 18th-20th century SPECIALIST: Country furniture & metalware GENERAL: Treen, pottery, glass & furniture.
**Walpole Highway Antiques Centre,** Main Road, Walpole Highway, PE14 7RN TEL: 881033 PARKING: Own carpark OPEN: 7 days 10.30-5 MIN: £1 MAX: £2000 GENERAL: 35 dealers in centre with varied, constantly changing stock.

## PETERBOROUGH (01733)

**Fitzwilliam Antiques Centres Ltd.**, Fitzwilliam Street PE1 2RX TEL: 65415 PARKING Own carpark OPEN: Mon-Sat 10-5, Sun 12-5 MIN: £5 MAX: £5000+ GENERAL: 40+ dealers showing quality stock including porcelain, furniture, pine, jewellery, glass, maps, books, toys, silver, commemorative coins OTHER INFO: Peterborough is a development city with an 11th century cathedral, 5 miles from the M1. Many good hotels, leisure park, Queensgate Shopping Centre.
**Old Soke Books**, 68 Burghley Road, PE1 2QE TEL: 64147 PARKING: Medium OPEN: Tues-Sat 10.30-5.30 MIN: £1 MAX: £300 PERIOD: 19th century GENERAL: Mostly secondhand and old books, good selection of prints, some paintings & small antiques.

## WERRINGTON (01733)

**G Smith & Son (Peterboro') Ltd,** The Mill House, 1379 Lincoln Road, PE4 6LT TEL: 571630 PARKING: Easy OPEN: 9.30-5, no Sundays MIN: Few £s MAX: £2500 PERIOD: 18th-20th century SPECIALIST: Furniture & clocks GENERAL: Bric a brac, restoration.

## WANSFORD-IN-ENGLAND (01780)

**Lamps & Candles,** 16 London Road, PE8 6JB TEL & FAX: 783999 PARKING: Easy OPEN: Tues-Fri 9.30-1, 2-6, Sat 9-1, 2.30-6 MIN: £50 MAX: £10,000 PERIOD: 19th-20th century SPECIALIST: Period lighting OTHER INFO: Opposite the renowned Haycock Hotel on crossroads A1/A47.

**Old House Antiques**, 16 London Road, PE8 6JB TEL: 783462, 783999 FAX: 783452 PARKING Easy OPEN: Tues-Sat 9.30-6 & by appt PERIOD: 19th-20th century SPECIALIST: Period lighting 1850's-1950's GENERAL: Glass, lighting, candles

## SAWTRY (01487)

**A Barn Full of Brass Beds**, Manor Farm, St Judiths Lane, PE17 5XE TEL: 832664 PARKING: Own carpark OPEN: By appt MIN: £250 MAX: £1000 PERIOD: 19th century SPECIALIST: 200 antique brass & iron beds.

## RAMSEY (01487)

**Abbey Antiques**, 63 Great Whyte, PE17 1HL TEL: 814753 PARKING Easy OPEN: Tues-Sun 10-5 MIN: £3 MAX: £1500 PERIOD: 19th-20th century SPECIALIST: Collectables: Doulton, Beswick, Carlton, Goss, Victoriana, Wade, Shelley. Small furniture OTHER INFO: Enesco, Mabel Lucie Attwell, figurines. we have formed special club: 'Memories UK' for collectors of Memories of Yesterday Mabel Lucie Attwell figurines.

## WARBOYS (01487)

**Warboys' Antiques**, Old Church School, High Street, PE17 2RH TEL: 823686 FAX: (01480) 496296 PARKING Own carpark OPEN: Tues-Sat 11-5 MIN: £1 MAX: £2500 PERIOD: 19th-20th century SPECIALIST: Biscuit tins, advertising, sporting items GENERAL: 2000 sq ft of best selection of collectables in Cambs. OTHER INFO: Warboys is one of historic centres of English witchcraft.

## SOMERSHAM (01487)

**TW Pawson Clocks**, 31 High Street, PE17 3JA TEL: 841537 ASSNS: BWCMG PARKING: Easy OPEN: Mon-Fri 9.30-6 Sat 9.30-1 MIN: £100 MAX: £5000 PERIOD: 18th-19th century SPECIALIST: Clocks & barometers GENERAL: Repair & restoration of antique clocks & barometers OTHER INFO: On the edge of the Fens in a typical Fenland farming village.

## WILLINGHAM (01954)

**Willingham Antiques**, 27 Green Street, CB4 5JA TEL: 60283 PARKING Easy OPEN: Mon-Wed, Fri-Sun 10-5 MIN: £5 MAX: £1000 PERIOD: 18th-19th century GENERAL: General antiques OTHER INFO: Good food, pubs, good parking outside.

## ST IVES (01480)

**BR Knight & Sons**, Quay Court, Bull Lane off Bridge Street, PE17 4AR TEL: 468295, 300042 PARKING Easy OPEN: Mon, Fri-Sat 11-3 MIN: £1 MAX: £250 PERIOD: 18th-20th century SPECIALIST: Art, pottery, pictures by Huntingdonshire artists GENERAL: Pottery, porcelain, pictures, prints, costume & Victorian jewellery OTHER INFO: Historic town in Cromwell country, the 15th century bridge with a chapel in the middle, is one of only three in England. Light meals at Lizzy's on riverside quay.

## SOUTHOE (01480)

**Midloe Grange Antiques & Design,** Rectory Lane, PE18 9YD TEL: 404029 FAX: 471658 PARKING: Own carpark OPEN: Mon-Fri 8-5, weekends by appt MIN: £10 MAX: £4500 PERIOD: 17th-19th century GENERAL: Country & decorative pine.

## ST NEOTS (01480)

**Tavistock Antiques,** Cross Hall Manor, Eaton Ford PE19 4AH TEL: 472082 FAX: 407736 OPEN: By appt MIN: £500 MAX: £20,000 PERIOD: 18th century SPECIALIST: English furniture & decorative items.

# Bedfordshire & Northants

Perhaps the counties of Bedfordshire and Northamptonshire lack the telling scenery of Devon or Cornwall or Cumbria but in their own way they have much to offer the visitor. The countryside is still beautiful and typically English with green fields surrounded by hedges, small villages with thatched cottages and towns that are rich in history.

The tour starts in **Ampthill**, once the site of a 15th century castle, it is a pleasant town with many fine Georgian buildings. The largely 15th century church has a peculiar memorial: the tomb of Colonel Richard Nicolls is inside the church with the cannonball which killed him set above.

Crossing briefly into Buckinghamshire, **Olney** is next. Standing on the River Ouse, the town has had a long association with boot making. William Cowper lived here between 1768 and 1786 and his home in Market Place is now the Cowper and Newton Museum (the Reverend John Newton wrote *Amazing Grace*). Cowper and Newton memorabilia is on display and there is an exhibition of bobbins and lace.

Travelling north, **Castle Ashby** is so-called because a castle has stood here since the 11th century. The original had disappeared by the 16th century and then in 1574 Lord Compton started construction of the present building which is more grand house than castle.

Now the route comes to the county town of **Northampton**, also well-known for the making of shoes. The Central Museum and Art Gallery in Guildhall Road has the largest collection of boots and shoes in the country as well as displays on the town's history from prehistoric times to the present day.

There are a number of fine country houses nearby. For example, Holdenby House stands seven miles to the north west. This was once the largest Elizabethan house in England and was used as a prison for Charles I during the Civil War. Another fine house is Cottesbrooke Hall, a magnificent Queen Anne building with an excellent collection of sporting and equestrian pictures, furniture and porcelain. Then, of course, there is Althorp, childhood home of the Princess of Wales. Standing 6 miles north west, it has been the home of the Spenser family since 1508. This too has a wonderful collection of pictures including Reynolds, Gainsboroughs, Rubens, Van Dycks, together with fine French furniture and rare porcelain..

After calling at the villages of **West Haddon** and **Arthingworth**, the route comes to **Market Harborough** on the River Welland. This town, in the centre of hunting country, has many fine Georgian buildings. The old grammar school was built in 1614 and stands on wooden pillars. The church of St Dionysius is said to have been founded by John of Gaunt and dates from between the 13th and 15th centuries. Just two miles west on the A427, **Lubenham** is next before the route turns south to **Kettering**, on the banks of the River Ise and best known for the manufacture of footwear. The remains of a Roman settlement have been found nearby and some of the finds sit in the local museum. Three miles north stands Boughton House. It was built in the grand manner, on the site of an earlier monastery, by Ralph Montagu, one-time ambassador to the Court of Louis XIV. The French influence is strongly reflected in the building and the magnificent treasures inside including works by El Greco, Murillo, Caracci and 40 Van Dyck sketches.

Continuing along the A6 the tour reaches **Finedon** where The Old Bell is one of the earliest inns in the country. The church has a 133 feet spire and an unusual carved strainer-arch in the nave. Two miles north east is Wellington Tower, built in commemoration of the Duke of Wellington's visit.

Nearby **Wellingborough** is another Northamptonshire town associated with footwear. On the River Nene, its church dates from the 14th and 15th centuries and All Hallows church hall is a 17th century stone built house. Five miles away, **Rushden** also has a beautiful church.

12 miles south on the A6, **Bedford** is next. This town has been in existence since Saxon times.

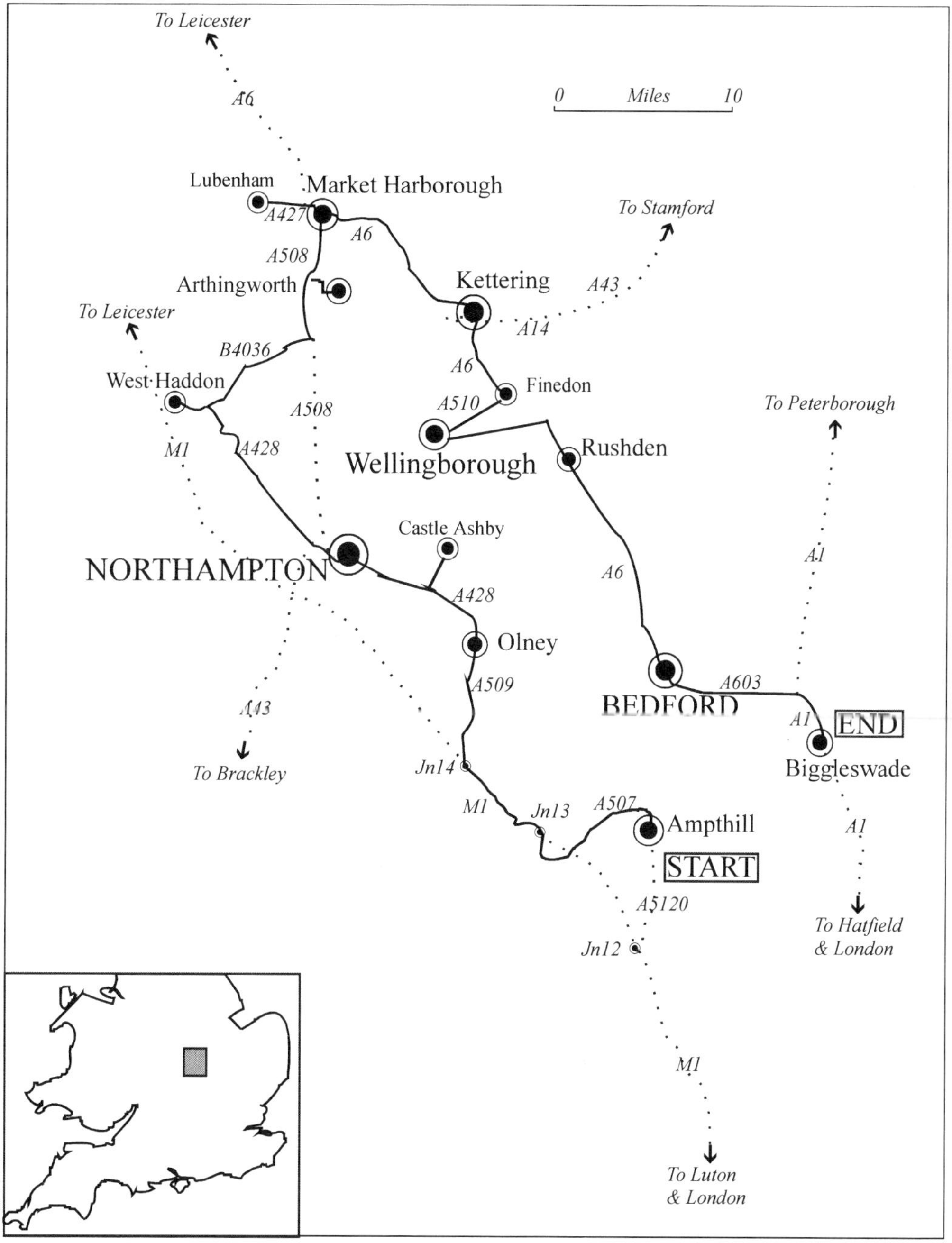
To Leicester
A6
0 Miles 10
Lubenham
Market Harborough
A427
A6
To Stamford
A508
Arthingworth
Kettering
A43
To Leicester
A14
B4036
A6
West Haddon
Finedon
A510
A508
To Peterborough
Rushden
M1
A428
Wellingborough
Castle Ashby
A1
NORTHAMPTON
A6
A428
Olney
A509
A603
A43
BEDFORD
A1
END
To Brackley
Jn14
Biggleswade
M1
Jn13
A507
Ampthill
A1
START
A5120
To Hatfield
& London
Jn12
M1
To Luton
& London

It was sacked and burned by the Danes in 1010 and a castle built here by the Normans of which only the mound remains. St Peter's Church still has some Saxon stonework bearing burnmarks, said to have been made during the Danish attack. John Bunyan was imprisoned in Bedford gaol and wrote *The Pilgrim's Progress* whilst there. The Bunyan Meeting Library and Museum in Mill street contains all the surviving relics of John Bunyan as well as copies of *The Pilgrim's Progress* in 169 languages. The Cecil Higgins Art Gallery & Museum in Castle Close should have special interest for lovers of antiques. Here they have re-created the Victorian home of a prosperous brewer.

The final stop is **Biggleswade** perhaps best known for its aerodrome and the Shuttleworth Collection of cars and aeroplanes. It was started by Richard Shuttleworth in the 1920s. On the outbreak of war he joined, naturally enough, the RAF but was unfortunately killed in 1940. His mother preserved the collection as a memorial to her son.

## ANTIQUE DEALERS

### AMPTHILL (01525)

**Ampthill Antiques**, 4 Market Square, MK45 2PJ TEL: 403344 PARKING: Easy OPEN: Mon-Sat 9.30-5, Sun 2-5 MIN: £1 MAX: £4000 PERIOD: 18th-20th century GENERAL: Jewellery, Clarice Cliff, etc, clocks OTHER INFO: Bunyan Country & Houghton House.

**Robert Harman**, 30 Church Street, MK45 2EH TEL: 402322 ASSNS: BADA, LAPADA OPEN: Mon-Sat 9.30-5 MIN: £200 MAX: £50,000 PERIOD: 17th-early 19th century SPECIALIST: Tea caddies, works of art GENERAL: Furniture.

**The Pine Parlour**, 82A Dunstable Street, MK45 2JS TEL: 403030 PARKING: Easy OPEN: Tues-Sun 10-5 MIN: £5 MAX: £800 PERIOD: 19th-20th century SPECIALIST: Georgian & Victorian pine furniture GENERAL: Kitchenalia, country bygones & interesting cast iron objects including Victorian mangles.

**S & S Timms Antiques Ltd**, 20 Dunstable Street, MK45 2JT TEL: 403067 & 0860 482995 FAX: 715883 ASSNS: LAPADA PARKING: Medium OPEN: Mon-Fri 9.30-5, Sat 10-4 or by appt MIN: £100 MAX: £8000 PERIOD: 18th-20th century GENERAL: Furniture, copper, brass & fine art.

### OLNEY (01234)

**Fenlan Antiques**, 17B Stile Brook Road, Yardley Industrial Estate, MK46 5EA TEL: 711799 PARKING: Own carpark OPEN: Mon-Fri 8.30-5.30, Sat 9.30-1 MIN: £20 MAX: £3500 PERIOD: 19th-20th century SPECIALIST: Furniture & restoration products & sundries OTHER INFO: Mainly workshop for restoration/cabinet making. Trade & public welcome. Village atmosphere, reasonably close to other antique outlets 12-15 mile radius.

**Market Square Antiques**, 20 Market Place, MK46 4BA TEL: 712172 PARKING: Easy OPEN: Mon-Sat 10-5, Sun 1-5 MIN: £10 MAX: £5000 PERIOD: 18th-20th century GENERAL: Furniture, porcelain, silver, glass OTHER INFO: Market town (market Thursdays). Also Cowper Museum, Church Park.

**Olney Antique Centre**, Rose Court, Market Place, MK46 4BA TEL: 712172 PARKING: Easy OPEN: Mon-Sat 10-5, Sun 1-5 MIN: £1 MAX: £1000 PERIOD: 18th-20th century GENERAL: General antiques.

**John Overland Antiques**, 7 Rose Court, Market Place, MK46 4BY TEL: 712351 PARKING: Own carpark OPEN: Mon-Sat 9.30-5 MIN: £5 MAX: £5000 PERIOD: 17th-19th century SPECIALIST: Country oak, Georgian mahogany GENERAL: Furniture & Vienna regulators, dial clocks OTHER INFO: Market town, 10 mins from M1.

**Pine Antiques**, 10 Market Place, MK46 4EA TEL: 711065 FAX: 510226 PARKING: Easy OPEN: Mon, Tues, Thurs, Fri 10-5, Sat 9.30-5.30 Sun 12-5 MAX: £800 PERIOD: 19th-20th century GENERAL: Pine & reclaimed timber furniture made to customers' requirements OTHER INFO: Famous pancake race, William Cowper Museum, good tearooms.

**Robert Unsworth Antiques,** 1 Weston Road, MK16 5BD TEL: 711210 PARKING: Easy OPEN: 10-4.30, Sun 12-4.30 MIN: £50 MAX: £2500 PERIOD: 18th-19th century SPECIALIST: Furniture.

## CASTLE ASHBY (01604)

**Geoffrey S Wright (Fine Paintings)**, The Old Farmyard, NN7 1LF TEL: 696787 ASSNS: FATG PARKING: Own carpark OPEN: 10-5.30 MIN: £100 MAX: £10,000 PERIOD: 19th-20th century SPECIALIST: British oils & watercolours GENERAL: Interior design accessories, decorative furniture & furnishings.

## NORTHAMPTON (01604)

**Buley Antiques**, 164 Kettering Road TEL: 31588, 491577 PARKING: Medium OPEN: Mon-Sat 10.30-4 MIN: £5 MAX: £200 PERIOD 19th-20th century GENERAL: Antiques & bric-a-brac OTHER INFO: Museums, parks, hotels.

**F & CH Cave**, 111 Kettering Road TEL: 38278 PARKING: Easy OPEN: Mon-Wed, Fri, Sat 9-5.30 MIN: £200 MAX: £8000 PERIOD 17th-19th century SPECIALIST: Antique & decorative furniture OTHER INFO: Large basement devoted to antiques only (ground floor & windows display new furniture), Swallow Hotel 5 Star, excellent meals & rooms, St. Matthews Church contains Henry Moore's Madonna & Graham Sutherland paintings. One of only 3 surviving Queen Eleanor's Crosses (the one at Charing Cross is a replica).

**Nostalgia Antiques**, 190 Kettering Road TEL: 33823 PARKING: Easy OPEN: Mon-Sat 10-5 MIN: £1 MAX: £400 PERIOD 19th-20th century SPECIALIST: Clocks, watches GENERAL: Militaria, tin plate, model cars, general antiques OTHER INFO: ° mile from town centre.

**Occultique**, 73 Kettering Road, NN1 4AW TEL: 27727 FAX: 603860 ASSNS: ABA PARKING: Medium OPEN: Mon-Sat 10-5 MIN: £1 MAX: £750 PERIOD 20th century SPECIALIST: Unusual, bizarre, occult & Oriental books & artifacts OTHER INFO: French Partridge, Houghton. Tourist info: Mr Grant's House, 10 St Giles Square.

**The Old Brigade**, 10a Harborough Road, Kingsthorpe, NN2 7AZ TEL: 719389 ASSNS: Arms & Militaria Society PARKING: Easy OPEN: Mon-Sat 10.30-5 MIN: £5 MAX: £5000 PERIOD 19th-20th century SPECIALIST: Antique arms & militaria, Third Reich items OTHER INFO: Trains from Euston (London) 1 hour.

**Penny's Antiques**, 83 Kettering Road, NN1 4AW TEL: 32429 PARKING: Easy OPEN: Mon-Wed 11-4, Fri 11-4, Sat 10-5 MIN: £1 MAX: £250 PERIOD 19th-20th century SPECIALIST: Chairs & pictures GENERAL: General antiques OTHER INFO: 200 year old shop, close to town centre, 2 other antique shops close & large furniture store.Hotels: Plough, Grand, Angel, Langham & Moathouse in or near town centre.

**Regent House Antiques**, Royal Terrace, NN1 3RF TEL: 37992 PARKING: Own carpark OPEN: Mon-Fri 10.30-5 MIN: £150 MAX: £15,000 PERIOD 17th-19th century SPECIALIST: Georgian furniture OTHER INFO: This detached Georgian house is furnished with antiques that are for sale. Near Regent Square, St. Sepulchre's Church (one of England's 4 remaining round churches) 5 mins walk, Lime Trees Hotel (2 star), nearby at 8 Langham Place.

**Talent Pastimes Ltd**, 85 Kettering Road, NN1 4AW TEL: 36396 PARKING: Medium OPEN: Mon-Sat 9-5 PERIOD: 18th-20th century SPECIALIST: UK stamps & postal history GENERAL: Postcards, cigarette cards OTHER INFO: 10 mins from town centre.

## WEST HADDON (01788)

**Antiques**, 9 West End, NN6 7AY TEL: 510772 PARKING: Easy OPEN: Tues-Sat 10-5 MIN: £30 MAX: £4500 PERIOD: 17th-19th century SPECIALIST: Copper, brass & ironwork GENERAL: Country furniture, metalwork & domestic items.

## ARTHINGWORTH (01858)

**Coughton Galleries Ltd**, The Old Manor, LE16 8JT TEL: 86436 FAX: 86535 PARKING: Own carpark OPEN: Wed-Thur, Sat-Sun 10.30-5 MIN: £150 MAX: £5,000 PERIOD: 20th century GENERAL: Modern British & Irish oils & watercolours.

## MARKET HARBOROUGH (01858)

**Abbey Antiques**, 17 Abbey Street, LE16 9AA TEL: 462282 PARKING: Easy OPEN: 10.30-5 MIN: £1 MAX: £2000 PERIOD: 19th century GENERAL: Smalls of all kinds, furniture, old pine OTHER INFO: Good hotels with restaurants: The Three Swans & The Angel.

**Graftons of Market Harborough,** 92 St Mary's Road, LE16 7DX TEL: 433557 PARKING: Own carpark OPEN: 10-5, closed Wed pm MIN: £5 MAX: £1000 PERIOD: 18th-19th century

SPECIALIST: Agricultural & farming prints GENERAL: Oils, watercolours, prints.

**Richard Kimbell Ltd**, Rockingham Road, LE16 7PT TEL: 433444 FAX: 461301 PARKING: Own carpark OPEN: Mon-Sat 9-6, Sun 10.30-4.30 MIN: £1 MAX: £3000 PERIOD: 19th century SPECIALIST: Antique & reproduction pine GENERAL: Country furniture & crafts.

**J Stamp & Sons**, The Chestnuts, 15 Kettering Road, LE16 8AN TEL: 462524 FAX: 465643 PARKING: Own carpark OPEN: Mon-Fri 8-5, Sat 9-12.30 & by appt MIN: £50 MAX: £,000 PERIOD: 18th-19th century SPECIALIST: Mahogany, oak, walnut furniture OTHER INFO: Restorers.

**Duncan Watts Oriental Rugs**, 90 St Mary's Road TEL & FAX: 462620 ASSNS: LAPADA PARKING: Easy OPEN: By appt MIN: £20 MAX: £2500 PERIOD: 19th-20th century SPECIALIST: Oriental rugs only.

## LUBENHAM (01858)

**Leicestershire Sporting Gallery,** 62 Main Street, LE16 9DG TEL: 465787 ASSNS: Racecourse BPA PARKING: Own carpark OPEN: 10-5 MIN: £2 PERIOD: 19th century SPECIALIST: Original Vanity Fair cartoons, sporting books, prints & oils, horse brasses, Furniture, old maps, medals, militaria.

## KETTERING (01536)

**Antiques Warehouse**, 53 Havelock Street, NN16 9PZ TEL: 510522 PARKING: Own carpark OPEN: Mon-Sat 9-5.30 MIN: £2 MAX: £3000 PERIOD 18th-19th century SPECIALIST: Pine furniture, oak, fireplaces & stoves, also reproduction.

**Alexis Brook**, 74 Lower Street, NN16 8DL TEL: 513854 PARKING: Own carpark OPEN: Lucky chance or by appt MIN: £1 MAX: £1000 PERIOD 19th century GENERAL: Mainly tôle, glass, pottery, porcelain, small furniture, bygones.

**Dragon Antiques,** 85 Rockingham Road, NN16 8LA TEL: 517017 PARKING: Easy OPEN: 10-4 MIN: £5 MAX: £4000 PERIOD: 19th-20th century SPECIALIST: Pictures OTHER INFO: Picture framing.

**CW Ward Antiques**, 40 Lower Street, NN16 8DJ TEL: 513537 PARKING: Easy OPEN: Mon-Sat 10-4 MIN: £10 MAX: £3500 PERIOD 18th-20th century GENERAL: General antiques OTHER INFO: Rockingham Castle, Royal Hotel, Sir Alfred East Art Gallery.

## FINEDON (01933)

**Aspidistra Antiques**, 51 High Street, NN9 5JN TEL: 680196, (0860) 682771 PARKING: Easy OPEN: 7days 10-5.30 MIN: £1 MAX: £1000 PERIOD 18th-20th century SPECIALIST: Art Nouveau & Deco GENERAL: Victoriana OTHER INFO: Very good restaurant/hotel: The Tudor Gate.

**Simon Banks Antiques**, Quaker Lodge, Church Street, NN9 5NA TEL: 680371, mobile 0374 740508 PARKING: Easy MIN: £1 MAX: £3500 PERIOD: 18th-20th century SPECIALIST: Edwardian inlaid furniture GENERAL: Mahogany & oak, shipping furniture OTHER INFO: Near Bell Inn reputedly one of the oldest in England.

**Jean Burnett Antiques**, 31 High Street, NN9 5JN TEL: 680430 PARKING: Easy OPEN: Mon-Sat 10-1, 2.30-5 MIN: £5 MAX: £1500 PERIOD 18th-19th century SPECIALIST: Needlework tools & accessories, samplers, embroidered pictures GENERAL: Some country furniture, general antiques OTHER INFO: Tudor Gate Hotel next door, we can even boast of the oldest licensed premises in England, The Bell, snacks & meals. 2 antique centres, 2 warehouses & 3 shops in Finedon.

**MC Chapman Antiques**, 12-20 Regent Street TEL: 681688 FAX: 681688 PARKING: Own carpark OPEN: Mon-Fri 9-5 PERIOD 18th-19th century SPECIALIST: Furniture GENERAL: Furnishings & decorative items.

**Dales of Finedon**, 1 High Street TEL: 680973 PARKING: Easy OPEN: Mon-Sat 10-5, Sun 2-5 MIN: £1 MAX: £5,000 PERIOD: 18th-20th century GENERAL: Furniture, ceramics, silver, glassware OTHER INFO: 5 other antique shops, Tudor Gate Hotel & pubs within 400 yds.

**EK Antiques,** 37 High Street, NN9 5JN TEL: 681882 PARKING: Easy OPEN: Daily 9.30-5.30, Sun 11-5.30 MIN: £5 MAX: £5000 PERIOD: 18th-20th century SPECIALIST: Victorian, Edwardian, solid oak furniture GENERAL: Porcelain, glass, china, pictures, decorative items, metalware, pictures, needlework OTHER INFO: Tudor Gate Hotel next door.

**Finedon Antiques**, 1-3 Church Street TEL: 681260 FAX: 681688 PARKING: Own carpark OPEN: Mon-Sat 9.30-5.30, Sun 2-5 PERIOD 18th-20th century SPECIALIST: Furniture GENERAL: Covering whole spectrum of the antiques & collectables trade OTHER INFO: 6 shops & 2 large warehouses, good Tudor Gate Hotel & The Bell, oldest inn in England.

## WELLINGBOROUGH (01933)

**Park Book Shop**, 12 Park Road, NN8 4PG TEL: 222592 PARKING: Easy OPEN: Mon-Wed, Fri, Sat 10-5 MIN: £1 MAX: £250 PERIOD 19th-20th century GENERAL: Topography, art, antiques, history, hobbies.

**Park Gallery**, 16 Cannon Street, NN8 5DJ TEL: 222592 PARKING: Easy OPEN: Mon-Wed, Fri, Sat 10-5 MIN: £2 MAX: £500 PERIOD: 18th-20th century SPECIALIST: Local maps & topography GENERAL: Prints, picture framing.

**Bryan Perkins Antiques**, 52 Cannon Street, NN8 4DJ TEL: 228812 PARKING: Own carpark OPEN: Mon-Fri 9-5.30, Sat 9-12.30 MIN: £1 MAX: £10,000 PERIOD: 18th-19th century SPECIALIST: Victorian dining tables, chests of drawers GENERAL: Mahogany furniture OTHER INFO: Near Althorp House, Boughton, Burghley etc. Our own good B&B.

## RUSHDEN (01933)

**Sherwood Antiques**, 59 Little Street, NN10 0LS TEL: 53265 PARKING: Easy OPEN: Tues, Wed, Fri, Sat 12-5 PERIOD: 19th century.

**Shire Antiques**, 111 High Street South, NN10 1OL TEL: 315567 PARKING: Easy OPEN: Mon-Sat 9.30-6 MIN: £5 MAX: £1,000 PERIOD 19th-20th century GENERAL: Clocks, porcelain, pine, mahogany, oak, sewing machines, typewriters, gramophones.

## BEDFORD (01234)

**Manor Antiques**, The Manor House, Cottonend Road, Wilstead MK45 3BT TEL: 740262 PARKING: Own carpark OPEN: Mon-Sat 10-5 MIN: £55 MAX: £5000 PERIOD: 19th century SPECIALIST: Dining furniture & good quality accessories OTHER INFO: 15 mins drive to Woburn Abbey & large antique centre and 10 mins from Ampthill with many antique shops.

## BIGGLESWADE (01767)

**Shortmead Antiques**, 46 Shortmead Street, SG18 0AP TEL: 601780 PARKING: Easy OPEN: Mon-Wed, Fri, Sat 10-4 MIN: £5 MAX: £1500 PERIOD: 18th-20th century GENERAL: General antiques OTHER INFO: Very picturesque village ½ mile from A1, 5 mins drive from Old Warden Aircraft Museum.

# East Midlands

*Stratford-upon-Avon*

This tour covers the rural heart of England, a countryside that has been created and tended by man from earliest times. History is evident throughout the region. Many battles in the War of the Roses and the Civil War took place in this area and William Shakespeare, the greatest ever English writer, was born in Stratford-upon-Avon. Amongst the historic market towns and charming villages, tourists on this route will also see an English new town at Milton Keynes.

The first visit is to **Whitchurch**, Buckinghamshire. The village has a fine church with a 15th century painting in the north aisle and the earthmound to the west is all that is left of Bolebec Castle. Six miles away along the A413, **Winslow** has a 17th century hall that is one of the few private buildings that can be definitely attributed to Sir Christopher Wren. The tour continues through **Steeple Claydon** and **Twyford** where the church has a two storied porch enclosing a Norman doorway.

Going via **Tingewick,** the next call is **Brackley**, a small town with a number of 18th century houses in the High Street and a church with an early English tower. After stopping in **Croughton**, the tour continues to the small villages of **Clifton** and then to **Deddington** where it is said that Charles I spent a night at Castle Farm. Then detour to **North Aston.** North on the A4260, **Banbury** dates from Saxon times but little remains from before the 17th century. In the past the residents of the town had little respect for ancient buildings. For example, in the 18th century the local church was blown up because nobody wanted to pay for restoration. Puritans destroyed the original cross made famous by the nursery rhyme, the one seen today is a replica erected in 1859. The cake shop that made Banbury synonymous with tarts was demolished as recently as 1967 although the original shop front now hangs in the museum. There was also a 12th century castle, covering three acres, but this was demolished after holding out for the King during the Civil War.

After visiting the village of **Kineton** the route moves to **Stratford-upon-Avon**, home of the Royal Shakespeare Company. The town has many fine buildings but, above all, it is William Shakespeare that brings visitors here. Stratford has five principal properties associated with Shakespeare but in the summer visitors usually have to queue. Anne Hathaway's Cottage is a delightful thatched house, her abode before marrying Shakespeare. Another of the properties is Shakespeare's Birthplace, displaying many rare items as well as the BBC Television Costume Exhibition. Hall's Croft was the home of the Bard's daughter and her husband. Then there is New Place, Shakespeare's last home, with its lovely Elizabethan knot garden. Finally, the Shakespeare Countryside Museum at Mary Arden's House, Wilmcote about three and a half miles from Stratford, is a Tudor farmhouse and the home of Shakespeare's mother.

Nearby **Bidford-on-Avon** is a charming village also with Shakespearean associations. Nearby **Alcester** (pronounced Olster) is a picturesque town on the rivers Alne and Arrow. Ragley Hall stands two miles away on the A435 and is a magnificent baroque mansion containing collections

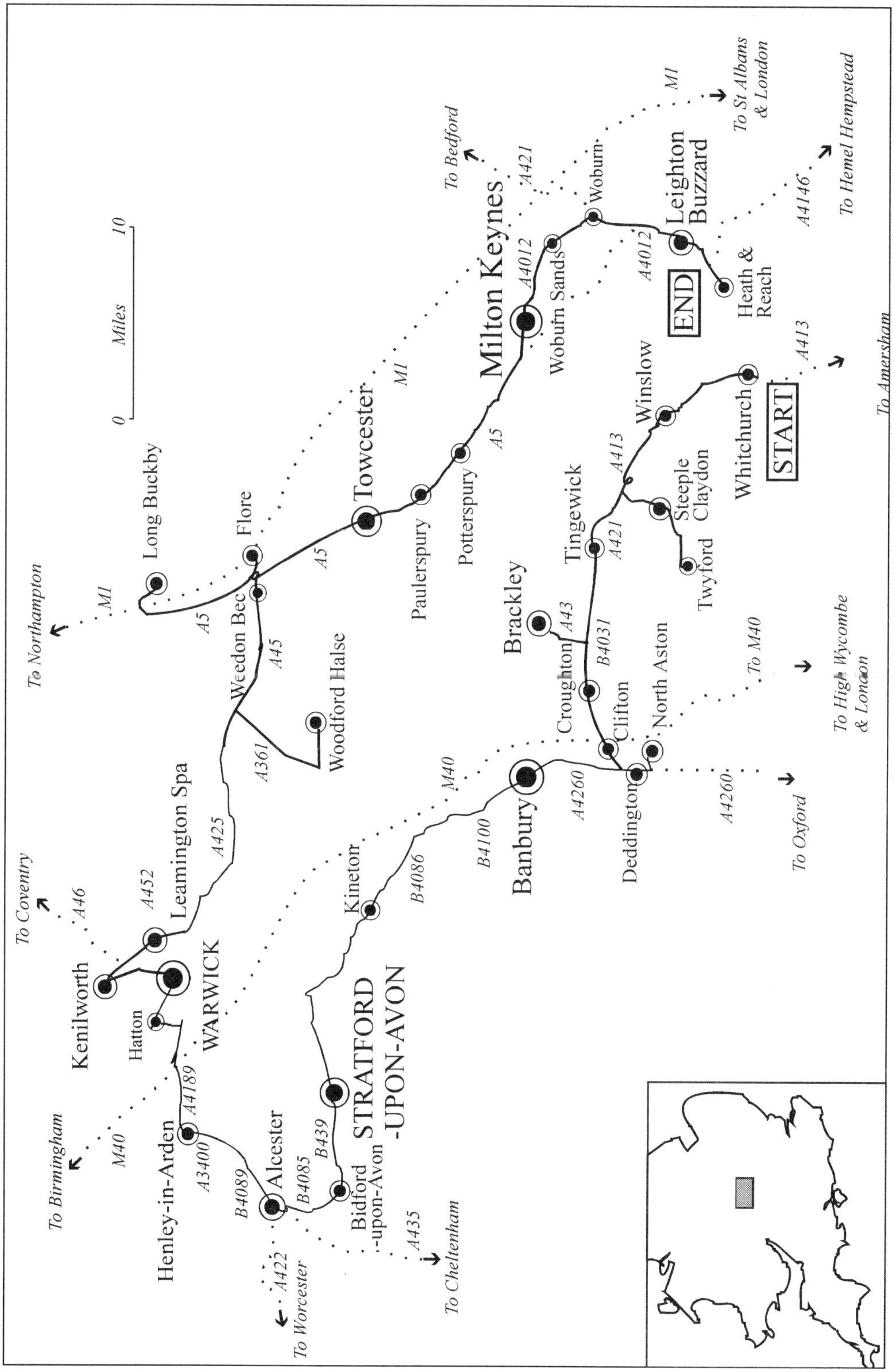
START
END
Whitchurch
Winslow
Steeple Claydon
Twyford
Tingewick
Brackley
Croughton
Clifton
North Aston
Deddington
Banbury
Kineton
STRATFORD -UPON-AVON
Bidford -upon-Avon
Alcester
Henley-in-Arden
Hatton
WARWICK
Kenilworth
Leamington Spa
Woodford Halse
Weedon Bec
Long Buckby
Flore
Towcester
Paulerspury
Potterspury
Milton Keynes
Woburn Sands
Woburn
Leighton Buzzard
Heath & Reach
Miles
0
10
To Northampton
To Coventry
To Birmingham
To Worcester
To Cheltenham
To Oxford
To High Wycombe & London
To M40
To Amersham
To Hemel Hempstead
To St Albans & London
To Bedford
A413
A421
A43
B4031
A4260
B4100
B4086
B439
B4085
B4089
A3400
A4189
A422
A435
M40
A46
A452
A425
A361
A45
A5
M1
A4012
A4146

*The Lord Leycester Hospital, Warwick*

of fine paintings, ceramics, furniture and works of art. **Henley-in-Arden** is next. It once stood in the ancient forest of Arden although little of the forest remains today. The town has several buildings dating from the 15th century onwards including the timbered Guildhall from 1448.

Crossing the motorway the route comes to the village of **Hatton** before arriving in **Warwick**. This town possesses the finest medieval castle in England. Possibly this was the site of a Saxon defensive mound against the Danes, standing as it does on the River Avon. In 1068 William the Conqueror gave the site and borough to Henry de Newburgh who started the castle by building a motte and shell keep. It was during the 14th century that Thomas Beauchamp, Earl of Warwick, built the castle that largely survives today. The best known Earl of Warwick was nicknamed 'Kingmaker' for his role in the Wars of the Roses. He met his death at the Battle of Barnet in 1471. Right at the end of the 15th century, another Earl of Warwick was executed for his part in the Perkin Warbeck plot (it was claimed that Perkin Warbeck was the son of Edward IV and rightful heir to the throne). Another Earl, John Dudley, was executed in 1554 after being involved in the attempt to put Lady Jane Grey on the throne. Owners of Warwick Castle seemed to have had an unfortunate record of choosing the wrong side.

Nowadays the Castle has much to offer. There are battlements and towers, a dungeon, a torture chamber and state apartments with a wonderful collection of pictures by Rubens, Van Dyck, etc. Owned by a subsidiary of Madame Tussauds, an award winning exhibition is titled *'A Royal Weekend Party 1898'*. Other notable buildings include the 15th century Beauchamp Chapel in St Mary's Church containing the Purbeck marble tomb of Richard Beauchamp, Earl of Warwick, who died in 1439 and the Lord Leycester Hospital, built in 1571 by Robert Dudley, Earl of Leicester.

**Kenilworth** also has a famous castle, but this is a ruin. Started in the early 12th century and in the 13th century, it was held by Simon de Montfort who rebelled against Henry III. Simon de Montfort was killed in the Battle of Evesham in 1265 although his followers held the castle against all attacks for another six months. It was only illness and starvation that caused them to surrender. It was given to John of Gaunt and in the 16th century, Elizabeth I gave it to her favourite, Robert Dudley,

Earl of Leicester. In the 17th century Parliamentary forces demolished part of the keep, walls and towers to prevent further military use.

The nearby town of **Royal Leamington Spa** (the 'Royal' was given by Queen Victoria after a visit to the town in 1838) stands on the River Leam and the Grand Union Canal. With its natural spring waters, it has baths,Regency terraces and the Royal Pump Room.

The tour continues east through the villages of **Woodhouse Halse** and **Weedon Bec** before detouring north along the A5 to **Long Buckby**. **Flore**, next, is a pleasant riverside village with thatched limestone cottages. Still on the A5, **Towcester** (pronounced Toe-ster) stands astride the old Roman road of Watling Street. Although once the Roman settlement of *Lactodorum*, it was as a coaching town in the 18th and 19th centuries that prosperity really came One of the many coaching inns, the Saracen's Head, was featured in Dickens' *Pickwick Papers*. Along the A5 via **Paulerspury** and **Potterspury** is **Milton Keynes**. A new town started in 1967, it has engulfed some of the local small villages. Known for the grid-like street plan and, humorously, concrete cows, after some 25 years it is now establishing an identity. The home of the Open University, there is also an extremely good shopping centre. Nearby, the villages of **Woburn Sands** and **Woburn** are quite overshadowed by Woburn Abbey, home of the Dukes of Bedford for over 350 years. This is probably the most famous of the great English houses open to the public. It contains collections of furniture, silver and pictures including works by Canaletto, Van Dyck, Rembrandt, Gainsborough, Velazques, etc. Also on display is a wonderful Sevres dinner service presented to Duke of Bedford by Louis XV. In the grounds there is a wildlife park and an antiques centre.

Further south, **Leighton Buzzard** is the last call. Prehistoric and Roman remains have been found in this ancient town as well as three Saxon cemeteries. The most notable building is its church, All Saints. Started at the end of the 13th century the spire rises to a height of 190 feet. Unfortunately parts of the building were damaged by fire in 1985 although some of the best features escaped.

Amongst these is the 13th century oak lectern, said to be the oldest in Britain. The font and the sanctus bell, both possibly older than the church itself, also survived. The last stop is in the oddly named village of **Heath and Reach**.

## ANTIQUE DEALERS

### WHITCHURCH (01296)

**Deerstalker Antiques**, 28 High Street, HP22 4JT TEL: 641505 PARKING: Easy OPEN: Tues, Wed, Thurs, Sat 10-5.30 MIN: £1 MAX: £3000 PERIOD: 19th-20th century SPECIALIST: Georgian chests of drawers GENERAL: Bric-a-brac, furniture.

### WINSLOW (01296)

**Medina**, 8 High Street, MK18 3HF TEL: 712468 OPEN: Mon-Sat 9.30-6 MIN: £5 MAX: £1000 SPECIALIST: Antiquarian maps & prints GENERAL: Watercolours, oils, prints etc OTHER INFO: Bell Hotel & restaurants.

**Winslow Antiques Centre**, 15 Market Square, MK18 3AB TEL: 714540 PARKING: Easy OPEN: Mon-Sat 10-5 Sun 1-5 MIN: £1 MAX: £3000 PERIOD: 17th-20th century GENERAL: Silver, jewellery, furniture, porcelain, glass, pottery, etc OTHER INFO: Winebar, bistro, good coffee shop opposite. Close to Winslow Hall & Clayden House.

### STEEPLE CLAYDON (01296)

**Antique & Vintage Arms & Armour**
**The Beeches, Chaloners Hill, MK18 2PE TEL: 738255 FAX: 730810 PARKING: Own carpark OPEN: By appt MIN: £50 MAX: £16,500 PERIOD: 17th century-1920 SPECIALIST: American old west guns, Indian items & equipment of the cowboy era. Also American Cival War items including pistols & guns. Our latest colour catalogue of American and European arms is now available price £5.**

### TWYFORD (01296)

**Adrian Hornsey Ltd,** Three Bridge Mill, MK18 4DY TEL & FAX: 738373 PARKING: Own carpark OPEN: Mon-Fri 9-5, Sat 9-4 MIN: £10 MAX: £10,000 PERIOD: 17th-20th century GENERAL: Furniture OTHER INFO: Largest trade/retail antique centre in Central England, 55,000 sq ft.

### TINGEWICK (01280)

**Marshall Antiques**, The Antique Shop, Main Street, MK18 4NL TEL: 848546 PARKING: Easy OPEN: Mon-Sat 10-5 MIN: £10 MAX: £2000 PERIOD: 17th-19th century SPECIALIST: Longcase clocks GENERAL: Country furniture.

**Tingewick Antiques Centre**, Heritage House, Main Street, MK18 4RB TEL: 848219 PARKING: Easy OPEN: Mon-Thurs, Sat 10-5.30, Sun 11-5 MIN: £1 MAX: £2000 PERIOD: 18th-20th century SPECIALIST: Roll top desks GENERAL: Furniture, china, collectables.

### BRACKLEY (01280)

**Brackley Antiques**, Hollywood House, 69 High Street, NN13 7BW TEL: 703362 PARKING: Own carpark OPEN: Mon-Sat 10-6 MIN: £1 MAX: £2000 PERIOD: 19th-20th century GENERAL: Traditionally upholstered 19th century chairs & sofas, china, pottery, furniture, collectables.

**The Old Hall Bookshop**, 32 Market Place TEL: 704146 ASSNS: ABA, PBFA PARKING: Easy OPEN: Mon-Sat 9.30-1, 2-5.30 MIN: £1 MAX: £1000+ PERIOD: 19th-20th century SPECIALIST: Local topography, travel, art, literature, sporting, children GENERAL: Large general stock OTHER INFO: The Old Hall is a fine 18th century house set in the middle of the Market Place. The Gardens at Stowe nearby.

**Right Angle**, 24 Manor Road, NN13 6AJ TEL: 702462 FAX: 701228 ASSNS: FATG PARKING: Easy OPEN: Mon-Sat 9.30-1, 2-5.30, (Weds am only) MIN: £4 MAX: £1500 PERIOD: 18th-20th century SPECIALIST: Engravings GENERAL: Watercolours, oils, etchings, chromolithographs.

### CROUGHTON (01869)

**Croughton Antiques,** 29 High Street, NN13 5LT TEL: 810203 PARKING: Easy OPEN: Wed-Sun 10-6 MIN: £5 MAX: £1500 PERIOD: 19th-20th century SPECIALIST: Traditionally restored furniture, smalls & decorators items OTHER INFO: Family run business, Lyn, Tony and son, Neil Cross.

## CLIFTON (01869)

LOGO

**Castle Antiques Ltd**, Manor Farm, OX15 0PA TEL: 338688 ASSNS: LAPADA PARKING: Own carpark OPEN: Mon-Sat 10-6, Sun 10-4 MIN: £1 MAX: £3000 PERIOD: 18th-20th century GENERAL: Furniture, metalware, silver, china & glass. OTHER INFO: Large showroom, 6 miles from exit 10 M40. 1° miles from Deddington.

## DEDDINGTON (01869)

**Deddington Antiques Centre**, Market Place, OX15 0TT TEL: 338968 PARKING: Easy OPEN: Mon-Sat 10-5 MIN: £1 MAX: £1000 PERIOD: 18th-20th century GENERAL: Furniture, porcelain, china, silver, linen, pictures.

**Rookery Antiques,** Hudson Street, OX15 0SW TEL: 338045 PARKING: Easy OPEN: Mon-Sat 10-5.30 Sun 11-1.30 MIN: £2 MAX: £2000 PERIOD: 18th-20th century GENERAL: Mainly antique furniture & country pieces, interesting mixture of smalls OTHER INFO: Lovely village restaurants, tea rooms & various shops, lovely church, also hotels & pubs.

## NORTH ASTON (01869)

**Elizabeth Harvey-Lee,** 1 West Cottages, Middle Aston Road, OX6 3QB TEL: 347164 FAX: 347956 PARKING: Easy OPEN: By appt only MIN: £100 MAX: £5000 PERIOD: 1490-1940 SPECIALIST: Artists' etchings & engravings.

## BANBURY (01295)

**Judy Vedmore - Furniture & Antiques**, 42 Parson's Street, OX16 8NA TEL: 269626 PARKING: Medium OPEN: Tues-Sat 10-5 MIN: £2 MAX: £4000 PERIOD: 18th-20th century GENERAL: Silver, unusual books, general antiques & collectables OTHER INFO: Right item at right price, right present, right investment. Early & late swim at Leisure Centre.

## KINETON (01926)

**The Old Mill Antique Furniture Exporters,** Mill Lane TEL: 640971 PARKING: Own carpark OPEN: Mon-Fri 8.30-5.30, Sat 9.30-1 MIN: £50 MAX: £5,000 PERIOD: 18th-20th century SPECIALIST: 10,000 sq ft warehouse of furniture for all export markets OTHER INFO: Excellent Walton Hall Hotel 4 miles.

## STRATFORD-ON-AVON (01789)

**The Antique Shop,** 30 Henley Street TEL: 297249 shop but best on private-205883 PARKING: Medium OPEN: 10-5 MIN: £20 MAX: £200 PERIOD: 18th-20th century SPECIALIST: English pottery, porcelain, glass, books GENERAL: Objets d'art, silver, jewellery etc, collectors items and range of decoratives.

**The Antiques Arcade,** 10-11 Sheep Street OPEN: 10-5.30 GENERAL: General antiques.

**Arbour Antiques Ltd**, Poets Arbour, Sheep Street, CV37 6EF TEL: 293453 PARKING: Difficult OPEN: Mon-Fri 9-5.30 MIN: £100 MAX: £20,000 PERIOD: 16th-19th century SPECIALIST: Arms & armour.

**Art Deco Ceramics**, Unit 3-4, Stratford Antique Arcade, Ely Street, CV37 6LN TEL: 204351 & 299524 PARKING: Medium OPEN: 10-5, closed Thurs & Sun MIN: £10 MAX: £1500 PERIOD: 20th century SPECIALIST: Art Deco ceramics GENERAL: Hand-painted pottery of the 1920s & 30s, some post-war designer items OTHER INFO: We are authors of *Collecting Clarice Cliff, The Colourful World of Clarice Cliff & Collecting Art Deco Ceramics* (world-wide postal service).

**Jean A Bateman,** 41 Sheep sTreet, CV37 6EE TEL: 298494 ASSNS: LAPADA PARKING: Medium OPEN: Mon-Sat 9.30-5 MIN: £10 MAX: £10,000 PERIOD: 18th-20th century SPECIALIST: Antique jewellery GENERAL: Jewels, needlework, scent bottles, miniatures, etc.

**Howards Jewellers,** 44a Wood Street, CV37 6JZ TEL: 205404 FAX: 293652 ASSNS: NAG PARKING: Medium OPEN: 9.30-5.30 MIN: £18 MAX: £60,000 PERIOD: 18th-20th century SPECIALIST: Fine antique & period jewellery and silver.

**The Loquens Gallery**, The Minories, Rother Street TEL: 297706 PARKING: Own carpark OPEN: Mon-Sat 9.15-5 or by appt PERIOD: 18th-20th century SPECIALIST: Fine Victorian watercolours, oils GENERAL: Prints, etchings.

**Stratford Antiques Centre,** 59-60 Ely Street, CV37 6LN TEL: 204180 & 297496 PARKING: Difficult weekdays, easy Sundays OPEN: 7days 10-5.30 MIN: £1 MAX: £3000 PERIOD: 19th-20th century GENERAL: Silver, jewellery, furniture, pottery, collectables OTHER INFO: Near town centre, cafe serving snacks & meals, housed in 17th century building.

**The Stratford Bookshop,** 45A Rother Street, CV37 6LT TEL: 298362 PARKING: Easy OPEN: Mon-Sat 10-6 MIN: £1 MAX: £200 PERIOD: 18th-20th century GENERAL: Second hand, antiquarian & out of print books.

**Robert Vaughan Antiquarian Booksellers**, 20 Chapel Street, CV37 6EP TEL: 205312 ASSNS: ABA, PBFA PARKING: Medium OPEN: Mon-Sat 9.30-6 MIN: £5 MAX: £25,000 PERIOD: 18th-20th century SPECIALIST: Shakespeare, Elizabethan, Jacobean dramatists. Theatre & allied subjects GENERAL: Good English literatures, fine bindings OTHER INFO: Shakespeare's birthplace & burial place, both 5 mins walk.

**Jennifer Wall Antiques,** 10-11 Sheep Street TEL: 294659 PARKING: Easy OPEN: 10-5.30 MIN: £10 MAX: £800 PERIOD: 19th-20th century SPECIALIST: Silver, silver plate, jewellery GENERAL: Porcelain, books, lighting, lace, furniture OTHER INFO: Surrounded by good wine bars, restaurants, theatres, shops & every Shakespearian effect known to man.

## BIDFORD-ON-AVON (01789)

**Bidford Antique Centre,** 94-96 High Street TEL: 773680 PARKING: Easy OPEN: Mon, Wed-Sat 10-5, Tues 10-7, Sun 2-5 MIN: 50p MAX: £1000 GENERAL: Antique collectables, furniture, books, records, linen.

## ALCESTER (01789)

**Malthouse Antiques Centre**, 4 Market Place, B49 5AE TEL: 764032 PARKING: Easy OPEN: Mon-Sat 10-5, Sun 2-5 MIN: £1 MAX: £2000 PERIOD: 19th century GENERAL: Furniture, silver, porcelain, kitchenalia, pictures, objets d'art, etc OTHER INFO: Pleasant market town with plenty to interest visitors, only 8 miles from Stratford-upon-Avon.

## HENLEY-IN-ARDEN (01564)

**The Chadwick Gallery**, 2 Doctors Lane (off High Street), B95 5AW TEL: 794820 ASSNS: LAPADA PARKING: Own carpark OPEN: Tues-Wed, Fri-Sat 10-5 MIN: £50 MAX: £5,000 PERIOD: 19th-

20th century GEN-ERAL: Watercolours, etchings.
**Colmore Galleries Ltd**, 52 High Street, B95 5AN TEL & FAX: 792938 ASSNS: LAPADA PARKING: Easy OPEN: Mon-Fri 11-5.30, Sat 11-4.30 MIN: £100 PERIOD: 19th-20th century SPECIALIST: Victorian oils & watercolours GENERAL: Modern paintings & signed limited editions.
**GB Horton - The Arden Gallery**, 54 High Street, B95 5AN TEL: 792520 PARKING: Medium OPEN: Mon-Fri 1-6 MIN: £1 MAX: £2,000 PERIOD: 19th-20th century GENERAL: Watercolours and oils, miniatures.
**Lacy Gallery,** 56 High Street, TEL: 793073 PARKING: Easy OPEN: Tues, Weds, Thurs 10-1 SPECIALIST: Oils, watercolours & prints, art reference books.
**Jasper Marsh**, 3 High Street TEL: 792088 ASSNS: BADA PARKING: Medium OPEN: Mon-Sat 10-5.30 MIN: £100 MAX: £5,000 PERIOD: 18th-19th century GENERAL: Mahogany & oak furniture.

## HATTON (01926)

**Antiques Corner**, Unit 42, Hatton Country World, CV35 8XA TEL: 499731 & 842405 PARKING: Own carpark OPEN: 7 days 10-5 MIN: £2 MAX: £1,000 PERIOD: 19th-20th century GENERAL: China, glass, furniture, clocks, linen, jewellery, old phones, prints OTHER INFO: Pub & restaurant on site by spring 1995. Next to largest flight of locks on canal system.
**Summersons Antique Restoration**, 15 Carthorse Walk, CV35 8XA TEL: 843443 ASSNS: CMBHI PARKING: Own carpark OPEN: 9.30-5 MIN: £75 MAX: £4000 PERIOD: 18th-19th century SPECIALIST: Clocks & barometers OTHER INFO: Part of Hatton Country World complex.

## WARWICK (01926)

**Duncan Allsop,** 26 Smith Street, CV34 4HS TEL: 493266 ASSNS: ABA PARKING: Own carpark OPEN: 9.30-5.30 PERIOD: 17th-20th century SPECIALIST: Antiquarian & second hand books.
**Apollo Antiques Ltd,** The Saltisford, CV34 4TD TEL: 494746 FAX: 401477 ASSNS: LAPADA PARKING: Easy OPEN: Mon-Fri 9-6, Sat 9.30-12.30 or by appt MIN: £100 MAX: £35,000 PERIOD: 18th-19th century SPECIALIST: Arts & Crafts, Art Nouveau furniture GENERAL: Continental furniture, marquetry & inlaid furniture, shipping goods, decorative bronzes & objects of art OTHER INFO: 20 mins from Birmingham International Airport, 90 mins from Central London via M40, good local motels & historical Warwickshire surroundings.
**John Goodwin & Sons**, Units F & M, Budbrooke Industrial Estate, Budbrooke Road, CV34 5XH TEL: 491191 FAX: 491191 PARKING: Own carpark OPEN: Mon-Fri 9-5.30, Sat 10-4 MIN: £5 MAX: £5,000 PERIOD: 18th-20th century SPECIALIST: 19th, early 20th century furniture.
**Patrick & Gillian Morley Antiques**, 62 West Street, CV34 6AN TEL: 494464 FAX: 400531 ASSNS: LAPADA PARKING: Own carpark OPEN: Mon-Fri 9-5.30 MIN: £50 MAX: £25,000 PERIOD: 17th-20th century SPECIALIST: Quality period furniture GENERAL: Unusual items.
**Martin Payne Antiques**, 30 Brook Street, CV34 4BL TEL: 494948 ASSNS: LAPADA PARKING: Easy OPEN: Mon-Sat 10-5.30 MIN: £10 MAX: £9,000 PERIOD: 18th-20th century SPECIALIST: Antique & collectable silver.
**Smith Street Antique Centre**, 7 Smith Street TEL: 497864, 400554 PARKING: Medium OPEN: Mon-Sat 10-5 MIN: £1 MAX: £15,000 PERIOD: 18th-20th century SPECIALIST: Military, Oriental, taxidermy GENERAL: Silver, plate,glass, cigarette cards, porcelain, golfing memorabilia, furniture OTHER INFO: St. Johns Museum, Dolls Museum.
**Don Spencer Antiques**, 36a Market Place, CV34 4SH TEL: 407989 PARKING: Easy OPEN: Mon-Sat 10-5 MIN: £500 MAX: £3000 PERIOD: 19th century SPECIALIST: Antique desks GENERAL: Victorian furniture.
**The Tao Antiques,** 59 Smith Street, CV34 4HU PARKING: Medium OPEN: 10.30-5.45 MIN: £5 MAX: £1000 PERIOD: 19th-20th century GENERAL: China, plate, silver, clocks, furniture.
**Vintage Antiques Centre**, 36 Market Place TEL: 491527 ASSNS: WADA PARKING: Easy OPEN: Six days 10-5 MIN: £1 MAX: £500 PERIOD: 19th-20th century SPECIALIST: Glass, ceramics, GENERAL: Collectables.
**Warwick Antiques**, 16-18 High Street, CV34 4AP TEL: 492482 FAX: 493867 PARKING: Own carpark OPEN: 9-5 MIN: £1 MAX: £5,000 PERIOD: 19th-20th century SPECIALIST: General antiques.
**Warwick Antique Centre**, 20 High Street, CV34 4AP TEL: 491382 PARKING: Own carpark OPEN: 10-5 MIN: 50p MAX: £2000 PERIOD: 18th-20th century GENERAL: Silver, jewellery, porcelain, glass, fur-

niture, toys, coins, books, militaria, teddy bears, pens, Derby OTHER INFO: Good trade call. Warwick Races.

**Westgate Antiques**, 28 West Street, CV34 6AN TEL & FAX: 494106 ASSNS: LAPADA PARKING: Easy OPEN: Mon-Sat 10-5.30 or by appt MIN: £20 MAX: £10,000 PERIOD: 18th-20th century SPECIALIST: Silver & plate GENERAL: Glass, boxes, decorative items.

## KENILWORTH (01926)

**Castle Gallery**, 32 Castle Hill, CV8 1NB TEL: 58727 PARKING: Easy OPEN: Tues, Fri-Sun 11-5 MIN: £50 MAX: £3,000 PERIOD: 18th-20th century GENERAL: British watercolours & drawings, also contemporary OTHER INFO: Picturesque town, close to dramatically ruined Kenilworth Castle.

**Janice Paull**, Beehive House, 125 Warwick Road, CV8 1HY TEL: 55253, (0831) 691254 FAX: 863384 ASSNS: BADA, LAPADA PARKING: Own carpark OPEN: By appt PERIOD: 19th century SPECIALIST: Mason's & other ironstone ware GENERAL: Pottery, porcelain OTHER INFO: Organiser of the Kenilworth Antiques Fair, 27th-31st March & 9th-13th October 1996 at the Chesford Grange Hotel (see page 293). Furniture dateline 1830, porcelain 1890

## LEAMINGTON SPA (01926)

**Olive Green Ltd**, 12 Station Approach, Avenue Road, CV31 5NN TEL: (0860) 613610 PARKING: Easy OPEN: Thurs-Sat 10-5 & by appt MIN: £5 MAX: £2,000 PERIOD: 18th-20th century SPECIALIST: 19th century furniture, decorative arts GENERAL: Furniture & allied arts OTHER INFO: Art Gallery, Manor House hotel.

**The Incandescent Lighting Company**, 36 Regent Street, CV32 5EG TEL: 422421 PARKING: Easy OPEN: 9.30-5.30 MIN: £20 MAX: £2,500 SPECIALIST: 19th-20th century electric lighting OTHER INFO: Charming Regency town a few hundred yards from neighbouring Warwick and its castle & wealth of antique shops.

**Kings Cottage Antiques**, 4 Windsor Street TEL: 422927 PARKING: Medium OPEN: 9.30-5.30 MIN: £100 MAX: £10,000 PERIOD: 16th-18th century SPECIALIST: 2000 sq ft of oak & country furniture GENERAL: Furniture for restoration.

**Leamington Antique Centre**, 20 Regent Street TEL: 429679 PARKING: Easy OPEN: Mon-Sat 9-6 MIN: £1 MAX: £2,000 PERIOD: 19th-20th century GENERAL: Pine, shipping items & bric-a-brac.

**Yesterdays**, 21 Portland Street, CV32 5EZ TEL: 450238 PARKING: Easy OPEN: Thurs-Sat 10-5 MIN: £5 MAX: £3000 PERIOD: 18th-20th century GENERAL: 19th century decorative mahogany furniture, pretty china & framed prints OTHER INFO: *Homes & Antiques* magazine, Jan 1994, nominated us as Britain's Friendliest Antique Shop.

## WOODFORD HALSE (01327)

**The Corner Cupboard**, 14-18 Station Road, NN11 3RB TEL: 60725 PARKING: Easy OPEN: Closed Tues MIN: £10 MAX: £800 PERIOD: 19th-20th century SPECIALIST: Victorian brass & iron bedsteads, stripped pine, English & Continental furniture, etc OTHER INFO: Opposite a famous large shoe shop renown for its exceptional value.

## WEEDON BEC (01327)

**Architectural Antiques of Northants,** The Woodyard, NN7 4LB, 2° miles north of Weedon on A5 TEL: 349249 FAX: 349397 PARKING: Own carpark OPEN: Mon-Sat 9-5, Sun 11-5 MIN: £25 MAX: £14,000 PERIOD: 17th-20th century SPECIALIST: Architectural antiques GENERAL: Victorian shop fittings OTHER INFO: Tea rooms & gift shop on site. Premises are Victorian model farm buildings.

**Rococo Antiques**, 5 New Street, Lower Weedon, NN7 4QS TEL: 341288 PARKING: Easy OPEN: Mon-Sat 10-5.30 MIN: £5 MAX: £3000 PERIOD: 18th-20th century SPECIALIST: Brass & iron bedsteads, fireplaces GENERAL: Ironwork, pine furniture, doors OTHER INFO: Prettiest & best stocked shop in Weedon.

**The Village Antique Market**, 62 High Street, NN7 4QD TEL: 342015 PARKING: Own carpark OPEN: 7 days 10-5.30 PERIOD 18th-20th century OTHER INFO: On Grand Union Canal at A45/A5 junction. 40 dealers. 3 hotels, 1 pub.

## LONG BUCKBY (01327)

**Long Buckby Antiques,** 17 Church Street, NN5 7RE TEL: 843487 PARKING: Easy OPEN: Mon-Sat 8-5 MIN: £1 MAX: £3000 PERIOD: 18th-20th century GENERAL: Furniture & shipping goods OTHER INFO: Next door, at 15 Church Street, we run the Antique Coffee Pot, a licensed restaurant, open all day, also selling antiques on display.

## FLORE (01327)

**Christopher Jones Antiques,** Flore House, The Avenue, NN7 4LZ TEL: 342165 FAX: 349230 PARKING: Own carpark OPEN: 10-5 weekdays, 11-4.30 MIN: £30 PERIOD: 18th-20th century SPECIALIST: Decorative English & Continental furniture and effects.

## TOWCESTER (01327)

**Clark Galleries**, 215 Watling Street, NN12 6BX TEL: 352957 ASSNS: Ass. British Picture Restorers PARKING: Medium OPEN: Mon-Fri 9-5.30, Sat 9.30-4 MIN: £150 MAX: £25,000 PERIOD 18th -20th century SPECIALIST: Oils of all types OTHER INFO: Some watercolours & prints. Fine art reliners & restorers. Excellent hotel: Saracen's Head, Pickwick restaurant, a good coffee shop.

**Ron Green Antiques**, 209, 227 & 239 Watling Street TEL: 350387 PARKING: Easy OPEN: Mon-Sat 8.30-5.30 MIN: £25 MAX: £10,000 PERIOD 17th-19th century SPECIALIST: English & Continental furniture, decorative items OTHER INFO: Early coaching inn: Saracens Head lies between our shops and was used by Charles Dickens.

**Shelron Collectors Shop**, 9° Brackley Road, NN12 6DH TEL: 350242 ASSNS: Postcard Traders Assn, Cartophilic Society PARKING: Easy OPEN: Tues-Sat 10-4 MIN: £1 MAX: £200 PERIOD 19th-20th century GENERAL: Mostly paper. bric-a-brac, models, books, all types of cards (playing, cigarette, post, trade etc) maps, prints OTHER INFO: Saracen's Head Hotel (mentioned in Dicken's Pickwick Papers) 1 min. walk.

## PAULERSPURY (01327)

**Malcolm Cameron**, The Antique Galleries, Watling Street, NN12 7LQ TEL: 811238 ASSNS: BADA PARKING: Own carpark OPEN: Mon-Sat 9-5.30 MIN: £400 MAX: £8000 PERIOD 17th-18th century SPECIALIST: English furniture & barometers.

## POTTERSPURY (01908)

**Reindeer Antiques Ltd**, 43 Watling Street, NN12 7QD TEL: 542407, 542200 FAX: 542121 ASSNS: BADA, LAPADA PARKING: Own carpark OPEN: Mon-Sat 9-6 PERIOD 18th century SPECIALIST: Furniture GENERAL: Oak, statuary, period accessories, mirrors etc OTHER INFO: Large showrooms. Near Cock Inn. Also Bull Inn at Stony Stratford-both famous for Cock & Bull story.

## MILTON KEYNES (01908)

**Temple Lighting/Jeanne Temple Antiques**, Stockwell House, Wavendon, MK17 8LS TEL: 583597 FAX: 281149 PARKING: Own carpark OPEN: Mon-Sat 10-5 MIN: £20 MAX: £2000 PERIOD: 19th-early 20th century SPECIALIST: Light fittings GENERAL: Furniture & collectables.

## WOBURN SANDS (01908)

**Haydon House Antiques**, Station Road, MK17 8RX TEL: 582447 ASSNS: LAPADA PARKING: Own carpark OPEN: Mon-Fri 10-5.30, Sat-Sun 10-1 MIN: £5 MAX: £6000 PERIOD: 18th-19th century GENERAL: General antiques OTHER INFO: Bedford Arms Hotel, Woburn.

**Woburn Sands Antique Centre**, The Old Bakery, 1 Russell Street, MK17 8NU TEL: 584827, 583024 PARKING: Own carpark OPEN: Mon-Sat 10-1, 2-5 MIN: £1 MAX: £2000 PERIOD: 18th-19th century GENERAL: Brass, glass, furniture.

## WOBURN (01525)

**Applecross Antiques**, Woburn Abbey Antiques Centre, MK43 0TP TEL: 290350 OPEN: Normal PARKING: Own carpark OPEN: Nov-Easter 11-5, Easter Sunday - Oct 10-6 MIN: £50 MAX: £1,000 PERIOD: 17th-19th century SPECIALIST: Blue & White transfer ware, Staffordshire figures GENERAL: Silver, ceramics, prints, needlework. **Sefton Antiques**, Woburn Abbey Antique Centre, MK43 0TP TEL: 290350 OPEN: Normal PARKING: Own carpark OPEN: Nov-Easter 11-5, Easter Sunday-Oct 10-6 MIN: £50 MAX: £3000 PERIOD: 17th-19th century SPECIALIST: Brass candlesticks, papier maché, Tunbridge Ware, pewter GENERAL: General antiques OTHER INFO: All stock pre-1860.

**Christopher Sykes Antiques**, The Old Parsonage, Bedford Street, MK17 9QL TEL: 290259 FAX: 290061 PARKING: Easy OPEN: Mon-Sat 9-.30 MIN: £5 MAX: £5000 PERIOD: 18th-20th century SPECIALIST: Corkscrews & wine related antiques GENERAL: Scientific & medical instruments OTHER INFO: 1 mile from Woburn Abbey with Animal Kingdom & antiques market.

**Town Hall Antiques**, Market Place MK17 9PZ TEL: 290950 PARKING: Easy OPEN: Tues-Sun 11-5.30 MIN: £1 MAX: £5000 PERIOD: 18th-20th century SPECIALIST: Porcelain, furniture, toys, prints, childrens books, kitchenalia, small silver. OTHER INFO: Black Horse, Catering Pub of the Year 1994, plus 8 other good places to eat.

**Woburn Abbey Antiques Centre**, South Court, Woburn Abbey, MK43 0TP TEL: 290350 FAX: 290271 PARKING: Own carpark OPEN: Seven days Easter Sunday-31st Oct 10-6, 1st Nov-Easter Saturday 11-5, closed 24th-26th Dec MIN: £1 MAX: £5000 GENERAL: 17th-19th century furniture, paintings, prints, silver, clocks, glass, porcelain, objets d'art OTHER INFO: 40 shops and 12 fitted showcases on 2 floors.

## LEIGHTON BUZZARD (01525)

**David Ball Antiques**, 59 North Street, LU7 7EQ TEL: 210753, 382954 ASSNS: LAPADA PARKING: Easy OPEN: Mon 10-5 or by appt MIN: £10 MAX: £3-4000 PERIOD: 18th-20th century GENERAL: Georgian & Victorian furniture, clocks, barometers, and unusual items.

**Linslade Antiques**, 1 New Road, Linslade TEL: 378348 PARKING: Own carpark OPEN: Mon-Sat 9.30-5.30, Sun 1-5 MIN: £1 MAX: £3000 PERIOD: 17th-20th century GENERAL: General antiques OTHER INFO: 200 yards mainline station, close Woburn Abbey.

**Linslade Antiques**, 16 Wing Road, Linslade TEL: 378348 PARKING: Own carpark OPEN: Mon-Sat 9.30-5.30, Sun 1-5 MIN: £1 MAX: £3000 PERIOD: 17th-20th century GENERAL: General antiques.

## HEATH & REACH (01525)

**Brindleys**, Woburn Road, LU7 0AR TEL: 237750 & 237831 PARKING: Own carpark OPEN: Mon-Sat 10-5, Sun 12-5 MIN: £2 MAX: £5000 PERIOD: 18th-20th century GENERAL: Pottery, porcelain, oils & furniture OTHER INFO: 15-20 dealers.

**Charterhouse Gallery Ltd**, 26 Birds Hill, LU7 0AQ TEL: 237379 FAX: 237379 ASSNS: LAPADA PARKING: Own carpark OPEN: Mon-Thurs, Sat 10-1, 2-5 PERIOD: 19th-early 20th century SPECIALIST: Watercolours & fine art restoration & framing on own premises.

# Hereford & Worcester

This is a region famous for Hereford cattle, orchards and Elgar. Part of the Welsh Marches, there are castles, Roman and earlier fortifications built in defence of this border country. The Malvern Hills, which account for some 40 square miles of the area, provide a number of fine viewpoints for the lovely countryside below.

The start is the spa town of **Droitwich** where mineral baths are supplied with water from 200 feet below ground. This was an ancient settlement and a centre for the supply of salt in the Iron Age.TheDroitwich Heritage Centre, Victoria Square, displays the story from these early times. Included in the exhibits are salt making artefacts from the Iron Age to Elizabethan and later times. They also have a skeleton and preserved brain, from the skull, the face has been reconstructed.

*The Feathers Hotel, Ludlow*

**Kidderminster**, next, stands on the Staffordshire and Worcestershire Canal. It was renowned for carpet-making and the birthplace of Sir Rowland Hill who inaugurated the penny post. Hartlebury Castle, in the village of the same name, stands five miles south. Owned by the Bishops of Worcester for over 1000 years and sacked during the Civil War and rebuilt later, the medieval great hall has fine plasterwork and a fine collection of portraits of the bishops. It is also the Hereford and Worcester County Museum with displays of the social history of the area from earlist times to the 1900s.

Travelling west via **Bewdley** and pretty **Cleobury Mortimer**, the route crosses briefly into Shropshire to visit **Ludlow**, most famous for a 11th century castle, one of the 32 built in the Welsh Marches. Perched on a cliff overlooking the Rivers Teme and Corve, the castle has seen much action over the centuries. Richard III's nephews, the two princes, lived here before they were moved to the Tower of London and their deaths. The town has much to offer including the 18th century Hosyer's almshouses, the 14th century grammar school, the 15th century Guildhall and a butter cross from 1744. Also of note is St Laurence's Church, a 'wool' church, so called being built from the prosperity brought by wool in the Middle Ages. It has some particularly fine stained glass windows.

Back in Hereford & Worcester, the tour now reaches **Leominster** (pronounced Lemster), another town which prospered through the medieval wool trade. There are many fine black and white houses including Grange Court, a supreme example of this type of architecture. There is also the fine 12th century priory church of St Peter and St Paul built on the site of a 9th century nunnery. Unfortunately a 17th century fire largely destroyed the building and only in the 19th century was it fully restored.

The route reaches its most westerly point at **Hay-on-Wye**, known for the enormous number of antiquarian and secondhand bookshops. This small town is in fact just over the border in Wales. It has a long history, traces of which may be seen in the scant remains of a Roman fort on the north bank of the River Wye and in the ruins of the Castle built by the Normans. Destroyed by Owen

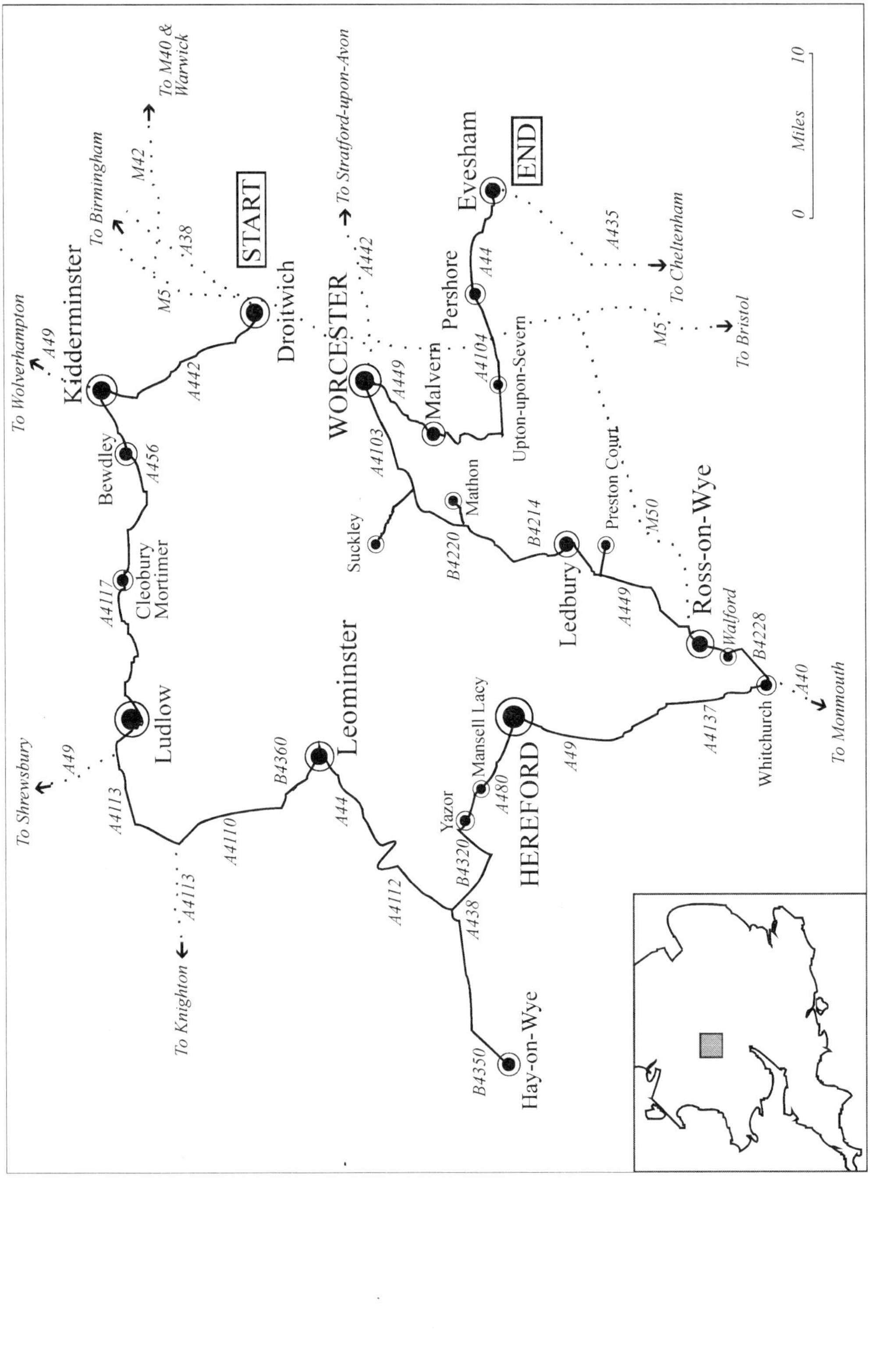
START
END
Kidderminster
Droitwich
WORCESTER
Malvern
Pershore
Evesham
Upton-upon-Severn
Bewdley
Cleobury Mortimer
Ludlow
Leominster
Suckley
Mathon
Preston Court
Ledbury
Ross-on-Wye
Walford
Whitchurch
HEREFORD
Mansell Lacy
Yazor
Hay-on-Wye
To Wolverhampton
To Birmingham
To M40 & Warwick
To Stratford-upon-Avon
To Cheltenham
To Bristol
To Monmouth
To Shrewsbury
To Knighton
A49
M5
A38
M42
A442
A456
A4117
A4113
A4110
B4360
A44
A4112
A438
B4320
A480
B4350
A4103
A449
A4104
B4220
B4214
M50
A4137
B4228
A40
A435
0
Miles
10

*Worcester*

Glendower but then rebuilt, however little is left today as it was largely knocked down during the Civil War.

Returning to England, the tour continues through the villages of **Yazor** and **Mansell Lacy** to **Hereford**, once the capital of West Mercia. Standing on the River Wye, this city has been the seat of the bishop since the 7th century. A Saxon church was replaced by the present cathedral in the 11th century but has had many later modifications. It has the largest chained library in the world with almost 1450 books including a copy of the Anglo-Saxon Chronicle dating from the 9th century.

The town has several good museums including Hereford City Museum and Art Gallery in Broad Street, the Cider Museum and King Offa Cider Brandy Distillery in Pomona Place, the Jacobean period museum of The Old House in High Town and the Churchill Gardens Museum in Venn's Lane with an extensive collection of costume and also fine furniture and watercolours.

The tour proceeds to its most southerly point, the town of **Whitchurch** before turning back, via the little village of **Walford,** to **Ross-on-Wye**, an excellent base for exploring the beautiful Forest of Dean and the Wye Valley. This historic town goes back at least to Saxon times with several buildings of note including the 17th century Market Hall and John Kyrle's house opposite. John Kyrle was responsible for giving Ross a public water supply, also laying out the public gardens in 1693.

After visiting **Preston Court**, next comes **Ledbury**, the birthplace of Poet Laureate, John Masefield, in 1878. Again there are the black and white houses that are such a feature of this area. The route passes through the villages of **Mathon** and **Suckley** before reaching **Worcester,** on the River Severn. This beautiful cathedral city, stands at a natural river ford, it was of strategic importance and also the site of a Norman castle, little of which remains. The scene of battles in the 12th century war between King Stephen and the Empress Matilda, it was also subjected to raids by the Danes sweeping up the river. The cathedral was built of the local sandstone in the

11th and 12th centuries with some later additions. However, the softness of the stone has meant considerable restoration and rebuilding in the mid 19th century so little remains of the original stone carvings. The cathedral contains the tomb and a Purbeck marble effigy of King John dating from 1232, the earliest royal effigy in the country.

One of the many notable buildings in the city is The Greyfriars, a fine 15th century town house built by a wealthy local brewer. Another remarkable edifice is the magnificent Guildhall. During the Civil War Worcester was solidly Royalist and the Guildhall illustrates this with statues of Charles I and Charles II on the facade together with a model of Oliver Cromwell's head nailed by the ears above a doorway. The city's museums include the Dyson Perrins Museum of Worcester Porcelain in Severn Street, the 15th century timber framed Commandery in Sidbury and The Elgar Birthplace in Crown East Lane.

Nearby **Great Malvern** is one of several towns with Malvern in the name. It is dominated by the Worcestershire Beacon which rises to 1395 feet. The spring that brought prosperity to the town as a spa starts on its slopes and also provides the world famous Malvern Water. The Beacon is designated as an area of outstanding natural beauty. The town is also well-known for its public school, Malvern College.

The tour travels east, first to **Upton-on-Severn** and then **Pershore**, famous for its plums. A handsome Georgian town, it is set amongst orchards. The final destination is **Evesham**, centre of the Vale of Evesham and also noted for fruit growing. A cross stands in the town to the memory of Simon de Montfort, killed in the Battle of Evesham in 1265, an event which signalled the end of the barons' revolt against Henry III. The town has a number of old buildings: the 14th century Almonry, the Tudor Round House an Walker Hall from the 15th century.

## ANTIQUE DEALERS

### DROITWICH (01299)

**Grant Books**, The Golf Gallery, New Road, Cutnum Green, WR9 0PQ TEL: 851588 FAX: 851446 ASSNS: PBFA, U.S. & British Golf Collectors Societies PARKING: Easy OPEN: 9-5 & by appt MIN: £5 MAX: £2,000 PERIOD: 19th-20th century SPECIALIST: Golf books, prints, clubs, ephemera OTHER INFO: Publishers of limited edition golf books. Relaxing brine baths.

### KIDDERMINSTER (01562)

**BBM Jewellery, Coins & Antiques**, 8-9 Lion Street, DY10 1PT TEL: 744118 FAX: 825954 ASSNS: BJA PARKING: Easy OPEN: 10-5 closed Tues MIN: £1 MAX: £8500 PERIOD: 19th-20th century SPECIALIST: Antique jewellery GENERAL: Secondhand jewellery, diamonds.

### BEWDLEY (01299)

**Menteith Toys**, 89 Welch Gate, DY12 2AX TEL: 403238 PARKING: Easy OPEN: Sat 10.30-5.30, Sun 2-5 or by appt MIN: £3 MAX: £100 PERIOD: 20th century SPECIALIST: Antique toys, Dinkys, Corgis, teddy bears GENERAL: Trains, Scalextric, tinplate, dolls, everything for the collector OTHER INFO: Visit our beautiful Georgian town situated on the River Severn, why not bring a picnic (some for the ducks too), we'd love to see you.

### CLEOBURY MORTIMER (01299)

**Antique Centre**, Childe Road, DY14 9PA TEL: 270513 PARKING: Own carpark OPEN: Mon-Sat 10-5, Sun 11-5 MIN: £1 MAX: £3500 PERIOD: 17th-20th century GENERAL: Antique beds, Georgian, Victorian, Edwardian furniture, smalls, bric-a-brac, architectural items.

### LUDLOW (01584)

**DW & AB Bayliss Antiques**, 22-24 Old Street, SY8 1NP TEL: 873634 PARKING: Easy OPEN: 9-5 PERIOD: 18th-19th century SPECIALIST: Paintings GENERAL: Furniture, decorative items.

**RG CAVE & SONS LTD**
**17 BROAD STREET, SY8 1NG TEL & FAX: 01584 873568 ASSNS: BADA, LAPADA PARKING: EASY OPEN: MON-SAT 9.30-5.30 MIN: £20 MAX: £8000 PERIOD: 17TH-19TH CENTURY SPECIALIST: 18TH CENTURY ENGLISH FURNITURE GENERAL: GENERAL ANTIQUES OTHER INFO: PROBATE & INSURANCE VALUATIONS.**

**JA Clegg,** 12 Old Street, SY8 1NP TEL & FAX: 873176 OPEN: 8.15-5, PERIOD: 17th-18th century SPECIALIST: Period furniture.

**CURIOSITY SHOP**
**127 OLD STREET, SY8 1NU TEL: 875927 PARKING: EASY OPEN: MON-SAT 9-5.30 & BY APPT MIN: £20 MAX: £20,000 PERIOD: 17TH-19TH CENTURY SPECIALIST: CLOCKS, WEAPONS & EARLY OAK GENERAL: MILITARIA, MUSIC BOXES, COUNTRY FURNITURE.**

**Valentyne Dawes Gallery,** Chuch Street, SY8 1AP TEL: 874160 FAX: 825249 PARKING: 10-5.30 MIN: £200 MAX: £25,000 SPECIALIST: Marine paintings GENERAL: 19th century paintings, 17th century furniture.

**Dickinson's Architectural Antiques & Interiors,** 140 Corve Street, SY8 2PG TEL: 876207 PARKING: Easy OPEN: Mon-Sat 10-1, 2-5 MIN: £2 MAX: £3000 PERIOD: 19th century SPECIALIST: Period bathrooms GENERAL: Fireplaces, lighting, doors, interior fittings etc.

**Friars Antiques,** 87 Old Street, SY8 1NS TEL: 876087 PARKING: Easy OPEN: 9-5.30 PERIOD: 18th-20th century SPECIALIST: Staffordshire figures GENERAL: Furniture, paintings.

**Garrard Antiques,** 139A Corve Street, SY8 2PG TEL & FAX: 876727 PARKING: Easy OPEN: Mon-Sat 10-5 MIN: £10 MAX: £3000 PERIOD: 18th-19th century SPECIALIST: Oils & watercolours 1830-1930 GENERAL: Pine & country furniture, elm & fruitwood.

**G & D Ginger,** 5 Corve Street, SY8 1DA TEL: 876939 PARKING: Easy OPEN: Mon-Sat 8.30-5.30 & by appt MIN: £100 MAX: £10,000 PERIOD: 18th century SPECIALIST: Country furniture GENERAL: All types of antique furniture.

**Pepper Lane Antique Centre,** Pepper Lane, SY8 1PX TEL: 876494 PARKING: Medium OPEN: Mon-Sat 10-5 MIN: £1 MAX: £1500 PERIOD: 19th-20th century GENERAL: General antiques OTHER INFO: Market on Mon, Fri, Sat.

**St Leonards Restorations,** St Leonards Antiques Centre, Corve Street, SY8 1DL TEL: 875573 PARKING: Own carpark OPEN: Mon-Sat 9-5 MIN: £10 MAX: £3500 PERIOD: 18th-20th century GENERAL: Longcase clocks, furniture, porcelain, metalware, collectables, interesting bygones.

**M & R Taylor Antiques,** 53 Broad Street, SY8 1NH TEL: 874169 PARKING: Easy OPEN: Mon-Sat 9-6 & by appt MIN: £25 MAX: £4000 PERIOD: 17th-late 19th century GENERAL: Furniture, brass, treen etc OTHER INFO: Unicorn Inn.

**Teme Valley Antiques,** 1 The Bull Ring, SY8 1AD TEL: 874686 ASSNS: NAG PARKING: Easy OPEN: 10-5 MIN: £5 MAX: £2,500 PERIOD: 17th-20th century SPECIALIST: Portrait miniatures GENERAL: General antiques.

**Temeside Antique Centre,** St John's Lane, SY8 1PE TEL: 873481 PARKING: Easy OPEN: 9-5.15 PERIOD: 18th-20th century GENERAL: Pine, oak furniture, general antiques, china, paintings, etc.

## LEOMINSTER (01568)

**The Barometer Shop,** New Street, HR6 8BT TEL: 610200, 613652 PARKING: Own carpark OPEN: 9-5.30 closed Wed MIN: £45 MAX: £8500 PERIOD: 18th-20th century SPECIALIST: Clocks & barometers GENERAL: Period furniture OTHER INFO: The Banfield Collection of barometers at Churchill Gardens Museum, Hereford.

**Chapman Antiques,** 2 Bridge Street, HR6 8DX TEL: 615803, mobile 0836 566146 ASSNS: LAPADA PARKING: Easy OPEN: Mon-Sat 9.30-5.30 MIN: £200 GENERAL: Fine quality 17th to early 19th century furniture OTHER INFO: In an antique area, we already specialise in U.S. market.

**Coltsfoot Gallery,** Hatfield, HR6 0SF TEL: 760277 PARKING: Own carpark OPEN: 9-5 & by appt PERIOD: 19th-20th century SPECIALIST: Sporting prints GENERAL: Watercolours, prints, landscape, sporting & wildlife OTHER INFO: Restoration & conservation of works of art on paper.

**Court's Miscellany,** 48A Bridge Street, HR6 8DZ TEL: 612995 PARKING: Medium OPEN: Mon-Sat 10.30-5 MIN: 25p MAX: £1500 PERIOD: mainly 19th-20th century SPECIALIST: Collectables, social history GENERAL: Commemoratives.

**Farmers Antiques,** 26A Broad Street, HR6 8BS TEL: 611413 FAX: 611141 PARKING: Easy OPEN: Wed-Sat 11-4 & by appt MIN: £10 MAX: £10,000 PERIOD: 18th-20th century SPECIALIST: Antiques in 4 new premises adjoining premises of Farmers Gallery.

**Farmers Gallery,** 26A Broad Street, HR6 8BS TEL: 611413 FAX: 611141 PARKING: Easy OPEN: Wed-Sat 11-4 & by appt MIN: £10 MAX: £10,000 PERIOD: 18th-20th century SPECIALIST: Oils, watercolours, miniatures, prints.

**The Granary Coffee House,** 6 South Street, TEL: 614290 PARKING: Easy OPEN: Mon-Sat 9-3 MIN: 50p PERIOD: 19th-20th century GENERAL: Prints, bric a brac, books, linen, china, glass, etc OTHER INFO: Small market of 9 units above a coffee shop serving excellent refreshments.

**Jeffery Hammond Antiques**, Shaftesbury House, 38 Broad Street, HR6 8BS. TEL & FAX: 614876 ASSNS: LAPADA PARKING: Own carpark OPEN: Mon-Sat 9-6 ring bell out of hours MIN: £500 MAX: £20,000 PERIOD: 17th-early 19th century SPECIALIST: Furniture, some clocks & pictures OTHER INFO: The town is set where the English plains meet the Welsh mountains. Its turbulent past has witnessed the battles of Celt, Roman, Saxon, Dane, Norman, Plantagenet, Tudor, Roundhead & Royalist. All have left their mark.

**Hubbard Antiques**
**Bridge Street, HR6 8DU TEL: 614362 ASSNS: BADA, LAPADA PARKING: Own carpark OPEN: Mon-Sat 9-5 & by appt (resident) MIN: £20 MAX: £10,000 PERIOD: 17th-19th century SPECIALIST: Welsh oak dressers GENERAL: Country oak furniture, brass & copper OTHER INFO: On signposted trail of 'black & white' half timbered houses. Hope End Hotel, Marsh Country Hotel.**

**Jennings of Leominster**, 30 Bridge Street, HR6 8DX TEL: 612946 PARKING: Medium OPEN: Mon-Sat 9.30-6 MIN: £20 MAX: £10,000 PERIOD: 17th-19th century SPECIALIST: Period furniture & clocks.

**Leominster Antiques Market**, 14 Broad Street, HR6 8BS TEL: 612189 PARKING: Easy OPEN: Mon-Sat 10-5 MIN: £5 MAX: £1000 PERIOD: 18th-20th century GENERAL: 10 dealers on offering a wide range of quality antiques.

## HAY-ON-WYE (01497)

**Antique Market,** 6 Market Street, HR3 5AD TEL: 820175 PARKING: Medium OPEN: 10-5 MIN: 50p PERIOD: 19th century GENERAL: China, furniture, glass, collectables, etc.

**Richard Booth Bookshops Ltd,** 44 Lion Street, HR3 5AA TEL: 820322 FAX: 821150 PARKING: Medium OPEN: 9-8 summer, 9-5.30 winter MIN: £1 PERIOD: 17th-20th century SPECIALIST: Over 400,000 books covering most subjects.

**Hebbards of Hay,** 7 Market Street, HR3 5AF TEL: 820413 PARKING: Own carpark OPEN: Mon-Sat 9-5 MIN: £10 MAX: £1000 PERIOD: 18th-20th century SPECIALIST: 18th-19th century pottery GENERAL: Pottery & porcelain, collectables, blue & white OTHER INFO: Opposite Post Office.

**Tamara Le Bailly Antiques,** 5 Market Street, HR3 5AF TEL: 821157 FAX: 821091 PARKING: Easy OPEN: 10.30-5.30 PERIOD: 17th-20th century GENERAL: Oak & country furniture, decorative items, lightings, pictures, prints, metalware, textiles.

**Mark Westwood Books,** High Town, HR3 5AF TEL: 820068 FAX: 821641 ASSNS: ABA, PBFA PARKING: Easy OPEN: Mon-Sat (Sun in summer) 11-5 MIN: £1 MAX: £5000 PERIOD: 17th-20th century SPECIALIST: Antiquarian books on history of science & medicine GENERAL: Antiquarian & secondhand books.

**Bryan Wigington, Antique Furniture Restorations,** Chapel School Room, 1 Heolydwr, HR3 5AT TEL: 820545 ASSNS: BAFRA PARKING: Own carpark OPEN: 10-6 & by appt MIN: £10 MAX: £5000 PERIOD: 17th-19th century SPECIALIST: Well restored furniture GENERAL: Small stock, some interesting smalls, the odd picture, pewter, treen, metalware, olf tools, interesting old timbers, bits, carvings, etc OTHER INFO: This is the town of books by the million, good bookcases are scarcer (if you'd rather, I can take you fishing!).

## YAZOR (01981)

**MP & OJ Russell Antiques**, The Old Vicarage TEL: 22674 PARKING: Easy OPEN: Anytime but appt usual MIN: £50 MAX: £50,000 PERIOD: 17th-19th century SPECIALIST: Oak & country furniture GENERAL: Other furniture (not pine).

## MANSELL LACEY (01981)

**Bernard & Catherine Gay Pictures & Antiques,** The Old School House, HR4 7HQ TEL: 590269 PARKING: Own carpark OPEN: 9-6 MIN: £10 MAX: £5000 PERIOD: 17th-20th century SPECIALIST: Paintings & prints GENERAL: Smalls, ceramics, glass, furniture etc OTHER INFO: A Victoran Gothic pile, travel rated by *Pilgrim's Progress*. We also offer B&B. Coach parties by appt.

## HEREFORD (01432)

**Antiques & Bygones**, 47 St Owen Street TEL: 276241 PARKING: Easy OPEN: Seven days 8-6 PERIOD: 18th-20th century GENERAL: Antiques

& bygones OTHER INFO: Restaurant next door.
**I & JL Brown Ltd**, 58 Commercial Road, HR1 2BP TEL: 358895 FAX: 275338 PARKING: Easy OPEN: Mon-Sat 9-5.30 MIN: £10 MAX: £10,000 PERIOD: 18th-19th century SPECIALIST: UK's largest source (56,000 sq ft) of English country & French provincial furniture.
**Chatelain,** Whitmore Cross, Tillington HR4 8LE TEL: 760034 FAX: 350389 PARKING: Own carpark OPEN: 9.30-5 MIN: £200 MAX: £5000 PERIOD: 19th century SPECIALIST: Bedsand mirrors.
**GE Richards & Son (Antiques)**, 57 Blueschool Street, HR1 2AR TEL: 267840 PARKING: Own carpark OPEN: Mon-Sat 9-5 MIN: £5 MAX: £5000 PERIOD: 18th-20th century GENERAL: Antiques & reproductions.
**Warings of Hereford,** 45-47 St Owen Street TEL: 276241 PARKING: Easy OPEN: 7 days 9-5 PERIOD: 19th-20th century GENERAL: Antiques, bygones & pine.

## WHITCHURCH (01600)

**Olivers of Whitchurch**, The Square, HR9 6DJ TEL: 890662 PARKING: Own carpark OPEN: Mon-Sat 10-5.30 MIN: £100 MAX: £950 PERIOD: 19th-20th century SPECIALIST: Victorian & Edwardian brass & iron bedsteads, mattresses & bases GENERAL: Pine furniture, scales, metalware.

## WALFORD (01989)

**Old Pine Shop**, Warryfield Barn, Walford, HR9 5QW TEL: 566331, 768278 FAX: 566331 PARKING: Easy OPEN: Tues, Thurs-Sat 9.30-1, 2-5 MIN: £2 MAX: £2000 PERIOD: 18th-20th century SPECIALIST: Stained glass & leaded light windows GENERAL: Pine, brass & iron bedsteads, restoration OTHER INFO: A stripping service available.
**Robson Antiques,** Little Howle Farm, Howle Hill, HR9 5SL TEL: 768128 PARKING: Own carpark OPEN: 7days 9-till late summer, 9-5.30 winter MIN: £5 MAX: £3000 PERIOD: 17th-19th century GENERAL: Very large stock of furniture, early Georgian to late Edwardian (a few pieces of 1940s) OTHER INFO: In 18th century stone barns, beautiful courtyard with shire horses.

## ROSS-ON-WYE (01989)

**Baileys Architectural Antiques**, The Engine Shed, Ashburton Industrial Estate, HR9 7BW TEL: 563015 FAX: 768172 PARKING: Own carpark OPEN: Mon-Fri 9-5, Sat 10-5 MIN: £3.50 MAX: £3000 PERIOD: 19th-20th century SPECIALIST: Original & traditional fireplaces, bathrooms, unfitted kitchens, pictures, lighting, tiles.
**Fritz Fryer Decorative Antique Lighting**, 12 Brookend Street, HR9 7EG TEL: 567416 FAX: 566742 ASSNS: LAPADA PARKING: Easy OPEN: Mon-Sat 10-5.30 MIN: £30 MAX: £3000 SPECIALIST: Decorative lighting 1830-1930 OTHER INFO: No traffic jams!
**Robert Green Antiques**, 46 High Street, HR9 5HG TEL: 567504 PARKING: Medium OPEN: 10-5 MIN: £1 MAX: £5000 PERIOD: 18th-20th century SPECIALIST: Dining tables GENERAL: Mahogany furniture, silver, jewellery, glass, china.
**Robin Lloyd Antiques**, 23-24 Brookend Street, HR9 7EE TEL: 62123 FAX: 768145 PARKING: Easy OPEN: Mon-Sat 10-5 MIN: £5 MAX: £5000 PERIOD: 17th-19th century SPECIALIST: Oak, country furniture, brass candlesticks GENERAL: Anything decorative or unusual, good trade call OTHER INFO: Museum of Advertising, Button Museum. The Pheasants in Eddycross Street, best restaurant in W.Midlands.
**Relics**, 19 High Street, HR9 5BZ TEL: 64539 PARKING: Medium OPEN: Mon-Sat 10-5, Wed 10-1 MIN: £1 MAX: £1000 PERIOD: 19th-20th century SPECIALIST: Silver, jewellery GENERAL: General antiques.
**Ross Old Book & Print Shop**, 51-52 High Street, HR9 5HH ASSNS: PBFA PARKING: Medium OPEN: Mon-Sat 10-5 MIN: £1 MAX: probably £1000 PERIOD: 17th-20th century SPECIALIST: Topographical maps & prints GENERAL: Antiquarian & secondhand books.
**Trecilla Antiques**, 36 High Street, HR9 5HD TEL: 63010 PARKING: Own carpark OPEN: Mon-Sat 9.30-5, but Wed am only MIN: £5 MAX: £3000 PERIOD: 17th-20th century SPECIALIST: Arms & period furniture GENERAL: 6 showrooms of something for all OTHER INFO: Next to Old Market House in beautiful 'Jewel of the Wye'. Markets Thurs & Sats.

## PRESTON COURT (01531)

**Serendipity**, The Tythings, HR8 2LL TEL: 660245 FAX: 660421 PARKING: Own carpark OPEN: Mon-Sat 9-5 or anytime by appt MIN: £5 MAX: £15,000+ PERIOD: 17th-20th century SPECIAL-

IST: Traditional furniture, 4 poster beds OTHER INFO: In courtyard of our Elizabethan manor On B4215 between Preston Cross & Dymock.

## LEDBURY (01531)

**John Nash Antiques & Interiors,** Tudor House, 17c High Street, HR8 1DS TEL: 635714 FAX: 635050 PARKING: Easy OPEN: 9.30-5.30 PERIOD: 18th-19th century GENERAL: Mahogany & walnut furniture & decorative items.

**York House of Ledbury**, 155 The Homend TEL: 634687 PARKING: Easy OPEN: Mon, Tues, Thurs-Sat 9.30-1, 2-5.30 MIN: £10 MAX: £5000 PERIOD: 18th-19th century GENERAL: Furniture, glass, silver plate, decoratives.

## MATHON (01684)

**Phipps & Company Ltd**, Mathon Court, WR13 5NZ TEL: 892242 FAX: 575226 PARKING: Own carpark OPEN: By appt MIN: £100 MAX: £50,000+ PERIOD: 20th century SPECIALIST: Modern British paintings & sculpture OTHER INFO: The British Camp on the Malvern Hills is UK's highest Iron Age hill fort.

## SUCKLEY (01886)

**Holloways,** Lower Court, WR6 5DE TEL & FAX: 884665 PARKING: Own carpark MIN: £5 MAX: £5000 PERIOD: 18th-20th century SPECIALIST: Garden antiques only.

## WORCESTER (01905)

**The Antique Map & Print Gallery,** 61 Sidbury, WR1 2HU TEL & FAX: 612926 PARKING: Easy OPEN: 9-5.30 MIN: £4 MAX: £12,000 PERIOD: 17th-20th century SPECIALIST: Maps, topography, atlases & handcoloured plate books, prints GENERAL: We try to cover every subject.

**Antique Warehouse**, rear 74 Droitwich Road TEL: 27493 PARKING: Own carpark OPEN: Mon-Fri 8-6, Sat 10-4.30 MAX: £2,000 PERIOD: 19th century GENERAL: Victorian pine.

**Antiques & Curios,** 50 Upper Tything, WR1 1JZ TEL: 25412 PARKING: Easy OPEN: 9-5.30 MIN: £5 MAX: £1500 PERIOD: 18th-20th century GENERAL: Quality furniture, mirrors, pictures, curios, etc OTHER INFO: Over 2000 sq ft of stock.

**Andrew Boyle (Booksellers) Ltd**, 21 Friar Street, WR1 2NA TEL: 611700 ASSNS: ABA, PBFA PARKING: Medium OPEN: Mon-Wed, Fri 9.30-4 MIN: £6 MAX: £1000 PERIOD: 17th-20th century GENERAL: Most subjects.

**Bygones by the Cathedral**, 32 College Street TEL: 25388 ASSNS: LAPADA, Fellow Gemmological Assn of GB PARKING: Medium OPEN: Mon-Sat 9.30-1, 2-5.30 MIN: £10+ MAX: £20,000 PERIOD: 17th-20th century SPECIALIST: Jewellery, Worcester china GENERAL: General antiques OTHER INFO: Anything that makes us smile.

**Bygones of Worcester**, 55 Sidbury, WR1 2HU TEL: 23132 ASSNS: LAPADA, Fellow Gemmological Assn of GB PARKING: Medium OPEN: Mon-Sat 9.30-1, 2-5.30 MIN: £10 MAX: £20,000 PERIOD: 17th-20th century SPECIALIST: Worcester porcelain GENERAL: General antiques, pottery, jewellery, eccentricities, the odd dinosaur's egg & narwals horn.

**Grays Antiques,** 49 & 50A Upper Tythings & 58 Lowesmoor, WR1 1JZ TEL & FAX: 724456 PARKING: Medium OPEN: Mon-Sat 8.30-5.30 MIN: £50 MAX: £6000 PERIOD: 18th-20th century GENERAL: Pottery, porcelain, furniture, prints.

**Jean Hodge Antiques**, Peachley Manor, Hallows Lane, Lower Broadheath WR2 6QL TEL: 640255 PARKING: Own carpark OPEN: Seven days from 9am MIN: £5 MAX: £2500 PERIOD: 18th-19th century SPECIALIST: Period furniture.

**Sarah Hodge Antiques**, Peachley Manor, Hallows Lane, Lower Broadheath WR2 6QL TEL: 640255 PARKING: Own carpark OPEN: Seven days from 9am MIN: £5 MAX: £2500 PERIOD: 18th-19th century SPECIALIST: Furniture, kitchenalia, pine OTHER INFO: Open all hours. 4 large showrooms.

**The Original Choice Ltd**, 56 The Tything TEL: 613330 PARKING: Medium OPEN: Mon-Sat 10-6, Sun 1-5.30 MIN: £2 MAX: £20,000 PERIOD: 18th-20th century SPECIALIST: Fireplaces, stained glass.

**The Tything Antique Market**, 49 The Tything TEL: 610597 PARKING: Medium OPEN: Mon-Sat 10-5 PERIOD: 17th-20th century GENERAL: Wide range of quality items.

**Worcester Antiques Centre**, Reindeer Court, WR1 4DF TEL & FAX: 610593 PARKING: Easy OPEN: Mon-Sat 10-5 MIN: £5 MAX: £5000 PERIOD: 1750-1940 SPECIALIST: Royal Worcester, Coalport & other English factories, silver, jewellery, Arts & Crafts, Art Nouveau, Art Deco, kitchenalia, glass, books, prints, furniture, oak & mahogany.

## MALVERN (01684)

**Carlton Antiques,** 43 Worcester Road, WR14 4RB TEL: 573092 PARKING: Medium OPEN: Weekdays 10-6, Sun 1-6 MIN: £70 MAX: £2000 PERIOD: 19th-20th century SPECIALIST: Postcards GENERAL: Cottage furniture, pictures.

**Joan Coates of Malvern,** 26 St Ann's Road, WR14 4RG TEL: 575509 PARKING: Medium OPEN: Thurs-Fri 10-1, 2.30-5.30, Sat 10-1 MIN: £8 MAX: £450 PERIOD: 18th-20th century SPECIALIST: Small silver & old English ware GENERAL: Decoratives & small furniture, brass & copper.

**Kimber & Son Antiques**, 6 Lower Howsell Road, Malvern Link, WR14 1EF TEL: 574339 PARKING: Own carpark OPEN: Mon-Fri 9-1, 2-5, Sat 9-12.30 MIN: £20 MAX: £20,000 PERIOD: 18th-19th century GENERAL: General furnishings & decorative smalls.

**Gandolfi House**, 211-213 Wells Road, Malvern Wells, WR14 4HF TEL: 569747 PARKING: Easy OPEN: Tues-Sat 10-5.30 MIN: £10 MAX: £5,000 SPECIALIST: 19th, 20th century watercolours, oils, prints, Art Deco pottery GENERAL: 18th, 19th century furniture, glass, fire irons.

**Malvern Studios**, 56 Cowleigh Road TEL: 574913 ASSNS: BAFRA, UKIC, Museum & Galleries Commission listed PARKING: Own carpark OPEN: Mon-Thurs 9-5.15, Fri-Sat 9-4.45 PERIOD: 17th-20th century SPECIALIST: Satinwood & painted furniture when possible GENERAL: Period furniture from single chair to D-end dining tables. Restoration workshops for any furniture but specialising in boule & gilt, hand polishing.

**St James Antiques**, De Lys, Wells Road, WR14 4JL TEL: 563404 PARKING: Own carpark OPEN: 9-5 & by appt MIN: £50 MAX: £1000 PERIOD: 19th-20th century SPECIALIST: Continental pine GENERAL: Importers.

**Whitmore,** Teynham Lodge, Chase Road, Upper Colwall, WR13 6DT TEL & FAX: 540651 ASSNS: BNTA PARKING: Easy MIN: £1 MAX: £500 PERIOD: 17th-20th century SPECIALIST: Tokens & commemorative medallions GENERAL: Numismatic OTHER INFO: Strictly a postal business but para-numismatists made welcome with or without a parachute.

## UPTON-UPON-SEVERN (01684)

**Highway Gallery,** 40 Old Street, WR8 0HW TEL: 592645 PARKING: Easy OPEN: 10-5, closed Mon & Thurs MIN: £150 MAX: £10,000 PERIOD: 19th-20th century SPECIALIST: Oils & watercolours OTHER INFO: River town famous for Jazz Festival & for the number of pubs.

## PERSHORE (01386)

**Hansen Chard Antiques**, 126 High Street, WR10 1EA TEL: 553423 ASSNS: BHI PARKING: Easy OPEN: Tues-Wed, Fri-Sat 10-5 & by appt MIN: £5 MAX: around £3000 PERIOD: 18th-19th century SPECIALIST: Clocks & barometers.

**Look-In Antiques**, 134b High Street (main A44) TEL: 556776 PARKING: Medium OPEN: Mon-Sat 10.15-5.15 MIN: £1-4 MAX: £550 PERIOD: 19th-20th century GENERAL: Furniture all types, except the very large, and general antiques OTHER INFO: The town is of great historical interest having celebrated the millenium of its Royal Charter. There are 5 Georgian houses in Bridge Street which continues from High Street. Fine Abbey was occupied by Cistercian monks until early this century.

**Penoyre Antiques**, 9 Bridge Street, WR10 1AJ TEL: 553522 FAX: (01905) 754129 PARKING: Easy OPEN: Mon-Wed, Fri-Sat 9.30-1, 2-5.30 MIN: £24 MAX: £24,000 PERIOD: 18th-19th century GENERAL: Georgian mahogany dining room furniture OTHER INFO: The Angel is acoaching inn and the original model for JM Barrie's *Quality Street.*

**SW Antiques**, Abbey Showrooms, Newlands, WR10 1BP TEL: 555580 FAX: 556205 PARKING: Own carpark OPEN: Mon-Sat 9-5, Sun 10.30-4.30 MIN: £50 MAX: £8000 PERIOD: 19th-20th century SPECIALIST: Victorian & Edwardian bedroom furniture.

## EVESHAM (01386)

**Magpie Antiques & Jewellers,** 61 High Street & 2 Port Street, WR11 6AN TEL: 41631 ASSNS: LAPADA PARKING: Medium OPEN: Mon-Sat 9-5.30 MIN: 50p MAX: £10,000 PERIOD: 17th-20th century SPECIALIST: Jewellery, silver, china (Port St) GENERAL: Militaria, medals, furniture, stamps, coins, etc (High St).

# Shropshire

Powerful lords, strong castles and the marauding Welsh played a large part in the history and shaping of Shropshire. The north-western part of the county is an area of hills and valleys whilst further east the land levels out into a plain, making ideal dairy farming country and giving a typically English landscape. In the south, hills provide far more dramatic scenery.

**Wellington** is first. This now forms part of Telford but still has half timbered houses standing in narrow streets. Close by is the Wrekin, a hill rising sharply to 1335 feet and giving dramatic views over the surrounding countryside. Excavations have revealed that this was the site of a major Iron Age fort, possbily the base for the Cornovii tribe. The new town of **Telford** was built on the worked out Shropshire coalfield. This area had been damaged by the coal workings and, in the 1960s, a new town on the site appeared the best way to use the land. This was an area of great importance during the Industrial Revolution and was at the cutting edge of 19th century technology. The Ironbridge Gorge Museum, five miles from Telford, has a number of sites and exhibits showing the industrial importance of this region. The Blists Hill Open Air Museum, covering 42 acres, is a working Victorian industrial community showing a foundry, candle factory, saw mill, printing shop, etc. This was the site of the first iron bridge in the world and there is an exhibition and information centre relating to this. The Jackfield Tile Museum, housed in a former tileworks, displays a large collection of tiles. The Tar Tunnel is an 18th century tunnel for the mining of bitumen and visitors may go underground.

**Shifnal** (the antique shop is at nearby tiny Neachley) has few ancient buildings left because a disastrous fire in 1591 destroyed much of the town. The church of St Andrew did survive, however, and contains a Norman chancel arch which has a carving of the 'green man' on it, as a pagan symbol this is most unusual in a church. Five miles north stands Weston Park, a grand 17th century house set in 1000 acres of parkland. The grounds include formal gardens, a rose garden, an Italian broderie and an arboretum. In the house is an excellent collection of antiques and paintings including works by Van Dyck and Gainsborough.

Continuing south, the route comes to the quiet market town of **Bridgnorth**. Divided by the River Severn, this was once a busy river port and a producer of iron and carpets. Features of note include a fine 16th century half timbered house, elegant Georgian houses in East Castle Street, several timber framed buildings including the Swan Inn, and the last remnant of a castle and a tower which leans at an angle three times greater than the Leaning Tower of Pisa. The town stands on a sandstone bluff and it has the Cliff Railway built in 1892 and still working. Now electric, originally the cars were powered by running water in and out of tanks beneath them. The feat of engineering can only be appreciated when it is realised that the gradient on the cliff is two in three, making it the steepest railway in England.

**Much Wenlock** is set on the extreme north eastern side of Wenlock Edge. This old market town contains picturesque black and white buildings in narrow streets. It was sacked by the Danes and then rebuilt by Lady Godiva's husband, Leofric. Raynald's Mansion from 1682 and the 15th century timbered Guildhall resting on wooden pillars are of particular interest.

Next is **Craven Arms**, a 19th century new town named for the existing inn. The town, planned as a centre where several railways lines intersected, quickly becoming an important centre for selling sheep. A mile south is the 13th century Stokesay Castle. The nearby village of **Bishop's Castle** had, until 1832, the distinction of being England's smallest borough and was represented by two Members of Parliament. It is a picturesque place with Georgian and timber-framed buildings in the High Street. A particularly striking house is the Elizabethan 'house on crutches'—the gables are supported by posts.

The tour now turns north to the market town of **Church Stretton**, given a charter by King John in 1214. An unexpected feature of St Laurence's Church is the female fertility figure, a Sheila-na-gig, built into the wall above the disused North Door. A hill-fort, Caer Caradoc, stands about a

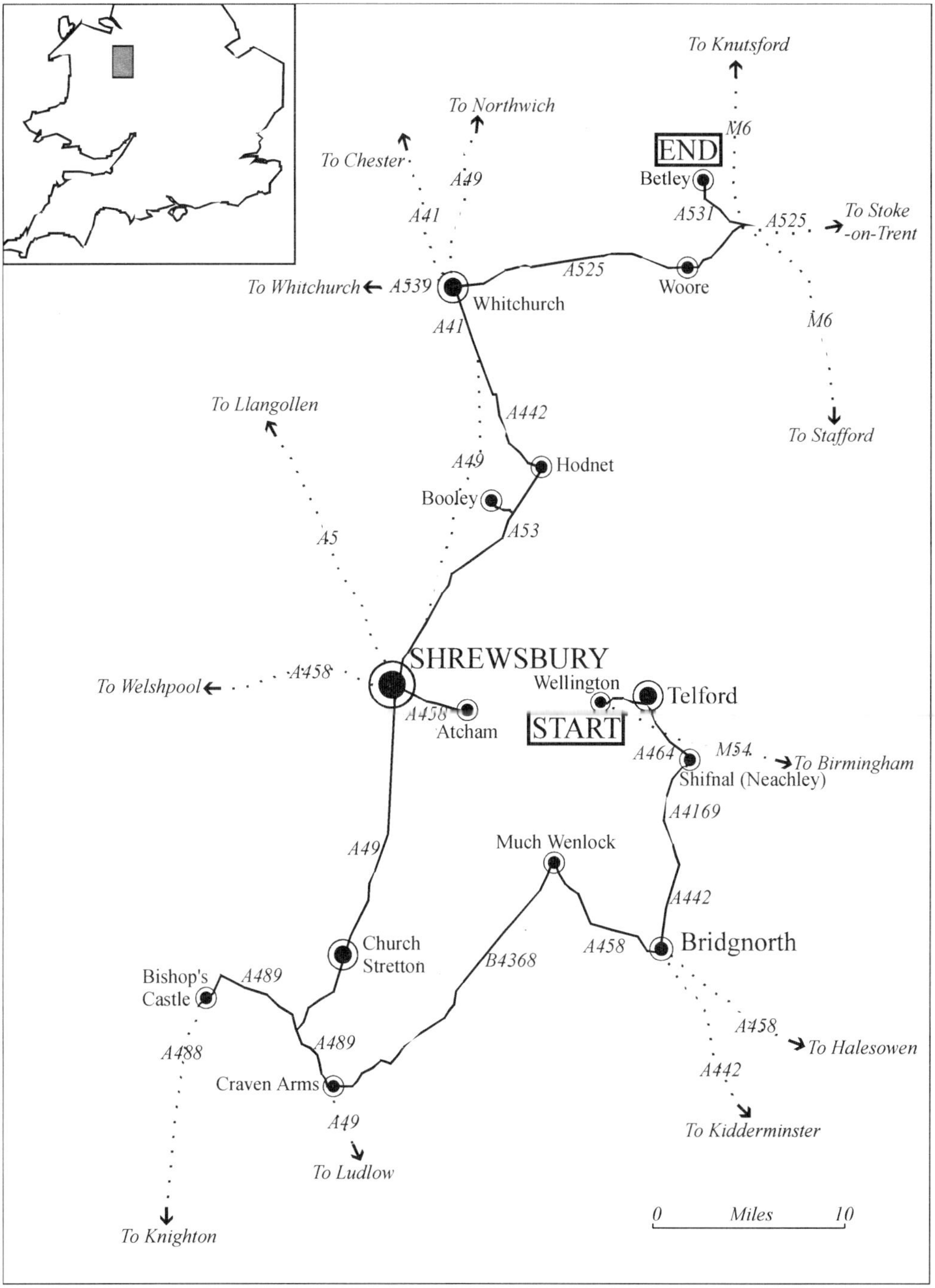
To Knutsford
M6
END
Betley
To Northwich
To Chester
A49
A41
A531
A525
To Stoke -on-Trent
A525
Woore
To Whitchurch
A539
Whitchurch
A41
M6
To Stafford
To Llangollen
A442
A49
Hodnet
Booley
A53
A5
SHREWSBURY
Wellington
Telford
To Welshpool
A458
A458
Atcham
START
A464
M54
To Birmingham
Shifnal (Neachley)
A4169
Much Wenlock
A49
A442
Church Stretton
Bridgnorth
A458
B4368
Bishop's Castle
A489
A489
A458
To Halesowen
A488
Craven Arms
A442
A49
To Kidderminster
To Ludlow
To Knighton
0 Miles 10

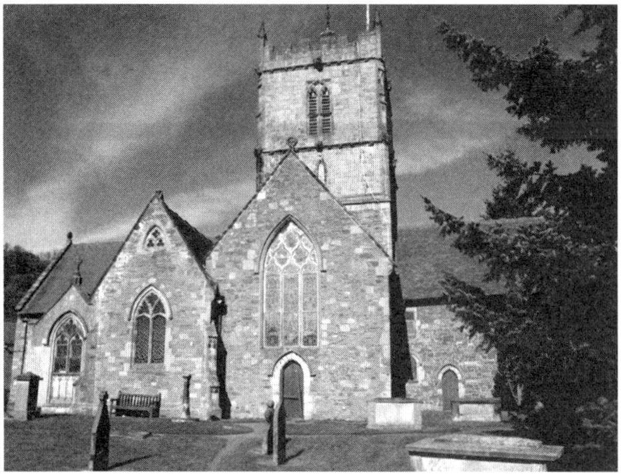
*St Laurence's Church, Church Stretton*

mile west of the town. The British chieftain, Caractacus, is said to have fought his final battle with the Romans here.

**Shrewsbury,** 11 miles north, stands on the River Severn. Its centre is a jumble of narrow, crooked streets lined with many timbered and half timbered shops and houses including the house in Wyle Cop where Henry Vll probably stayed prior to the Battle of Bosworth in 1485. A more recent building is the town's fine railway station built in Tudor style. The several good museums include the Georgian Clive House in College Hill which has an outstanding collection of Shropshire porcelain and art and the Radbrook Culinary Museum in Radbrook Road has a unique exhibition of domestic and household items. There is also the Coleham Pumping Station at Old Coleham with a preserved beam engine and Rowley's House Museum, in a 17th century mansion in Barker Street, displays exhibits ranging from archaeology to local history. Shrewsbury Castle stands on a bend of the River Severn giving it a natural moat. The site of a Saxon fort, it was built in the 11th century and partly rebuilt in the 13th century. In the Middle Ages the castle was used as a base for attacking the Welsh and saw action again during the Civil War as a Royalist stronghold but captured by Parliamentary forces in 1644. After Charles II came to the throne it passed into private hands and was eventually remodelled by Thomas Telford in the 18th century.

Taking the B4380 for three miles, is **Atcham**, sited on a river of the same name. This pleasant village has a seven arch bridge, built in 1768. Its Norman church was built with Roman stones taken from Wroxeter and contains roof timbers at least 500 years old. Now take the A53 north east to arrive first in **Booley** and then **Hodnet**, a large and pretty village. The only Grade I landscape in Shropshire may be found three miles away at Hawkstone Park. It contains cliffs, caves, woodlands, towers, monuments and steep rock paths. This is dramatic and unusual scenery much used for filming *The Chronicles of Narnia* and *One Foot in the Past*. Another local attraction is the award winning Hodnet Hall Gardens.

Continuing north, **Whitchurch** is on the site of the Roman town of *Mediolanum*. Little remains of the Roman settlement and the present town is mostly Queen Anne in style. East, on the A525, the village of **Woore** comes next followed by the final destination, **Betley**, on the A531.

## ANTIQUE DEALERS

### WELLINGTON (01952)

**Haygate Antiques,** Haygate Gallery, 40 Haygate Road, TF1 1QT TEL: 248553 PARKING: Easy OPEN: 9-5, closed Wed MIN: £20 MAX: £2000 PERIOD: 19th-20th century SPECIALIST: Watercolours GENERAL: Small antiques & decorative items.

**Brian James Antiques,** The Old Maltings, The Lawns, TF1 3AF TEL: 256592 ASSNS: GMC PARKING: Own carpark OPEN: Mon-Fri 9-5, Sat 9-1 MIN: £50 MAX: £2000 PERIOD: 18th-20th century SPECIALIST: Chests of drawers GENERAL: Conversion, full restoration facilities, large stock.

**Bernie Pugh Antiques**, 120 High Street, TF1 1JU TEL: 256184 Mobile: 0860 219944 PARKING: Medium OPEN: Mon, Tues Thurs-Sat 10-12, 1-

5.30, Weds 10-12 PERIOD: 19th-20th, some 18th century SPECIALIST: We try to deal in the unusual OTHER INFO: Good B&B 5 mins, Birtley house, Holyhead Rd.

## TELFORD (01952)

**Gallery 6**, 6 Church Street, BroseleyTF12 5DG TEL: 882860 PARKING: Own carpark OPEN: 11-6 (resident) MIN: £100 MAX: £2000 SPECIALIST: 20th century oils, watercolours, etchings GENERAL: 19th-20th century same inc contemporary OTHER INFO: Broseley has many houses associated with the Industrial Revolution, Ironbridge and its earliest iron bridge in the world.

**Granny's Attic**, 33 Market Street, Oakengates TEL: 610330 PARKING: Medium OPEN: 10-5 not Thurs PERIOD: 17th-20th century GENERAL: Exciting wide range, bit of everything.

**Ironbridge Antique Centre,** Dale End, Ironbridge TF8 7DS TEL: 433784 PARKING: Own carpark OPEN: Mon-Sat 10-5, Sun 2-5 MIN: 50p MAX: £1000 PERIOD: 19th-20th century GENERAL: Furniture, smalls OTHER INFO: Tourist area, site of the first iron bridge, hotels, B&Bs, restaurants.

**Telford Antique Centre,** High Street, TF1 1JW TEL: 256450 PARKING: Own carpark OPEN: Mon-Sat 10-5 Sun: 2-5 MIN: £1 MAX: £2000 PERIOD: 19th-20th century GENERAL: Furniture, fireplaces, china, militaria, books, glass. OTHER INFO: This building was once the old Chad Valley factory which made teddy bears.

## NEACHLEY (01902)

**Doveridge House of Neachley**, Neach Hill, Long Lane, TF11 8PJ TEL: 373131-2 ASSNS: BADA, CINOA, LAPADA PARKING: Own carpark OPEN: Seven days 9-5 MIN: £30 MAX: £15,000 PERIOD: 17th-19th century SPECIALIST: Furniture GENERAL: General antiques OTHER INFO: Directions: M54, Jn 3, then A41 ° mile south east.

## BRIDGNORTH (01746)

**English Heritage of Bridgnorth**, 2 Whitburn Street, WV16 4QN TEL: 762097 PARKING: Medium OPEN: Mon-Sat 9.30-5 MIN: £1 MAX: £1500 PERIOD: 19th-20th century SPECIALIST: Jewellery, militaria GENERAL: General antiques OTHER INFO: Near Ironbridge Gorge Museum, numerous pubs, Severn Valley Railway.

**Micawber Antiques**, 64 St Mary's Street TEL: 763254 PARKING: Easy OPEN: 10-5 MIN: £5 MAX: £1000 PERIOD: 19th century SPECIALIST: Early 19th century English porcelain GENERAL: General antiques OTHER INFO: Situated in mainly 16th century-timbered St Mary's Street. Best B&B at delightful Mary Champion's.

**Parmenter Antiques**, 5 Central Court, High Street.WV16 4DQ TEL: 765599 FAX: 767480 PARKING: Easy OPEN: 10-5 MIN: £5 MAX: £2000 PERIOD: 17th-20th century SPECIALIST: Furniture GENERAL: Objects, pictures, jewellery OTHER INFO: Town Hall is medieval barn on piers straddling High Street. The remaining stump of our castle leans at alarming angle (worse than Leaning Tower of Pisa), England's only funicular railway.

## MUCH WENLOCK (01952)

**Cruck House Antiques**, 23 Barrow Street, TF13 6EN TEL: 727165 PARKING: Easy OPEN: 10-5 MIN: £2 MAX: £1000 PERIOD: 18th-20th century SPECIALIST: Silver, watercolours GENERAL: Small furniture, pictures, small items.

**Wenlock Fine Art**, 3 The Square, TF13 6LX TEL: 728232 PARKING: Easy OPEN: 10-5 MIN: £100 MAX: £10,000 SPECIALIST: Some 19th but mainly 20th century British paintings OTHER INFO: Ceramics & sculpture.

## CRAVEN ARMS (01588)

**I & S Antiques,** Ludlow Road, SY7 9QL TEL: 672263 PARKING: Own carpark OPEN: Mon-Sat 9-5.30, Sun 10.30-4.30 MIN: 50p MAX: £5000 PERIOD: 19th century SPECIALIST: Pine, shipping goods, country furniture, bric a brac.

## BISHOP'S CASTLE (01588)

**Ark Antiques,** 9 Market Square TEL: 638608 PARKING: Easy OPEN: Tues, Thurs-Sat 10.30-4.30 PERIOD: 17th-20th century SPECIALIST: Country furniture, brass & iron beds GENERAL: Metalware, chimney cranes, pottery, country land & gardening tools OTHER INFO: Very early town with numerous pubs & good reasonable accommodation. My stock is cheap, good & real!

## CHURCH STRETTON (01694)

**Antiques On The Square**, 2 Sandford Court, Sandford Avenue, SY6 6DA TEL: 724111, 723072, Mobile (0831) 336052 ASSNS: Art Deco Dealers

Assn PARKING: Own carpark OPEN: Mon-Tues, Thurs-Sat 9.30-5, Wed 9-1 MIN: £10 MAX: £5000 PERIOD: 20th century SPECIALIST: Clarice Cliff, Susie Cooper, pottery, 1930's Art Deco, etc OTHER INFO: Thursday market, Longmynde Hotel, Stretton House Hotel, Spa water.

**Old Barn Antiques**, High Street, SY6 6BX. TEL: 723742 & 722294 ASSNS: LAPADA PARKING: Own carpark OPEN: By appt MIN: £150 MAX: £14,000 PERIOD: 18th-19th century SPECIALIST: Furniture & furnishings.

**Stretton Antiques Market**, 36 Sandford Avenue, SY6 6BH TEL: 723718 FAX: 781502 PARKING: Easy OPEN: Mon-Sat 9.30-5.30, Sun 10.30-4.30 MIN: £1 MAX: £3000 PERIOD: 19th-20th century GENERAL: Furniture & collectables.

## SHREWSBURY (01743)

**Candle Lane Books**, 28-31 Princess Street, SY1 1SL TEL: 365301 PARKING: Medium OPEN: Mon-Sat 9.30-1, 2-5 PERIOD: 19th-20th century SPECIALIST: Large stock of antiquarian & secondhand books.

**Hutton Antiques**, 18 Princess Street, SY1 1LP TEL: 245810 PARKING: Easy OPEN: 10-4, closed Thurs MIN: £5 MAX: £1700 PERIOD: 18th-19th century SPECIALIST: Silver & porcelain GENERAL: General antiques OTHER INFO: Clive House Museum (Coalport porcelain), Military Museum.

**FC Manser & Son Ltd**, 53-54 Wyle Cop, SY1 1XJ TEL: 351120 FAX: 271047 ASSNS: LAPADA PARKING: Own carpark OPEN: 9-5 MIN: £5 MAX: £12,000 PERIOD: 18th-20th century GENERAL: General antiques OTHER INFO: Right in medieval town centre. Hotels: Lion, Prince Rupert, Albrighton. Country Friends restaurant.

**Princess Antique Centre,** 14A The Square TEL: 343701 PARKING: Medium OPEN: Mon-Sat 9.30-5.30 MIN: £1 MAX: £2000 PERIOD: 19th-20th century GENERAL: Porcelain, china, furniture, militaria, clothes, toys, curios, fireplaces.

**Raleigh Antiques**, 23 Belle Vue Road, SY3 7LN TEL: 359552 ASSNS: Founder Guild of Antique Dealers & Restorers PARKING: Medium OPEN: Mon-Sat 9.30-5 MIN: £2 MAX: £10,000 PERIOD: 18th-20th century GENERAL: General antiques OTHER INFO: Excellent hotels: The Prince Rupert (need to book) & The Lion. Annual event:

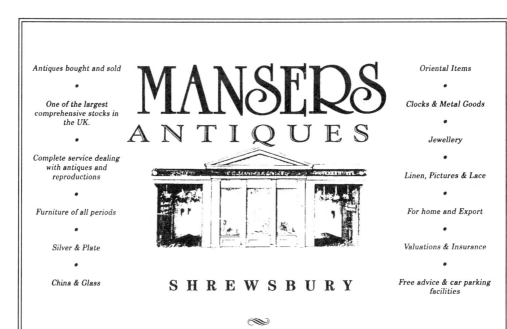

Shrewsbury Flower Show, second Fri & Sat in August, attended by 85,000 visitors.
**Shrewsbury Antique Centre,** 15 Princess House, The Square, SY1 1JZ TEL: 247704 PARKING: Medium OPEN: Mon-Sat 9.30-5.30 PERIOD: 18th-20th century GENERAL: Silver, porcelain, china, furniture, jewellery, glass, collectables.
**Shrewsbury Antique Market**, Frankwell Quay Warehouse, SY3 8LG TEL: 350916 PARKING: Easy OPEN: Mon-Sat 9.30-5 MIN: 50p MAX: £1500 PERIOD: 19th-20th century GENERAL: Furniture, glass, china, clothes, curios, prints & books.
**Tiffany Antiques**, Unit 1, Welshbridge Antique Centre, 135 Frankwell TEL: 257425, mobile 0370 380261 PARKING: Easy OPEN: 9.30-5.30, Sun 12-5 MIN: £5 MAX: £600 PERIOD: 19th-20th century SPECIALIST: Antique brass & copper GENERAL: All collectables OTHER INFO: Brother Cadfael town. Auction rooms along the road from antique centre. Good pub next door for meals.
**Welsh Bridge Antique Centre,** 135 Frankwell, S3 8JX TEL: 248822 OPEN: Mon-Sat 9.30-5.30, Sun 12-5 PARKING: Easy MIN: £1 MAX: £1000 PERIOD: 19th-20th century GENERAL: General antiques & collectables.
**Wyle Cop Antiques**, The Old School (off Wyle Cop), SY1 1UT TEL: 231180 PARKING: Medium OPEN: Mon-Sat 9.30-5.30 PERIOD: 19th-20th century GENERAL: Mainly furniture.

## ATCHAM (01952)

**Mytton Antiques**, 2-3 Norton Cottages, Norton Crossroads, SY4 4UM TEL: 740229 FAX: 461154 PARKING: Own carpark OPEN: Mon-Sat 10-5 MIN: £5 MAX: £5000 PERIOD: 18th-19th century SPECIALIST: Country oak furniture, longcase clocks GENERAL: Mahogany, oak 1700-1900, general antiques OTHER INFO: There is a good country house B&B to a few miles away.

## BOOLEY (01939)

**Marcus Moore Antiques & Restorations**, Booley House, SY4 4LY TEL: 200333 PARKING: Own carpark OPEN: Anytime by appt MIN: £5 MAX: £5000 PERIOD: 17th-19th century SPECIALIST: Georgian mahogany, oak, pine. 19th cent. furniture.

## HODNET (01630)

**Hodnet Antiques**, 13a Shrewsbury Street TEL: 638591 PARKING: Easy OPEN: Variable & by appt MIN: £1 MAX: £5000 SPECIALIST: Porcelain, pottery, glass, furniture, etc OTHER INFO: Most stock from local private houses. Hodnet Hall Gardens open April-Sept.

## WHITCHURCH (01948)

**Dodington Antiques**, 15 Dodington, SY13 1EA TEL: 663399 PARKING: Easy OPEN: By appt MIN: £25 MAX: £7000 PERIOD: 18th-19th century SPECIALIST: Country oak & mahogany furniture OTHER INFO: Also at The Old Music Hall (2 doors away).

## WOORE (01630)

**The Mount Antiquarian Gallery,** 12 Nantwich Road, CW3 9BA TEL: 647277 PARKING: Easy OPEN: Erratic but reliable at weekends MIN: £2 MAX: £500+ PERIOD: 17th-20th century (a little 15th & 16th) SPECIALIST: Maps, paintings & prints OTHER INFO. Customers are warned that the proprietor is said to be noisy and rude but doesn't actually bite. Ask to see the garden.
**No7 Antiques,** 7 Nantwich Road, CW3 9SA TEL & FAX: 647118 PARKING: Easy OPEN: 10-5, closed Mon MIN: £5 MAX: £2000 PERIOD: 17th-20th century SPECIALIST: Kitchenalia GENERAL: Country furniture, treen, metalware, porcelain OTHER INFO: 3 good pubs in village, 2 mins from Bridgemere Garden World.
**Peter Wain,** 7 Nantwich Road, CW3 9DA TEL & FAX: 647118 ASSNS: BADA, CINOA PARKING: Easy OPEN: 10-5, closed Mon MIN: £200 MAX: £10,000 PERIOD: 17th-20th century SPECIALIST: Oriental ceramics.

## BETLEY (01270)

**Betley Court Gallery**, Main Road, CW3 9BH TEL: 820652 FAX 820122 PARKING: Own carpark OPEN: Anytime (resident) MIN: £20 MAX: £2500 PERIOD: 18th-20th century SPECIALIST: Doulton Lambeth, Wedgwood GENERAL: Oils, watercolours, ceramics, furniture

# Central England

*Chamberlain Square, Birmingham*
*By courtesy of Birmingham City Council*

The West Midlands and Staffordshire are often thought of as being industrial areas and many visitors do not realise that both counties have a lot to offer. Its true that Birmingham in particular was in the forefront of the Industrial Revolution. The wealth that this brought into the city then has left a legacy of important and imposing public buildings. In Staffordshire, similarly, the growth in factories during the last century led to prosperity and increasing population. However, the county is still largely rural and and includes a part of the Peak District.

The tour starts in the SE outskirts of Birmingham, at **Solihull** which has the Tudor timber framed houses of Solihull Hall and Old Berry Hall. Continuing on via **Coleshill,** and then **Sutton Coldfield** with its 16th century church and grammar school, **Birmingham** is England's biggest city after London so to get around successfully it is essential to get an excellent street map and details of things to see and do from the Tourist Information Centre.

There are many relics of Birmingham's medieval past. Aston Hall, two miles from the centre, is an imposing house built around 1620 with splendid Jacobean plaster work and many rooms furnished in period style. It also has good collections of tapestries, paintings, furniture, glass and ceramics. Three miles out stands Blakesley Hall, a timber framed yeoman's cottage from the late16th century furnished in the style of the period. In Edgbaston, two miles out, is reputedly 'Birmingham's most eccentric building', Perrott's Folly built in 1758, a 96 foot high tower with seven floors.

The city has a number of fascinating museums. The largest is the Birmingham Museum and Art Gallery in Chamberlain Square with several large departments ranging from Fine Art to Natural History. For lovers of cars there is Autoworld at the Patrick Collection in Lifford Lane and the Museum of Science and Industry, Newhall Street, also has transport exhibits as well as other industrial and scientific items.

Leaving Birmingham, north-west is industrial **Walsall**. Birthplace of Jerome K. Jerome, author of *Three Men in a Boat*, this town still has traces of its past before the Industrial Revolution. A few remnants still exist of the 14th century castle demolished in 1646 and involved in the Civil War. The Museum and Art Gallery in Lichfield Street also has a local history gallery. The Walsall Leather Centre Museum, housed in a Victorian factory in Wisemore, gives a fascinating glimpse of the past with displays showing leather production from tanning to finishing. There are also demonstrations in authentic period workshops.

Taking the A461 the trip comes to **Lichfield**, with its famous cathedral developed around the tomb of St. Chad. Work was started in the 12th century although little is now in evidence. The present construction dates from the 14th and 15th centuries and is unique in having three spires. Although marked by pollution, it is a delightful building, with much stone carving and decoration on the outside. There has been violence, for during the Civil War, the cathedral and close

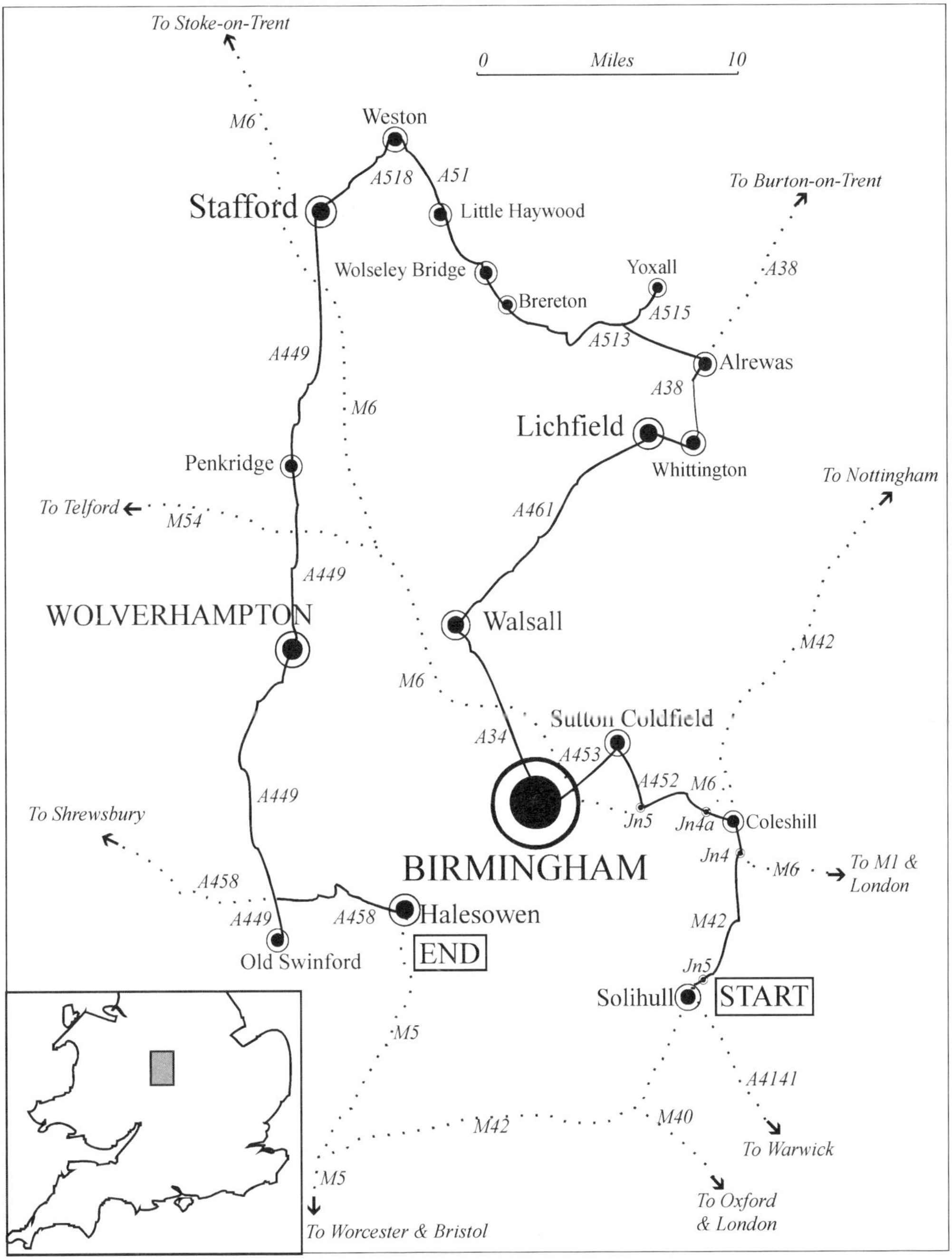
To Stoke-on-Trent
0 Miles 10
M6
Weston
A518
A51
Stafford
Little Haywood
To Burton-on-Trent
Wolseley Bridge
Yoxall
A38
Brereton
A515
A513
A449
Alrewas
A38
M6
Lichfield
Penkridge
Whittington
To Nottingham
To Telford
M54
A461
A449
WOLVERHAMPTON
Walsall
M42
M6
Sutton Coldfield
A34
A453
A452
M6
To Shrewsbury
A449
Jn5
Jn4a
Coleshill
Jn4
M6
To M1 & London
BIRMINGHAM
A458
A449
A458
Halesowen
M42
Old Swinford
END
Jn5
Solihull
START
M5
A4141
M42
M40
To Warwick
M5
To Oxford & London
To Worcester & Bristol

*Aston Hall. By courtesy of Birmingham City Council*

formed a Royalist enclave and consequently came under siege in the1640's. In the attacks the central spire was shot down, medieval windows broken, tombs were smashed, lead was stripped off the roof and books and records were burnt. However, one precious item was saved: a copy of the Gospels made by the monks of Lindisfarne in 730 AD and now kept in the Chapter House. Much of the damage was repaired in the reign of Charles II and a statue of him is on the West Front. More restoration work was carried out from 1790 through to Victorian times because the sandstone, from which the cathedral was built, was crumbling badly and at one time it appeared that the nave might collapse.

The town is charming with many18th century houses standing in old narrow streets. It was the birthplace of Samuel Johnson and David Garrick, amongst others, and Johnson's parents are buried here. There is also the Samuel Johnson Birthplace Museum in Breadmarket Street. Another museum is the Lichfield Heritage Exhibition, Treasury and Munument Room in the Market Square covering the city's history as well as displaying regimental plate, mace, state sword, Ashmole Cup, etc. The route continues through the villages of **Whittington**, home of the Staffordshire Regiment and with a museum dedicated to them, and then **Alrewas**, very pretty with black and white houses. **Yoxall**, is most ly a conservation area,. **Brereton** and**Wolseley Bridge** are next, followed by **Little Haywood** and **Weston**.

**Stafford** retains much of its original medieval street layout although it has lost many of the black and white, half-timbered houses. Of the survivors, High House is perhaps the most interesting. It is probably the largest timber-framed house in England, built in 1595 and also very likely sheltered Charles I and Prince Rupert in 1642. There are collections of furniture, costume, paintings, ceramics and rare 18th and 19th century wallpapers.

Stafford was the home and birthplace of Izaak Walton, author of *The Compleat Angler*. Born in 1593 and baptised in the local church, his home at Shallowfield is now a memorial to his work and life. The fine neo-classical Shugborough Hall stands six miles east on the A513. Completed in 1693 and the seat of the Earls of Lichfield, the hall is set in beautiful gardens and parkland containing a working rare breeds farm.

Turning south, the village of **Penkridge** is followed by industrial **Wolverhampton**. Here Bantock House in Bradmore is famous for its collection of English painted enamels and Jappaned ware from the West Midlands. Painted enamels are also the subject of the Bilsom Museum and Art Gallery in Mount Pleasant although the museum includes displays on the social and industrial history of the area. Wightwick Manor, three miles west on the A454, is a 19th century house whose interior shows the strong influence of William Morris and the Pre-Raphaelites. The final calls are on **Old Swinford** and then **Halesowen**.

## ANTIQUE DEALERS

### SOLIHULL (0121)

**Renaissance Antiques**, 18 Marshall Lake Road, Shirley, B90 4PL TEL: 745 5140 PARKING: Medium OPEN: Mon-Sat 9-5 PERIOD: 18th-20th century GENERAL: Wide range. Restoration & re-upholstering.

### COLESHILL (01675)

**Coleshill Interiors & Antiques,** 12-14 High Street, B46 1AZ TEL & FAX. 462931 ASSNS: LAPADA PARKING: Own carpark OPEN: Tues-Sat 9.30-5 MIN: £50 MAX: £10,000 PERIOD: 18th-20th century SPECIALIST: Continental porcelain GENERAL: Furniture, silver, jewellery, OTHER INFO: 2 miles from NEC, 14 pubs, 2 restaurants.

### SUTTON COLDFIELD (0121)

**M Allen Watchmaker**, 76a Walsall Road, Four Oaks, B74 4QY TEL: 308 6117 PARKING: Easy OPEN: Mon-Sat 9-5.30 MIN: £75 MAX: £4000 PERIOD: 18th-20th century SPECIALIST: Vintage gold wristwatches GENERAL: Clocks, watches from U.S., Germany, France. All repairs.

**Thomas Coulborn & Sons**, Vesey Manor, 64 Birmingham Road, B72 1QP TEL: 354 3974 FAX: 354 4614 ASSNS: BADA PARKING: Own carpark OPEN: Mon-Sat 9.15-1, 2-5.30 MIN: £500+ PERIOD: 18th-19th century SPECIALIST: English & French furniture, giltwood mirrors. Finest furniture outside London.

**Driffold Gallery**, The Smithy, 78 Birmingham Road TEL: 355 5433 PARKING: Own carpark OPEN: Mon-Sat 10-5.30 MIN: £100 MAX: £12,000 PERIOD: 19th-20th century GENERAL: Oil paintings & watercolours + original illustrations OTHER INFO: Part of our premises date back to 14th century. Henry VIII is believed to have visited The Smithy whilst hunting in park.

**Osbornes Antiques**, 91 Chester Road, New Oscott, B73 5BA TEL: 355 6667 FAX: 354 7166 PARKING: Easy OPEN: Mon 9-1, 2-4, Tues-Fri 9-1, 2-5, Sat 9.15-12.15 MIN: £50 MAX: £6000 SPECIALIST: Barometers, clocks, barographs GENERAL: Small inlaid furniture OTHER INFO: Scientific glass blowers (thermometers & tubes), & restorers on premises.

**H & RL Parry Ltd,** 23 Maney Corner, B72 1QL TEL: 354 1178 PARKING: Medium OPEN: 9.30-5 MIN: £75 MAX: £2/3500 PERIOD: 18th-19th century SPECIALIST: Silver & jewellery.

**Robert & Mary Taylor**, Windy Ridge, Worcester Lane, Four Oaks, B75 5QS TEL: 308 4209 FAX: 323 3473 PARKING: Own carpark OPEN: By appt MIN: £5 MAX: £2000 PERIOD: 20th century SPECIALIST: Corgi & Dinky Toys GENERAL: All collectable toys & diecast models OTHER INFO: Mainly export to US & Japan.

### BIRMINGHAM (0121)

**Always Antiques**, 285 Vicarage Road, Kings Heath, B14 7NE. TEL: 444 8701 PARKING: Easy OPEN: Thurs-Sat 9.30-6 MIN: £10 MAX: £1 000 PERIOD: 19th-20th century SPECIALIST: Ceramics GENERAL: 1930's furniture OTHER INFO: Weekly markets. 3 miles city centre, ICC centre.

**Architectural Antiques of Moseley Ltd,** 23A St Mary's Road, Moseley, B13 8HW TEL: 442 4546 PARKING: Own carpark OPEN: thurs-Sat 10-6, Sun 10-3 MIN: £5 MAX: £15,000 PERIOD: 18th-20th century SPECIALIST: Sympathetic renovation to 18th & 19th century properties GENERAL:

Architectural items, garden statuary.

**Peter Asbury Antiques,** 162 Vicarage Road, Langley, Oldbury B68 8JA TEL: 558 0579 PARKING: Own carpark OPEN: Mon-Sat 9.30-5 MIN: 10p MAX: £350 PERIOD: 18th-20th century GENERAL: Clocks, china, glass, old dolls, toys, general antiques OTHER INFO: Private toy museum, open by appt only.

**Ashleigh House Antiques**, 5 Westbourne Road, Edgbaston, B15 3TH TEL: 454 6283 FAX: 454 6283 PARKING: Own carpark OPEN: By appt MIN: £200 MAX: £10,000 PERIOD: 18th-19th century SPECIALIST: Regency furniture, French clocks, paintings GENERAL: Antique furniture, clocks, Oriental & Continental works of art, ivories, bronzes OTHER INFO: We are large listed mansion, accommodation overnight for bona fide buyers by prior appt.

**Barnt Green Antiques**, 93 Hewell Road, Barnt Green, B45 8NL TEL: 445 4942 ASSNS: BAFRA PARKING: Easy OPEN: Mon-Fri 9-5.30, Sat 9-1 MIN: £50 MAX: £50,000+ PERIOD: 18th-19th century SPECIALIST: Furniture, some 17th century stock OTHER INFO: Close to Lickey Hills.

**Birmingham Bookshop**, 567 Bristol Road, B29 6AF TEL: 472 8556 PARKING: Easy OPEN: Tues-Sat 11-4 PERIOD: 20th century SPECIALIST: Books & prints.

**Andrew Brooker-Cary,** The Old Bakehouse, Station Road, Harborne TEL: 428 1928 PARKING: Easy OPEN: 10-5.30, closed Wed MIN: £40 MAX: £1500 PERIOD: 18th-20th century SPECIALIST: Lighting, mirrors GENERAL: Pine furniture, fireplaces, garden items.

**Format of Birmingham Ltd,** 18-19 Bennetts Hill, B2 5QJ TEL: 643 2058 FAX: 643 2210 PARKING: Medium SPECIALIST: Coins, medals & banknotes.

**Garratt Antiques Ltd**, 35 Stephenson Street, B2 4BH TEL: 643 9507 FAX: (0283) 791725 ASSNS: GMC, BJA, NAG PARKING: Medium OPEN: 10-5 MIN: £2 MAX: £10,000+ PERIOD: 19th-20th century SPECIALIST: Jewellery, Birmingham silver, British paintings, crystal GENERAL: General antiques OTHER INFO: Come and join us for tea or coffee. Enjoy browsing in our friendly shop.

**The Graves Gallery**, (estd 1752), 3 The Spencers, Augusta Street, Hockley TEL: 212 1635 ASSNS: FATG PARKING: Own carpark OPEN: 10.30-4.30 MIN: £65 MAX: £4000 PERIOD: 19th-20th century SPECIALIST: Silverplate, studio pottery GENERAL: Oils & watercolours OTHER INFO: Restoration, framing, valuations. In heart of jewellery quarter with the best restaurants.

**Bob Harris & Sons**, 2071 Coventry Road, Sheldon, B26 3DY TEL: 743 2259 FAX: 743 2259 ASSNS: LAPADA PARKING: Own carpark OPEN: 9-6 MIN: £5 MAX: £ 8500 PERIOD: 18th-20th century SPECIALIST: Furniture, Staffordshire figures, GENERAL: Metalware, shipping goods OTHER INFO: 3 miles from NEC.

**Holliday Wharf Antique Centre**, 164-166 Holliday Street TEL: 643 9900 ASSNS: LAPADA PARKING: Own carpark OPEN: 9-5.30 MIN: £10 MAX: £50,000 PERIOD: 18th-20th century SPECIALIST: Early oak & metalware, Georgian mahogany GENERAL: Decorative items, walnut, inlaid furniture, good shipping stock, porcelain, silver, paintings OTHER INFO: Rear of Hyatt Hotel.

**John Hubbard Antiques**, 224-226 Court Oak Road, Harbourne, B32 2EG TEL: 426 1694 FAX: 428 1214 ASSNS: LAPADA PARKING: Own carpark OPEN: Mon-Sat 9-6 MIN: £20 MAX: £15,000 PERIOD: 18th-19th century SPECIALIST: Furniture GENERAL: Paintings, watercolours, clocks, lighting & decorative items OTHER INFO: 2 mins from world famous award-winning Egon Ronay-recommended Jonathan restaurant & hotel, all furnished with antiques.

**Huddington International Trade Warehouse**, 73 Western Road, Hockley, B18 7QD TEL: 523 8862 FAX: 554 1741 PARKING: Medium OPEN: 9-4.30 MIN: £5 PERIOD: 17th-20th century SPECIALIST: Furniture OTHER INFO: On A4157 next to Dudley Road Hospital.

**James Antiques - Canalside,** Gas Street Basin, off Gas Street, B1 2JU TEL: 643 3131 PARKING: Medium OPEN: Tues-Thurs, Sat & Sun 12-5 or by appt MIN: 50p MAX: £250 PERIOD: 19th-20th century GENERAL: General antiques, bric a brac, canal art, decorative items, canal & general books, maps OTHER INFO: Canal boat trips outside door.

**Kestrel House**, 72 Gravelly Hill, North Erdington, B23 6BB TEL: 373 2375 ASSNS: ATD, FIBD PARKING: Own carpark OPEN: Mon-Sat 10-7 MIN: £5 MAX: £500 PERIOD: 19th-20th century SPECIALIST: Oils & watercolours GENERAL: Mainly antiques & general goods. Regular auction.

**March Medals**, 113 Gravely Hill North, B23 6BJ TEL: 384 4901 PARKING: Own carpark OPEN:

10-5 MIN: £5 MAX: £5000 PERIOD: 19th-20th century SPECIALIST: Orders, decorations & medals GENERAL: Militaria.

**F Meek's,** 22 Warstone Lane, Hockley, B18 6JE TEL: 236 9058 FAX: 212 0301 ASSNS: British Horological PARKING: Medium OPEN: 9-5.30 SPECIALIST: Watch & clock materials GENERAL: Vintage wristwatches & clocks.

**Moseley Pianos**, Unit L, 68 Wyreley Road, Witton, B6 7BN TEL: 327 2701, (0831) 560518 PARKING: Easy OPEN: Mon-Thurs 10-2 or anytime by appt MIN: £100 MAX: £5000 PERIOD: 19th-20th century SPECIALIST: Secondhand upright & grand pianos some with ornate cabinets. Specialising in the export trade OTHER INFO: Facilities for loading & packing containers.

**Piccadilly Jewellers**, 10 Piccadilly Arcade, New Street, B2 4HD TEL: 643 5791 FAX: 631 2167 ASSNS: NAG PARKING: Medium OPEN: Mon-Sat 9.30-5 MIN: £15 MAX: £10,000 PERIOD: 19th-20th century SPECIALIST: Antique jewellery & silverware.

**Treasure Chest Antique & Bric-a-Brac Centre**, 1407 Pershore Road, Stirchley, B30 2JR TEL: 459 4587 FAX: 458 3705 PARKING: Own carpark OPEN: Mon-Sat 9-5.45, Sun 10-5 PERIOD: 20th century GENERAL: Antiques & bric-a-brac.

**Warley Antique Centre**, 146 Pottery Road, Oldbury, B68 9HD TEL: 434 3813 PARKING: Easy OPEN: Mon-Sat 10-6, Sun 11-4 PERIOD: 19th-20th century SPECIALIST: Ruskin pottery, dolls GENERAL: China, furniture, pottery, clocks, pictures OTHER INFO: 50 dealers. Close to M5 jct 3.

## WALSALL (01922)

**Cobwebs Antiques**, 639 Bloxwich Road, Leamore, WS3 2BQ TEL: 21798 PARKING: Easy OPEN: Tues, Wed, Fri, Sat 11-5 MIN: £5 MAX: £400 PERIOD: 19th-20th century SPECIALIST: Glass GENERAL: General antiques, bric a brac OTHER INFO: Very good Leather Museum.

**The Doghouse,** 309 Bloxwich Road, WS2 7BD TEL: 30829 FAX: 31236 PARKING: Own carpark OPEN: 9-5.30, Sun phone first MIN: 50p MAX: £5000 PERIOD: 17th-20th century GENERAL: Trade & retail furniture. 5000 sq ft warehouse stocked with everything from clocks to fireplaces OTHER INFO: Walsall has 3 market days.

**LP Furniture (Midlands) Ltd**, The Old Brewery, Short Acre Street, WS2 8HW TEL: & FAX: 746764 PARKING: Own carpark OPEN: 9-5 MIN: £50 MAX: £5000 PERIOD: 19th-20th century SPECIALIST: French furniture GENERAL: Continental furniture, 1930s English walnut.

**Nicholls Jewellers**, 57 George Street TEL: 641081 PARKING: Easy OPEN: Mon-Sat 9-5 PERIOD: 20th century SPECIALIST: Antique rings, pendants etc GENERAL: New & secondhand jewellery.

**Past and Present**, 66 George Street, WS1 1RS TEL: 611151 PARKING: Easy OPEN: Mon-Sat 9.30-5.30 MIN: £4 MAX: £3000 PERIOD: 18th & 20th century GENERAL: General antiques, a veritable pot pourri, all reasonably priced OTHER INFO: Shop close to thriving old established open air market.

**Walsall Antiques Centre**, 7a The Digbeth Arcade, WS1 1RE TEL: 725163/5 PARKING: Easy OPEN: Mon-Sat 10-6 MIN: £2 MAX: £ 5,000 PERIOD: 18th-20th century SPECIALIST: Royal, military & political commerative pottery & porcelain GENERAL: General antiques.

## LICHFIELD (01543)

**Mike Abrahams Books**, Cranmere Court, Walsall Road, WS13 6RF TEL: 256200 ASSNS: PBFA PARKING: Easy OPEN: Seven days 10-6 by appt, private premises. MIN: £1 MAX: £1000 PERIOD: 19th-20th century SPECIALIST: Books: antiquarian, childrens, topographical, transport, collecting, military, illustrated, magic, gypsies, witchcraft.

**The Antique Shop**, 31 Tamworth Street. WS13 6JP TEL:268324 PARKING: Easy OPEN: Mon-Sat 9.30-5.30, occasionally closed 1.30-2.30 MIN: £3 MAX: £1000 PERIOD: 19th century GENERAL: General antiques OTHER INFO: Heritage Exhibition. Hotels: The George, Little Barrow, Swinfen Hall. Thrales restaurant.

**Images at the Staffs Bookshop,** 4-6 Dam Street, WS13 6AA TEL: 264093 PARKING: Easy OPEN: Mon-Sat 9.30-5.30 MIN: £5 PERIOD: 17th-20th century SPECIALIST: Childhood, objects and books. Antiquarian books of all kinds. Printed ephemera OTHER INFO: 13th century cathedral, Teddy Bear Museum.

**Cordelia & Perdy's Antique Junk Shop**, 53 Tamworth Street, WS13 6JW TEL: 263223 PARKING: Medium OPEN: Mon, Thurs-Sat 10-4 MIN: £1 MAX: £350 PERIOD: 19th & 20th century GENERAL: Wide range, buying only from house clearances OTHER INFO: Features on *Songs on Praise* , *What's My Line* & *Down Your Way*. It's better to be looked over than overlooked!

**The Tudor of Lichfield Antique Centre,** Bore Street, WS13 6LL TEL: 263951 PARKING: Easy (Lots of Pay & Display carparks) OPEN: Mon-Sat 10-5 MIN: 50p MAX: £2000 PERIOD: 17th-19th century GENERAL: General antiques & good period furniture OTHER INFO: The Antiques Centre is situated above an old-established restaurant in a black and white timbered building.

## WHITTINGTON (01543)

**Milestone Antiques**, 5 Main Street, WS14 9JU TEL: 432248 ASSNS: LAPADA PARKING: Easy OPEN: Thur-Sat 10-6, Sun 11-3 MIN: £10 MAX: £6000 PERIOD: 18th & 19th century SPECIALIST: Coalport GENERAL: English furniture and decorative items, no reproduction OTHER INFO: 2 good old pubs in village serving excellent food.

## ALREWAS (01283)

**Poley Antiques,** 5 Main Street, DE13 7AA TEL: 791151 PARKING: Own carpark OPEN: Thurs-Sat 10-5.30 MIN: £1 MAX: £800 PERIOD: 18th-1940 SPECIALIST: British ceramics GENERAL: China, glass, metalware, small silver, small furniture, silver plate.

## YOXALL (01543)

**Armson's of Yoxall Antiques**, The Hollies, DE13 8NH TEL & FAX: 472352 ASSNS: LAPADA PARKING: Own carpark OPEN: Mon-Fri 9-5, Sat 9-12 noon MIN: £20 MAX: £5000 PERIOD: 17th-19th century SPECIALIST: Practical antique furniture GENERAL: Furniture OTHER INFO: Many useful trade calls in area. 30 mins from Birmingham Airport, NEC, M1, M6 & M42.

**HW Heron & Son Ltd**, 1 King Street, DE13 8NF TEL: 472266 ASSNS: LAPADA PARKING: Mon-Fri 9-6 OPEN: Mon-Fri 9-6, Sat 10.30-5.30, Sun 2-6 MIN: £20 MAX: £5000 PERIOD: 18th & 19th century SPECIALIST: Early 19th century porcelain GENERAL: English ceramics and small items.

## BRERETON (01889)

**Rugeley Antique Centre,** 161-163 Main Road, WS15 1DX TEL: 577166 PARKING: Own carpark OPEN: Mon-Sat 9-5, Sun 12-4.30 MIN: £1 MAX: No limit PERIOD: 19th & 20th century GENERAL: 26

dealers with varying stock of furniture and smalls OTHER INFO: Also B&B in self-contained unit.

## WOLSELEY BRIDGE (01889)

**Jalna Antiques,** The Old Barn, ST17 0XJ TEL: 881381 PARKING: Own carpark OPEN: 10-5 MIN: £20 MAX: £3000 PERIOD: 18th-19th century SPECIALIST: Chairs & couches GENERAL: Furniture.

## LITTLE HAYWOOD (01889)

**Jalna Antiques,** Coley Lane, ST18 0UP TEL: 881381 PARKING: Own carpark OPEN: Resident on premises MIN: £20 MAX: £3000 PERIOD: 18th-19th century SPECIALIST: Chairs & chaise longues GENERAL: Furniture.

## WESTON (01889)

**Weston Antique Gallery**, Boat Lane, ST18 0HU TEL: 270450 PARKING: Own OPEN: Wed-Sat 10-5.30 MIN: £10 MAX: £750 PERIOD: 17th-early 20th century century SPECIALIST: Antique maps & prints of Staffordshire GENERAL: General antiques OTHER INFO: We are located between Wedgwood Visitor Centre & Shugborough Hall.

## STAFFORD (01785)

**Windmill Antiques**, 9 Castle Hill, Broadeye TEL: 228505 PARKING: Easy OPEN: Mon-Sat 10-5 MIN: £1 MAX: £2000 PERIOD: 18th-20th century SPECIALIST: Tools, Staffordshire figures, glass GENERAL: Very wide range OTHER INFO: The shop is situated next to an ancient windmill.

## PENKRIDGE (01785)

**Golden Oldies,** 5 Crown Bridge, ST19 5NH TEL: 714722 PARKING: Easy OPEN: Mon 9.30-1.30, Tues-Sat 9.30-5.30 MIN: £5 MAX: £2000 PERIOD: 19th-20th century GENERAL: Furniture OTHER INFO: Good pubs, hotels & restaurants. 17th century stocks & jail, 13th century church.

## WOLVERHAMPTON (01902)

**Golden Oldies,** 5 St George's Parade, WV2 1AZ TEL: 22397 PARKING: Medium OPEN: Tues-Sat 10-5 PERIOD: 20th century GENERAL: Furniture.

**Pendeford House Antiques,** Pendeford Avenue, Tettenhall, WV6 9EG TEL: 756175 PARKING: Own carpark OPEN: 10.30-5, closed Thurs & Sun MIN: £1 MAX: £2000 PERIOD: 18th-20th century GENERAL: China, clocks, furniture, brass, silver, glass, paintings, jewellery, linen.

**Martin Quick Antiques Ltd**, 323 Tettenhall Road, WV6 0JZ TEL: 754703 FAX: 756889 ASSNS: LAPADA PARKING: Easy OPEN: Mon-Fri 9-5.30, Sat 9-4 MIN: £10 MAX: £5000 PERIOD: 18th-20th century SPECIALIST: Large stock of antique beds GENERAL: Furniture from all periods.

**Tatters Decorative Antiques,** 9 Upper Green, Tettenhall, WV6 8QQ TEL: 756500 PARKING: Easy OPEN: Mon, Wed, Fri, Sat 10-5 MIN: £5 MAX: £800 PERIOD: 19th century SPECIALIST: Textiles, decorative GENERAL: Staffordshire, small furniture.

**Martin Taylor Antiques**, 140b Tettenhall Road, WV6 0BQ TEL: 751166, after hours (01785) 284539 FAX: 746502 ASSNS: LAPADA PARKING: Easy OPEN: Mon-Fri 8.30-5.30, Sat 9.30-1.30 & by appt MIN: £50 MAX: £5000+ PERIOD: 18th-19th century SPECIALIST: Continental 19th century walnut, marquetry inlaid.

## OLD SWINFORD (01384)

**Old Swinford Gallery**, 106 Hagley Road, DY8 1QV TEL: 395577 PARKING: Easy OPEN: Tues-Fri 9.30-5, Sat 9.30-1 MIN: £50 MAX: £5,000 PERIOD: Some 18th, but mainly 19th-early 20th century SPECIALIST: Oils, watercolours, maps, antiquarian prints.

## HALESOWEN (0121)

**Clent Books**, 52 Summer Hill, B63 3BU TEL: 550 0309, home (01299) 401090 PARKING: Easy OPEN: Mon-Sat 10-4 MIN: £4 MAX: £300 PERIOD: 18th-20th century SPECIALIST: Topography, history, local history, 9000 books OTHER INFO: Good cup of coffee.

## West Midlands to Leicestershire

This largely rural region has been settled since prehistoric times and so the landscape is one mainly hewn by man. There are rounded hills and small woods, rivers and canals, pretty villages and attractive towns. The area remains largely undiscovered by tourists who therefore miss out on its gentle beauty.

The first stop is the city of **Coventry**. Developed from a small Saxon settlement, the past prosperity came from wool. Supposedly Leofric, Earl of Mercia, began this prosperous business in the 11th century when he started a monastery and gave the monks land for sheep. It was this same Leofric whose wife pleaded with him to cut taxes but he told her she could ride through the streets naked before he did so. The story goes that Godiva took him at his word after first instructing the residents of the town to stay indoors with their shutters closed. As a result of Godiva's ride, taxes were indeed cut. An 18th century addition to the story said that Peeping Tom broke the ban on watching Godiva and was struck blind as a consequence. Figures portraying Godiva and Tom re-enact the scene every hour on a clock over Hertford Street.

During the Civil War Coventry was held for Parliament and captured Royalists were imprisoned there. On the Restoration of the monarchy the city was ordered to knock down its walls which was done but the twelve gates were left standing, two of which may still be seen today in Lady Herbert's Garden.

Prosperity continued and clock making and silk weaving also became important until the 19th century when Coventry could no longer compete with imports. However, engineering was established and the city became a manufacturing base for the motor car. During the Second World War the factories became a major target for German bombing and the raid suffered on the 14th November 1940 is said to have been the worst inflicted on any British town. About 40 acres of the city were flattened. Of approximately1000 buildings in the centre only 30 were left undamaged. That night the cathedral of St Michael was almost completely destroyed; only the spire and outer walls were left standing. These are linked to the new cathedral, completed in 1962, by a canopied porch.

In spite of the bombing many medieval buildings have survived. There is the 14th century Guildhall of St Mary, the Tudor almshouses of Ford's Hospital and Cheylesmore Manor House dating originally from 1230.

The tour now moves on to **Bulkington,** whose church has a font made from a Roman marble column, followed by **Hinckley**, a centre for the hosiery industry. The village of **Shenton** lies just a couple of miles south of **Market Bosworth** and closeby Bosworth Field whereRichard III fought his final battle against Henry Tudor. This brought to an end the Plantagenet dynasty and established the Tudor line on the throne of England. The Bosworth Battlefield Visitor Centre and Country Park has exhibitions, models and film on the battle.

After the villages of **Measham** and **Coalville**, named for its one-time principal industry, **Tonge** is next followed by **Loughborough**, the second largest town in Leicestershire. It has a most unusual First World War Memorial, the Carillon Tower which houses 47 bells. There is also a Bell Foundry Museum in Freehold Street and displays on the art of bell foundry.

Going via **Quorndon**, long associated with the famous Quorn Hunt, and **Woodhouse Eaves**, **Leicester** follows. This city has been in existence since Roman times and contains plenty of historic buildings and good museums. However, like many English towns and cities, it was the Industrial Revolution and the coming of the railways that really brought prosperity causing enormous expansion from quiet market town to busy metropolis.

Jewry Wall is the city's only visible relic of the Romans and was part of the public baths. Overlooking the excavated site stands the Jewry Wall Museum with exhibitions covering its history from earliest times to the 16th century. Leicester Castle dates from the 11th century and stands on the site of an earlier Saxon fortification. Newarke was a 14th century addition to the castle and once

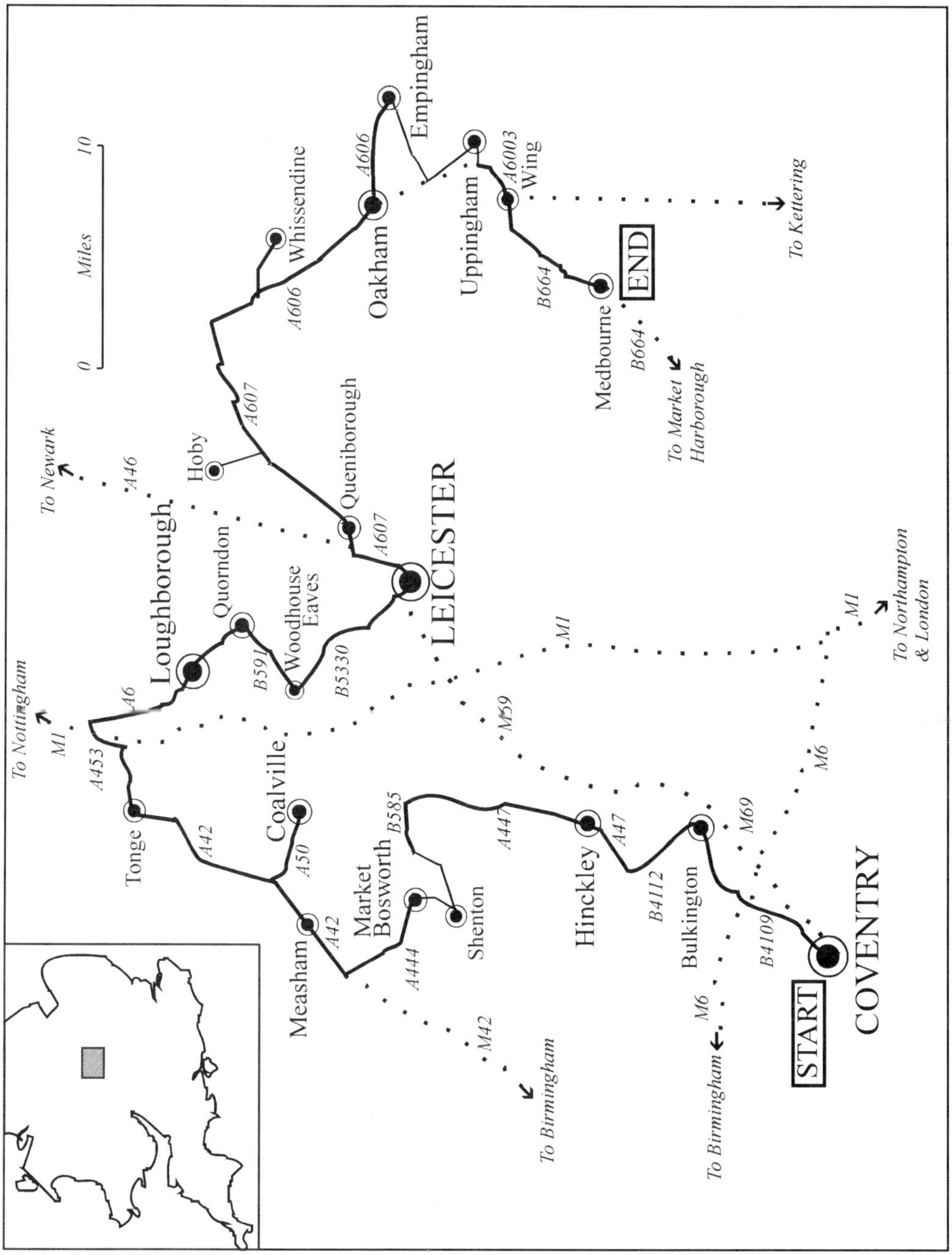

Miles
0
10
START
COVENTRY
END
LEICESTER
Loughborough
Quorndon
Woodhouse Eaves
Queniborough
Hoby
Whissendine
Oakham
Empingham
Uppingham
Wing
Medbourne
Coalville
Tonge
Measham
Market Bosworth
Shenton
Hinckley
Bulkington
To Nottingham
To Newark
To Kettering
To Market Harborough
To Northampton & London
To Birmingham
To Birmingham
A6
A46
A607
A606
A6003
B664
B664
M1
M1
M1
A453
A42
A42
A50
B591
B5330
M69
M69
A444
M42
B585
A447
A47
B4112
B4109
M6
M6

enclosed a church which has since disappeared. Newarke now houses a museum covering social history from the 16th century to the present day. It also has a fine collection of clocks.

The church of St Nicholas is of Saxon origin and may have been built as early as the 7th century. Stone from Roman buildings was used in its construction and, although Saxon in style, it does incorporate a Norman doorway. The 14th century St Martin's Church was upgraded to a cathedral in 1927. Unfortunately, by the 19th century, the fabric of the church was so decayed that it was extensively restored so reflecting Victorian design rather than that of its origins.

**Queniborough** and **Hoby** villages are next, then **Whissendine** with its beautiful early-English to perpendicular church which has some quite fine window tracery. Taking the A606, the tour arrives in the quiet country town of **Oakham**. It was the capital of Rutland, England's smallest county, until the 1974 boundary changes merged Rutland with Leicestershire but this process is now being reversed. Its 12th century castle contains a unique collection of horseshoes. There was a tradition that any peer of the realm passing through Rutland should present an inscribed horseshoe to the lord of the manor. The Rutland County Museum, housed in an 18th century cavalry riding school, tells the story of life in the county with exhibits of agricultural implements, wagons, local crafts and domestic items.

Moving on via country roads through **Empingham** and then **Wing,** the route comes to **Uppingham**, a small ancient market town probably best known for its public school. The town traces it origins back to Saxon times and received a market charter in the late 13th century. St Peter & St Paul's church dates from the 14th century but was restored in the 19th century, largely eliminating the earlier building. However, the church still has figures dating from the early 13th century as well as an Elizabethan pulpit.

Lastly **Medbourne** has been a settlement since Roman times. There is a medieval packhorse bridge crossing the stream and the parish church dates from the 13th and 14th century.

# ANTIQUE DEALERS

## COVENTRY (01203)

**Memories Antiques**, 400a Stoney Stanton Road, CV1 5DH TEL: 687994 PARKING: Own carpark OPEN: Mon, Tues, Thurs-Sat 10-5, Sun by appt PERIOD: 19th-20th century SPECIALIST: China GENERAL: Antiques, collectables, Royal Doulton.

## BULKINGTON (01203)

**Sport & Country Gallery**, Northwood House, 121 Weston Lane, CV12 9RX TEL: 314335 ASSNS: LAPADA PARKING: Own carpark OPEN: Anytime by appt MIN: £100 MAX: £6,000 PERIOD: 19th-20th century SPECIALIST: Sporting paintings, bronzes GENERAL: Oils, watercolours, furniture.

## HINKLEY (01455)

**House Things Antiques**, Trinity Lane, 44 Mansion Street, LE10 0AU TEL: 618518 PARKING: Easy OPEN: Mon-Sat 10-6 MIN: £1 MAX: £500 PERIOD: 19th-20th century GENERAL: Brass & iron beds, fireplaces, furniture, clocks, general artifacts. Many unusual items OTHER INFO: Renown for hansom cab (original on show), Axe & Compass, canals. Kings Hotel.

## SHENTON (01455)

**Whitemoors Antiques & Crafts Centre,** Main Street, CV13 6BZ TEL: 212250 PARKING: Own carpark OPEN: Wed-Sun 11-5, inc Bank Holidays MIN: £1 MAX: £2000 PERIOD: 18th-20th century SPECIALIST: Crystal paperweights (new & old) GENERAL: 12 different dealers with a complete variety of antiques, curios, works of art, books, etc OTHER INFO: The centre boasts galleries, tearooms, beautiful gardens, next to river. Sited immediately below Bosworth Battlefield in village of Shenton. Whitemoors is where Henry Tudor camped the night before the battle at which Richard III was killed. See 'Perseus' a 7ft bronze, in all his naked glory.

## MARKET BOSWORTH (01455)

**Corner Cottage Antiques**, 5 Market Place, The Square, CV13 0LF TEL: 290344 PARKING: Easy OPEN: Mon-Sat 10-5 MIN: £5 MAX: £5000 PERIOD: 18th-20th century GENERAL: General antiques OTHER INFO: Historic Battle of Bosworth site, Water Sports Centre, Sharkestone Steam Railway (summer only).

## MEASHAM (01530)

**Ashley House Antiques**, 61 High Street, DE12 7HR TEL: 273568 shop, 373655 home ASSNS: National Brass Society PARKING: Easy OPEN: Thurs, Fri, Sat 11-5 or by appt MIN: £25 MAX: £2750 PERIOD: 19th-20th century SPECIALIST: Longcase & wall clocks, Measham bargeware teapots, ancient horse brasses (expert on this subject) GENERAL: Inlaid furniture, oil lamps, general antiques. OTHER INFO: 2 miles from Market Bosworth, scene of historic battle. Good hotels.

## COALVILLE (01530)

**Keystone Antiques**, 9 Ashby Road (A50), LE67 3LF TEL: 835966 ASSNS: LAPADA, NAG (registered valuer), Fellow Gemmological Assn PARKING: Own carpark OPEN: Mon-Tues, Thur-Fri 10-5, Sat 10-4.30 MIN: £20 MAX: £2500 PERIOD: 18th-20th century SPECIALIST: Victorian, Edwardian jewellery & silver GENERAL: Glass, books, collectables OTHER INFO: Snibston Discovery Park & Industrial Museum

## TONGE (01332)

**C Reynolds Antiques**, The Spindles, DE7 1BD TEL: 862609 FAX: 862609 PARKING: Own carpark OPEN: By appt MIN: £100 upwards SPECIALIST: Unusual clocks & watches OTHER INFO: 3 miles from East Midlands Airport and the Motor Museum.

## LOUGHBOROUGH (01509)

**Lowe of Loughborough,** Great House, 37-40 Churchgate, LE11 1UE TEL: 212554 OPEN: 8-5.30 MIN: £1 MAX: £10,000 PERIOD: 1700-1900 SPECIALIST: Georgian furniture GENERAL: Furniture & soft furnishings OTHER INFO: Medieval great hall with 16 showrooms. King Henry VII's room where Henry slept prior to the Battle of Bosworth according to local history.

## QUORNDON (01509)

**Quorn Pine & Decoratives**, The Mills, Leicester Road TEL: 416031 ASSNS: GMC PARKING: Own carpark OPEN: Mon-Sat 9-6, Sun 2-5 MIN: £5 MAX: £2000 PERIOD: 19th-20th century SPECIALIST: Pine furniture GENERAL: Reproduction pine, kitchenalia, new & old decorative items OTHER INFO: Home of Quorn Hunt, favourite of Prince Charles.

## WOODHOUSE EAVES (01509)

**Paddock Antiques**, The Old Smithy, Brand Hill, LE12 8SS TEL: 890264 PARKING: Easy OPEN: Thurs-Sat 10-5.30 MIN: £20 MAX: £5000 PERIOD: 18th-20th century SPECIALIST: Fine English & Continental china GENERAL: Glass & small furniture.

## LEICESTER (0116)

**Boulevard Antiques**, Old Dairy, Western Boulevard, LE2 7BU TEL: 254 1201 FAX: 854315 PARKING: Own carpark OPEN: Mon-Sat 9-6, Sun 10-5 MIN: £1 MAX: £2500 PERIOD: 19th-20th century GENERAL: Furniture, a few smalls.

**Britains Heritage**, Shaftesbury Hall, 3 Holy Bones TEL: 251 9592 FAX: 243 3233 PARKING: Medium OPEN: Mon-Fri 9.30-5.30, Sat 9.30-5, Sun 2-5 MIN: £5 MAX: £10,000 PERIOD: 18th-20th century SPECIALIST: Fully restored English & French fireplaces GENERAL: Fireside accessories OTHER INFO: UK delivery/fitting. Next to historic Roman Jewry Wall & old part of city.

**Corrys Antiques**, 24-26 Francis Street Stoney-gate, LE2 2BD TEL: 270 3794 FAX: 270 3794 ASSNS: LAPADA PARKING: Own carpark OPEN: Mon-Sat 9-5.30 MIN: £10 MAX: £15,000 PERIOD: 18th-19th century GENERAL: Furniture, paintings, silver, porcelain, jewellery OTHER INFO: City's southside exclusive shopping area. Quality shops.

**Letty's Antiques**, 6 Rutland Street, LE1 1RA TEL: 262 6435 PARKING: Medium OPEN: Mon-Wed, Fri, Sat 9.30-5 MIN: £1 MAX: £3500 PERIOD: 19th-20th century SPECIALIST: Jewellery, silverware GENERAL: Small secondhand antique items.

**Montague Antiques**, 60 Montague Road (off Queen's Road nr university), LE2 1TH TEL: 720 6485 ASSNS: LAPADA PARKING: Easy OPEN: 10-6, closed Wed & Sun MIN: £1 MAX: £800 PERIOD: 18th-20th century GENERAL: Furniture, collectables, glass, china (no jewellery).

**Walter Moores & Son**, 89 Wellington Street, LE1 6HJ TEL: 255 1402 PARKING: Own carpark OPEN: Tues-Fri 8.30-5.30, Sat 8.30-12.30 MIN: £15 MAX: £15,000 PERIOD: 17th-19th century GENERAL: Furniture OTHER INFO: 5 mins walk from station.

**The Rug Gallery**, 50 Montague Road, Clarendon Park, LE2 1TH TEL: 270 0085 (24 hrs) PARKING: Easy OPEN: Sat only 10-4 or by appt MIN: £10 MAX: £5000 PERIOD: 19th-20th century SPECIALIST: Oriental rugs & kilims old & new GENERAL: Furniture, textiles, jewellery from Central Asia.

## QUENIBOROUGH (0116)

**J Green & Son**, 1 Coppice Lane, LE7 3DR TEL: 260 6682 FAX: 260 6882 PARKING: Own carpark OPEN: By appt MIN: £200 MAX: £30,000 PERIOD: 17th-19th century GENERAL: 18th & early 19th century furniture, clocks & pictures.

## HOBY (01664)

**Withers of Leicester**, The Old Rutland, 6 Regent Road TEL: 434803 PARKING: Own carpark OPEN: Seven days 9-6 MIN: £100 MAX: £5000 PERIOD: 17th-19th century GENERAL: Furniture and decorative objects OTHER INFO: Ragdale Hall Health Hydro in next village, convenient for dealers who feel they have over-expanded.

## WHISSENDINE (0166)

**Old Bakehouse Pine Furniture**, 11 Main Street, LE15 7ES TEL: 479691 PARKING: Own carpark OPEN: Erratic MIN: £25 MAX: £500 PERIOD: 19th-20th century GENERAL: Pine furniture OTHER INFO: B&B available.

## OAKHAM (01572)

**Gallery Antiques,** 17 Mill Street, LE15 6EA TEL & FAX: 755094 ASSNS: LAPADA PARKING: Easy OPEN: 9.30-5.30 daily MAX: £10,000 PERIOD: 17th-19th century SPECIALIST: French beds GENERAL: English furniture + full range of Continental items OTHER INFO: Shop dates from 1550 in centre of town one mile from Rutland Water, the largest man-made lake in England.

**Old House Gallery**, 13-15 Market Place TEL: 755538 PARKING: Easy OPEN: 10-1, 2-5 MIN: £5 MAX: £5000 PERIOD: 17th-20th century SPECIALIST: Paintings, prints, antique maps GENERAL: Studio ceramics, sculpture OTHER INFO: Small interesting gallery with easy friendly relaxed atmosphere.

## EMPINGHAM (01780)

**Churchgate Antiques**, 13 Church Street, LE15 8PN TEL: 460528 PARKING: Easy OPEN: Afternoons MIN: £5 MAX: £3000 PERIOD: 18th-20th century SPECIALIST: Doulton GENERAL: Furniture, silver, pictures OTHER INFO: 1 mile from Rutland Water & good range of water pursuits.

**Old Bakery Antiques**, The Old Bakery, Church Street, LE15 8PN TEL: 460243 PARKING: Easy OPEN: Mostly seven days 10-6 but check for midweek MIN: £15 MAX: £3500 PERIOD: 17th-20th century SPECIALIST: Dining tables & chairs GENERAL: Oak furniture, some brass, copper, prints, porcelain OTHER INFO: At Dam end of Rutland Water. Rutland is the county expected to be reborn.

## WING (01572)

**Robert Bingley Antiques**, Church Street TEL: 737725 FAX: 737284 PARKING: Own carpark OPEN: Mon-Sat 9-5, Sun 11-4 MIN: £20 MAX: £5000 PERIOD: 18th-19th century GENERAL: Huge shop (4000 sq ft/10 rooms) mainly of furniture. Some smalls OTHER INFO: Beautiful countryside around Rutland Water.

## UPPINGHAM (01572)

**Bay House Antiques**, 33 High Street East, LE15 9PY TEL: 821045 PARKING: Easy OPEN: Mon-Sat 10-5 MIN: £5 MAX: £1500 PERIOD: 19th century GENERAL: Pottery, porcelain, metalware, Victorian, Edwardian furniture, small agricultural items OTHER INFO: Small historic market town with excellent facilities.

**Clutter,** 14A Orange Street, LE15 9SQ TEL: 823745 PARKING: Easy OPEN: Mon-Fri 10-5, Sat 10-6 MIN: 50p MAX: £3000 PERIOD: 18th-20th century SPECIALIST: Textiles & costume GENERAL: Linen, lace, chenilles, silver, parlour & kitchen clutter OTHER INFO: Customers are sometimes asked to use a one-way system when busy: we are very tiny & very cluttered!

**John Garner Fine Art & Antiques**, 51-53 High Street East, LE15 9PY TEL: 823607 FAX: 821654 ASSNS: FATG, GMC PARKING: Med-ium OPEN: 9-5.30 MIN: £1 MAX: £10,000+ PERIOD: 18th-20th century SPECIALIST: 19th century oils & furniture GENERAL: Dining suites, sporting pictures, prints OTHER INFO: The Old Vicarage, Laxton B&B £13.

**Gilberts,** 8 Ayston Road, LE15 9RL TEL: 823486 PARKING: Easy OPEN: Mon, Tues 9-1, 2-5, Wed-Sat 9.30-5 MIN: £5 MAX: £2500 PERIOD: 19th-20th century GENERAL: Furniture.

**Goldmark Books,** Orange House, Orange Street, LE15 9SQ TEL: 822694 FAX: 821503 PARKING: Easy OPEN: Mon-Sat 9.30-5.30 & Sun pm MIN: £1 MAX: £2000 PERIOD: 17th-20th century SPECIALIST: Art, literature, poetry, antiques GENERAL: 30,000 books on all subjects OTHER INFO: Warm welcome with a free cup of coffee. Great contemporary art gallery next door.

**Marc Oxley Fine Art,** 8-10 Orange Street, LE15 9SQ TEL: 822334 PARKING: Medium OPEN: Mon-Sat 9.30-5.30, Sun 2.30-5.30 MIN: £5 MAX: £500 PERIOD: 1650-1950 SPECIALIST: Victorian watercolours & drawings GENERAL: I have approx 500 original watercolours & drawings OTHER INFO: A beautiful market town built of honey coloured stone situated in the heart of England's smallest county, Rutland.

**TJ Roberts Antiques**, 39-41 High Street East, LE15 9PY TEL: 821493 PARKING: Easy OPEN: Mon-Sat 9.30-5.30 MIN: £25 MAX: £5000 PERIOD: 17th-19th century GENERAL: Furniture, general antiques OTHER INFO: Historic market town with famous public school.

**E & C Royall**, 3 Printers Yard TEL: (01858) 565744 PARKING: Medium OPEN: 10-5 closed Thurs MIN: £10 MAX: £1000 PERIOD: 18th-20th century SPECIALIST: Oriental ivories & bronzes GENERAL: Jewellery, furniture, pictures, objets

**Tattersall's**, 14 Orange Street, LE15 9SQ TEL: 821171 PARKING: Easy OPEN: 9.30-5 not Thurs MIN: £45 MAX: £4500 PERIOD: 19th-20th century SPECIALIST: Persian rugs, antiques, old & new rugs, upholstery, some mirrors.

## MEDBOURNE (01858)

**E & C Royall**, 10 Waterfall Way TEL: 565744 PARKING: Easy OPEN: 8.30-5 MIN: £10 MAX: £500 PERIOD: 18th-20th century SPECIALIST: Ivories, Oriental bronzes, restoration GENERAL: European furniture, jewellery, pictures OTHER INFO: All forms of restoration undertaken.

# Lincolnshire

Lincolnshire has some of the England's richest agricultural land, much of it reclaimed from drained fens or the sea. The county is largely flat, even the Lincolnshire Wolds, running parallel to the coast, only rise to 550 feet at their highest point. There have been settlements here since the Stone Age. The Romans built their roads and forts. Later, in the 9th and 10th centuries, much of the county was settled by Danes. The Black Death in the 14th century left many villages depopulated and it is said that there are more than 200 lost villages in Lincolnshire.

**Stamford**, the starting point, is a lovely stone-built town, with many fine Georgian buildings, and has prospered in the past. In Norman times it was a centre for great religious houses and their schools, then later, from the 12th century, wool soon became important. Astride the Great North Road, Stamford was also a great coaching town still having many fine inns. One of the old buildings, Browne's Hospital founded in 1483, now houses a museum including a good collection of medieval stained glass.

A most memorable mansion, Burghley House, stands a mile east. Built by William Cecil, the first Lord Burghley, he designed much of the house himself, envisaging it as being a house fit for Queen Elizabeth I to visit, as indeed she did. William Cecil was farsighted, or perhaps just lucky, because he supported Elizabeth when her half-sister, Mary, was on the throne which could have been dangerous if not actually fatal. When Elizabeth became Queen, William Cecil's fortunes rose correspondingly as he was made Lord High Treasurer.

The state rooms are breathtaking with painted figures appearing to leap from walls and ceilings. In contrast, there is the opportunity to see below-stairs in the Old Kitchen – a vast room containing more than 260 copper cooking utensils. Burghley House is not just the creation of William Cecil but also of his descendents who all brought something to the mansion. The walls and ceilings were painted in the 18th century to such marvellous effect, Grinling Gibbons carvings are in evidence and the park was landscaped by Capability Brown. A house not to be missed.

After first stopping at **West Deeping**, the route continues to old **Market Deeping**, on the River Welland situated on the edge of the Fens. Once a town of some regional importance now not even a market is held here. A point of interest is the oldest rectory (13th century ) in the country still used for its original purpose. There are several fine historic houses and a good restored perpendicular church with a rood-loft doorway.

Following the B1357, the village of **Weston St Mary** comes next, then the market town of **Holbeach**, one of the bulb-growing centres of Lincolnshire, and then **Gedney**. Nearby, another pretty market town, **Long Sutton**, has a perpendicular church with a detached 162 feet high timber and lead spire considered one of the finest in the country. An indoor tropical butterfly garden may also be found here, where the butterflies fly free. At the village of **Sutton Bridge** legend has it King John lost his treasure in nearby Cross Keys Wash

Now the tour calls at **Kirton** before arriving in **Boston**. In 1630, about ten years after the Pilgrim Fathers had left for the New World, a group of Puritans set sail from Boston for America and there founded the town of Boston, Massachusetts. The church of St Botolph's contains a memorial to John Cotton, the leader and minister of this band of Puritan settlers, as well as to the five Lincolnshire men who became governors of the state of Massachusetts. It also has elaborately carved 14th century misericords, a chancel with a fine medieval painted ceiling, a 272 foot high tower from the top of which, on a clear day Lincoln is visible 20 miles away. The Guildhall, now used as a museum and dating from the 15th century, contains the original cells occupied by the Pilgrim Fathers in 1607 after their first unsuccesful attempt to escape to Holland in search of religious freedom.

700 years ago Boston was a thriving port but by the 16th century declined due to silting of the River Witham. However the drainage of the fens and improvements to the river channel such as the opening of the Grand Sluice in the 18th century brought changes so that by the 19th century the

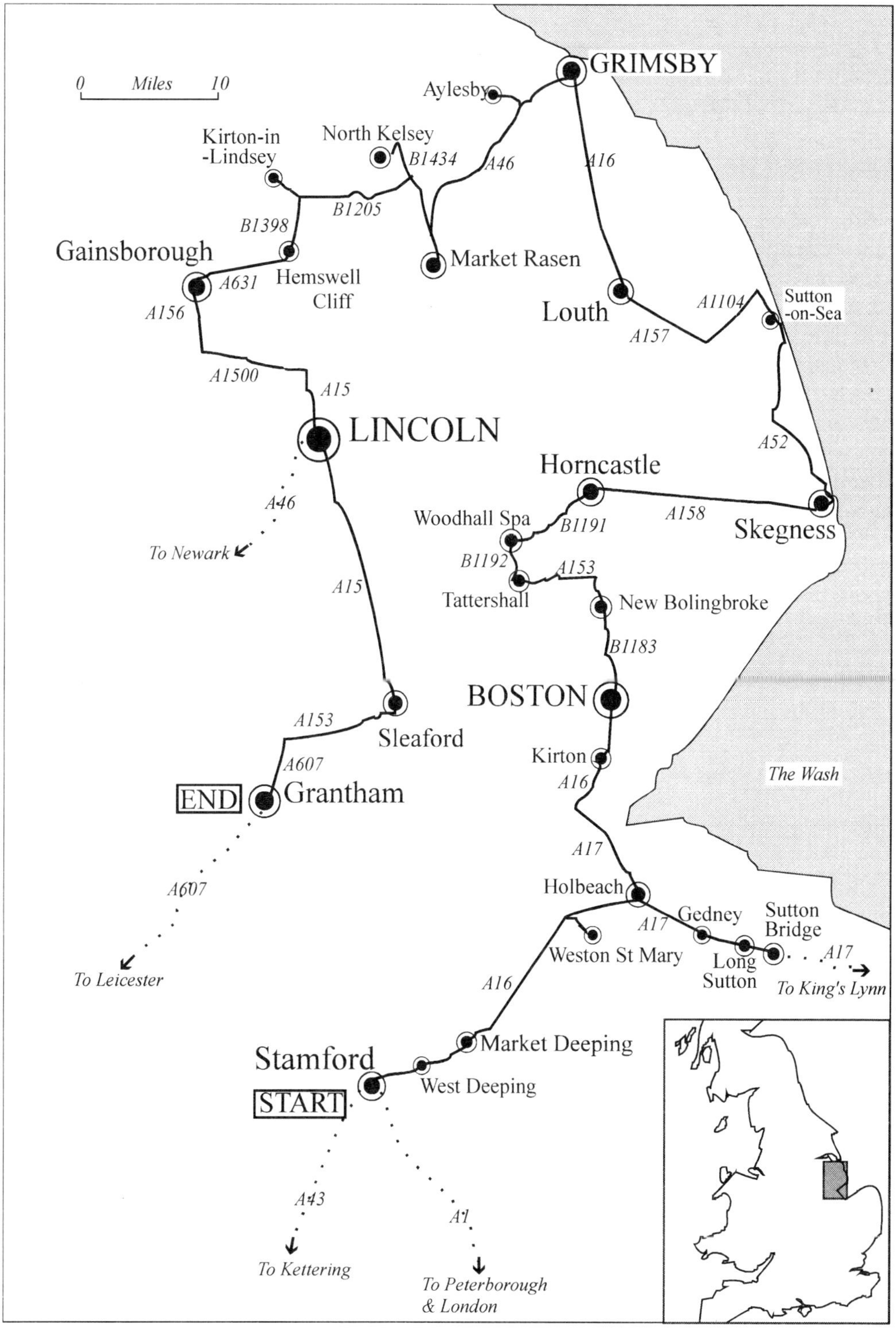
0 Miles 10
GRIMSBY
Aylesby
North Kelsey
Kirton-in
-Lindsey
B1434
A46
A16
B1205
B1398
Gainsborough
Hemswell
Cliff
Market Rasen
A631
A156
Louth
A1104
Sutton
-on-Sea
A157
A1500
A15
LINCOLN
A52
Horncastle
Woodhall Spa
B1191
A158
Skegness
A46
To Newark
B1192
A153
Tattershall
New Bolingbroke
A15
B1183
BOSTON
A153
Sleaford
Kirton
A607
The Wash
END
Grantham
A16
A17
A607
Holbeach
Gedney
Sutton
Bridge
A17
Weston St Mary
Long
Sutton
A17
To Leicester
A16
To King's Lynn
Market Deeping
Stamford
START
West Deeping
A43
A1
To Kettering
To Peterborough
& London

docks were, and continue to be, busy and profitable.

The route continues through **New Bolingbroke** and **Tattershall**, where the 15th century castle is one of the finest examples of a fortified brick castle in the country. It was built on the site of 13th century castle by Ralph, Lord Cromwell who was, for a while, treasurer for the King's Exchequer. In 1911 a group of Americans bought the tower and intended to dismantle it and ship it back to the United States. This was prevented by Lord Curzon of Kedleston who bought the castle presenting it to the National Trust. The next stop is **Woodhall Spa** and then **Horncastle**, site of a Roman fort. Although parts of the Roman wall survive, the town is mostly 19th century.

Heading for the coast, **Skegness** and, smaller, quieter, **Sutton-on-Sea** just to the north are both seaside resorts with beautiful sandy beaches and lovely gardens. Sutton is set behind a seawall with pleasure gardens. Inland, the fine Georgian town of **Louth** has a 295 foot spire on the church of St James, the highest in Lincolnshire, it can be seen from miles around.

Back on the coast, **Grimsby** on Humberside is almost synonymous with fishing and during the 19th century was the world's largest fishing port. The National Fishing Heritage Centre charts the course of the industry in the area. Inland again, the village of **Aylesby** is followed by **Market Rasen**, best known nowadays for its racecourse. Many Roman remains have been found in the town and there are also numerous elegant Georgian houses.

The tour proceeds to the small villages of **North Kelsey, Kirton-in-Lindsey** and then **Hemswell Cliff** before arriving in **Gainsborough**. This town stands on the River Trent and the three-arched bridge here is 18th century. The Old Hall is a 15th to 16th century manor house where Richard III, Henry VIII and Katherine Howard, one of Henry VIII's wives, all stayed.

Next, the historic city of **Lincoln** was once a Roman colony where veteran legionaries were given grants of land when they retired. Its most distinctive feature is the cathedral standing on a hill rising to 200 feet above the city. The first was built by Bishop Remigius in 1072 but burnt down and was rebuilt by Bishop Alexander the Magnificent in 1140, work continuing right up until the 15th century. It has a fine west front, said to symbolise Heaven's Gate, and the wonderful Angel Choir has the largest eight-light window in the country. This cathedral is most magnificent and has so many splendid things to see that the best way to appreciate it is to visit the cathedral bookshop first.

The Bishop's Palace is noteworthy. By the17th century the palace was a ruin and it was only in the late 19th century that restoration work began. Excavations have uncovered the medieval layout of the palace which dates from the 12th to 15th centuries. Lincoln's other major landmark is its castle, built on the site of a Roman fortress. The castle was started in 1068 and houses were demolished to make room for its six acre site. Today the walls and keep still stand.

**Sleaford**, on the River Slea, has a church dating from the 12th to 15th century with a tower and a spire. Other old buildings include the Vicarage, dating from 1568, the Manor House from 14th century onwards and the Black Bull inn where a carved stone depicts bull-baiting and is dated 1689. There was once a castle here, but all that is left are a few mounds and pieces of stone.

The last stop is historic **Grantham** on the River Witham, birthplace of Sir Isaac Newton and Margaret Thatcher.. It has benefited through the centuries from being on the Great North Road and has one of the oldest inns in the country, The Angel and Royal in the High Street. Reputedly King John held court here in 1213 and Richard III signed the Duke of Buckingham's death warrant in 1483. Another inn, the Beehive, has a real beehive for its sign. Seven miles south stands Woolsthorpe Manor, birthplace of Sir Isaac Newton and where it is said the apple fell from the tree and hit him on the head leading to him formulate the theory of gravity. There is also the National Trust property of Belton House three miles north east on the A607 to Lincoln. This is a late 17th century house with a plasterwork ceiling by Edward Goudge, carvings of the Grinling Gibbons school, portraits, furniture, tapestries and memorabilia of the Duke of Windsor.

Another stately home, again seven miles away off the A607 towards Nottingham, is Belvoir

Castle, (pronounced Beever) seat of the Dukes of Rutland. There was once a Norman castle here but the present building, magnificent as it is, dates from 1816. From here the visitor gets a splendid view over the Vale of Belvoir. The castle contains many treasures and interesting militaria. There is also a fine Statue Garden with 17th century sculptures.

## ANTIQUE DEALERS

### STAMFORD (01780)

**Graham Pickett Antiques,** 29 Water Street, PE9 2NJ TEL: 481064 PARKING: Easy OPEN: 10-5 closed Thurs & Sun MIN: £10 MAX: £5000 PERIOD: 17th-19th century SPECIALIST: Country furniture, French beds GENERAL: Metalware & decorative items OTHER INFO: One mile from Burghley House open Easter to Oct. Stamford was used by BBC for Middlemarch.

**St George's Antiques**, St George's Square, PE9 2BN TEL: 54117 PARKING: Easy OPEN: Mon-Fri 9-4.30 MIN: £5 MAX: £5000 PERIOD: 19th century SPECIALIST: Silver GENERAL: Furniture

**St Martins Antiques & Crafts Centre**, 23a High Street, St Martins, PE9 2LE TEL: 481158 FAX: 481158 PARKING: Own carpark OPEN: 10-5 (or 5.30) MIN: £3 MAX: £10,000 PERIOD: 18th-20th century SPECIALIST: Military history books GENERAL: General antiques, militaria, nauticalia OTHER INFO: Coffee shop. One of finest stone towns in Europe.

**St Mary's Galleries**, 5 St Mary's Hill, PE9 2DP TEL: 64159 PARKING: Own carpark OPEN: 9-5 MIN: £10 MAX: £8000 PERIOD: 17th-19th century GENERAL: Jewellery, pictures, furniture & unusual items.

**Staniland (Booksellers)**, 4-5 St. George's Street, PE9 2BJ TEL: 55800 ASSNS: PBFA PARKING: Medium OPEN: Mon-Sat 10-5 MIN: £1 MAX: £1000 PERIOD: 17th-20th century SPECIALIST: Local topography & architecture GENERAL: About 25,000 books in 8 rooms. All subjects. OTHER INFO: George Hotel, famous coaching inn, 5 churches. Stamford is famous for its well-preserved stone architecture dating from 16th-18th century.

**Stamford Antiques Centre,** Broad Street, PE9 1PX TEL: 62605 PARKING: Easy GENERAL: Antiques & collectables, 45 dealers.

**Andrew Thomas Antiques**, 10 North Street, PE9 2YN TEL & FAX: 62236 PARKING: Easy OPEN: Mon-Sat 9-6 with variable lunchbreak MIN: £5 MAX: £2500 PERIOD: 18th-20th century SPECIALIST: Painted, pine & country furniture GENERAL: Early metalware & decorative items. We buy from Holland, Germany, Czechoslovakia & Romania.

### WEST DEEPING (01778)

**Quality Antiques,** The Barn 43A King Street, PE6 9HP TEL: 342053 PARKING: Easy OPEN: 7 days 9-6 MIN: £20 MAX: £3500 PERIOD: 18th-19th century GENERAL: Furniture, clocks, beds, soft furnishings, smalls OTHER INFO: Showroom in a listed building dating from 1786.

### MARKET DEEPING (01778)

**Portland House Antiques**, 23 Church Street, PE6 8AN TEL: 347129 PARKING: Easy OPEN: Mon-Sat 10-4.30 or by appt MIN: £100 MAX: £10,000 PERIOD: 18th-20th century GENERAL: Furniture, decorative arts OTHER INFO: George Hotel, Stamford.

### WESTON ST MARYS (01406)

**Dean's Antiques**, The Walnuts, PE12 6JB TEL: 370429 PARKING: Own carpark OPEN: 10-4 MIN: £1 MAX: £200 PERIOD: 19th-20th century SPECIALIST: Farm & country bygones GENERAL: Pine & general furniture, bric-a-brac, brass, copper, old tools OTHER INFO: Display of old farm tools, kitchen & dairy bygones.

### HOLBEACH (01406)

**PJ Cassidy (Books)**, 1 Boston Road, PE12 7LR TEL: 426322 FAX: 426322 PARKING: Easy OPEN: Mon-Sat 10-6 MIN: £1 MAX: £150+ PERIOD: 17th-20th century SPECIALIST: Antique maps, prints & books OTHER INFO: Small market town, with 3 good hotels.

### GEDNEY (01406)

**Paul Johnston**, Chapel Gate, PE12 0DB TEL: 362414

ASSNS: BADA PARKING: Easy OPEN: 10-6. Specialist dealer in 17th-18th century English oak furniture OTHER INFO: Gedney Church well worth visiting, excellent pub food nearby

## LONG SUTTON (01406)

**JW Talton**, 15-19 Market Street, PE12 9DD TEL: 362147 PARKING: Easy OPEN: 9-5 except Weds 9-12 MIN: £15 MAX: £1000 PERIOD: 19th-20th century GENERAL: Small furniture, silver + plate, porcelain.

**Trade Antiques,** 7 Market Street, PE12 9EF TEL: 363758 PARKING: Easy OPEN: By appt MIN: £5 MAX: £1000 PERIOD: 19th century SPECIALIST: Pocket watches GENERAL: Furniture.

## SUTTON BRIDGE (01406)

**The Antique Shop**, 100 Bridge Road, PE12 9SA TEL: 350535 PARKING: Easy OPEN: 9-5.30 MIN: £5 MAX: £4000 PERIOD: 19th century SPECIALIST: Oil lamps, tables & chairs, sideboards GENERAL: China, brass.

**Bridge Antiques**, 32 Bridge Road, PE12 9UA TEL: 350704 PARKING: Own carpark OPEN: Mon-Fri 8-5 or by appt MIN: £25+ PERIOD: 20th century SPECIALIST: Jacobean style, barleytwist, pineapple, linen fold GENERAL: 250 pieces selected 1920's oak & walnut furniture.

**Old Barn Antiques Warehouse**, 220 New Road, PE12 9QE TEL: 350435 mobile 0850 254674 PARKING: Own carpark OPEN: Mon-Sat 9-5.30 MIN: £5 MAX: £2000 PERIOD: 19th-20th century SPECIALIST: Furniture GENERAL: 10,000sq ft of oak, mahogany, pine, shipping furniture.

## KIRTON (01205)

**Kirton Antiques**, 3 High Street, PE20 1DR TEL: 722595, 722134 FAX: 722895 ASSNS: LAPADA PARKING: Own carpark OPEN: Mon-Fri 8.30-5, Sat 8.30-12, but anytime by appt MIN: £1 MAX: £10,000 PERIOD: 17th-20th century SPECIALIST: Chests of drawers GENERAL: General antiques OTHER INFO: Guildhall Museum, Boston, incorporating cells where Pilgrim Fathers were kept prior to sailing for Boston, Mass.

## BOSTON (01205)

**Tony Coda Antiques,** 121 High Street, PE21 8TJ TEL: 352754 PARKING: Easy OPEN: 10-5 MIN: £5 MAX: £2000 PERIOD: 17th-20th century GENERAL: Clocks, paintings, furniture, china, smalls OTHER INFO: Boston is the home of the famous church & landmark 'The Stumps'.

**Mary Holland Antiques**, 7a Red Lion Street, PE21 0PH TEL: 363791, home 353840 PARKING: Easy OPEN: Tues-Wed, Fri-Sat 10-5 & by appt MIN: £1 MAX: £1000 PERIOD: 19th-20th century GENERAL: General antiques OTHER INFO: The Boston Stump, White Hart Hotel, Shod Friars Hall, The Docks. Wormgate, Guildhall, library. Weds & Sat. market day. (Wed also auction).

**Past & Present,** 31 Horncastle Road, PE21 9BU TEL: 361424 PARKING: Easy OPEN: Tues-Sat 11-5 MIN: £1 SPECIALIST: Watercolours, prints of Boston GENERAL: Antiques, collectables.

**Portobello Row**, 93-95 High Street TEL: 368692 PARKING: Own carpark OPEN: Tues-Wed, Fri-Sat 10-4, Mon & Thurs 10-2.45 MIN: £1 PERIOD: 19th-20th century SPECIALIST: Blue & white china, postcards, 40-60's clothing, lamps, postcards OTHER INFO: 9 dealers. Market days Wed & Sat. White Hart & New England hotels.

## NEW BOLINGBROKE (01205)

**Junktion,** The Old Railway Station, PE22 7LN TEL: 480087 & 480086 FAX: 480132 PARKING:

Own carpark OPEN: Wed, Thurs, Sat 10-5 MIN: £1 MAX: £2000 PERIOD: 19th-20th century SPECIALIST: Early advertising, mechanical music GENERAL: Collectables, bygones, large unusual decorative stock.

## TATTERSHALL (01526)

**Wayside Antiques**, Market Place, LN4 4LQ TEL: 342436 PARKING: Easy OPEN: Mon-Sat 10-5 but anytime by appt MIN: £2 MAX: £2000 PERIOD: 18th-20th century GENERAL: Furniture, clocks etc OTHER INFO: Near Tattershall Castle.

## WOODHALL SPA (01526)

**Underwoodhall Antiques,** Shop 4, Broadway Centre TEL: 353815 PARKING: Easy OPEN: 10-5 MIN: £1 MAX: £500 PERIOD: 19th-20th century SPECIALIST: Postcards, Worcester, Royal Doulton GENERAL: General antiques OTHER INFO: Tearoom attached, association with RAF Dambusters 617 Squadron.

**VOC Antiques,** 27 Witham Road, LN10 6RW TEL: 352753 ASSNS: LAPADA PARKING: Own carpark OPEN: Mon Sat 9.30 5.30, Sun 2 5 MIN: £50 MAX: £5000 PERIOD: 17th-19th century SPECIALIST: Furniture GENERAL: Clocks, barometers, metalwork, porcelain & pictures OTHER INFO: Locally a tournament class golf course. 25 mins from Lincoln & 10 mins from Horncastle.

## HORNCASTLE (01507)

**Clare Boam**, 22 North Street, LN9 5DX TEL: 522381 PARKING: Easy OPEN: Mon-Sat 9-5, Sun 2-4.30 MIN: £1 MAX: £1000 PERIOD: 19th-20th century GENERAL: Bric-a-brac, general furniture OTHER INFO: Admiral Rodney Hotel.

**Robert Kitching,** 9-11 West Street, LN9 5JE TEL: 522120 PARKING: Mon-Sat 9.30-5.30 GENERAL: Clocks & general antiques.

**Lincolnshire Antiques Centre**, 26 Bridge Street, LN9 5HZ TEL: 527794 FAX: 526670 PARKING: Own carpark OPEN: Mon-Sat 9-5 or by appt MIN: £1 MAX: £5000 PERIOD: 17th-20th century GENERAL: Furniture, jewellery, silver, collectables OTHER INFO: 30+ dealers under one roof. Produce, game & general auction held in our courtyard every Sat at 10.30am

**Seaview Antiques**, Stanhope Road, LN9 6AA TEL: 524524 FAX: 526946 PARKING: Own carpark OPEN: Mon-Sat 9-5 MIN: £20 MAX: £10,000 PERIOD: 19th-20th century SPECIALIST: French country tables & armoires GENERAL: Furniture, soft furnishings, decorative items, brassware.

**Laurence Shaw Antiques**, 77 East Street, LN9 7AA TEL: 527638 PARKING: Own carpark OPEN: 8.30-5 MIN: £10 MAX: £10,000 PERIOD: 17th-19th century SPECIALIST: Books GENERAL: Wide range of quality antiques, 20th century books OTHER INFO: Next to Tourist Info and famous Magpies restaurant.

**York House Antiques,** 20 North Street, LN9 5DX TEL: 726399 PARKING: Medium OPEN: Mon-Sat 10-5, Sun 2-5 MIN: 50p MAX: £500 PERIOD: 19th-20th century GENERAL: Antiques, bric a brac, collectables.

## SKEGNESS (01754)

**Romantiques,** 93 Roman Bank, PE25 2SW TEL: 767879 PARKING: Easy OPEN: 9-5 PERIOD: 18th-20th century SPECIALIST: Clocks GENERAL: Smalls, pcitures, furniture, lighting, jewellery. Combine a visit with dat at seaside. Be prepared for a long walk to the sea.

## SUTTON-ON-SEA (01507)

**Knicks Knacks Antiques,** 41 High Street, LN12 2EY TEL: 441916 PARKING: Easy OPEN: 10-1, 2-5 MIN: 50p MAX: £800 PERIOD: 19th-20th century SPECIALIST: Brass, iron beds, lighting, fireplaces, Deco GENERAL: Bric-a-brac, linen, cast iron, brass, copper, bygones OTHER INFO: Small furniture warehouse at the back of our shop.

## LOUTH (01507)

**The Old Maltings Antique & Collectors Centre,** Aswell Street TEL: 600366 & 358744 PARKING: Own carpark OPEN: 9.30-4.30 MIN: 50p MAX: £3000+ PERIOD: 17th-20th century GENERAL: Something for everybody.

## GRIMSBY (01472)

**Bell Antiques,** 68A Harold Street TEL: 695110 PARKING: Easy OPEN: By appt only SPECIALIST: Antique pine OTHER INFO: Fishing Heritage Centre & docks.

**Scarthoe Gifts & Antiques,** 38A Louth Road, Scathoe, DN33 2EP TEL: 877394 PARKING: Easy OPEN: 10-5, closed Mon & Thurs PERIOD: 20th century GENERAL: Old prints, engravings, china, jewellery.

## AYLESBY (01472)

**Robin Fowler Period Clocks**, Washingdales, DN37 7LH TEL: 751335 ASSNS: BHI, GMC PARKING: Own carpark OPEN: By appt MIN: £200 MAX: £10,000 PERIOD: 17th-19th century SPECIALIST: Clocks & barometers.

## MARKET RASEN (01673)

**Harwood Tate**, Church Mill, Caistor Road, LN8 3HX TEL: 843579 PARKING: Own carpark OPEN: Mon-Fri 9-5.30, Sat 10-1 MIN: £25 MAX: £5000 PERIOD: 18th-19th century GENERAL: Oak, mahogany, rosewood furniture, clocks, paintings, prints, textiles, ornamentals.

## NORTH KELSEY (01652)

**Moorpine**, Station Yard TEL: 678036 PARKING: Own carpark OPEN: Mon-Fri 9-5, Sat AM & Sun PM MIN: £10 MAX: £1,000 PERIOD: 19th century GENERAL: English & continental pine.

## KIRTON-IN-LINDSEY (01652)

**Keith Van Hefflin**, 12 High Street TEL & FAX: 648044 PARKING: Own carpark OPEN: 10-5 MIN: 50p MAX: £250,000 PERIOD: 17th-20th century SPECIALIST: Jewellery OTHER INFO: Original working windmill, gliding club. Private guide anywhere in England (Mr. McDonald).

## HEMSWELL CLIFF (01427)

**Astra House**, The Guardroom, Old RAF Hemswell (nr Caenby Corner), DN21 5TU TEL & FAX: 668312 PARKING: Own carpark OPEN: Seven days 10-5 MIN: £1 MAX: £5000 PERIOD: 19th-20th century SPECIALIST: Continental furniture GENERAL: Old & new pine, shipping goods, smalls, collectables, almost anything pre 1950 OTHER INFO: 35 unitholders, further 300+ units within 400 yds.

**Hemswell Antiques Centres**, Caenby Corner Estate, DN21 5TJ TEL: 668389 FAX: 668935 PARKING: Own carpark OPEN: Seven days 10-5 MIN: £1 MAX: £20,000 PERIOD: 18th-20th century SPECIALIST: Period, pine & shipping furniture GENERAL: Longcase clocks, barometers, jewellery, prints, books, silver, pictures, ceramics & collectables OTHER INFO: 300 dealers in UK's largest antique centre, own licensed restaurant & coffee shop, accommodation arranged. Lincoln 10 miles.

**Second Time Around**, Antique Centre I, Caenby Corner Estate, DN21 5TJ TEL: 668389 mobile: (0860) 679495 FAX: 668935 OPEN: 7 days 10-5 MIN: £1350 MAX: £12,000 PERIOD: 17th-20th century SPECIALIST: Longcase clocks GEN-ERAL: Other smaller decorative clocks.

## GAINSBOROUGH (01427)

**Pilgrims Antiques Centre**, 66 Church Street, DN21 2TR TEL: 810897 PARKING: Medium OPEN: Tues, Thurs-Sat 10-4.30 MIN: £5 MAX: £500 PERIOD: 19th century SPECIALIST: Jewellery & silver GENERAL: Furniture, pine, smalls, linen OTHER INFO: Close to 16th century Old Hall, opposite unusual Regency parish church.

## LINCOLN (01522)

**C & KE Dring Antiques**, 111 High Street, LN5 7PY TEL: 540733 PARKING: Medium OPEN: 10-5 MIN: £5 MAX: £2000 PERIOD: 18th-20th century SPECIALIST: Inlaid furniture GENERAL: Toys, prints, clocks & shipping etc OTHER INFO: Cathedral, Castle, Roman remains, City Museum, Museum of Lincolnshire Life. Good facilities.

**David J Hansord & Son**, 32 Steep Hill, LN2 1LU TEL:

30044 ASSNS: BADA PARKING: Easy OPEN: Mon-Sat 10-5 MIN: £100 MAX: £50,000 PERIOD: 17th-18th century GENERAL: English furniture, clocks, barometers & scientific instruments, works of art.

**Harlequin Gallery/Golden Good Books,** 20-22 Steep Hill, LN2 1LT TEL: 522589 ASSNS: PBFA PARKING: Restricted access OPEN: 10.30-1.30, 2.30-5.30 PERIOD: 17th-20th century GENERAL: Antiquarian & secondhand books, maps & prints.

**Dorrian Lambert Antiques,** 64 Steep Hill TEL: 545916 PARKING: Easy OPEN: Mon, Tues, Thurs-Sat 10.30-5 MIN: £10 MAX: £5000 PERIOD: 18th-20th century SPECIALIST: Sporting antiques GENERAL: Jewellery, collectables, small furniture pottery, metalwork OTHER INFO: Opposite Jews House (one of the oldest buildings in Europe).

**Mansions,** 5 Eastgate, LN2 1QA TEL: 513631 PARKING: Easy OPEN: Mon-Sat 10-5 MIN: £10 MAX: £500 PERIOD: 18th-20th century SPECIALIST: Period lighting GENERAL: Beaded & decorative items, fabrics, small furniture OTHER INFO: People remark that our shop is one of the smallest but most crammed full in the country.

**Mansions,** Cobb Hall, St Pauls Lane, LN1 3AL TEL: 513631 PARKING: Easy OPEN: Mon-Sat 10-5 MIN: £10 MAX: £500 PERIOD: 18th-20th century SPECIALIST: Period lighting GENERAL: Beaded & decorative items, fabrics, small furniture, papier maché.

**Richard Pullen Jewellers,** 28 The Strait, LN2 1JD TEL: 537170 ASSNS: NAG PARKING: Easy OPEN: Mon, Tues, Thurs-Sat 10-4.30 MIN: £20 MAX: £3000 PERIOD: 19th-20th century SPECIALIST: Antique silver & jewellery.

**J & R Ratcliffe,** 46 Steep Hill, LN2 1LU TEL: 537438 PARKING: Easy OPEN: 10-5 MIN: £5 MAX: £5000 PERIOD: 17th-19th century SPECIALIST: Old English & Continental furniture GENERAL: General antiques.

**Rowletts of Lincoln,** 338 High Street, LN5 7DQ TEL: 524139 PARKING: Easy OPEN: 9-5 MIN: £1 MAX: £5000 PERIOD: 19th-20th century SPECIALIST: Late Victorian & Edwardian jewel-lery. GENERAL: Diamond & other jewellery.

**Second Time Around,** Castle Villa, 14 Drury Lane, LN1 3BN TEL: 543167, mobile: (0860) 679495 PARKING: Medium OPEN: By appt evenings & weekends MIN: £1350 MAX: £12,000 PERIOD: 17th-20th century SPECIALIST: Longcase clocks.

**20th Century Frocks,** 65 Steep Hill, LN1 1YN TEL: 545916 PARKING: Easy OPEN: 11-4.30 MIN: £5 MAX: £250 PERIOD: 20th century SPECIALIST: 1920s-30s ladies clothes and accessories, good examples of 1940s, 50s, 60s.



## SLEAFORD (01205)

**Victoriana,** 1 Jermyn Street TEL: 722785 PARKING: Easy OPEN: Mon, Fri & most Sats 10.30-5 MIN: £1 MAX: £250 PERIOD: 19th-20th century GENERAL: Silver, glass, china, linen, jewellery, cases of cutlery, etc OTHER INFO: Visit Coglesford Mill. At last free parking for 2 hours within 50 yards of the shop.

## GRANTHAM (01476)

**The Attic,** 84 Westgate, NG31 6LE TEL: 64990 PARKING: Easy OPEN: 8.30-6 MIN: £1 MAX: £1500 PERIOD: 19th-20th century GENERAL: General antiques.

**Grantham Clocks,** 30 Lodge Way, NG31 8DD TEL: 61784 ASSNS: BHI PARKING: Easy OPEN: By appt MIN: £20 MAX: £4000 PERIOD: 18th-20th century SPECIALIST: Antique clocks GENERAL: Full range of clocks only, restoration guaranteed OTHER INFO: Grantham is birthplace of Isaac Newton & Margaret Thatcher.

**Grantham Furniture Emporium,** 4-6 Wharf Road TEL: 62967 PARKING: Own carpark OPEN: Tues, Thurs-Sat 10-5, Sun 11-5 MIN: £1 MAX: £3000 PERIOD: 19th-20th century GENERAL: 3000 sq ft of Victorian, Edwardian, 20's & shipping furniture OTHER INFO: Australian owners. Good town facilties. Belton Woods Country Club.

**Notions,** 2a Market Place, NG31 6LQ TEL: 63603 PARKING: Easy OPEN: 10-5, Sun 2-5 MIN: £1 MAX: £500 GENERAL: Furniture & decorative items from Victorian to 1960's.

# Nottinghamshire and South Yorkshire

*Newstead Abbey, about 5 miles north of Nottingham*
*By courtesy of Nottingham City Council*

Robin Hood, coal and steel are the things that people associate with this region. Now most of the mines have gone as have the steelworks. The industrialised towns are still here but there is also wonderful countryside, pretty villages and charming market towns.

The tour starts just off the M1, in **Beeston** with an industrial late 19th century history. Once a village it seems now almost absorbed by the built-up suburbs stretching from Derby to Nottingham. Nevertheless there is a Beeston Old Village Trail and a South Beeston Industrial Trail to follow. **Nottingham**, next door, is most famous for Robin Hood and his long-running battle with the Sheriff. Unfortunately, there is no proof that such a person ever existed and there are many theories about the source of the legend. Some think he is a composite of different men and others that source harks back to the pagan myths of the green man, a fertility symbol.

Nottingham Castle is the most outstanding feature. William the Conqueror built a castle here soon after taking power. Much action was seen over the centuries, Prince John capturing it in 1191 and it was recaptured by his brother, King Richard I, three years later. Richard III stationed himself here while awaiting news of Henry Tudor's landing in the country. He was killed at the Battle of Bosworth and the Tudor line established on the throne of England. Another king, Charles I, used Nottingham Castle as his headquarters after fleeing from London. He gathered his army here before moving on eventually to win the Battle of Edgehill. Later the Parliamentary Forces took the castle and after the Civil War much of it was demolished. Rebuilt in an Italian style in 1679 but burnt down by a Luddite mob in 1831, it was later restored and now houses a museum with displays of pictures, decorative arts, militaria and a History of Nottingham Exhibition. There is much to see in

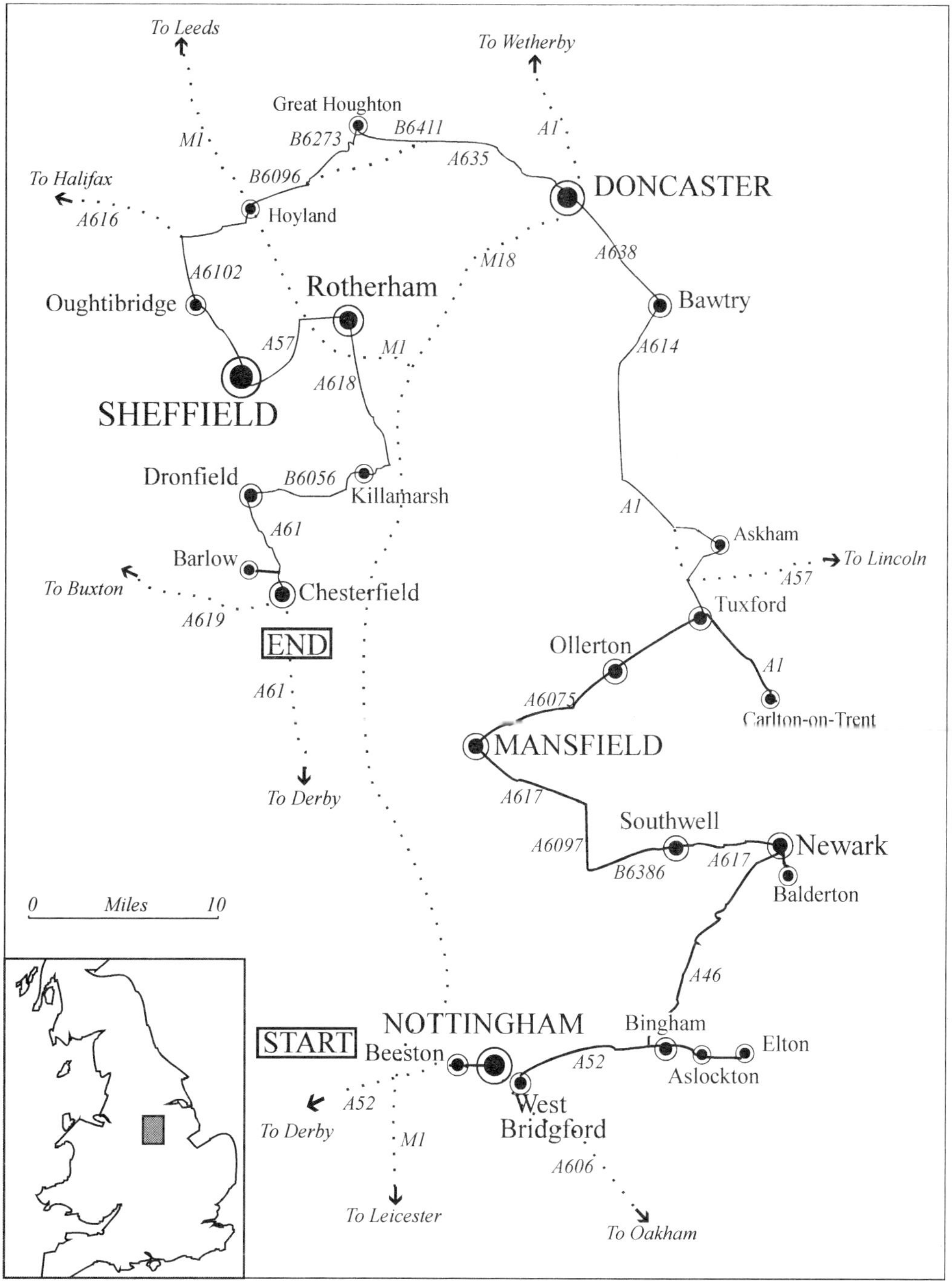
To Leeds
To Wetherby
Great Houghton
B6411
B6273
M1
A1
A635
To Halifax
B6096
DONCASTER
A616
Hoyland
M18
A638
A6102
Rotherham
Bawtry
Oughtibridge
A57
M1
A614
A618
SHEFFIELD
Dronfield
B6056
Killamarsh
A1
A61
Askham
Barlow
To Lincoln
A57
To Buxton
Chesterfield
Tuxford
A619
END
Ollerton
A1
A61
A6075
Carlton-on-Trent
MANSFIELD
To Derby
A617
Southwell
A6097
Newark
B6386
A617
Balderton
0 Miles 10
A46
NOTTINGHAM
Bingham
START
Beeston
Elton
A52
Aslockton
A52
West Bridgford
To Derby
M1
A606
To Leicester
To Oakham

*Robin Hood. By courtesy of Nottingham City Council*

this historic city, including several Georgian houses in Castle Street, St. Peter's Church with some 13th century features and the Cathedral built by Pugin. A racecourse also exists and the famous cricket ground at Trent Bridge. The city contains several good museums, amongst which are The Lace Centre in Castle Road, Museum of Costumes and Textiles, Castlegate, the Canal Museum in Canal Street and Brewhouse Yard Museum at the foot of Castle Rock.

The journey now continues via **West Bridgford** to nearby **Bingham** with an early church which has parts dating from the 13th century and includes a Norman font. **Aslockton** village is perhaps best known as the birthplace of Thomas Cranmer, Archbishop of Canterbury during the reign of Henry VIII, and **Elton**, nearby, with the fine romantic style Elton Hall, dating from the 15th century. This belonged to the Proby family for three hundred years and visitors may see their remarkable collections of furniture, paintings, including Gainsboroughs, Reynolds, Constables, and books, including Henry VIII's prayer missal.

Next is ancient **Newark**, astride the River Trent and close to a junction of the Great North Road and the Roman Fosse Way. A major feature is the ruins of Newark Castle. Although there had been several fortifications built on the site earlier, the main castle was constructed in 1123 by the Bishop of Lincoln. King John died here in October 1216 after travelling from Wisbech. During the Civil War Newark was a Royalist stronghold which led to the castle being besieged three times. On the last occasion in 1645, King Charles I was on his way to relieve it when he encountered Parliamentary troops and fought the Battle of Naseby where he suffered his final defeat. The King and other survivors escaped to Newark but left later for Oxford. The following year he was taken and Newark Castle surrendered. The castle was rendered undefendable and never rebuilt.

The particularly fine St Mary Magdalen, the earliest part of which, the crypt, dates from the early 12th century. The remainder of the church was built between the 13th and 16th centuries with much fine stone and wood carving and stained glass windows. One of only dozen Flemish brasses in the country is kept here. The crypt contains the church's treasury which includes some very fine plate.

Another striking feature is the Town Hall, said to be one of the best Georgian town halls in England. It has a fine collection of civic plate dating mostly from the 17th and 18th centuries, also paintings and historical records. An excellent collection of dolls and juvenalia can be found at the Vina Cooke Museum in Millgate. A Folk Museum is in the same street and Winfield Airfield houses the Newark Air Museum.

After visiting **Balderton**, the lovely small town of **Southwell** is next. In the mid 10th century, Southwell Minster was built on the site of a Roman villa. It was later replaced by the existing Norman church, built in the 12th century. Amongst the many excellent features in the cathedral, the best known is probably the wonderful stone carving in the chapter house where the 13th century stone-carvers sculpted near lifelike leaves. The Minster has always been the most important church in the county and under the direct control of the Archbishops of York. However this position was lost in the mid 19th century and it became just the local parish church. In 1884 a new diocese was formed and Southwell Minster attained cathedral status.

**Mansfield**, 13 miles northwest, now is just on the eastern edge of Sherwood Forest but the centre oak of the forest actually stood in the town's Westgate until the 1940s when it had to be felled. A plaque marks the spot. **Ollerton**, the next call, has a watermill dating from the early 18th century although one has been here since Norman times. **Tuxford** village was once an important coach stop as shown by the large Georgian inn, the Newcastle Arms. At nearby **Carlton-on-Trent** stands Carlton Hall, built in 1765 and boasting a beautiful drawing room and an ancient cedar in the grounds.

Turning north via **Askham** on the A631, **Bawtry** stands on the Great North Road, one of the major coaching routes. The Crown Inn is a relic of those days. There are also 18th century almhouses and an animal pound, once used for strays. Nearby **Doncaster,** a busy industrial town, has existed as early as Roman times. The Mansion House is of particular note being one of only three in the country that were built as the mayor's residence. Started in 1745, it is a fine Georgian building containing a ballroom with an ornamental ceiling and Adam style fireplaces.

The route now visits **Great Houghton, Hoyland** and then **Oughtibridge** before arriving in **Sheffield**., an industrial and university city, on the River Don and most famous for steel and cutlery. The city has a Roman Catholic cathedral of partly 14th to 15th century origin which was originally the parish church. On the outskirts are the remains of the 12th century Beauchief Abbey and there are several Georgian houses in Paradise Square.

The next stop, industrial **Rotherham** in South Yorkshire, is also on the River Don. It has a bridge with a restored 15th century chapel on it and there is also a fine perpendicular church. The notable Clifton Park Museum is housed in a late 18th century mansion and the rooms are furnished in period style. There are displays of Victoriana, Roman antiquities, local history, glass making, etc.

Turning south via **Killamarsh** and then west, **Dronfield**, in Derbyshire, contains a number of 18th century houses and the church dates back, in parts, to the 14th century. Inside is a good example of a Jacobean pulpit and a brass of two priests dates back to about 1390.

The village of **Barlow** is next followed finally by the ancient market town of **Chesterfield,** also mentioned in the Domesday Book. George Stephenson, the famous railway engineer, lived at Tapton House, just north east, and he supervised the building of the railway through Chesterfield. His grave may be found in Trinity Church. The town is most famous for it 14th century church, All Saints, with the twisted spire. The Peacock Heritage Centre is a charming museum housed in a 16th century timber framed building, restored in 1981.

## ANTIQUE DEALERS

### BEESTON (0115)

**Elizabeth Bailey**, 33 Chilwell Road TEL: 225 5685 PARKING: Easy OPEN: Mon 2-5.30, Tues, Wed, Fri, Sat 10-1, 2-5.30 GENERAL: Antiques, Victoriana & decorative items.

### NOTTINGHAM (0115)

**NJ Doris**, 170 Derby Road, NG7 1LR TEL: 978 1194 PARKING: Medium OPEN: Mon-Wed, Fri-Sat 10-5 MIN: £1 MAX: £1000 PERIOD: 18th-20th century GENERAL: Antiquarian & secondhand books: military, theology, English Literature, natural history, huntings OTHER INFO: Derby road is city's antique centre.

**Golden Cage**, 99 Derby Road, Canning Circus TEL: 941 1600 PARKING: Easy OPEN: Mon-Sat 10-5 MIN: £20 MAX: £500 PERIOD: 20th century SPECIALIST: Period clothes GENERAL: Unusual clothing, furs, boas, morning suits, toppers, one-off waistcoats OTHER INFO: We dress people from the Clothes Show Magazine.

**Hockley Coins**, 170 Derby Road, NG7 1LR TEL: 979 0667 PARKING: Easy OPEN: 10-4, closed Thurs

MIN: £1 MAX: £100 PERIOD: Roman, 17th-20th century SPECIALIST: English hammered GENERAL: Coins, cigarette cards, medals, army badges.

**Melville Kemp Ltd**, 79-81 Derby Road, NG1 5BA TEL: 941 7055 FAX: 941 7055 ASSNS: NAG, LAPADA, NADA PARKING: Easy OPEN: Mon-Wed, Fri-Sat 9-5.30 MIN: £30 MAX: £25,000 PERIOD: 19th-20th century SPECIALIST: Probably the finest & most unusual selection of antique jewellery, silver, fob & pocket watches GENERAL: Porcelain & glass.

**Lustre Metal Antiques Nottingham Ltd**, 10-12 The Cattle Market, Meadow Lane, NG2 3GY TEL: 986 3523, mobile 0374 877937 PARKING: Own carpark OPEN: Mon-Sat 9.30-4.30 & by appt MIN: £2 MAX: £3000+ PERIOD: 18th-20th century SPECIALIST: Victorian brass & iron beds, fireplaces, mantels GENERAL: Brass, cast iron, fenders, fire irons, hanging lights, garden vases etc.

**Pegasus Antiques**, 62 Derby Road, NG1 5FD TEL: 947 4220 ASSNS: NAG, NADA PARKING: Easy OPEN: Mon-Sat 9.30-5 MIN: £5 MAX: £5000 PERIOD: 17th-late 19th century GENERAL: Quality furniture, also copper, small silver & jewellery , some 19th century brass & porcelain.

**David & Carole Potter**, 76 Derby Road, NG1 5FD TEL: 941 7911 ASSNS: LAPADA PARKING: Easy OPEN: Tues-Sat 10-5 MIN: £50 MAX: £15,000 PERIOD: 18th-19th century GENERAL: General antiques.

**Val Smith Coins Books & Collectors Centre**, 170 Derby Road, NG7 1LR TEL: 978 1194 ASSNS: IPM, Notts Numismatic Society PARKING: Easy OPEN: 10-5 MIN: £1 MAX: £500 PERIOD: 18th-20th century SPECIALIST: Postcards, banknotes, bullion GENERAL: Coins, medals, jewellery.

**Top Hat Antique Centre**, 66-72 Derby Road, NG1 5FD TEL: 941 9143 ASSNS: NADA PARKING: Easy OPEN: Mon-Sat 9.30-5 MIN: £1 MAX: £5000 PERIOD: 18th-20th century GENERAL: Victorian, Edwardian furniture, general antiques OTHER INFO: Good tourist town, major attractions 5 mins.

**Trident Arms**, 74 Derby Road, NG1 5FD TEL: 941 3307 FAX: 941 4199 ASSNS: NADA & Gun Trade Assn PARKING: Easy OPEN: Mon-Fri 9.30-5, Sat 10-4 PERIOD: 17th-20th century SPECIALIST: Antique & modern weapons & militaria OTHER INFO: One of the largest stocks in UK.

## WEST BRIDGFORD (0115)

**Bridgford Antiques**, 2a Rushworth Avenue, NG2 7LF TEL: 282 1835 PARKING: Easy OPEN: Mon-Sat 10-5 MIN: £1 MAX: £500 PERIOD: 19th-20th century GENERAL: Shipping goods, bric-a-brac, postcards OTHER INFO: Close Notts cricket & football grounds. Lithuanian spoken (honest).

**Joan Cotton Antiques**, 5 Davies Road TEL: 281 3043 PARKING: Own carpark OPEN: 9-5 except Wed MIN: £20 MAX: £80 PERIOD: 20th century SPECIALIST: Jewellery & silver GENERAL: Smalls (no furniture).

**Moultons**, 5 Portland Road, NG2 6DN TEL: 281 4354 PARKING: Easy OPEN: Tues-Sat 10-5 MIN: £2 MAX: £2000 PERIOD: 18th-20th century SPECIALIST: Pine, fabric & curtains GENERAL: Oak & mahogany, kitchenalia, glass, silver plate OTHER INFO: 1 mile from Holme Pierpoort Hall, Vale of Belvoir, close to city centre.

## BINGHAM (01949)

**EM Cheshire**, The Manor House, Market Place TEL: 838864 ASSNS: BADA, LAPADA PARKING: Easy OPEN: Mon-Sat 10-5 MIN: £250 MAX: £10,000 PERIOD: 17th-19th century SPECIALIST: Furniture GENERAL: Early metal, treen OTHER INFO: Small town, good market place, good food shops, good inns.

## ASLOCKTON (01949)

**Jane Neville Gallery**, Elm House, Abbey Lane, NG13 9AE TEL: 50220 FAX: 51337 ASSNS: FATG PARKING: Easy OPEN: 9-5 weekdays, phone for other times MIN: £10 MAX: £5000 PERIOD: 20th century SPECIALIST: Sporting, wildlife & countryside pictures GENERAL: English art & limited edition prints OTHER INFO: Rural village with good inn food.

## ELTON (01949)

**Rectory Bungalow Workshop & Studio**, 1 Main Road, NG13 9LF TEL: 850878 PARKING: Easy OPEN: Saturdays 9.30-4.30 summer & 10-12, 2-3 winter or by appt MIN: £1 MAX: £5000 PERIOD: 17th-20th century SPECIALIST: Handpainted furniture GENERAL: Country furniture & 17th-19th century decoratives OTHER INFO: Manor Arms pub behind shop, Belvoir Castle 3 miles, Langar House Hotel & restaurant 5.

## NEWARK (01636)

**Castlegate Antiques Centre**, 55 Castle Gate, TEL:

700076 PARKING: Easy OPEN: Mon-Sat 9-5.30 MIN: £50 MAX: £5000 PERIOD: 17th-19th century GENERAL: Furniture, plus small stock of decorative items & paintings. Book shop, art reference & childrens OTHER INFO: Newark Castle currently undergoing restoration, was partly demolished by Oliver Cromwell.

**D & G Antiques**, 11 Kings Road, NG24 1EW TEL: 702782 PARKING: Own spaces OPEN: 9.30-5 MIN: £20 MAX: £1500 PERIOD: 18th-20th century GENERAL: Victorian & some period up to 1930 OTHER INFO: New direct connection to Paris & Brussels through Eurotunnel, due 1996.

**D & V Antiques**, 4a Northgate, NG24 1EZ TEL: 71888 PARKING: Medium OPEN: Mon-Thurs, Sat 9.30-5 MIN: £1 MAX: £1000 PERIOD: 19th-20th century GENERAL: Furniture, bric-a-brac, lamps OTHER INFO: Gannets cafe & Appleton Hotel.

**Newark Antiques Centre**, Regent House, Lombard Street, NG24 1XR TEL: 605504 PARKING: Medium OPEN: Mon-Sat 9.30-5, Suns & Bank Holidays 11-4 MIN: £20 MAX: £5000 PERIOD: 18th-20th century SPECIALIST: Longcase clocks, textiles, jewellery GENERAL: Furniture, pine, porcelain, militaria, glass, silver, collectables OTHER INFO: 55 units & 18 display cabinets, tearoom.

**Newark Antiques Warehouse**, Kelham Road, NG24 1BX TEL: 74869 FAX: 612933 PARKING: Own carpark OPEN: Mon-Fri 8.30-5.30, Sat 9.30-4 MIN: £25 MAX: £10,000 PERIOD: 17th-20th century GENERAL: Oak, mahogany, walnut furniture & shipping goods OTHER INFO: Trade warehouse, very large stock changing daily.

**Portland Antiques**, 20 Portland Street, NG24 4XG TEL: 701478 PARKING: Easy OPEN: 9.30-4.30 closed Mon-Thurs MIN: £1 PERIOD: 17th-20th century GENERAL: Wide range of quality stock.

**Portland Street Antiques Centre**, 27-31 Portland Street, NG24 4XF TEL: 74397 PARKING: Easy OPEN: 10-5 MIN: £1 MAX: £5000 PERIOD: 19th-20th century SPECIALIST: Militaria, coins, silver, taxidermy (DoE licence) GENERAL: Antiquarian books, taxidermy, furniture, caramics, silver, longcase clocks, Art Deco, colletables OTHER INFO: Our antiques centre is housed on the three floors of a reportedly haunted Victorian schoolhouse.

**Second Time Around,** Newark Antique Centre, Lombard Street TEL: 605504 & (01522) 543167 (home) PARKING: Own carpark OPEN: 7 days 9.30-5 MIN: £1350 MAX: £12,000 PERIOD: 17th-20th century SPECIALIST: Longcase & bracket clocks GENERAL: All other clocks up to 1940.

**Jack Spratt Antiques**, Unit 5, George Street, NG24 1LU TEL: 707714 FAX: 640595 PARKING: Own carpark OPEN: Mon-Fri 8-5.30, Sat 8-4 MIN: £10 MAX: £2,000 PERIOD: 19th-20th century SPECIALIST: Oak, fruitwood, pine furniture GENERAL: Every possible item in pine OTHER INFO: Largest pine warehouse in the Midlands.

**Tudor Rose Antiques**, 12-13 Market Place TEL: 610311 PARKING: Easy OPEN: MIN: £5 MAX: £10,000 PERIOD: 17th-19th century SPECIALIST: Country furniture GENERAL: Treen, metalware, silver, jewellery, pottery, porcelain, etc.

**Wade-Smith & Read**, 1-3 Castlegate TEL: 73792 PARKING: Medium OPEN: Mon-Wed, Fri, Sat 9-5 & by appt MIN: £200 MAX: £12,000 PERIOD: 17th-20th century SPECIALIST: Early oak & walnut GENERAL: English furniture 17th & 18th century OTHER INFO: Fine town hall by John Carr of York, 1770. Millgate House Hotel.

## BALDERTON (01636)

**Blacksmiths Forge Antiques**, 74 Main Street, NG24 3NP TEL: 700008 PARKING: Own carpark MIN: £5 MAX: £800 PERIOD: 19th-20th century SPECIALIST: Pine, cast iron fireplaces GENERAL: Original pine furniture, pottery, fireplaces.

## SOUTHWELL (01636)

**Strouds of Southwell Antiques**, 3-7 Church Street, NG25 0HG TEL: 815001 FAX: 813064 PARKING: Easy OPEN: Mon-Sat 10-5 MIN: £10 MAX: £50,000 PERIOD: 17th-19th century SPECIALIST: Period furniture, pewter, farmhouse tables GENERAL: Longcase clocks, paintings etc OTHER INFO: Opposite the amazing Minster, huge early cathedral in this tiny market town..

## MANSFIELD (01623)

**The Bookshelf**, 7a Albert Street, NG18 1EA TEL: 648231 PARKING: Medium OPEN: Mon, Tues, Thurs-Sat 9.30-5, Wed 10-2 MIN: £1 PERIOD: 17th-20th century GENERAL: All from Archeology to Zeus OTHER INFO: Mansfield Museum. Sherwood Forest Visitor Centre at nearby Edwinstowe includes Robin Hood Exhibition.

## OLLERTON (01623)

**Hamlyn Lodge**, Station Road, NG22 9BN TEL:

823600 PARKING: Own carpark OPEN: Tues-Sat 10-5, Sun 12-4 & bank hols MIN: £30 MAX: £4000 PERIOD: 18th-20th century SPECIALIST: Furniture only, original & restored condition. All restorations & cabinet-making inhouse OTHER INFO: Housed in converted 18th century farmhouse.

## TUXFORD (01777)

**Sally Mitchell's Gallery,** 9 Eldon Street, TEL: 870580 PARKING: Easy OPEN: Mon-Sat 10-5 PERIOD: 19th-20th century SPECIALIST: Animal & country paintings & prints OTHER INFO: Two doors from a coaching inn, The Newcastle Arms.

## CARLTON-ON-TRENT (01636)

**Granny's Attic,** 308 Carlton Hill, NG4 1GD TEL: 265204 PARKING: Easy OPEN: 10-4 PERIOD: 18th-20th century GENERAL: Antiques, bric a brac, dolls house furniture, etc OTHER INFO: Proprietor has a sense of humour.

**S Pembleton (Antiques),** 306 Carlton Hill TEL: 265204 PARKING: Easy OPEN: 9-5.30, closed Mon & Wed MIN: £5 MAX: £500 PERIOD: 18th-20th century SPECIALIST: Clocks & watches GENERAL: Furniture, china & glass, collectables

## ASKHAM (01777)

**Sally Mitchell Fine Arts,** Thornlea, Askham, NG22 0RN TEL: 838234 ASSNS: FATG PARKING: Own carpark OPEN: By appt or by appt MIN: £20 MAX: £5000 PERIOD: 19th-20th century SPECIALIST: Animal & country paintings OTHER Surrounded by animals, horses, dogs, cats, chickens (rare breeds), ducks, peacocks & sheep (Jacobs).

## BAWTRY (01302)

**Swan Antiques**, 2 Swan Street, DN10 6JQ TEL: 710301 PARKING: Easy OPEN: Seven days 10-5 MIN: £1 MAX: £5000 PERIOD: 18th-20th century SPECIALIST: Early porcelain & pottery GENERAL: General antiques.

**Treasure House (Bawtry) Ltd**, 4-10 Swan Street TEL: 710621 PARKING: Easy OPEN: 10-5, closed Wed MIN: £1 MAX: £3000 PERIOD: 19th-20th century SPECIALIST: Cigarette cards GENERAL: General antiques OTHER INFO: We are an antiques centre with 13 dealers.

**Timothy D Wilson**, Grove House, Wharf Street, DN10 6HZ. TEL: 710040 ASSNS: LAPADA PARKING: Easy OPEN: Resident, phone call advisable MIN: £20 MAX: £30,000 PERIOD: 17th-19th century SPECIALIST: English oak furniture & accessories, Windsor chairs OTHER INFO: An 18th century crossroads for the coaching trade. Surrounding villages are birthplaces of the Pilgrim Fathers.

## DONCASTER (01302)

**Fishlake Antiques,** Adjacent Vine Cottage, Hay Green Corner, Fishlake, DN7 5LA TEL: 841411 PARKING: Own carpark OPEN: Any by appt MAX: £1500 PERIOD: 18th-20th century SPECIALIST: Country pine & clocks GENERAL: Furniture OTHER INFO: Excellent pub lunch.

**Keith Stones Grandfather Clocks**, 5 Ellers Drive, Bessacart, DN4 7DL TEL: 535258 PARKING: Easy OPEN: By appt MIN: £600 MAX: £2500 PERIOD: 18th-19th century SPECIALIST: Longcase clocks, painted dials.

## GREAT HOUGHTON (01226)

**Farmhouse Antiques,** 7 High Street, S72 0AA TEL: 754057 PARKING: Easy OPEN: Mon/Thurs 1-5, Sat 10-12, 1-5 MIN: £1 MAX: £2500 PERIOD: 19th-20th century SPECIALIST: Stripped pine, Susie Cooper GENERAL: Victorian, Edwardian furniture, porcelain, glass, pictures, jewellery, Art Deco OTHER INFO: 15 mins Nostell Priory.

## HOYLAND (01226)

**Charisma Antiques**, St Paul's Former Methodist Church, Market Street, S74 9QR TEL: 747599 PARKING: Easy OPEN: Mon-Sat 10-5 MIN: £5 MAX: £2,500 GENERAL: General antiques OTHER INFO: 1809 Methodist chapel with 3 floors

## OUGHTIBRIDGE (0114)

**Julie Goddard Antiques**, 7-9 Langsett Road South, S30 3GY TEL: 286 2261 PARKING: Own carpark OPEN: Mon, Thurs-Sat 10-4.30, closed Tues pm MIN: £10 MAX: £2500 PERIOD: 18th-19th century SPECIALIST: 19th century furniture GENERAL: Collectables & decorative items OTHER INFO: Very scenic, hilly Pennine village close to M1 (J36) & Holmfirth.

## SHEFFIELD (0114)

**A & C Antiques**, 239 Abbeydale Road, S7 9FJ TEL: 258 9161 PARKING: Easy OPEN: Mon-Sat 10.30-5 MIN: £5 MAX: £ 2,000 PERIOD: 19th-20th century SPECIALIST: Jewellery & quality smalls OTHER INFO: Chatsworth House, Derbyshire, Abbeydale Ind. Hamlet, Peak district.

**Aristocrat Antique Bedsteads,** 113 Wolseley Road, S8 0ZT TEL & FAX: 255 4384 PARKING: Easy OPEN: Weekdays 10-4, Sat 10-5.30, Sun by appt MIN: £200 MAX: £5000 PERIOD: 19th century SPECIALIST: Bedsteads, accompanying furniture.

**Anita's Holme Antiques,** 144 Holme Lane, S6 4JW TEL:233 6698 PARKING: Easy OPEN: 9-5 MIN: £3 MAX: £250 PERIOD: 20th century SPECIALIST: China & plates GENERAL: Cross section.

**Dronfield Antiques,** 375 Abbeydale Road, S7 1FS TEL: 255 0172 FAX: 255 6024 PARKING: Easy OPEN: Mon-Wed, Fri, Sat 10.30-5 MIN: £1 MAX: £2000 PERIOD: 19th-20th century GENERAL: Interesting bric-a-brac, Victorian, Edwardian & 1920's plus shipping furniture.

**Fulwood Antiques & Basement Gallery,** 7 Brookland Avenue, S10 4GA TEL: 230 7387 PARKING: Easy OPEN: Wed, Fri 10-5, Sat 10-1 or by appt MIN: £1 MAX: £5000 PERIOD: 18th-19th century SPECIALIST: Watercolour & oils GENERAL: General antiques.

**Fun Antiques,** 72 Abbeydale Road, S7 1FD TEL: 255 3424 FAX: 258 8599 PARKING: Easy OPEN: By appt only MIN: £10 MAX: £1000 PERIOD: 19th-20th century SPECIALIST: Early toys, advertising items, black art, fairground arcade machines, dolls & teddy bears, sporting items, Disney - general decorative eccentricities.

**DJ Green Antiques,** 334 Abbeydale Road, S7 1FN TEL & FAX: 255 0881 ASSNS: LAPADA PARKING: Easy OPEN: Mon-Sat 9.30-5 MIN: £20 MAX: £5,000 PERIOD: 18th-20th century SPECIALIST: Mainly furniture GENERAL: Silver + plate, glass, pictures etc.

**Hibbert Brothers Ltd,** 117 Norfolk Street, S1 2JE TEL: 272 2038 ASSNS: FATG PARKING: Easy OPEN: Mon-Sat 9-5.30 MIN: £20 MAX: £30,000 PERIOD: 19th-20th century SPECIALIST: Paintings of the area GENERAL: Fine original oil paintings & watercolours OTHER INFO: Next to Town Hall Crucilla & Lyceum theatres & new Nova Hotel all within 50 yds.

**Paraphernalia,** 66-68 Abbeydale Road TEL: 255 0203 PARKING: Easy OPEN: 9.30-5 MIN: £1 MAX: £600 PERIOD: 19th-20th century SPECIALIST: Brass & iron beds, lighting, kitchenalia, china, etc.

**Sheffield Antiques Emporium,** 15 Clyde Road, S8 0YD TEL: 258 4863 PARKING: Easy MIN: £5 MAX: £1000 PERIOD: 19th century (varies) GENERAL: 40 dealers selling books, militaria, kitchenalia, linen, glass, collectables, furniture, toys, clocks, pine, etc OTHER INFO: Friendly antique centre with excellent cafe.

**Sheffield Pine Centre,** 356-358 South Road, Walkley, S6 3TE. TEL: 233 6103, 258 7458 PARKING: Easy OPEN: Mon-Sat 9-5.30 MIN: £5 MAX: £1000 PERIOD: 18th-20th century SPECIALIST: Stripped pine GENERAL: Victorian, Edwardian furniture OTHER INFO: Workshop at Lowfield Cutlery Forge, Guernsey Road, Heeley, S2 4HG.

**Tilleys Vintage Magazine Shops,** 281 Shoreham Street, S1 4SS TEL: 275 2442 PARKING: Easy OPEN: Tues-Sat 9.30-1.30, 3-4.30 MIN: £1.50 MAX: £1000 PERIOD: 19th-20th century SPECIALIST: Magazines GENERAL: Comics, programmes, newspapers, postcards, posters, annuals, cigarette cards, etc.

**Turn of the Century Antiques,** 48-50 Barber Road, Crookesmoor, S10 1ED TEL: 267 0947 PARKING: Easy OPEN: 10-6 approx MIN: £10 MAX: £10,000 PERIOD: 17th 19th century SPECIALIST: 18th century longcase clocks, all clock restoration/repair GENERAL: Furniture, oils & watercolours.

## ROTHERHAM (01709)

**Roger Appleyard Ltd.,** Eastwood Trading Estate, S65 1SL TEL: 367670 FAX: 829395 ASSNS: LAPADA PARKING: Own carpark OPEN: Mon-Fri 9-5 MIN: £5 MAX: £5000 PERIOD: 19th-20th century SPECIALIST: Display accessories GENERAL: Furniture OTHER INFO: 10,000 sq ft warehouse.

**Barbican Bookshop,** 24 Fossgate, YO1 2TA TEL & FAX: 653643 ASSNS: PBFA, BA PARKING: Medium OPEN: Mon-Sat 9-5.30 MIN: £1 MAX: £400 SPECIALIST: Theological & topographical books GENERAL: Antiquarian & second hand books on most subjects.

**John Shaw Antiques Ltd,** 103 Rawmarsh Hill, Parkgate, S62 6DL TEL: 522340 PARKING: Easy OPEN: Mon-Sat 9-5, Sun 10-4 MIN: £10 MAX: £10,000 PERIOD: 18th-20th century GENERAL From a glass fish to a stuffed fish.

**Philip Turner Antiques,** 94a Broad Street, Parkgate TEL: 524640 PARKING: Easy OPEN: 9-5.30 & anytime by appt MIN: £50 MAX: £1000 PERIOD: 19th-20th century SPECIALIST: Oak furniture c

1900 GENERAL: Furniture particularly suitable for German, Japanese & American markets.

## KILLAMARSH (0114)

**Hauenplan's Architectural Emporium,** The Old Station, Station Road, S31 8EN TEL: 248 9972 PARKING: Own carpark OPEN: Tues-Sat 10-4 MIN: £5 MAX: £25,000 PERIOD: 18th-20th century SPECIALIST: Architectural fittings, decorative & garden items.

## DRONFIELD (01246)

**Bardwell Antiques,** 51 Chesterfield Road, S18 6XA TEL: 412183 PARKING: Easy OPEN: Mon-Sat 9-5 MIN: £1 MAX: £2000 PERIOD: 18th-20th century GENERAL: All types of furniture, pottery.

## BARLOW (0114)

**Hackney House Antiques,** Hackney Lane, S18 5TG TEL: 289 0248 PARKING: Own carpark OPEN: Tues-Sun 9-6 MIN: £25 (prints) MAX: £1,500 (clocks) PERIOD: 19th-20th century GENERAL: General antiques OTHER INFO: Tearoom & restaurant on site.

## CHESTERFIELD (01246)

**Polly Coleman Antiques,** 424 Chatsworth Road, Brampton, S40 3BD TEL: 202225 & 278146 PARKING: Easy OPEN: Thurs & Fri 11-4.30, Sat 2-5 MIN: £5 MAX: £1500 PERIOD: 19th-20th century (pre 1930) SPECIALIST: Paintings & signed prints GENERAL: Chairs, porcelain & unusual decorative items.

**Anthony D Goodlad,** 26 Fairfield Road, Brockwell, S40 4TP TEL: 204004 PARKING: Easy OPEN: 10-5 but by appt only MIN: £1 MAX: £300 PERIOD: 19th-20th century SPECIALIST: Militaria chiefly World War I & II.

**Ian Morris,** 479 Chatsworth Road, S40 3AD TEL: 235120 PARKING: Easy OPEN: Mon-Fri 9-5, Sat 12-5 MIN: £1 MAX: £2000 PERIOD: 18th-20th century GENERAL: Furniture, paintings, smalls, Shipping items OTHER INFO: 8 miles to Chatsworth and Hardwick Hall, 10 miles Haddon Hall, Peak District National Park 4 miles.

**Tilleys Vintage Magazine Shop,** 29-31 South Street North, New Whittington, S43 2AA TEL: 454270 PARKING: Easy OPEN: Mon-Sat normally 10-6, but pls phone first MIN: £1 MAX: £250 PERIOD: 19th-20th century SPECIALIST: Magazines GENERAL: Newspapers. OTHER INFO: Wholesale only. 15 pubs & clubs within 1 mile of the shop. 30 mins drive from our retail shop in Sheffield.

**Brian Yates Antiques & Restorations,** 420 Chatsworth Road, S40 3BQ TEL & FAX: 220395 PARKING: Own carpark OPEN: Mon-Sat 9.30-5.30 MIN: £50 MAX: £5000 PERIOD: 17th-19th century SPECIALIST: Oak & country furniture plus accessories GENERAL: Longcase clocks, brass, copper, Staffordshire figures, porcelain, etc OTHER INFO: It is said the crooked spire will straighten if a virgin marries in the church.

# Derbyshire and Staffordshire

Although there are plenty of picturesque villages and beautiful countryside, it is industry that is most closely associated with this area. Stoke-on-Trent is world-famous for its pottery, Derby for its porcelain and Burton-on-Trent for its beer.

The first stop is in **Shardlow**, on the Trent and Mersey Canal, followed by the ancient county town of **Derby** on the River Derwent is first Originally the site of a Roman camp, by the time of the Norman Conquest the population had risen to 2000. In the early 18th century silk mills were opened and the town's industrial base expanded even more with the coming of the railways. A big locomotive and coach works was sited here as was a Rolls-Royce factory and a statue of Sir Henry Royce may be found in the Arboretum Park. Royal Crown Derby Porcelain is still producing fine bone china here. There is also a cathedral built in 1727 incorporating a tower built 200 years earlier. The city has several noteworthy buildings such as St Peter's Church, mentioned in the Domesday Book, the former 16th century Derby School The County Hall's facade is mid 17th century. Amongst the museums are the Derby Industrial Museum in the Silk Mill off Full Street, Pickford's House Museum, Friar Gate, which is a Georgian townhouse exhibiting items of social history, and the Royal Crown Derby Museum in Osmaston Road.

The tour continues to **Heanor**, a town that once had many coal mines, now closed leaving behind spoil heaps which have had to be cleaned up and the land made good for present and future use. **Alfreton** comes next followed by **Belper**, situated on the River Derwent. Its position on the river brought it prosperity through the textiles industry as water powered the mills, some of which still stand in the north of the town. Nearby **Duffield** once had one of the largest Norman castles in the country with a keep almost as big as the White Tower in the Tower of London. Now only the foundations may be seen. **Ashbourne**, on the edge of the Peak District, is next. This market town has many buildings of interest including the many Georgian houses in Church Street, the 15th century timber framed Gingerbread Shop and the Green Man and Black's Head Royal Hotel claiming to have the longest inn name in the country. The town's church is also excellent with the oldest parts dating from the 13th century. Strangers visiting the town on Shrove Tuesday or Ash Wednesday get a big surprise because the traditional game of football is played then. However, it is quite unlike the usual form of the game. The goals are three miles apart and the two teams consist of hundreds of men. Shops board up their windows which is probably wise as there are very few rules.

About halfway between Ashbourne and Stoke-on-Trent stands the famous Alton Towers pleasure park, probably one of the most popular places in Britain for children of all ages. The less well known Alton Castle nearby is also worth seeing. The original castle was Saxon but the Normans built their own stronghold on the site in 1175. By the early 15th century it had passed to the Earl of Shrewsbury. During the Civil War the castle was held for King Charles but was destroyed by Parliamentary Forces. In the mid 19th century the Earl of Shrewsbury commissioned the architect, Pugin who had designed the Houses of Parliament, to rebuild the castle, but to a much more romantic design. However, work stopped when both the Earl and Pugin died. Now work has started again and it is open to the public.

After visiting the villages of **Yeaveley** and **Kingsley, Cheddleton** follows. It has a charming museum: Cheddleton Flint Mill, dating back 700 years, and having twin waterwheels used for grinding flint. Nearby **Stoke-on-Trent** is famous as the centre of the potteries and the North Staffordshire coalfield. Stoke was also the 'Five Towns', the setting in Arnold Bennett's novels. However, as the home of Wedgwood, Minton, Doulton and Spode, it is pottery and porcelain that most people associate with the town. As might be expected, there are several pottery museums. The Minton Museum in London Road, the Wedgwood Museum in Barlaston, the Sir Henry Doulton Gallery, Nile Street, Burslem, the Gladstone Pottery Museum, Uttoxeter Road, Longton, featuring a restored Victorian pottery factory, the Etruria Industrial Museum, Lower Bedford Street,

## Derbyshire and Staffordshire

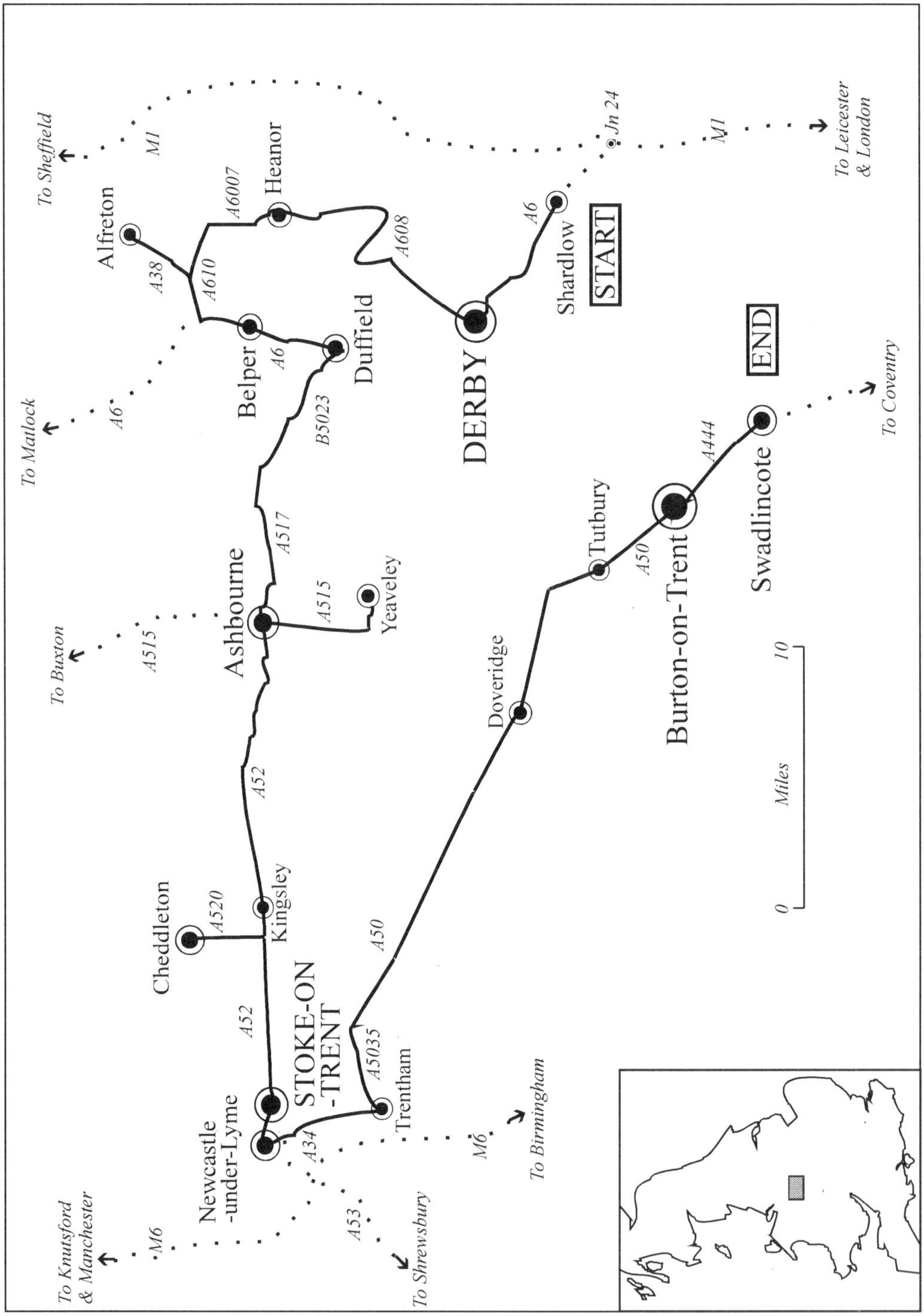

Etruria, with the only surviving steam-powered potters mill.

Stoke was also important for coal mining and the great slagheaps (coal mining waste) may be seen in the town. However, they are not the eyesore that might be expected. They have been landscaped, and planted to make a park. Nearby Keele University helped the town with this, because it is very difficult to get anything to grow on slagheaps so they served as an experimental area for the University.

The neighbouring town of **Newcastle-under-Lyme** is a much quieter and more residential place than Stoke although for many centuries this was the largest town in Staffordshire. It is believed that Newcastle received its charter in the latter half of the 12th century and it quickly became the main market town for north Staffordshire. The local museum in Brampton Park displays Staffordshire pottery, toys and social history. It also recreates a Victorian street. In the eight acres of grounds there is an aviary and a wildlife garden.

On the outskirts of Stoke, **Trentham** has really lovely gardens covering 800 acres and containing woodland and park with facilities for fishing and boating amongst many other activities and amusements. After stopping in **Doveridge** the route arrives in **Tutbury**, whose castle has strong royal associations. It once belonged to John of Gaunt and later Mary, Queen of Scots was imprisoned here for a while. Now only ruins remain. The origins of the town are Anglo-Saxon and it has historically been a centre for glass making, a craft that still continues here. The town's oldest building, the 16th century Dog and Partridge, was a coaching inn and it has retained it quaint appearance.

The beer-making town of **Burton-on-Trent** had, at one time, more than forty breweries. The Bass Museum, Visitor Centre and Shire Horse Stables in Horninglow Street tells the story of brewing and its part in the town's history. There are also shire horses and their stables on show as well as a collection of horse drawn and vintage vehicles.The tour comes to an end in Swadlincote.

## ANTIQUE DEALERS

### SHARDLOW (01332)

**Shardlow Antiques Warehouse,** 24 The Wharf, DE72 2GH TEL: 792899 PARKING: Own carpark OPEN: Mon-Sat 10.30-4 Sun 12-4 PERIOD: 17th-20th century SPECIALIST: Furniture OTHER INFO: Situated at the side of the canal.

### DERBY (01332)

**Abbey House Antiques**, 115 Woods Lane, DE3 3UE TEL: 31426 FAX: 31426 PARKING: Easy OPEN: By appt only PERIOD: 18th-20th century SPECIALIST: Antique dolls, teddies & all things juvenile GENERAL: Bespoke pine furniture.

**Tanglewood**, Tanglewood Mill, Coke Street, DE1 1NE TEL & FAX: 346005 PARKING: Own carpark OPEN: Mon-Fri 9-5 or by appt MIN: £2 MAX: £2000 PERIOD: 18th-20th century SPECIALIST: Antique Irish pine GENERAL: Pine & decorative items OTHER INFO: 8 miles from M1 via A52.

### HEANOR (01773)

**Bygones**, 23c Derby Road TEL: 768513 PARKING: Easy OPEN: 10-5 closed Mon & Wed MIN: £1 MAX: £1000 PERIOD: 19th-20th century SPECIALIST: Langleyware GENERAL: General antiques OTHER INFO: Art gallery on 2 floors. Picture framing service.

### ALFRETON (01773)

**South Street Trading Co**, 31-32 South Street, Riddings DE55 4EJ TEL & FAX: 541527 PARKING: Medium OPEN: Mon-Fri 9-5 or by appt MIN: £5 MAX: £12,000 PERIOD: 20th century SPECIALIST: Live steam models GENERAL: Advertising items, railwayana.

### BELPER (01773)

**Belper Antiques Centre**, 2 Queen Street, DE56 1NR TEL: 823002 PARKING: Free 100 yds OPEN: Mon-Sat 10.30-5 MIN: £1 MAX: £2000 PERIOD: 18th-20th century GENERAL: Quality antiques.

**Sweetings Antiques**, 1 & 1a The Butts, DE56 1HX TEL: 825930 PARKING: Easy OPEN: Mon-Sat 9.30-5.30 MIN: £1 MAX: £3000 PERIOD: 19th-20th century SPECIALIST: Old stripped pine, hand

stripped satin walnut GENERAL: Furniture and general antiques OTHER INFO: Alton Towers, Haddon Hall, Factory Shops.
**Wayside Antiques,** 62 Town Street, DE56 4GG TEL: 840346 PARKING: Own carpark OPEN: Mon-Sat 10-6 MIN: £10 MAX: £6000 PERIOD: 18th-20th century SPECIALIST: Furniture GENERAL: Silver, prints, watercolours, porcelain, boxes.

## DUFFIELD (01332)

**Dragon Antiques**, 1 Tamworth Street, TEL: 842332 ASSNS: GMC PARKING: Easy OPEN: Mon-Sat 9.30-5.30 MIN: £5 MAX: £5000 PERIOD: 18th-20th century SPECIALIST: Longcase, bracket & mantel clocks GENERAL: General antiques.

## ASHBOURNE (01335)

**Yvonne Adams,** 47 Church Street TEL: 346466 PARKING: Easy OPEN: Tues & Weds AM MIN: £30 MAX: £2000 PERIOD: 17th-19th century SPECIALIST: Oak and country furniture and general antiques.
**Pamela Elsom - Antiques,** 5 Church Street, DE6 1AE TEL: 343468 ASSNS: LAPADA PARKING: Easy OPEN: Mon 2-5, Tues, Thurs-Sat 10-5 MAX: £5000 PERIOD: 17th-19th century GENERAL: Furniture, general antiques, secondhand books.
**Manion Antiques**, 23 Church Street, DE6 1AE TEL: 343207 PARKING: Easy OPEN: Thurs-Sat 10-5 & by appt MIN: £20 MAX: £2000 PERIOD: 18th-19th century GENERAL: Wide selection of quality antiques.
**Pine & Decorative Items,** 38 Church Street, DE6 1AJ TEL & FAX: 300061 PARKING: Easy OPEN: 10.30-5 MIN: £10 MAX: £2000 PERIOD: 18th-20th century SPECIALIST: Pine, decorative items.
**Rose Antiques**, 37 Church Street TEL: 343822 PARKING: Easy OPEN: 10-5 SPECIALIST: General antiques.
**Spurrier-Smith Antiques**, 28, 39-41 Church Street DE6 1AJ TEL: 343669 ASSNS: LAPADA PARKING: Own carpark OPEN: Mon, Tues, Thurs-Sat 10-5.30 MIN: £5 MAX: £15,000 PERIOD: 17th-20th century SPECIALIST: Furniture & fine art. We have a large collection from the Vung Tau Cargo, c. 1690, rare & beautiful pottery which spent 300 years under the sea. GENERAL: Metalwork, glass, china, decorative items, garden furniture, instruments OTHER INFO: We often have large unusual fairground items. 7 showrooms & warehouse.
**Kenneth Upchurch**, 30b Church Street TEL: Derby (0332) 754499 PARKING: Medium OPEN: 11.15-5 MIN: £10 MAX: £1500 PERIOD: 19th century SPECIALIST: Oils GENERAL: Watercolours, some 18th-19th century pottery & porcelain.

## YEAVELEY (01335)

**Gravelly Bank Pine Antiques,** TEL & FAX: 330237 PARKING: Own carpark OPEN: Seven days a week 9-7 MIN: £10 MAX: £850 PERIOD: 18th-20th century SPECIALIST: Pine furniture OTHER INFO: Good pub within walking distance.

## KINGSLEY (01538)

**Country Cottage Interiors**, Newhall Farmhouse, Hazles Cross Road, ST10 2AY TEL:754762 PARKING: Own carpark OPEN: 8.30-5 MIN: £1 MAX: £800 PERIOD: 18th-19th century GENERAL: Stripped & unstripped period English pine & kitchenalia OTHER INFO: Beautiful area. Small (4-5) self-catering cottage on premises.

## CHEDDLETON (01538)

**Jewel Antiques**, Whitegates, 63 Basford Bridge Lane TEL: 360744 PARKING: Own carpark Easy OPEN: By appt MIN: £50 MAX: £5000 PERIOD: 18th-20th century SPECIALIST: Oil lamps, jewellery, paintings GENERAL: Small furniture.

## STOKE-ON-TRENT (01782)

**Ann's Antiques**, 26 Leek Road, Stockton Brook TEL: 503991 PARKING: Easy OPEN: Mon-Wed, Fri-Sat 10-5 MAX: £1000 PERIOD: 19th-20th century GENERAL: Furniture, jewellery, pottery & architectural items.
**Castle Antiques**, 113 Victoria Street, Hartshill, ST4 6EU TEL: 625168 PARKING: Easy OPEN: Mon-Wed, Fri, Sat 10.30-3.30 PERIOD: 18th-20th century GENERAL: Victorian & Edwardian furniture.
**Potteries Antique Centre,** 271 Waterloo Road, Cobridge, ST6 3HR TEL: 201455 FAX: 201518 OPEN: 7 days 10-6 MIN: £1 MAX: £10,000 PERIOD: 18th-20th century SPECIALIST: Royal Doulton, Beswick & Wade GENERAL: Furniture, shipping goods, collectables.

## NEWCASTLE-U-LYME (01782)

**Kip Errington Antiques,** 63 George Street, ST5 1JT TEL: 632822 PARKING: Easy OPEN: 10-4 MIN: £10 MAX: £1500 PERIOD: 18th-20th century SPECIALIST: English & Arabic GENERAL:

English & French furniture, etc OTHER INFO: Antique market in town centre every Tuesday.

## TRENTHAM (01782)

**England's Museum of Print**, The Courtyard, Trentham Gardens, Stone Road, ST4 8AX TEL: 657341 ASSNS: International Arts Guild PARKING: Own carpark OPEN: 11-5, closed Tues MIN: £8 MAX: £3000 SPECIALIST: 19th-20th century etchings & lithos GENERAL: Full range of printed artwork OTHER INFO: In Trentham Gardens, Capability Brown's gardens, there are restaurants on site, a lake (water-ski to us), caravan site, Sir Charles Barry listed building.

## DOVERIDGE (01889)

**Pine Antiques**, Bell Farm, Yelt Lane, DE6 5JU TEL & FAX: 564898 PARKING: Own carpark OPEN: Wed & Sat 9-5.30, Sun 12.30-4.30 PERIOD: 18th-20th century SPECIALIST: Original English & Welsh pine GENERAL: Country furniture.

## TUTBURY (01283)

**Town & Country Antiques**, 40 Monk Street, DE13 9NA TEL & FAX: 520556 PARKING: Easy OPEN: 7 days a week 10-5.30 MIN: £1 MAX: £1000 PERIOD: 19th century GENERAL: Original pine furniture, linen & lace.

**Tutbury Mill Antiques**, 6 Lower High Street, DE13 9LU TEL: 815999 PARKING: Own carpark OPEN: 9-5 MIN: £1 MAX: £3500 PERIOD: 18th-20th century SPECIALIST: Country furniture, Victoriana GENERAL: Shipping, smalls OTHER INFO: Large converted mill with 12 other country shops inc restaurant and B&B. Off High Street with 15th century inn and 2 glassworks open to public and 12th century castle.

## BURTON-ON-TRENT (01283)

**Derby Street Antique Emporium**, 138 Derby Street, DE14 2LF TEL: 515202 PARKING: Own carpark OPEN: Mon-Sat 9.30-5.30 MIN: £5 MAX: £5000 PERIOD: 19th century GENERAL: Good cross section OTHER INFO: Also monthly auction last Thursday of every month.

**C & R Scattergood**, 132 Branston Road, DE14 3DQ TEL: 546695 ASSNS: LAPADA PARKING: Own carpark OPEN: Mon-Sat 9-6 MIN: £100 MAX: £10,000 PERIOD: 17th-20th century SPECIALIST: Wemyss pottery GENERAL: Ceramics & glass.

## SWADLINCOTE (01283)

**Wooden Box Antiques**, 32 High Street, DE11 7EH TEL: 212014 PARKING: Own carpark OPEN: 9.30-5.30 MIN: 50p MAX: £600 PERIOD: 19th century SPECIALIST: Original pine furniture, cast iron fireplaces GENERAL: Furniture OTHER INFO: Rear loading, close to ski centre.

# The Peak District

Although usually thought of as being in Derbyshire, the Peak District covers parts of Staffordshire, Cheshire and South Yorkshire. Now a National Park, it is justly famous for the magnificence of its dramatic scenery ranging from heather-covered moorlands to spectacular gorges and valleys cut by rivers through limestone cliffs. The southern part of the area is known as Low Peak or White Peak because of the white limestone rock here. This is beautiful country, much gentler and less intimidating than the northern area called High Peak or Dark Peak. The rock there is gritstone and much of the area is wild peat moorland. There are fewer roads and villages but there is some of the most dramatic scenery in the Peak District.

The tour starts at **Leek** in Staffordshire, just outside the National Park boundary. The town is an important market place for the area and was also important for its silk mills. Although many of the buildings only date from the 19th century, there are survivors from earlier. The Church of St Edward the Confessor was built in 1297, perhaps on the site of an earlier Saxon church. It has 13th century rose windows, a ducking stool and other interesting features surviving from a thousand year history including a Danish or Saxon pillar in the churchyard.

Crossing into Cheshire, the truly ancient **Congleton** on the River Dane comes next. Evidence suggests that a settlement existed here as early as the Stone Age. However, the town only grew after the Normans arrived. Four miles away, on the A34, stands a gem of a 15th century house: Little Moreton Hall, a black and white, timber-framed building and probably the most perfect example of a 15th century moated manor house still in existence.

Moving on via the village of **Siddington**, the tour arrives in **Macclesfield**. A silk manufacturing town with several 18th and 19th century mills, the story of its associations with silk are displayed in the Macclesfield Silk Museum and Heritage Centre in Roe Street. Paradise Mill in Old Park Lane gives demonstrations of hand-weaving and displays 26 silk hand looms. Another fascinating museum is the Jodrell Bank Science Centre and Arboretum with its 76m Lovell telescope and displays on astronomy, space and communications.

Five miles north stands Adlington Hall partly built in the mid 15th century but with roots literally much older. At the heart of this typical Cheshire black and white house are two oak trees carved into pillars but with their roots still in the ground. Originally this area had been forest, some of which had been cleared to build a hunting lodge incorporating the two oaks. When the lodge was demolished this wonderful house was built around the oak pillars and they are all that remains of the original forest. The black and white features are Elizabethan and the South Front of the house was built in 1757. Also there is a magnificent organ, the largest 17th century one in England, which was once played by Handel.

**Alderley Edge**, next, is a market town and takes the name from sandstone cliffs a mile away. Although its buildings are mostly 19th century it reputedly has the oldest timber framed house in Cheshire, Chorley Old Hall. There is also a most unusual watermill at Nether Alderley, 1° miles out on the A34. Because the stream upon which this 16th century mill stands was too small to provide enough power, a dam was built to make a small reservoir to remedy the situation with three more built later.

Nearby **Wilmslow** has an award winning museum 1° miles north. Quarry Bank Mill, owned by the National Trust, has the largest working waterwheel in the country and displays the history of the cotton industry. It also recreates an Apprentice House of the 1830s, where pauper children working in the mill lived. Moving on, **Poynton**, a suburb of Stockport on the Macclesfield Canal, was formerly an important mining area with sixty working pits at the beginning of this century. Two miles away, **Marple Bridge** sits at the junction of the Rivers Goyt and Etherow, and the Peak Forest and the Macclesfield Canal. The canals were important to the industrial development of the town during the 19th century but now they are used for recreation. Following the A57, the route reaches its most northerly point at **Glossop** in Derbyshire, whose prosperity came from cotton and woollen

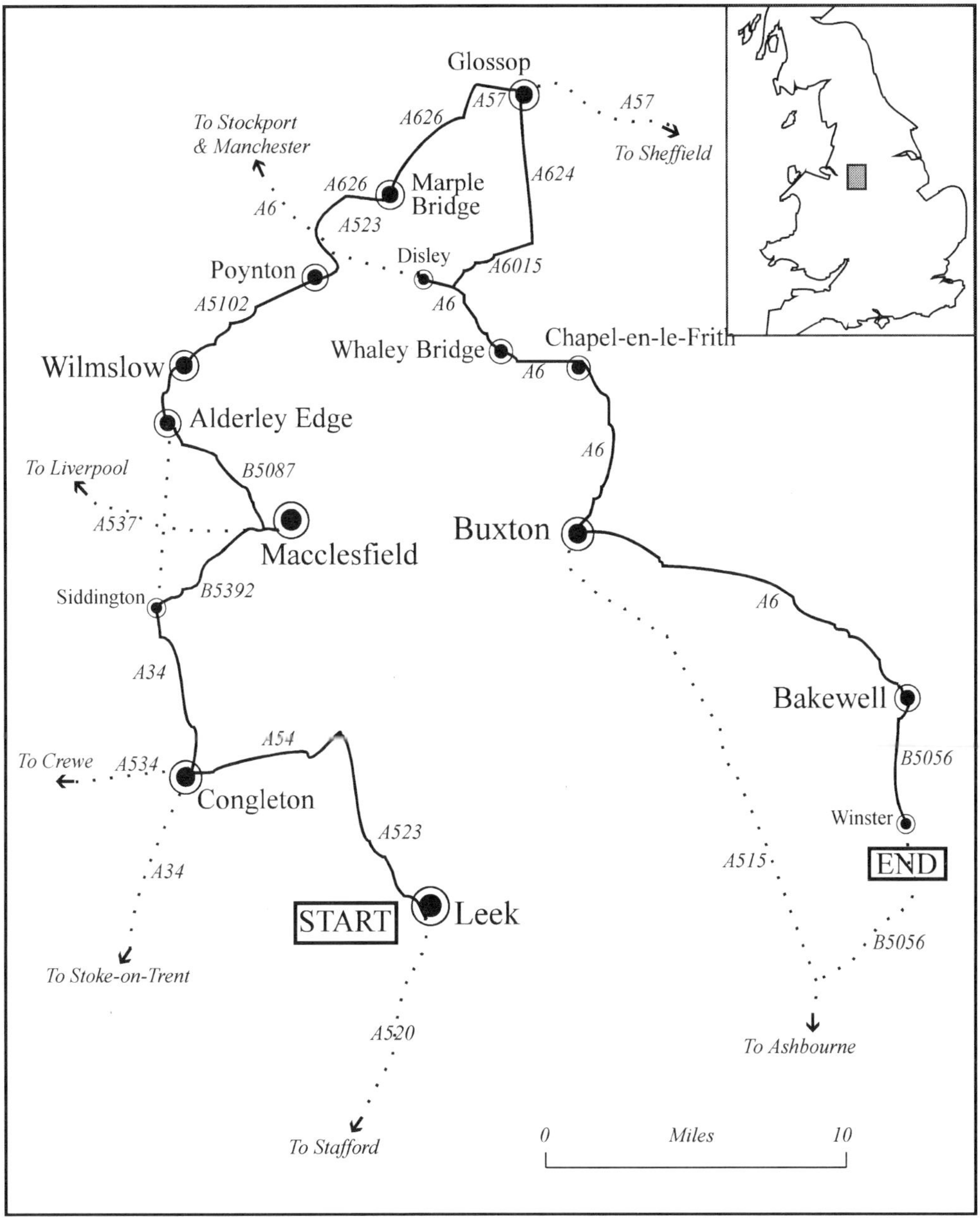
Glossop
A57
A57
To Sheffield
A626
A624
To Stockport
& Manchester
A626
Marple
Bridge
A6
A523
Disley
A6015
Poynton
A6
A5102
Wilmslow
Whaley Bridge
Chapel-en-le-Frith
A6
Alderley Edge
A6
To Liverpool
B5087
A537
Buxton
Macclesfield
Siddington
B5392
A6
A34
Bakewell
A54
To Crewe
A534
B5056
Congleton
A523
Winster
A34
A515
END
START
Leek
B5056
To Stoke-on-Trent
A520
To Ashbourne
To Stafford
0
Miles
10

mills. A mile north west are the remains of the Roman fort of Melandra Castle covering about two acres.

Turning south, the magnificent Lyme Park near **Disley** is the largest house in Cheshire dating from the 16th century. Inside there are tapestries, carvings by Grinling Gibbons and a collection of English clocks. Back in Derbyshire, **Whaley Bridge** was the final point on the Peak Forest Canal. Here goods from Lancashire were off-loaded from the boats, taken up the steep slope by a stationary engine and thence by tramway to another canal for onward shipment to the Midlands. Nearby **Chapel-en-le-Frith** takes its name from the chapel built in the 13th century, *frith* means forest, so it was the chapel in the forest. It was replaced in the 14th century by the present church.

**Buxton**, possibly the most famous of Peak District towns, stands at 1000 feet above sea level and is the highest town in England. It is famous for its natural mineral water and the Romans built baths here and a number of Roman roads centred on the town. The reputation of the water continued through the centuries. Mary, Queen of Scots came here, while a prisoner, to cure her rheumatism. In the late 18th century the Duke of Devonshire built The Crescent, a copy of Bath's Royal Crescent, in an effort to turn Buxton into a spa town to rival Bath.

A charming small opera house is the centre of the prestigious Buxton International Festival of Music and the Arts every July. The 23 acres of Pavilion Gardens with pleasant walks are a must. Buxton Museum and Art Gallery in Terrace Road displays local geology, archeology and history. Also a good open market exists in Higher Buxton.

Poole's Cavern, on the southern edge of Buxton, has some remarkable limestone formations, many of them given names. There is evidence that the cave was inhabited by Stone Age man and that the Romans used it as a temple. Poole is said to have been a medieval outlaw who used the cavern as his hide-out. Six miles from Buxton, on the A537, stands the Cat and Fiddle, at 1690 feet above sea level it is said to be the highest public house in England and a good place to stop and look at the views.

Southeast, the tour comes to **Bakewell** in the centre of the Peak District and a mecca for visitors. The town is probably most famous for its pudding which was created by accident when a cook at the Rutland Hotel misunderstood instructions. Many of the buildings are Victorian but the church is 12th-14th century and has a Saxon cross in the churchyard. The Old House Museum is an early Tudor house with wattle and daub interior walls. On display are a Victorian kitchen, costumes, lace, craftsmen's tools, and toys.

Nearby Chatsworth is one of the most famous houses in England. This magnificent mansion, owned by the Dukes of Devonshire, was started in 1687 and is a treasure house of priceless pictures, books, furniture and works of art. The house is set in beautiful gardens with a maze and the Emperor Fountain, the highest gravity fed fountain in the world, able to rise to a height of 260 feet. This house is not to be missed and needs at least a day to see it.

Another house that must be visited is Haddon Hall, two miles southeast on the A6. A perfectly preserved 12th century manor house owned by the Duke of Rutland who also owns Belvoir Castle, it was preserved because, in the 18th century, the family inherited Belvoir leaving Haddon Hall empty. At the beginning of this century the ninth Duke decided to restore it. Time had stopped at Haddon, no alterations had been made for two hundred years. Now it gives a window onto life from the 12th to 18th centuries. It also contains a fascinating museum of things people had lost over the years that workmen found under floorboards and in nooks and crannies.

The tour ends in the large village of **Winster**, once a lead-mining centre.

## ANTIQUE DEALERS

### LEEK (01538)

**Anvil Antiques Ltd.**, Mills Cross Street, ST13 6BL TEL: 371657 FAX: 385118 PARKING: Own carpark OPEN: Mon-Sat 9-6 PERIOD: 18th-19th century SPECIALIST: Architectural items GENERAL: Antique & reproduction pine a speciality, both for home & export markets.

**Sylvia Chapman Antiques**, 56 St Edward Street, ST13 5DL TEL: 399116 PARKING: Easy OPEN: 12-5.30, closed Thurs & Sun MIN: £25 MAX: £500 PERIOD: 19th & early 20th century SPECIALIST: Pottery, cranberry & coloured glass GENERAL: Antiques, small furniture, kitchenalia.

**Compton Mill Antique Centre**, Compton, ST13 5NJ TEL: 373396 FAX: 399092 PARKING: Own carpark OPEN: Mon-Sat 9-6, Sun 1-5.30 MIN: £1 MAX: £2000 PERIOD: 19th century SPECIALIST: Antique & reproduction pine GENERAL: 40,000 sq ft shipping furniture, oak, mahogany, pine etc, bric-a-brac OTHER INFO: Own restaurant, container packing service, hotels arranged, car to & from Manchester Airport.

**England's Gallery**, Ball Haye House, 1 Ball Haye Terrace, ST13 6AP TEL: 373451 ASSNS: International Arts Guild PARKING: Easy OPEN: Tues-Sat 10-5 MIN: £95 MAX: £50,000 PERIOD: 19th-20th century GENERAL: Victorian oils & watercolours OTHER INFO: Bespoke framing, restoration & art materials.

**Gemini Trading**, Limes Mill, Abbotts Road, ST13 6EY TEL: 387834 FAX: 399819 PARKING: Easy OPEN: Mon-Fri 9-5 or by appt MIN: £5 MAX: £900 PERIOD: 19th-20th century SPECIALIST: Pine furniture GENERAL: Kitchenalia & decoratives OTHER INFO: Good pub meals opposite.

**Roger Haynes Antique Finder**, 31 Compton, ST13 5NJ TEL: 385161 FAX: 385161 PARKING: Easy OPEN: Mon-Fri 9.30-6 but appt a must as 99% is export trade PERIOD: 19th-20th century SPECIALIST: Pine furniture (no reproduction whatsoever) GENERAL: Great stock of decorative accessories.

**Johnsons**, Park Works, Park Road, ST13 8SA TEL: 386745 FAX: 384862 PARKING: Easy OPEN: Mon-Sat 9-6 & by appt MIN: £5 MAX: £2000 PERIOD: 18th-19th century SPECIALIST: Period pine furniture GENERAL: Antique pine, decorative smalls, bespoke reproduction pine furniture.

**Leek Antiques Centre**, 4-6 Brook Street, ST13 5JE TEL: 398475 PARKING: Easy OPEN: 10-5 MIN: £1 MAX: £2000 PERIOD: 19th-20th century SPECIALIST: (12 dealers) furniture, pottery, porcelain, pine, gallery.

**Molland Antique Mirrors,** 40 Compton, ST13 5NH TEL & FAX: 372553 PARKING: Easy OPEN: Mon-Sat 9-6 Sun by appt MIN: £100 MAX: £2500 PERIOD: 19th century SPECIALIST: Gilt mirrors OTHER INFO: Restoration service available.

**Odeon Antiques**, 76-78 St Edward Street, ST13 5DL TEL & FAX: 387188 PARKING: Easy OPEN: Mon-Sat 9-5 MIN: £5 MAX: £2000 PERIOD: 19th-20th century SPECIALIST: Lighting, beds GENERAL: Pine, collectables.

**Old & New**, 59 St Edward Street, ST13 5DN TEL: 384174 PARKING: Easy OPEN: 9-6 MIN: £25 MAX: £650 PERIOD: 20th century SPECIALIST: Edwardian, Art Deco.

**Pine Emporium,** 57 St Edward Street TEL: 388449 & (01374) 455200 PARKING: Medium OPEN: 6 days 10-5 MIN: £2 MAX: £1000 PERIOD: 19th-20th century SPECIALIST: Victorian pine.

### CONGLETON (01260)

**The Antique Shop**, 2 Cross Street TEL: 298909 PARKING: Easy OPEN: Mon, Tues, Thurs-Sat 10-4.30 MIN: £5 MAX: £500 PERIOD: 19th-20th century SPECIALIST: Large quantity of pottery & stripped furniture OTHER INFO: 5 antique shops here & bric-a-brac markets on Tues and Fri.

**Little's Collectables**, 8-10 Little Street, CW12 1AR TEL: 299098 PARKING: Easy OPEN: 9.30-5.30 MIN: £1 MAX: £800 PERIOD: 18th-19th century GENERAL: Victorian furniture, pictures, china, glass, Wedgwood, Doulton. Collectables up to present day OTHER INFO: Shop is 1610 all with original beams. Winebar/bistro next door. Lion & Swan, 17th century hotel above.

**Pine Too**, 8-10 Rood Hill, CW12 1LG TEL: 279228 FAX: 279228 PARKING: Easy OPEN: Mon-Sat 9.30-5.30 MIN: £2 MAX: £1000 PERIOD: 19th-20th century SPECIALIST: Pine, genuine old & reproduction GENERAL: Bespoke production.

### SIDDINGTON (01625)

**Gordon L Bagshaw**, The Old Smithy, Capesthorne Estate Yard, SK11 9JX TEL & FAX: 860909

ASSNS: Northern Ceramics Assn PARKING: Own carpark OPEN: Mon-Sat by appt MIN: £5 MAX: £2000 PERIOD: 18th-19th century SPECIALIST: Full or museum restoration of pottery, porcelain, clock dials & cases, etc GENERAL: Small furniture, ceramics, pictures, clocks OTHER INFO: Fully qualified lecturer in antiques & antique restoration.

## MACCLESFIELD (01625)

**Paula Bolton Antiques**, 83-85 Chestergate, SK11 6DG TEL: 433033 FAX: 430033 PARKING: Own carpark OPEN: Mon-Sat 10-5.30 MIN: £5 MAX: £4000 PERIOD: 19th century GENERAL: General antiques & collectables.

**Philip Brooks**, 6 West Bank Road off Prestbury Road, Upton, SK10 3BT TEL: 426275 PARKING: Easy OPEN: By appt only MIN: £50 MAX: £1000 PERIOD: 19th-20th century SPECIALIST: Oils & watercolours, British & foreign impressionists.

**Cheshire Antiques**, 88-90 Chestergate TEL: 423268 PARKING: Easy OPEN: 11-5 not Weds MIN: £50 MAX: £4-5000 PERIOD: 17th-20th century GENERAL: Early oak, Georgian, Victorian mahogany tables, chairs, longcase clocks & barometers OTHER INFO: Prestbury Village, olde worlde & very pretty.

**Robert Copperfield, English Homes Antiques**, 5-7 Chester Road, SK11 8DG TEL: 511233 PARKING: Medium OPEN: Mon-Sat 10-5 PERIOD: 17th-20th century SPECIALIST: English & Continental furniture OTHER INFO: The oldest established antiques business in Macclesfield.

**The Hidden Gem,** 3 Chester Road TEL: 433884 & 828348 PARKING: Own carpark OPEN: Sat & by appt MIN: £15 MAX: £2500 PERIOD: 18th-20th century GENERAL: Paintings, furniture, early electric lamps & converted gas fittings OTHER INFO: Macclesfield is home to the English silk industry with good exhibitions including a working mill. Nearby Alderley Edge is the haunt of witches, ancient and modern.

**DJ Massey & Son**, 47 Chestergate TEL: 616133 PARKING: Easy OPEN: Mon-Sat 9-5.30 MIN: £20 MAX: £6000 PERIOD: 20th century SPECIALIST: Secondhand wristwatches & jewellery.

## ALDERLEY EDGE (01625)

**Alderley Antiques**, 17 London Road, SK9 7JT TEL: 583468 ASSNS: LAPADA PARKING: Easy OPEN: Mon, Tues, Thurs-Sat 10-1, 2-5, Wed 10-1 MIN: £100 MAX: £15,000 PERIOD: 18th-19th century SPECIALIST: Georgian furniture GENERAL: Furniture, clocks, paintings, silver, objets d'art OTHER INFO: Area of natural beauty.

**Anthony Baker Antiques**, 14 London Road, SK9 7JS TEL: 582674 ASSNS: LAPADA PARKING: Easy OPEN: Tues-Sat 10-5.30 MIN: £5 MAX: £3000 PERIOD: 18th-19th century. GENERAL: Furniture, collectables.

**Brook Lane Antiques**, 67 Brook Lane, SK9 7RW TEL: 584896 PARKING: Own carpark OPEN: Mon-Sat 9-5 MIN: £3 MAX: £3000 PERIOD: 19th-20th century GENERAL: Furniture, beds, bric-a-brac OTHER INFO: 30 mins to ancient City of Chester, 15 mins to old village of Knutsford.

**Sara Frances Antiques**, 2 West Street, SK9 7EG TEL: 585549 FAX: 586015 PARKING: Easy OPEN: Tues-Sat 10-5.30 MIN: £50 MAX: £4000 SPECIALIST: 17th, 18th century oak & country furniture GENERAL: 19th century decoratives & soft furnishings OTHER INFO: No.15 Winebar, The Edge Hotel, Tatton Hall (Knutsford).

## WILMSLOW (01625)

**Peter Bosson**, 10b Swan Street, SK9 1HE TEL: 525250, 527857 ASSNS: Antiquarian Horological Assn PARKING: Medium OPEN: Tues, Thurs-Sat 10-12.45, 2.15-5 MIN: £10 MAX: £5000 PERIOD: 18th-20th century SPECIALIST: Barographs GENERAL: Clocks, barometers, scientific instruments OTHER INFO: Styal Mill (NT), Stanneylands Hotel, The Bank café/winebar (50 yards), 3 miles Manchester airport.

## POYNTON (01625)

**Harper Fine Paintings**, Overdale, Woodford Road, SK12 1ED TEL: 879105 PARKING: Own carpark OPEN: 10-9 MIN: £100 MAX: £40,000 PERIOD: 18th-20th century SPECIALIST: Victorian oils and early Victorian watercolours OTHER INFO: Mottram Hall Hotel, Shrigley Hall (country hotel).

**Recollections**, 1st floor, 77 Park Lane, SK12 1RD TEL: 859373 PARKING: Easy OPEN: Mon, Tues, Thurs-Sat 10-5 MIN: £1 MAX: £500 PERIOD: 19th-20th century SPECIALIST: Costume jewellery, antique linen & lace, popular collectables.

## MARPLE BRIDGE (0161)

**The Mulberry Bush**, 20 Town Street, SK6 5AA TEL: 427 8825 PARKING: Easy OPEN: 9-5 MIN:

£10 MAX: £5000 PERIOD: 18th-20th century GENERAL: Quality mix of furniture, smalls, collectables OTHER INFO: On riverside street in refurbished village. Our famous flight of canal locks.

## GLOSSOP (01457)

**Derbyshire Clocks**, 104 High Street West, SK13 8BB TEL: 862677 PARKING: Easy OPEN: 9-5 closed Tues MIN: £300 MAX: £5000 PERIOD: 18th-19th century SPECIALIST: English longcase, wall, bracket & Vienna wall clocks.

**Norfolk Square Antiques**, 16 Henry Street, (Norfolk Square), SK13 8BW TEL: 854052 PARKING: Medium OPEN: Mon-Sat 10-5 MIN: £1 MAX: £1500 PERIOD: 18th-20th century SPECIALIST: Ceramics GENERAL: Country furniture & objets d'art, watercolours.

## DISLEY (01663)

**Mill Farm Antiques**, 50 Market Street, SK12 2DT TEL: 764045 PARKING: Easy OPEN: Seven days 9-6 MIN: £75 MAX: £5000 PERIOD: 18th-20th century SPECIALIST: Pianos, clocks, mechanical music GENERAL: Shipping furniture & general antiques.

## WHALEY BRIDGE (01663)

**Nimbus Antiques**, 14 Chapel Road, SK12 7JZ TEL: 734248 PARKING: Own carpark OPEN: Mon-Sat 9-5.30, Sun 2-5.30 MIN: £100 MAX: £4000 PERIOD: 18th-19th century SPECIALIST: Furniture GENERAL: Wide furniture range, all restored & renovated on site.

## CHAPEL-EN-LE-FRITH (01298)

**The Clock House**, 48 Manchester Road, SK12 6SR TEL & FAX: 815174 ASSNS: BHI, AWCCCI (USA) PARKING: Easy OPEN: Seven days even bank hols 10-6 MIN: £10 MAX: £10,000 PERIOD: 17th-20th century SPECIALIST: Vintage wrist watches, jewellery GENERAL: Clocks, barometers. Repairs OTHER INFO: Producer of Teach Yourself video on clock repairs & dial restoration.

## BUXTON (01298)

**Antiques Warehouse**, 25 Lightwood Road, SK17 7BJ TEL: 72967, home 871932 FAX: 871932 PARKING: Own carpark OPEN: Mon-Sat 10-4.30 & by appt MIN: £5 MAX: £2000 PERIOD: 17th-20th century SPECIALIST: 19th century mahogany & unrestored brass & iron beds GENERAL: Furniture, some smalls & pictures, ideal for EEC, Australian and USA markets OTHER INFO: Buxton is famous for its well-dressing.

**Aquarius Antiques & Restoration**, 3a Church Street, SK17 6HD TEL: 72209 PARKING: Medium OPEN: 9.30-5.30 closed Mon, Wed MIN: £1 MAX: £800 PERIOD: 19th-20th century GENERAL: Mainly Victorian, Edwardian & Art Deco furniture, pictures, books, ceramics.

**G & J Claessens Antiques**, George Street, SK17 6AT TEL: 72198 ASSNS: LAPADA PARKING: Medium OPEN: Mon-Fri 10-5, Sat 10-2 MIN: £500 MAX: £10,000 PERIOD: 18th-19th century GENERAL: Victorian, Edwardian, clocks, marbles, bronzes, pictures, French furniture, decorative items.

**A & A Needham**, West End Galleries, 8 Cavendish Circus, SK17 6AT TEL: 24546 PARKING: Medium OPEN: Mon-Fri 9.30-5, Sat 9.30-1.30 PERIOD: 18th-19th century SPECIALIST: Bronzes GENERAL: Antique, works of art, furniture, clocks.

**What Now Antiques**, Cavendish Arcade, The Crescent, SK17 6BQ TEL: 27178 PARKING: Easy OPEN: Tues-Sat 10.30-5, Sun 2-5 MIN: £1 MAX: £1500 PERIOD: 19th-20th century SPECIALIST: Watercolours, golfing items, silver & plate ENERAL: Furniture & decorative items 1820-1950, & general antiques OTHER INFO: Shop in converted thermal baths in historic crescent. 5 antique shops 100 yds.

**Winstons,** The Old Courthouse, George Street, SK17 6AY TEL: 79379 PARKING: Medium OPEN: Mon-Sat 10-5.30, Sun 12-5.30 MIN: £2 MAX: £800 PERIOD: 19th-20th century SPECIALIST: Furniture GENERAL: Various.

## BAKEWELL (01629)

**Bakewell Antiques & Collectors Centre**, King Street, DE45 1DZ TEL: 812496 FAX: 814531 PARKING: Own small carpark OPEN: Mon-Sat 10-5, Sun 11-5 MIN: £1 MAX: £5000 PERIOD: 18th-20th century GENERAL: 15+ dealers. Furniture, ceramics, clocks, barometers, books, pictures, silver, decorative items OTHER INFO: Good refreshments on site.

**Beedham Antiques Ltd**, Holme Hall, DE45 1GE TEL: 813285 PARKING: Own carpark OPEN: By appt MIN: £500 MAX: £30,000 PERIOD: 16th-17th century SPECIALIST: English & Continental oak & other furniture & related objects.

**Chappell's Antiques & Fine Art**, King Street, DE45 1DZ TEL: 812496 FAX: 814531 ASSNS: BADA, LAPADA, CINOA PARKING: Own carpark OPEN: Mon-Sat 9.30-5.30 MIN: £20 MAX: £15,000 PERIOD: 18th-19th century SPECIALIST: Blue John & Derby porcelain GENERAL: Fine period English furniture, porcelain, clocks, barometers, metals, treen.

**Michael Goldstone**, Avenel Court, DE45 1DZ TEL: 812487 ASSNS: BADA, CINOA PARKING: Own carpark OPEN: Mon-Sat 9-6 MIN: £25 MAX: £20,000 PERIOD: 17th-18th century SPECIALIST: Early oak & country furniture OTHER INFO: Early market town with weekly market since 1326.

**Martin & Dorothy Harper**, King Street, DE45 1DZ TEL: 814757 ASSNS: LAPADA PARKING: Easy OPEN: Mon-Wed, Fri, Sat 10-5.30, MIN: £5 MAX: £5000 PERIOD: 18th-19th century GENERAL: Furniture & general antiques.

**Alan Hill Books**, 3 Buxton Road, TEL: 814841 ASSNS: PBFA PARKING: Difficult OPEN: Mon-Sat 10-5 MAX: £500 PERIOD: 17th-20th century SPECIALIST: Topographical books & maps GENERAL: Antiquarian & secondhand books, maps & prints.

**JHS Antiques** (Julian H Snodin), Stand 11, Bakewell Antique Centre, King Street, DE45 1DZ TEL: 812496 & 584624 PARKING: Medium OPEN: Mon-Sat 10-5, Sun 11-5 MIN: £25 MAX: £2500 PERIOD: 17th-19th century SPECIALIST: Staffordshire, treen GENERAL: Country & period furniture & decorative items OTHER INFO: The centre's cafe serves delicious Bakewell puddings.

**Lewis Antiques,** King Street, DE45 1DZ TEL: 813141 PARKING: Medium OPEN: 10-5 except Thurs MIN: £100 MAX: £8000 PERIOD: 17th-19th century GENERAL: Furniture, porcelain, clocks, barometers & pictures.

**Water Lane Antiques**, Water Lane, DE45 1EW TEL: 814161 PARKING: Easy OPEN: Mon-Sat 9.30-5.30 MIN: £50 MAX: £8000 PERIOD: 18th-19th century SPECIALIST: Ashford marble & Blue John GENERAL: Furniture & decorative items.

## WINSTER (01629)

**Winster Arts,** Kirby House, Main Street, DE4 2DH TEL: 650716 PARKING: Easy OPEN: Weekends only July & August MIN: £1 MAX: £6500 PERIOD: 19th-20th century SPECIALIST: Victorian Oriental goods OTHER INFO: Situated in a conservation area, an 18th century leadmining village, 2 good pubs serving meals.

# Cheshire

*Two tiered shopping galleries, Chester*

Cheshire is a county of small towns and villages. It is prime dairy farming country with typical lush green pastureland. Roman remains and black and white houses are what are usually associated with the area with Chester being the prime example of a Roman town.

**Knutsford**, the first stop on the tour, was the 'Cranford' of Elizabeth Gaskell's novel. The town has a number of the famous Cheshire black and white houses, a coaching inn, The Royal George, a Victorian Gothic town hall and Georgian houses. The town is also famous for its Mayday celebrations, said to be the most impressive in England. A fine Palladian mansion, Tabley House, is two miles west on the A5033. It is particularly known for its fine collection of English paintings. Another mansion, Tatton Park, stands outside the town. The present building was started in the late 18th century and the owners furnished it in lavish style, all of which can be seen today. Landscaped by Humphrey Repton, the gardens are superb incorporating Tatton and Melchett meres. They include an Italian terrace garden and a Japanese garden complete with Shinto temple.

From Knutsford the route goes west through the small villages of **Plumley** and **Lostock Graham** before arriving in **Northwich**, on the junction of the rivers Weaver and Dane. The town is situated by a large area of salt which has been extracted here since Roman times. This industry became even more important when, in the 17th century, rock salt was discovered nearby. This led to the making of brine in the 19th century. Pumping brine caused subsidence in the town's buildings and so timber-framed buildings were designed that could be raised to counteract the effect of the subsiding ground. Just five miles from Northwich, Arley Hall and Gardens may be visited. Although the house was only built in 1840, the estate has been in the same family for over 500 years. The Hall is a fine example of Victorian Jacobean style and contains oak panelling, plasterwork, pictures, furniture and porcelain. It stands in beautiful parkland and award winning gardens.

After **Davenham**, **Whitegate** is next and nearby is the seven acre Iron Age Eddisbury Hill hillfort, said to be the largest fortification of its kind in the county. At **Helsby**, to the north, there are two more Iron Age sites, one at Helsby Hill and the other, Woodhouse Hillfort, north of the village, although at the second there is little to be seen. Turning back south, the village of **Tarvin Sands** is followed by **Chester**, the only English city to have preserved all of its walls. Romans established

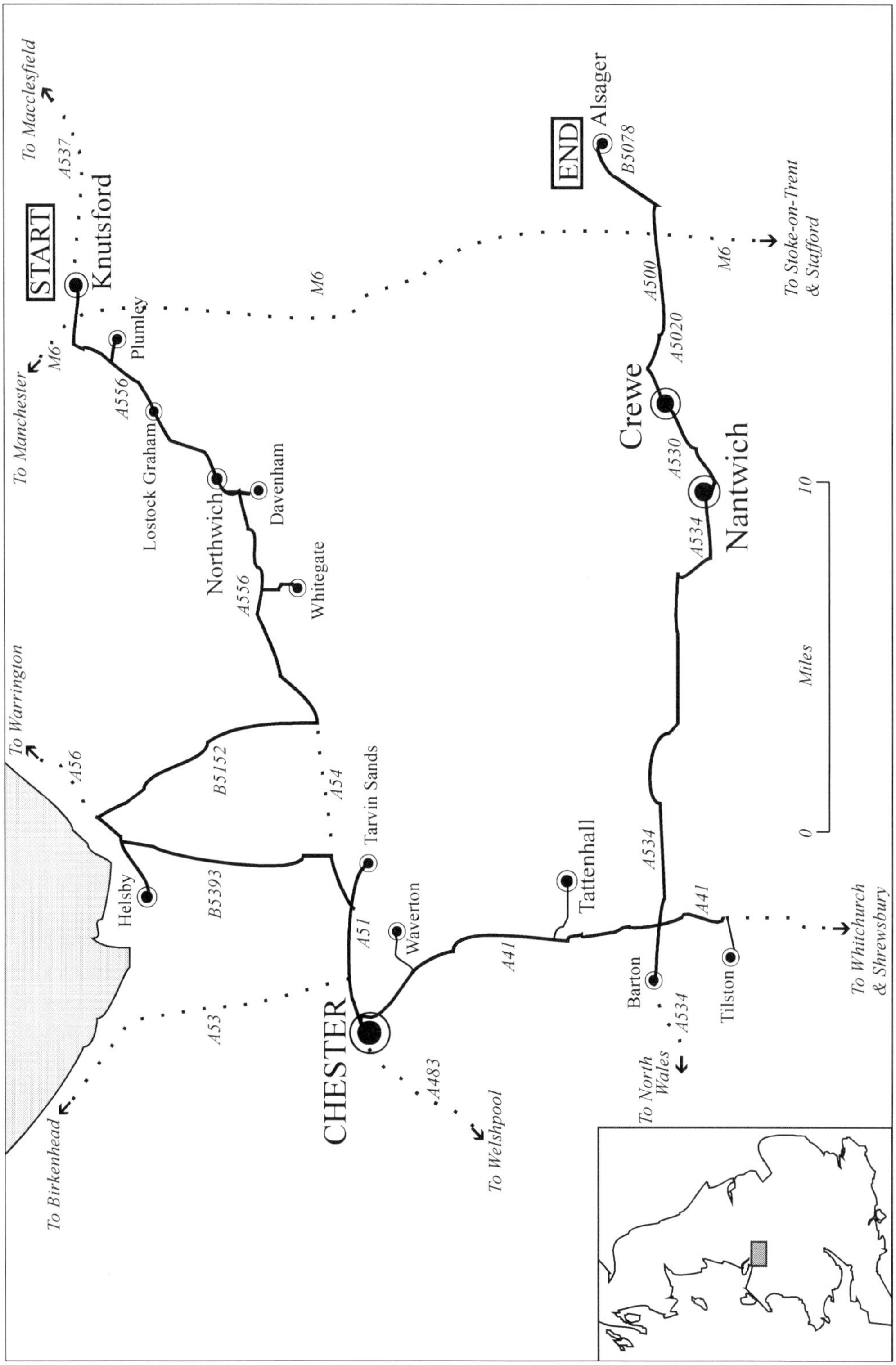
START
Knutsford
END
Alsager
CHESTER
Crewe
Nantwich
Northwich
Plumley
Lostock Graham
Davenham
Whitegate
Helsby
Tarvin Sands
Waverton
Tattenhall
Barton
Tilston
To Macclesfield
To Manchester
To Warrington
To Birkenhead
To Welshpool
To North Wales
To Whitchurch & Shrewsbury
To Stoke-on-Trent & Stafford
M6
A537
A556
A56
B5152
A54
B5393
A51
A53
A483
A41
A534
A530
A5020
A500
B5078
Miles
0
10

a fort here and it was home to a legion for the entire 300 years of their British occupation. A good place for more information on Chester in Roman times is the Grosvenor Museum which has a very fine collection of antiquities.

Chester has prospered through the centuries. First it was a successful port, but this ended in the 15th century when the River Dee silted up. However, commercial life was so strong by this time the town continued to thrive. Amongst other museums are the Chester Heritage Centre in Bridge Street Row, the early 14th century Water Tower and the 13th to 14th century King Charles Tower from where Charles I watched the defeat of his army at Rowton Moor in 1645. Both towers are on the City Walls.

The medieval two tier shopping galleries are the most famous of the many attractions. Another major landmark is the 800 year old cathedral. Built of sandstone, by the 19th century it was crumbling badly and was extensively restored by architect, Sir George Gilbert Scott and others. They had to replace the flying buttresses, windows, vaulted wooden ceilings, choir stalls and the organ.

Chester is extremely picturesque and much loved by most visitors. To really appreciate and see far more of the memorable sights, it is essential to visit the Tourist Information Centre in the Town Hall.

The tour continues south via **Waverton** to **Tattenhall, Barton** and then **Tilston** before turning east along the A49 to **Nantwich**, known from Roman times until the mid 19th century for salt production. The town has suffered badly in wars over the centuries. It resisted the Normans, suffered considerable damage from repeated Welsh attacks and was also caught up in the Civil War when the town was besieged by Royalists and had to be relieved by Parliamentary troops under the command of Sir Thomas Fairfax and Sir William Brereton. As if this was not enough, the town also had two devastating fires in 1438 and 1583. In spite of all this, it still has a fine 14th century church, impressive enough, both inside and out, to be called 'the cathedral of south Cheshire'. Another building that survived the last fire is the timber framed Sweetbriar Hall, built in the mid 15th century. In the High Street there are some lovely Elizabethan buildings overhanging the street and built after the later fire. Nearby Dorfold Hall, one mile west on the A534, is a Jacobean country house started in 1616 with later additions and alterations. It has particularly fine plaster ceilings using a Tudor rose, fleur-de-lys and thistle in the decoration to celebrate the joining of England, Scotland and Wales under James I in March 1603.

Keen gardeners, especially those with ponds and lakes, will hate to miss Stapeley Water Gardens, a mile south east on the A51. Covering over three acres, and boasting the world's largest water garden centre, it also houses the National Collection of *Nymphaea*, i.e. waterlilies, with over 350 varieties. There are also other water plants, pools and fountains as well as the Palms Tropical Oasis, a pavilion containing piranhas, parrots, monkeys and exotic plants.

Nearby **Crewe** is strongly associated with railways and its junction must be England's second busiest after the world-renowned Clapham Junction in southwest London. The first line to arrive in Crewe was the Warrington to Birmingham in 1837. Before the arrival of the railways Crewe was primarily an agricultural town but it became important for the manufacture of railway engines and the railways became the town's principal employer.

The final stop is the mainly agricultural town of **Alsager**, named for the most important local family.

## ANTIQUE DEALERS

### KNUTSFORD (01565)

**David Bedale**, 5-7 Minshull Street, WA16 6HG TEL: 653621 PARKING: Medium OPEN: Mon-Sat 9.30-1, 2-5.30 MIN: £100 MAX: £15,000 PERIOD: 17-19th century GENERAL: 18th-19th century furniture & unusual decorative items OTHER INFO: Tatton Park, La Belle Epoque restaurant, Cottons Hotel

**Cranford Galleries**, 10 King Street, WA16 6DL TEL: 633646 ASSNS: FATG PARKING: Medium OPEN: Mon, Tues, Thurs-Sat 11-1, 2.30-5 MIN: £50+ MAX: £3850+ PERIOD: 18th-19th century GENERAL: General antiques, picture framing.

**Glynn Interiors**, 92 King Street, WA16 6ED TEL: 634418 PARKING: Easy OPEN: Mon-Sat 10-5, closed Weds MIN: £50 MAX: £3000 PERIOD: 19th century SPECIALIST: Upholstery & inlaid furniture OTHER INFO: Excellent restaurant behind, the Courtyard Coffee House combined with first Penny Farthing Museum.

**Knutsford Antique Centre**, 16 King Street TEL: 755334 PARKING: Easy OPEN: Mon, Tues, Thurs-Sat 10-5, Sun 12-4 MIN: £5 MAX: £3000 PERIOD: 18th-20th century GENERAL: Very varied stock of antiques & collectables including paintings OTHER INFO: 8 dealers in this interesting centre in fashionable, historic town. 2miles from M6.

**Lion Gallery & Bookshop,** 15A Minshull Street, WA16 6HG TEL: 652915 mobile: (0850) 270796 FAX: 750142 PARKING: Easy OPEN: Fri 10.30-5, Sat 10-5, anytime by appt PERIOD:1600-1920 SPECIALIST: One of largest stocks in world of maps & print. Antiquarian books.

### PLUMLEY (01565)

**Coppelia Antiques**, Holford Lodge, Plumley Moor Road, WA16 9RS TEL: 722197 FAX: 722744 PARKING: Own carpark OPEN: 7 days 10-7 MIN: £100 MAX: £50,000 PERIOD: 17th-18th century SPECIALIST: Longcase clocks GENERAL: Quality Georgian furniture & clocks. All restoration done on premises OTHER INFO: Good food at local pubs, country location, only 4 mins M6, Jn 19.

### LOSTOCK GRAHAM (01606)

**Lostock Antiques**, 210 Manchester Road, CW9 7NN TEL: 45523 PARKING: Easy OPEN: Tues-Sat 10.30-5.30, Sun 1-5 MIN: £1 MAX: £1500 PERIOD: 19th century SPECIALIST: Our own brand of furniture polishes, lots of French mirrors, beds, etc GENERAL: Books, bric-a-brac, kitchenalia. Full restoration.

### NORTHWICH (01606)

**RW Hayward,** Blakemere Craft & Antique Centre, Chester Road, Sandiway CW8 2EB TEL: 883261 ASSNS: Guild of Antique Dealers & Restorers PARKING: Easy OPEN: Tues-Fri 10-5, Sat, Sun 10-5.30 MIN: £30 MAX: £2500 PERIOD: 19th-20th century GENERAL: Furniture & collectables.

### DAVENHAM (01606)

**Davenham Antique Centre,** 461 London Road, CW9 8NA TEL: 44350 PARKING: Easy OPEN: 10-5, closed Weds MIN: £1 MAX: £1000 PERIOD: 19th-20th century GENERAL: General antiques, a good selection of quality furniture.

**Forest Books of Cheshire**, at Magpie Antiques, 2-4 Church Street, CW9 8NA TEL: 44350 PARKING: Easy OPEN: Tues, Thurs, Sat 11-5, Fri & some Mons 2-5 not bank hols MIN: £1 MAX: £250+ PERIOD: 19th-20th century SPECIALIST: Wildlife, gardening, fishing & other English life, Cheshire & N.Wales, some prints & pictures.

**Magpie Antiques**, 2-4 Church Street, CW9 8NA TEL: (01829) 260360 (Home) PARKING: Easy OPEN: Tues, Thurs, Sat 11-5, Mon, Fri 2-5 MIN: £1 MAX: £250 PERIOD: 19th-20th century SPECIALIST: Country style items GENERAL: Pictures, smalls, some furniture etc OTHER INFO: Small conservation area, coaching inn, Northwich Salt Museum & salt-mining area.

### WHITEGATE (01606)

**The Antiques Shop**, Cinder Hill, CW8 2BH TEL: 882215 PARKING: Own carpark OPEN: Tues-Wed, Fri-Sat 10-5, Mon 2-5 MIN: £10 MAX: £2000 PERIOD: 18th-20th century GENERAL: General antiques OTHER INFO: Self-contained holiday bungalow in grounds.

### HELSBY (01928)

**Sweetbriar Gallery**, 106 Robin Hood Lane TEL: 723851 FAX: 723851 ASSNS: Paperweight Collectors Assn PARKING: Own carpark OPEN: By appt MIN: £2 MAX: £2500 PERIOD: 19th-20th century SPECIALIST: Paperweights (international dealer), perfume bottles, etchings, some other pictures, particulary wild life specialist artists: Tunnicliffe & Frank Brangwyn.

## TARVIN SANDS (01829)

**Cheshire Brick & Slate Company,** Brook House Farm, Salter's Bridge, CH3 8HL TEL: 740883 FAX: 740481 PARKING: Own carpark OPEN: Mon-Fri 8-5.30 Sat 8-4.30, Sun 10-4 MIN: 25p MAX: £5000 PERIOD: 19th-20th century GENERAL: All reclaimed building materials & architectural antiques OTHER INFO: 6 miles outside Chester, many dealers & places of interest in surrounding areas.

## CHESTER (01244)

**Abbey Antiques,** 24 Watergate Street, CH1 2LA TEL: 328802 OPEN: Mon-Sat 10-5 MIN: £5 MAX: £5000 SPECIALIST: Antique furniture, 19th century oils & watercolours OTHER INFO: Watergate Street is the antique centre of Chester.

**Adam Antiques**, 65 Watergate Row, CH1 2LE TEL: 319421 ASSNS: LAPADA PARKING: Easy OPEN: Mon-Sat 10-5 MIN: £10 MAX: £5000 PERIOD: 18th-20th century GENERAL: Decorative & traditional furniture, clocks, objets d'art.

**Albany Antiques,** Aldersley Hall, 47 Northgate Street, CH1 2HQ TEL: 324885 PARKING: Own carpark OPEN: Mon-Sat 8.30-5.30 MIN: £1 MAX: £300 PERIOD: 19th-20th century SPECIALIST: Art Deco ceramics GENERAL: 70+ different ceramics factories, linen, dolls, teddies.

**Angela Antiques**, 32 Christleton Road, CH3 5UG TEL: 351562 PARKING: Easy OPEN: 10-5 MIN: £2 MAX: £400 PERIOD: 19th-20th century GENERAL: Collectables, pine, lace, linen, decorative items OTHER INFO: By superb riverside B&B's-River Peace, The Moorings.

**The Antique Shop**, 40 Watergate Street, CH1 2LA TEL: 316286 PARKING: Medium OPEN: Mon-Sat 10-5.30 MIN: £5 MAX: £500 PERIOD: 18th-20th century SPECIALIST: Metalware, Doulton, Blue & White, pot lids, Maling, military.

**Avalon Stamp & Postcard Shop**, 1 City Walls/ Rufus Court, Northgate Street, CH1 2JG TEL: 318406 PARKING: Difficult OPEN: 9.30-5.30 MIN: £1 PERIOD: 19th-20th century SPECIALIST: Stamps, postcards.

**Barn Antiques**, 25 Christleton Road, Boughton TEL: 344928 PARKING: Easy OPEN: Mon-Sat 9-5 MIN: £10 MAX: £500 PERIOD: 19th-20th century GENERAL: Shipping & medium priced antiques.

**Baron Fine Art**, 68 Watergate Street, CH1 2LA TEL: 342520 ASSNS: LAPADA PARKING: Medium OPEN: Mon-Sat 9.45-5.30 MIN: £25 MAX: £30,000 PERIOD: 19th-20th century GENERAL: Watercolours, oils & etchings OTHER INFO: Also good centre for touring N.Wales, Liverpool etc.

**Cameo Antiques,** 19 Watergate Street, CH1 4BP TEL: 311467 OPEN: Mon-Sat 9-5 MIN: £10 MAX: £3000 PERIOD: 19th-20th century SPECIALIST: Jewellery, silver, ceramics GENERAL: Small furniture, decorative items.

**Cestrian Antiques,** 22 Watergate Row, CH1 2LD TEL: 400444 PARKING: Medium OPEN: Mon-Sat 10-5.30 MIN: £1 MAX: £3000 PERIOD: 17th-20th century SPECIALIST: Small occasional furniture GENERAL: General Antiques OTHER INFO: In the centre of the main antiques area of Chester, free glasses of wine or sherry or coffee provided at various times of the year.

**Chester Furniture Cave**, The Old Chapel, Christleton Road, Boughton TEL: 314798 PARKING: Easy OPEN: Mon-Sat 9.30-5 MIN: £50 MAX: £5000 PERIOD: 18th-20th century GENERAL: Good quality shipping & antique furniture.

**Dales of Chester,** 16 Christleton Road, Boughton, CH3 5UP TEL & FAX: 317737 PARKING: Easy OPEN: 10-5 MIN: £10 MAX: £5000 PERIOD: 18th-20th century SPECIALIST: Figures GENERAL: Furniture, china, copper, brass.

**Farmhouse Antiques**, 23 Christleton Road, Boughton TEL: 322478 PARKING: Medium OPEN: Mon-Sat 9-5 MIN: 1p MAX: £5850 PERIOD: 19th-20th century SPECIALIST: Early 19th century longcase clocks GENERAL: Country type stock, kitchenalia, Blue & White china, book sets, old golf clubs, mechanical music.

**Erica & Hugo Harper,** 31 Christleton Road TEL: 323004 PARKING: Medium OPEN: 10-4.45 MIN: 50p MAX: £50 GENERAL: China & bric a brac OTHER INFO: We have moved here after having a successful junk shop in Watergate Row for 30 years.

**Jamandic Ltd**, 22 Bridge Street Row, CH1 1NN TEL: 312822 FAX: 349756 ASSNS: Fellow Interior Designer & Decorators Association (IDDA) PARKING: Easy OPEN: Mon-Fri 9-5.30, Sat 10-1 MIN: £300 MAX: £20,000 PERIOD: 18th-20th century SPECIALIST: Decorative furniture and accessories.

**KAYES (M KAYE LTD)**
**9 ST MICHAELS ROW, CH1 1EF TEL: 327149 FAX: 318404 ASSNS: NAG PARKING: EASY OPEN: 9.30-5 MIN: £10 MAX: £20,000 PERIOD: 19TH-20TH CENTURY SPECIALIST: ENGLISH SILVER 1700-1939. JEWELLERY & RINGS 1870-1930. HIGHLY STOCKED IN EDWARDIAN & LATE VICTORIAN SILVER & JEWELLERY. HIGH VALUE IN GEM SET STOCK. OTHER INFO: CHESTER IS 'GROWING' TO BE WITHOUT DOUBT THE JEWELLERY & SILVER CITY OF THE NORTH. IN THE CENTRE IS THE BEAUTIFUL ST MICHAEL'S ARCADE, IN THE CENTRE OF WHICH IS OUR SHOP.**

**Lowe & Sons**, 11 Bridge Street Row, CH1 1PD TEL: 325850 FAX: 345536 ASSNS: NAG, CMJ PARKING: Medium OPEN: Mon-Sat 9.15-5.15 PERIOD: 18th-20th century SPECIALIST: Silver & jewellery OTHER INFO: An old Victorian shop with gallery. The company was established in 1770 & has been in these premises since 1804.

**Made of Honour**, 11 City Walls, CH1 1LD TEL: 314208 PARKING: Medium OPEN: Mon-Sat 10-5.30 MIN: £2 MAX: £1000 PERIOD: 18th-19th century SPECIALIST: English pottery & porcelain, Staffordshire figures, textiles, woodwork, beadworks GENERAL: Decorative & collectors items, books, prints & watercolours.

**Richard Nicholson of Chester**, 25 Watergate Street, CH1 2LB TEL: 326818 FAX: 336138 PARKING: Medium OPEN: Mon-Sat 10-1, 2.15-5 MIN: £1 MAX: £3000 PERIOD: 17th-20th century GENERAL: Antiquarian maps & prints OTHER INFO: Map catalogue subscription service.

**Richmond Galleries**, Ground floor, Watergate Buildings, New Crane Street, CH1 4JE TEL: 317602 PARKING: Easy OPEN: Mon-Sat 9.45-5.15 MIN: £20 MAX: £1000 PERIOD: 18th-20th century SPECIALIST: Antique pine, Spanish, French, country furniture & decorative items.

**Stothert Antiquarian Books**, 4 Nicholas Street, CH1 2NX TEL: 340756 OPEN: Mon-Sat 9.30-1, 2-5.30 MIN: 50p MAX: £1000 PERIOD: 17th-20th century GENERAL: Unusual books.

**Watergate Antiques**, 56 Watergate Street, CH1 2LD TEL: 344516 FAX: 320520 PARKING: Own carpark OPEN: Mon-Sat 9.30-5 MIN: £20 MAX: £12,000 PERIOD: 18th-19th century SPECIALIST: Silver & silver plate, ceramics GENERAL: Glass, militaria.

## WAVERTON (01244)

**J Alan Hulme**, 52 Mount Way, Waverton, CH3 7QF TEL: 336472 ASSNS: IMCOS PARKING: Easy OPEN: 9-8 by prior appt MIN: £1 MAX: £350 PERIOD: 17th-20th century SPECIALIST: UK county maps, engravings of topographical views, fashion, flowers, humour, birds, sporting, Vanity Fair.

## TATTENHALL (01829)

**Great Northern Architectural Antiques Co Ltd,** New Russia Hall, Chester Road, CH3 9AH TEL: 70796 FAX: 70971 PARKING: Own carpark OPEN: 7 days 9.30-4.30 MIN: £5 MAX: £10,000 PERIOD: 19th century SPECIALIST: Doors & sanitaryware GENERAL: Fireplaces, architectural antiques & reclaimed materials OTHER INFO: 15,000 sq ft of showrooms, pleasantly situated amongst some of Cheshire's best known attractions.

## BARTON (01829)

**Derek Rayment Antiques**, Orchard House, SY14 7HT TEL: 270429 ASSNS: BADA, LAPADA PARKING: Own carpark OPEN: Anytime by appt MIN: £60 MAX: £10,000+ PERIOD: 18th-19th century SPECIALIST: Only barometers.

## TILSTON (01829)

**Well House Antiques**, The Well House, SY14 7DP TEL: 250332 PARKING: Own carpark OPEN: Wed-Sat 9.30-4.30 & by appt (advisable to phone first) MIN: £5 MAX: £1000+ PERIOD: 18th-20th century GENERAL: General antiques OTHER INFO: Victorian parlour & garden on show.

## NANTWICH (01270)

**Rex Boyer Antiques**, Townwell House, 52 Welsh Row, CW5 5EJ TEL: 625953 ASSNS: LAPADA PARKING: Own carpark OPEN: Normal (resident) MIN: £50 MAX: £12,000 PERIOD: 18th-19th century SPECIALIST: English furniture.

**Chapel Antiques**, 47 Hospital Street, CW5 5RL TEL: 629508 PARKING: Easy OPEN: 9.30-5.30

closed Mon & Wed pm MIN: £5 MAX: £3500 PERIOD: 17th-19th century GENERAL: General antiques. Furniture repairs & restorations

**Roderick Gibson**, 70-72 Hospital Street, CW5 5RP TEL: 625301 FAX: 629603 ASSNS: LAPADA PARKING: Medium OPEN: Mon-Sat 9-5.30 MIN: £3 MAX: £3000 PERIOD: 18th-19th century GENERAL: Antique & reproduction furniture, smalls & garden statuary.

**Lions & Unicorns Commemoratives**, Kiltearn House, 33 Hospital Street, CW5 5RL TEL: 628892 FAX: 626646 ASSNS: Commemorative Collectors Club (CCC) PARKING: Own carpark OPEN: Anytime by appt MIN: £1 MAX: £350 PERIOD: 19th-20th century SPECIALIST: Commemoratives of the Royals & the famous in all mediums, china, glass, textiles, tin & paper GENERAL: General antiques OTHER INFO: Lamb Hotel, Crown Hote.

**Love Lane Antiques**, Love Lane TEL: 626239 PARKING: Easy OPEN: Mon, Tues, Thurs-Sat 10-5 GENERAL: General antiques & collectables.

**Nantwich Antiques,** The Manor House, 7 Beam Street, CW5 5LR TEL: 610615 FAX: 610637 OPEN: Mon-Sat 9-5 MIN: £1 MAX: £2500 PERIOD: 19th century SPECIALIST: Indian furniture & decorative items GENERAL: Country furniture.

**Nantwich Art Deco & Decorative Arts**, 87 Welsh Row, CW5 5ET TEL: 624876 PARKING: Easy OPEN: Mon, Thurs-Sat 10-5 MIN: £1 MAX: £300 PERIOD: 20th century SPECIALIST: Art Deco, ceramics. 1930's pottery, cabinets, mirrors.

**Richardson Antiques**, 89 Hospital Street, CW5 5RU TEL: 625963 PARKING: Easy OPEN: Mon-Sat 9.30-5.30 MIN: £1 MAX: £5000 PERIOD: 18th-19th century GENERAL: General antiques.

**Andrew Turner Antiques,** 54 Hospital Street, CW5 5RP TEL: 625009 PARKING: Easy OPEN: 10-5, closed Mon & Wed pm MIN: £10 MAX: £5000 PERIOD: 17th-19th century GENERAL: Silver, mostly pre 1830, furniture, pottery & porcelain.

**Wyche House Antiques**, The Old Surgery, 50 Welsh Row TEL: 627179 ASSNS: LAPADA PARKING: Easy MIN: £15 MAX: £10,000 PERIOD: 18th-20th century SPECIALIST: Cranberry Glass GENERAL: 17th-19th century furniture, 18th & 19th century china. Good selection of silver items.

## CREWE (01270)

**Steven Blackhurst**, 102 Edleston Road TEL: 258617, 665991 PARKING: Difficult OPEN: 9.30-5, closed Wed MIN: £10 MAX: £600 PERIOD: 19th-20th century GENERAL: Stripped pine, some reproduction pine, dried flowers etc OTHER INFO: Good chiropodist near, useful for hikers!

## ALSAGER (01270)

**Forest Books of Cheshire**, The Bookshop Upstairs, 14b Lawton Road, ST7 2AF TEL: 882618 PARKING: Easy OPEN: Tues, Sat 11-5.30, Thurs, Fri 11-7, closed bank hols & fortnight in Feb and Aug MIN: £1 MAX: £900 PERIOD: 19th-20th century SPECIALIST: British wildlife, agriculture, gardening, birds, fishing, drama GENERAL: Wide but emphasis on history & other higher educations OTHER INFO: Some print & paper emphemera.

# Manchester to Liverpool

This tour of North Cheshire, Lancashire and Merseyside encompasses the cradle of the Industrial Revolution and visits the towns and cities that grew and prospered in the 19th century. Today, unfortunately, some of these are in decline as they have lost their main industries and now struggle to find new paths to prosperity.

**Warrington** in Cheshire, first, was the site of a settlement in pre-Roman times thanks to its situation on a crossing point on the River Mersey. The Romans also settled here but little remains of their occupation. The town became prosperous in the 18th and 19th century and has left a legacy of fine houses from that period. The museum in Bold Street displays collections of natural history, geology, ethnology and Egyptology. It also contains exhibits relating to the prehistoric, Roman and later local history.

The route continues along the A56 to the pretty village of **Bowdon**, mentioned in the Domesday Book, and then to the ancient borough of **Altrincham**, granted its charter in 1290, although there is nothing left to see of that distant past. The National Trust property of Dunham Massey stands 3 miles to the south west of the town. This fine 18th century house has a good collection of Huguenot silver, furniture and family portraits and is set in a lovely garden and deer park.

**Cheadle Hulme** and **Bramhall** act as residential suburbs for Manchester and the next stop, **Stockport**. Standing on the junction of the rivers Tame and Goyt, there has been a settlement here since Roman times. The town really began to grow in the 13th century when a weekly market was started. In the 19th century the Industrial Revolution brought prosperity but also great misery to the working people, documented by Frederick Engels in his classic work. The mill chimneys, once such a feature, were immortalised by L.S. Lowry in his paintings. Stockport Museum in Turncroft Lane has displays on the history of the town from prehistoric times to the present day.

**Manchester** is one of the great English cities. It still retains some of the magnificent Victorian commercial and industrial buildings built at the height of its prosperity as the primary centre in Lancashire for coal and cotton. Great expansion occurred during the 18th and 19th centuries with the Industrial Revolution. This was further encouraged by the opening of the Manchester Ship Canal in 1894, connecting the city to Liverpool.

The Industrial Revolution might have brought wealth to the few but it increased the poverty and misery of the masses living in filthy slums and working in appalling conditions. By 1819 calls for Parliamentary reform had increased considerably. At that time only the landed classes were represented in Parliament and the growing industrial cities like Manchester had no representation at all. Parliament would do nothing to help the desperate working classes so, in the eyes of many, it was thought Parliament should be changed. Agitation and demonstrations grew, *Habeas Corpus* was suspended and seditious meetings were banned. This caused a fresh wave of demonstrations throughout the country.

All this discontent and unrest culminated, on the 16th August 1819, with the Peterloo Massacre. On that date a crowd of some 80,000 people gathered on St Peter's Fields in Manchester to hear a Radical speaker. The crowd was peaceful and contained many women and children. On seeing the size of the crowd the magistrates panicked and read the Riot Act and then ordered the yeomanry to arrest the speaker. They, in their turn, also panicked and charged the crowd with sabres which resulted in eleven people killed and hundreds injured. The name Peterloo was given as an ironic reference to the Battle of Waterloo four years earlier.

During the 19th century, Manchester's prosperity continued unchecked. The great Gothic town hall, covering nearly two acres and completed in 1877, stands as a monument to the Victorian industrialists. The city was badly damaged during the Second World War but other great Victorian buildings also survive. The City Art Gallery, in Mosley Street, was designed by Sir Charles Barry, who also designed the Houses of Parliament. Originally the building was the headquarters of the Royal Manchester Institution for the Promotion of Literature, Science and the Arts.

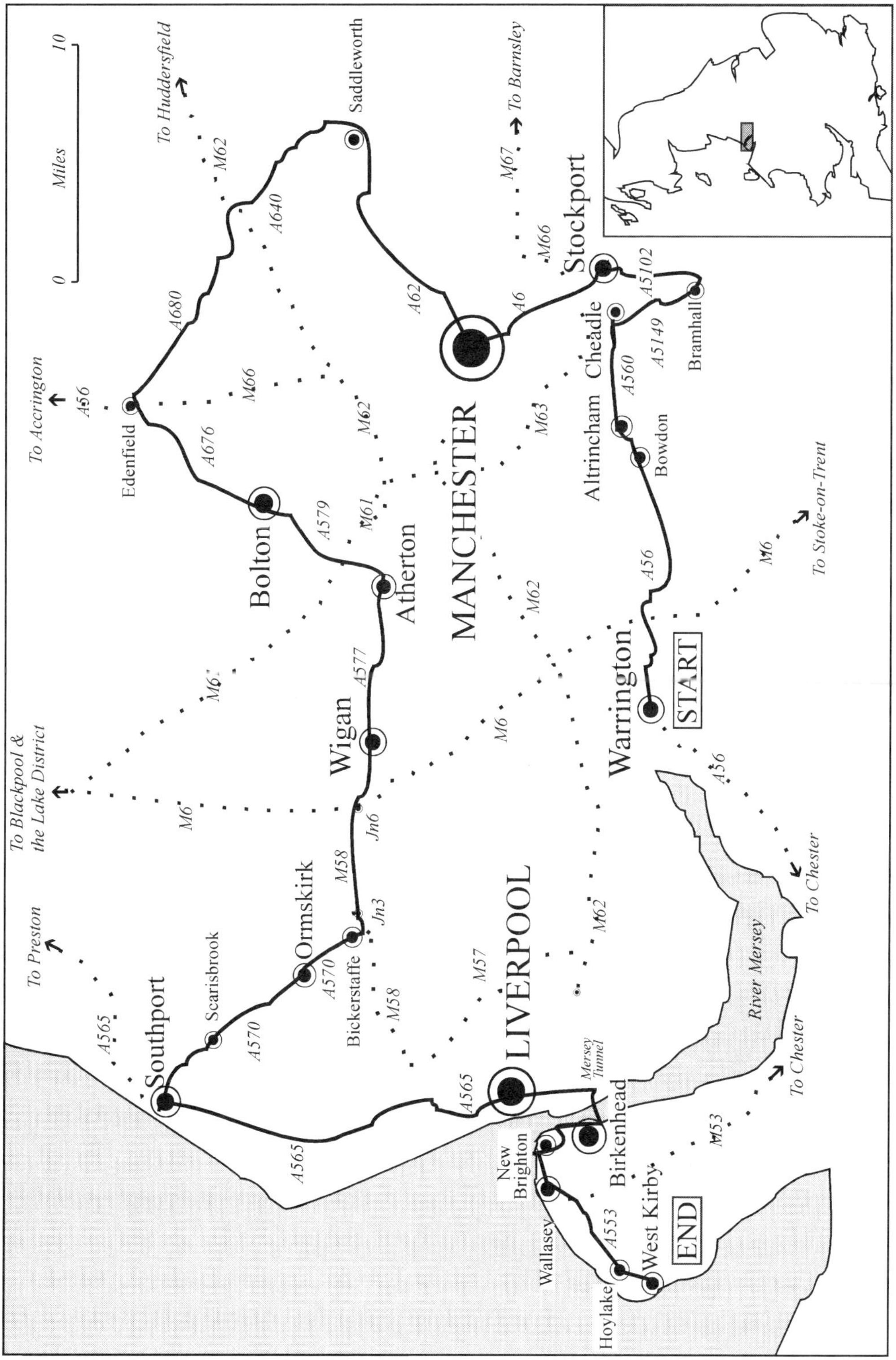
Miles
0
10
To Huddersfield
M62
Saddleworth
To Barnsley
M67
M66
Stockport
A640
A680
A62
A6
A5102
Bramhall
A5149
Cheadle
A560
To Accrington
A56
M66
Edenfield
A676
MANCHESTER
M62
M63
Altrincham
Bowdon
Bolton
A579
M61
Atherton
A56
To Stoke-on-Trent
M6
M62
Warrington
START
A577
M61
Wigan
M6
To Blackpool & the Lake District
M6
Jn6
M58
A56
To Chester
Ormskirk
Jn3
LIVERPOOL
M62
To Preston
Scarisbrook
A570
Bickerstaffe
M58
M57
River Mersey
A565
Southport
A570
A565
Mersey Tunnel
Birkenhead
To Chester
M53
A565
New Brighton
Wallasey
A553
West Kirby
END
Hoylake

Now it contains an extremely fine and important collection of pictures including works by Turner, Gainsborough, Stubbs, Boucher, etc. There is also a good collection of Pre-Raphaelite and Victorian paintings. There are many other fine museums and galleries. An unusual one is the Greater Manchester Police Museum in Newton Street. This is set in a Victorian police station and features a reconstructed 1920s Charge Office, cells and collections of uniforms and other exhibits.

Manchester is also a city of culture. Its major theatre, in the Royal Exchange, puts on many plays just before they go to the West End of London. The Free Trade Hall, extensively damaged by bombing in the Second World War but now rebuilt, is the home of the world famous Hallé Orchestra. The city also had the first free library in Europe, the Chetham Library opened in 1656 funded by a bequest from Humphrey Chetham. The John Rylands Library, also originally funded by a local family, has an amazing collection of medieval books including a Gutenburg Bible, books printed by William Caxton and manuscripts dating back to 3000BC. Additionally it has a superb collection of jewelled medieval bindings. Manchester's third great library, the Central Library, is reputed to have one of the largest collections of books in the country.

The city's Victorian splendour can blind the visitor to its older attractions. Manchester Cathedral dates from the 15th century and was built for a college of priests to pray for for souls of benefactors. The church was restored and enlarged when it became a cathedral in 1847 but much of the older fabric survives in spite of a damage caused by a landmine during the Second World War. The choir stalls are particularly fine examples of 16th century woodcarving. The medieval shopping streets of The Shambles were destroyed by bombing but the 14th century Wellington Inn has survived and now stands incongruously surrounded by modern shops.

Leaving Manchester the tour visits **Saddleworth, Edenfield** and then **Bolton**. For many years, Bolton meant cotton; it was one of the great Lancashire centres for fine weaving and spinning of cotton. Two important inventions of the Industrial Revolution were made by residents of the town: the spinning mule by Samuel Crompton and the water frame by Arkwright. These helped to revolutionise the cotton industry.

Two miles north east of the centre stands Hall i' th' Wood, the 15th century home of Samuel Crompton now containing some of his relics. The house is very picturesque and interesting in its own right. Built in 1483 in the post and plaster style, extensions were added in 1591 and 1648. Samuel Crompton was living here in the last quarter of the 18th century.

One and a half miles out is another very old and interesting house, Smithills Hall. This is one of the oldest manor houses in Lancashire and a house has stood on this site since the 14th century. The Great Hall has an open timber roof and is the oldest part of the building which has been added to and improved over the centuries giving it a most attractive, if haphazard, appearance.

Back in the town, the Old Man and Scythe inn dates from the 13th century and it was here, in October 1641, that the Earl of Derby was put up for the night by Cromwell before being beheaded next day in the market place in retaliation for a Royalist massacre.

**Atherton** comes next, then **Wigan**, once an important coal-mining town but still dating back to Roman times. It was made famous by George Orwell's book, *The Road to Wigan Pier*. The pier in question was a wharf on the Leeds to Liverpool canal and is now the site of a living museum dedicated to showing local life at the turn of the century and includes a Victorian schoolroom, a music hall and working steam engines.

The tour now visits **Bickerstaffe** and then **Ormskirk** which received its charter as a market town in 1286 although very few ancient buildings survive. It does have some Georgian houses in Burscough Street including the fine Knowles House built in the 1770s. The local church of St Peter and St Paul is unusual in having both a tower and a spire side by side. The tower is 15th century while the spire was built about a hundred years later. There is a 12th century window in the chancel and four 15th century effigies.

The route now heads for the coast via **Scarisbrook** to arrive in **Southport**, an attractive seaside resort with miles of sandy beach and beautiful public gardens. As the home of the Royal

Birkdale Golf Course, it is known for its golf. The Atkinson Art Gallery in Lord Street has displays of art from the 18th to 20th centuries as well as collection of English glass and Chinese porcelain. The Botanic Gardens Museum in Churchtown has exhibits of local history, natural history, Victoriana, dolls and Liverpool porcelain.

Following the A565, **Liverpool** is next. The city started as a small settlement on the north bank of the Mersey in the 1st century AD, by the 12th century it had grown into a busy fishing port when granted a charter by King John. However, the port's trade with the Indies and the Americas in the 17th and 18th centuries brought real prosperity. Initially the trade was in sugar and slaves but, with the coming of steam ships, the port expanded further until, at its height, Liverpool had seven miles of docks and was the terminus for Cunard and White Star liners.

The best known landmark is the Royal Liver Building on the banks of the Mersey. It has two cathedrals, one Anglican completed in 1978, and the other Roman Catholic, finished in 1967. Another building of note is St George's Hall, described as the finest example of the Greco-Roman style in Europe, which was built in 1854. Liverpool Town Hall, completed in 1754, was designed by John Wood who also designed many of the elegant buildings in Bath.

As might be expected, there are many interesting museums and galleries. The Walker Art Gallery is said to be one of the finest in Europe with collections of European art from the 14th century to the present day and includes work by Rubens, Rembrandt, Poussin, Monet, Seurat and Degas. The Museum of Labour History is housed in the former Sessions House and is devoted to the last 150 years of working class life on Merseyside. Then there is the award-winning Merseyside Maritime Museum on Albert Dock with floating exhibits and working displays. This museum tells the story of Liverpool from small hamlet to major international port.

The city also has a number of historic houses. In the centre Bluecoat Chambers is a fine Queen Anne building with a cobbled quadrangle. Next there is Croxteth Hall and Rare Breeds Centre five miles north east of the city centre and set in a 500 acre country park with a superb collection of animals. Perhaps the best known of the ancient buildings is Speke Hall near the city's airport. This is an Elizabethan half-timbered house built around a courtyard. Its attractions include the Great Hall, priest holes, Jacobean plasterwork and extensive gardens and woodlands.

Now using the Mersey Tunnel, the tour crosses to the Wirral peninsula and **Birkenhead**, originally a small village built around a 12th century priory. It began to grow when the Laird shipbuilding yards were opened in 1824 and the docks in 1847. Nearby **New Brighton** stands on the mouth of the Mersey and has developed as a seaside resort and residential area. Neighbouring **Wallasey** is largely an extension of Birkenhead and the two towns are only separated by the docks. The tour continues to **Hoylake**, a settlement in pre-Roman times. Now it is a pleasant holiday resort with sandy beaches and safe bathing. The last stop is in **West Kirby**, also on the coast and offering bathing beaches and golf.

## ANTIQUE DEALERS

### WARRINGTON (01925)

**A Baker & Sons**, 10 Cairo Street, WA1 1ED TEL: 33706 FAX: 33706 ASSNS: NAG PARKING: Medium OPEN: 9.30-4.50 MIN: £10 MAX: £10,000 SPECIALIST: 18th-19th century vinaigrettes GENERAL: 19th-20th silver & jewellery OTHER INFO: 86 years in same family. Royal Garden Hotel, Lord Daresbury Hotel.

**The Rocking Chair Antiques**, Unit 3, St Peters Way, WA2 7BL TEL: 652409 FAX: 652409 PARKING: Easy OPEN: 9-5 GENERAL: Shipping items 1900-1930.

**Victoriana Antiques**, 85a Walton Road, Stockton Heath TEL: 263263, 261035 PARKING: Own carpark OPEN: Tues-Wed, Fri-Sat 1-5 & by appt MIN: £5 MAX: £1500+ PERIOD: 18th-20th century SPECIALIST: Antique metals (fireside furniture, decorative items). 1900-1930 lighting GENERAL: Smaller items of furniture 1800-1930 OTHER INFO: Birthplace of Lewis Carroll.

### BOWDON (0161)

**Eureka Antiques**

**7A Church Brow, WA14 2SF TEL: 926 9722 PARKING: Medium OPEN: By appt MIN: £10 MAX: £12,000 PERIOD: 19th century SPECIALIST: Agate jewellery, Tartanware, 19th century furniture GENERAL: Coloured glass, antique collectables, snuff, patch boxes, etc. OTHER INFO: Also 105 Portobello Rd, London W8 Sats only.**

### ALTRINCHAM (0161)

**Altrincham Antiques**, 39 Hale Road, WA14 2EY TEL: 941 3554, (0836) 316366 FAX: 941 3554 PARKING: Own carpark OPEN: Mon-Sun 10-6 MIN: £5 MAX: £5000 PERIOD: 19th-20th century SPECIALIST: Mixed as well as the unusual OTHER INFO: Prop hire. The mere fact that I am in this trade is of great amusement to my bank manager!

**Cottage Antiques**, Rose Cottage, Hasty Lane, Hales Barn, Ringway, WA15 8UT TEL: 980 7961 PARKING: Own carpark OPEN: Mon-Sat 9-6 & by appt MIN: £5 MAX: £10,000 PERIOD: 17th-20th century GENERAL: General antiques OTHER INFO: 5 mins Manchester Airport, 1 min from M56, J6 & 5 major hotels. Tatton Park House & Gardens, Dunham Park House & Gardens, Warry Bank Mill.

**Halo Antiques**, Charles Madan Building, Atlantic Street WA14 5DA TEL: 941 1800 FAX: 929 9565 PARKING: Own carpark OPEN: 8-6 MIN: £100 MAX: £2000 SPECIALIST: Pine from reclaimed timber only. Massive stocks OTHER INFO: Trade only. By appointment only.

**Robert Redford Antiques & Interiors,** 48 New Street, WA14 2QS TEL: 929 8171 PARKING: Easy OPEN: 10-6, closed Mon & Weds MIN: £10 MAX: £2500 PERIOD: 19th century GENERAL: Small furniture, silver, porcelain, glass, items of interest, clocks OTHER INFO: We also run an excellent B&B in a large Victorian house close to the town centre.

**Squires Antiques**, 25 Regent Road, WA14 1RX TEL: 928 0749 PARKING: Own carpark OPEN: Tues, Thurs-Sat 10-5 MIN: £10 PERIOD: 19th-20th century SPECIALIST: Small silver & decorative items, gifts GENERAL: General antiques.

### CHEADLE HULME (0161)

**Allan's Antiques**, 10 Ravenoak Road, SK8 7DL TEL: 485 3132 PARKING: Medium OPEN: Mon, Tues, Thurs-Sat 10-1, 2-5 MIN: £1 MAX: £5000 PERIOD: 18-20th century SPECIALIST: Silver esp. cutlery GENERAL: Furniture, smalls OTHER INFO: Near one of UK's finest half timbered buildings, Millington Hall, 17th century restaurant.

### STOCKPORT (0161)

**ER Antiques Centre**, 122 Wellington Street (off Wellington Road), SK1 1YH TEL: 429 6646, home 480 5598 PARKING: Medium OPEN: Mon-Sat 12-5.30, Weds pm only MIN: £1 MAX: £250+ PERIOD: 19th-20th century SPECIALIST: Pressed & cut coloured glass, Victorian collectables GENERAL: Aladdin's cave of small gift items: jewellery, costume, real curios 1870-1930's, silver + plate, lots of Blue & White OTHER INFO: 6 dealers. We adore cats & stock Winstanleys. Owner is a clairvoyant & psychometrist.

**Halcyon Antiques**, 435 Buxton Road, Great Moor, SK2 7HE TEL: 483 5038 PARKING: Easy OPEN: Mon-Sat 10-5 MIN: £1 MAX: £2000 PERIOD: 18th-20th century GENERAL: Porcelain, glass, silver, furniture, jewellery, linen, pictures.

**Highland Antiques Export,** 67 Wellington Road North, SK4 2LP TEL: 476 6660 FAX: 476 6669 PARKING: Own carpark OPEN: Mon-Sat 9-5 MIN: £5 MAX: £13,000 PERIOD: 18th-20th century SPECIALIST: Japanese & Oriental GENERAL: Silver & plate, Persian carpets, paintings, English pottery, etc.

**Howarth Antiques**, 147 Wellington Road North, Heaton Norris TEL: 443 1096 FAX: 443 1096 PARKING: Easy OPEN: Mon-Sat 10-5, Sun 11.30-5 MIN: £20 MAX: £2000 PERIOD: 18th-20th century SPECIALIST: Chaise longues GENERAL: From bric-a-brac to dining suites.

**Imperial Antiques**, 295 Buxton Road, Great Moor, SK2 7NR TEL: 483 3322 FAX: 483 3322 ASSNS: LAPADA PARKING: Easy OPEN: 9.30-5 MIN: £10 MAX: £5000 PERIOD: 18th-20th century SPECIALIST: Oriental and Persian carpets GENERAL: Silver + plate ware.

**Limited Editions**, 35 King Street East, SK1 1XJ TEL: 480 1239 PARKING: Own carpark OPEN: Mon-Wed, Fri-Sat 9.45-6 MIN: £5 MAX: £20,000 PERIOD: 18th-20th century SPECIALIST: 50+ tables & set of chairs GENERAL: Furniture & upholstery, some smalls OTHER INFO: Full restoration facilities available including upholstery.

**Nostalgia,** 61 Shaw Heath, SK3 8BH Tel: 477 7706 PARKING: Own carpark PERIOD: 18th-18th century SPECIALIST: Marble chimneypieces GENERAL: Complete range of antique fireplaces, in excess of 1000 in stock.

**Page Antiques**, 424 Buxton Road, Great Moor TEL: 483 9202 PARKING: Own carpark OPEN: 10-5.30 MIN: £1 MAX: £3000 PERIOD: 18th-20th century SPECIALIST: Furniture GENERAL: Silver, china, metalware, etc.

## BRAMHALL (0161)

**David H Dickinson Antiques & Fine Art**, P.O.Box 29, SK7 2EJ TEL: 440 0688 ASSNS: LAPADA PARKING: Own carpark OPEN: Strictly by appt only MIN: £500 MAX: £50,000 PERIOD: 18th-19th century SPECIALIST: Extraordinary works of art & decoration GENERAL: For interior decorator trade OTHER INFO: Near Manchester Airport.

## MANCHESTER (0161)

**Antique Fireplaces,** 1090 Stockport Road, Levenshulme M19 2US TEL: 431 8075 OPEN: 7 days 9-6 MIN: £150 MAX: £1000 PERIOD: 19th-20th century SPECIALIST: Fireplaces.

**AS Antique Galleries**, 26 Broad Street, Pendleton, Salford, M6 5BY TEL: 737 5938 FAX: 737 6626 PARKING: Easy OPEN: Normal MIN: £50 MAX: £10,000 PERIOD: 19th-20th century SPECIALIST: Enormous stock Art Nouveau, Arts & Crafts, Art Deco, bronzes, ivories, glass, furniture, silver etc GENERAL: Victorian & earlier furniture, lighting, metalware OTHER INFO: 5 mins drive from city centre.

**Bulldog Antiques**, 393 Bury New Road, Prestwich, M25 8UB TEL: 798 9277, home 790 7153 PARKING: Easy OPEN: Mon-Sat 10.30-5.30 MIN: £25 MAX: £10,000 PERIOD: 18th-20th century SPECIALIST: Furniture, clocks GENERAL: General antiques OTHER INFO: Local period tavern, B&B, 15th century with good food.

**Henry Donn Gallery**, 138-142 Bury New Road, Whitefield, M45 6AD TEL: 766 8819 ASSNS: FATG PARKING: Own carpark OPEN: Mon-Sat 9.30-5.15 MIN: £25 MAX: £10,000 PERIOD: 20th century SPECIALIST: Modern British GENERAL: Oils, watercolours, pastels, sculpture OTHER INFO: The largest private gallery in the north west, area equals 3 shops with displays on 2 floors. Framing, valuations, restoration.

**Failsworth Mill Antiques**, Ashton Road West, Failsworth, M35 0ER TEL: 684 7440 PARKING: Own carpark OPEN: Mon-Fri 9-5 MIN: £5 MAX: £10,000 PERIOD: 18th-20th century GENERAL: Former cotton mill now with 50,000 sq ft antique & French furniture, architectural antiques.

**Forest Books in Manchester**, The Ginnel Gallery, 18-22 Lloyd Street, M2 5WA TEL: 834 0747 PARKING: Medium OPEN: Mon-Sat 10-5.30 MIN: £1 MAX: £1000 PERIOD: 17th-20th century SPECIALIST: Collecting, drama. art history, local interests, drama, attractive literature GENERAL: Prints, pictures, postcards OTHER INFO: Next to Town Hall & Granada Studios.

**Garson & Co Ltd**, 47 Houldsworth Street, Piccadilly, M1 2ES TEL: 236 9393 FAX: 236 4211 PARKING:Own carpark OPEN: Mon-Fri 8-5 MIN: £20 MAX: £50,000 PERIOD: 17th-20th century SPECIALIST: Carved gold French mirrors, tables GENERAL: Backgammon, bronzes, paintings, prints, watercolours, telescopes, private chapel altars, books etc OTHER INFO: Clients' comments: 'Another world, mindboggling, too much to see in one trip'

**The Ginnel Gallery Antique Centre**, Basement, 18-22 Lloyd Street, M2 5WA TEL: 833 9037 PARKING: Medium OPEN: Mon-Sat 9.30-5.30 MIN: £2 MAX: £5000 PERIOD: 17th-20th century SPECIALIST: Art Deco, antiquarian books, 1950's & 60's GENERAL: Furniture, pottery, glass, books OTHER INFO: Large city site with restaurant.

**Kenworthys Ltd,** 226 Stamford Street, Ashton-under-Lyme, OL6 7LW TEL: 330 3043 ASSNS: BADA PARKING: Easy OPEN: Mon-Sat 10-5, closed Tues MIN: £5 MAX: 15,000 PERIOD: 17th-20th century GENERAL: Jewellery, silver.

**Levenshulme Antique Village,** 965 Stockport Road, Levenshulme TEL: 956 4644 PARKING: Own carpark OPEN: 7 days 10-5 MIN: £5 MAX: £5000 PERIOD: 19th-20th century GENERAL: Furniture, bric a brac, all aspects of antique & pine OTHER INFO: We have a courtyard with pine stripping services and a cafeteria with home cooked food.

**Manchester Antique Company**, 95 Lapwing Lane, West Didsbury TEL: 434 7752 PARKING: Own carpark OPEN: Mon-Sat 9.30-5 MIN: £20 MAX: £35,000 PERIOD 17th-20th century SPECIALIST: Continental furniture, Dutch marqetry GENERAL: 35,000 sq ft of shipping goods to period furniture etc. Vast stock of walnut OTHER INFO: 5 mins city centre, lawn tennis club opposite.

**Marks Antiques**, 16 Waterloo Street, Oldham, OL1 1SQ TEL: 624 5975 FAX: 624 5975 PARKING: Easy OPEN: Mon-Sat 9.30-5 MIN: £50 MAX: £1000 PERIOD: 17th-20th century SPECIALIST: Jewellery GENERAL: Furniture, porcelain OTHER INFO: Also Marks Pawnbrokers. Spend £500 and also spend the night in our 17th century Manor House.

**Village Antiques**, 416 Bury New Road, Prestwich M25 5BD TEL: 773 3612 PARKING: Easy OPEN: Mon-Sat 10-5 but Wed 10-1 MIN: £5 MAX: £2500 PERIOD: 17th-20th century GENERAL: Furniture, antiques OTHER INFO: Browsers welcome.

## SADDLEWORTH (01457)

**Oldfield Cottage Antiques,** Queen Anne Gallery, 64 High Street, Uppermill, Saddleworth, OL3 6HA TEL: 874728 FAX: 0161-628 2812 PARKING: Easy OPEN: Mon, Weds-Sat 9.30-5.30, Tues & Sun 11-5 MIN: £1 MAX: £1000 PERIOD: 20th century SPECIALIST: Pine furniture & kitchenalia OTHER INFO: Uppermill is a major tourist attraction with many unusual shops to browse in, a museum, canal barge trips, etc.

## EDENFIELD (01706)

**The Antique Shop**, 17 Market Street, BL0 0JA TEL: 823107, 822351 PARKING: Easy OPEN: Mon-Sat 10-4 MIN: £5 MAX: £5,000 PERIOD: 18th-20th century GENERAL: General antiques items OTHER INFO: Close to M66-J1. Local steam train, theatre, trout farm, 10pin bowling.

## BOLTON (01204)

**Bolton Antiques Centre**, Central Street, BL1 2AB TEL: 362694 PARKING: Easy OPEN: Mon-Sat 10-5, Sun 11-4.30 PERIOD: 19th century GENERAL: Antiques, collectables, jewellery.

**Drop Dial Antiques,** Last Drop Village, Hospital Road, Bromley Cross BL7 9PZ TEL: 307186 PARKING: Own carpark OPEN: Every afternoon except Mon or by appt MIN: £120 PERIOD: 18th-20th century SPECIALIST: Clocks OTHER INFO: Within an hotel complex offering a restaurant, teashop & Sunday antiques market.

**G Oakes & Son**, 160-162 Blackburn Road, BL1 8DR TEL: 26587 PARKING: Easy OPEN: Mon-Sat 9-5 MIN: £5 MAX: £1500 PERIOD: 19th-20th century SPECIALIST: Shipping goods GENERAL: Antiques, Victorian, quality 20th century furniture.

**Park Galleries Antiques & Fine Art**, BL1 4SJ TEL: 529827, (0161) 7645853 PARKING: Easy OPEN: Thurs-Sat 11-5 & anytime by appt MIN: £5 MAX: £4000 PERIOD: 17th-early 20th century SPECIALIST: Antique & period furniture GENERAL: Porcelain, pottery, metalware, miniatures, decoratives, 19th century oils.

**Tiffany Antiques**, Bolton Antique Centre, Central Street, BL1 2AB TEL: 362694, home (01270) 257425 PARKING: Easy OPEN: Seven days 9.30-5 MIN: £3 MAX: £300 PERIOD: 19th-20th century GENERAL: Collectables, ceramics, glass OTHER INFO: La Curio café in antique centre.

## ATHERTON (01942)

**Victoria's**, 144-146 Bolton Road TEL: 882311 PARKING: Easy OPEN: Mon-Sat 10-5.30 MIN: £2 MAX: £2000 PERIOD: 19th century SPECIALIST: Pine & furniture GENERAL: Cornucopia.

## WIGAN (01942)

**Colin de Rouffignac**, 57 Wigan Lane, WN1 2LF

TEL: 37927 ASSNS: BNTA PARKING: Easy OPEN: Mon, Tues, Thurs-Sat 10-5 MIN: £5 MAX: £10,000 PERIOD: 18th-20th century SPECIALIST: Paintings GENERAL: Jewellery, furniture.

**Whatnot Antiques**, 90 Wigan Lane, WN1 2LF TEL: 491880 PARKING: Easy OPEN: Mon, Tues, Thurs-Fri 10-5, Sat 2-5 MIN: £1 MAX: £2000 PERIOD: 17th-20th century GENERAL: Good range of general antiques OTHER INFO: A visit to Wigan Pier a must.

## BICKERSTAFFE (01695)

**EW Webster Antiques**, Wash Farm, L39 0HG TEL: 24326 FAX: 50363 PARKING: Own carpark OPEN: Anytime by appt PERIOD: 1680-1830 GENERAL: Georgian furniture, needlework, decorative items.

## ORMSKIRK (01695)

**Alan Grice Antiques**. 106 Aughton Street, L39 3BS TEL: 572007 PARKING: Own carpark OPEN: Mon-Sat 10-6 MIN: £80 MAX: £3500 PERIOD: 17th-20th century SPECIALIST: English furniture.

## SCARISBRICK (01704)

**Carr Cross Gallery**, Southport Road TEL: 880638 PARKING: Easy OPEN: Mon-Sat 10-5 MIN: £50 MAX: £2000 PERIOD: 18th-19th century SPECIALIST: Fireplaces, architectural antiques.

## SOUTHPORT (01704)

**CK Broadhurst & Co Ltd**, 5-7 Market Street, PR8 1HD TEL: 532064, 534110 FAX: 542009 ASSNS: ABA, PBFA PARKING: Easy OPEN: Mon-Sat 9-5.30 MIN: £1 MAX: £5000+ PERIOD: 18th-20th century SPECIALIST: Art, architecture, modern firsts, topography, private press. GENERAL: All subjects.

**Decor Galleries**, 52 Lord Street, PR8 1QB TEL: 535734 PARKING: Easy OPEN: Mon-Sat 9.30-5 MIN: £150 MAX: £4000 PERIOD: 19th-20th century SPECIALIST: Furniture, lamps GENERAL: 19th century antiques, decorative fittings, fabrics.

**The Spinning Wheel Antiques,** 1 Liverpool Road, Birkdale, PR8 4AR TEL: 568245 & 567613 PARKING: Easy OPEN: 10.30-5, closed Tues MIN: £1 MAX: £2000 PERIOD: 19th-20th century SPECIALIST: Old golf, coins, banknotes.

**Tony Sutcliffe Antiques,** 37A Linaker Street TEL: 537068 & 533465 PARKING: Own carpark OPEN: 8.30-5 MIN: £10 MAX: £2500 PERIOD: 19th-20th century GENERAL: Victorian & shipping goods for Japan.

## LIVERPOOL (0151)

**Architectural Antiques**, 60 St Johns Road, Waterloo, L22 9GQ TEL: 949 0819 PARKING: Easy OPEN: Mon-Sat 10-5 MIN: £50 MAX: £3000 PERIOD: 18th-19th century SPECIALIST: Antique fireplaces GENERAL: Stripped pine, panel, doors, rolltop baths, Belfast sinks OTHER INFO: 5 mins seafront. Everchanging stock.

**Edwards**, 45a Whitechapel, L1 6DT TEL: 236 2909 ASSNS: FGA PARKING: Medium OPEN: Mon-Fri 10-4 MAX: £500 PERIOD: 19th-20th century SPECIALIST: Jewellery or silver OTHER INFO: In city centre.

**Lyver & Boydell Galleries**, 15 Castle Street, L2 4SX TEL: 236 3256 ASSNS: LAPADA, FATG PARKING: Medium OPEN: Mon-Sat 10.30-5.30 MIN: £5 MAX: £10,000 PERIOD: 18th-20th century SPECIALIST: Victorian and earlier oils & watercolours GENERAL: Antique maps & prints OTHER INFO: Conservation area in city centre. Close to famous Albert Dock.

**Magg's Antiques Ltd**, 26-28 Fleet Street, L1 4AR TEL: 708 0221 FAX: 708 0221 PARKING: Medium OPEN: Mon-Fri 9-5 MIN: £20 MAX: £2000 PERIOD: 17th-19th century SPECIALIST: Chests of drawers GENERAL: Victorian & Edwardian furniture, 1920's Shipping goods.

**E Pryor & Son,** 110 London Road, L3 5NL TEL: 709 1361 ASSNS: NAG, BJA PARKING: Medium OPEN: 8-4, closed Wed MIN: £20 MAX: £5000 PERIOD: 18th-20th century SPECIALIST: Largest collection of silver in the area GENERAL: Jewellery, porcelain, pottery, coins, paintings OTHER INFO: St George's Hall, one of the most architecturally beautiful buildings in the country, is just 400 yards away.

**Ryan-Wood Antiques**, 102 Seel Street, L1 4BT TEL: 709 7776 FAX: 709 3203 PARKING: Easy OPEN: Mon-Sat 9.30-5 MIN: £5 MAX: £15,000 PERIOD: 18th-20th century GENERAL: Furniture, glass, china, silver & plate, pictures OTHER INFO: Close to tourist attractions, art galleries etc.

**Stefani Antiques,** 497 Smithdown Road, L15 5AE TEL: 734 1932 PARKING: Easy OPEN: 10-5.30 PERIOD: 17th-20th century GENERAL: Furniture, silver, pottery, porcelain, jewellery, Art Deco &

Nouveau OTHER INFO: 2 mins from Penny Lane.
**Swainbank's Ltd,** 50-56 Fox Street, L3 3BQ & Christchurch, 170 Kensington, L7 2RJ TEL & FAX: 260 9466 PARKING: Easy OPEN: Mon-Fri 9-5 MIN: £10 PERIOD: 19th century GENERAL: Furniture & bric a brac.

## BIRKENHEAD (0151)

**Bodhouse Antiques**, 379 Newchester Road, L62 9AB TEL & FAX: 644 9494 PARKING: Own carpark OPEN: Mon-Fri 9-5 & by appt MIN £:10 MAX: £4000 PERIOD: 19th century SPECIALIST: Inlaid furniture GENERAL: General antiques OTHER INFO: Fluent Italian, good knowledge other European languages, packing, courier service.

## NEW BRIGHTON (0151)

**Arbiter**, 10 Atherton Street TEL: L45 2NY TEL: 639 1159 PARKING: Easy OPEN: Tues-Sat 1-5 or by appt MIN: £10 MAX: £1000+ PERIOD: 3500 BC-1970's SPECIALIST: Oriental & ethnic, Arts and Crafts movement including good Art Deco, named items and small antiquities OTHER INFO: Past president China Trade Society.

## WALLASEY (0151)

**Decade Antiques,** 62 Grove Road, L45 3HW TEL: 638 0433 PARKING: Easy OPEN: 10.30-5 MIN: £5 MAX: £1500 PERIOD: 19th-20th century GENERAL: Decorative antiques, textiles, Continental furniture OTHER INFO: Near seafront, 15 mins from Albert Dock, Liverpool, 20 mins from the Lady Lever Gallery, Port Sunlight with its wonderful collection of furniture in a period set-up.
**Victoria Antiques,** 155-157 Brighton Street, L44 8DU TEL: 639 0080 PARKING: Easy OPEN: 6 days 9.30-5.30 MIN: £15 MAX: £2000 PERIOD: 19th century GENERAL: Furniture.

## HOYLAKE (0151)

**The Clock Shop**, The Quadrant, L47 2EE TEL: 632 1888 ASSNS: BHI, BWCMG PARKING: Easy OPEN: Mon-Fri 9-5, Sat 10-2 MIN: £20 MAX: £4000 PERIOD: 18th-20th century SPECIALIST: Clocks & barometers GENERAL: Jewellery OTHER INFO: 5 mins Royal Liverpool Golf.
**Hoylake Antique Centre,** 128-130 Market Street, L47 3BH TEL: 632 4231 PARKING: Easy OPEN: 9.15-5.30, closed Wed MIN: £10 MAX: £1500 PERIOD: 19th century SPECIALIST: 18th century porcelain GENERAL: Furniture, ceramics, pictures.
**Market Antiques**, 80 Market Street, L47 3BB TEL: 632 4059 FAX: 632 4059 PARKING: Easy OPEN: Thurs, Fri 10-1, 2.15-5, Sat 10-5 MIN: £1 MAX: £2000 PERIOD: 17th-20th century SPECIALIST: Furniture GENERAL: Small range of furnishings OTHER INFO: Good sunsets.

## WEST KIRBY (0151)

**Mrs Constance Dilger,** Helen Horswill Antiques, 62 Grange Road, L48 4EG TEL: 625 7517 PARKING: Easy OPEN: 10-5 or by appt MIN: £9 MAX: £250 PERIOD: 19th century SPECIALIST: Staffordshire figures GENERAL: Cranberry glass, porcelain & pottery.
**Helen Horswill Antique & Decorative Arts**, 62 Grange Road, L48 4EG TEL: 625 2803/8660 PARKING: Easy OPEN: Mon-Sat 10-1, 2.30-5 or by appt MIN: £5 MAX: £5000 PERIOD: 17th-20th century GENERAL: Country furniture & artifacts, Victorian & Edwardian upholstered sofas & chairs OTHER INFO: Good cafés & bistros etc.

# Lancashire

The picture that Lancashire conjures for many is of dark, satanic mills, cobbled streets and workers in clogs. However true this might have been for some of the major towns and cities a hundred years ago, now it is quite outdated. Most of the mills have gone and the towns and cities are like many others in the rest of England. Lancashire is still quite a rural county outside the conurbations and contains designated Areas of Outstanding Natural Beauty like the Forest of Bowland.

The tour starts in **Blackpool**, synonymous with English holiday making and famous for the tower, pier and illuminations. Its career as a holiday resort started in the 18th century but the coming of the railways in 1846 really began the meteoric rise to become the most famous of English seaside towns. Traditionally Lancashire factories and mills shut down for a week in the summer and their workers brought prosperity to the town as, determined to enjoy themselves, they descended on it. Everything in Blackpool is geared for fun: the renowned Tower Ballroom, the seven miles of bathing beaches, the Golden Mile, the crazy golf courses, amusement arcades, theatres, three piers, the Pleasure Beach, water slides, trams, etc.

Nearby **Lytham St Anne's** offers a complete contrast to its brash neighbour. The town is the result of an amalgamation between Lytham, mentioned in the Domesday book, and St Anne's. The intention of joining the two places was to stop Blackpool swallowing both villages. The town, laid out as a garden city in the late 18th and early 19th centuries, offers few concessions to holiday makers. Visitors to Lytham St Anne's come for the peace and quiet, pleasant walks and, famously, golf at the Royal Lytham St Anne's Golf Club, one of the venues for the British Open Championships.

Now heading east, **Preston**, on the River Ribble has a long, honourable history. In 1179 it was the first town in Lancashire to receive a borough charter and in 1328 received the right to hold a trade fair every twenty years. In 1815 the town was again the first outside London to have gas-lit streets and the by-pass, built in 1958, was the first stretch of motorway in Britain. It became an important centre for cotton spinning and engineering during the 19th century as well as the centre for the county council. The Harris Museum and Art Gallery is housed in a magnificent Greek Revival building, completed in 1893 and contains a good collection of British paintings as well as displays of ceramics, glass and costume.

Five miles east, on the A675, is Hoghton Tower. A 16th century fortified hilltop mansion where James I knighted a joint of beef, hence sirloin. The house contains collections of Chinese teapots, dolls houses and documents relating to the mansion.

After first calling at **Samlesbury**, the tour moves to **Longridge**, standing between the valleys of the Rivers Ribble and Hodder. This was the site of extensive quarries providing the fine sandstone used in many 19th century Lancashire buildings. On Higher Road there is a group of twenty cottages called Club Row, built between 1794 and 1804, said to be the oldest houses in Lancashire to be built by the members of a building society.

Just over ten miles further east, **Whalley** is a very attractive town of ancient origin. Standing on the River Calder, its bridge still retains some medieval masonry. One feature is the Cistercian abbey established in the 13th century. Now all that remains are some walls and a gateway in the grounds of the abbot's house which was rebuilt after the Dissolution and used as a residence by a local family. The nearby church of St Mary is even older than the abbey and must stand on the site of a pre-Norman church demonstrated by the three earlier crosses in the churchyard. Of more recent origins, the viaduct that looms over the town is an impressive feat of engineering. More than 600 yards long and opened in 1850, this viaduct was constructed across the wide valley of the Calder as part of the Blackburn to Clitheroe railway. **Sabden**, next, is reached on a steep country road

The route moves on by another country road to the ancient market town of **Clitheroe**. The castle here was built on a limestone hill at the end of the 12th century. At only about 35 feet square, the

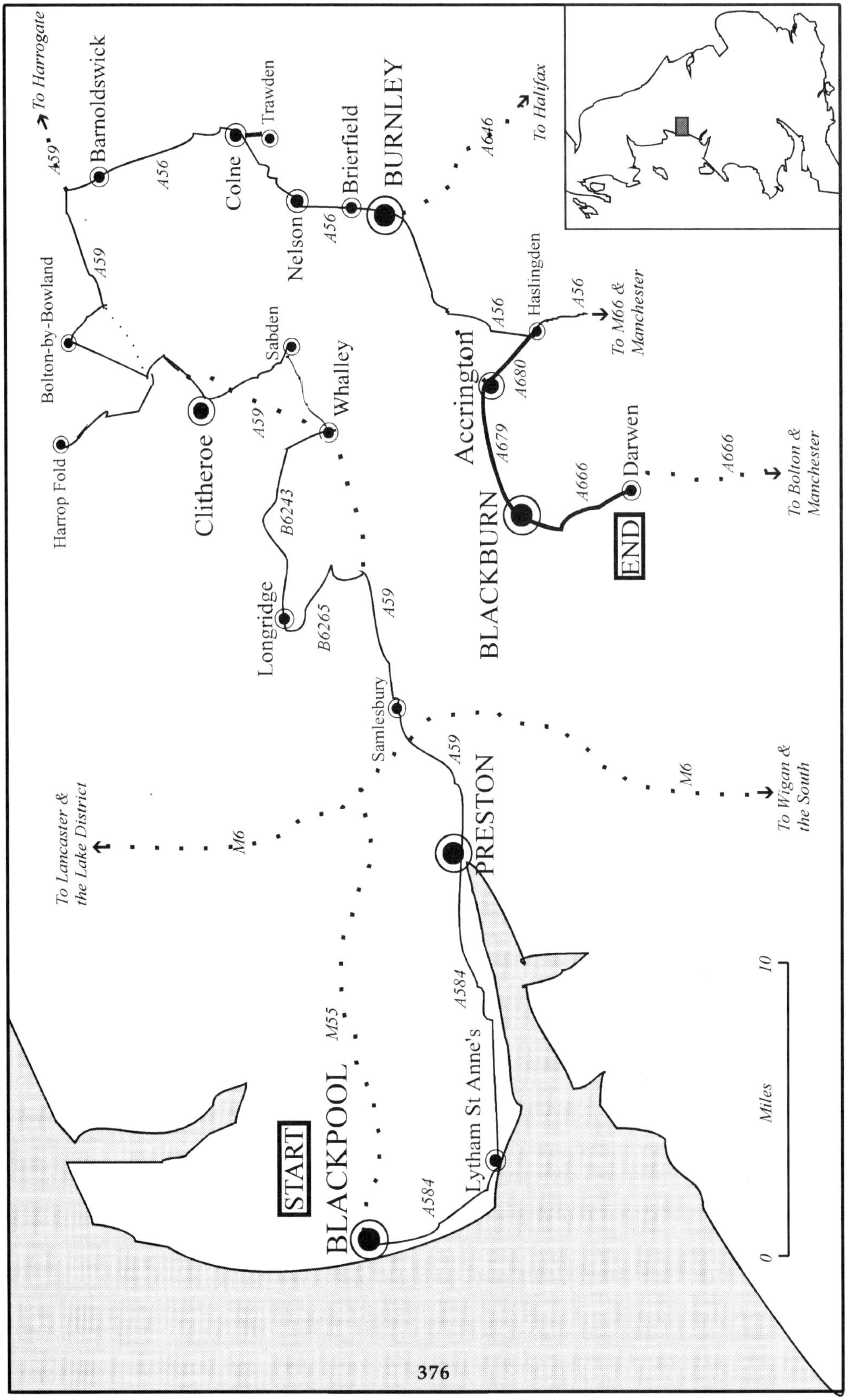
START
BLACKPOOL
Lytham St Anne's
A584
M55
PRESTON
To Lancaster & the Lake District
M6
Samlesbury
A59
To Wigan & the South
Longridge
B6265
B6243
Harrop Fold
Clitheroe
Bolton-by-Bowland
Sabden
Whalley
Barnoldswick
To Harrogate
A56
Colne
Trawden
Nelson
Brierfield
BURNLEY
A646
To Halifax
Haslingden
To M66 & Manchester
Accrington
A680
A679
BLACKBURN
A666
Darwen
END
To Bolton & Manchester
Miles
0
10

keep is said to be the smallest in the country. During the Civil War, the castle was held for the King but was taken by Parliament and slighted, although it was restored in the mid 19th century. Six miles due north via Chatburn and then Grindleton on yet more unclassified roads, is the hamlet of **Harrop Fold**. This is followed by **Bolton-by-Bowland**, a quiet pretty village with a perpendicular church built in the mid 15th century and having an extremely fine tower.

**Barnoldswick**, next, was in Yorkshire until the boundary changes of 1974. Up to the 1930s the town's prosperity was based upon cotton weaving but then Rolls Royce set up a factory to manufacture engines. St Mary-le-Gill, the medieval perpendicular parish church contains Jacobean pews and a three decker pulpit. Further south, in the old town of **Colne**, the British in India Museum displays paintings, photographs, coins, medals, diorama, etc.

The route continues through **Trawden** and **Nelson**, named for a pub where the local railway station was built in 1849, and then **Brierfield** before reaching **Burnley**, near the junction of the rivers Brun and Calder and surrounded by hills. This was a medieval market town which prospered during the Industrial Revolution after the Leeds and Liverpool Canal was built through the town at the end of the 18th century. Like many other Lancashire towns, its wealth came from coal and cotton. The 14th century Towneley Hall houses a museum and art gallery and the collections include oak furniture, oils and watercolours and decorative arts. There is also an exhibition on local crafts and industries.

Detouring slightly, **Haslingden** comes next, followed by **Accrington**. Standing on the crossing point of two turnpikes, it was just a small village until the 19th century. Again the opening of the Leeds Liverpool Canal in 1801 and the coming of the railway in 1847 brought about Accrington's industrial growth. The prosperity was based upon weaving, brick-making and engineering. Although the church of St James dates from 1763 the remainder of the important public buildings are solidly Victorian. Haworth Art Gallery is reputed to have the finest collection of Tiffany glass in the world.

Nearby **Blackburn**, has been a textiles centre since Flemish weavers settled here in the 14th century. However, the Leeds Liverpool Canal brought about its 19th century prosperity, demonstrated by the fine Cotton Exchange from 1865. The Lewis Textile Museum illustrates the history of cotton, much of which is associated with the city. Blackburn became a cathedral city in 1926 when its fine Gothic revival style parish church, St Mary's, was upgraded to a cathedral.

Neighbouring **Darwen**, the final call, is situated in a narrow valley cut by the river for which the town is named. The original settlement started on the east bank but growth in the 19th century took place along the A666 road, then a turnpike. Originally, cotton was the prime industry but gradually the mills were turned over to making paper. A mile south, on the A666, stands the India Mill Chimney. Unmissable because of the 300 feet height, it was built in 1867 in the style of an Italian belltower. Outside India Mill a 450 horse power cross compound steam engine from 1905 is displayed.

## ANTIQUE DEALERS

### BLACKPOOL (01253)

**Peter Christian Antiques,** 400-402 Waterloo Road, FY4 4BL TEL: 763268 PARKING: Easy OPEN: Mon-Sat 10-5 MIN: £20 MAX: £5000 PERIOD: 19th-20th century SPECIALIST: Decorative arts, pine GENERAL: General antiques.

**R & L Coins,** 521 Lytham Road, FY4 1RJ TEL: 343081 FAX: 408058 ASSNS: BNTA PARKING: Own carpark OPEN: Mon-Fri 10-4 PERIOD: Roman to 20th century SPECIALIST: Coins, jewellery.

**RH Latham Antiques & Pine,** 45 Whitegate Drive, FY3 9DG TEL: 393950 PARKING: Easy MIN: £1 MAX: £3000 PERIOD: 19th--20th century SPECIALIST: Antique pine.

### LYTHAM ST ANNES (01253)

**The Snuff Box,** 5 Market Buildings, Hastings Place, FY8 4ES TEL: 738656 PARKING: Easy OPEN: Mon, Tues, Thurs-Sat 10-5 MIN: £1 MAX: £1000

PERIOD: 19th-20th century SPECIALIST: Silver, plate, jewellery, watches GENERAL: Smalls OTHER INFO: German spoken.

## PRESTON (01772)

**The Antique Centre**, 56 Garstang Road, PR1 1NA TEL: 882078 FAX: 885115 PARKING: Own carpark OPEN: Mon-Sat 9-5.30, Sun 10.30-5.30 MIN: £5 MAX: £25,000 PERIOD: 17th-20th century GENERAL: 32 dealers, antiques, collectables.

**Peter Guy's Period Interiors**, 26-30 New Hall Lane, PR1 4DU TEL: 703771 FAX: 703771 ASSNS: LAPADA PARKING: Own carpark OPEN: Mon-Sat 9.30-5.30 MIN: £10 MAX: £10,000 PERIOD: 18th-20th century SPECIALIST: Georgian case furniture GENERAL: French & English furniture & accessories.

**KC Antiques**, The Antique Centre, 56 Garstang Road, PR1 1NA TEL: 882078 FAX: 885115 PARKING: Easy OPEN: Mon-Sat 9-5.30, Sun 10.30-5.30 PERIOD: 18th-19th century GENERAL: Quality mahogany, pine & oak.

**Orchard Antiques**, 447 Blackpool Road, Lane Ends, Ashton TEL: 769749 PARKING: Easy OPEN: Tues-Sat 10-5.30 MIN: £5 MAX: £350 PERIOD: 18th-20th century SPECIALIST: Deco, old porcelain, small furniture, linen.

**Swag**, 24-26 Leyland Road, Penwortham, PR1 9XS TEL: 744970 PARKING: Medium OPEN: Mon-Sat 10-6 MIN: £1 MAX: £2500 PERIOD: 19th-20th century SPECIALIST: Antique dolls GENERAL: General antiques.

**Ray Wade Antiques**, 113 New Hall Lane, PR1 5PB TEL: 792950, home (01253) 700815 PARKING: Easy OPEN: 10-5.30 MIN: £10 MAX: £5000 PERIOD: 18th-19th century SPECIALIST: Decorative antiques GENERAL: Furniture, ceramics, glass, bronzes, etc OTHER INFO: Restoration available. Valuations for probate etc.

## SAMLESBURY (01254)

**Samlesbury Hall Ltd**, Preston New Road, PR5 0UP TEL: 812010 FAX: 812174 PARKING: Own carpark OPEN: 11-4.30 GENERAL: From bric-a-brac & collectables to expensive antiques OTHER INFO: We are a 14th century black & white timbered Manor House, (Entrance £2 to Hall itself).

## LONGRIDGE (01772)

**Charnley Fine Arts**, Charnley House, Preston Road TEL: 782800 FAX: 785068 PARKING: Own carpark OPEN: Anytime by appt MIN: £100 MAX: £10,000 PERIOD: 17th-20th century SPECIALIST: Victorian watercolours GENERAL: Paintings OTHER INFO: Near M6 juncs 31 & 32, B&B in Georgian Farmhouse.

**Kitchenalia**, The Old Bakery, 36 Inglewhite Road, PR3 3JS TEL: 785411 PARKING: Easy OPEN: Mon, Tues, Thur-Sat 10-5 MIN: £1 MAX: £1000 PERIOD: 19th-20th century SPECIALIST: Kitchen collectables GENERAL: Pine furniture, butchers blocks, pews & 'what's that for' items.

## WHALLEY (01254)

**Edmund Davies & Son Antiques**, 32 King Street, BB6 9SL TEL: 823764 PARKING: Easy OPEN: Mon-Sat 10-5.30 MIN: £2 MAX: £5000 PERIOD: 17th-19th century SPECIALIST: Longcase clocks GENERAL: Oak & country furniture, especially rush seated chairs OTHER INFO: Trade warehouse.

## SABDEN (01282)

**Pendle Antiques Centre Ltd**, Union Mill, Wait Street, BB6 9ED TEL: 776311 FAX: 778643 PARKING: Own carpark OPEN: Seven days 10-5 MIN: £1 MAX: £10,000 PERIOD: 19th-20th century SPECIALIST: Furniture GENERAL: Furniture, pine, painted furniture, bric-a-brac.

## CLITHEROE (01200)

**Lee's Antiques,** 59 Whalley Road, BB7 1EE TEL: 24921 & 25441 PARKING: Easy OPEN: Mon, Tues, Thurs, Fri 10.30-5 MIN: 1p MAX: £2000 PERIOD: 20th century GENERAL: Very wide selection.

**Rebecca Antiques,** 22 Moor Lane, BB7 1BE TEL: 29461 PARKING: Medium OPEN: Thurs-Sat 9-5 MIN: £1 MAX: £2000 GENERAL: Kitchenalia, advertising, garden, unusual furniture & objects with emphasis on the decorative OTHER INFO: Cowman's famous Sausage Shop.

## HARROP FOLD HAMLET (01200)

**Harrop Fold Clocks,** BB7 4PJ TEL: 447665 PARKING: Own carpark OPEN: By appt only MIN: £1500 MAX: £8000 PERIOD: 18th century SPECIALIST: Longcase clocks GENERAL: English wall clocks OTHER INFO: 2 self catering holiday cottages all year (brochure). Directions: 6 miles due north of Clitheroe via Chatburn & Grindleton.

## BOLTON-BY-BOWLAND (01200)

**Marian Howard Farmhouse Antiques**, Corner Shop, 23 Main Street TEL: 447294, 446244 PARKING: Easy OPEN: Sat, Sun, Bank hols only 12-4.30 & by appt PERIOD: 19th-20th century SPECIALIST: Large stock patchwork, white lace & table linen GENERAL: Victoriana & jewellery.

## BARNOLDSWICK (01282)

**Roy W Bunn**, 34-36 Church Street TEL: 813703 ASSNS: LAPADA PARKING: Easy OPEN: By appt only MIN: £50 MAX: £1000 PERIOD: 19th century SPECIALIST: Staffordshire figures.

## COLNE (01282)

**Decollectables,** 123 Albert Road, BB8 0BT TEL: 869268 & 0860 296582 PARKING: Easy OPEN: 10-4, closed Tues & Sun MIN: £5 MAX: £500 PERIOD: 20th century SPECIALIST: Carltonware, shelley, Sylvac GENERAL: Art Deco ceramics.

## TRAWDEN (01282)

**The Old Rock**, Keighley Road TEL: 869478 FAX: 865193 PARKING: Own carpark OPEN: Mon-Fri 9-5, Sat, Sun 10-4 MIN: £3 MAX: £2500 PERIOD: 18th-20th century SPECIALIST: Stained glass GENERAL: Furniture OTHER INFO: Brontë's Haworth 9 miles, Wycollar 1 mile.

## NELSON (01282)

**Margaret's Antiques,** 79a Scotland Road, BB9 7UY TEL: 613158 PARKING: Medium OPEN: 10-4 MIN: £10 MAX: £100.

## BRIERFIELD (01282)

**JH Blakey & Sons**, Burnley Road, BB9 5AD TEL: 613593 FAX: 617550 PARKING: Easy OPEN: Mon-Fri 8-5.30, Sat 8-12 PERIOD: 18th-20th century GENERAL: Good range of furniture.

## BURNLEY (01282)

**Brun Lea Antiques,** 3-5 Standish Street, BB11 1AP & Dane House Mill, Dane House Road, BB10 1NZ TEL: 413513 FAX: 832769 PARKING: Easy MIN: £1 MAX: £10,000 PERIOD: 18th-20th century GENERAL: Across the board OTHER INFO: Dane House Mill is warehouse on canal side, approx 30,000 sq ft. Please ring for directions.

## HASLINGDEN (01706)

**PJ Brown Antiques,** 8 Church Street, BB4 5QU TEL: 224888 PARKING: Easy OPEN: Mon-Fri 10-5, Sat 10-4 MIN: 50p MAX: £5000 PERIOD: 19th-20th century GENERAL: Antiques & shipping goods (in large shop & warehouse) OTHER INFO: East Lancs Railway, Helmshore Textile Museum, close to M66, M65 & M62.

**Clifton House Antiques,** 198 Blackburn Road TEL: 214895 PARKING: Easy OPEN: 10-5 MIN: £5 MAX: £500 PERIOD: 19th-20th century GENERAL: Furniture & pottery.

**Fieldings Antiques,** 176-180 Blackburn Road, BB4 5HW TEL: 214254 & 263358 PARKING: Easy OPEN: 10.30-5 MIN: £50 MAX: £2500 PERIOD: 18th-20th century SPECIALIST: Clocks GENERAL: General antiques & furniture.

**P Norgrove (Antique Clocks),** 38 Bury Road, BB4 5PL TEL: 211995 PARKING: Easy OPEN: Most weekdays, always Sat 10-5 MIN: £50 MAX: £5000 PERIOD: 18th-20th century SPECIALIST: Clocks.

## ACCRINGTON (01254 )

**Coin & Jewellery Shop**, 129a Blackburn Road, BB5 0AA TEL: 384757 PARKING: Medium OPEN: Mon, Tues, Thurs-Sat 9.30-5 PERIOD: 19th-20th century SPECIALIST: Coins & medals GENERAL: Badges, tins, smalls, jewellery.

## BLACKBURN (01254)

**Ancient & Modern Antiques,** 56 Bank Top, BB2 1TB TEL: 263256 PARKING: Easy OPEN: 9.30-5.30 MIN: £10 MAX: £5000 SPECIALIST: Victorian jewellery & diamonds GENERAL: Antiques, militaria, etc. OTHER INFO: Valuations, repairs.

**RC Lynch Antiques**, 726 Preston Old Road, Feniscowles TEL: 209943 PARKING: Own carpark OPEN: Mon-Sat 9.30-5 MIN: £1 MAX: £2000+ PERIOD: 17th-20th century SPECIALIST: Fireplaces, pictures, violins, cellos GENERAL: Musical instruments, fireplaces, furniture, pottery.

## DARWEN (01254)

**KC Antiques**, 538 Bolton Road TEL: 772252 PARKING: Easy OPEN: Mon-Sat 9-5, Sun 1-4 PERIOD: 18th-19th century GENERAL: Quality mahogany, pine, oak.

# Huddersfield to Settle

Ostensibly this is a very industrialised area but it still contains much beautiful countryside. The Pennines are the predominant feature and separate Yorkshire from Lancashire. They form a region of wild moorland and deep river valleys. The industrial towns at the southern end of this tour were important during the industrial revolution and most have imposing Victorian architecture to show for it. Now, they are neither as smoky or as unpleasant as might be supposed, and have much to offer the visitor.

The tour starts in the village of **Shepley** and then **Mirfield**, where the Brontes went to school at Roe Head. **Huddersfield** comes next. This was the old woollen centre for the West Riding of Yorkshire and has built its prosperity on cloth. The Tolson Museum illustrates the growth and development of the town and its relationship to the cloth industry. The museum is housed in Ravensknowle Hall, an Italianate mansion built in the mid 19th century by a local textile manufacturer. **Halifax,** following, is well known for its industrial textiles and as the headquarters of England's biggest building society. Its perpendicular church dates from 1490 and inside there is a life-size figure known as Old Tristram who holds an alms box. The town hall was designed by Sir Charles Barry who also designed the Houses of Parliament. Piece Hall, in Thomas Street, was built in 1779 as a cloth-market. Shibden Hall stands close to the town on the A58 and is an early 15th century half-timbered house furnished with articles from the 17th and 18th centuries.

Nearby **Sowerby Bridge** sits on the junction of the Rochdale Canal and the Calder & Hebble Navigation (another canal). Not only did this allow woollen goods to be transported far more easily but the town also became important for trans-shipment between the two canals. Some of the 18th century buildings in the canal basin have space beneath to allow barges to enter and goods to be transferred under cover.

A small detour is made to visit **Walsden** before going to **Bradford**. This university city has for long been associated with the wool industry. It has been a cathedral city since 1920 when its parish church was upgraded. The National Museum of Photography, Film and Television may be found here in Pictureville and is said to be the most popular museum outside London. Another unusual museum is the Colour Museum in Gratton Road. This explores the many facets of the world of colour and its uses.

**Saltaire** is the next astounding stop on the River Aire. This is no normal call because Sir Titus Salt developed the entire village from the 1850s to remove his workers from the Victorian grime and hovels of the inner city and let up to 3000 of them live in a model clime whilst they worked happily at his massive new 1200 loom cloth mill there. Everything was thought of: a beautiful church, good-sized houses, town hall, school, park, mechanics institute and the streets named after Sir Titus's family. Even today many of these houses are much sought after. Saltaire is definitely worth your time, leisurely boat trips and all.

**Bingley**, next, on the Leeds and Liverpool Canal was the original home of Airedale terriers, first bred for hunting otters. Here the Canal passes through two staircase locks where much of the original machinery may be seen. Four miles west of **Keighley** (pronounced Keethley), at the junction of the Rivers Aire and Worth, is possibly the most famous tourist attraction in Yorkshire: the Brontë Parsonage and Museum. This Georgian parsonage was the home of the Brontës and is furnished in the period of the family with many of their relics including furniture, clothes, manuscripts and drawings. A less well-known attraction is the Vintage Railway Carriage Museum at the Railway Station in Haworth where there is a collection of railway carriages, steam engines and railway posters.

After visiting the small village of **Cross Hills**, the tour moves into North Yorkshire and **Skipton**, an important market town on the Airedale Moors at the farthest point north of the Leeds and Liverpool Canal. Real growth began at the end of the 18th century although there was a settlement here much earlier as shown by the castle and the church. Skipton Castle was started in the 11th

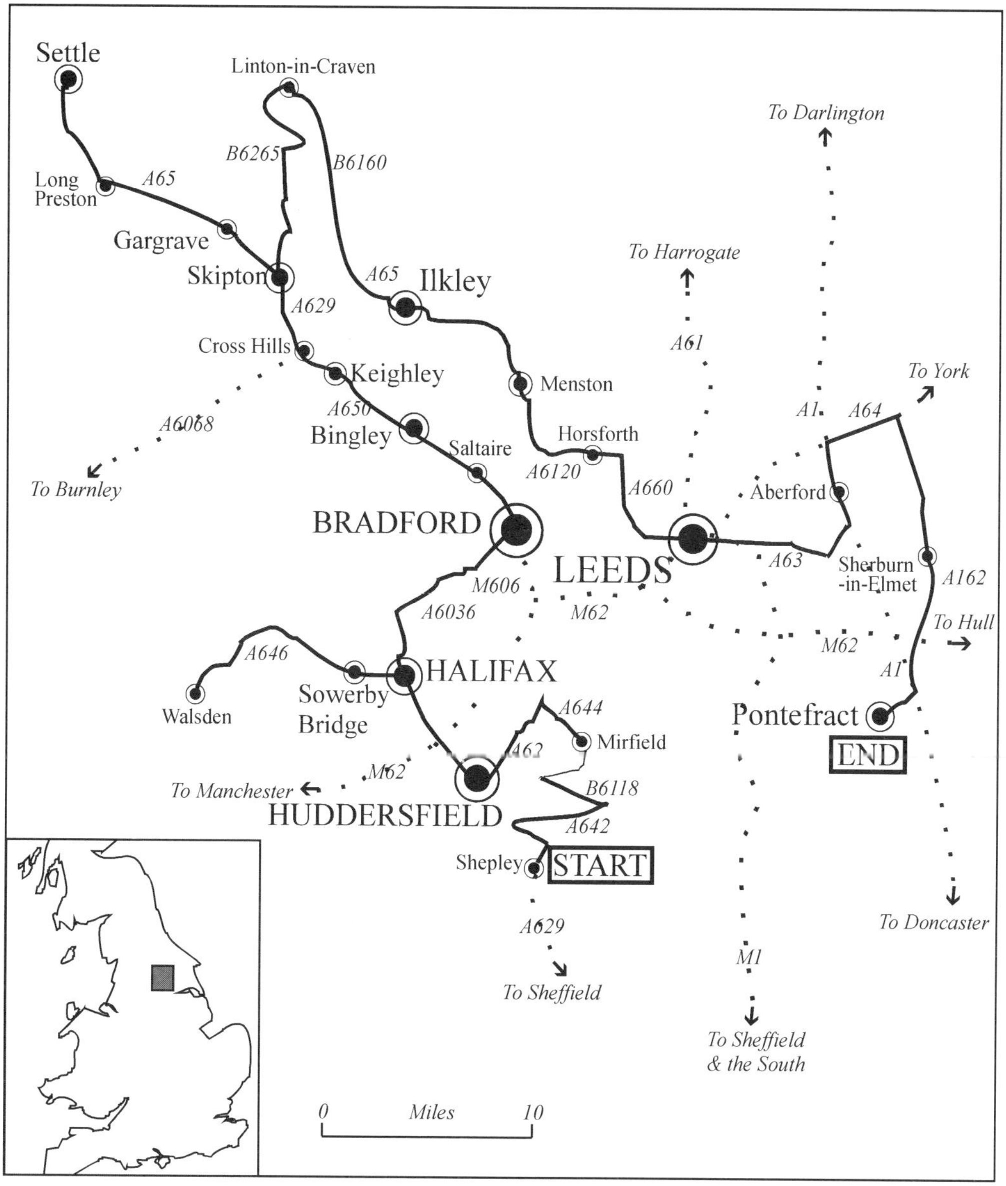
Settle
Linton-in-Craven
To Darlington
B6265
B6160
Long Preston
A65
Gargrave
To Harrogate
Skipton
A65
Ilkley
A629
A61
Cross Hills
Keighley
Menston
To York
A1
A64
A6068
A650
Bingley
Horsforth
Saltaire
To Burnley
A6120
A660
Aberford
BRADFORD
LEEDS
A63
Sherburn -in-Elmet
M606
A162
A6036
M62
To Hull
M62
A646
HALIFAX
A1
Sowerby Bridge
Walsden
A644
Pontefract
Mirfield
END
M62
To Manchester
B6118
HUDDERSFIELD
A642
Shepley
START
A629
To Doncaster
M1
To Sheffield
To Sheffield & the South
0
Miles
10

*Ribblehead Viaduct on the Settle to Carlisle Railway*

century and is one of the most complete and best preserved medieval castles in the country. It came into the hands of the Clifford family in 1309 and they have made many alterations and additions to it over the centuries. Monuments to the Cliffords are also found in the town's perpendicular church. Another important edifice is Bolton Abbey, once an Augustinian priory. Built on the site of a Saxon manor, this was one of the most wealthy and powerful religious establishments in the county. At the time of the Dissolution of the Monasteries the monks surrendered and the nave of the abbey was saved for use as the parish church. The remainder of the buildings are ruins. This is now all part of the estate of the Duke of Devonshire and is set in beautiful parkland which includes nature trails and riverside walks.

Further on, the route calls on **Gargrave**, at a crossing point in the Pennines, then **Long Preston**, with the remains of a Roman fort next to the church. **Settle**, a small market town set beneath limestone cliffs in Ribblesdale, is on the main road from Yorkshire to Cumbria. It gives the impression of a solidly Georgian town but look into the courts and alleys and earlier houses may be seen. Of particular interest is the 17th century building, The Folly, with its elaborate front. Just 6 miles north, on the Settle and Carlisle Railway, is a magnificent spectacle surely not to be missed: the 1876 Ribblehead 24-arch viaduct—a mecca for camera fans, not to say railway buffs worldwide.

**Linton-in-Craven** village has packhorse and clapper bridges across its stream and in the church there is an unusual crucifix dating from the 10th century. Returning to West Yorkshire, **Ilkley** started life as a Roman fort standing at 750 feet above sea level on Ilkley Moor; possibly not a choice posting in Roman times. Now, however, it is elegant with late Victorian buildings. Growth was due to establishment as a spa town and it became the favoured resort for Bradford wool magnates in the 19th century. A small 16th century manor house in Castle Yard displays items of local history from Roman times to the 19th century.

After stopping in **Menston** and **Horsforth**, the tour moves to **Leeds**, an important industrial and commercial centre still retaining a number of historic buildings. Amongst these, St Peter's Church has an Anglo-Saxon cross, St John's Church has a wealth of 17th century woodwork, the grammar school was founded in 1552 and there are numerous Victorian buildings that reflect the city's 19th century prosperity. Five miles east of Leeds stands Temple Newsam, so named because the estate originally belonged to the Knights Templar. The 17th century house was the birthplace of Lord Darnley and a centre for the plots surrounding Mary Queen of Scots. The house contains fine collections of furniture, silver, ceramics and pictures.

Another wonderful country house, Harewood House, can be found 8 miles north. Built in the 18th century and designed by John Carr and Robert Adams, it is still the home of the Lascelles family and contains superb ceilings, plasterwork and Chippendale furniture as well as collections of English and Italian paintings and Sevres and Chinese porcelain.

Turning east, **Aberford** once stood on the Great North Road and was an important coaching stop. Still retaining most of the 18th century buildings, it has several features of particular note. There are two coaching inns, a ruined windmill and, surprisingly, an arch, in Parlington Park, was erected in 1783 to celebrate the American War of Independence. On it is inscribed, 'Liberty in North America triumphant.'

After calling at **Sherburn-in-Elmet**, the final destination is **Pontefract**. This town is well-known for Pontefract cakes, little rounds of liquorice. In the late 19th century, the a liquorice factory was housed in the grounds of Pontefract Castle. The castle was built in the late 11th century and saw much action. During the Civil War it was originally held for the King but changed hands several times after prolonged sieges. Eventually it was slighted by Parliamentary forces. The town itself has several Georgian buildings although redevelopment of Pontefract has in some cases been unsympathetic.

## ANTIQUE DEALERS

### SHEPLEY (01484)

**DW Dyson Antique Weapons**, Woodlea, HD8 8ES TEL: 607331 FAX: 604114 ASSNS: GMC, Arms & Armour Society, Reg. firearms dealer, OMRS PARKING: Own carpark OPEN: Anytime by appt MIN: £100 MAX: £000's PERIOD: 17th-20th century SPECIALIST: Arms & armour, restoration, miniature guns & intricate presentation pieces made. British Gallantry medals always in stock.

### MIRFIELD (01924)

**Lawn & Lace**, 5 Knowl Road TEL: 491083 PARKING: Own carpark OPEN: Wed-Sat 9.30-5.30 PERIOD: 19th-20th century SPECIALIST: Lace, textiles, dolls GENERAL: Small furniture, ceramics OTHER INFO: Some older textiles.

### HUDDERSFIELD (01484)

**Beau Monde Antiques**, 343a Bradford Road, Fartown, HD2 2QF TEL: 427565 PARKING: Easy OPEN: Mon-Sat 9.30-6, Wed AM only MIN: £1 MAX: £500 PERIOD: 19th-20th century GENERAL: Mixed.

**Peter Berry Antiques**, 119 Wakefield Road, Moldgreen, HD5 9AN TEL: 544229 PARKING: Easy OPEN: Mon-Sat 10-5.30 MIN: £20 MAX: £5000 PERIOD: 18th-19th century SPECIALIST: Furniture & its finest quality restoration, early pottery particularly Leeds creamware GENERAL: Complementary china, pottery, pictures OTHER INFO: Highest level restoration.

**Fillans Antiques**, 2 Market Walk TEL: 531609 FAX: 432688 ASSNS: NAG, Gemological Assn of GB PARKING: Medium OPEN: 9.30-5 PERIOD: 19th-20th century SPECIALIST: Fine Victorian, Edwardian jewellery GENERAL: Secondhand & antique jewellery, silver.

**Huddersfield Antiques**, 170 Wakefield Road, Mold Green, HD5 6AW TEL: 539747 PARKING: Easy OPEN: 10.30-4.30 PERIOD: 19th-20th century GENERAL: Shipping furniture, Victoriana, postcards, pianos, collectables.

**KLM & Co Antiques,** The Antique Shop, Wakefield Road, Lepton, HD8 0EL TEL: 607763 PARKING: Own carpark OPEN: Mon-Sat 10.30-5 MIN: £5 MAX: £1500 GENERAL: Antiques including pine.

### HALIFAX (01422)

**Ken Balme Antiques**, 10-12 Keighley Road, Ovenden, HX2 8AL TEL: 344193 PARKING: Medium (around the back) OPEN: Mon-Tues, Thurs-Sat 9.30-5 MIN: £1 MAX: £400 PERIOD: 19-20th century GENERAL: Commemorative ware, Victorian glass, candlesticks, blue & white pottery OTHER INFO: Shop built 1887, ancient jailhouse & stocks nearby.

**Simon Haley**, 89 Northgate TEL: 360434 PARKING: Easy OPEN: 10.30-5 MIN: 1p MAX: £2000 PERIOD: 17th-20th century SPECIALIST: Toys GENERAL: General antiques.

**Halifax Antique Centre**, Queens Road, (nr King Cross A58) TEL: 366657 PARKING: Own carpark OPEN: Tues-Sat 10-5 PERIOD: 19th-20th century SPECIALIST: Art deco, costume, mechanical music, jewellery etc.

**Muir Hewitt Art Deco Originals**, Halifax Antiques Centre, Queens Road, TEL: 366657 & 202744 PARKING: Own carpark OPEN: 10.30-5 SPECIALIST: Art Deco pottery including Susie Cooper, Clarice Cliff, Charlotte Rhead, furniture lighting & mirrors.

**Andy Thornton Architectural Antiques Ltd,** Victoria Mills, Stainland Road, Greetland, HX4 8AD TEL: 377314 FAX: 310372 OPEN: Mon-Fri 8.30-5.30, Sat 9-5, Sun 10-5 MIN: £5 MAX: £50,000 PERIOD: 19th century SPECIALIST: Architectural antiques GENERAL: Original panelling, fire surrounds, doors, stained glass.

## SOWERBY BRIDGE (01422)

**Memory Lane**, 69 Wakefield Road TEL: 833223 FAX: 883324 PARKING: Easy OPEN: Mon-Sat 10-5 MIN: £1 PERIOD: 19th-20th century SPECIALIST: Pine, oak, dolls, teddies, toys GENERAL: Every & anything.

**Talking Point Antiques**, 66 West Street TEL: 834126 PARKING: Easy OPEN: Thurs-Sat 10.30-5.30 & by appt MIN: £1 PERIOD: 19th-20th century SPECIALIST: Windup gramophones, 78's & related items GENERAL: English pottery & porcelain (with restoration available), decorative items, curios OTHER INFO: Pennine market town with canal marina.

## WALSDEN (01706)

**Cottage Antiques Ltd**, 788 Rochdale Road, OL14 7UA TEL: 813612 PARKING: Own carpark OPEN: Tues-Sun 10-4.30 MIN: £1 MAX: £1500 PERIOD: 18th-20th century GENERAL: Continental decorated country furniture.

## BRADFORD (01274)

**Langleys Ltd**, 59 Godwin Street, BD1 2SH TEL: 722280 ASSNS: NAG PARKING: Difficult OPEN: Mon, Tues, Thurs-Sat 9-5 MIN: £200 MAX: £8000 PERIOD: 18th-20th century SPECIALIST: Early/mid Victorian, Art Deco GENERAL: Fine early diamond & gem sets, jewellery to present day.

## SALTAIRE (01274)

**Carlton Antiques & Fine Art,** 1 Victoria Road, BD18 3LA TEL: 530611 PARKING: Easy OPEN: Thurs-Sun 10.30-5.30 MIN: £50 MAX: £5000 PERIOD: 17th-20th century SPECIALIST: 19th-early 20th century oils & watercolours GENERAL: Early Georgian to Victorian oak, walnut & mahogany furniture & clocks OTHER INFO: The shop is situated in the heart of the historic model village of Saltaire, opposite Salts Mill housing the '1853 Gallery' of David Hockney pictures.

**The Titus Gallery,** 1 Daisy Place, Saltaire Road, BD18 4NA TEL & FAX: 581894 PARKING: Own carpark OPEN: 10-5.30 MIN: £50 MAX: £30,000 PERIOD: 17th-20th century SPECIALIST: Paintings GENERAL: Occasional furniture OTHER INFO: On site artist's working studio

## BINGLEY (01274)

**Bingley Antiques Centre**, Keighley Road TEL: 567316 PARKING: Own carpark OPEN: Mon, Wed-Fri 9.30-5, Tues 10-5, Sat 9-5, Sun 2-5 MIN: £1 MAX: £5000 PERIOD: 17th-20th century GENERAL: Quality antiques mainly £150 up to £1500 OTHER INFO: Also warehouse. of shipping goods.

## KEIGHLEY (01535)

**Keighley Antiques**, 153 East Parade, BD21 5HX TEL: 663439 PARKING: Medium OPEN: 10-5 MIN: £5 MAX: £1000 PERIOD: 18th-20th century SPECIALIST: Jewellery GENERAL: Bric-a-brac, china.

## CROSS HILLS (01535)

**Heathcote Antiques**, 1 Aire Street Junction, BD20

7RT TEL: 635250 PARKING: Own carpark OPEN: 10-5.30 MIN: £5 MAX: £5000 PERIOD: 19th-20th century SPECIALIST: Old unrestored pine GENERAL: Clocks, wide variety of smalls, porcelain, pottery, (especially Blue & White), small furniture.

## SKIPTON (01756)

**Adamson Armoury**, 70 Otley Street, BD23 1ET TEL: 791355 PARKING: Medium OPEN: Mon-Sat 9.30-4.30 MIN: £20 MAX: £1000 PERIOD: 17th-20th century SPECIALIST: Antique edge weapons GENERAL: Antique weapons.

**Corn Mill Antiques**, High Corn Mill, Chapel Hill, BD23 1NL TEL: 792440 PARKING: Own carpark OPEN: Mon, Thurs-Sat 10-4 MIN: £10 MAX: £5000 PERIOD: 19th-20th century GENERAL: Quality furniture, porcelain, clocks etc OTHER INFO: Next to good coffee house, near castle.

## GARGRAVE (01756)

**Antiques at Forge Cottage,** 22A High Street, BD23 3RB TEL: 748272 OPEN: Tues, Thurs, Sat 10-4.45, Mon, Wed Fri 2-4.45 PERIOD: late 18th-early 20th century SPECIALIST: Glass, porcelain, metalware GENERAL: Small silver, jewellery, collectables.

**Harry Blackburn Antiques**, 9 East Street, BD23 3RS TEL: 749796 PARKING: Easy OPEN: 10-5 PERIOD: 19th-20th century GENERAL: Furniture, metalwork, pottery glass OTHER INFO: B&B's etc plentiful.

**Bernard Dickinson**, The Estate Yard, West Street TEL: 748257 PARKING: Own carpark OPEN: 9-5.30 PERIOD: 17th-18th century SPECIALIST: English oak & walnut GENERAL: Furniture.

**Gargrave Gallery**, 48 High Street, BD23 3RB TEL: 749641 PARKING: Easy OPEN: Appt advisable MIN: £3 MAX: £3000 PERIOD: 18th-20th century SPECIALIST: Clocks, barometers GENERAL: General antiques.

**RN Myers**, Endsleigh House, High Street, BD23 3LX TEL: 749587 ASSNS: BADA PARKING: Easy OPEN: Mon-Sat 9-5.30 & by appt MIN: £15 MAX: £15,000 PERIOD: 17th-early 19th century SPECIALIST: Furniture & porcelain GENERAL: Pottery, metalware, pictures, prints.

## LONG PRESTON (01729)

**Gary K Blissett**, Summerfield, 3 Station Road, BD23 4NH TEL: 840384 PARKING: Easy OPEN: By appt MIN: £50 MAX: £3000 PERIOD: 19th-20th century GENERAL: Paintings & watercolours.

## SETTLE (01729)

**Anderson Slater Antiques,** 6 Duke Street, BD24 9DW TEL: 822051 PARKING: Medium OPEN: 10-5, closed Wed MIN: £60 MAX: £4000 PERIOD: 18th-19th century SPECIALIST: Furniture GENERAL: Pictures, porcelain, decorative items.

**Folly Antiques**, The Folly, Chapel Street PARKING: Easy OPEN: Mon-Sat 10-5.30 MIN: £35 MAX: £6000 PERIOD: 17th-19th century SPECIALIST: Jewellery, furniture GENERAL: Antiques OTHER INFO: In part of 17th century manor house near main square.

**Mary Milnthorpe & Daughters,** The Antique Shop, Market Place, BD24 9DX TEL: 822331 PARKING: Easy OPEN: 9.30-12.30, 1.45-5, closed Wed & Sun PERIOD: 18th-20th century SPECIALIST: Jewellery & silver.

**Nan Books**, Roundabout, 41 Duke Street, BD24 9AJ TEL: 823324 PARKING: Easy OPEN: Tues, Fri, Sat 11-12.30, 2-5.30 MIN: £1 MAX: £500 PERIOD: 18th-19th century SPECIALIST: Glass, ceramics OTHER INFO: Tourist centre for Yorkshire Dales, Settle-Carlisle railway.

**Roy Precious**, King William House, High Street, BD24 9EX TEL: 823946 PARKING: Easy OPEN: 10-5.30 closed Weds, phone call advised MIN: £20 MAX: £6,000 PERIOD: 17th-18th century SPECIALIST: Oak & country furniture, portraits GENERAL: Some pottery, treen & pewter, period mahogany & walnut OTHER INFO: Blue Goose, Falcon Manor, Royal Oak.

**Well Cottage Antiques**, High Street, BD24 9EX TEL: 823593 PARKING: Easy OPEN: Thurs-Sat 10-5.30 MIN: £1 MAX: £350 PERIOD: 19th-20th century SPECIALIST: Framed cigarette cards, cricket pictures GENERAL: China, pine, collectables OTHER INFO: Market Tues, ° day Weds.

## LINTON-IN-CRAVEN (01756)

**Ings House Antiques,** Thorpe Lane, BD23 5HL TEL: 730301 PARKING: Own carpark OPEN: 9-6 MIN: £5 MAX: £1000 PERIOD: 18th-20th century GENERAL: Victoriana, country furniture, curios, porcelain, metalware, tools OTHER INFO: Very close to award winning restaurant, Angel at Hetton. Ings House initially appears to be in the middle of nowhere but is an Aladdin's Cave.

## ILKLEY (01943)

**Burrow & Rapier**, 37 The Grove, LS29 0QN TEL: 817631 PARKING: Easy OPEN: Mon-Sat 10-5.30 MIN: £5 MAX: £8000 PERIOD: 19th century GENERAL: Fine furniture, antiques, reproduction items OTHER INFO: Opposite Monkmaris restaurant, French, German spoken.

**Manor Barn,** Burnside Mill, Main Street, Addingham, LS29 0PJ TEL: 830176 FAX: 830991 PARKING: Own carpark OPEN: Mon-Sat 8-5.30, Sun 11-4 MIN: 50p MAX: £2000 PERIOD: 19th century SPECIALIST: Pine GENERAL: Furniture OTHER INFO: On the edge of Ilkley Moor, pleasant village, lots of pubs & nearby accommodation.

## MENSTON (01943)

**Park Antiques**, 2 Northview, Main Street, LS29 6JW TEL: 872392 PARKING: Easy OPEN: Seven days 10-6.30 MIN: £400 MAX: £5,000 PERIOD: 19th century SPECIALIST: Quality rosewood, walnut & mahogany. Soft furnishings, clocks OTHER INFO: Harry Ramsden's world famous fish'n'chips ° mile, Emmerdale Farm's Woolpack Inn 1° miles.

## HORSFORTH (0113)

**Bill Thirkill Antiques**, Springfield Cottage, 107 West End Lane, LS18 5ES TEL: 258 9160 PARKING: Own carpark OPEN: 8.30 onwards MIN: £15 MAX: £2,200 PERIOD: 18th-19th century SPECIALIST: Porcelain, pottery GENERAL: Furniture, metalware, musical.

## LEEDS (0113)

**The Antique Exchange**, 400 KirkstallRoad, LS4 2JX TEL: 274 3513 PARKING: Easy OPEN: Mon, Thur-Sat 10.30-3 MIN: £199 MAX: £3000 PERIOD: 19th-20th century SPECIALIST: Satin walnut & ash bedroom furniture.

**Bishop House Antiques,** 169 Town Street, Rodley, LS13 1HW TEL: 256 3071 PARKING: Medium OPEN: Sat 2-5.30 PEROD: 19th century GEN-ERAL: General antiques, porcelain, glass.

**Coins International,** 1-2 Melbourne Street, LS2 7PS TEL: 243 4230 FAX: 234 5544 PARKING: Own carpark OPEN: Mon-Fri 9-5 MIN: £25 MAX: £25,000 PERIOD: BC-20th century SPECIALIST: British gold coins, banknotes GENERAL: Ancient, medieval & modern coins, proof sets, Maundy Coins, gold & bullion coins OTHER INFO: We are always anxious to buy all types of coins.

**Geary Antiques**, 114 Richardshaw Lane, Pudsey,

LS28 6BN TEL: 256 4122 PARKING: Own carpark OPEN: Mon, Tues, Thurs-Sat 10-5.30, Sun 12-4 MAX: £5,000 SPECIALIST: Georgian, Victorian, Edwardian furniture, upholstery. Restoration.

**J Howorth Antiques & Collectables,** 169 Cardigan Road (off Burley Road), Burley, LS6 1QL TEL: 230 6204 PARKING: Easy OPEN: 11-5.30, Sun 12.30-5.30, closed Tues MIN: 50p MAX: £2000 PERIOD: 19th-20th century GENERAL: House clearance specialist, silver, plate, chimney pots, fireplaces OTHER INFO: On main road to Headingley Cricket Ground. We hire props to Yorkshire TV.

**White Cross Antiques,** 141 Otley Road, Guiseley, LS20 8LZ TEL: 287 8945 OPEN: Varies, usually Mon-Fri 11-7, Sun after 11am, closed Sat MIN: £1 MAX: £4000 PERIOD: 17th-20th century GENERAL: Bric a brac, porcelain, china, glass, furniture, clocks, pictures, gramophones OTHER INFO: 100 yds from famous Harry Ramsden's fish & chip emporium.

**Windsor House Antiques Ltd,** 18-20 Benson Street, LS7 1BL TEL: 244 4666 FAX: 242 6394 ASSNS: LAPADA PARKING: Own carpark OPEN: Mon-Fri 8-5 & by appt MIN: £50 MAX: £100,000 PERIOD: 18th-20th century SPECIALIST: European bronzes, works or art, Orientalist paintings GENERAL: Enormous stocks 18th-19th century furniture & objects OTHER INFO: B&B's & hotels organised for prospective clients.

**Year Dot,** 15 Market Street Arcade, LS1 6DH TEL: 246 0860 PARKING: Difficult OPEN: 9.30-5 MIN: £1 MAX: £1250 PERIOD: 18th-20th century GENERAL: Jewellery, pottery, small furniture

## ABERFORD (0113)

**Aberford Pine,** Hicklam House, LS25 3DP TEL: 281 3209 FAX: 281 3121 PARKING: Own carpark OPEN: Mon-Sat 9-5.30, Sun 10-5.30 MIN: £10 MAX: £3000 PERIOD: 19th century GENERAL: Pine, collectables, some oak & mahogany, prints, etc OTHER INFO: Situated just off the A1, 7 miles south of Wetherby. 20 showrooms with changing & variable stock.

## SHERBURN-IN-ELMET (01977)

**Drey Antique Centre,** 56 Low Street, LS25 6BA TEL: 681404 PARKING: Easy OPEN: Daily 10-5, closed Wed MIN: £2 MAX: £2000 PERIOD: 19th century SPECIALIST: Country furniture GENERAL: Collectables, Doulton figures, character jugs, Yorkshire books, paintings.

## PONTEFRACT (01977)

**Cottage Antiques,** 5 Ropergate End TEL. 611146 PARKING: Easy OPEN: 5 days 12 noon-4 MIN: £5 MAX: £1000 PERIOD: 19th century SPECIALIST: Antique stripped pine & satinwood GENERAL: Bedroom & kitchen furniture, linen, china, decorative items.

# York to the North Yorkshire Coast

York Minster and the Shambles

The North Yorkshire coast boasts plenty of sandy beaches but it is not a benign seaboard. Much land has been lost to the sea through erosion, from farmland, isolated cottages to whole villages. Spurn Head, at the mouth of the Humber, has been built up as the sea has eroded the beaches and coastline and deposited the material here. Inland, the scenery varies from the extreme flatness of the region around Holderness, to the north of the Humber, to the rounded hills of the Yorkshire Wolds. Further contrast is found in the Plain of York, which again is relatively flat countryside. All of this is rich agricultural land and the hand of man has had a considerable impact on the scenery over the centuries.

The tour starts in **York**. This city, rich in history, can only be covered briefly here. All visitors should go to the Tourist Information Centre and also to the exhibition, the York Story in the Heritage Centre in Castlegate.

Initially, York was founded as the Roman settlement of *Eboracum*. It was established as a fort and military headquarters to keep down potential rebellions and to guard against raids by the northern tribes. It continued in importance after the Romans left. Much of the medieval walls and many historic buildings still exist.

No visit would be complete without seeing York Minster, the largest medieval cathedral in Britain. The magnificence of Durham Cathedral and the great Yorkshire Cistercian abbeys spurred on the authorities here to build an even greater cathedral. Construction of the present building started in the 13th century and took about 250 years to complete. The cathedral has so many wonderful things to see. Amongst these are the glorious windows with their original glass,. indeed the largest collection of medieval glass in Britain. The Minster was spared during the Civil War because the citizens surrendered to Sir Thomas Fairfax, leading the Parliamentary army, on condition that none of their churches, including the Minster, would be damaged.

Another fascinating feature is the Shambles, an area of narrow cobbled streets dating from the 18th century and earlier with their original buildings. Noteworthy also is Fairfax House in Castlegate, described as a classic masterpiece of 18th century architecture and reputed to be one of the finest townhouses in England. It contains a superb collection of 18th century furniture and clocks collected by Noel Terry, the former owner.

There are numerous museums including the National Railway Museum in Leeman Road, York Castle Museum detailing social history, the Yorkshire Museum which contains collections of

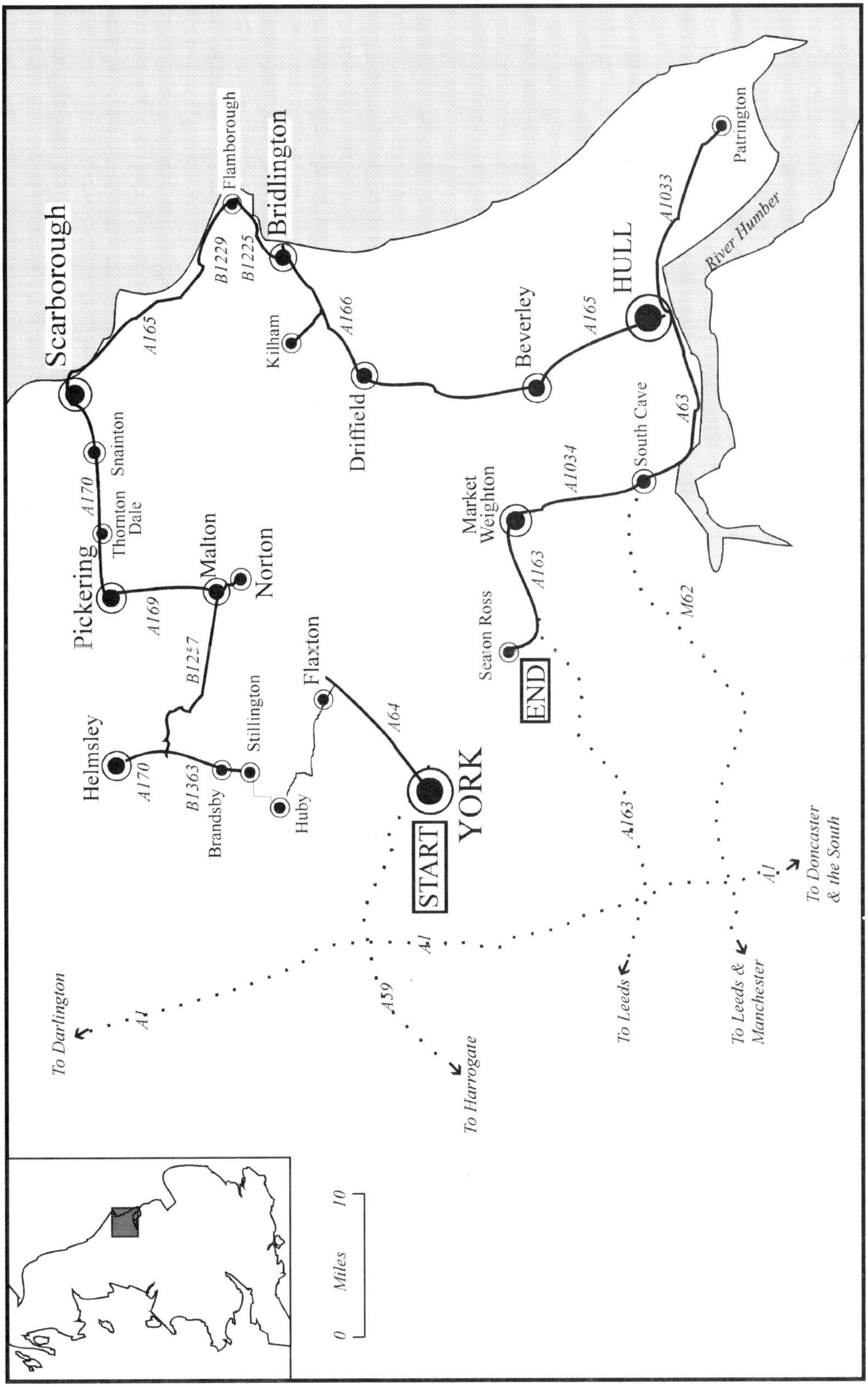
Scarborough
Flamborough
Bridlington
B1229
B1225
A165
Kilham
A166
Driffield
Beverley
A165
HULL
A1033
Patrington
River Humber
Snainton
A170
Thornton Dale
Pickering
A169
Malton
Norton
South Cave
A63
A1034
Market Weighton
A163
Seaton Ross
END
M62
B1257
Flaxton
A64
Stillington
Helmsley
A170
B1363
Brandsby
Huby
YORK
START
A163
A1
A59
To Darlington
To Harrogate
To Leeds
To Leeds & Manchester
To Doncaster & the South
Miles
0
10

*Heavily eroded cliffs near Flamborough Head*

Roman, Anglo-Saxon and Viking artefacts and the Yorkshire Museum of Farming at Murton which is set in an eight acre country park.

**Flaxton** lies 10 miles north east, off the A64, and then country roads lead to **Huby** and, then Stillington, before climbing wooded slopes to nearby **Brandsby** where the 18th century church has a stone cupola on a charming hipped roof supported internally by cross vaulted Doric columns. **Helmsley**, a pretty stone-built town standing just three miles from the ruins of the magnificent Rievaulx Abbey, is sited in a beautiful steep wooded valley by the River Rye. The Cistercian abbey was founded in 1131. For a century it prospered becoming very wealthy. However, the extensive building works imposed a heavy burden and by the 13th century the abbey was deep in debt. At the height, there were 140 monks and 500 lay brothers but by the time of the Dissolution only 22 monks remained.

Helmsley is overlooked by the ruins of a once impregnable castle. Started in the late 12th century, there were alterations and additions throughout the following five centuries. The first real action seen was in the Civil War when it withstood a siege by the Parliamentary general, Sir Thomas Fairfax. This lasted three months until the castle garrison surrendered. At that time the Duke of Buckingham owned the castle, he later married Sir Thomas Fairfax's daughter. Towards the end of the 17th century it was sold to Sir Charles Duncombe, a London banker, whose family later built Duncombe Park. This fine country house is near the town centre. Built in the early 18th century, it is surrounded by beautiful gardens and parkland.

Taking the B1257, the route now reaches **Malton**, the site of a Roman fort. The town began to prosper when the River Derwent, upon which it stands, was made navigable in the 18th century. Six miles west is the magnificent mansion, Castle Howard. A castle in name only, this palatial construction was designed by Vanbrugh and built between 1699 and 1726. It is set in beautiful parkland and contains many impressive rooms and fine collections of pictures, statuary, costume and furniture.

After visiting **Norton** just on the opposite river bank , the tour arrives in **Pickering**. Situated on the edge of the North Yorkshire Moors there has been a settlement here since before the Norman Conquest. Acastle was probably first built in the 12th century. Set in good hunting country, during the Middles Ages it was frequently host to the reigning monarchs of the day and saw action in various raids by the Scots and rebellions by local lords. By the 16th century though quite decayed some repair work was done but it was largely uninhabited with only the Mill Tower being used as a prison and the chapel as a courthouse. After two centuries of neglect, restoration work was finally done in 1926. The Beck Isle Museum of Rural Life, is housed in a Regency building and displays collections relating to rural life over the last 200 hundred years. At Pickering Station there is a steam railway to Grosmont, near Whitby. The line was built by George Stephenson in the 1830s and passes through wonderful scenery.

Now taking the A170, the route stops in the picturesque villages of **Thornton le Dale** and **Snainton** before reaching the coast and **Scarborough**. Sited on two bays, the town came to

*The seafront at Scarborough*

prominence as a spa and holiday resort as early as the 17th century. However, the history goes back much further. Bronze Age remains have been found on the site of Scarborough Casle. Built on a headland between the two bays and 300 feet above sea level, it is a naturally defensible position. The Romans set up a beacon here to give warning of Saxon raiders. As skeletons have been found on the site showing clear signs of violence, apparently Saxons must indeed have raided the area, certainly the town was sacked by Norsemen in the 11th century. The castle begun in 1135 was involved in much action. The first attack came on it at the beginning of the 14th century when it was held by Piers Gaveston, a favourite of the king, Edward II. A group of discontented barons mounted a siege and starvation eventually forced surrender. A few years later the Scots attacked the town but failed to take the castle.

During the Civil War Scarborough was staunchly Royalist and the castle was again beseiged, this time for 18 months. Once again only starvation forced the garrison to surrender. The defence during the long siege were so impressive that, on surrender, the defenders were allowed to march out of the castle with flags flying and to the beat of drums. After that the castle saw little action until the First World War when it came under fire from two German cruisers, so receiving the distinction of being one of the few English castles to have been shelled by the Germans.

Further down the coast on the A165 is **Flamborough**. At Flamborough Head the chalk wolds meet the sea in a series of dramatic cliffs and eroded into intricate shapes. An octagonal lighthouse stands on top of the Head. In the local church there is a 15th century rood screen.

The next call, the seaside resort of **Bridlington**, has good sandy beaches and a harbour for trawlers. The old part of the town lies about a mile inland and was originally built around an Augustinian priory which now serves as the parish church. Set on the cliffs overlooking Bridlington Bay stands Sewerby Hall built between 1714 and 1720. Its 50 acres of gardens include an old English walled garden, a small zoo and an aviary. There is also a museum dedicated to the aviator, Amy Johnson. Another great house, Burton Agnes Hall, lies six miles south west. This is an outstanding example of Elizabethan architecture and contains collections of antique furniture, porcelain and the largest collection in the north of French Impressionist and Modern paintings including Renoir, Pissaro, Corot, Utrillo, Gauguin, Augustus John, etc.

Inland, via the village of **Kilham**, is **Driffield** (properly called Great Driffield), a busy market town. Its most prominent feature is the 110 foot high tower of the 15th century church. Sledmere House is eight miles north west. Originally built in the mid 18th century, the house was burnt down in 1911. However, during the First World War it was reconstructed and restored and contains much of the original furniture and pictures.

Travelling south, **Beverley**, although now in Humberside, was once the capital of the East Riding of Yorkshire. The Minster with its twin towers dominates the town. Started in the 13th century, it is reputed to be one of the finest Gothic buildings in Europe. The decorated style of ecclesiastical architecture is demonstrated to good effect in the Percy tomb, particularly in its canopy. Other notable points are the east window with its original glass, the 17th century woodcarving on the choir stalls and the Saxon *fridstol* or sanctuary chair beside the altar which is where, it is thought, an official sat to hear pleas for sanctuary.

Other notable and historic buildings exist. North Bar is the only remaining 15th century gateway of the five that once allowed access through the town walls. Another church of particular interest, St Mary's, was the Minster's chapel of ease and was also Norman in origin although it has been altered and enlarged over the centuries. The Guildhall, in Register Square, has an outstanding example of stucco work in its ceiling showing the all-seeing figure of Justice. The Guildhall was bought by the council in 1500 for use as a town hall and it now contains the Mayor's Parlour and Tourist Information Office.

The tour now arrives in **Hull**, more properly called Kingston-upon-Hull. Standing on the mouth of the River Humber, its prosperity has been based on the fishing industry, now in decline. There is much of interest. Blaydes House, in the High Street, is a mid Georgian merchant's house with a fine staircase and panelled rooms. Wilberforce House, also in the High Street, was the birthplace of William Wilberforce who fought for the abolition of slavery; it now houses a museum to commemorate his struggle. One of the oldest secular buildings in the town is the Old Grammar School, built in the late 16th century. This contains a museum showing the town's history. Standing about seven miles north east is Burton Constable, a magnificent Elizabethan house built about 1570, containing a fine collection of furniture, pictures, works of art and 18th century scientific instruments.

There is now a detour on to Spurn Head to visit **Patrington** before continuing to **South Cave** followed by **Market Weighton** (pronounced Weeton). Once the home of William Bradley, the Market Weighton Giant, at 7ft 9ins he is reputed to be the tallest Englishman ever.and in 1820 was buried in the local churchyard with a plaque. Another one, with his footprint drawn on it, marks his home, Bradley House, on the corner of York Road. His chair may be seen in the Londesborough Arms Hotel in the High Street. The tour ends in the village of **Seaton Ross,** and now only about 14 miles from the start at York.

# ANTIQUE DEALERS

## YORK (01904)

**Barbara Cattle**, 45 Stonegate, YO1 2AW TEL: 623862 ASSNS: BADA OPEN: 9-5.30 PERIOD: 18th-20th century SPECIALIST: Silver & jewellery.

**Barker Court Antiques**, 44 Gillygate, YO3 7EQ TEL: 622611 PARKING: Easy OPEN: 10.30-5.30 MIN: £3 MAX: £100 PERIOD: 19th-20th century SPECIALIST: EP flatware, studio glass GENERAL: Collectables OTHER INFO: Close to Minster & Art Gallery. Personally recommended Mamma Mia & Waggon & Horses.

**Bishopgate Antiques,** 23-24 Bishopgate Street, YO2 1JH TEL: 623893 FAX: 626511 PARKING: Medium OPEN: 6 days 9.15-6 MIN: 50p MAX: £3000 PERIOD: 18th-20th century GENERAL: Clocks, scientific instruments, porcelain, funriture, brassware OTHER INFO: Excellent ghost walk.

**Bobbins Wool Crafts Antiques**, 31-33 Goodramgate, YO1 2LS TEL: 653597 PARKING: Medium OPEN: Mon -Sat 10-5.30 MIN: £2 MAX: £1000 PERIOD: 19th-20th century SPECIALIST: Oil lamps GENERAL: Antiques & collectables

**The Emporium,** 77 Walmgate, YO1 2TZ TEL: 634124 PARKING: Easy OPEN: 10-5, closed Tues & Sun MIN: 50p MAX: £1000 PERIOD: 19th-20th century GENERAL: Furniture, Art Deco Victoriana, glass, silver, unusual collectables OTHER INFO: Opposite the Spread Eagle pub, best real ale & food in York, great place to leave husbands whilst you browse in peace! Shop is located in a half-timbered building, circa 1425.

**Golden Memories of York,** 141 Newgate, YO1 2LA TEL: 655883 ASSNS: NAG PARKING: Medium OPEN: Mon-Thurs 9-5, Fri, Sat 9-5.30 MIN: £5 MAX: £3000 PERIOD: 19th-20th century SPECIALIST: Antique jewellery & silver.

**Holgate Antiques**, 52 Holgate Road, YO2 4AB TEL: 630005 PARKING: Easy OPEN: Mon-Sat 10-5 MIN: £5 MAX: £2000 PERIOD: 19th-20th century SPECIALIST: Pine GENERAL: Bric-a-brac, mahogany furniture OTHER INFO: Holmewood House Hotel.

**Minster Antiques,** 24 Goodramgate, YO1 2LG TEL: 655481 PARKING: Medium OPEN: 10-5 MIN: £5 MAX: £500 PERIOD: 19th-20th century SPECIALIST: Brass, copper, collectors items OTHER INFO: Close to York Minster in pedestrian area, browsers welcome.

**Minstergate Bookshop,** 8 Minster Gates, YO1 2HL TEL: 621812 ASSNS: PBFA PARKING: Difficult OPEN: 7 days 10-5.30 MIN: £1 MAX: £10,000 PERIOD: 18th-20th century SPECIALIST: Antiquarian books & prints.

**Robert Morrison & Son**, Trentholme House, 131 The Mount, YO2 2DA TEL: 655394 ASSNS: BADA PARKING: Own carpark OPEN: Mon-Fri 9.30-5, Sat 9.30-1 MIN: £100 MAX: £33,000 PERIOD: 18th-19th century SPECIALIST: British furniture, circa 1700-1870 GENERAL: Selection of antiques of this period.

**O'Flynn Antiquarian Books, Maps & Prints,** 35 Micklegate, YO1 1JH TEL: 641404 FAX: 611872 PARKING: Medium OPEN: Mon-Sat 9-6, Sun 1-6 MIN: 40p MAX: £5000 PERIOD: 17th-20th century SPECIALIST: Early printed books & maps GENERAL: Maps & prints, also natural history, sporting, shipping, railways, architectural, etc.

**Ken Spelman**, 70 Micklegate, YO1 1LF TEL: 624414 FAX: 626276 ASSNS: ABA, PBFA PARKING: Easy OPEN: Mon-Sat 9-5.30 MIN: £1 MAX: £15,000 PERIOD: 17th-20th century SPECIALIST: Fine arts, English Literature (18th century) GENERAL: 40,000 books on all subjects, catalogues issued worldwide OTHER INFO: Open coal fire, 19th century shelving.

**Thacker's**, 42 Fossgate TEL: 633077 PARKING: Medium OPEN: 10-5 MIN: £5 MAX: £5000 PERIOD: 17th-20th century SPECIALIST: Silver, furniture, glass, porcelain OTHER INFO: Next door to one of the oldest buildings in England, Merchant Adventurers Hall.

**York Antiques Centre**, 2 Lendal, YO1 2AA TEL: 641445 PARKING: Medium OPEN: MIN: £5 MAX: £5000 PERIOD: 18th-20th century SPECIALIST: Silver, porcelain, militaria, toys GENERAL: Antiques & collectables OTHER INFO: Greek restaurant in building.

## FLAXTON (01904)

**Elm Tree Antiques**, YO6 7RJ TEL: 468462 FAX: 468728 PARKING: Own carpark OPEN: Mon-Sat 9-5, Sun 10-5 MIN: £5 MAX: £10,000 PERIOD: 18th-20th century SPECIALIST: Dining furniture, Staffordshire figures GENERAL: Antiques & furniture OTHER INFO: 10 mins from Castle Howard.

## HUBY (01423)

**Haworth Antiques**, Harrogate Road, LS17 0EF TEL: 734293, (0831) 692263 ASSNS: BWCMG PARKING: Own carpark OPEN: 10-5 & by appt MIN: £100 MAX: £4,000 PERIOD: 18th-20th century SPECIALIST: Antique clock & clocks restoration OTHER INFO: 6 SW Harrogate.

## STILLINGTON (01347)

**Pond Cottage Antiques**, Brandsby Road TEL: 810796 FAX: 810796 PARKING: Own carpark OPEN: 9-7 MIN: £1 MAX: £900 PERIOD: 19th-20th century SPECIALIST: Pine & kitchen antiques GENERAL: Antique & reproduction pine, kitchenalia, dairy items OTHER INFO: B&B accom available 2 or more nights, listed in *Staying off the Beaten Track.*

## BRANDSBY (01347)

**LL Ward & Son**, Bar House, YO6 4RQ TEL: 888651 ASSNS: GMC PARKING: Own carpark OPEN: 9-6 PERIOD: 18th-19th century SPECIALIST: Antique stripped pine.

## HELMSLEY (01439)

**Rievaulx Books**, 18 High Street, YO6 5AG TEL: 70912 PARKING: Easy OPEN: Mon-Sat10.30-5, Sun 2-5 MIN: £1 MAX: £200 PERIOD: 19th-20th century SPECIALIST: Art, architecture & 20th century wood engravings GENERAL: Secondhand & antiquarian books.

**Westway Pine**, Bondgate & Carlton Lane TEL: 771399 & 770172 PARKING: Easy OPEN: Mon-Sat 9-5.30, Sat 10-5 or by appt MIN: £20 MAX: £2000 PERIOD: 18th-20th century SPECIALIST: Pine furniture (restored) OTHER INFO: We offer en-suite B&B's.

**York Cottage Antiques**, 7 Church Street, YO6 5AD TEL: 70833 ASSNS: LAPADA PARKING: Own carpark OPEN: 10-4 MIN: £5 MAX: £5000 PERIOD: 17th-19th century SPECIALIST: Metalware, oak & country furniture.

## MALTON (01653)

**Malton Antiques Market,** 2 Old Maltongate, YO17 0EG TEL: 692732 PARKING: Own carpark (limited space) OPEN: 10-12.30, 2-5 MIN: 310 MAX: £2000 PERIOD: 18th-19th century SPECIALIST: Furniture GENERAL: Pottery, porcelain, brass, copper, silver OTHER INFO: Castle Howard 7 miles, Eden Camp War Museum 2 miles.

**Matthew Maw**, 18 Castlegate, YO17 0DT TEL: 694638 PARKING: Easy OPEN: Mon-Sat 9-5 MIN: £10 MAX: £2000 PERIOD: 19th-20th century GENERAL: Traditional furniture, shipping goods (no smalls).

## NORTON (01653)

**Northern Antiques Company,** 2 Parliament Street, YO17 9HE TEL: 697520 FAX: 694699 PARKING: Own carpark OPEN: Mon-Fri 9-1, 2-5, Sat 9.30-12.30 PERIOD: 18th-19th century GENERAL: An eclectic mix of country furniture, cast iron beds & upholstered furniture OTHER INFO: The shop is upstairs, over the top of the Aga shop. Over the road is an excellent pub, The Cornucopia.

## PICKERING (01751)

**Antiques & Things**, Southgate TEL: 476142 PARKING: Own carpark OPEN: 10-5, closed Wed MIN: £1 MAX: £1000 PERIOD: 19th-20th century GENERAL: Mixture, pottery, smalls, furniture etc OTHER INFO: Highly commended en-suite B&B. Excellent holdiay centre.

**Country Collector,** 11-12 Birdgate (top of Market Place), YO18 7AL TEL: 477481 PARKING: Easy OPEN: Tues, Thurs-Sat 10-5 MIN: £5 MAX: £500

PERIOD: 19th-20th century SPECIALIST: English decorative ceramics, blue & white china, Art Deco pottery GENERAL: Pine furniture, glass, metalware, collectables OTHER INFO: Tourist Information Centre was voted best in the country. Steam Railway & award winning Beck Isle Museum.

**CH Reynolds Antiques,** 122 Eastgate, YO18 7DW TEL: 472785 PARKING: Easy OPEN: Seven days 9.30-5.30 MIN: £5+ PERIOD: 18th-20th century GENERAL: General antiques.

## THORNTON DALE (01751)

**Stable Antiques**, 4 Pickering Road, YO18 7LG TEL: 474332 & 474435 for appts & info PARKING: Medium OPEN: From 2pm & by appt, closed Mon MIN: £3 MAX: £700 PERIOD: 19th-20th century SPECIALIST: Porcelain, furniture GENERAL: Silver, brass, glass, unusual containers OTHER INFO: Carpark with lake & woodland 2 mins on foot. Nearby renowned Brompton Forge Restaurant.

## SNAINTON (01723)

**Cottage Antiques**, 19 High Street, YO13 9AE TEL: 859577 PARKING: Medium OPEN: Mon-Fri 8.30-5, Sat 8.30-12 MIN: £1 MAX: £4000 PERIOD: 18th-19th century SPECIALIST: Longcase clocks & Victorian rocking horses OTHER INFO: Hand made furniture & antique shops in village.

## SCARBOROUGH (01723)

**Hanover Antiques,** 10 Hanover Road, YO11 1LS TEL: 374175 PARKING: Medium OPEN: 11-3 MIN: £1 MAX: £500 PERIOD: 19th-20th century SPECIALIST: Militaria, medals, badges, bayonets GENERAL: Pottery, bric a brac, etc OTHER INFO: Close to Stephen Joseph Theatre.

## FLAMBOROUGH (01262)

**Lesley Berry Antiques**, The Manor House, YO15 1PD TEL: 850943 PARKING: Own carpark OPEN: 9.30-6 MIN: £2 MAX: £1500 PERIOD: 17th-19th century GENERAL: General antiques OTHER INFO: Accommodation available.

## BRIDLINGTON (01262)

**CJ & AJ Dixon Ltd (Military Medals),** 23 Prospect Street, YO15 2AE TEL: 603348 & 676877 FAX: 606600 ASSNS: BNTA, OMRS, OMSA, MMSSA, MCCC PARKING: Easy OPEN: Mon-Fri 9.30-5, Sat by appt MIN: £5 MAX: £20,000 PERIOD: 18th-20th century SPECIALIST: Gallantry groups & Victorian campaigns GENERAL: British orders, medals decorations.

**Priory Antiques**, 47-49 High Street, YO16 4PR TEL: 601365 PARKING: Easy OPEN: Tues, Wed, Fri 10-5 MIN: £5 MAX: £4500 PERIOD: 18th-19th century SPECIALIST: Furniture GENERAL: Metalware, clocks, barometers OTHER INFO: Best fish 'n' chips for miles.

## KILHAM (01262)

**Old Ropery Antiques,** East Street, YO25 0SG TEL: 420233 PARKING: Easy OPEN: Tues-Sat 9-5 MIN: £100 MAX: £6000 PERIOD: 17th-18th century SPECIALIST: Clocks & barometers GENERAL: Some furniture & scientific instruments OTHER INFO: Kilham is a small village set in the heart of the Yorkshire Wolds, of which it was once the capital.

## DRIFFIELD (01377)

**Antique Pine & Furniture Shop**, Smith & Smith Designs, 58a Middle Street North, YO25 7SU TEL: 256321 PARKING: Easy OPEN: Mon-Sat 9.30-5 MIN: £25 MAX: £2000 PERIOD: 18th-20th century SPECIALIST: Pine & country furniture.

**The Crested China Company**, Station House, YO25 7PY TEL: 257042, 255002 PARKING: Own carpark OPEN: By appt or take a chance MIN: £1 MAX: £400 mostly PERIOD: Mainly 1880-1930 SPECIALIST: Goss & crested china OTHER INFO: Bell Hotel, superb facilities.

## BEVERLEY (01482)

**Hawley Antiques,** 5 North Bar Within TEL: 868193 ASSNS: LAPADA PARKING: Easy OPEN: 9.30-5 MIN: £10 MAX: £5000 PERIOD: 18th-19th century GENERAL: Furniture & general antiques.

**James Starkey Fine Art**, 49 Highgate, HU17 0DN TEL: 881179 FAX: 861644 PARKING: Easy OPEN: Mon-Fri 10-5, Sat 10-1 MIN: £20 MAX: £20,000 PERIOD: 17th-20th century SPECIALIST: Modern marine works GENERAL: Few antiques & paintings OTHER INFO: In the shadow of Beverley Minster. Local hotel - Beverley Arms.

## HULL (01482)

**Avenue Antiques,** 24 Princes Avenue, HU5 3QA TEL: 445342 PARKING: Medium OPEN: Tues,

Wed, Fri, Sat 10.30-5 MIN: £2.50 MAX: £750 PERIOD: 20th century SPECIALIST: Art Deco ceramics & collectables OTHER INFO: Hull now boasts a rejuvenated old town area with many interesting buildings, museums & a marina.

**Grannies Parlour & Grannies Treasures Antique Centre**, 33 Anlaby Road, HUI 2PG TEL: 228258 PARKING: Medium OPEN: Mon-Sat 11-5 MIN: £1 MAX: £500 PERIOD: 19th-20th century SPECIALIST: Advertising items, dolls, teddies, kitchenalia GENERAL: All collectables & antiques OTHER INFO: Town centre 10 mins.

**De Grey Antiques,** 96 De Grey Street, Beverley Road, HU5 2SB TEL: 442184 PARKING: Easy OPEN: 10.30-5.30 MIN: £5 MAX: £700 PERIOD: 19th century GENERAL: Glass, china, paintings, metalware, furniture.

**David K Hakeney Antiques**, Albion House, Albion Street, HU1 3TE TEL & FAX: 228190, mobile 0860 507774 ASSNS: LAPADA PARKING: Own carpark OPEN: Mon-Sat 10-6 or by appt MIN: £10 MAX: £5000 PERIOD: 19th century GENERAL: General antiques, porcelain, decorative items OTHER INFO: New premises after 23 years in George Street.

**David K Hakeney Antiques Trade Warehouse**, 400 Wincolmlee TEL: 228190, (0860) 507774 FAX: 228190 ASSNS: LAPADA PARKING: Medium OPEN: Mon-Fri 10-5, Sat 10-1 MIN: £10 MAX: £5000 PERIOD: 18th-20th century GENERAL: General antiques.

**Imperial Antiques**, 397 Hessle Road, HU3 4EH TEL & FAX: 327439 PARKING: Easy OPEN: 9-6 MIN: £50 MAX: £1000 PERIOD: 18th-19th century SPECIALIST: Antique & old stripped pine OTHER INFO: Sunnybank Hotel.

**Lesley's Antiques,** 329 Hessle Road, HU3 4BL TEL: 323986 & 646280 PARKING: Easy OPEN: 10-4 MIN: £5 MAX: £200 PERIOD: 19th-20th century SPECIALIST: Victoriana GENERAL: Smalls & some earlier items OTHER INFO: Our Victorian shop is an antique in itself. We endeavour to create an authentic Victorian atmosphere.

**Pearson Antiques,** 4 Dalton Street, off Cleveland Street TEL: 29647 OPEN: Mon-Fri 10-5 MIN: £5 MAX: £1000 PERIOD: 18th-20th century SPECIALIST: Victorian full-size models GENERAL: Furniture, shipping goods, pottery etc.

## PATRINGTON (01964)

**Clyde Antiques,** 12 Market Place TEL: 630650 PARKING: Easy OPEN: Tues, Thurs-Sat 10-5 MIN: £3 MAX: £2000 PERIOD: 18th-20th century GENERAL: General antiques OTHER INFO: Supposedly Patrington has the most beautiful village church in England.

## SOUTH CAVE (01430)

**The Old Copper Shop & Posthouse Antiques**, 69 & 75 Market Place TEL: 423988 PARKING: Easy OPEN: Mon, Wed-Sat 9.30-4.30 MIN: £5 MAX: £1000 PERIOD: 19th-20th century GENERAL: General antiques.

**Penny Farthing Antiques**, 60 Market Place, HU15 2AT TEL: 422958 PARKING: Easy OPEN: Mon-Sat 9.30-5 MIN: £5 MAX: £3000 PERIOD: 18th-20th century SPECIALIST: Brass & iron bedsteads GENERAL: General antiques & collectables.

## MARKET WEIGHTON (01430)

**Houghton Hall Antiques**, Cliffe-Northcave Road (1 mile), YO4 3RE TEL: 873234 PARKING: Own carpark OPEN: Seven days 8.30-4.30 MIN: £5 MAX: £6000 PERIOD: 17th-20th century SPECIALIST: Furniture GENERAL: General antiques OTHER INFO: Londesborough Arms Hotel & restaurant, George Hotel Beverley.

## SEATON ROSS (01759)

**Lewis Hickson MBHI,** Rosewell TEL: 318850 ASSNS: BHI PARKING: Own carpark OPEN: By appt MIN: £500 MAX: £5000 PERIOD: 17th-19th century SPECIALIST: Longcase & bracket clocks OTHER INFO: Comprehensive specialised repair service on the premises to all antique clocks.

# North Yorkshire

*The Wakeman's House, Ripon*

This tour stays mainly on the Plain of York, a rich farming region, between the North Yorkshire Moors to the east and the Yorkshire Dales to the west, both with magnificent scenery. The region is full of history and contains many picturesque towns and villages.The remains of many large religious houses may still be seen.

**Boston Spa**, in West Yorkshire, is the first to be visited. On the River Wharfe, the town became a well-known spa until nearby Harrogate became the fashionable place in the area for taking the waters. However, with the Georgian houses, it still retains an air of elegance. Crossing into North Yorkshire, the route comes via **Kirk Deighton** to **Knaresborough**. Sited on a steep gorge cut by the River Nidd, terraces of houses rise up the sides and cobbled lanes run down to the river. There are also the remains of a castle originally started by Serlo de Burg who received the land from William the Conqueror. Richard II was imprisoned here for a time and one of the knights who killed Thomas à Becket, Sir Hugh de Morville, stayed here. Another local attraction is the Dropping Well whose water has such a high mineral content that objects dropped into it petrify. Legend has it that the prophetess, Mother Shipton, was born in a nearby cave. The grandest of Gothic Revival houses is four miles west. Allerton Park's Great Hall and Dining Room are reputed to be amongst England's finest carved wood rooms

Only four miles away is the elegant town of **Harrogat**e, a relative upstart that owes its existence to the 18th century fashion for spa water. The original spring was discovered in the then Knaresborough Forest in 1571 by a local man. He had the soil around paved and it was named Tewit Well. At the end of the 18th century the town started to grow although the centre was mostly constructed in the 19th century. An original spring is still marked by a domed building in The Stray, the common that runs around the southern side of Harrogate. The Royal Pump Room Museum, an octagonal building from 1842, stands over a sulphur spring and also houses the local museum.

The tour continues through the villages of **Killinghall, Markington** and **Birstwith** and then arrives in **Pateley Bridge**. In the summer, this very attractive town gives the impression of being full of flowers from the hanging baskets and window boxes that adorn the houses. The Nidderdale Museum, displaying aspects of 19th century Dales life, is housed in the town's former workhouse.

Next is **Ripon** standing at the meeting of the Rivers Cover, Skell and Ure. The cathedral is the most outstanding feature of this thriving market town conferring upon it the status of city. It was built over many centuries and the structure well illustrates the evolution and change that took place in ecclesiastical architecture. The crypt was built in 670 AD by St Wilfrid to protect the bones of saints. His church, built above the crypt, was destroyed by marauding Danes but rebuilt by visiting Archbishops of York . Because a succession of Archbishops were responsible for the rebuilding the mixture of architectural styles occurred. The chapter house dates from

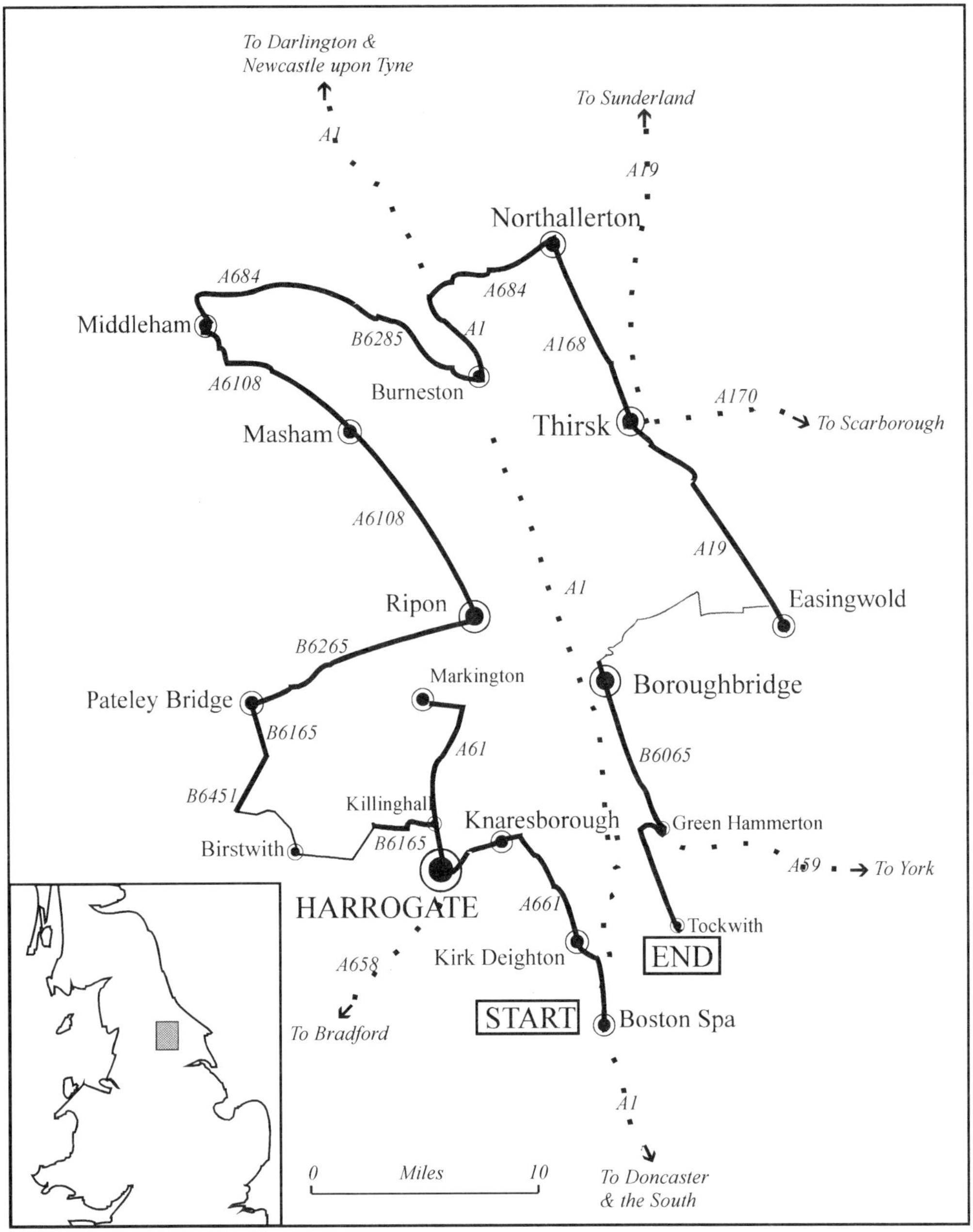
To Darlington &
Newcastle upon Tyne
A1
To Sunderland
A19
Northallerton
A684
Middleham
A684
B6285
A1
A168
Burneston
A6108
A170
Thirsk
To Scarborough
Masham
A6108
A19
A1
Ripon
Easingwold
B6265
Markington
Boroughbridge
Pateley Bridge
B6165
A61
B6065
B6451
Killinghall
Knaresborough
Green Hammerton
Birstwith
B6165
A59
To York
HARROGATE
A661
Tockwith
A658
Kirk Deighton
END
To Bradford
START
Boston Spa
A1
0
Miles
10
To Doncaster
& the South

*The Royal Pump Room Museum, Harrogate*
*By courtesy of Harrogate International Centre*

about the 12th century and is typical of the Norman style. The Early-English style may be seen in the simple beauty of the west front. In contrast, the east windows are a breath-taking example of the Decorated style from approximately the 14th century. The Perpendicular style, unique to English stonemasons, may be seen in the reconstructed medieval nave. After the Reformation, the Archbishops of York no longer held such importance and Ripon's church lost its prime purpose, but continued to serve as the parish church even though now too large. However, by 1836 came designation as the cathedral for this part of Yorkshire as the area's population had grown considerably and a separate diocese was deemed necessary. Restoration work and upgrading of the interior was carried out and included an Arts and Craft movement pulpit made from bronze and marble and the fine reredos behind the high altar.

A 90 feet high obelisk surmounted by a weather vane in the shape of a wakeman's horn stands in Ripon market square. In medieval times the wakeman was responsible for sounding the horn each night to summon the Town Watch to their duty. Although the office of Wakeman was replaced by the Mayor in 1617 the Hornblower still sounds the horn from each corner of the market square at 9pm every evening. The house of the last Wakeman and the first Mayor of Ripon may be seen at the corner of the square.

There are a number of charming places to visit near Ripon. Amongst these are the ruins of Fountains Abbey, now awarded World Heritage status. These still beautiful ruins are all that remain of one of the richest Cistercian abbeys in England. Three miles south off the A61 there is a fine example of a moated manor house, Markenfield Hall. Then four miles south east is Newby Hall, a lovely Adam style house.

Continuing along the A6108, **Masham**, on the River Ure, is pretty with a large market place and famous for a very strong local beer, Threakston's Old Peculiar. Further on, **Middleham** is closely associated with Richard III. The ruined castle, once his home, was started in the latter part of the 12th century.and later became part of the estate of the Earl of Warwick. When he was killed in the Battle of Barnet in 1471 it passed to the Crown and was given to Richard of Gloucester, later Richard III. After Richard's defeat at the Battle of Bosworth it again passed to the Crown and was neglected until it fell into ruins. The stump of a cross in the market square is thought to represent Richard III's heraldic boar.

The village of **Burneston** is next followed by the capital of North Yorkshire, **Northallerton**. A settlement has stood here since Roman times and now it is a busy centre for the district as well as for visitors to the area. **Thirsk**, nine miles away, was the birthplace of the founder of Lord's Cricket Ground, Thomas Lord. A pretty market town it is ideally situated for exploring the North Yorkshire Moors. Sutton Bank, a few miles east is a precipitous escarpment from which hang-gliders take off. There are beautiful views from the top..

After detouring along the A19 to **Easingwold**, the route arrives,via country roads, in **Boroughbridge**. Once on a major coaching road, it has the large inns typical of coaching towns. Now largely bypassed the town is still a quiet pleasant place to visit. On the River Ure, its bridge was once a crossing place between the former West and North Ridings of Yorkshire. Outside the town stands the Devil's Arrows, three 20 feet high monoliths dating from the Bronze Age. Aldborough, to the south east, is a charming village which, 2000 years ago, was once the main settlement for a Celtic tribe in the area. The remains of a Roman town have also been found here and the local museum displays the finds, including pottery, glass and metalwork.

This tour ends by visiting the villages of **Green Hammerton** and **Tockwith** which is about a mile from the battlefield of Marston Moor where, in 1644, Parliamentary troops fought and won the decisive battle of the Civil War against the Royalists.

## ANTIQUE DEALERS

### BOSTON SPA (01937)

**London House Oriental Rugs & Carpets**, 238-240 High Street, LS23 6AD TEL: 845123 PARKING: Easy OPEN: Mon-Sat 9.30-5.30 MIN: £20 MAX: £800 PERIOD: 19th-20th century SPECIALIST: 200 12-25 ft lengths GENERAL: 4000 fine decorative oriental rugs OTHER INFO: Smallest spa in England, 1 min off A1.

### KIRK DEIGHTON (01937)

**Elden Antiques**, 23 Ashdale View, LS22 4DS TEL: 584770 PARKING: Own carpark OPEN: 8.30-6 MIN: £5 MAX: £1500 PERIOD: 18th-20th century GENERAL: Furniture, china, pottery, brassware.

### KNARESBOROUGH (01423)

**Robert Aagard Ltd**, Frogmire House, Stockwell Road, HG5 0JP TEL: 864805 FAX: 869356 PARKING: Own carpark OPEN: 9.30-5 PERIOD: 18th-20th century SPECIALIST: Antique fire surrounds.

**Bowkett,** 9 Abbey Road, HG5 8HY TEL: 866112 PARKING: Easy OPEN: 9-6 MIN: 50p MAX: £500 PERIOD: 19th-20th century GENERAL: Furniture, books, bric a brac, collectors items.

**Milton J Holgate,** 36 Gracious Street, HG5 8DS TEL: 865219 ASSNS: BADA PARKING: Medium OPEN: 9-5.30, closed Thurs PERIOD: 17th-20th century SPECIALIST: Pre-1830 fine English furniture GENERAL: Antique accessories OTHER INFO: Knaresborough is an historic market town with a Norman castle, river with cliffed gorge. Several famous historic characters like the soothsayer, Mother Shipton, & the roadbuilder, Blind Jack.

**Gordon Reece Gallery,** 24 Finicle Street, HG5 8AA TEL: 866219 FAX: 868165 PARKING: Own carpark OPEN: Mon-Wed, Fri, Sat 10.30-5, Sun 2-5 MIN: £5 MAX: £6000 PERIOD: 17th-20th century SPECIALIST: Over 2000 fine old kilim rugs GENERAL: Tribal & folk arts, Oriental ceramics from 3000BC onwards OTHER INFO: 9 exhibitions a year focusing on the artefacts of non-European cultures.

**Reflections,** 23 Waterside, HG5 8DE TEL: 862005 PARKING: Medium OPEN: Tues-Sun 11-5.30 MIN: £5 MAX: £1000 PERIOD: 19th-20th century GENERAL: Small Victorian & later furniture, collectables, pictures, prints OTHER INFO: Picturesque riverside location.

**Charles Shaw Antiques**, The Old Vicarage, 2 Station Road (off A59), HG5 9AA TEL: 867715 PARKING: Own carpark OPEN: 8-6 MIN: £10 MAX: £7000 PERIOD: 17th-20th century

SPECIALIST: Taxidermy & country items GENERAL: Old books & pictures, antiques.

**John Thompson Antiques**, Swadforth House, Gracious Street, HG5 8DT TEL: 864698 ASSNS: LAPADA PARKING: Own carpark OPEN: 9-5.30 closed Thurs MIN: £100 MAX: £30,000 PERIOD: 18th-19th century SPECIALIST: Clocks & musical boxes GENERAL: Furniture, decorative items.

## HARROGATE (01423)

**Bloomers Antique Costume & Textiles**, 41 Cheltenham Crescent, HG1 1DN TEL: 569389 PARKING: Difficult OPEN: 11-5 MIN: £1 MAX: £1500 PERIOD: 18th-20th century SPECIALIST: Antique lace & fans GENERAL: All textiles inc shawls, quilts, linens, costume & accessories, beadwork, embroideries.

**Derbyshire Antiques Ltd**, 27 Montpellier Parade, HG1 2TG TEL: 503115 PARKING: Easy OPEN: Mon-Sat 10-5.30 MIN: £50 MAX: £20,000 PERIOD: 17th-18th century SPECIALIST: Oak, walnut GENERAL: Furniture, decorative items.

**Dragon Antiques**, 10 Dragon Road, HG1 5DF TEL: 562037 PARKING: Very easy OPEN: Mon-Sat 11-6 & by appt MIN: £5 MAX: £1750 PERIOD: 19th-20th century GENERAL: Glass, china pottery, cameras. OTHER INFO: Art Deco cabinets.

**The Ginnel Antique Centre**, The Ginnel, HG1 2RB TEL: 508857 PARKING: Easy OPEN: Mon-Sat 9.30-5.30 MIN: £5 MAX: £10,000 PERIOD: 18th-20th century SPECIALIST: Silver GENERAL: Furniture, porcelain, paintings, silver, jewellery.

**Grandads Attic**

**2 Granville Road, HG1 2BY TEL: 503003 PARKING: Own carpark OPEN: 10-5 MIN: 25p MAX: £75-100 (occasionally over £100) PERIOD: 19th-20th century SPECIALIST: All types of old planes, tools GENERAL: Kitchenalia, agricultural & garden tools. Small amount of china OTHER INFO: One visitor came into my shop & remarked "What a strange little shop!" Most say it is like a museum, I say at least you can buy any item. Plenty of interesting surrounding countryside, Heartbeat country about 25 miles from Harrogate.**

**Michael Green Traditional Interiors**, Library House, Regent Parade TEL: 560452 PARKING: Easy OPEN: Mon-Fri 9-5.30, Sat 9-4 MIN: £3 MAX: £2500 PERIOD: 18th-20th century SPECIALIST: Pine furniture GENERAL: Old kitchen treasures, Victorian doors, collectables, kitchenalia. Restoration OTHER INFO: Delightful position overlooking Christchurch Stray.

**Grove Collectors Centre,** Grove Road, HG1 5EW TEL: 561680 PARKING: Own carpark OPEN: Mon-Thurs, Sat 10-4.30 MIN: £1 MAX: £2000 PERIOD: 19th-20th century SPECIALIST: All collectables GENERAL: Furniture, bric a brac, china, glass, silver.

**Havelocks Antique Pine,** 27 Westmoreland Street, HG1 5AY TEL: 506721 PARKING: Easy OPEN: 7 days 10-5 MIN: £5 MAX: £1000 PERIOD: 18th-19th century SPECIALIST: Unusual period pieces GENERAL: Early Victorian pine furniture.

**Haworth Antiques**, 26 Cold Bath Road, HG2 0NA TEL: 521401 ASSNS: BCWMG PARKING: Own carpark OPEN: Mon-Sat 10-5 & by appt MIN: £50 MAX: £4000 PERIOD: 18th-20th century SPECIALIST: Antique clocks, clock restoration GENERAL: Useful furniture OTHER INFO: We back on to Crown Hotel. Excellent restaurants.

**London House Oriental Rugs & Carpets**, 9 Montpellier Parade, HG1 2TJ TEL: 567167 PARKING: Easy OPEN: Mon-Sat 10.30-5.30 MIN: £20 MAX: £8000 PERIOD: 19th-20th century SPECIALIST: 200 individual carpets (12-25 ft) GENERAL: 4000 decorative individual Oriental carpets & rugs.

**Charles Lumb & Sons Ltd**, 2 Montpellier Gardens, HG1 2TF TEL: 503776 FAX: 530074 ASSNS: BADA PARKING: Easy OPEN: Mon-Sat 9-1, 2-6 MIN: £50 MAX: £25,000 PERIOD: 18th-19th century SPECIALIST: English furniture & decorative accessories OTHER INFO: Close to Drum & Monkey restaurant.

**McTague of Harrogate**, 17-19 Cheltenham Mount, HG1 1DW TEL: 567086 ASSNS: FATG PARKING: Easy OPEN: Mon-Sat 9.30-5.30 MIN: £5 MAX: £1000 PERIOD: 18th-19th century SPECIALIST: Prints, watercolours GENERAL: Some oils.

**Montpellier Gallery,** 12 Montpellier Street, HG1 2TQ TEL: 500460 FAX: 528400 PARKING: Easy OPEN: Tues-Sat 10-5.30 PERIOD: 20th century GENERAL: Paintings, prints, bronzes, sculpture, interior design.

**Ogden of Harrogate Ltd,** 38 James Street, HG1 1RQ TEL: 504123 FAX: 522283 ASSNS: NAG,

BADA PARKING: Easy MIN: £50 MAX: £50,000 PERIOD: 19th-20th century SPECIALIST: Jewellery & silver GENERAL: Silver plate, watches, clocks.

**Paraphernalia**, 38a Cold Bath Road, HG1 0NA TEL: 567968 PARKING: Easy OPEN: Weekdays 10-5 MIN: £1 MAX: £250 PERIOD: 19th-20th century SPECIALIST: Old postcards, Goss & crested china GENERAL: Commemoratives, small furniture, decorative items & collectables OTHER INFO: Browsers welcome. Valley Gardens café 300 yards.

**Parker Gallery**, The Ginnel Antique Centre, Corn Exchange Buildings, HG1 2RB TEL: 567182 PARKING: Easy OPEN: Mon-Sat 9.30-5.30 MIN: £50 MAX: £3000 PERIOD: 19th-20th century SPECIALIST: Yorkshire impressionists GENERAL: Oils & watercolours.

**Paul M Peters Antiques**, 15 Bower Road, HG1 1BE TEL: 560118 ASSNS: LAPADA PARKING: Own carpark OPEN: Mon-Fri 10-5 MIN: £10 MAX: £5000 PERIOD: 17th-20th century SPECIALIST: Oriental & European ceramics & works of art OTHER INFO: 99% business done with the trade.

**Elaine Phillips Antiques Ltd,** 1-2 Royal Parade, HG1 2SZ TEL: 569745 ASSNS: BADA, CINOA PARKING: Easy OPEN: Mon-Sat 9.30-5.03 & by appt PERIOD: 17th-18th century SPECIALIST: English oak & associated items GENERAL: English furniture, metalware, treen, textiles, interior design service.

**Smith's The Rink Ltd**, Dragon Road, HG1 5DR TEL: 567890 FAX: 520416 PARKING: Easy OPEN: Mon-Sat 9-5.30 MIN: £70 MAX: £60,000 PERIOD: 17th-20th century SPECIALIST: English Edwardian, English & French Victorian furniture.

**Sutcliffe Galleries**, 5 Royal Parade, HG1 2SZ TEL: 562976 FAX: 528729 ASSNS: BADA, CINOA PARKING: Medium OPEN: Mon-Sat 10-1, 2-5 MIN: £1500 MAX: £40,000 PERIOD: 19th century SPECIALIST: Fine British & European oil paintings OTHER INFO: Fine restaurants.

**Thorntons of Harrogate,** 1 Montpellier Galleries, HG1 2TF TEL: 504118 ASSNS: LAPADA PARKING: Easy OPEN: 9.30-5.30 MIN: £50 MAX: £30,000 PERIOD: 17th-19th century SPECIALIST: Clocks, barometers GENERAL: Furniture, ceramics, objects, paintings, bronzes, etc.

**Walker Galleries Ltd**, 6 Montpellier Galleries, HG1 2TF TEL & FAX: 567933 ASSNS: BADA, LAPADA PARKING: Medium OPEN: Mon-Sat 9.30-5.30 MIN: £50 MAX: £25,000 PERIOD: 19th-20th century SPECIALIST: Paintings & watercolours OTHER INFO: Next door to excellent Drum & Monkey fish restaurant. Separate contemporary gallery at 16 Crescent Road.

**Christopher Warner**, 15 Princes Street, HG1 1NG TEL: 503617 ASSNS: BADA PARKING: Medium OPEN: Daily 10-5 MIN: £100 MAX: £16,500 PERIOD: 17th-20th century as available SPECIALIST: 18th-19th century silver GENERAL: Quality secondhand & modern jewellery, some silver OTHER INFO: Historic castles, National Trust.

**Windmill Antiques**, 4 Montpellier Mews, HG1 2TJ TEL: 530502 ASSNS: LAPADA PARKING: Easy OPEN: Mon-Sat 10-5.30 MIN: £20 MAX: £3500 PERIOD: 18th-19th century SPECIALIST: Writing & jewellery boxes, Victorian rocking horses, child's chairs GENERAL: Quality furniture, copper, brass & boxes, caddies, some silver OTHER INFO: In pretty courtyard with other antique shops & restaurants closeby.

**Yorkshire Country Living & Antiques,** Riverside Cellars, The Mill, Glasshouses, HG3 5QH TEL: 711947 & 711223 PARKING: Own carpark OPEN: 11-30-4.30, closed Mon & Tues or by appt MIN: £10 MAX: £2000 PERIOD: 17th-19th century SPECIALIST: Oak & country furniture & decorative items at realistic prices OTHER INFO: Tearooms & wine tasting, etc.

## KILLINGHALL (01423)

**Norwood House Antiques**, 88 Ripon Road, HG3 2DH TEL: 506468 PARKING: Easy OPEN: 10-5, closed Wed MIN: £50 MAX: £10,000 PERIOD: 18th-19th century GENERAL: English & Continental porcelain, furniture, prints, paintings, bronzes.

## MARKINGTON (01765)

**Daleside Antiques**, Hinks Hall Lane, HG3 3NU TEL: 677888 FAX: 677886 PARKING: Own carpark OPEN: Mon-Sat 7-6 MIN: £10 MAX: £4000 PERIOD: 18th-19th century SPECIALIST: Pine furniture & architectural wooden features.

## BIRSTWITH (01423)

**John Pearson Antique Clock Restoration**, Church Cottage, HG3 2NG TEL: 770828 ASSNS: BHI PARKING: Own carpark OPEN: Anytime by appt MIN: £1000 PERIOD: 17th-19th century

SPECIALIST: English longcase clocks GENERAL: Carriage, wall, bracket & French clocks OTHER INFO: Complete restoration for every single part, internationally recognised especially for clock dials.

## PATELEY BRIDGE (01423)

**Cat in the Window Antiques**, 22 High Street, HG3 5JU TEL: 711343 PARKING: Easy OPEN: Tues, Thurs-Sat 2-5 & by appt MIN: £1 MAX: £500 PERIOD: 19th-20th century SPECIALIST: Linens, metals GENERAL: Small furniture, collectables, baubles, bangles & beads. Pictures, ceramics, glass + lots more OTHER INFO: Pretty town, wonderful scenery, lots of flowers in spring & summer, Magical pre-Christmas.

**Brian Loomes**, Calf Haugh Farmhouse, HG3 5HW TEL: 711163 PARKING: Own carpark OPEN: 6 days by appt MIN: £300 MAX: £10,000 PERIOD: 17th-19th century SPECIALIST: British clocks only (large stock), Author of many clock reference books OTHER INFO: Very picturesque area, good walking country known as Little Switzerland.

## RIPON (01765)

**Balmain Antiques**, 13 High Skellgate, HG4 1BA TEL: 601294 PARKING: Own carpark PERIOD: 18th-19th century GENERAL: General antiques.

**Sigma Antiques & Fine Art**, Water Skellgate TEL: 603163 FAX: 690933 PARKING: Medium OPEN: Mon-Sat 10.30-5 & by appt MIN: £2 MAX: £50,000 PERIOD: 17th-20th century GENERAL: Huge stock, furniture, decorative items, bronze, porcelain, jewellery, paintings, silver, objets d'art etc OTHER INFO: Occasional antiquities. Fountain Abbey, Studley Royal, Newby Hall, Harewood House.

## MASHAM (01765)

**Aura Antiques**, 1-3 Silver Street, HG4 4DX TEL: 689315 PARKING: Own carpark OPEN: Mon-Sat 9.30-5 MIN: £10 MAX: £5000 PERIOD: 18th-19th century SPECIALIST: Period mahogany especially dining furniture GENERAL: Antiques & furniture OTHER INFO: Next to Floodlite Restaurant.

## MIDDLEHAM (01969)

**White Boar Antiques & Books**, Kirkgate, DL8 4PF TEL: 23901 PARKING: Easy OPEN: 10-5.30 MAX: £1000 PERIOD: 19th-20th century SPECIALIST: Books GENERAL: Small china, porcelain OTHER INFO: Good facilities



## BURNESTON (01677)

**W Greenwood Fine Art**, The Gallery, Oakdene, DL8 2JE TEL: 424830, 423217 PARKING: Own carpark OPEN: By appt MIN: £100 MAX: £5000 PERIOD: 18th-20th century SPECIALIST: Oils & watercolours of Yorkshire GENERAL: Paintings & frames.

## NORTHALLERTON (01609)

**Antique & Art**, 7 Central Arcade, DL7 8PY TEL: 772051 PARKING: Easy OPEN: Mon-Wed, Fri, Sat 10-4 MIN: £5 MAX: £2500 PERIOD: 19th-20th century GENERAL: Mainly small items, silver, EPNS, china, furniture.

**Collectors Corner**, 145-146 High Street TEL: 777623 PARKING: Easy OPEN: Mon-Sat 10-12.30, 1.30-4 MIN: £2 MAX: £200 PERIOD: 18th-20th century SPECIALIST: Clothes, books, postcards GENERAL: Abundance of mixed smalls OTHER INFO: Market days Wed & Sat.

## THIRSK (01845)

**Cottage Antiques,** 1 Market Place TEL: 522536 PARKING: Easy OPEN: 9-5, closed Wed MIN: £10 MAX: £2000 PERIOD: 18th-20th century SPECIALIST: Pottery & porcelain, brass & copper GENERAL: Country farmhouse furniture OTHER INFO: James Herriot's (the famous vet) town, hotels, restaurants, B&Bs aplenty.

## EASINGWOLD (01347)

**42 Antiques**, Long Street TEL: 821078 PARKING: Easy OPEN: Mon-Sat 9-6 PERIOD: 18th-20th century GENERAL: This 'n' that, good antiques when possible OTHER INFO: The fun shop, everything sold on the minimum profit.

**Old Flames**, 30 Long Street, YO6 3HT TEL: 821188 PARKING: Easy OPEN: Mon-Sat 10-5 MIN: £60 MAX: £2500 PERIOD: 18th-19th century SPECIALIST: Original fireplaces GENERAL: Architectural antiques, period lighting.

**White House Farm Antiques,** Whitehouse Farm, Thirsk Road, YO6 3NF TEL: 821479 PARKING: Own carpark OPEN: By phone call MIN: £5 MAX: £5000 PERIOD: 18th-20th century SPECIALIST: Architectural.

## BOROUGHBRIDGE (01423)

**Jeffrey Bates**, Bridge Street, YO5 9LA TEL & FAX: 324258 PARKING: Own carpark OPEN: Mon-Wed, Fri, Sat 10.30-5 MIN: £5 MAX: £2500 PERIOD: 18th-19th century SPECIALIST: Objects of vertu, pictures, canes, instruments GENERAL: Unusual decorative collectors' items, silver, books on India & Asia.

**Collectables,** 2 The Stoneyard, 12 Fishergate, YO5 9AL TEL: 324374 FAX: (01937 580396) PARKING: Own carpark OPEN: Wed-Sat 11-5.30 MIN: £10 MAX: £1000 MIN: £10 MAX: £1000 PERIOD: 19th-20th century GENERAL: Small furniture, porcelain, glass, silver & copper, art, originals & prints OTHER INFO: Many interesting local inns including The Crown Hotel where Mary Queen of Scots met her fellow conspirators.

**Country Antiques**, 38 High Street, YO5 9AW TEL: 340300 PARKING: Easy OPEN: Mon-Sat 10-4 PERIOD: 18th-19th century SPECIALIST: Silver of all periods GENERAL: Small furniture, treen, metalware.

**Joan Eyles Antiques,** The Stone Yard, 12 Fishergate, YO5 9AL TEL: 322481 & 323367 OPEN: Fri & Sat or by appt MIN: £10 MAX: £1000 PERIOD: 18th-19th century SPECIALIST: Fireplace furniture GENERAL: Small items of all kinds, small furniture OTHER INFO: 2 good hotels.

**Galloway Antiques**, High Street, YO5 9AW TEL: 324602 ASSNS: LAPADA PARKING: Easy OPEN: Mon-Sat 9.15-5.15, Sun 11-4 MIN: £30 MAX: £10,000 PERIOD: 17th-20th century GENERAL: Furniture, paintings, decorative items.

**Anthony Graham Antiques**, Aberure, Bridge Street, YO5 9LA TEL: 323952 PARKING: Own carpark OPEN: Mon-Wed, Fri, Sat 10.30-5 MIN: £5 MAX: £2000 PERIOD: 18th-19th century GENERAL: Smaller items, some furniture, prints.

**St James House Antiques**, 7 St James House TEL: 322508 PARKING: Own carpark OPEN: Mon-Wed, Fri, Sat 9-5.30 MIN: £5 MAX: £5,000 PERIOD: 18th-19th century GENERAL: General antiques. Restoration.

**RS Wilson & Sons**, 4 Hall Square, YO5 9AN TEL: 322417 ASSNS: BADA PARKING: Easy OPEN: Mon-Sat 9-5.30 but Thurs closed pm PERIOD: 17th-19th century GENERAL: Furniture & accessories.

## GREEN HAMMERTON (01423)

**The Main Pine Company**, Grangewood, The Green, YO5 8DB TEL: 330451 FAX: 331278 PARKING: Own carpark OPEN: Mon-Sat 9-5, Sun 11-4 MIN: £1 MAX: £5,000 PERIOD: 18th-20th century SPECIALIST: Antique pine.

## TOCKWITH (01423)

**Raymond Tomlinson (Antiques) Ltd**, Moorside, YO5 8QG TEL: 358833 FAX: 358188 ASSNS: LAPADA PARKING: Own carpark OPEN: Mon-Fri 8-5, Sat 9-4.30 (trade only) MIN: £5 MAX: £5000 PERIOD: 18th-20th century SPECIALIST: Longcase clocks, Oriental ceramics GENERAL: 52,000 sq ft warehouse of antique & repro furniture. OTHER INFO: Phone for map & directions. Export & packing service. Large restoration facility.

# The Lake District

*A view of Lake Bassenthwaite seen from the B5292*

The Lake District, in Cumbria, now mostly a National Park covering about 900 square miles, contains magnificent lakes and windswept fell.This is a dramatically beautiful region with some of England's highest mountains.

The first stop, however, is in Lancashire just outstide the Lake District. Standing on the River Lune, the county town of **Lancaster** has been in existence since at least Roman times. The Roman fortress of *Longoricum* stood on the site of the present castle and traces of the fosse may still be seen on the north side of the hill. The castle was started in 1094 and later enlarged by John of Gaunt, the Earl of Lancaster and father of Henry IV. Further additions were made in Elizabethan times.

The River Lune is tidal at this point and much of Lancaster's medieval prosperity came through its role as a port. This continued throughout the centuries and by the 18th century Lancaster was the fourth busiest slave-trading port in England. The Custom House on St George's Quay dates from this period and now houses the Maritime Museum. Another museum, at 15 Castle Hill, is an artisan's house furnished in the style of 1820. In Castle Street stands the 1620-built Judges Lodgings, the town's oldest house. Between 1826 and 1975 it was used by visiting judges ccoming for the assizes three times a year. Lancaster also has a Roman Catholic cathedral and a university.

Next come **Middleham** and **Yealand Conyers** with a Friends' Meeting House dating from 1692 although damaged by fire and largely rebuilt in the middle of the 18th century. The visit to **Holme** brings the tour into the Lake District and is followed by **Kendal**. The economy of this ancient market town was originally based upon wool but now it is the administrative centre for the Lake District National Park and a popular tourist destination. There are a number of notable buildings. Kendal Castle was the birthplace of Catherine Parr, the last wife of Henry VIII. The impressive Georgian house, Abbot Hall, stands near the parish church. This house contains

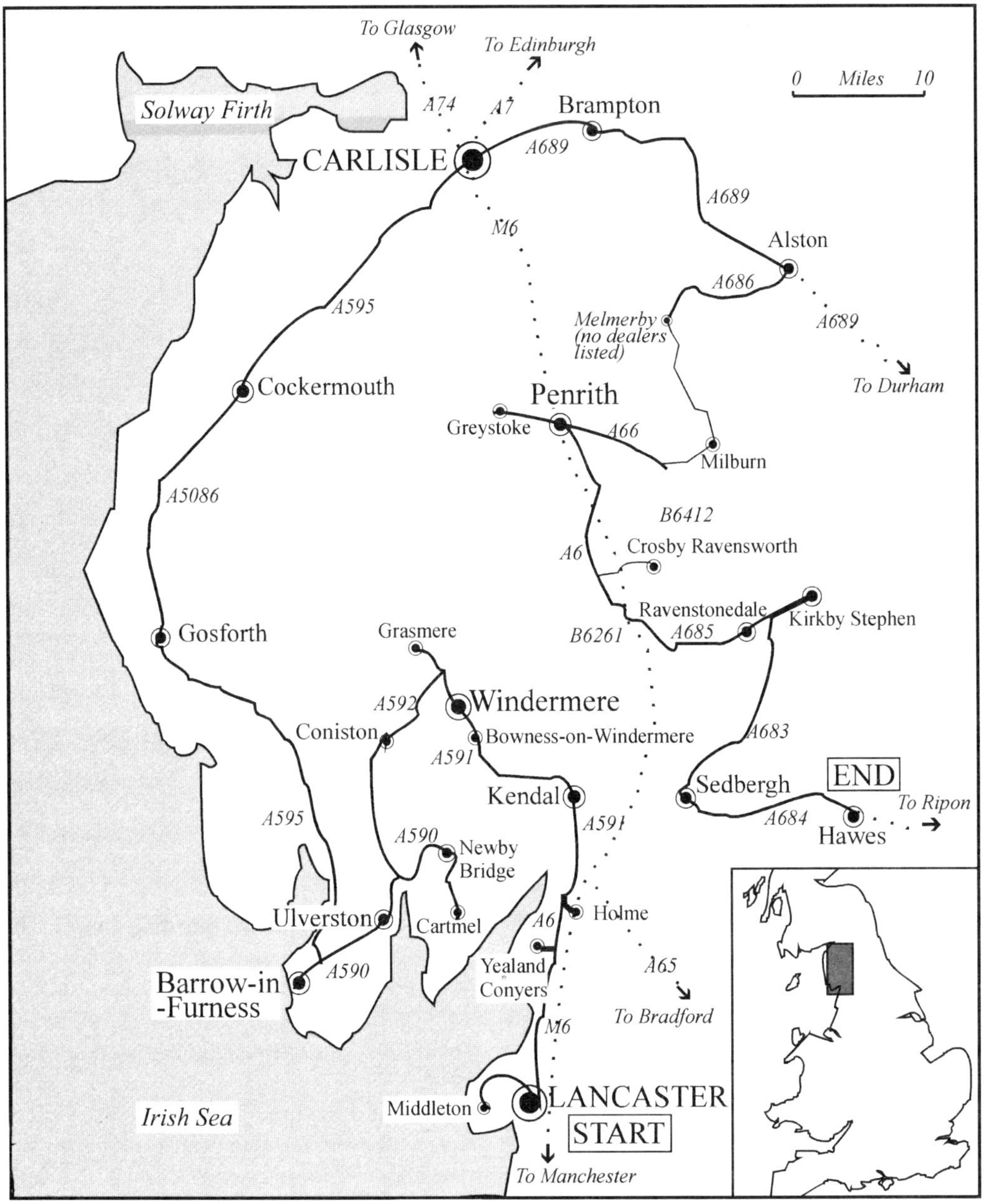


collections of portraits by George Romney and Daniel Gardner as well as Lake District landscapes. There is also a collection of furniture by Gillows of Lancaster. The adjacent Museum of Lakeland Life and Industry features displays of everything from hip baths to sheep dips.

Northwest is **Bowness-on-Windermere**, an old settlement that expanded with the coming of the railways. Dotted around the encircling hills are the mansions built by 19th century Lancastrian industrialists. The town is now a tourism centre with good facilities for water sports as well as boat trips around the lake. Nearby **Windermere**, surprisingly, stands almost a mile away from its lake and grew up around the railway station.

Next is Rydall Water and **Grasmere**, one of the best known of lakeland villages because of its association with William Wordsworth. His home, Dove Cottage, is a popular tourist attraction

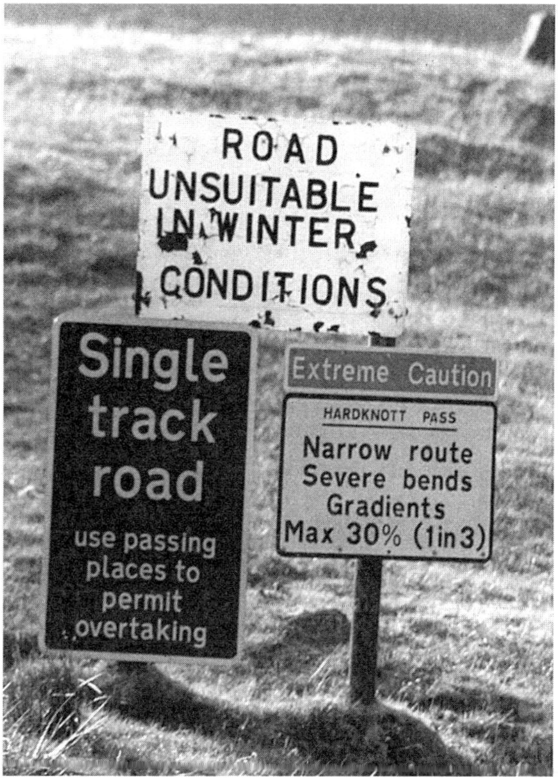


*Warning signs at the beginning of Hardknott Pass*

here. The poet is buried in the churchyard as are members of his family and also Hartley Coleridge.

Just off the A593 near Ambleside, there is a very popular drive through Wrynose Pass and continues into Hardknott Pass. This road is only suitable for motorists (and passengers) with nerves of steel and cars in good mechanical order. Much of the road is single track with gradients of 1 in 3 in places. Numerous road signs warn of its unsuitability for use in winter conditions. However, the views are breathtakingly beautiful right through both passes, partcularly so at *Mediobogdum*, now called Hardknott Castle, the Roman fort that commands the pass. The highest peaks of the Lake District can be seen from here as can the sea at Ravenglass. The fort, built in the 2nd century AD, covers some three acres and considerable remains are visible. It was not manned by imperial legions but by auxiliaries recruited from the Roman province of Dalmatia in former Yugoslavia. As little has changed in nearly two thousand years, it can be seen that this must have been a desperately lonely and uncomfortable posting especially for Southern Europeans.

Back on the tour, next comes **Coniston** at the north west edge of Coniston Water. The original industries were mining and quarrying but now most income comes from tourism. Overlooked by the 2635 feet high Coniston Old Man, it is ideally located for walkers exploring the surrounding peaks. Sir Donald Campbell was killed on Coniston Water when he attempted to beat his own world water speed record in 1967. Although his body was never found there is a memorial in the village.

To the south via the pretty **Newby Bridge**, **Cartmel** is a pleasant old town once the site of an important priory. Much of the building was destroyed during the Dissolution but the church is still in use for the parish community. Nearby **Ulvertson** has an unusual monument on Hoad Hill, a replica of Eddystone Lighthouse, built as a memorial to Sir John Barrow, the founder of the Royal Geographical Society. The hill also provides an excellent view of the surrounding countryside.

Ulverston was once important for iron-ore and charcoal especially after a canal was built to the sea in 18th century. However with the development of nearby **Barrow-in-Furness**, industry declined. By contrast Barrow has grown over the last 100 years from a small village to a major town. Its growth started with the Industrial Revolution and the coming of railways in 1846. It became a centre for engineering and shipbuilding; the Polaris submarine was built here. One and a half miles north the impressive ruins of Furness Abbey stand. Built from local sandstone in the 12th century, by the time of the 1537 Dissolution of the Monasteries, this abbey was one of the richest. Its wealth may still be judged by the sheer size and beauty of the extensive ruins.

The route now runs parallel to the coast along the A595 until it reaches **Gosforth** whose most notable feature is a collection of Anglo-Saxon and Norse crosses in the churchyard of St Mary's. One of these is 14 feet high and carved from red sandstone, depicting figures from Norse mythology and Christianity.

Along the A595 **Cockermouth**, next, was the birthplace of William Wordsworth and Fletcher Christian who led the mutiny on the Bounty. Astride the Rivers Cocker and Derwent, it has a castle, the earliest parts of which date from the mid 13th and 14th centuries with 18th and 19th century additions.

Moving on, **Carlisle** first achieved importance as the Roman headquarters for the area. As a border town it suffered centuries of hostilities with the Scots. After the Norman Conquest William had to take an army north to subdue the local inhabitants and import English peasants to colonise the region. In 1092 William II started work on Carlisle Castle sited on a bluff above the River Eden. Over the centuries the castle survived many battles and sieges and, on occasion, was taken by the Scots and then retaken by the English. It was not until the 16th century that relations between the Scots and English improved enough for constant battles and skirmishes to cease. In 1568 it was used for two months as a prison for Mary, Queen of Scots. In 1596 it again came under attack when Lord Scott of Buccleugh attempted to rescue a follower imprisoned there for raiding cattle. During the Civil War the castle changed hands frequently. First it held out for the King and was taken by Parliament and then retaken by Royalists. However, after the Roundhead victory at Preston the castle was finally taken by Parliamentary troops.

The last real action was during the Jacobite Rebellion of 1745 when Bonnie Prince Charlie led a Scottish army to try to regain the throne. He got as far as Derby from where he was forced to retreat to Carlisle by the Duke of Cumberland. Prince Charles left about 400 Highland soldiers to defend the castle but the Duke of Cumberland triumphed. Carlisle Castle was then used as a prison for Scots captured after the Battle of Culloden prior to their execution.

The city also has a fine cathedral built in the local sandstone. Founded by Henry I about 1120, it became a cathedral in 1133 but suffered considerably in the Scottish raids and was eventually finished in the late 14th century. During the Civil War Parliamentary forces destroyed part of the nave which has never been replaced and leaves it as one of the smallest cathedrals in England. It has a splendid medieval glass east window and fine 15th century choir stalls.

Following the A69, **Brampton** is next. Although granted its Charter in 1252, it has few ancient buildings because it was the target for raids by the Scots and suffered greatly as a result. The Tourist Information Centre is housed in the octagonal Moot Hall built in 1817. Nearby the town is Naworth Castle, a border fortress built in 1335 which later passed into the hands of the powerful Howard family. To the north of Brampton can be seen some of the few surviving Cumbrian sections of Hadrian's Wall.

The next call, **Alston**, at 919 feet above sea level, is reputed to be England's highest market town. It grew up as a result of lead mining in neighbouring hills which has been carried out since Roman times.Taking country roads (landmark villages are Melmerby, which marks the turn-off from the A686, then Ousby, Skirwith and Blencarn), **Milburn** has a large village green around which most of the buildings stand making a pleasant picture. The tour continues to **Penrith**, a prosperous market town which also suffered attacks by the Scots. Beacon Hill, rising over the town, was the site of many warning fires. Penrith Castle was built in the late 14th century to provide protection from the Scots. Richard of Gloucester, later to become Richard III, was its keeper when he held the title Lord Warden of the Western Marches. It later passed to the Earl of Warwick, nicknamed Kingmaker, and his badge, a bear and ragged staff, may be seen on the north west corner of the tower of St Andrew's Church.

The route detours westward to visit **Greystoke** with its large church dating from the middle of the 13th century and closely associated over the centuries with the Barons of Greystoke Castle. It contains some fine medieval glass, miserichords and carved stalls.

**Crosby Ravenscroft** is followed by **Ravenstonedale**, the church of St Oswald was built in the middle of the 18th century on the site of a much earlier one, some of which has survived. From the earlier church comes a most unusual pulpit with three levels. At the lowest level sat the clerk, on the second the vicar took the service and the sermon was preached from the topmost level. Nearby **Kirkby Stephen**, 600 feet above the Eden Valley has a 13th century church with a number of carved stones that pre-date the Norman Conquest including one with the Danish devil, Loki, carved upon it.

Although **Sedbergh** has officially been in Cumbria since the boundary changes of 1974, it still remains part of the Yorkshire Dales National Park and is an ideal centre for walkers exploring the beautiful surrounding countryside. The town contains some buildings of note. Amongst these is Sedbergh School founded in 1525. The restored church of St. Andrew was originally Norman and contains a number of interesting monuments.

Following the A684, the final stop is the village of **Hawes** in North Yorkshire. Here the Upper Dales Folk Museum has displays on life in the Dales including peat cutting, hand knitting and cheese making.

# ANTIQUE DEALERS

## LANCASTER (01524)

**Assembly Rooms Market,** King Street TEL: 66627 PARKING: Easy OPEN: Thur-Sat 10-4.30 MIN: 50p MAX: £500 PERIOD: 19th-20th century SPECIALIST: Costume GENERAL: Antiques, collectables, trains & railways, jewellery OTHER INFO: Georgian building in Heritage City, castle, Gillow Furniture Museum.

**GB Antiques Ltd**, The Antique Centre, Lancaster Leisure Park, Old Hornsea Pottery, Wyresdale Road, LA1 3LA TEL: 844734 FAX: 844735 PARKING: Own carpark OPEN: Seven days 10-5 MIN: £5 MAX: £6000 PERIOD: 19th-20th century GENERAL: 110 dealers & 36,000 sq ft of pine, mahogany, oak linen, Art Deco, glass, porcelain, dolls & teddies OTHER INFO: Café on site.

**Lancastrian Antiques & Tearooms,** 66 Penny Street, LA1 1XF TEL: 843764 PARKING: Easy OPEN: Tues-Sat 10-4.30 PERIOD: 19th-20th century GENERAL: Small furniture, silver, brac a brac OTHER INFO: Our customers tells us that we sell the best cup of coffee and home-made cakes.

**Vicary Antiques**, 18a Brock Street TEL: 843322 PARKING: Medium OPEN: Mon, Tues, Thurs-Sat 10-5 MIN: £1 MAX: £1000+ PERIOD: 19th-20th century SPECIALIST: Paintings 1880-1950, Arts & Crafts, furniture, metalware, etchings, art pottery GENERAL: Books, fabrics.

## MIDDLETON VILLAGE (01524)

**G & G Exports**, 25 Middleton Road, LA3 3JS TEL & FAX: 851565 PARKING: Own carpark OPEN: Seven days 9.30-5.30 but anytime by appt MIN: £30 MAX: £1000 PERIOD: 20th century SPECIALIST: Shipping furniture GENERAL: 20,000 sq ft of oak, walnut, mahogany & some pine.

## YEALAND CONYERS (01524)

**M & I Finch Antiques/Hector Finch Lighting**, 15-17 Yealand Road, LA5 9SG TEL: 732212 PARKING: Own carpark OPEN: Mon-Sat 10-6 MIN: £50 MAX: £7000 PERIOD: 18th-20th century SPECIALIST: Lighting GENERAL: Period furniture, some prints & smalls OTHER INFO: Pretty village with Grade II houses, Leighton House, (open summer), home of Gillow family. New Inn.

## HOLME (01524)

**JBW Antiques**, Duke Street, LA6 1PY TEL: 781377, PARKING: Own carpark OPEN: Mon-Fri 9-5, Sat 9-4 MIN: £5 MAX: £500 PERIOD: 18th-20th century SPECIALIST: Continental porcelain GENERAL: General antiques OTHER INFO: Next to MG Centre, classic car complex. 20 mins south of Bowness.

## KENDAL (01539)

**Below Stairs**, 125 Stricklandgate TEL: 741278 PARKING: Medium OPEN: Mon-Sat 10-4 MIN: £10 MAX: £500 PERIOD: 19th-20th century GENERAL: Metalware, china, glass.

**The Silver Thimble**, 39 Allhallows Lane TEL: 731456 PARKING: Medium OPEN: Mon-Sat 10-4 MIN: £1 MAX: £2500 PERIOD: 19th-20th century SPECIALIST: Cranberry & coloured glass GENERAL: General antiques OTHER INFO: Often referred to by customers as the cleanest, prettiest, well-displayed shop they have ever visited. Themed window displays every month.

## BOWNESS-ON-WINDERMERE (01539)

**Unicorn Antiques**, 1 Longlands, Lake Road, LA23 3LN TEL: 488747 PARKING: Medium OPEN: Seven days 10.30-5.30 MIN: £1 MAX: £2000 PERIOD: 19th-20th century SPECIALIST: Bottles & salt glaze jars c.1900 GENERAL: General antiques OTHER INFO: Beatrix Potter House.

**Utopia Antiques Ltd**, Lake Road, LA23 2JG TEL: 488464 PARKING: Own carpark OPEN: Mon-Sat 10-5 MIN: £10 MAX: £3000 PERIOD: 19th-20th century SPECIALIST: Antique pine furniture GENERAL: Pine & decorative accessories, aromatic products.

**White Elephant Antiques**, 66 Quarry Rigg TEL: 446962 PARKING: Own carpark OPEN: Seven days 9.30-5.30 MIN: £1 MAX: £1000 PERIOD: 18th-20th century SPECIALIST: Copper, brass GENERAL: Bric-a-brac, furniture OTHER INFO: Totaly unskilled owner who sells the odd treasure for buttons and doesn't even know it.

## WINDERMERE (01539)

**Birdcage Antiques**, College Road, LA23 1BX TEL: 445063 PARKING: Own carpark OPEN: Wed, Fri, Sat 10-5 MIN: £50 MAX: £1000 PERIOD: 19th-early 20th century SPECIALIST: Oil, gas, electric lighting GENERAL: Antiques & collectables.

**Joseph Thornton Antiques,** 4 Victoria Street LA23 1AB TEL: 442930 Mobile: 0378 147190 PARKING: Easy OPEN: 10-12, 1-4 or by appt MIN: 50p MAX: £15,000 PERIOD: 17th-20th century GENERAL: Furniture & bric a brac, clocks, silver, paintings, decorators items. OTHER INFO: 50 metres from railway station, hotels all around.

## GRASMERE (01539)

**Aladdins Cave Antiques**, Helm House, Langdale Road, LA22 9SU TEL: 435774 PARKING: Easy OPEN: Seven days 10-5 MIN: £1 MAX: £1000 PERIOD: 19th-20th century GENERAL: Brass, copper, coloured glass, treen, Lake District books & prints, furniture OTHER INFO: Dove Cottage (Wordsworth), Lake & boating, famous hotel: Michael's Nook, Beatrix Potter's house 12 miles.

**Andrew & Kay Saalmans**, The Stables, College Street, LA22 9SW TEL: 435453 PARKING: Easy OPEN: 10-6 MIN: £1 MAX: £250 PERIOD: 19th-20th century GENERAL: Brass & copperware, silver + plate, books, prints.

## CONISTON (01539)

**The Old Man Antiques**, Yewdale Road, LA21 8DU TEL: 441389 PARKING: Easy OPEN: Seven days 9.30-4.30 Easter-November MIN: £2 MAX: £1000 PERIOD: 19th-20th century SPECIALIST: Barometers as available GENERAL: Silver, glass, clocks, smalls OTHER INFO: The only antiques shop in Coniston, where Sir Donald Campbell sank with Bluebird attempting water speed record. At foot of famous mountain mined for copper & slate since the Stone Age.

## NEWBY BRIDGE (01539)

**Shire Antiques**, The Post House, High Newton, Newton-in-Cartmel, LA11 6JQ TEL: 531431 PARKING: Own carpark OPEN: 9-5 inc Sun, closed Tues MIN: £100 MAX: £20,000 PERIOD: 17th-18th century SPECIALIST: Early oak furniture GENERAL: Some early brass & metalware, oak carvings & decorative items OTHER INFO: Situated 100 yds off the A590 in village of High Newton, 3 miles east of Newby Bridge. Other good quality antique shops within 3 miles.

**Town Head Antiques**, LA12 8NP TEL: 531321 FAX: 530019 ASSNS: LAPADA PARKING: Own carpark OPEN: 9-1, 2-5 MIN: £5 MAX: £15,000 PERIOD: 18th-19th century GENERAL: Period furniture & general antiques OTHER INFO: In wing of large country house on the shores of Lake Windemere.

## CARTMEL (01539)

**Anthemion**, LA11 6QD TEL: 536295 ASSNS: BADA, LAPADA PARKING: Easy OPEN: Seven days 10-5.30, closed only 5 days a year (race days & Christmas Day) MIN: £50 MAX: £30,000 PERIOD: 17th-19th century SPECIALIST: English period furniture with associated decorative items OTHER INFO: This may look like a quiet sleepy village, but come and see for yourself.

**Peter Bain Smith Bookseller**, Old Market Square, LA11 6QB TEL: 536369 PARKING: Easy OPEN: Seven days 11-5.30 Summer, Wed-Sun 1.30-4.30 Winter MIN: £1 MAX: £300 PERIOD: 19th-20th century SPECIALIST: Local topography, English classics, childrens' GENERAL: Most subject, wide selection OTHER INFO: 4 pubs.

**Norman Kerr Antiquarian Booksellers**,

Gatehouse Bookshop & Priory Barn, LA11 6PX TEL: 536247 ASSNS: ABA, PBFA OPEN: By appt only please PERIOD: 17th-20th century GENERAL: Antiquarian & other quality books OTHER INFO: Unspoilt village on southern fringe of Lake district dominated by its 12 century Priory Church. Good Food Guide hotels.

## ULVERSTON (01229)

**Smiths Court Antiques,** Lower Brook Street TEL: 581324 PARKING: Easy OPEN: 11-4, closed Wed MIN: £5 MAX: £1200 PERIOD: 19th-20th century GENERAL: Smalls, brass, copper, silver, china, glass.

## BARROW-IN-FURNESS (01229)

**Henry Vincent**, 239 Rawlinson Street TEL: 823432 PARKING: Medium OPEN: 9.30-4, closed Thurs & Sun MIN: £1 MAX: £150 PERIOD: 20th century GENERAL: Furniture, weapons, coins, paintings, bric a brac.

## GOSFORTH (01946)

**Archie Miles Bookshop**, Beck Place, CA20 1AT TEL: 725792 PARKING: Easy OPEN: Tues-Sat 10-5.30 & by appt MIN: £1 MAX: £1,500 PERIOD: 17th-20th century SPECIALIST: English Literature, illustrated books, topography GENERAL: Most subjects OTHER INFO: In Lake District National Park, Ravenglass & Eskdale Railway, Muncaster Castle, Gardens & Owl Centre, Wastwater, working watermill all within 6 miles.

## COCKERMOUTH (01900)

**Antique Market Cockermouth,** Main Street TEL: 824346 PARKING: Medium OPEN: Mon-Sat 10-5 MIN: 50p MAX: £1000 PERIOD: 19th-20th century SPECIALIST: Linen, tools, ephemera GENERAL: Furniture, kitchenalia, pictures, etc.

**Cockermouth Antiques**, 5 Station Street, CA13 9QW TEL: 826746 PARKING: Easy OPEN: Mon-Sat 10-5 MIN: £1 MAX: £2000 PERIOD: 17th-20th century GENERAL: General antiques.

**Holmes Antiques**, 1 Market Square, CA13 9NH TEL: 826114 & 78364 PARKING: Easy OPEN: 10-5, closed Thur & Sun MIN: £1 MAX: £5000 PERIOD: 18th-20th century SPECIALIST: Paintings GENERAL: Furniture ^ fine antiques OTHER INFO: Wordsworth House (birthplace of William Wordsworth), Toy, mining & printing museums.



## CARLISLE (01228)

**Carlisle Antiques Centre,** Cecil Hall, 46 Cecil Street, CA1 1NT TEL: 36910 FAX: 36910 PARKING: Easy OPEN: Mon-Sat 9-5 MIN: 20p MAX: £5000 PERIOD: 19th-20th century SPECIALIST: Furniture, clocks GENERAL: Everything including shipping for dealers OTHER INFO: Restaurant on premises, toilets, telephone. Lots of shops & furniture warehouse.

**JW Clements**, 19 Fisher Street, CA3 8RF TEL: 25565 ASSNS: Cumbrian ADA PARKING: Difficult OPEN: Mon-Wed, Fri, Sat 9.30-5 MIN: £20 MAX: £5,000 PERIOD: 19th-20th century SPECIALIST: Jewellery GENERAL: Silver, ceramics OTHER INFO: Cathedral, Castle, Tulle House Museum.

**Langley Antiques,** The Forge, Corby Hill, CA4 8PL TEL: 560899 PARKING: Own carpark OPEN: 10.30-5, closed Thurs MIN: £50 MAX: £5000 PERIOD: 18th-20th century SPECIALIST: Furniture, clocks GENERAL: Porcelain & pottery, clocks & barometers.

**Saint Nicholas Galleries (Antiques) Ltd,** 28 London Road, CA1 2EL TEL: 34425 PARKING: Medium OPEN: 9.30-5, closed Thurs MIN: £1 PERIOD: 18th-20th century SPECIALIST: Jewellery GENERAL: General antiques OTHER INFO: Situated in a row of guest houses.

**Second Sight Antiques**, 4a Mary Street, CA2 6JZ TEL: 35922, 591525 ASSNS: FSB PARKING: Easy OPEN: Mon-Wed, Fri, Sat 10-5 MIN: £1 MAX: £3000 PERIOD: 17th-20th century

GENERAL: General antiques OTHER INFO: New reclaimed pine furniture. Hotel opposite.

**Souvenir Antiques**, 4 Kinmont Arcade, Treasury Court, Fisher Street TEL: 40281 PARKING: Medium OPEN: Mon-Sat 10-5 MIN: £1 MAX: £500 PERIOD: 19th-20th SPECIALIST: Antique maps of Cumbria GENERAL: Ceramics & good variety of collectables including Roman coins OTHER INFO: In quiet courtyard off pedestrianised precinct in historic city.

## BRAMPTON (01228)

**Mary Fell Antiques**, (Collectors Corner), 32-34 Main Street, CA8 1RS TEL: 22224 PARKING: Own carpark OPEN: Mon-Sat 11-5 MIN: £10 MAX: £2,000 PERIOD: 18th-20th century SPECIALIST: Fine porcelain GENERAL: General antiques OTHER INFO: Interesting collectables. Small market town close to Roman Wall.

## ALSTON (01434)

**Just Glass**, Brownside Coach House, CA9 3BP TEL: 381263 PARKING: Own carpark OPEN: Mon, Wed-Sat 10-6 but Oct-Easter by appt only MIN: £10 MAX: £500 PERIOD: 18th century to 1920 SPECIALIST: North east pressed glass GENERAL: Georgian, Victorian decorative glass OTHER INFO: We are also Egon Ronay recommemded small tearoom (since 1978) with superb full service & home-baked food.

## MILBURN (01768)

**Netherley Cottage Antiques**, CA10 1TN TEL: 361403 PARKING: Own carpark OPEN: Thursdays 9-5.30 but almost anytime by appt MIN: £1 MAX: £120 PERIOD: 18th-20th century SPECIALIST: Kitchenalia GENERAL: Treen, unusual country pieces, some watercolours, books & prints OTHER INFO: Facing attractive village green, welcome to walk around garden.

## PENRITH (01768)

**Antiques of Penrith**, 4 Corney Square, CA11 7PX TEL: 62801 PARKING: Easy OPEN: Mon-Sat 10-12, 1.30-5 MIN: £1 MAX: £ thousands PERIOD: 18th-20th century GENERAL: Huge variety & extensive stock of furniture, brass, copper, china, Staffordshire, pewter, glass, silver + plate.

**Joseph James**, Corney Square, CA11 7PX TEL: 62065 PARKING: Medium OPEN: Mon, Tues, Thurs-Sat 9-5.30 MIN: £2 MAX: £1,500 PERIOD: 18th-20th century GENERAL: Furniture, porcelain, glass

**Penrith Coin & Stamp Centre/Gray Jewellers**, 37 King Street, CA11 7AY TEL: 64185 PARKING: Easy OPEN: Mon-Sat 9-5.30 but closed Weds in winter MIN: £5 MAX: £5000 PERIOD: 18th-19th century SPECIALIST: Coins from Roman up to date GENERAL: Antique gold & silver jewellery.

**Jane Pollock Antiques**, 4 Castlegate, CA11 7HZ TEL: 67211 PARKING: Easy OPEN: Mon, Tues, Thurs-Sat 9.30-5 MIN: £5 MAX: £5000 PERIOD: 18th-20th century SPECIALIST: Silver GENERAL: Pottery, porcelain, wooden boxes, collectables OTHER INFO: Hornby Hall country house accommodation (tel: 891114).

## GREYSTOKE (01768)

**Pelican Antiques,** The Pelican, Church Road, CA11 0TW TEL: 483477 PARKING: Easy OPEN: Preferably by appt MIN: £5 MAX: £400 GENERAL: Small curio items, metals, china, glass.

**Roadside Antiques**, Watsons Farm, Greystoke Gill,

CA11 0UQ TEL: 483279 PARKING: Own carpark OPEN: Seven days 10-6 MIN: £1 MAX: £2500 PERIOD: 19th-20th century SPECIALIST: Porcelain GENERAL: Quality Victorian & Edwardian antiques, furniture, jewellery & paintings OTHER INFO: Beckstones Art Gallery (quality modern original paintings), Herdwick Inn, Penruddock, Clickham Inn, between Greystoke & Penrith.

## CROSBY RAVENSWORTH (01931)

**Jennywell Hall Antiques**, CA10 3JP TEL: 715288 PARKING: Own carpark OPEN: Most times but phonecall advisable (resident) MIN: £10 MAX: £2000 PERIOD: 18th-19th century GENERAL: Oak & mahogany furniture, pictures, glass, ceramics, decorative items OTHER INFO: 4 self-catering holiday cottages associated with us.

## RAVENSTONEDALE (01539)

**The Book House**, CA17 4NQ TEL: 623634 PARKING: Easy OPEN: Mon, Wed-Sat 9-5 MIN: £1 MAX: £1000 PERIOD: 19th-20th century SPECIALIST: Industrial history, railways, gardening, old girls GENERAL: Secondhand & antiquarian books only OTHER INFO: Good centre for Northern Dales & Eden Valley. We offer comfortable B&B.

## KIRKBY STEPHEN (01768)

**Haughey Antiques**, 28-30 Market Street, CA17 4QW TEL: 371302 ASSNS: LAPADA PARKING: Own carpark OPEN: Mon-Sat 10-5 PERIOD: 17th-19th century GENERAL: Furniture, clocks, garden statuary.

**David Hill Antiques**, 36 Market Square TEL: 371598 PARKING: Easy OPEN: Mon-Sat 9.30-4 MIN: £1 MAX: £950 PERIOD: 19th-20th century SPECIALIST: Ironware, clocks GENERAL: Bric-a-brac.

**Mortlake Antiques**, 32-34 Market Street, CA17 4QW TEL: 371666 PARKING: Easy OPEN: Mon-Sat 9.30-5 summer, Mon, Fri, Sat 10-5 winter MIN: £1 MAX: £2000 PERIOD: 19th-20th century SPECIALIST: Original pine & stripped furniture GENERAL: Kitchen items, stoneware, metalware, pressed glass, treen OTHER INFO: We also offert mountain bike hire - go for a hike on a bike.

## SEDBERGH (01539)

**RFG Hullett & Son**, 6 Finkle Street, LA10 5BZ TEL: 620298 FAX: 621396 ASSNS: ABA PARKING: Easy OPEN: Mon-Sat 10-12, 1.15-5 MIN: £10 MAX: £10,000 PERIOD: Incunabala to modern firsts SPECIALIST: Fine antiquarian books & general antiquarian books: topography, natural history, fine arts

**Stable Antiques**, 15 Back Lane, LA10 5AQ TEL: 620251 PARKING: Easy OPEN: Mon-Sat 9-6 & by appt MIN: £1 MAX: £1000 PERIOD: 17th-20th century SPECIALIST: Metal & treen GENERAL: China, glass, prints, silver, small furniture OTHER INFO: B&B above shop, dogs welcome, children by arrangement.

## HAWES (01969)

**Sturmans Antiques**, Main Street, DL8 3QW TEL: 667742 ASSNS: LAPADA PARKING: Medium OPEN: Seven days 10-5.30 MIN: £1 MAX: £5000 PERIOD: 18th-20th century SPECIALIST: Furniture GENERAL: Oils & watercolours, porcelain, glassware, metalware. Good selection longcase & wall clocks OTHER INFO: Highest market town in Yorkshire in heart of Herriot Country.

# The Far North East

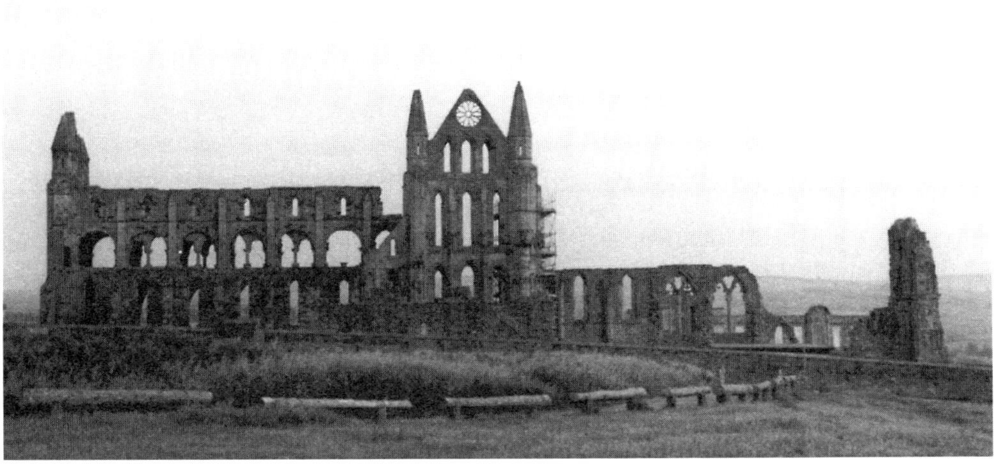

*Whitby Abbey*

This final English trip takes in five counties: North Yorkshire, Cleveland, County Durham, Tyne & Wear and Northumberland. On the North Yorkshire Moors Bronze Age man cleared the forests for agriculture leaving behind moorland as well as barrows and stone cairns. Medieval monks in the great Yorkshire abbeys also cut down trees to clear areas for sheep and for making charcoal. Without trees the soil became acid and was swept away by wind and water leaving only enough nutrients for heather, grass and bracken. In Northumbria the hand of man can also be seen in the Border Forest, the largest man-made forest in Europe and planted by the Forestry Commission. However, this is wild terrain with the rugged Cheviot Hills in the west and rocky cliffs on the east coast facing the cold North Sea. The Romans built their wall south of this county and over the centuries the region was the scene of many battles and skirmishes between the English and Scots. Tyne & Wear was one of the main ship-buildings areas in the country, but now that has gone as have many of the mines in Cleveland and Durham.

The village of **Sleights** is first and then **Whitby**, at the mouth of the River Esk. It is a popular holiday resort with a picturesque harbour, good safe beaches and close to the North Yorkshire National Park. Forming a distinctive landmark on the cliffs above Whitby are the ruins of a 13th century abbey. Bram Stoker, creator of Dracula, and Captain Cook were past residents. Captain Cook's house may be seen in Grape Lane. Another connection with the famous seafarer may be found at **Great Ayton**. Here he went to school and the building is now a Captain Cook museum.

The route crosses into Cleveland to visit **Yarm** and then **Eaglescliffe** where the notable railway viaduct dominates the town which contains many Georgian buildings. Nearby **Darlington**, in County Durham, was originally an Anglo-Saxon settlement whose prosperity was founded on wool then later linen and carpet making. As these declined the manufacture of locomotives and railway wagons and bridge building took their place.The Railway Centre and Museum has many exhibits of interest including Stephenson's Locomotion.

After a short detour to **Manfield**, the route continues west to **Barnard Castle**, named for its castle overlooking the River Tees from a clifftop. Dating from the 11th century, it was long subject to ownership disputes. Over a window of one of the many building is a carving of a wild boar, probably dating from the period when it was occupied by Richard, Duke of Gloucester, later

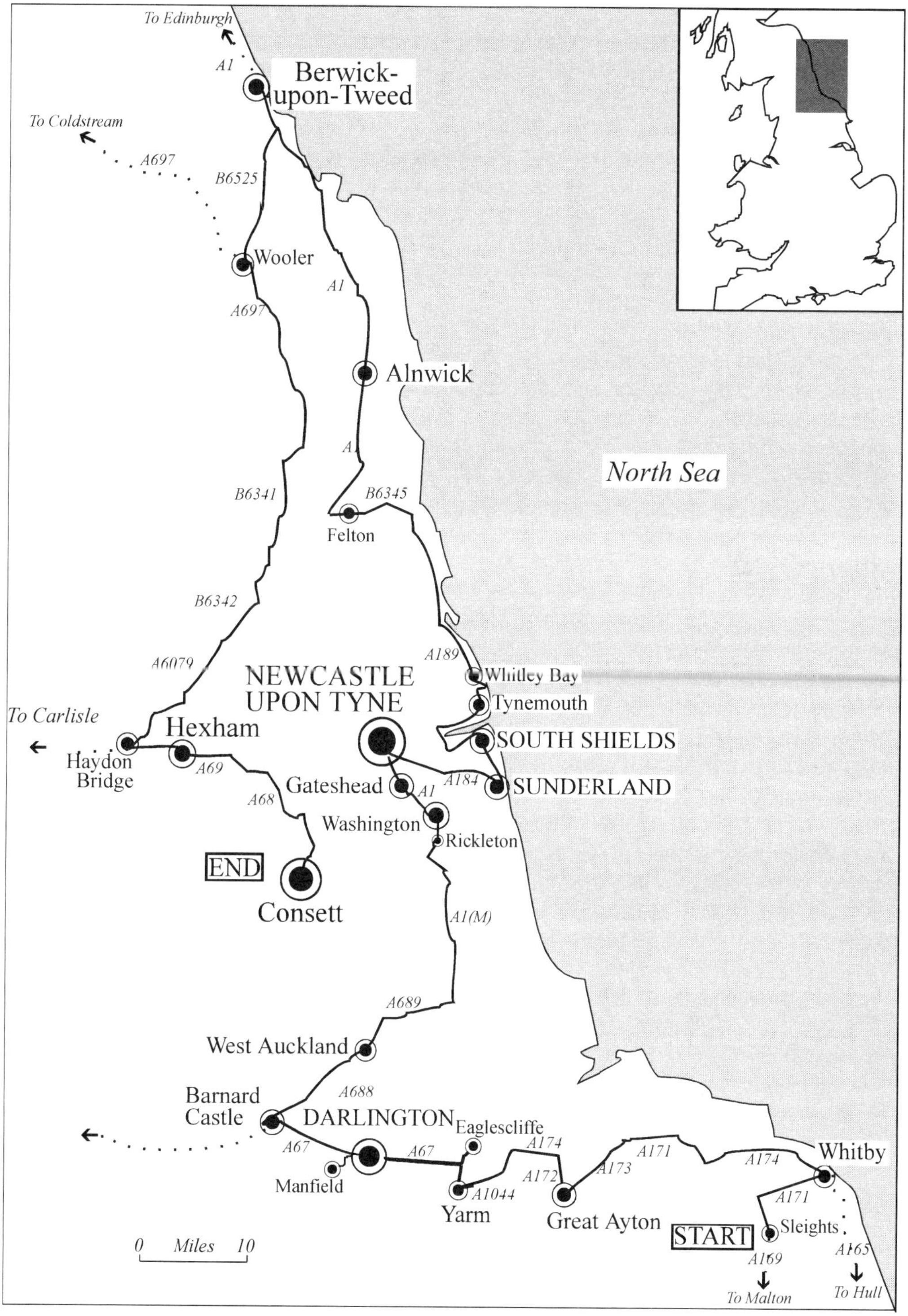
To Edinburgh
A1
Berwick-upon-Tweed
To Coldstream
A697
B6525
Wooler
A1
A697
Alnwick
A1
North Sea
B6341
B6345
Felton
B6342
A6079
A189
NEWCASTLE UPON TYNE
Whitley Bay
Tynemouth
To Carlisle
Hexham
SOUTH SHIELDS
Haydon Bridge
A69
A184
Gateshead
A1
SUNDERLAND
A68
Washington
Rickleton
END
Consett
A1(M)
A689
West Auckland
Barnard Castle
A688
DARLINGTON
Egglescliffe
A67
A67
A174
A171
A174
Whitby
Manfield
A172
A173
A1044
A171
Yarm
Great Ayton
START
Sleights
A169
A165
To Malton
To Hull
0 Miles 10

*Whitby Harbour*

Richard III. It contains a magnificent hall built by the Bishop of Durham in the 13th century.

The town has much to see. The covered market cross is so big that it served as the town hall during the 18th century. Charles Dickens reputedly wrote *Nicholas Nickleby* at he King's Head inn. Also of note is the spectacular Bowes Museum set in 20 acres of gardens and strongly reminiscent of a French chateau. It contains collections of paintings, furniture, tapestries, porcelain, glass, jewellery, sculpture and metalwork.

Five miles east along the A688, is Raby Castle, one of the largest 14th century castles in Britain and built by the Nevill family. Seeing action in the Civil War when taken in a surprise attack by Royalist troops, it now contains a fine collection of English, Dutch and Flemish pictures and good period furniture; there is also an exhibition of horse-drawn carriages and fire engines.

The tour continues via **West Auckland**, where Roman remains have been found nearby, **Rickleton** and then **Washington**, in the county of Tyne & Wear. The ancestors of George Washington once lived at Washington Old Hall before they moved to Sulgrave.

**Gateshead**, on the Tyne, is next. The town has been closely associated with ship building and repair. Five bridges connect it to **Newcastle**, the most recent Tyne Bridge has a single span of 531 feet reaching up to 200 feet above the river. Newcastle was also noted for shipbuilding as well as coal mining, locomotives and armaments. This ancient town was established by the Romans because of its proximity to Hadrian's Wall. Later it became the cathedral city for the region. The cathedral's most notable feature is a tower, built around 1450. The pinnacled flying buttresses holding up a small spire give the construction a touch of flamboyance and examples of the decorated style may be seen in the canopy over the font and on some of the windows.

The castle is also interesting. Constructed on the site of a Roman camp, the present building was started by Robert, eldest son of William the Conqueror. Improvements were made over the centuries and action was seen in the border wars. Indeed it changed hands on occasion and was once held by King David of Scotland. Its history is told in the Castle Keep Museum.

The University of Newcastle runs four museums: the Hancock Museum deals with natural history and Ancient Egypt, the Hatton Gallery has displays of contemporary and historical art, the Museum of Antiquities has prehistoric, Roman, Anglo-Saxon and medieval items and the Shefton Museum of Greek Art and Archaelogy contains Greek artefacts starting from Minoan times.

Nearby **Sunderland**, on the River Wear, was another ship building centre., but other industries included pottery and glass-making. Four miles west is Hylton Castle dating from 1400. Seven miles away, **South Shields** was the site of the Roman fort of *Arbeia*, built to defend the eastern end of Hadrian's Wall. Crossing the Tyne, the next stop is**Tynemouth**. The ruins of the castle and priory occupy a good defensive position on a headland. The priory was established in the 11th century on the site of an earlier monastery. During the border wars with the Scots a fortified gatehouse was added which persuaded Henry VIII to turn the priory into a royal castle after the Dissolution of the

*Bowes Museum, Barnard Castle*

Monasteries. Adjoining **Whitley Bay** is a pleasant seaside resort with good sandy beaches.

The tour continues north with a call on **Felton** in Northumberland, and then on to **Alnwick**, once the county town. The Percy family, Dukes of Northumberland, have dominated this area for almost 700 years. Alnwick Castle was built in the 12th century and bought by Henry de Percy in 1309 who strengthened it against Scottish raiders. The Percys were ill-fated with nine of the Lords of Alnwick meeting violent deaths. Eventually the castle fell into disrepair until 1764 when rebuilding was started. Outside, it is the very picture of what a castle should be, but the interior is a model of civilisation with collections of fine furniture, Meissen china and pictures, including works by Titian, Van Dyck and Canaletto. It also contains one of the country's oldest private museums, open to the public, and displays prehistoric to Viking artefacts.

**Berwick-on-Tweed**, next, is England's most northerly town and has seen much fighting in the border wars. It changed hands thirteen times until finally surrendereding to the English in 1482. Of particular note are the town walls which were replaced in the Elizabethan period. Built to withstand gunpowder, they are up to ten feet thick in places. Berwick has a wealth of historical buildings including 18th century houses and one of the few churches to have been built during Oliver Cromwell's Commonwealth. Berwick Barracks, in the centre, contains a museum chronicling the history of the King's Own Scottish Borderers. The early 18th century Barracks, designed to house 36 officers and 600 men, were built in three blocks around a square, the fourth side being a beautifully decorated gatehouse.

Turning south, **Wooler** sits astride the River Till and the north east edge of the Cheviot Hills. There is a mound of a Norman castle here but most of the houses date from the late 19th century as the town suffered a disastrous fire in 1862. Although the next stop is fifty miles south, there is beautiful scenery and two noteworthy National Trust houses to break up the journey. The first, Cragside, about four miles from the junction of the A697 and B6341, was built in the 19th century by the inventor and industrialist, William Armstrong. The house is a Victorian fantasy incorporating Tudor black and white architecture with Gothic. Armstrong blasted the site out of a hill creating a romantic backdrop for his dream house. Inside the rooms are magnificent, a fitting place to entertain his wealthy, titled and royal customers. Cragside is also notable for being the first house in the world to use hydro electricity. The other house is Wallington, about 15 miles further south on the B6342. It was built in the late 17th century and then remodelled about fifty years later. In the 19th century the internal courtyard was roofed in and makes a central hall. The house contains notable collections of porcelain, pictures and furniture. The surrounding grounds are beautiful but it is the conservatory that claims the interest of gardeners where there is a famous collection of fuchsia one of which is 80 years old.

**Haydon Bridge** lies at the end of this drive followed by **Hexham**, a pretty town well placed for exploring Hadrian's Wall and other Roman remains in the area. The very large church was once a great abbey. Dating from about 1200 it contains many features including a Saxon crypt. There are numerous old and interesting buildings in the town, amonst them, the old prison dating from 1330 and now housing the Tourist Information Offices and the 15th century Moot Hall.

About four miles north on the A6079, is Chesters Fort, a Roman fortification built as part of Hadrian's Wall. Characteristically, the Romans did not bend their wall to go round the River Tyne, instead they built a bridge and the fort was to defend this. The excavated site is well maintained in a beautiful valley. Amongst the excavations may be seen the bathhouse and an underground strongroom where the legion's pay and standards were kept. On the site there is also a museum displaying Roman finds from several of the sites in Northumberland.

The tour ends in **Consett**, famous for its steelworks which, at their height, produced more than a million tons of steel annually.

## ANTIQUE DEALERS

### SLEIGHTS (01947)

**Coach House Antiques**, 75 Coach Road, YO22 5BT TEL: 810313 PARKING: Easy OPEN: 10-5 summer, 10.30-4.30 winter MIN: £1 MAX: £750 PERIOD: 18th-20th century SPECIALIST: Oak & country furniture GENERAL: Unusual & decorative items.

### WHITBY (01947)

**The Bazaar**, Skinner Street, YO21 3AH TEL: 602281 PARKING: Easy OPEN: Mon-Sat 10-5.30 MIN: £1 MAX: £450 PERIOD: 18th-20th century GENERAL: General antiques OTHER INFO: Whitby, historic architecture. Well worth visiting.

**Bobbins Wool, Crafts & Antiques,** Wesley Hall, Church Street, YO22 4DE TEL: 600585 PARKING: Difficult OPEN: 7 days (except Jan & Feb) 10.30-5ish MIN: £1.25 MAX: £150 PERIOD: 19th-20th century SPECIALIST: Oil lamps, spares & repairs GENERAL: Bottles, bric a brac, kitchenalia, kitsch & tat, bobbins, mill relics OTHER INFO: In the heart of the old cobbled pedestrian area of Whitby, full of pubs, eating places & special shops.

**Caedmon House**, 14 Station Square TEL: 602120, 603930 PARKING: Medium OPEN: 10-5 MIN: £2 MAX: £2500 PERIOD: 19th-20th century SPECIALIST: Dresden china, old dolls, small furniture, toys GENERAL: House clearances, Victorian crystoleums & lustres, Sunderland pottery, Moorcroft old & new OTHER INFO: Bramstoker wrote Dracula here, best museum in the North, Heartbeat country, Captain James Cook's Trail. Shop is called after Caedmon, the first English poet who lived in Whitby Abbey at time of Lady Hilda. At the synod here date for Easter was set for Christians worldwide. (Wow! What Disney would give for all this history).

**The Mount Antiques**, Khyber Pass, YO21 3HD TEL: 604516 PARKING: Own carpark OPEN: 10.15-4.30 MIN: £10 MAX: £2500 PERIOD: 18th-19th century GENERAL: General antiques.

**Whalers Lodge Antiques,** 139 Church Street TEL: 605042 PARKING: Difficult OPEN: Variable PERIOD: 19th-20th century GENERAL: Collectables, jet jewellery, antiques OTHER INFO: On the old side of Whitby - between Market Place & abbey.

### GREAT AYTON (01642)

**The Great Ayton Bookshop,** 47 & 53 High Street, TS9 6NH TEL: 723358 ASSNS: PBFA PARKING: Medium OPEN: Tues, Thurs-Sat 10-5.30, Wed 10-2, Sun 2-5.30 MIN: 25p MAX: £200 PERIOD: Occasionally 17-19th century, mostly 20th century GENERAL: Books, prints, postcards OTHER INFO: Captain Cook attended school in the village & there is a small museum.

## YARM (01642)

**Ruby Snowden Antiques,** 20 High Street, TS15 9AE TEL: 785363 PARKING: Easy OPEN: Mon-Sat 9-5 MIN: £5 MAX: £2000 PERIOD: 18th-20th century GENERAL: Furniture & smalls.

## EAGLESCLIFFE (01642)

**TB & R Jordan,** Aslak, Aislaby, TS16 0QN TEL: 782599 FAX: 780473 ASSNS: LAPADA OPEN: By appt MIN: £30 MAX: £6000 PERIOD: 19th-20th century SPECIALIST: Special interest in 'Staithe Group' artists GENERAL: British oils and watercolours. Some contemporary works.

## DARLINGTON (01325)

**Robin Finnegan Jewellers**, 83 Skinnergate, DL3 7LX TEL: 489820 FAX: 357674 ASSNS: NAG, Gemmological Assn of GB PARKING: Medium OPEN: Mon-Sat 10-5.30 MIN: £1 MAX: £20,000 PERIOD: 17th-20th century SPECIALIST: Jewellery, coins, medals, collectors items GENERAL: New, secondhand & antique jewellery, smalls OTHER INFO: Friendly family firm sometimes close to insanity that lets chipmunks in the shop, so nobody too serious please.

**Nichol & Hill**, 20-22 Grange Road, DL1 5NG TEL: 375431 FAX: 382863 PARKING: Medium OPEN: Mon-Fri 8.30-5, Sat 10-5 MIN: £100 MAX: £3000 PERIOD: 19th-early 20th century SPECIALIST: Furniture GENERAL: Complete restoration & upholstery service.

**Alan Ramsey Antiques**, 10 Dudley Road, Yarm Road Industrial Estate, DL1 4GG TEL: 361679, (01642) 711311 PARKING: Own carpark OPEN: Tues, Thurs, Fri 10-3 PERIOD: 19th-20th century GENERAL: 2000 sq ft antique furniture OTHER INFO: Trade only.

## MANFIELD (01325)

**DD White Antiques**, Lucy Cross Cottage, DL2 2RJ TEL: 374303 PARKING: Own carpark OPEN: By appt MIN: £40 MAX: £2000 PERIOD: 18th-20th century GENERAL: Shipping furniture OTHER INFO: Headlam Hall Hotel, Black Bull.

## BARNARD CASTLE (01833)

**The Collector,** Douglas House, 23-25 The Bank, DL12 8PH TEL: 37783 PARKING: Easy OPEN: Mon-Sat 10-5 or phone if closed MIN: £3 MAX: £3000 PERIOD: 17th-19th century SPECIALIST: Early oak & country furniture, restoration of early furniture GENERAL: Furnishings & decorative items OTHER INFO: One of the earliest buildings in the country is across the street & also the best restaurant, once owned by Richard III.

**Stephanie Grant Art & Antiques**, The Ancient Manor House, 38-40 The Bank TEL: 37437 PARKING: Easy OPEN: Mon-Sat 10-5 other dealers, Stephanie Grant by appt MIN: £1 MAX: £5000 PERIOD: 17th-20th century SPECIALIST: Paintings, pine & oak furniture GENERAL: Smalls, rugs, pottery, silver etc OTHER INFO: Property said to have belonged to stewards to Henry VII & James I.

**Joan & David White Antiques**, Neville House, 10 The Bank TEL: 344595 & 374303 PARKING: Medium OPEN: Wed, Fri, Sat 11-5 MIN: £10 MAX: £1800 PERIOD: 18th-20th century GENERAL: Furniture, decorative & shipping items OTHER INFO: High Force (highest waterfall in England).

## WEST AUCKLAND (01388)

**Eden House Antiques**, 10 Staindrop Road, DL14 9JX TEL: 833013 ASSNS: GMC PARKING: Own carpark OPEN: Mon-Sat 10-6.30 MIN: £1 PERIOD: 18th-20th century GENERAL: General antiques & reproduction furniture OTHER INFO: Home of Mary Ann Cotton, famous multiple murderess. 13th century Manor House Hotel.

## RICKLETON (0191)

**Harold J Carr Antiques**, Field House, NE38 9HQ TEL & FAX: 388 6442 ASSNS: LAPADA PARKING: Difficult OPEN: By appt only PERIOD: 19th-20th century GENERAL: Export furniture, shipping oak, walnut & mahogany.

## WASHINGTON (0191)

**Grate Expectations (Fireplaces),** Unit 6, Lee Close, Pattinson North Industrial Estate, NE38 8QA TEL: 416 0609 FAX: 417 9946 PARKING: Easy OPEN: Mon-Sat 9-5 MIN: £75 MAX: £850 PERIOD: 19th century-1930s SPECIALIST: Iron, wood, marble fireplaces OTHER INFO: Near Washington Waterfowl Park & Penshaw Monument.

## GATESHEAD (0191)

**N Jewett**, 639-643 Durham Road, Lowfell, NE9 5HA TEL: 487 7636 PARKING: Easy OPEN: Mon-

Sat 10-5 MIN: £250 MAX: £3000 PERIOD: 18th-20th century SPECIALIST: Furniture.

**Metro Antiques,** 31 The Boulevard, Antique Village, Metrocentre, NE11 9YP TEL: 460 0340 PARKING: Easy OPEN: Mon-Sat 10-8 Sun 11-5 PERIOD: 19th-20th century GENERAL: Antique, second hand, collectables, reproduction.

**Sovereign Antiques**, 35 The Boulevard, Antique Village, Metro Centre, NE11 9YN TEL: 460 9604 PARKING: Easy (Metrocentre) OPEN: Mon-Sat 10-8, Thurs till 9pm MIN: £5 MAX: £8000 PERIOD: 18th-20th century SPECIALIST: Jewellery, silver, maps & prints.

## NEWCASTLE-ON-TYNE (0191)

**Causey Antiques**, Causey Street, Gosforth TEL: 285 9062 PARKING: Difficult OPEN: Thurs-Sat 10-4 MIN: £1 MAX: £600 PERIOD: 17th-20th century GENERAL: China, furniture, medals, toys, glass, clocks, gold & silver OTHER INFO: Gosforth Park Hotel & Racecourse.

**Davidson's the Jewellers Ltd,** 94-96 Grey Street, NE1 6AG TEL: 232 2551 PARKING: Medium, OPEN: Mon-Sat 9-5 MIN: £300 MAX: £30,000 PERIOD: 19th-20th century SPECIALIST: Early Victorian GENERAL: Fine gems OTHER INFO: Grey Street is one of the finest examples of Georgian architecture in Europe.

**Dean Art Gallery**, 42 Dean Street, NE1 1PG TEL: 232 1208 PARKING: Medium OPEN: Mon-Fri 10-5, Sat 10-1 MIN: £300 MAX: £5000 PERIOD: 19th-20th century SPECIALIST: Period local artists GENERAL: Oils & watercolours & some rare prints OTHER INFO: Surtees & Vermont hotels very near.

**H & S Collectables**, 149 Salters Road, Gosforth, NE3 2UT TEL: 284 6626, home 286 3498 PARKING: Easy OPEN: Mon-sat 10-5 MIN: £5 MAX: £900 PERIOD: 19th-20th century SPECIALIST: Tyneside Malingware 1890-1963 GENERAL: Antiques & Victoriana, clocks, small furniture, silver, decorative items, collectables OTHER INFO: Valuations. Off Gosforth High Street.

**Anna Harrison Antiques,** 49 Great North Road, Gosforth NE3 2HH TEL: 284 3202 FAX: 284 6689 ASSNS: LAPADA PARKING: Own carpark OPEN: 9-5 MIN: £15 MAX: £5000 PERIOD: 18th-20th century SPECIALIST: 18th century English china GENERAL: Furniture.

**Geoffrey Hugall Antiques**, 19 Clayton Road, Jesmond, NE2 4RP TEL: 281 8408 PARKING: Easy OPEN: Mon-Fri 10-5, Sat 10-4 PERIOD: 18th-19th century GENERAL: Quality general antiques.

**Intercoin**, 103 Clayton Street, NE1 5PZ TEL: 232 2064 PARKING: Easy OPEN: Mon-Sat 9-5 PERIOD: All periods, ancient to modern SPECIALIST: Coins, medals, banknotes, silver, small antiques OTHER INFO: Free identification & valuations.

**MacDonald Fine Art**, 2 Ashburton Road, Gosforth, NE3 4XN TEL: 285 6188, 284 4214 PARKING: Easy OPEN: Mon-Fri 10-1, 2-5.30, Sat 10-1 MIN: £50 MAX: £3000 PERIOD: 19th-20th century SPECIALIST: Watercolours & oils.

**Shiners Architectural Reclamation Ltd,** 123 Jesmond Road, NE2 1JY TEL: 281 6474 OPEN: Mon-Sat 9-5 MIN: £1 MAX: £3000 PERIOD: 18th-20th century SPECIALIST: Fireplaces GENERAL: Architectural antiques OTHER INFO: Next to an Italian restaurant, plenty of hotels.

## SUNDERLAND (0191)

**Peter Smith Antiques**, 12-14 Borough Road, SR1 1EP TEL: 567 3537 FAX: 514 2286 ASSNS: LAPADA PARKING: Easy OPEN: Mon-Fri 9.30-4.30, Sat 9.30-1 MIN: £5 MAX: £10,000 PERIOD:18th-20th century GENERAL: Furniture, clocks OTHER INFO: Good beaches.

## SOUTH SHIELDS (0191)

**The Curiosity Shop**, 16 Frederick Street, NE33 5EA TEL: 456 5560 ASSNS: FSB PARKING: Easy OPEN: Mon-Sat 9-5, closed Wed MIN: £5 MAX: £3000 PERIOD: 19th-20th century GENERAL: Furniture, antiques, Royal Doulton OTHER INFO: Best range of Indian restaurants in UK

## TYNEMOUTH (0191)

**Maggie Mays**, Preston Road (opposite Gunner Inn), NE29 0LJ TEL: 237 6933, (0850) 907049 PARKING: Easy OPEN: Mon, Thurs-Sat 11-6 MIN: £10 MAX: £10,000 PERIOD: 19th-20th century SPECIALIST: Local artist & Northumbria GENERAL: Antiques & furniture, Art Deco, mechanical music, brass fenders, lamps, rugs, pine, beds etc OTHER INFO: A real antique shop with an eccentric owner who can repair most things, even pianolas. Don't be disappointed if he won't sell something as he is a compulsive magpie!

**Renaissance Antiques**, 11 Front Street, NE30 4RG TEL: 259 5555 PARKING: Easy OPEN: Mon, Tues, Sat 10.30-12.30, 2-3.45 MIN: £5 MAX:

£1000 PERIOD: 19th-20th century GENERAL: Furniture, bric-a-brac.
**Ian Sharp Antiques**, 23 Front Street, NE30 4DX TEL: 296 0656 ASSNS: LAPADA PARKING: Easy OPEN: Mon-sat 10-5.30 & by appt MIN: £50 MAX: £5000 PERIOD: 18th-19th century SPECIALIST: Northeastern pottery, local artists' oils & watercolours GENERAL: Furniture, pottery, porcelain, decorative items OTHER INFO: Pretty village dominated by The Priory & Castle burial place of Northumberland kings & saints.

## WHITLEY BAY (0191)

**The Bric-a-Brac Shop**, 195 Park View, NE26 3RD TEL: 252 6141 PARKING: Medium OPEN: Mon-Sat 10-1, 3-5 MIN: £1 MAX: £4000 PERIOD: 19th-20th century GENERAL: Furniture, china, silver, curios, bric-a-brac.

## FELTON (01670)

**Felton Park Antiques,** NE65 9HN TEL: 787319 PARKING: Own carpark OPEN: Strictly by appt only MIN: £5 MAX: £500 PERIOD: 18th-19th century SPECIALIST: Early ceramics, Newhall, blue & white, Sunderland Lustre, & small furniture OTHER INFO: Northumberland is beautiful, but don't tell anyone else!

## ALNWICK (01665)

**Bailiffgate Antique Pine,** 22 Bailiffgate, NE66 1LX TEL: 603616 PARKING: Easy OPEN: 10-4.30 Wed MIN: £4.50 MAX: £1500 PERIOD: 19th-20th century SPECIALIST: Victorian pine furniture.
**Pottergate Antiques,** 24 Narrowgate, NE66 1JG TEL: 510034 PARKING: Medium OPEN: Mon-Sat 10-5 MIN: £20 MAX: £3000 PERIOD: 19th century GENERAL: Furniture, decorative objects, jewellery OTHER INFO: B&B open all year, T & L Shell, Dukesryde, Longhoughton Road, Lesbury.

## BERWICK-ON-TWEED (01289)

**J & D Stewart,** 6 West Street, Norham, TD15 2LB TEL: 382376 PARKING: Easy OPEN: 9-6 MIN: £2 MAX: £100 PERIOD: 19th-20th century GENERAL: Victoriana & collectables OTHER INFO: Castle & Norman church. Good B&Bs.
**Treasure Chest**, 43 Bridge Street TEL: 307736 PARKING: Medium OPEN: 10.30-4 MIN: £1 MAX: £400 PERIOD: 19th-20th century GENERAL: Pine & other furniture OTHER INFO: Award winning restaurant next door. with B&B.

## WOOLER (01668)

**Millers Antiques**, 1-5 Church Street, NE71 6BZ TEL: 81500, 7281 PARKING: Easy OPEN: By appt MIN: £50 MAX: £10,000 PERIOD: 17th-20th century GENERAL: 30,000 sq ft Georgian, Regency, Victorian furniture.

## HAYDON BRIDGE (01434)

**Cain & Main, The Violin Shop**, 27 Hencotes, NE46 2EQ TEL: 607897 PARKING: Medium OPEN: Mon-Sat 10-5 MIN: £5 MAX: £15,000 PERIOD: 18th-20th century SPECIALIST: Violins, violas, cellos, bows GENERAL: Occasionally other instruments OTHER INFO: Glass case of unusual violin family instruments on display, fine new violins made on premises, restoration.
**Haydon Bridge Antiques**, 3 Shaftoe Street, NE47 6JX TEL: 684200 & 684461 PARKING: Easy OPEN: Tues, Wed, Fri, Sat 11-5.30 & by appt MIN: £1 MAX: £4000 PERIOD: 18th-20th century GENERAL: Furniture, paintings, china, bric-a-brac, furnishing pieces OTHER INFO: Next to wonderful restaurant/B&B furnished with antiques.
**Revival - Traditional Beds,** The Oddfellows Hall, Shaftoe Street, BE47 6BQ TEL: 684755 PARKING: Easy MIN: £5 MAX: £2500 PERIOD: 17th-20th century SPECIALIST: Beds including four posters OTHER INFO: Licensed restaurant & teashop, B&B.

## HEXHAM (01434)

**Arthur Boaden Antiques**, 29-30 Market Place, NE46 3PB TEL: 603187 ASSNS: LAPADA PARKING: Medium OPEN: Mon-Sat 9-12.30, 1.30-5 MIN: £1 MAX: £5000 PERIOD: 19th-20th century GENERAL: Antique, secondhand & reproduction furniture, general antiques.
**JA & T Hedley**, 3 St Mary's Chare TEL: 602317 PARKING: Easy OPEN: Mon-Sat 9-5 MIN: £1 MAX: £3000 PERIOD: 18th-20th century GENERAL: Furniture, porcelain, glass & sundries OTHER INFO: Furniture restorers.

## CONSETT (01207)

**Harry Raine**, Kelvinside House, Villa Real, DH8 6BL TEL: 503935 PARKING: Easy OPEN: Anytime by appt MIN: £200 MAX: £4-6000 PERIOD: 18th-19th century GENERAL: Furniture.

# Southern Scotland

*St Mary's Loch, approximately 15 miles west of Selkirk*
*By courtesy of the Scottish Tourist Board. Photograph by Harvey Wood.*

For centuries the border country was the scene of fierce fighting between the England and Scotland. There were also raids and skirmishes between the Scottish clans making life here uncertain and dangerous. Remnants of those battles can be seen in strong castles and ruined abbeys. Now, however, the farmlands and rugged moors are peaceful and beautiful. This area is known as the Scottish Lowlands but the name can be deceptive as there are mountains here too, some rising to over 2500 feet.

The tour starts right on the border at **Coldstream**, on the River Tweed, the town that gave its name to the Regiment of the Coldstream Guards. It is at a natural ford of the river which was used as a crossing point for English and Scottish armies throughout the centuries. Just west stands The Hirsel, family seat of the late Sir Alec Douglas-Home, who was briefly Prime Minister in the early 1960's. The large grounds and museum are open to the public where details of the family story are shown as well as displays of tools, archaeology and natural history. Nearby is Flodden Field, the bloody battleground where, in 1513, the Scots were routed by the English. The song *The Flowers of the Forest* is said to be a lament for the 10,000 deaths there.

Taking the A698, the next stop is in **Jedburgh**. The abbey here was started in the beginning of the 12th century and is still a beautiful red sandstone building in spite of now being a ruin. Another attraction is Mary Queen of Scots' House in Queen Street. Rrecently refurbished, it tells the story of the Queen who stayed here in 1566. Castle Jail and Museum in Castlegate relates the history of the town and with an exhibition on prison life.

15 miles north west is **Selkirk** This ancient burgh supplied 80 men to fight against the English at the Battle of Flodden but only one returned carrying a captured English standard which is now paraded during Selkirk's Common Riding in June. This ceremony involves riding on horseback around the borders of the town and goes back to the lawless times when encroachment was rife.

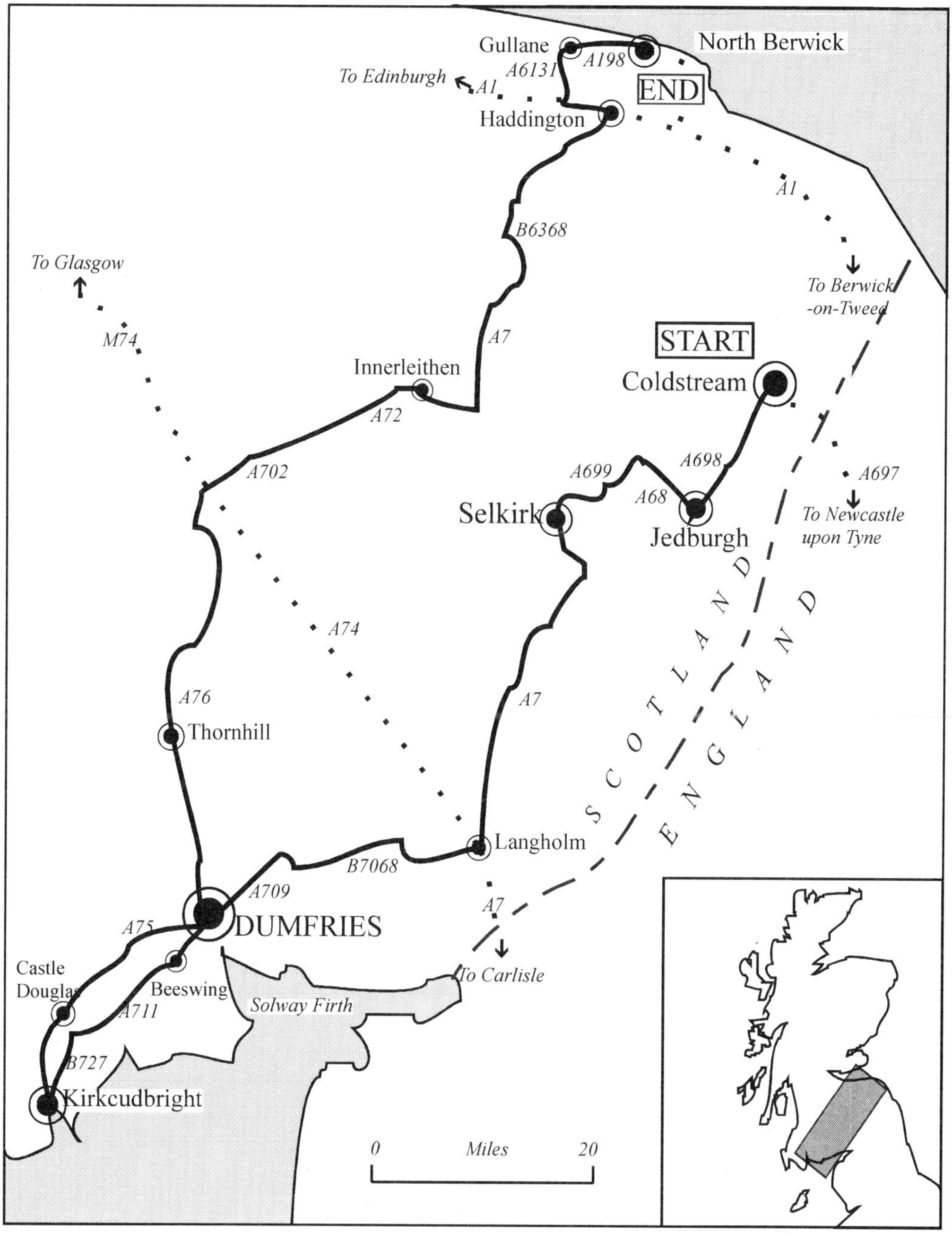
Gullane
North Berwick
A198
A6131
To Edinburgh
A1
END
Haddington
A1
B6368
To Glasgow
To Berwick
-on-Tweed
M74
A7
START
Innerleithen
Coldstream
A72
A702
A699
A698
A697
A68
Selkirk
Jedburgh
To Newcastle
upon Tyne
A74
SCOTLAND
ENGLAND
A76
A7
Thornhill
Langholm
B7068
A709
A7
A75
DUMFRIES
Castle
Douglas
Beeswing
To Carlisle
A711
Solway Firth
B727
Kirkcudbright
0
Miles
20

The town has a statue to the brave man who returned from Flodden as well as one of Sir Walter Scott, the novelist and also Sherriff of Selkirk. His home, Abbotsford House, may be seen at Melrose, about 5 miles north-east off the A7. A third statue in the town is of Doctor Mungo Park, the explorer who found the source of the River Niger. The Georgian mansion of Bowhill stands 3 miles west on the A708 and contains a wonderful collection of paintings including works by Canaletto, Gainsborough and Reynolds.

Further south-west, the mill town, **Langholm,** was the home of the ancestors of Neil Armstrong, the first man on the moon. Thomas Telford, the engineer, was born here and worked as an apprentice on one of the town's many bridges. A picturesque town on the confluence of the rivers Esk, Wauchope and Ewes, the oldest part consists of narrow twisting streets whilst across the river the newer buildings, dating from the 18th century, display the elegance associated with the period.

The route moves on to **Dumfries** on the River Nith. This red sandstone town was the departure point for many Scots emigrating to the New World. Scots drovers walked cattle from here nearly 300 miles to Huntingdon in England and so Huntingdon is one of the places, with their mileages from Dumfries, listed on Midsteeple, a former tollbooth in the town centre. Robert Burns also lived here for the last five years of his life and the Robert Burns Centre in Mill Road contains an exhibition on the poet and his local story. The house in Burns Street, where he spent his last three years, is also open to the public. The Dumfries Museum has a *camera obscura*, dating from the mid 19th century. At the top of a converted windmill, it gives a panoramic view of the town and surrounding countryside.

After first visiting the village of **Beeswing**, the tour reaches its most westerly point and the seaside town of **Kirkcudbright** (pronounced Kircoobree), meaning the church of St Cuthbert. The ruined Mclellan's Castle overlooks the harbour. Built in 1582 from the stones of a disused friary, it was once an elegant mansion. Other points of interest are the Market Cross dating from 1610 and the Tollbooth, originally built in the early 15th century but with later additions. The 12th century Dundrennan Abbey, also now a ruin, stands on the A711 five miles away. There is much of note in the abbey but perhaps the connection with Mary Queen of Scots gives a particular fascination. The tragic queen spent her last night in Scotland in the Abbey before seeking sanctuary from Queen Elizabeth I in England.

Turning back north-east, **Castle Douglas** is on Carlingwark Loch. Nearby the ruined Threave Castle stands on an island in the loch and was the stronghold of the much-feared Black Douglases. Built in the late 14th century, as the base for a powerful family, it saw many battles. The Douglases boasted that the gallows knob over the doorway of the castle 'never wanted a tassel.' Threave Garden may be found a mile west of the castle off the A75. These magnificent, much-visited gardens house the National Trust for Scotland's horticultural school.

Another castle stands just three miles north of the next stop in **Thornhill**. Drumlanrig Castle, built on the site of another Douglas stronghold in pink sandstone in the late 17th century, is in extensive and beautiful grounds consisting of woods and parkland. It contains a magnificent collection of art: pictures by Rembrandt and Holbein, Louis XIV furniture and relics of Bonnie Prince Charlie, the Young Pretender.

**Innerleithen**, on the confluence of the River Tweed and Leithen Water, contains the Robert Smail's Printing Works, started in 1866 and closed in 1985. However, the works were never modernised so the visitor can step back into a Victorian workshop. **Haddington**, next, received its royal charter in the 12th century although the elegant buildings date mostly from the 17th-19th centuries. One of the earlier buildings is the Church of St Mary, built in the 14th century. Noteworthy also is the Jane Welsh Carlyle Museum in Lodge Street. Jane Welsh was the wife of Thomas Carlyle and the museum is housed in her home. It is still furnished in the style of the early 19th century and displays portraits of people associated with the couple. There are two fine houses nearby: Lennoxlove, owned by the Duke of Hamilton, contains a superb collection of works of art including the Casket, ring and death mask of Mary Queen of Scots and Stevenson House, dating mainly from the mid 16th century has fine pictures and furniture

**Gullane**, less than eight miles away, is well-known for Muirfield golf course. Nearby **North Berwick**, the last stop on this tour, is also a golfer's paradise being surrounded by golf courses. This ancient town became popular as a holiday resort during the 19th century and the buildings mostly date from that period. The ruined Auld Kirk stands beside the tiny harbour. The church was the scene of a black magic rite in the 16th century designed to cause the death of the king, James VI. A volcanic plug, Berwick Law, rises behind the town to a height of 613 feet. A steep climb will bring the fit visitor to the top where there is a watchtower, a relic of the Napoleonic Wars, and an arch made from a whale's jawbone.

## ANTIQUE DEALERS

### COLDSTREAM (01890)

**Coldstream Antiques,** 44 High Street, TD12 4AS TEL: 882552 PARKING: Easy OPEN: Mon-Sat 9-6, Sun by appt MIN: £5 MAX: £5000 PERIOD: 18th-19th century GENERAL: Furniture, clocks, small objects of interest.

**Fraser Antiques,** 65 High Street, TD12 4DL TEL & FAX: 882450 PARKING: Easy OPEN: Wed-Fri 10-5 or by appt MIN: £10 MAX: £3000 PERIOD: 18th-20th century GENERAL: Porcelain, silver, glass, furniture, decorative items.

### JEDBURGH (01835)

**Mainhill Gallery,** Ancrum, TD8 6XA TEL: 830518 PARKING: Own carpark OPEN: 7 days 10.30-5.30 MIN: £20 MAX: £10,000 PERIOD: 19th-20th century SPECIALIST: Scottish artists GENERAL: Etchings, watercolours, oils & sculpture OTHER INFO: Quiet & picturesque village close to main north/south trunk road, A68. We can advise on local accommodation, etc.

### SELKIRK (01750)

**Heatherlie Antiques,** 6-8 Terrace, TD7 5AH TEL: 20114 PARKING: Easp OPEN: Mon-Fri 9.30-12.30, 2-5, Sat 9.30-12.30 MIN: £1 MAX: Approx £4000 PERIOD: 19th-20th century GENERAL: General antiques OTHER INFO: Near Abbotsford House, home of Sir Walter Scott who was also Sheriff of Selkirk. The Court House can still be visited. St Mary's Lock, a well known beauty spot, iwithin easy reach lying between Selkirk and Moffat.

### LANGHOLM (01387)

**The Antiques Shop,** 96 High Street, DG13 0DH TEL: 380238 PARKING: Difficult OPEN: 10.30-5.30, closed Wed pm MIN: 50p MAX: £2000 PERIOD: 18th-19th century GENERAL: Jewellery, china, glass, pictures, books, rugs, furniture warehouse nearby OTHER INFO: Tradional Scottish border town. Good centre for hill walking.

### DUMFRIES (01387)

**Dix Antiques,** 100 English Street, DG1 2BY TEL: 64234 PARKING: Difficult OPEN: 10-4.30 MIN: £5 MAX: £1000 PERIOD: 19th-20th century GENERAL: Furniture, clocks, smalls, jewellery.

### BEESWING (01387)

**Cairnyard Antiques,** DG2 8JE TEL: 730218 PARKING: Mon-Sat 10-5 MIN: 50p MAX: £5000 PERIOD: 19th-20th century GENERAL: China, silver, clocks, furniture OTHER INFO: Beeswing (named after a racehorse) is on A711, 5 miles from Dumfries.

### KIRKCUDBRIGHT (01557)

**The Antique Shop,** 69 St Mary Street, DG6 4DU TEL: 330239 PARKING: Easy OPEN: 10-5 MIN: £1 MAX: £1500 PERIOD: 19th-20th century SPECIALIST: Victoriana, Art Nouveau & Deco GENERAL: General antiques, collectors items, linen, lace, kitchenalia, furniture, books.

**Osborne,** 41 Castle Street, DG6 4JD TEL: 330441 FAX: 331791 PARKING: Easy OPEN: 9-12.30, 1.30-5 PERIOD: 17th-20th century.

### CASTLE DOUGLAS (01556)

**Bendall,** 221-223, King Street, DG7 1DT TEL & FAX: 502113 PARKING: Easy OPEN: 9-5 PERIOD: 17th-20th century.

### THORNHILL (01848)

**Thornhill Gallery,** 47-48 Drumlanrig Street, DG3 5LJ TEL: 335566 PARKING: Easy OPEN: Mon-

Sat 9-5.30 MIN: £5 MAX: £1000 PERIOD: 18th-20th century GENERAL: Small antiques centre with wide range of stock OTHER INFO: Golf course nearby, salmon & trout fishing locally, B&B is available at Thornhill Gallery.

## INNERLEITHEN (0131)

**Antiques,** 16 High Street, EH44 6HF TEL: 225 6343 & (01896) 870355 PARKING: Easy MIN: £1 MAX: £500 PERIOD: 19th-20th century SPECIALIST: China, glass GENERAL: Small furniture, linen, general antiques.

## HADDINGTON (01620)

**Elm House Antiques,** Church Street, EH41 3EX TEL: 823413 PARKING: Easy OPEN: Sat 10-1, 2-5, weekdays by appt PERIOD: 18th-19th century SPECIALIST: English ceramics, Scottish pottery, blue & white earthenware GENERAL: Furniture & silver OTHER INFO: Close to 15th century bridge & large medieval church.

**Leslie & Leslie,** 77 Market Street, EH41 3JJ TEL & FAX: 822241 PARKING: Medium OPEN: Mon-Fri 9-1, 2-5 MIN: £5 MAX: £2500 PERIOD: 19th-20th century GENERAL: General antiques.

## GULLANE (01620)

**Gullane Antiques,** 5 Rosebery Place TEL: 842326 PARKING: Easy OPEN: Mon, Tues, Fri, Sat 10.30-1, 2.30-5, Thurs 2.30-5 MIN: 50p MAX: £1000 PERIOD: 19th-20th century GENERAL: China, glass, collectables, some jewellery & furniture.

## NORTH BERWICK (01620)

**Fraser Antiques,** 129 High Street, EH39 4HB TEL: 892722 FAX: 01890 882450 PARKING: Easy OPEN: Sat 9.30-12.30 or by appt MIN: £10 MAX: £3000 PERIOD: 18th-20th century GENERAL: Porcelain, silver, glass, furniture, decorative items. antiques OTHER INFO: Within walking distance of Royal Troon Golf Club.

# Strathclyde to Oban

*City Chambers, Glasgow*
*By courtesy of the Scottish Tourist Board*

The tour, which includes parts of central region of Scotland, is one of great contrasts. Glasgow, Scotland's second great city, is a busy centre of industry and culture whilst tranquil beautiful countryside and lovely coastal scenery are close by.

**Prestwick**, first, is on the west coast; and apart from having an international airport, is a renowned golfing and holiday resort. Neighbouring **Troon** also has several golf courses and good beaches. Further north, **Saltcoats** gets its name from the saltworks and at low tide fossilised trees may be seen in the harbour.

The ferry to reach the next stop, **Brodick** on the **Isle of Arran**, leaves from Ardrossan, adjoining Saltcoats. The island was a popular holiday destination for Glaswegians and has beautiful scenery with highlands in the north and lowlands in the south, a reflection of Scotland itself, in fact. Only about 20 miles long by 10 miles wide and largely unspoilt, much of Arran is moorland and mountains with settlements around the coast. Brodick is the main town and port for the island situated on a sandy bay. Brodick Castle was built on the site of a Viking stronghold and dates from the 13th century with later additions. During the Civil War the castle was held for Parliament until the islanders massacred the garrison. Now the castle contains collections of silver, porcelain, furniture and paintings and is set in lovely gardens. To the north the mountain of Goatfell rises to a height of 2866 feet.

Returning to the mainland, Largs is truly an ancient settlement with local traces of habitation from the Neolithic and Iron Ages being found. The Pencil Tower on the sea shore is a monument to the battle fought by the Scots, under King Alexander III in 1263, against the Norsemen who had held the Hebrides and Isle of Man for centuries. The battle was ferocious and lasted for two days. Eventually the Scots won and, as a result, the Hebrides and the Isle of Man became part of Scotland. Kelburn Castle and Country Centre stands to the south of the town and has been the home of the Boyle family for 800 years. The castle, dating from the 13th century, is surrounded by magnificent gardens and dramatic natural scenery.

The route turns inland to the town of **Kilbarchan**, famous for the weaving of tartan, and then to **Paisley**. The centre for making shawls, the town gave the name to a particular pattern thought to have originated from an Indian design brought here in the 18th century by returning soldiers. The museum and art gallery in the High Street has a world famous collection of Paisley shawls as well as exhibitions on local history.

After first visiting **Barrhead** the tour continues to **Langside** and then to **Glasgow**, Scotland's

## Strathclyde to Oban

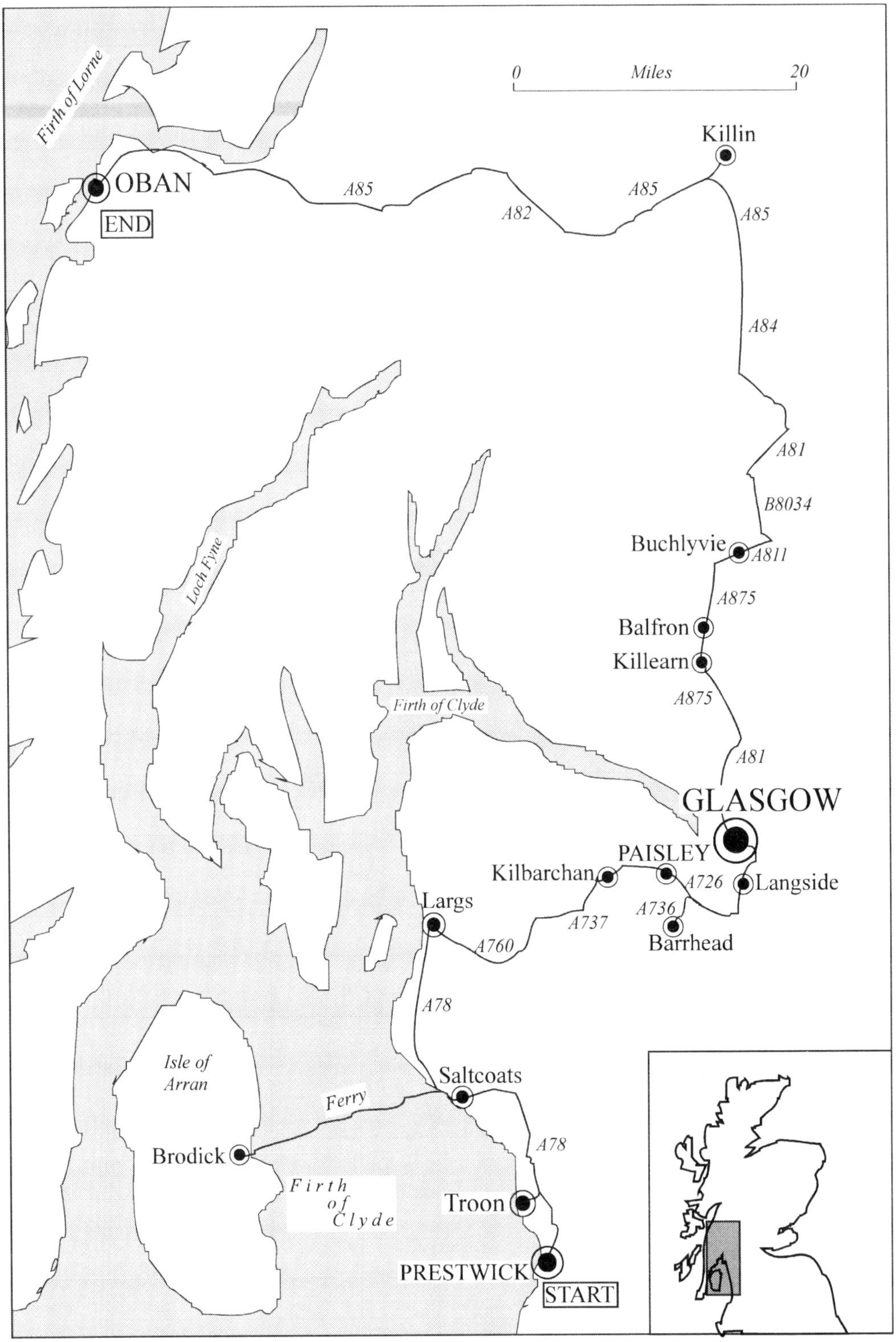

*Castle Stalker on the shores of Loch Linnhe*
*By courtesy of the Scottish Tourist Board*

second city. Settlement here probably started in the 6th century around the site of the present cathedral where a church built by the city's patron saint, St Mungo, stood. The cathedral, an outstanding example of Early English Gothic, was built on the site of this early church in the 13th century although there are a few remains of earlier work in the Lower Church. Inside there is much to see including a 15th century stone screen, magnificent fan vaulting and modern stained glass windows.

For many years Glasgow had a poor image as a dirty, slum city but this has now been dispelled especially as it won the award of Cultural Capital of Europe in 1990, its renowned Mitchell Library is one of the largest in Europe. Now the slums have gone and the imposing Victorian buildings have been cleaned. Also home to the Scottish Opera, there are not one but two universities, Glasgow and Strathclyde plus many museums and art galleries. Amongst the most notable are the Art Gallery and Museum in Kelvingrove which contains a fine collection of art including works by Botticelli, Rembrandt, Millet, Monet and Van Gogh. A special emphasis is on Scottish artists especially the Glasgow Boys and Scottish Colourists. Displayed are decorative arts, arms and armour, archaeology, antiquities, etc. The Hunterian Art Gallery, Hillhead Street, contains collections of the work of Charles Rennie Mackintosh and includes reconstructions of the interiors from his house. In contrast, The Tenement House at 145 Buccleuch Street, Garnethill, shows how the working classes lived at the end of the 19th century.

Historic Glasgow has many more interesting places, this is just a small sample as the trip now continues north, to the village of **Killearn** and then **Balfron**, where there is a legend that, in the distant past, all the children of the village were eaten by wolves. After the next call in **Buchlyvie** there is some 35 miles of truly lovely driving to **Killin**, on the River Dochart and a mile to the south of Loch Tay. The village is a popular centre with holiday-makers in both summer and winter. The church dates only from the mid 18th century but was built on the site of a much earlier one and inside there is a 9th century septagonal font. The Reverend James Stewart is commemorated in front of the church as he was the first person to translate the New Testament into Gaelic. Finlarig Castle stands near the town on the shore of Loch Tay. Now a ruin, it was once the centre of the notorious Clan Campbell. A beheading pit is near the castle where a primitive guillotine, called the Maiden, was once used.

Fifty miles west the route terminates at the **Oban** set on a sheltered bay. The town's busy harbour has ferries running from here to the Hebrides as well as excursion boats, yachts and fishing trawlers. Another charming feature is McCaig's Tower, a replica of the Colosseum, built in 1897 by a local man. The ruins of the 12th to 13th century Dunollie Castle, may be seen to the north. Another stronghold stands about twelve miles north of Oban. Castle Stalker, on the shores of Loch Linnhe, was built in the 16th century and has since been restored. For gardeners, Arduine (pronounced Ardooney) Garden, 20 miles south of Oban, is a must. Started at the turn of the century, restored in the 1970s and now run by the National Trust for Scotland, it contains nationally important collections of rhododendrons, azaleas and magnolias. There are also many other rare and beautiful trees and shrubs.

## ANTIQUE DEALERS

### PRESTWICK (01292)

**Yer Granny's Attic at the Lee Glass Works,** 176 Main Street, KA9 1PG TEL: 76312 PARKING: Easy OPEN: Tues-Sat 10-6 MIN: £1 MAX: Generally under £100 PERIOD: 19th-20th century SPECIALIST: Stained glass (mirrors, lamps, windows) GENERAL: Collectables, bric a brac OTHER INFO: We share space with the stained glass making business.

### TROON (01292)

**Old Troon Sporting Antiques,** 49 Ayr Street, KA10 6EB TEL: 311822 FAX: 313111 PARKING: Medium PERIOD: 19th-20th century SPECIALIST: Gold antiques & art GENERAL: Some general antiques OTHER INFO: Within walking distance of Royal Troon Golf Club.

### SALTCOATS (01294)

**Narducci Antiques,** 57 Raise Street, KA21 5QT TEL: 461687, 467137 & (01475) 672612 FAX: 461687 PARKING: Own carpark OPEN: By appt, trade & shippers anytime PERIOD: 19th-20th century SPECIALIST: Large selection of antique furniture & shipping goods, packing & shipping anywhere, road haulage to Europe OTHER INFO: Situated on West Coast between Ayr & Largs. Trade buyers collected from Glasgow Airport or railway station. Easy access by road.

### ISLE OF ARRAN (01770)

**Kames Antiques & Jewellery,** Shore Road, Brodick KA27 8AJ TEL & FAX: 302213 PARKING: Own carpark MIN: £2 MAX: £6500 PERIOD: 18th-20th century SPECIALIST: Jewellery GENERAL: Furniture, porcelain, objets d'art, silver, paintings, prints, artists material OTHER INFO: 2 shops located on Scotland's premier holiday island, the most attractive on the West coast.

### LARGS (01475)

**Narducci Antiques,** 11-13 Waterside Street TEL: 672612 FAX: 461687 PARKING: Own carpark OPEN: Tues, Thurs, Sat 2.30-5.30, trade anytime by appt PERIOD:19th-20th century GENERAL: Large selection of antique furniture & shipping goods. Packing & shipping anywhere. Road haulage to Europe OTHER INFO: Situated in North Ayrshire coastal town. Popular tourist spot. Lovely scenery, good hotels & restaurants, famous ice cream parlour. Easy access by road, 40 mins from Glasgow Airport, trade buyers collected from airport.

### KILBARCHAN (01505)

**Gardner's the Antique Shop,** Wardend, Kibbleston Road, PA10 2PN TEL & FAX: 702292 ASSNS: LAPADA PARKING: Own carpark OPEN: Mon-Fri 9-6, Sat 10-1, trade by appt other times MIN: £1 MAX: £8000 PERIOD: 18th-20th century GENERAL: 11 large rooms & sheds of furniture, porcelain, silver, metalware, pictures, unusual collectables OTHER INFO: Kilbarchan is one of the original weaving villages for Paisley shawls, etc & is a conservation area with a weaver's cott open to the public.

## PAISLEY (0141)

**Paisley Fine Books,** 17 Corsebar Crescent, PA2 9QA TEL & FAX: 884 2661 OPEN: 9-9 MIN: £2 MAX: £500 SPECIALIST: Books on antiques, architecture, art, garden history & design OTHER INFO: Postal business worldwide, free catalogue, free book search service.

## BARRHEAD (0141)

**CPR Antiques Services,** 96 Main Street, G78 1SE TEL: 881 5379 PARKING: Medium OPEN: 10-1, 1.30-5, closed Tues & Sun MIN: £2 SPECIALIST: Brass.

## LANGSIDE (0141)

**Butler's Furniture Galleries,** 24-26 Millbrae Road, Langside, G42 9TU TEL: 632 9853 & 639 3396 PARKING: Own carpark OPEN: Mon-Fri 9.30-5.30 MIN: £5 MAX: £4000 PERIOD: 19th century GENERAL: Furniture, some silver, Persian rugs, smalls OTHER INFO: I am on the site of the famous Battle of Langside involving Mary Queen of Scots.

**Den of Antiquity,** Langside Lane, 539 Victoria Road, G42 8BH TEL & FAX: 423 7122 PARKING: Own carpark OPEN: Mon-Sat 9.30-5.30, Sun 12-5 MIN: £5 MAX: £2000 PERIOD: 20th century SPECIALIST: Pine GENERAL: Mahogany, oak.

**Renaissance Furniture Store,** 103 Niddrie Road, G42 8PR TEL: 423 0022 PARKING: Easy OPEN: Tues-Fri 10.30-5, Sat & Sun 12-5 MIN: £5 MAX: £1200 PERIOD: 19th-20th century SPECIALIST: Fireplaces GENERAL: Clean (often refurbished) large furniture, clocks, Art Nouveau, smalls OTHER INFO: Near to the Burrell Collection.

## GLASGOW (0141)

**Albany Antiques,** 1347 Argyle Street, G3 8AD TEL: 339 4267 ASSNS: LAPADA PARKING: Mon-Fri 9.30-5.30 MIN: £5 MAX: £5000 PERIOD: 19th century SPECIALIST: Edwardian & Victorian furniture GENERAL: Oriental ceramics & works of art OTHER INFO: Next to Janssens & opposite Kelvingrove Art Gallery & Museum.

**All Our Yesterdays,** 6 Park Road, Kelvinbridge TEL: 334 7788 FAX: 339 8994 PARKING: Easy OPEN: Mon-Thurs 11.30-5.30, Fri, Sat 10-5.45 MIN: £5 MAX: £600 PERIOD: 1880-1945 SPECIALIST: Kitchenalia, oddities, Doulton, Lambeth, stoneware, collectables, etc OTHER INFO: This Aladdin's Cave is the Harrods of the junk shops: free search service available, what we don't have we will find.

**E.A.S.Y. (Edinburgh & Glasgow Architectural Salvage Yard)** 85-87 Colvend Street, G40 4DU TEL: 556 7772 FAX: 556 5552 PARKING: Easy PERIOD: 18th-20th century GENERAL: Doors, counters, panelling, stairways, fireplaces, light fittings, gates, columns, marble slabs, etc.

**Jean Megahy Antiques,** 481 Great Western Road, G12 8HL TEL: 334 1315 PARKING: Easy OPEN: Mon-Fri 10-5, Sat 10-1 MIN: £30 MAX: £5000 PERIOD: 18th-20th century GENERAL: Furniture, glass, brass, silver, ceramics, clocks, light fittings.

**Pastimes,** 140 Maryhill Road, G20 7QS TEL: 331 1008 PARKING: Easy OPEN: Mon-Sat 10-5 MIN: £1 MAX: £1000 PERIOD: 20th century SPECIALIST: Dinky & Corgi toys GENERAL: Other vintage toys, model railways, dolls houses, tinplate, also militaria (by appt) OTHER INFO: We organise

the Glasgow vintage toy auctions 4 times a year.
**Tim Wright Antiques,** Richmond Chambers, 147 Bath Street, G2 4SQ TEL: 221 0364 ASSNS: LAPADA OPEN: Mon-Fri 9.45-5, Sat 10.30-2 MIN: £50 MAX: £7000 PERIOD: 18th-20th century SPECIALIST: Lots of decorative smalls GENERAL: 2000 sq ft of quality furniture, metalware, ceramics, glass, silver.

## KILLEARN (01360)

**Country Antiques,** TEL: 770215 PARKING: Easy OPEN: 9.30-5.30 MIN: £5 MAX: £300 PERIOD: 19th century GENERAL: Small decorative antiques, pre 1920 OTHER INFO: Shop adjoins an excellent kitchenware shop with every conceivable gadget & lovely pottery.

## BALFRON (01360)

**Amphora Galleries,** 16-18 Buchanan Street, G63 0TT TEL: 440329 PARKING: Easy OPEN: 10-5.30 or by appt MIN: £15 MAX: £5000 PERIOD: 18th-20th century SPECIALIST: Upholstery GENERAL: Furniture, porcelain, decorative items OTHER INFO: 15 miles from Stirling & 12 miles from Loch Lomond, delightful scenery.

## BUCHLYVIE (01360)

**Amphora Galleries,** 22 Main Street, FK8 3LX TEL: 850203 PARKING: Easy OPEN: 10-5.30 or by appt MIN: £15 MAX: £5000 PERIOD: 18th-20th century SPECIALIST: Upholstery GENERAL: Furniture, porcelain, decorative items.

## KILLIN (01567)

**Maureen H Gauld,** Craiglea Main Street, FK21 8UE TEL: 820475 PARKING: Own carpark OPEN: Mon-Sat 10-5, March to Oct MIN: £1 MAX: £4000 PERIOD: 18th-20th century SPECIALIST: Scottish paintings, etchings GENERAL: Furniture, silver, china, etc.

## OBAN (01631)

**Oban Antiques,** 35 Stevenson Street, PA34 5NA TEL: 66203 PARKING: Medium MIN: £10 MAX: £2000 PERIOD: 19th-20th century GENERAL: Ceramics, glass, jewellery, furniture, prints, silver, plate, books, metalware, pictures, etc OTHER INFO: Can recommend good B&B, Oban good centre for Iona & other islands & general touring.

# Edinburgh to St Andrews

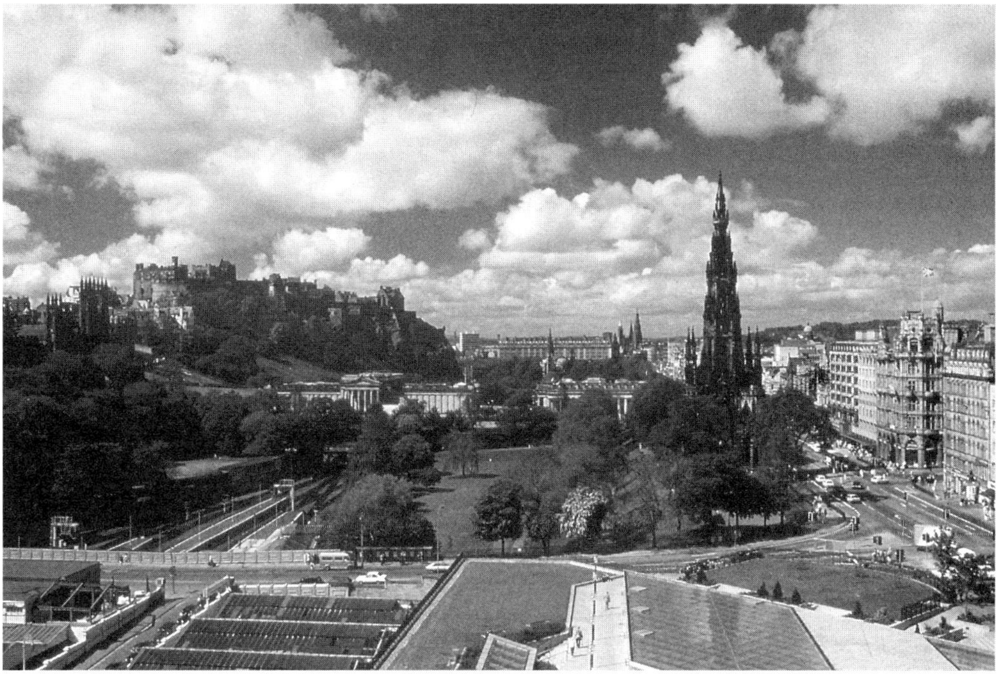

*Princes Street, Edinburgh*
*By courtesy of the Scottish Tourist Board*

Capital cities, golf and, as always in Scotland, beautiful scenery are all part of this tour. It visits Edinburgh, the present capital, and Perth, the former. These cities and most of the towns and villages are heavy with history and this is reflected in their architecture, museums and monuments.

The trip starts with **Edinburgh**, the capital and a beautiful and imposing city. This has been the site of a settlement since at least the Bronze Age as archaealogical remains found on Castle Rock prove. The city is dominated by the castle situated on a volcanic plug of rock and the town grew up around it in from the 11th century. Here Mary Queen of Scots gave birth to James VI of Scotland who also became James I of England. The Scottish Crown Jewels are kept within the castle in the Old Royal Palace and the Scottish United Services Museum has exhibitions of the uniforms, arms, medals, etc of the Scottish armed forces. In the surrounding park, on Princes Street, there is the oldest floral clock in the world, constructed in 1903. At the opposite end of the gardens is the Church of St John, built by William Burn in 1817 and containing a remarkable collection of 19th century stained glass.

The Royal Mile, one of the most famous streets in Scotland, runs from Edinburgh Castle to Holyrood Abbey. It was the hub from which the city spread outwards and there are so many places to visit. At the castle end of the Royal Mile stands the Scotch Whisky Heritage Centre which recounts the history of whisky over 300 years and also tells how the drink is made. A *camera obscura* is situated nearby in the Outlook Tower from which the whole panorama of Edinburgh may be seen while visitors listen to a commentary. Gladstone's Land, a six storey tenement built in 1620, stands further west along the Royal Mile. Owned by the National Trust for Scotland, the building has been restored as a typical home of the period. Three museums exist on the Royal Mile. The Museum of Childhood contains large collections of dolls, toys, games and costume. The People's Story, near the eastern end , is housed in a former tollbooth and recounts the history of Edinburgh's residents from the 18th century onwards. Huntly House Museum stands almost opposite and con-

# Edinburgh to St Andrews

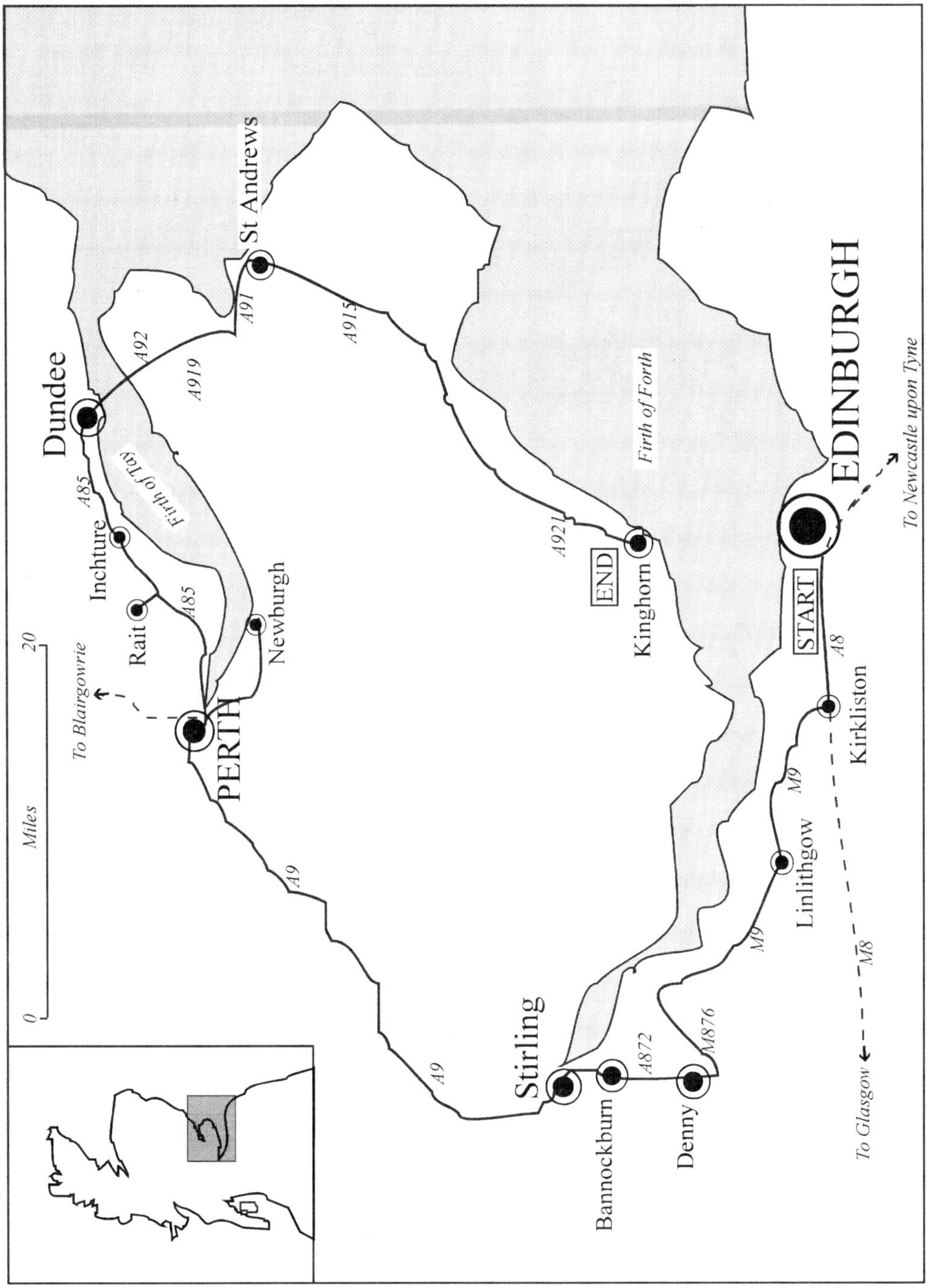

*Drummond Castle Gardens between Stirling and Perth*
*By courtesy of the Scottish Tourist Board*

tains important collections of silver, glass and Scottish pottery as well as exhibitions on local history and topography and relics of Field Marshall Earl Haig. There are many other charming and historic buildings in the Royal Mile, this is only a small selection.

The Palace of Holyrood House and Holyrood Abbey stand at the eastern end. Holyrood Palace is the official residence of the Queen in Scotland. Although there has been a palace here since the early 16th century, built around the abbey's guest house, the present building is largely late 17th century. Bonnie Prince Charlie, the Young Pretender, stayed here in 1745. Edinburgh Castle was held by the English and a cannonball may be seen embedded in a house at the castle end. It is said to have been fired at Holyrood Palace and the Young Pretender. Little now survives of Holyrood Abbey except for the ruined church although it was once a great and powerful religious house founded in 1128.

Edinburgh contains many other museums These include the City Art Centre at 2 Market Street,with works by late 19th and 20th century artists. There are two other important art galleries: the Scottish National Portrait Gallery at 1 Queen Street and the Scottish National Gallery of Modern Art in Belford Road. The Royal Museum of Scotland, Chambers Street, contains the national collections of decorative arts, natural history, geology, technology, etc. The National Gallery of Scotland, The Mound, has excellent exhibitions of pictures including works by El Greco, Rembrandt, Vermeer, Turner, Constable, Degas, Monet, etc.

Turning west out of Edinburgh, the tour visits first **Kirkliston** and then **Linlithgow**, site of the great royal palace, birthplace of Mary, Queen of Scots. Most of the present building dates from the 15th to 16th centuries although some parts survive from the early 14th century. In the Church of St Michael, dating mostly from the 15th century, legend has it that James IV was warned by a ghost against war with the English just before the disastrous Battle of Flodden.

The village of **Denny** comes next followed then by **Bannockburn**, two miles north, the 13th century battleground where Robert the Bruce defeated the English to maintain an independent Scotland. The Bannockburn Heritage Centre traces the history of Scotland, and its quest for freedom from the English, from early times to the union of the two countries under one king in 1603. The village lies just south of the battlefield and largely grew during the 19th century when mills were built. Now it is almost a suburb of Stirling.

Continuing into **Stirling**, this grew up around a castle standing atop a 250 foot rock. The original timber-built fortress was the home of King Alexander I who died there in 1124. In the 13th century it was rebuilt in stone, nowadays, after ages of modifications most of the castle dates from the 15th and 16th centuries. Another landmark, Mar's Wark, is nearby and is the remains of a mansion started by the Earl of Mar in the 16th century but never fully completed.

A pleasant 30 mile drive now skirts the 2364 foot Ben Cleuch, a charming viewpoint,and passes through the quaintly named village of Dollar. Approximately midway between the Stirling and Perth there is a detour that is a must for all gardeners. Drummond Castle stands on the A822 and its superb gardens are open to the public. They were originally designed and planted in the early 17th century and were restored in the 19th century. The most important and famous feature is the multifaceted sundial dating from 1630. The gardens extend over a series of terraces, the highest of which gives a view over the gardens and from there it may be seen that the the lowest garden is laid out in the shape of a St Andrew's Cross.

Next, **Perth**, was once the capital of Scotland. A settlement was established at Scone (pronounced Skoon) just two miles north and this became the Scottish capital in the 9th century. However, in the 13th century the town was destroyed by floods and the status of capital was transferred to Perth. Traditionally Scone Palace was where Scottish kings were crowned. The present building was constructed in the early 19th century around 16th century remains of the earlier palace. It contains an outstanding collection of china, furniture, ivories, needlework and clocks.

In Perth John Knox preached his sermon against idolatry in St John's Kirk which led to the wrecking of churches throughout the country and also to the destruction of Scone Palace and Abbey. The Kirk originally dated from 1243 but is now mostly 15th century. Balhousie Castle, by North Inch Park, houses the regimental Museum of the Black Watch. The Art Gallery and Museum in George Street covers art, costume, local and natural history and whisky distilling. Sir Walter Scott wrote about the 'fair maid of Perth' and the Fair Maid's House in North Port is now used as a gallery for Scottish arts and crafts. It is also possible to visit a local whisky distillery run by Dewar's and the Caithness Glassworks.

Next there is a short detour to the southern side of the Tay and the town of **Newburgh,** with its 18th century houses, before returning, almost back to Perth, to visit the villages of **Rait** and **Inchture**. The route now reaches **Dundee**, a busy port and industrial city. In the centre volcanic rock, the Law of Dundee, rises to a height of 571 feet giving good views over the city and surrounding countryside. There are several excellent museums. The Barrack Street Museum has displays on natural history and includes the Tay Whale which swam up the Tay in 1883. Broughty Castle Museum, on the banks of the Tay at Broughty Ferry, has exhibitions of local history, arms and armour and whaling. It is housed in a 15th century castle which was attacked by the English in the 1547 and then again in 1651 leaving it in ruins but restored in the 1861. A superb collection of 19th and 20th century Scottish paintings, prints, drawings, sculpture, furniture, clocks, etc, are housed in the McManus Galleries in Albert Square. The Galleries also contain costume, antiquities and displays on life in the area from prehistoric times to the 19th century. The Mills Observatory, Balgay Park, is Britain's only full-time public observatory. As well as offering allowing public use of the telescope, there are exhibitions of telescopes and scientific instruments.

Crossing the Firth of Tay by way of the Tay Road Bridge, the tour reaches the North Sea at **St Andrews** in Fife, world famous for the Royal and Ancient Golf Club, the controlling body for golf worldwide. The ruins of the cathedral, once the largest in Scotland, are impressive. Construction started in the mid 12th century and was finished about 150 years later. It was unaffected by the Dissolution of the Monasteries and appararently fell into ruins through neglect. Stones from the cathedral have been used in other buildings in the town. St Andrews Castle was built as the bishop's palace in the 13th century although rebuilt and altered in later centuries. Finally a charming coastal drive brings this tour to an end in the village of **Kinghorn** with a lovely sandy beach area of Burnisland on the Firth of Forth, only 25 miles short of Edinburgh again.

## ANTIQUE DEALERS

## EDINBURGH (0131)

**Another World,** 25 Candlemaker Row, EH1 2QG TEL: 225 1988 PARKING: Easy OPEN: Wed, Fri, Sat 1-4.30 MIN: £20 MAX: £1000 PERIOD: 17th-19th century SPECIALIST: Netsuke & Japanese sword fittings GENERAL: Oriental antiques OTHER INFO: Just down from Greyfriars Bobby, in the old part of Edinburgh.

**Paddy Barrass,** 15 The Grassmarket EH1 2HS TEL: 226 3087 PARKING: Easy OPEN: Mon-Fri 12-6, Sat 10.30-5.30 MAC: £200 PERIOD: 19th-20th century SPECIALIST: Linen, period clothing.

**Laurance Black Ltd, Antiques of Scotland,** 60

Thistle Street, EH2 1EN TEL: 220 3387 PARKING: Medium OPEN: Mon-Fri 10-5, Sat 10-1 MIN: £5 MAX: £30,000 PERIOD: 18th-20th century SPECIALIST: Scottish furniture, tartanware GENERAL: Furniture, paintings, treen, glass, pottery, textiles.

**Joseph Bonnar, Jewellers,** 72 Thistle Street, EH2 1EN TEL: 226 2811 FAX: 225 9438 PARKING: Medium OPEN: Mon-Sat 10.30-5 MIN: £25 MAX: £15,000 PERIOD: 17th-20th century, sometimes ancient jewellery SPECIALIST: Antique & period jewellery, silver OTHER INFO: We have the most comprehensive stock of old jewellery in Scotland.

**Bourne Fine Art,** 4 Dundas Street, EH3 6HZ TEL & FAX: 557 4050 PARKING: Easy OPEN: Mon-Fri 10-6, Sat 10-1 MIN: £20 PERIOD: 18th-20th century SPECIALIST: The Colourists GENERAL: Scottish paintings.

**Calton Gallery,** 10 Royal Terrace, EH7 5AB TEL: 556 1010 FAX: 558 1150 PARKING: Easy OPEN: Mon-Fri 10-6, Sat 10-1 MIN: £100 MAX: £50,000 PERIOD: 19th century-1940 SPECIALIST: Scottish oils & watercolours, marine oils & watercolours GENERAL: British & Continental paintings & watercolours, animalier bronzes OTHER INFO: Gallery is in an elegant Georgian townhouse, on three floors.

**Carson Clark Gallery,** 173 Canongate, The Royal Mile, EH8 8BN TEL & FAX: 556 4710 PARKING: Easy OPEN: Mon-Sat 10.30-5.30 MIN: £10 MAX: £2000+ PERIOD: 16th-19th century SPECIALIST: Maps & sea-charts of all parts of the world OTHER INFO: We have thousands of maps so one day's visit may not be long enough so bring a campbed or sleeping bag!

**DL Cavanagh,** 49 Cockburn Street, EH1 1BS TEL: 226 3391 OPEN: 11-5 PERIOD: 18th-20th century SPECIALIST: Silver, jewellery, coins & medals GENERAL: Antiques & curios OTHER INFO: 2 mins from Princes Street.

**Collector Centre,** 127 Gilmore Place, EH3 9PP TEL: 229 1059 PARKING: Medium OPEN: 10-6, closed Wed & Sun, or by appt MIN: 50p MAX: £1000 PERIOD: 18th-20th century GENERAL: Silver, glass, porcelain & pottery, ephemera, pictures, collectables, etc OTHER INFO: 5 mins from King's Theatre, watch swans on canal nearby. International Festivals of Jazz & Dance.

**Craiglea Clocks,** 88 Comiston Road, EH10 5QJ Tel: 452 8568 PARKING: Medium OPEN: 10-5 MIN: £50 MAX: £5000 PERIOD: 18th-20th century SPECIALIST: Clocks & barometers.

**E.A.S.Y. (Edinburgh & Glasgow Architectural Salvage Yard)** Unit 6 Couper Street, EH6 6HH TEL: 554 7077 FAX: 554 3070 PARKING: Easy PERIOD: 18th-20th century GENERAL: Doors, counters, panelling, stairways, fireplaces, light fittings, gates, columns, marble slabs, etc.

**Donald Ellis Antiques,** Bruntsfield Clocks, 7 Bruntsfield Place, EH10 4HN TEL: 229 4720 PARKING: Medium OPEN: 9.30-5.30, closed Wed pm MIN: £5 MAX: £5000 PERIOD: 17th-20th century SPECIALIST: Clocks GENERAL: Furniture & decorative antiques OTHER INFO: Busy, bustling area of antique shops, restaurants, theatres, hotels etc, just south of city centre.

**Dunedin Antiques Ltd,** 4 North West Circus Place, EH3 6ST TEL: 220 1574 FAX: 556 4423 PARKING: Easy OPEN: 10-5 MIN: £75 MAX: £15,000 PERIOD: 18th-19th century SPECIALIST: Chimney pieces, overmantel mirrors, etc GENERAL: Furniture, decorative items, metalware OTHER INFO: Proprietor also caters for up-market B&B, hosts of good pubs & restaurants nearby.

**Pamela George Antiques,** 37 Thistle Street, EH2 1DY TEL: 225 6350 & 225 2159 PARKING: Medium OPEN: Mon-Sat 11-3 MIN: £10 MAX: £1000 PERIOD: 18th-20th century SPECIALIST: Scottish ceramics GENERAL: Antiques, small furniture, collectables, blue & white ceramics, etc OTHER INFO: Thistle Street has a number of good pubs & restaurants and is only minutes away from Princes Street, main railway station, etc.

**Georgian Antiques,** 10 Pattison Street, Leith Links, EH6 7HF TEL: 552 7286 FAX: 553 6299 ASSNS: LAPADA PARKING: Easy OPEN: Mon-Fri 8.30-5.30, Sat 10-2 MIN: £5 MAX: £25,000 PERIOD: 18th-20th century GENERAL: Shipping, commercial Victorian, Edwardian, Georgian, smalls & good stock for private buyers.

**Gladrags,** 17 Henderson Row, EH3 5DH TEL: 557 1916 OPEN: Tues-Sat 10.30-6 MIN: £10 MAX: £500 SPECIALIST: Period clothes, Victorian to 1960s, linen, accessories, costume jewellery.

**Goodwins Antiques Ltd,** 15-16 Queensferry Street, EH2 4QW TEL: 225 4717 FAX: 220 1412 PARKING: Medium OPEN: Mon-Fri 9.30-5.30, Sat 9.30-5 SPECIALIST: Antique jewellery, porcelain, silver OTHER INFO: Insurance, probate, valuations.

**Goodwins at the Sheraton Grand,** 1 Festival

Square, EH3 9SR TEL: 229 9131 ext 5808 OPEN: Mon-Fri 9.30-5.30, Sat 9.30-5 SPECIALIST: Antique jewellery, porcelain, silver.

**Hand in Hand,** 3 NW Circus Place, EH3 6ST TEL & FAX: 226 3598 PARKING: Medium OPEN: 10-5.30, closed Mon MIN: £1 MAX: £2000 PERIOD: 18th-20th century SPECIALIST: Fine linens for bed & table GENERAL: Paisley shawls, lace, costume & accessories, soft furnishings OTHER INFO: Florentines, the famous French patisserie & coffee shop, next door but one, very yummy.

**Elizabeth Humphrey,** 48 Thistle Street, EH2 1EN TEL: 226 3625 PARKING: Difficult OPEN: Every morning MIN: 50p MAX: £200 PERIOD: 19th-20th century SPECIALIST: Pottery, etchings GENERAL: Mixed.

**Malcolm Innes Gallery,** 67 George Street, EH2 2JG TEL & FAX: 226 4151 ASSNS: SLAD, Edinburgh Art Galleries Assn OPEN: 9.30-6 MIN: £100 MAX: £15,000 PERIOD: 19th-20th century SPECIALIST: Scottish, sporting, military oils, watercolours & prints.

**Kaimes Smithy Antiques,** 79 Howdenhall Road TEL & FAX: 441 2076 PARKING: Easy OPEN: Mon-Sat 1.30-5.30 MIN: £10 MAX: £2000 PERIOD: 18th-20th century GENERAL: 800 sq ft of display quality furniture, clocks, porcelain, glass, paintings, silver, curios OTHER INFO: 17th century smithy. Good eating places nearby.

**London Road Antiques,** 15 Earlston Place, EH7 5SU TEL: 652 2790 PARKING: Easy OPEN: Mon-Sat 11-5.30, Sun 1-5 MIN: £50 MAX: £5000 PERIOD: 18th-19th century SPECIALIST: Furniture GENERAL: Shipping pine trade store OTHER INFO: Period showrooms with particularly interesting lobby.

**McNaughton's Bookshop,** 3A-4A Haddington Place (Leith Walk), EH7 4AE TEL: 556 5897 FAX: 556 8220 ASSNS: ABA PARKING: Medium to difficult OPEN: Tues-Sat 9.30-5.30 MIN: 10p MAX: £2000 PERIOD: 17th-20th century GENERAL: Secondhand & antiquarian books on most subjects. Sometimes a few 16th century books OTHER INFO: This 1820s basement shop is situated on the edge of Edinburgh's Newtown, about 10 mins walk from Waverley Station & directly opposite Valvona & Crolla, widely considered to be the finest Italian delicatessan & wine merchant in Britain.

**Montresor,** 35 St Stephen Street, Stockbridge, EH3 5AH TEL: 220 6877 PARKING: Medium OPEN: 10.30-6 MIN: £25 PERIOD: 19th-20th century SPECIALIST: Costume jewellery, lighting, sundry glass, pottery, china OTHER INFO: Stockbridge has a pleasant village atmosphere with interesting shops and a short journey from Princes Street.

**Mulherron Antiques,** 83 Grassmarket, EH1 2HJ TEL: 226 5907 FAX: 226 2894 PARKING: Easy OPEN: Mon-Sat 10-6 MIN: £200 MAX: £30,000 PERIOD: 18th century SPECIALIST: Furniture GENERAL: Oriental rugs & carpets OTHER INFO: Edinburgh is like Rome, built on 7 hills & is a wonderful cultural centre.

**T & JW Neilson Ltd,** 76 Coburg Street, EH6 6HJ TEL: 554 4704 FAX: 555 2071 PARKING: Own carpark OPEN: Mon-Sat 9.30-5 MIN: £5 MAX: £15,000 PERIOD: 18th-20th century SPECIALIST: Fireplaces & accessories.

**Nest Egg Antiques,** 5 Grange Road TEL: 667 2328 PARKING: Easy OPEN: Mon-Sat 10-6 MIN: £5 MAX: £3600 PERIOD: 19th century SPECIALIST: Lighting, desks, beds, brassware GENERAL: Pine, furniture, etc.

**Now & Then Old Toys & Antiques,** 7-9 West Crosscauseway, EH8 9JW TEL & FAX: 668 2927 PARKING: Easy OPEN: Tues-Sat 10.30-5.30 MIN: £1 MAX: £1000 PERIOD: 20th century SPECIALIST: Tinplate toys, teddy bears, Dinky toys, antique telephones GENERAL: Advertising, children's books, biscuit tins, small furniture, gramophones, radios OTHER INFO: Museum of Childhood.

**The Open Eye Gallery,** 75-79 Cumberland Street, EH3 6RD TEL: 557 1020 ASSNS: Edinburgh Gallery Association PARKING: Easy OPEN: Mon-Fri 10-6, Sat 10-4 MIN: £10 MAX: £20,000 PERIOD: 20th century SPECIALIST: Early 20th century etchings & studio ceramics OTHER INFO: Craft Council listed gallery.

**Present Bygones,** 61 Thistle Street, EH2 1D TEL: 226 7646 PARKING: Medium OPEN: Mon-Sat 10-5 MIN: £1 MAX: £1000 PERIOD: 19th-20th century SPECIALIST: Ceramics, fans, needlework GENERAL: Furniture, decorative items, silver & jewellery.

**Rembrandt Antiques,** 183-189 Causewayside, EH9 1PH TEL: 662 4509 & 667 2328 PARKING: Easy OPEN: Mon-Sat 10-6 MIN: £5 MAX: £3600 PERIOD: 19th century SPECIALIST: Lighting, desks, beds, brass GENERAL: Pine, furniture, etc.

**Claudia Seaton Antiques & Books,** 2 Gillespie

Crescent, EH10 4HT TEL: 228 8654 PARKING: Medium OPEN: 10.30-4.30, closed Wed MIN: £5 MAX: £1000 PERIOD: 19th century SPECIALIST: Decorative antiques & textiles GENERAL: Furniture, jewellery & books.

**Stockbridge Antiques & Fine Art,** 8 Deanhaugh Street, EH4 1LY TEL: 332 1366 PARKING: Medium OPEN: Tues-Sat 2-5.30 PERIOD: 19th century SPECIALIST: Dolls, teddies, juvenalia GENERAL: Small furniture, pictures, prints, textiles, Oriental, porcelain OTHER INFO: Close to city centre, lovely scenic river walks, good pubs, village atmosphere, edge of Georgian Newtown, coffee shop next door.

**The Thrie Estaits,** 49 Dundas Street, EH3 6RS TEL: 556 7084 PARKING: Difficult OPEN: Mon-Fri 11-5.30 MIN: £10 MAX: £2000 PERIOD: 17th-20th century GENERAL: Mostly unusual and interesting items, smalls in various materials OTHER INFO: I have a lot of pregnant women in who never buy anything.

**Unicorn Antiques,** 65 Dundas Street, EH3 6RS TEL: 556 7176 PARKING: Medium OPEN: 10.30-6.30 MIN: 10p MAX: £400 PERIOD: 19th-20th century GENERAL: Cutlery & domesticware, bric a brac, small furniture OTHER INFO: Semi-basement shop, the original Aladdin's Cave according to my customers, browsers welcome, not for the claustrophobic.

**Whytock & Reid,** Sunbury House, Belford Mews, EH4 3DN TEL: 226 4911 FAX: 226 4595 PARKING: Own carpark OPEN: Mon-Fri 9-5.30, Sat 9-12.30 MIN: 350 MAX: £25,000 PERIOD: 18th-20th century SPECIALIST: Furniture designed by Sir Robert Lorimer GENERAL: Furniture, carpets & rugs.

**Wild Rose Antiques,** 15 Henderson Row, EH3 5DH TEL: 557 1916 OPEN: Tues-Sat 10.30-6 MIN: £10 MAX: £1500 PERIOD: 18th-20th century GENERAL: Silver, jewellery, glass, decorative, brass, copper, porcelain, pottery, small furniture.

**Young Antiques,** 36 Bruntsfield Place, EH10 4HJ TEL: 229 1361 PARKING: Easy OPEN: 10.30-5.30 MIN: £10 MAX: £15,000 PERIOD: 19th-20th century SPECIALIST: Ceramics GENERAL: Furniture, Persian rugs, oils.

## KIRKLISTON (0131)

**Breastmill Antiques,** Breastmill, EH29 9EA TEL: 333 4621 PARKING: Own carpark OPEN: 1.30-5.30, closed Tues & Wed in winter MIN: 50p MAX: £2500 PERIOD: 19th-20th century GENERAL: Porcelain, pictures, furniture & collectables OTHER INFO: Situated 2 miles from Forth Bridge in a 16th century mill

## LINLITHGOW (01506)

**Heritage Antiques,** 222 High Street, EH49 6BQ TEL: 847460 PARKING: Medium OPEN: 10-5 MIN: 50p MAX: £500 PERIOD: 19th-20th century GENERAL: Ceramics, jewellery, small furniture, bric a brac OTHER INFO: Linlithgow is a very historic town, Mary Queen of Scots was born in Linlithgow Palace.

## DENNY (01324)

**Ian Burton,** 74 Glasgow Road, FK6 5DN TEL: 823333 FAX: 825207 PARKING: Own carpark OPEN: By appt only PERIOD: 18th-19th century SPECIALIST: Clocks.

## BANNOCKBURN (01786)

**Old Mill Antiques (Stirling),** Old Murrayfield, 1A Main Street, FK7 8LZ TEL: 817130 FAX: 817239 PARKING: Medium OPEN: Mon-Fri 9-5, Sat 10-4 PERIOD: 18th-20th century SPECIALIST: Victorian fire pieces GENERAL: Architectural antiques, bric a brac.

## STIRLING (01786)

**Abbey Antiques,** 35 Friars Street, FK8 1HA TEL: 447840 PARKING: Medium OPEN: 9.30-5 MIN: £1 MAX: £2000 PERIOD: 19th-20th century SPECIALIST: Jewellery & silver GENERAL: Antiques & collectables.

## PERTH (01738)

**Forsyth Antiques,** 2 St Paul's Square TEL: 624877 PARKING: Easy OPEN: Mon-Sat 10-5 MIN: £1 MAX: £1500 PERIOD: 19th-20th century SPECIALIST: Scottish silver, Monart glass GENERAL: Silver, jewellery, furniture, caskets.

**Gallery One,** 1 St Paul's Square, PH1 5QW TEL: 624877 PARKING: Easy OPEN: Mon-Sat 10-5 MIN: £80 MAX: £7000 PERIOD: 19th-20th century SPECIALIST: Scottish pictures GENERAL: Prints, watercolours, oils.

**The George Street Gallery,** 38 George Street, PH1 5JL TEL: 638953 PARKING: Medium OPEN: 10-5, Sat 10-1 MIN: £30 MAX: £10,000 PERIOD:

20th century SPECIALIST: Scottish oils, watercolours, etchings, limited number of prints OTHER INFO: Perth is one of the most attractive cities in Scotland, an ideal centre for touring, fishing, shooting.

**Ian Murray's Antique Warehouse,** 21 Glasgow Road, PH2 0NZ TEL: 637222 PARKING: Own carpark OPEN: Mon-Fri 9-5, Sat 10-1 MIN: £25 MAX: £3000 PERIOD: 18th-20th century GENERAL: Furniture OTHER INFO: Largest antique warehouse north of the Forth, 20,000 sq ft.

**Roy Sim Antiques,** 77-79 Kinnoull Street, PH1 5EZ TEL & FAX: 629835 PARKING: Medium OPEN: Mon-Sat 10-5 MIN: £10 MAX: £15,000 PERIOD: 18th-19th century SPECIALIST: Furniture & objets d'art GENERAL: Clocks, silver OTHER INFO: 2400 sq ft of antiques for trade & retail.

**The Tay Street Gallery,** 70 Tay Street, PH2 8NN TEL: 620604 PARKING: Easy OPEN: Tues, Thurs-Fri 10-1, 2-3.30 MIN: £15 MAX: £5000 PERIOD: 17th-19th century SPECIALIST: Furniture for English & overseas (particularly American) trade buyers OTHER INFO: Bridges Restaurant next door, pub lunches 12noon-2pm, evenings 6pm-10pm.

## NEWBURGH (01337)

**Newburgh Antiques,** 222 High Street, KY14 6DZ TEL: 841026 PARKING: Easy OPEN: 10.30-12, 1.30-5 MIN: £1 MAX: £2500 PERIOD: 18th-19th century SPECIALIST: Wemyss ware GENERAL: Scottish pottery & watercolours, furniture, objects.

## RAIT (01821)

**Fair Finds,** Rait Village Antiques Centre, PH2 7RT TEL: 670379 PARKING: Own carpark OPEN: Mon-Sat 10-5 MIN: £50 MAX: £5000 PERIOD: 19th century SPECIALIST: Weymss ware GENERAL: Country house furnishings, silver, china, pine & decorative items.

**Guiscards,** Rait Antiques Centre, PH2 7RT TEL & FAX: 672392 PARKING: Own carpark OPEN 10.30- 5 MIN: £1 MAX: £2,500 PERIOD: 19th-20th century SPECIALIST: Textiles & beds GENERAL: Antiques of all sorts

**Joyce & Lindsay Newton Antiques,** The Steading, Rait Antiques Centre, PH2 7RT TEL: 670205 PARKING: Own carpark OPEN: Mon-Sat 10.30-5 MIN: £2 MAX: £2000 PERIOD: 19th-20th century SPECIALIST: Cushions, decorative furnishings GENERAL: Country house pine & some mahogany.

**Rait Antiques,** Rait Village Antique Centre, PH2 7RT TEL: 670318 PARKING: Own carpark OPEN: Mon-Fri 10-5 PERIOD: 18th-19th century SPECIALIST: Furniture GENERAL: Treen, woodworking tools.

**Tempemans Antiques,** The Millroom, PH2 7RT TEL: 670344 FAX: 670389 PARKING: Own carpark OPEN: Mon-Sat 10-5 Sun 1-4 MIN: £5 MAX: £12,000 PERIOD: 1870-1920 SPECIALIST: Antiques & decorative GENERAL: Oak & mahogany furniture OTHER INFO: Part of Rait Antique Centre, in total 7000 sq ft over the complete antiques spectrum.

## INCHTURE (01828)

**CS Moreton (Antiques)**
**Inchmartine House, PH14 9DD TEL: 686412 PARKING: Own carpark OPEN: Mon-Sat 9-5.30 MIN: £25 MAX: £10,000 PERIOD: 17th-19th century SPECIALIST: Old cabinet making tools GENERAL: Early oak, walnut & Georgian mahogany & Regency furniture & objects, Persian carpets & rugs.**

## DUNDEE (01382)

**Angus Antiques,** 4 St Andrews Street TEL: 322128 PARKING: Easy OPEN: Mon-Fri 10-4 MIN: £1 MAX: £10,000 PERIOD: 18th-20th century SPECIALIST: Military, collectables GENERAL: Gold, silver, Art Deco & Nouveau, advertising, tin toys, teddy bears, etc.

## ST ANDREWS (01334)

**Old St Andrews Gallery,** 9 Albany Place, KY16 9HH TEL: 477840 PARKING: Easy OPEN: Mon-Sat 10-5 MIN: £5 MAX: £20,000 PERIOD: 19th century SPECIALIST: Golf memorabilia, silver, jewellery GENERAL: Scottish jewellery, china, furniture.

## KINGHORN (01592)

**Pend Antiques,** 53 High Street, KY3 9UW TEL: 890140 PARKING: Easy OPEN: 11-5, closed Sun MIN: £1 MAX: £850 PERIOD: 19th-20th century GENERAL: Furniture, china, glass, linen, decorative items, etc OTHER INFO: Kinghorn starts the Fife Coastal Route known as Eaust Neuk, picturesque beaches, monument where Alexander III fell to his death.

# Tayside, Inverness, The Grampians

*Inverness Castle. By courtesy of the Scottish Tourist Board*
*Photograph by Harvey Wood*

The Scottish Highlands contain some of the loveliest countryside in Britain. Inland, towns and villages are few and there are only a small number of roads. For the most part, settlements are confined to the coast, sides of lochs and at crossroads. The Highlands shelter a range of flora and fauna rare or non-existent in other parts of Britain. Golden eagles, osprey, ptarmigans may all be seen by the dedicated or lucky visitor. Today the main source of income for the area comes from tourism and forestry.

**Blairgowrie** is the start. This small town is famous for growing raspberries and has the largest working water wheel in Scotland at Keathbank Mill. The trip continues to **Dunkeld** with a ruined cathedral. Celtic monks driven out of Iona by Norsemen came to Dunkeld in the 6th century bringing with them relics of St Columba. Here they established a monastery and later the town became the seat of a bishop. The cathedral dates, in parts, from the 12th century although most come from the 14th to 15th century. The choir of the cathedral now serves as parish church. The approach to the cathedral is lined by beautiful 17th century houses now in the care of the National Trust for Scotland.

**Pitlochry**, further north, is another popular town for holidaymakers and also plays host to Highland Games. An annual summer festival of drama and concerts is centred in the Pitlochry Festival Theatre. Loch Faskally lies just west and boats may be hired here. Salmon may also be seen, from an observation room, making their way upstream. The loch was man-made to provide hydro-electric power and a visitors' centre explains more about hydro-electricity and also how this can be compatible with the needs of salmon in Scottish rivers and lochs. There is much to see surrounding Pitlochry. To the south, at Aberfeldy, Cluny House stands in very lovely and interesting gardens containing many wonderful plants including primulas, Japanese acers and rhododendrons. Nearby, at Weem, the Castle Menzies is a good example of a 16th century fortified house. Bonnie Prince Charlie stopped here on his way to the Battle of Culloden in 1746. Another battle was fought to the

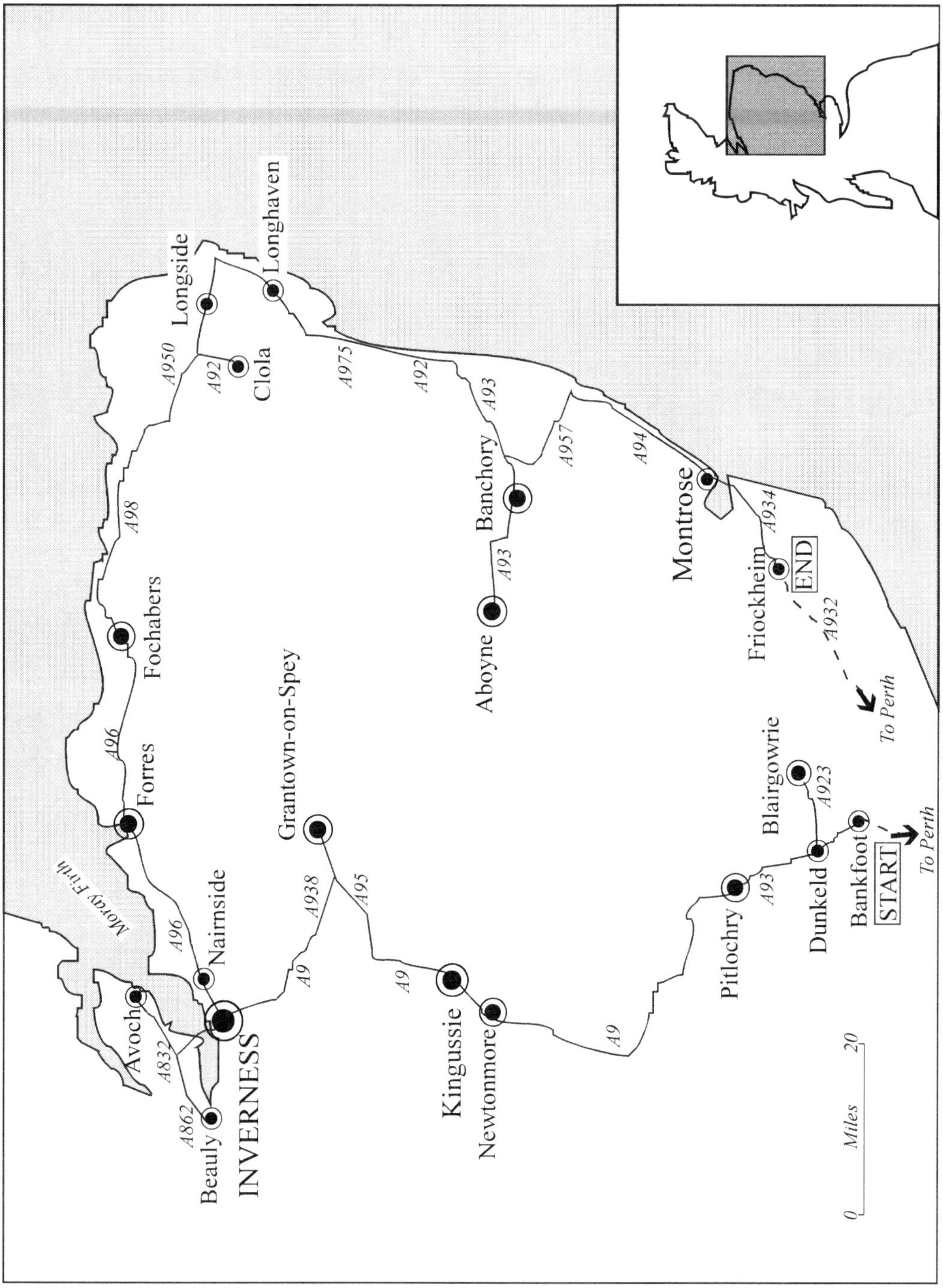

Longhaven
Longside
Clola
A950
A92
A975
A92
A93
A957
A94
Banchory
Montrose
A934
Friockheim
END
A932
To Perth
A98
A93
Aboyne
Fochabers
Grantown-on-Spey
A96
Forres
Moray Firth
Nairnside
A96
A938
A95
A9
A9
Blairgowrie
A923
Bankfoot
START
To Perth
Dunkeld
A93
Pitlochry
Avoch
A832
A862
Beauly
INVERNESS
Kingussie
Newtonmore
A9
0
Miles
20

north at Killiecrankie. Here Jacobite Highlanders defeated the forces of King William in 1689. The Scottish rebels were led by Bonnie Dundee who was killed in the battle. A memorial stone stands at the place he fell. Although the Jacobites won, the loss of their leader was decisive and they were defeated just three weeks later at Dunkeld. At Killiecrankie an English soldier is said to have leapt across an 18 foot wide ravine to escape and this feat is commemorated in the name Soldier's Leap.

**Newtonmore** comes next. This small highland town stands at the head of the Spey Valley, the Monadhliath Mountains lie to the north and the Grampians to the south. It is a centre for pony trekking, walking and touring. On the first Saturday in August the Newtonmore Highland Games are held. At **Kingussie,** a couple of miles further on, there is a fantastic folk museum. The town has a firm place in Scottish history. In the early 14th century it was taken from its feudal lords, the Comyns, by Robert the Bruce. Just over 400 years later the few survivors of Culloden retreated here where they were effectively deserted by the Young Pretender and told to find safety themselves. Further northeast again, **Grantown-on-Spey** sits on the junction of several roads and was founded in the late 18th century by Sir James Grant. This elegant town is now the centre for year-round holidays. In the winter there is skiing and in the summer it is a good base for touring the Highlands as well as for trout and salmon fishing.

Whilst not on the tour, the city of Inverness is well worth some time before visiting **Beauly**, a pleasant small town containing a ruined 13th century priory. The route carries on back through Inverness to **Avoch** on the Black Isle. This is, in fact, not an island but rather a wide peninsula with the Moray Firth to the south and Cromarty Firth to the north. The route turns back through Inverness to **Nairnside** next to the battlefield of Culloden, the last battle fought in mainland Britain and the death knell for hopes of restoring the Stuarts to the British throne. The Young Pretender, Bonnie Prince Charlie, fought the English army led by the Duke of Cumberland. The Prince's army numbered about 5000 Highlanders but they were tired, ill-fed and badly armed. In contrast, the English army was about 9000 strong with none of the handicaps suffered by the opposition. In spite of a fearsome resolve and great heroism in the face of overwhelming odds, the Highlanders were massacred. Less than 100 English soldiers died while over a 1000 Jacobites were killed in the battle. Worse, the Duke of Cumberland ordered all the wounded rebels killed and searches were carried out for days afterwards for any that might have escaped. The Well of the Dead may still be seen. Here wounded Jacobites were killed while trying to drink. There are also memorials in the form of the stones of the Graves of the Clans, the Memorial Cairn and the Irish Stone, in honour of Irishmen who fought with the Highlanders. The battlefield is now owned by the National Trust for Scotland and it has been restored its 18th century appearance. There is a visitors' centre which tells the story of the importance of this battle.

Twenty miles east on the A96, mainly along the Moray Firth, is ancient **Forres**, formerly the home of the kings of Scotland. In Shakespeare's *Macbeth* it was on the way to the court of Duncan at Forres that Macbeth encountered the three witches. However, by the 13th century the importance of the town declined and Scottish kings no longer held court here. Local history is recounted in the Falconer Museum in Tolbooth Street. The town still has its 19th century tolbooth and there is also a 15th century market cross. A 23 foot monolith, Sueno's Stone, stands to the east. The stone commemorates a battle but nobody knows for sure who was fighting whom although it is dated between the 9th and 11th centuries. The monolith is engraved with warriors, some lacking heads. Skeletons were excavated here in the early 19th century. Via Elgin and its beautiful ruined cathedral, **Fochabers** is the next call. This village originally stood by Gordon Castle but, when it was moved here in 1776, it was built to a grid-iron pattern.

Following the North Sea coast east, still on the A96, it is well worth calling at the fishing port of Buckie with its maritime museum and the quaint Cullen, built on two levels with its long railway viaduct, and pretty Portsoy harbour and a famous serpentine marble. Banff, is also an excellent stop before the tour continues another 20 miles to the villages of **Clola** and **Longside.** The main town of Peterhead with its grand bay lies just to the east, and just south is **Longhaven.**

Another 10 miles south via Cruden Bay, where the North Sea oil pipelines come ashore, is perhaps the most extensive, amazing and untouched dune system in Europe, in the Sands of Forvie Nature Reserve and 12 miles further south is northeast Scotland's main city, Aberdeen. There are so many historic and charming sights that a full day or more could easily be spent here. 15 miles southwest on the A93, this time inland again, **Banchory**, rises in a series of terraces above the River Dee. Just south of the town the Dee joins the River Feugh and the bridge here is an ideal spot for to see leaping salmon. To the south west Scolty Hill rises to a height of 1000 feet and is crowned by a memorial to General Burnett, who fought in the Napoleonic Wars and lived at nearby Crathes Castle. This romantic looking 16th century castle contains wonderful painted ceilings and is set in 600 acres of beautiful grounds. There are eight different gardens here and they contain many rare shrubs and plants. The gardens are separated by borders or by yew hedges dating from 1702. Twelve miles on is **Aboyne**, a village largely built in the late 19th century by Sir William Cunliffe Brookes, a Manchester banker. Set around a large village green, part of the earlier village, it is the scene of Highland Games in August. The nearby Glen Tanar, to the south west, is a beautiful setting and ideal for woodland walks.

Turning east, the route follows the coast road through the picturesque Stonehaven and Inverbervie to **Montrose.** The town stands on a spit of land with the sea to the east and the Montrose Basin, a tidal basin, to the west, now a valuable habitat for waterfowl. The elegant High Street contains buildings from the 18th century and there are several good museums and places of interest. The House of Dun, run by the National Trust for Scotland, overlooks the Basin and was built in 1730. The William Lamb Memorial Studio at 24 Market Street, displays sculpture, etchings, paintings and drawings of the famous sculptor. The Montrose Museum in Panmure Place covers the history of the town from prehistoric times onwards and includes the history of the port. Sunnyside Museum, at the Royal Sunnyside Hospital, tells the history of psychiatry in Scotland. The tour ends inland in **Friockheim**, 10 miles south west off the A934.

## ANTIQUE DEALERS

### BLAIRGOWRIE (01250)

**Roy Sim Antiques,** The Granary Warehouse, Lower Mill Street, PH10 6AQ TEL & FAX: 873860 PARKING: 9-5.30, Sun 12.30-5.30 MIN: £1 MAX: £1500 PERIOD: 19th-20th century GENERAL: 4500 sq ft of antiques, decorative & collectable items OTHER INFO: Ample parking, restaurant & coffee shop on site.

### DUNKELD (01350)

**Dunkeld Antiques,** Tay Terrace, PH8 0AQ TEL & FAX: 728832 PARKING: Easy OPEN: 10-5.30 7day - summer, 6 days - winter MIN: £5 MAX: £8000 PERIOD: 18th-19th century SPECIALIST: Fishing, dining furniture GENERAL: Books on Scotland, shooting, fishing OTHER INFO: Very attractive village on the banks of the Tay. Shop is a converted church.



### PITLOCHRY (01796)

**Blair Antiques**
**14 Bonnethill Road, PH16 5BS TEL & FAX: 472624 PARKING: Easy OPEN: 9-12.30, 2-5 MIN: £5 MAX: £5000 PERIOD: 18th-20th century GENERAL: Furniture, paintings, silver & plate, porcelain, glass OTHER INFO: Pitlochry is a good central location for a buying trip in Scotland with many hotels & B&Bs.**

### NEWTONMORE (01540)

**The Antique Shop,** Main Street, PH20 1DD TEL: 673272 PARKING: Easy OPEN: Daily in summer

MIN: £1 MAX: £1000 PERIOD: 19th-20th century GENERAL: Collectables, militaria, small furniture, paintings, prints, books.

## KINGUSSIE (01540)

**Mostly Pine,** 10 High Street, PH21 1HR TEL: 661838 PARKING: Easy OPEN: 10-5.30 MIN: £4 MAX: £4000 PERIOD: 20th century SPECIALIST: Country furniture OTHER INFO: Situated in Strathspey, hospitality & scenic beauty on River Spey, close to ski-ing area.

## GRANTOWN-ON-SPEY (01479)

**Strathspey Gallery,** 40 High Street, PH26 3EH TEL: 873290 FAX: 873383 ASSNS: LAPADA, HADA PARKING: Easy OPEN: 10-1, 2-5 MIN: £10 MAX: £3000 PERIOD: 17th-20th century SPECIALIST: Local artists paintings & prints GENERAL: Furniture, pcitures, pottery, porcelain OTHER INFO: The Spey Valley is a beautiful area and well worth a visit.

## BEAULY (01463)

**Iain Marr Antiques,** 3 Mid Street, IV4 7DP TEL: 782372 ASSNS: HADA PARKING: Easy OPEN: 10.30-1, 2-5.30, closed Thurs MIN: £5 MAX: £10,000 PERIOD: 19th century GENERAL: Silver, clocks, porcelain, paintings, furniture, arms.

## AVOCH (01381)

**Highland Antiques,** Old Post Office, IV9 8RQ TEL: 621000 ASSNS: HADA, PBFA PARKING: Own carpark OPEN: Mon-Sat 10.30-5, closed Thurs MIN: £5 MAX: £3000 PERIOD: 19th-20th century GENERAL: General antiques, paintings, books & prints OTHER INFO: Situated in a fishing village 8 miles north east of Inverness, with dophins, museums, cathedral. If shop is shut at lunchtime please call at the pub next door.

## NAIRNSIDE (01463)

**Gallery Persia,** Upper Myrtlefield, IV1 2BX TEL: 792198 PARKING: Own carpark OPEN: By appt MIN: £70 MAX: £4000+ PERIOD: 19th-20th century SPECIALIST: Oriental rugs.

## FORRES (01309)

**Michael Low (Antiques),** 45 High Street, IV36 0PB TEL: 673696 FAX: 672211 PARKING: Easy OPEN: 10-1, 2-5 MIN: £1 PERIOD: 18th-20th century GENERAL: Antiques, Victoriana & collectors items (no furniture).

## FOCHABERS (01343)

**Antiques (Fochabers),** 22 The Square, IV32 7DP TEL: 820838 PARKING: Easy OPEN: 10-5 MIN: 50p MAX: £1750 PERIOD: 19th-20th century SPECIALIST: Furniture GENERAL: Silver, longcase clocks, collectables OTHER INFO: 3 antique shops in village plus museum, parking available, good food.

**Pringle Antiques,** High Street, IV32 7EP TEL: 820362 FAX: 821291 PARKING: Own carpark MIN: £1 MAX: £5000 PERIOD: 18th-19th century GENERAL: From jewellery to furniture OTHER INFO: Shop situated in converted church. At rear a large folk museum displays over 4000 items of interest to all.

**Marianne Simpson,** 61-63 High Street, IV32 7DU TEL: 821192 PARKING: Easy OPEN: 10-1, 2-4, Easter-Oct Mon-Sat, Oct-Easter Tues, Thur, Sat MIN: 50p MAX: £100 PERIOD: 19th-20th century SPECIALIST: Books OTHER INFO: Not far from Baxters of Speyside.

## CLOLA BY MINTLAW (01771)

**Clola Antique Centre,** Shannas School House, AB42 8AE TEL & FAX: 624584 PARKING: Own carpark OPEN: 10-5 MIN: 50p MAX: £2500 PERIOD: 18th-20th century SPECIALIST: Jewellery GENERAL: Furniture, Victoriana, books.

## LONGSIDE (01779)

**Kudos Antiques,** 12 Cooper's Brae, AB42 7XU TEL: 821472 PARKING: Easy OPEN: 10-8.30 MIN: £1 MAX: £1600 PERIOD: 18th-19th century SPECIALIST: Country & pottery GENERAL: Period pine, fine furniture, country effects, old garden artefacts OTHER INFO: We specialise in the unusual, odd or quaint and pride ourselves on always having the most interesting things.

## LONGHAVEN (01779)

**Grannie Used to Have One,** Sanderling, AB42 7NX TEL: 813223 PARKING: Own carpark OPEN: Mon, Thurs, Fri 1-8, Sat 10-5, Sun 10-8 MIN: £1 MAX: £2000 PERIOD: 19th-20th century SPECIALIST: Scottish pottery & furniture GENERAL: Pottery, porcelain, furniture, kitchenalia, pictures, glass, toys EPNS OTHER

INFO: My business is run from my steadings (Scottish word for barn) & stables which look across to the ruins of Slains Castle where Bram Stoker stayed and got his inspiration to write *Dracula.*

## BANCHORY (01330)

**Bygones,** 6 Dee Street, AB31 3ST TEL: 823095 PARKING: Easy OPEN: 10.30-5, closed Sun MIN: £5 MAX: £1000 PERIOD: 19th-20th century GENERAL: Furniture & collectables OTHER INFO: Crathes Castle (SNT)

## ABOYNE (013398)

**Amber Antiques,** 1 Southside, Kincardine O'Neil, AB34 5AA TEL: 84338 & 84277 PARKING: Easy OPEN: 10-5 MIN: £1 MAX: £5000 PERIOD: 18th-20th century SPECIALIST: Amber, antiquarian & second hand books GENERAL: Furniture, linen, pictures, Eastern pieces, jewellery OTHER INFO: Situated in the oldest village in Deeside (Balmoral only ° mile away), local shop for the Royals. Excellent hotel opposite

## MONTROSE (01674)

**Harper-James,** 25-27 Baltic Street, DD10 8EX TEL & FAX: 671307 OPEN: Mon-Fri 9-5, Sat 10-4 MIN: £10 MAX: £7500 PERIOD: 17th-19th century SPECIALIST: Furniture GENERAL: Porcelain, pictures, carpets OTHER INFO: Restoration, upholstery & French polishing carried out on the premises.

## FRIOCKHEIM (01241)

**MJ & D Barclay Antiques,** 29 Gardyne Street, DD11 4SQ PARKING: Easy OPEN: 11-5.30, closed Thurs & Sun PERIOD: 19th-20th century GENERAL: Furniture, clocks, porcelain, china, jewellery, general antiques.

# South Wales

*Low tide at Aberaeron Harbour*

South Wales has much to offer: two large cities, Cardiff and Swansea, the Pembrokeshire Coast National Park, the Brecon Beacons National Park, the valley villages, beautiful gentle farmland set amidst rolling hills in the WyeValley and holiday resorts with safe sandy beaches. Wales has a distinctive character and history evident to even the most casual visitor.

The tour starts in **Brecon**,on the northern edge of the 520 square mile Brecon Beacons National Park. Mostly over 1000 feet above sea level with some peaks rising to well over 2000 feet, it includes the Brecon Beacons and the Black Mountains. Brecon itself grew up it around a late 11th century castle. Suffering sieges and raids in the wars between the warring Welsh clans and the English, much of the castle and town walls were destroyed during the Civil War in the 17th century as the townspeople wished to demonstrate their neutrality. The cathedral was promoted from a parish church in 1923. Originally an 11th century priory, most parts now date from 13th and 14th centuries and even earlier. The remains of a Roman fort, Y Gaer, three miles away, can be reached on foot by using the route of the Roman road.

By taking the B4520 and then the A470, the route arrives in **Newbridge** before turning for the coast and the seaside and university town of **Aberystwyth**. Suffering considerably during the feuds between rival Welsh warlords, an early castle, just earthworks, was destroyed repeatedly until another stronger one was built a mile away. It was started by the brother of Edward I, Edmund of Lancaster, and completed in 1284. This was also attacked and besieged by the Welsh but was not taken. At the beginning of the 15th century the town was destroyed by Owen Glendower's forces although the castle did not fall for a further two years, in 1404. The castle was finally destroyed during the English Civil War after it was held for the King but then surrendered. Parliamentary forces blew it up. A number of museums and galleries exist, the most important being probably the National Library of Wales said to contain three million books. Amongst the ancient and important manuscripts is the oldest surviving written in Welsh, the Black Book of Carmarthen. The library

# South Wales

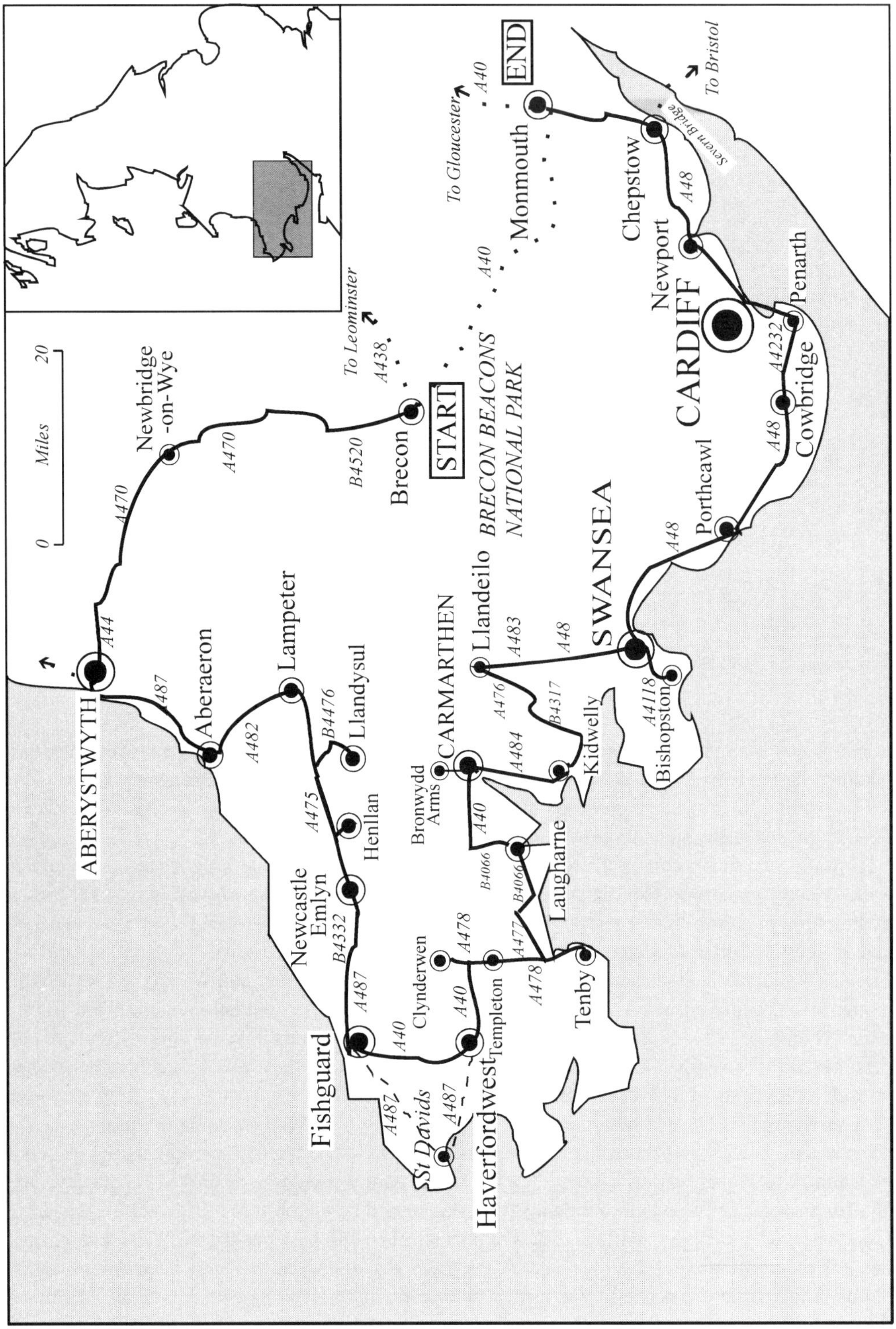

Miles
0
20
ABERYSTWYTH
A44
A470
Newbridge
-on-Wye
A470
B4520
Brecon
START
To Leominster
A438
BRECON BEACONS
NATIONAL PARK
A40
To Gloucester
A40
Monmouth
END
Chepstow
A48
Severn Bridge
To Bristol
Newport
CARDIFF
Penarth
A4232
Cowbridge
A48
Porthcawl
A48
SWANSEA
A4118
Bishopston
A48
Llandeilo
A483
CARMARTHEN
A476
B4317
Kidwelly
A484
Bronwydd
Arms
A40
Laugharne
B4066
B4066
A477
A478
Tenby
A478
Templeton
A40
Clynderwen
Haverfordwest
A487
St Davids
A487
Fishguard
A40
A487
B4332
Newcastle
Emlyn
Henllan
A475
B4476
Llandysul
Lampeter
A482
Aberaeron
487

St David's Cathedral

contains the Catherine Lewis Print Room exhibiting graphic art from the 15th century to modern times. The Aberystwyth Arts Centre, on the University campus, contains a theatre, four galleries, a concert hall and a studio with a year round programme of exhibitions, plays and concerts. There is also an exhibition of ceramics. The Ceredigion Museum, in Terrace Road and housed in a restored Edwardian theatre, has displays on local history, archaeology, geology, agriculture, lead mining and maritime history.

Taking the A487 coast road, the trip arrives in **Aberaeron**, at the mouth of the Aeron River. The pleasant seaside town has a number of elegant Georgian houses and its small harbour is popular with small boats and yachts. **Lampeter**, inland from Aberaeron, is another Georgian town and is home to St David's University, now part of the University of Wales. The route now turns west to visit **Llandysul** and **Henllan** before reaching **Newcastle Emlyn** with its 16th century castle ruins, slighted in the Civil War. Four miles east, off the A484, is the Museum of the Welsh Woollen Industry at Dre-fach Felindre, once the most important area in Wales for the production of wool. A working woollen mill and working exhibits show the manufacture from fleece to finished cloth.

Picturesque **Fishguard**, on the coast, has a harbour surrounded by steep cliffs. It was the last place in Britain to be invaded by foreign troops. The French landed soldiers here in 1797 and, tradition has it, they surrendered after mistaking the red-cloaks of Welsh women for the red uniforms of British soldiers. Jemima Nicholas, whose grave may be seen in the churchyard, took the surrender of 14 soldiers and, as a reward, was given a pension for the rest of her life. Nearby, Pen Caer is a wild rocky peninsula with cliffs rising to 400 feet above the sea. Strumble Head Lighthouse stands at the end of it and there is an Iron Age fort on the western side.

No visit to this area would be complete without a call at St David's Cathedral built in a river valley. Its presence makes St David's, little more than a village in size, the smallest city in Britain. The cathedral itself is large, imposing and beautiful. Traditionally it is said that St David, patron saint of Wales, founded a church here in the 6th century and his bones are believed to lie in a casket behind the High Altar. The church and village were destroyed by Viking raiders in 1088 but later rebuilt. The present cathedral dates from between the 12th and 15th centuries. In spite of the isolated position it was a place of pilgrimage with two journeys to St Davids equalling one to Rome. From William the Conqueror onwards, even kings made the pilgrimage to this lonely shrine. Over the years part of the building decayed but was restored in the 18th and 19th centuries with John Nash being responsible for rebuilding the West Front.

Back on the tour, **Haverfordwest** grew up around its Norman castle, built in the early 12th century. This was another Welsh town that suffered in the battles between the Welsh and English, being burnt down twice although the castle survived. The castle was held at different times for both sides in the Civil War. Finally, the Parliamentary Forces regained it in 1645 and it was slighted.

Several Georgian houses exist and the town is a designated Conservation Area.

After stopping in the villages of **Clynderwen** and **Templeton** the route carries on to the popular seaside resort of **Tenby**. This picturesque town, with its Georgian and Regency houses, has a lovely harbour from where visitors may take pleasure boats to Caldey Island. The town has ancient origins, possibly going back to Roman times. In the Middle Ages Tenby developed as a flourishing port, exporting coal and cloth and importing salt and wine. It declined in importance in the 17th and 18th centuries but the coming of the railways revived the economy and led to its development as a holiday resort. Points of note are the 15th century Tudor Merchant's House on Quay Hill and owned by the National Trust and the Tenby Museum and Art Gallery on Castle Hill. Here there are displays of Tenby's history from prehistoric times to the present day. The art gallery has exhibitions of work by local artists which include Gwen and Augustus John.

More Georgian houses may be seen in the next town, **Laugharne** on the River Taf. The town hall here includes a small prison and the 14th century church of St Martin's contains the remains of a Bronze Age man found during the building of local houses. There is also a 10th century cross and the poet, Dylan Thomas is buried in the churchyard. He spent the last part of his life in Laugharne and Dylan Thomas's Boathouse, where he wrote, is open to the public.

Turning north, **Carmarthen**, traditionally the birthplace of Merlin, son a princess and a spirit, or so she said, stands on a bluff above the River Tywi. This ancient settlement was the Roman town of *Caer Maridunum* and the remains of an amphitheatre survive. A castle was built here by the Normans and the town developed into an important port and wool centre. Its importance during the centuries although, during the Civil War the castle was slighted by Parliamentary troops. By the mid 19th to early 20th century Carmarthen declined as an industrial town but became the local administrative centre. The National Eisteddfod has been held here since the mid 15th century.

Just three miles away, **Bronwydd Arms** comes next followed by, 12 miles south, **Kidwelly** which grew up around a castle that still dominates the town. The well-preserved castle dates from the 13th century. The other major factor in the town's growth was the priory established in the 12th century. St Mary's Church, once part of it, dates from the 13th century but the spire has had to be replaced three times. It fell twice and then in the late 19th century was hit by lightning. The town is built at the convergence of two rivers, the Gwendraeth Fawr and the Gwendraeth Fach, the latter is crossed by a 14th century bridge. The Kidwelly Industrial Museum is housed in a former tinplate works and covers tinplate making, coal mining and railway engines. **Llandeilo** is where Dynefwr Castle stands above the river. This mansion stands on the site of an Iron Age fort which was succeeded by a stone castle. The present Gothic style house is surrounded by a beautiful landscaped park. This is supposed to be the site of Merlin's grave. The trip now turns south to **Swansea**, Wales' second largest city. Although the city name appears to be of Viking origin, no evidence exists of any settlement until the 11th century when the Normans built a castle later destroyed by Owen Glendower. In the Middle Ages Swansea's economy developed around coal mining and shipbuilding. It also gained importance as a port until, in the 18th century, it was the largest port in Wales. By this time metal smelting was contributing to the city's industrial growth which was further enhanced in 1798 by the opening of the Swansea Canal. Swansea's industrial base was widened further in 1918 when the first oil refinery opened nearby and the port expanded to take oil tankers.

This development as a port, certainly in modern times with deep draught vessels, was despite the limitations of the range of tidal rise and fall - reputed to be the world's greatest, thereby necessitating locks. During the Second World War the city was bombed heavily and much of the centre destroyed. Amongst buildings lost was the home of Beau Nash, who was born in here and went on to become the most fashionable figure in 18th century Bath. The wartime bombing led to a complete rebuilding of the city centre with modern pedestrian precincts and, in the Docks, a marina and centre for the arts.

A number of excellent museums and galleries exist. The Swansea Museum, Victoria Road, opened in 1835, is traditional, exhibiting collections on natural history, archaeology, Egyptology and Swansea and Nantgarw china. The Maritime and Industrial Museum housed in a turn of the century warehouse in the Maritime Quarter , has a number of historic vessels moored outside in the Marina. It tells the story of the city's industrial development from earliest times and includes a collection of vehicles ranging from horse-drawn carriages to lorries. A working woollen mill has been brought to the museum from Neath. The Glyn Vivian Art Gallery, in Alexandra Road, puts on temporary exhibitions although there are excellent permanent collections of Swansea and Nantgarw china and works by Welsh artists like Augustus John.

Swansea is not only industrial but also a popular centre for tourists with its easy access to the Gower peninsula, a designated Area of Outstanding Natural Beauty. Archaeological remains abound . The bones of exotic animals like lions, hippopotomus, mammoths and bears have been found in nearby caves. Iron Age forts and Neolithic bural chambers also exist. **Bishopston**, on the Gower Peninsula, stands near one of these, *Parc le Breos*. This is a multi-chambered tomb and contains the bones of about 25 people and was built about 6000 years ago. Nearby Cathole Cave shows evidence in the form of flint tools of habitation during the Paleolithic and Mesolithic periods.

Continuing along the coast, the route arrives in **Porthcawl**. In the 19th century efforts were made to develop the town as a port for exporting coal and iron. Although successful for a time, by the end of the century it was in decline. In 1907 the docks were closed and a few years later filled in, now providing a carpark for the visitors to the good beaches of Sandy Bay and Trecco Bay. Further east, **Cowbridge** is known as the capital of the Vale of Glamorgan. It stands on a Roman road but grew up in Norman times and still has 14th century walls and gatehouse. **Penarth**, the next call, developed from a small village in the 19th century to a popular town. Local businessmen, like mine-owners, found it a pleasant place to live and rumours speak of several resident millionaires. Now it is a seaside resort and a suburb of nearby Cardiff. One attractions is the Cosmeston Lakes Country Park and Medieval Village centred on two lakes and an excavated village. This village was abandoned by the early 15th century, probably because of the Black Death. Excavated buildings have been reconstructed to give visitors a picture of medieval village life.

Just five miles away , **Cardiff** is the largest city in Wales and the country's capital. Although there has been a settlement here since Roman times Cardiff only began to expand during the Industrial Revolution which brought great prosperity. In the early 19th century the population stood around 1000, by 1911 this had expanded to an astonishing 180,000. This enormous expansion occurred because Cardiff became the focal point for a number of routes. The Glamorganshire Canal, connecting the town to Merthyr Tydfil, was built at the end of the 18th century and the railway came in the mid 19th century. Between the construction of the canal and the railway, docks were dug here which successfully lead to further dockyard expansion throughout the latter half of the 19th century. By this time Cardiff was the world's leading coal exporter. After the First World War, exporting coal and iron declined but it continued to grow as the administrative and cultural centre for Wales although only officially declared as the Welsh capital in 1955.

Cardiff Castle dates from the beginning of settlement here and consists of the remains of the Roman fort and a Norman castle. It has been owned from the 16th century by the Herbert family and their descendents, the Marquesses of Bute, who had a considerable influence on the city. The 2nd Marquess built the first docks that led to Cardiff's prosperity. The 3rd Marquess restored the neglected castle in 1865 and it now contains magnificent interiors in Gothic, Arab and Greek styles designed by William Burges. The William de Morgan collection of tiles and ceramics are also displayed here.

The National Museum of Wales in Cathays Park stands in the city's elegant and imposing neo-classical centre and has important collections of paintings, silver, ceramics, silver, fossils and archaeological remains. The Welsh Industrial and Maritime Museum, Bute Street, contains working machines and interactive exhibits with the aim of telling the story of the development of Cardiff. Just four miles west, at St Fagans, the open air Welsh Folk Museum stands in 100 acres of parkland and shows buildings from all over Wales re-erected to give a picture of earlier Welsh life.

After stopping at **Maindee** (a Newport suburb), the route carries on to **Chepstow**, a medieval walled town on the River Wye. Chepstow Castle stands on limestone cliffs overlooking the river. It was built in the 11th century to guard the border between England and Wales and over the centuries was enlarged and strengthened. During the Civil War the castle was held for the King and came under siege twice. The second time the garrison actually fought to the death and a memorial plaque is in the Lower Ward. The town grew up around the castle and was an important local market It also developed as a port exporting timber from the Wye Valley. Isambard Kingdom Brunel designed the railway bridge and the station, The elegant road bridge was built by John Rennie in 1816. The parish church, St Mary's, was once part of the priory founded in the 11th century. The church is all that survives of the priory and was made into the parish church after the Dissolution of the Monasteries. Although the tower collapsed and was rebuilt, much of the building is Norman.

Turning inland on the A466, the route reaches the final stop, **Monmouth**, also on the River Wye. Another town with a long history, this was the Roman settlement of *Blestium*, although its later development was around the Norman castle, built originally in 1068 and rebuilt in the 12th century, to defend the border. The Monrow Bridge, dating from 1262, is the only one in Britain with a fortified gatehouse. The town itself is pretty and elegant with buildings from many periods. In Agincourt Square, so named because Henry V was born in the castle, was once the marketplace and contains the Shire Hall, dating from 1724.

## ANTIQUE DEALERS

### BRECON (01874)

**DG & AS Evans,** 7 The Struet, LD3 7LL TEL: 622714 PARKING: Easy OPEN: 9-1, 2-5, closed Wed pm MIN: £5 MAX: £800 PERIOD: 17th-19th century SPECIALIST: Prints & maps (Wales).

**Hazel of Brecon,** 2 Dukes Arcade, LD3 7AD TEL: 625274 PARKING: Medium OPEN: 10.30-5 MIN: £5 PERIOD: 18th-20th century SPECIALIST: Jewellery.

**Silvertimes,** 1 Dukes Arcade, LD3 7AD TEL: 625274 PARKING: Medium OPEN: 10.30-5 MIN: £10 PERIOD: 18th-20th century GENERAL: Silver, clocks, watches OTHER INFO: In courtyard of hotel.

### NEWBRIDGE-ON-WYE 901597)

**Allam Antiques,** Old Village Hall, LD2 3PM TEL: 860654 PARKING: Easy OPEN: Mon-Sat (Sun in summer) 11-6 MIN: £1 MAX: £2000 PERIOD: 18th-20th century GENERAL: Furniture & architectural items OTHER INFO: Newbridge has 3 pubs. Shop is near Royal Welsh Showground.

### ABERYSTWYTH (01970)

**Furniture Cave,** 33 Cambrian Street, SY23 1NZ TEL: 611234 PARKING: Medium OPEN: Wed 9-5, Sat 10-4 MIN: 50p MAX: £2000 PERIOD: 19th-20th century SPECIALIST: Pine GENERAL: Kitchen sink to Welsh oak, affordable furniture, cast iron, books, tools, ceramics, etc OTHER INFO: 2 floors of antiques set in university town by sea in beautiful mid-Wales. Plenty of restaurants, hotels & B&Bs.

**Howards of Aberystwyth,** 10 Alexandra Road (opposite railway station), SY23 1LE TEL & FAX: 624973 ASSNS: BADA, LAPADA PARKING: Easy OPEN: 10-5, closed Wed, Sun MIN: £25 MAX: £5000 PERIOD: 18th-20th century SPECIALIST: 18th-19th century British pottery GENERAL: Jewellery, maps, prints, brassware, country furniture, glass, silver OTHER INFO: Aberystwysth's claim to fame is that it has the highest number of books per person in the UK, also public houses.

### ABERAERON (01570)

**Collectomania,** Corner Shop, Albert Street TEL: 470597 PARKING: Easy OPEN: 10.30-5 MIN: £5 MAX: £1000 PERIOD: 19th century GENERAL: Good selection of china, collectables, some country furniture OTHER INFO: Aberaeron is a very beautiful seaside town with sea trade connections.

### LAMPETER (01570)

**Barn Antiques,** Market Street, SA48 7DR TEL:

423526 PARKING: Easy OPEN: 9-5.30 MIN: £2 MAX: £2500 PERIOD: 19th century SPECIALIST: Pine & country furniture GENERAL: Mixture of new & old, quality handmade furniture OTHER INFO: Full restoration service. Set in pretty university town within 30 mins of the coast.

## LLANDYSUL (01239)

**Ffynnon Las Antiques,** Ffynnon Las, Sarnau, SA44 6QT TEL: 654648 PARKING: Own carpark OPEN: 9-6 MIN: £5 MAX: £800 PERIOD: 19th-20th century SPECIALIST: Painted furniture, primitive paintings GENERAL: Pine furniture, some oak.

## HENLLAN (01559)

**Tortoiseshell Antiques,** Trebedw House, SA44 5TN TEL: 370943 OPEN: Only by appt, only do major London & provincial fairs MIN: £25 MAX: £3500 PERIOD: Small antiquities, 17th-19th century SPECIALIST: Carved ivories, tortoiseshell, fans, samplers.

## NEWCASTLE EMLYN (01239)

**Castle Antiques,** Market Square, SA30 9AE TEL. 710420 PARKING: Easy OPEN: Mon-Sat 9.30-5.30 MIN: £10 MAX: £3000 PERIOD: 18th-19th century GENERAL: Good quality furnishing antiques OTHER INFO: Located in 16th century cottage on approach to castle.

## FISHGUARD (01348)

**Manor House Antiques,** Manor House Hotel, Main Street, SA65 9HG TEL: 873260 PARKING: Medium OPEN: 9.30-5.30 MIN: £5 MAX: £750 PERIOD: 18th-20th century GENERAL: Porcelain, pottery, glass, small furniture OTHER INFO: Situated in hotel, excellent restaurant has been acclaimed by major guides.

## HAVERFORDWEST (01437)

**Kent House Antiques,** 13 Market Street, SA61 1NF TEL: 768175 PARKING: Medium OPEN: 10-5 MIN: £3 PERIOD: 19th-20th century SPECIALIST: Rugs GENERAL: Antiques, Victoriana, bric a brac, hand made rugs & interesting decor items.

**Gerald Oliver Antiques,** 14 Albany Terrace, St Thomas Green, SA61 1RH TEL: 762794 PARKING: Easy OPEN: 9-5, closed Thurs pm MIN: £1 MAX: £6000 PERIOD: 18th-19th century SPECIALIST: Welsh & country furniture GENERAL: Furniture, ceramics, brass, locally sourced when possible OTHER INFO: Pembrokeshire Coast National Park.

**Prendergast Antiques,** 162-164 Prendergast, SA61 2PQ TEL: 765695 PARKING: Easy OPEN: 10-5 MIN: £5 MAX: £2000 PERIOD: 18th-19th century GENERAL: Oak, mahogany, pine furniture, china, collectables, etc.

## CLYNDERWEN (01437)

**Jeremiah Antiques,** The Old Saddlery, Llandissilio, SA66 7TF TEL: 563848 PARKING: Easy OPEN: Mon-Sat 9-5 or by appt MIN: £50 MAX: £3500 PERIOD: 18th-19th century GENERAL: Mostly 19th century mahogany, walnut & rosewood furniture, light fittings OTHER INFO: Restoration & French polishing.

## TEMPLETON (01834)

**Barn Court Antiques,** Barn Court, SA67 8SL TEL: 861224 PARKING: Own carpark OPEN: 7 days 10-7 MIN: £5 MAX: £3000 PERIOD: 18th-19th century SPECIALIST: Furniture GENERAL: China & decorative items OTHER INFO: Ideal getaway weekend area, beaches, restuarants, leisure activities, lovely scenery.

## TENBY (01834)

**Audrey Bull Antiques,** 15 Upper Frog Street, SA70 7JD TEL: 843114 PARKING: Medium OPEN: 10-5.30 MIN: £10 MAX: £5000 PERIOD: 18th-19th century SPECIALIST: Jewellery GENERAL: Welsh country furniture, Georgian & Victorian furniture, silver, paintings, etc OTHER INFO: Tenby, enclosed within 14th century walls, is one of the most beautiful towns in Wales. Exccellent restaurants, call in for advice on where to eat.

**Clareston Antiques,** Warren Street, SA70 7JS TEL: 843350 PARKING: Medium OPEN: 10-1, 2-5 PERIOD: 18th-19th century SPECIALIST: Swansea pottery, porcelain, furniture.

## LAUGHARNE (01994)

**Neil Speed Antiques,** The Strand, SA33 4SZ TEL: 427412 PARKING: Easy OPEN: As often as possible but phone first MIN: £1 MAX: £3000 PERIOD: 17th-20th century SPECIALIST: Country furniture & related items GENERAL: Wide range including Welsh ceramics, quilts, local maps & prints.

## CARMARTHEN (01267)

**Carmarthen Antiques,** 75 Water Street, SA31 1PZ TEL: 235101 OPEN: 10-5.30 GENERAL: Oak, mahogany & pine furniture, china, paintings & decorative furnishings OTHER INFO: Housed in an elegant 4 storey Georgian building.

**Eynon Hughes Antiques,** Nott Square TEL: (01792) 651446 PARKING: Medium OPEN: Mon-Sat 9.30-5.30 MIN: £2 MAX: £2500 PERIOD: 18th-20th century GENERAL: Furniture, paintings, clocks, china OTHER INFO: Carmarthen market days Wed & Sat.

**Merlin Antiques,** Market Precinct, SA31 3LQ TEL: 237728 PARKING: Medium OPEN: 10-4.30, closed Mon MIN: £1 MAX: £600 PERIOD: 19th-20th century GENERAL: Pottery & porcelain, glass, small furniture, postcards OTHER INFO: Local market, on Wed & Sat, has half a dozen antique stalls.

## BRONWYDD ARMS (01267)

**Cwmgwili Mill Antiques,** SA33 6HX TEL: 231500 PARKING: Own carpark OPEN: 9-6 MIN: £10 MAX: £1000 PERIOD: 18th-20th century GENERAL: Oak, mahogany, pine, some bric a brac OTHER INFO: 3 miles north of Carmarthen.

## KIDWELLY (01554)

**Country Antiques,** Castle Mill, SA17 4UU TEL: 890534 ASSNS: LAPADA PARKING: Own carpark OPEN: Tues-Sat 10-5 MIN: £10 MAX: £25,000 PERIOD: 18th-19th century SPECIALIST: Folk art & furniture from Wales GENERAL: Mahogany, pine, pottery, etc.

## LLANDEILO (01558)

**James & Patricia Ash,** The Warehouse, Station Road, SA19 6NG TEL: 823726 PARKING: Own carpark OPEN: Mon-Fri 9-5 but advisable to phone first MIN: £50 MAX: £5000 PERIOD: 19th-20th century SPECIALIST: Victorian, Edwardian, pine furniture & Welsh country items OTHER INFO: Llandeilo is a small town set amidst beautiful countryside with good selection on interesting shops.

## SWANSEA (01792)

**Antique Emporium,** 76 St Helen's Road PARKING: Easy OPEN: Mon-Sat 10-5 MIN: 25p PERIOD: 19th-20th century SPECIALIST: Pictures, postcards, cast iron grates GENERAL: China, furniture, metalware, etc.

**Eynon Hughes Antiques,** Henrietta Street TEL: 651446 PARKING: Own carpark OPEN: Tues-Fri 11-4.30 MIN: £2 MAX: £2500 PERIOD: 18th-20th century GENERAL: Furniture, paintings, clocks, china OTHER INFO: Swansea has an interesting covered market renowned for its fish & cockles.

**Anne & Colin Hulbert (Antiques) Firearms Dealer,** 17 Approach Road, Manselton, SA5 8PD TEL: 653818 PARKING: Easy OPEN: 8-7 PERIOD: 19th century SPECIALIST: Shipping goods GENERAL: Retail items.

**Kim Scurlock,** 25 Russell Street, SA1 4HR TEL: 643085 PARKING: Easy OPEN: Mon-Fri 9.30-5, Sat 9.30-1 MIN: £25 MAX: £1000 PERIOD: 19th-20th century GENERAL: Pine & country furniture, china, glass & brass.

## BISHOPSTON (01792)

**Maybery Antiques,** 1 Brandy Cove Road, SA3 3HB TEL: 232550 PARKING: Easy OPEN: 11-5, closed Mon & Tues MIN: £1 MAX: £3000 PERIOD: 18th-20th century SPECIALIST: Porcelain - Swansea, Nantgarw, Royal Worcester GENERAL: Furniture, porcelain, pottery, paintings, general antiques OTHER INFO: Situated in National Trust area, near magnificent beaches.

**West Wales Antiques Company,** 18 Manselfield Road, Murton, SA3 3AR TEL: 234318 ASSNS: LAPADA PARKING: Easy OPEN: 10-1, 1-5 MIN: £50 MAX: £3200 PERIOD: 18th-19th century SPECIALIST: Nantgarw & Swansea porcelain GENERAL: Furniture, porcelain, silver, etc OTHER INFO: Shop situated on entrance to beautiful Gower coast.

## PORTHCAWL (01656)

**Harlequin Antiques,** Dock Street, CF36 3BL TEL: 785910 PARKING: Own carpark OPEN: Mon-Sat 9-5 MIN: £5 MAX: £1000 PERIOD: 18th-20th century SPECIALIST: Textiles GENERAL: Antiques OTHER INFO: The shop is situated in a public carpark overlooking harbour.

## COWBRIDGE (01446)

**Havard & Havard,** 59 Eastgate, CF7 7EL TEL: 775021 ASSNS: LAPADA PARKING: Easy OPEN: Tues, Thurs-Sat 10-5.30 MIN: £20 MAX: £10,000 PERIOD: 17th-19th century SPECIAL-

IST: Country furniture GENERAL: Oak, mahogany & walnut, metalware & samplers OTHER INFO: Cowbridge is an ancient market town, the shops are mostly small independent retailers, only 8 miles from Cardiff.

**Renaissance Antiques,** Northgate Way Arcade, 49 High Street, CF7 7AE TEL: 773893 & 774656 PARKING: Easy OPEN: 10.30-1, 2.15-5.30 MIN: £10 MAX: £2000 PERIOD: 18th-19th century SPECIALIST: Staffordshire figures GENERAL: Small furniture, metalware, paper mache, English pottery & glass, decorative items OTHER INFO: Good food in pubs & restaurants.

## PENARTH (01222)

**Corner Cupboard Antiques,** 4A Station Approach, CF44 2EE TEL: 705392 PARKING: Easy OPEN: 10-5, closed Wed & Sun PERIOD: 18th-20th century GENERAL: General antiques OTHER INFO: Just a few miles west of Swansea (Jn33 of M4), 5 mins from seafront, pier, promenade, various restaurants & several small hotels & B&Bs.

## CARDIFF (01222)

**Cardiff Antiques Centre,** 24 Morgan Arcade OPEN: Mon-Sat 10-5.30 MIN: £5 MAX: £7000 PERIOD: 19th century GENERAL: Cranberry glass, Gandy Welsh, clocks, furniture, Victoriana, jewellery, clothing, watercolours, 1930s Art Deco OTHER INFO: 14 dealers on 3 floors in a Victorian arcade in the heart of the city adjacent to David Morgan department store.

**Charlottes Antiques,** 129 Woodville Road, Cathays TEL: 759809 PARKING: Medium OPEN: 10-4 MIN: £5 MAX: £3000 PERIOD: 20th century GENERAL: Shipping antiques.

**Grandma's Goodies,** 31 Mortimer Road, Pontcanna, CF1 9JP TEL: 340901 OPEN: Thurs-Sat 10-5 & by appt MIN: £5 MAX: £350 PERIOD: 19th-20th century GENERAL: Lace, linen, china, jewellery, glass, small furniture OTHER INFO: Can browse uninterrupted or chat to owner, children & dogs welcome. Village atmosphere in Portcanna & plenty of hotels & B&Bs. On direct route to St Fagan's Folk Museum, approx 3 miles away.

**Manor House Fine Arts,** 73 Portcanna Street, CF1 9HS TEL: 227787 ASSNS: FATG PARKING: Easy OPEN: Tues, Thurs-Sat 10.30-5.30 MIN: £1 MAX: £4000 PERIOD: 1820-1994 SPECIALIST: Paintings, watercolours, prints OTHER INFO: We are a 15 min walk from city centre. Many good inexpensive B&Bs in Cathedral Road.

**Rowles Fine Antiques,** 24 Morgan Arcade TEL: 621443, mobile 0850 963454 PARKING: Medium OPEN: Mon-Sat 10-5.30 MIN: £5 MAX: £10,000 PERIOD: 19th-20th century SPECIALIST: Gaudy Welsh pottery, cranberry glass, oils lamps, clocks GENERAL: Furniture, pocelain, silver.

**San Domenico Stringed Instruments,** 175 Kings Road, CF1 9DF TEL: 235881 FAX: 344510 PARKING: Easy OPEN: Mon-Fri 10-4.30, Sat am only MIN: £300 MAX: £60,000 PERIOD: 18th-20th century SPECIALIST: Quality violins, violas, cellos & bows - the specialist violin shop in Wales OTHER INFO: Some of the best quality instruments and bows available, trades worldwide.

## MAINDEE (NEWPORT) (01633)

**Antiques of Newport,** 82 Chepstow Road, NP9 8ED TEL: 259935 & 255977 PARKING: Medium OPEN: 10.30-1, 2.30-5, closed Thurs MIN: £1 MAX: £1500 PERIOD: 18th-20th century SPECIALIST: Maps & prints GENERAL: Pottery, porcelain, silver, jewellery, fine art, etc.

## CHEPSTOW (01291)

**Glance Bank,** 17 Upper Church Street, NP6 5RX TEL: 626562 PARKING: Easy OPEN: 6 days 10ish-5.30 MIN: £2 MAX: £10,000 PERIOD: 17th-20th century SPECIALIST: Books, prints, maps, coins, medals, tokens, stamps, cap badges, banknotes, postcards OTHER INFO: 8 rooms in central town, 4 mins from Severn Bridge. Here there is one of Britain's most impressive castles on a high cliff abover the River Wye.

## MONMOUTH (01660)

**Carol Freeman Antiques,** The Gallery, Nailers Lane, NP5 3SE TEL: 772252 PARKING: Medium OPEN: Mon-Sat 10-5 PERIOD: 18th-20th century GENERAL: Furniture & general antiques.

# North and Mid Wales

*Powis Castle, near Welshpool*

The first part of this tour runs along the English-Welsh border with its history of raids and battles between the two countries. This has left a legacy of mostly Norman castles in various states of repair. Further along, the beautiful countryside of North Wales provides spectacular scenery with rugged mountains, river valleys and lakes. Much of this region is contained within the Snowdonia National Park, covering an area of 840 square miles and designated in 1951. At 3560 feet, Snowdon is the highest mountain in England and Wales. There are several tracks for walkers up the mountain and the Snowdon Mountain Railway ascends from Llanberis giving passengers spectacular views.

The route starts in the small border town of **Knighton** on the River Teme. Offa's Dyke runs across the south west side and a Heritage Centre gives information on the Dyke. Proceeding north, **Llanfair** is the centre for the Welshpool to Llanfair Railway and was reopened in 1963. The town's church was rebuilt in the 19th century on the site of a 13th century church and retains the original doorway, font, and early effigy of a knight.

Ten miles away medieval **Welshpool** contains many black and white timber-framed buildings happily mixing with later Georgian houses. It also has an original cockpit, now restored to its original state. Just a mile south, Powis Castle belonged to the Welsh princes and was built about 1300. Now it contains fine 16th century plasterwork, tapestries, paintings and furniture. In the town, on Canal Wharf, the Powysland Museum and Montgomery Canal Centre exhibits items of archaeology, the history of the railways, the canal and agricultural life.

Further north, **Chirk**, a small village on the border, is another settlement that owes its existence to a castle built there in 1310. This is an outstanding example of a Marcher castle (the border was referred to as the Marches). Continuously inhabited since completion, it is set in an 18th century landscaped park with a garden containing a ha-ha (sunken wall), a folly and good example of 19th century topiary. There are also many beautiful trees, shrubs and herbaceous borders. Nearby **Llangollen**, on the River Dee, holds an annual Eistedfodd in July attracting people worldwide. The

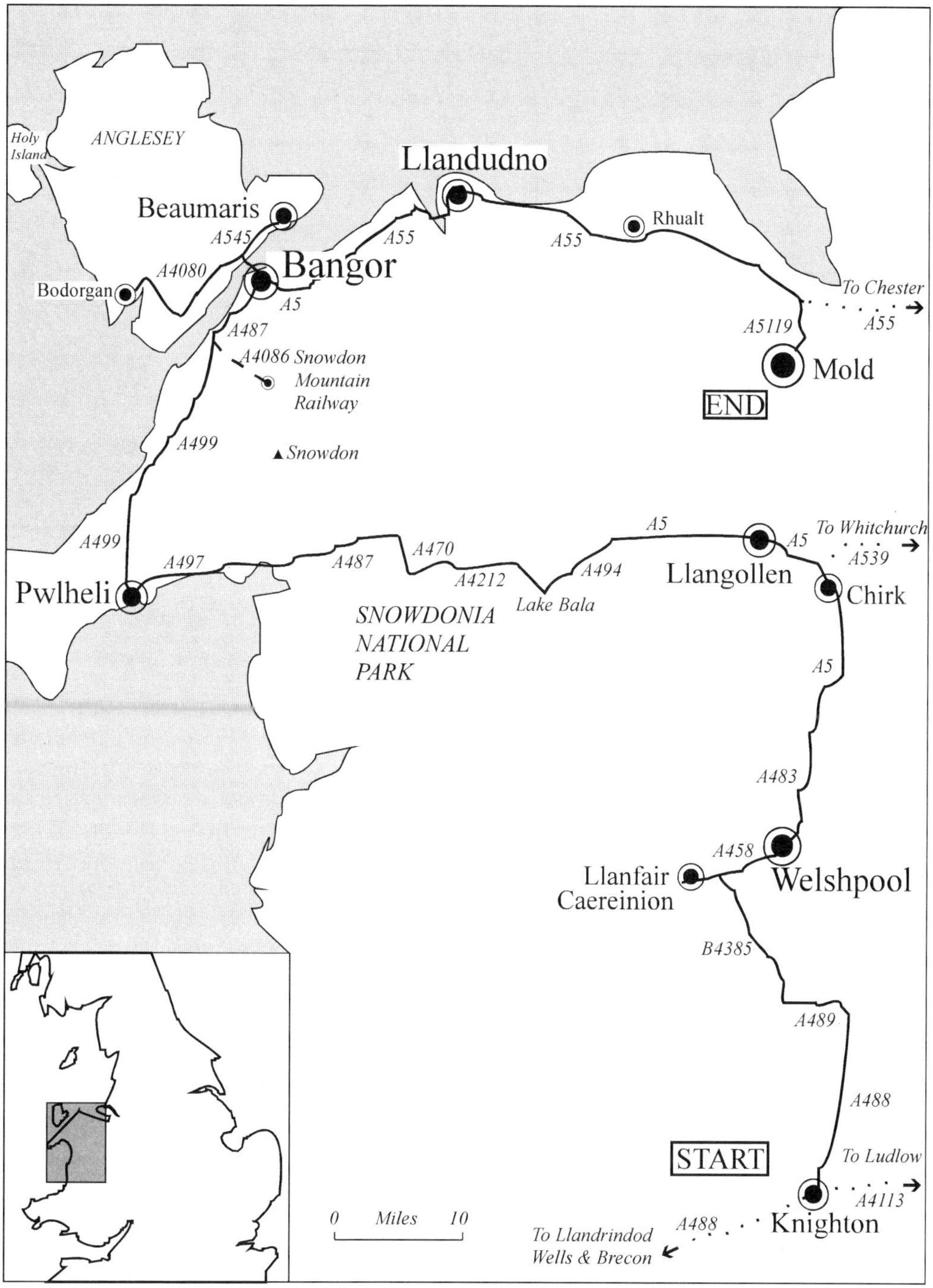
Holy Island
ANGLESEY
Llandudno
Beaumaris
A545
A55
A55
Rhualt
A4080
Bangor
Bodorgan
A5
To Chester
A487
A5119
A55
A4086 Snowdon
Mountain
Railway
Mold
END
A499
Snowdon
A5
To Whitchurch
A499
A5
A539
A497
A487
A470
A4212
A494
Llangollen
Chirk
Pwlheli
Lake Bala
SNOWDONIA
NATIONAL
PARK
A5
A483
A458
Llanfair
Caereinion
Welshpool
B4385
A489
A488
START
To Ludlow
A4113
0 Miles 10
A488
Knighton
To Llandrindod
Wells & Brecon

*Snowdon Mountain Railway By courtesy of the Wales Tourist Board*

town is perhaps best known for its two 'Ladies of Llangollen' who, from 1780 to 1831, lived in the house called Plas Newydd, now open to the public from April to October. They were two Irishwomen, Lady Eleanor Butler and Miss Sarah Ponsonby, who eloped together and and settled here. Their object was to devote themselves to 'friendship, celibacy and the knitting of blue stockings'. They attracted many famous visitors including the Duke of Wellington, Sir Walter Scott and William Wordsworth. Llangollen also has a castle, Castell Dinas Bran, standing on the north side of the Dee. It was originally an Iron Age fort, then a Welsh stronghold until the Normans built first a wooden fortification and then later, in the 13th century, a stone one. However, it saw little action but by the late 16th century had decayed in ruins. The Valle Crucis Abbey is also a ruin but gives a good idea of the original size as it includes the abbey church and some monastic buildings. The abbey was founded in the 13th century by the Welsh prince, Madog ap Gruffydd, and but fell into neglect after the Dissolution of the Monasteries in the 16th century.

The tour now heads west into the Snowdonia National Park. Bala Lake, the largest natural lake in Wales, is at the junction of the A494 and A4212. The route continues to the coast and the popular seaside resort of **Pwlheli**, with its long sandy beach. Crossing the Lleyn Peninsula and following the coast again brings the trip to **Bangor**, on the Menai Strait between the mainland and the island of Anglesey. This university and cathedral city is an ancient town which developed around a 6th century monastery. The Menai Bridge, connecting the Welsh mainland to Anglesey, was built constructed from 1819 to 1825, by Thomas Telford . He designed the then world's biggest suspension bridge to an Admiralty requirement that the Menai Strait should be open to even the tallest vessels. A Victorian fantasy, Penrhyn Castle, stands just east. This was designed by Thomas Hopper for George Pennant, owner of slate mines at Bethesda. Built in the first half of the 19th century, as a Norman castle complete with towers and a keep, it stands in 48 acres of cultivation ranging from a Victorian walled garden to one intended for wild flora. The bog garden contains some spectacular specimens including a giant fern tree and enormous gunnera.

Crossing the Menai Bridge, next is Anglesey. This island has a long history of settlement dating back to the Stone Age with many prehistoric sites. The scenery is largely pleasant farmland with dramatic cliffs on Holy Island. The first call on the island is to the village of **Bodorgan** in the extreme north-western corner and then on to **Beaumaris**, about four miles east of the Menai Bridge. Beaumaris was the main harbour for ferries to and from the mainland before the bridge was built. The castle here is a World Heritage Listed Site and was the last and biggest built by Edward I. The symmetrical moated castle was constructed in the late 13th century, although never quite finished. However, in the 15th century it was taken by Owen Glendower and then retaken by the English. During the Civil War the castle was held for the King but surrendered in 1646. After the restoration of Charles II it was given to the Bulkeley family who retained ownership until 1925. The town of Beaumaris is a lovely holiday resort with a harbour busy with small craft and pleasure boats running through the Menai Strait.

Back on the mainland, **Llandudno** is the largest seaside resort in Wales with a wide range of entertainment for visitors. It has a beautiful promenade along Orme Bay and a beautiful sandy beach. There has been a settlement here since the Bronze Age although it remained only a large village until the 19th century when a new town was planned and built to cater for holidaymakers. As a result there are many splendid Victorian buildings laid out in a grid pattern to provide a harmonious result. Since then, later development has not been allowed to spoil the town.

After leaving Llandudno the route follows the coastline to **Rhuallt** before turning south for the last town on this tour, **Mold**, the county town of Clwyd. The town's 15th century church has an charming frieze of animals and the painter, Richard Wilson, is buried in the churchyard.

# ANTIQUE DEALERS

## KNIGHTON (01547)

**Offa's Dyke Antique Centre,** 4 High Street, LD7 1AT TEL: 528635 PARKING: Easy OPEN: Mon-Sat 10-1, 2-5 MIN: £5 MAX: £2000 PERIOD: 18th-20th century SPECIALIST: Staffordshire figures, ceramics, glass GENERAL: Furniture, silver, jewellery, collectables.

**Islwyn Watkins Antiques,** 1 High Street, LD7 1AT TEL: 520145 & 528940 PARKING: Easy OPEN: Tues, Thurs-Sat 10-1, 2-5 MIN: £5 MAX: £1500 PERIOD: 18th-20th century SPECIALIST: 18th & 19th century and country pottery GENERAL: Small country furniture, bygones.

## LLANFAIR (01938)

**Heritage Restorations,** Maesglydfa, SY21 0HD TEL & FAX: 810384 PARKING: Own carpark OPEN: Mon-Sat 9-5.30 MIN: £5 MAX: £5000 PERIOD: 17th-19th century SPECIALIST: Very large stock (largest in Wales) of good original stripped pine, some oak & architectural items OTHER INFO: Good B&B nearby.

## WELSHPOOL (01938)

**FE Anderson & Son,** 5 High Street, SY21 7JP TEL: 553340 ASSNS: LAPADA PARKING: Own carpark OPEN: Mon-Fri 9-5, Sat 9-2 MIN: £30 MAX: £3500 SPECIALIST: Furniture, mirrors, etc OTHER INFO: This family business was established in 1842 and is adjacent to Powis Castle Park (National Trust).

**Horley Antiques,** 19 High Street, SY21 7JP TEL: 552421 PARKING: Medium OPEN: Mon-Fri 10-4 MAX: £1500 PERIOD: 19th-20th century SPECIALIST: Paintings GENERAL: Smalls.

## CHIRK (01691)

**Seventh Heaven Antique Beds,** Chirk Mill, LL14 5BU TEL: 777622 FAX: 777313 PARKING: Own carpark OPEN: Mon-Sat 9-5, Sun 10-4 MIN: £195 MAX: £10,000 PERIOD: 19th century SPECIALIST: Bedsteads GENERAL: Bedside tables, wardrobes, mattresses, linen OTHER INFO: Situated in an old corn mill once belonging to the Chirck Castle.

## LLANGOLLEN (01978)

**J & R Langford,** 12 Bridge Street, LL20 8PF TEL: 860182 PARKING: Own carpark OPEN: 9.30-5.30 MIN: £15 MAX: £5000 PERIOD: 19th-20th century GENERAL: Furniture, pottery, porcelain, paintings, silver, clocks, etc.

**Passers Buy,** Chapel Street/Oak Street, LL20 8NN TEL: 860861 PARKING: Easy OPEN: 11-5 MIN: £10 MAX: £2000 PERIOD: 18th-19th century SPECIALIST: Furniture GENERAL: Staffordshire figures, fairings, Gaudy Welsh & general antiques OTHER INFO: Famous for scenery & annual Eisteddfod. Home of famous 'Ladies of Llangollen'.

## PWLLHELI (01758)

**Rodney Adams Antiques,** Hall Place, 10 Penlan Street, LL53 5DH TEL: 613173 PARKING: Easy OPEN: 9-5 MIN: £10 MAX: £10,000 PERIOD: 18th-19th century SPECIALIST: Grandfather clocks, 30-50 in stock GENERAL: Furniture, furnishing pieces, oak & country OTHER INFO: It is an area of very special natural beauty. I have the largest collection of longcase clocks in Wales.

## BANGOR (01248)

**David Windsor Gallery,** 201 High Street, LL57 1NU TEL: 364639 ASSNS: FATG PARKING: Easy OPEN: 10-5, closed Wed MIN: £10 MAX: Variable PERIOD: 17th-20th century SPECIALIST: Maps, prints, lithographs, oils, watercolours, local interest OTHER INFO: Bangor is situated on the Menai Strait dividing the mainland from the Isle of Anglesey, beautiful coastline, mountains, etc.

## BODORGAN (01407)

**Michael Webb Fine Art,** Cefn-Llwyn, LL62 5DN TEL: 840336 ASSNS: LAPADA PARKING: Own carpark OPEN: By appt MIN: £50 MAX: £10,000 PERIOD: 18th-20th century SPECIALIST: Victorian oils & watercolours GENERAL: Oils, watercolours, etchings.

## BEAUMARIS (01248)

**Museum of Childhood,** 1 Castle Street, LL58 8AP TEL: 712498 ASSNS: Independent Museums Association PARKING: Easy OPEN: Easter-November MIN: 20p MAX: £190 PERIOD: 19th-20th century SPECIALIST: Bears, old toys GENERAL: Gift items, many based on museum exhibits OTHER INFO: 13th century castle opposite shop.

## LLANDUDNO (01492)

**CG Lee,** The Antique Shop, 24 Vaughan Street (nr Promenade), LL30 1AH TEL: 875575 PARKING: Medium OPEN: 9.30-5.30 PERIOD: 18th-19th century SPECIALIST: Jewellery, silver GENERAL: China, glass, furniture, metal goods.

## RHUALLT (01745)

**Barbara Trefor Antiques,** Rhuallt Hall, LL17 0TR TEL: 583604 PARKING: Own carpark OPEN: By appt MIN: £10 MAX: £5000 PERIOD: 18th-20th century GENERAL: Oak & country furniture, mahogany, walnut, clocks, bric a brac.

## MOLD (01352)

**Mold Antiques & Interiors,** The Old Chapel, 91 Wrexham Street, CH7 1HQ TEL: 752979 PARKING: 10-5, closed Sun & Thurs MIN: £1 MAX: £3000 PERIOD: 19th-20th century GENERAL: Furniture, ceramics, etc OTHER INFO: 1600 sq ft of antiques in a converted Victorian Welsh chapel.

# Northern Ireland

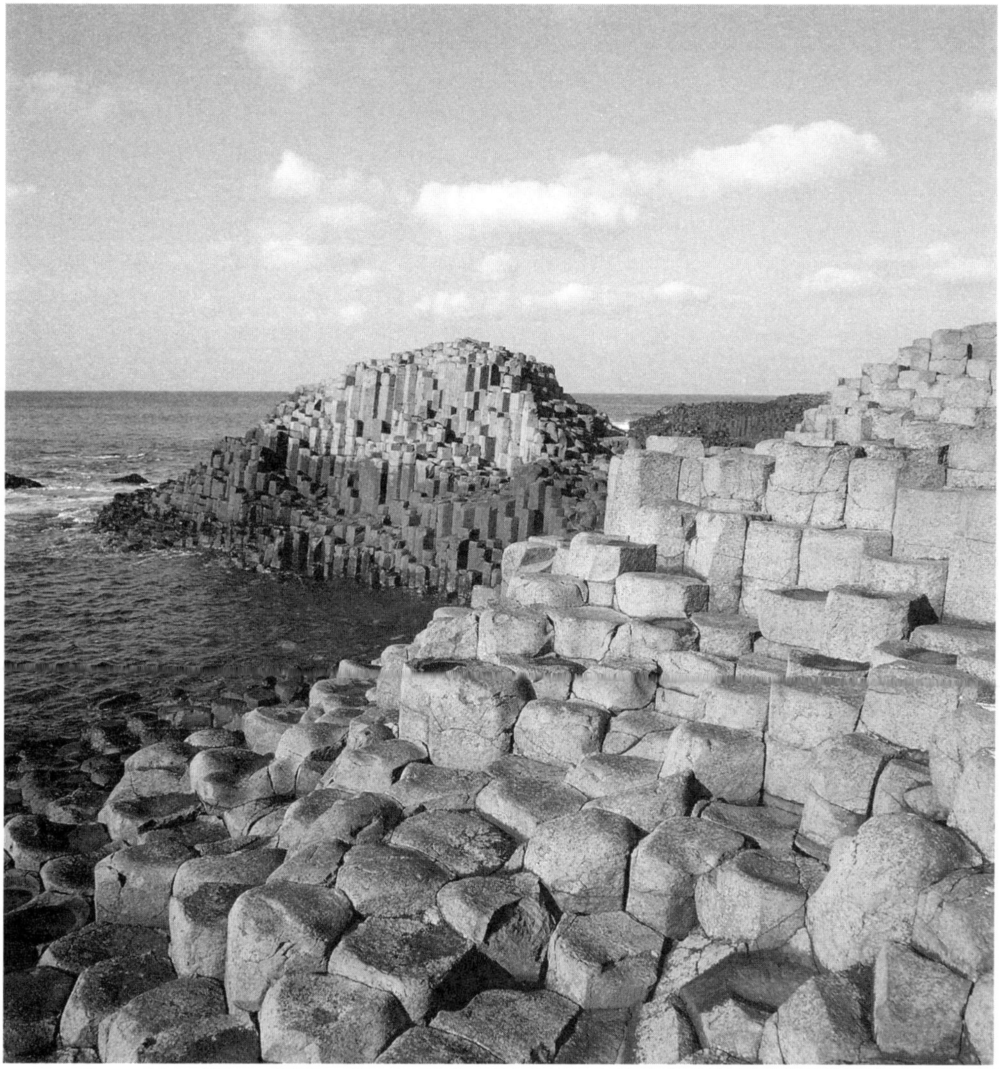

*The Giant's Causeway*

Northern Ireland is associated in most peoples mind with 'the troubles', the IRA, extreme Protestants, bombs and British army patrols in city streets. At the time of writing there is a ceasefire between the different factions and 'talks about talks' taking place. Although progress seems slow, experts think that there is now a chance of lasting peace. It has been said that the trouble with the Irish is that they never forget and with the British that they never remember. History is at the root of the 'Irish Troubles' starting centuries ago with the Anglo-Norman invasion of the island, through the battles with King William, the potato famine, absentee landlords and culminating in the partition of Ireland into north and south. The north was more industrially developed and prosperous and also contained a large Protestant majority, many being settlers brought from England and Scotland. A Parliament was set up at Stormont which governed Northern Ireland from 1922 until 1972. However, Protestants predominated and the Catholic minority complained of discrimination which exacerbated tensions between the two communities. This culminated in the Civil Rights marches of the late 1960s by Catholics. The level of violence increased

# Northern Ireland

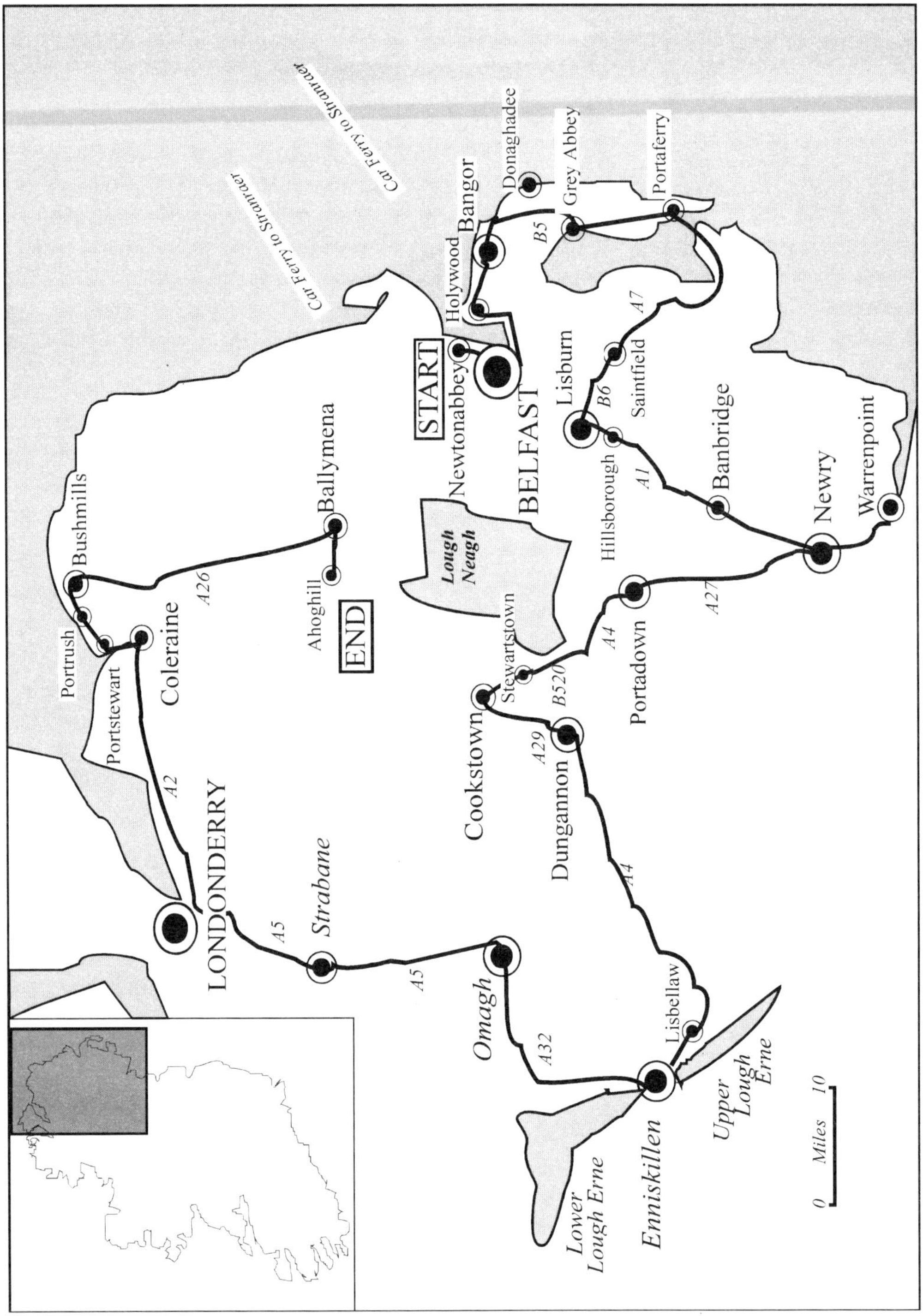

between Protestants and Catholics and, because the local police were seen as part of the problem, the British Army was sent into the province in August 1969, initially to a warm welcome by the Catholic minority. Since then there has been violence and outrages apparently perpertrated by both sides leading to a seemingly intractable problem.

In spite of all this, violence in the Province has never been all pervading as seen from outside and many people have had wonderful holidays there. It is a beautiful country with scenery ranging from the spectacular Antrim coastline to the fruit orchards of Fermanagh and includes moors, peat bogs, woodlands and lakes, including Lough Neagh, the largest lake in the British Isles.

The tour starts in **Newtownabbey** and then carries on to **Belfast**, the capital of Ulster. This city on the River Lagan has been the site of settlements since the Stone and Bronze Ages. In 1173 a Norman castle was built by a ford across the river and the town developed around it. Both town and castle were destroyed in the early 14th century and the area came under the control of the O'Neill clan. They forfeited their lands in 1603 and these were given to Sir Arthur Chichester who brought men from Devon into the area. At the same time Belfast was given a Royal Charter to build a quay. This expanded with the dredging of a channel in the 19th century to the point where the town grew into a major port and shipbuilding centre. During this period, Huguenots (French Protestants) found sanctuary from persecution in Belfast and they improved the weaving of fine linen which was already established here. The city has many impressive 19th century buildings which include St Anne's Cathedral, started in 1899 but not finished for another 82 years, the Albert Memorial Clocktower, built in 1867 and with a pronounced tilt to one side, the Grand Opera House, opened in 1895 with an opulent Victorian interior, and Belfast City Hall, started in 1898 and finished in 1906. The Crown Liquor Saloon, in Great Victoria Street, is a most unusual National Trust property. Built in 1885 and called the Railway Tavern, this pub is a supreme example of High Victorian taste with coloured and cut glass, classical pilasters, urns and cast-iron columns. The richly carved bar runs along one side of the room and facing it are a number of snugs, booths enclosed by wooden panels and coloured glass with doors to make them into private compartments. This pub is on every visitor's itinerary whether just for a drink or a meal of oysters or Irish stew.

After visiting **Holywood** the seaside town of **Bangor** comes next. It developed around a great 6th century abbey which was one of the most famous of the period, sending out missionaries to found other religious houses in Europe. It was sacked by Vikings but rebuilt in 1140 and continued until the Dissolution of the Monasteries. Now only a 14th century tower, incorporated into the local church, remains. One treasure survives, however, the Bangor Antiphony, a prayer book dating from about 680 AD and the earliest Irish text in existence, is kept in the Ambrosian Library in Milan. The 17th century Bangor Castle, overlooking the marina, still stands and has been made into the Town Hall. It also contains the North Down Heritage Centre which tells the story of Bangor Abbey and the town itself.

**Donaghadee** is just five miles along the coast on the Ards Peninsula which divides the Irish Sea from Strangford Lough. It is a picturesque small town with a large harbour. It is the closest Irish port to Britain with Portpatrick in Scotland being only 21miles away. During the 19th century mail boats travelled between the two towns until the business moved to the Stranraer-Larne route. Further south, **Grey Abbey** is named for the abbey, now in ruins, founded in 1193. **Portaferry**, next, stands at the southern end of the Ards Peninsula. This pleasant quiet small town is home to a Marine Biology Station which is housed in two Georgian houses on the Strangford Loch waterfront.

The tour continues via the short car ferry from Portaferry to Strangford and then to **Saintfield** followed by **Lisburn**. This industrial city is in the heart of the Ulster linen area and the local museum has an exhibition on the production of linen. The town is dominated by Christchurch Cathedral which was rebuilt in 1708 in the 'Planters Gothic' style (introduced by English and Scottish settlers in the 17th century). The graveyard contains several Huguenot graves including that of Samuel Louis Crommelin who was instrumental in introducing changes to improve linen weaving.

**Hillsborough**, five miles away, is an elegant Georgian town set around a central square. In the park there is a well-preserved 17th century fort, built to quell Irish rebels and where William III is said to have stayed in 1690 on his way to fight the Battle of the Boyne. Hillsborough Castle, nearby, is the official residence of the Secretary of State for Northern Ireland and it was here, in 1985, that Margaret Thatcher, then Prime Minister of Great Britain, and Garret Fitzgerald, then Taoiseach of Ireland, signed a treaty to ease relations between the two countries.

Following the A1, **Banbridge** comes next, followed by **Newry** which sits on the border between Ulster and the Irish Republic in a strategic gap in the mountains. Its position has led to much violence over the centuries. The original Norman castle was destroyed by Edward Bruce in the early 14th century and its replacement by one of the O'Neills in 1566. The town itself was burnt during the 'Troubles' in the late 17th century. Because of this few buildings survive from earlier times. The first Anglican church built in Ireland after the Reformation, St Patick's, was constructed here and still survives in spite of being seriously damaged when the town burnt. Nearby picturesque **Warrenpoint** on Carlingford Lough. has pleasure boat trips to see the Mountains of Mourne and the Cooley Peninsula.

The route now moves on to the industrial town of **Portadown** on the River Bann before reaching **Stewartstown**, and then **Cookstown.** with its very wide main street and, unusually, nearly all houses having their own garden This stemmed from the initial town planning around 1715. **Dungannon**, next, apart from being the capital of the region, is a very busy agricultural town and was once the centre for the O'Neills, Earls of Tyrone. After the fall of the O'Neills in the early 1700's, Scottish and English settlers came to the area and the town began to grow. 40 miles south west lies the village of **Lisbellaw** and 5 miles northwest is a touring 'must', the near border town of Enniskillen. Both Samuel Beckett and Oscar Wilde went to school here and the town centre actually sits on an island dividing Lough Erne. There is a fine castle, excellent museum facilities and by climbing the steps of the 100ft Coles Monument in Fonthill Park, wonderful views can be had. There are many antiquities in the area and an underground boat trip is available in the extremely popular Marble Arch Caves and Forest about 10 miles south.

25 miles northwest on the way to Londonderry, the county town of Tyrone, Omagh sits prettily on a steep slope over the junction of two rivers. It is a good touring base. Following the A5 20 miles north, the border town of Strabane is again just above two rivers. The A5 now continues along the east bank of the River Foyle another 14 miles to Ulster's second city, **Londonderry** or Derry, depending on which side of the religious and political divide the person comes from. Originally called Derry. It received the prefix 'London' in the 17th century when large parcels of land were given to London livery companies. The present Anglican cathedral stands on the site of the original abbey founded here in 546 AD by St Columba and burnt by Vikings about 250 years later. A great Norman church was built on the site in the 12th century which was again destroyed in 1566 when Shane O'Neill, Earl of Tyrone, attacked the town. Some forty years later the town was laid waste by Sir Cahir O'Doherty. However, he was killed shortly afterwards and his lands and that of the O'Neills were forfeited. This was the time land was given to London livery companies and the name changed, additionally, a large number of Protestant settlers were brought in.

The most famous episode in the city's history came in 1688 when the gates were shut on a regiment of soldiers supporting James II sent to hold the city for the Jacobite cause. James II landed in Ireland a few months later and put the city under siege with his 20,000 strong army and a boom was put across the River Foyle to prevent supplies being sent in by boat. The siege lasted for 105 days during which a large number of the city's people died. It was lifted when the boom was broken and relief ships sailed in.

Londonderry's violent history has left it few tangible legacies from the past although some parts of the city walls still survive. In the south west, on the walls, stands Roaring Meg, a cannon from the mid 17th century which was used during the siege. The Protestant St Columb's Cathedral stands on the site of the early abbey and was started in 1628 although the chancel was only completed in the late 19th century. A shell was fired into the town during the siege giving terms for surrender and this may be found in the porch of the cathedral.

The tour proceeds to **Coleraine**, another town where much land was given to London Livery Companies and consequently settled by English Protestants. At nearby Mountsandel flint tools dating from 6650 BC have been found. These are the earliest recorded finds left by man in Ireland. Continuing along the coast eastwards, **Portstewart** was a fashionable seaside resort in the 19th century as it has good sandy beaches. Neighbouring **Portrush** also has lovely beaches and is popular for holidays. On the same road, the A2, the route passes Dunluce Castle, built about 1300 and rebuilt in 1590 on a rock separated from the mainland. **Bushmills** comes next. This town is synonymous with whisky and the drink has been distilled in the town for centuries, even before it received its licence in 1608.

Bushmills is ideally situated for visitors to the Giant's Causeway. This natural wonder was only brought to the attention of a wide audience in 1740 when it was painted by an artist. The estimated 37,000 basalt columns were formed 60 million years ago when an underground volcanic eruption forced molten basalt through fissures in the earth's crust running from the north coast of Ireland through to the Isle of Skye and Staffa in the Faroes. Many of the columns are hexagonal, others have different numbers of sides ranging from five to ten. Parts of the Causeway have been given separate names including Chimney Point which gives the appearance of castle towers. So realistic is it that ships of the Spanish Armada fired upon it thinking it was Dunluce Castle. Further east along the coast, Carrick-a-Rede presents a challenge for the intrepid traveller. The island, Carrick-a-Rede, is a site for salmon fishers who set their nets on the north side. During the summer, from May to September, it is connected to the mainland by a rope bridge 66 feet long. If you dare the bridge, remember you have to come back and do not do it in a high wind. On the positive side, there have been very few accidents in the 200 years that the bridge has been used.

From Bushmills the tour turns inland to **Ballymena**, home of Ian Paisley and the county town of Antrim. **Ahoghill** is the final call.

## ANTIQUE DEALERS

### NEWTOWNABBEY (01232)

**New Abbey Antiques,** Caragh Lodge, Glen Road, Jordanstown, BT37 0RY TEL: 862036 FAX: 853281 ASSNS: IADA PARKING: Own carpark OPEN: 9.30-6 MIN: £30 MAX: £15,000 PERIOD: 18th-19th century SPECIALIST: Furniture GENERAL: Paintings & objects OTHER INFO: 15 mins from Belfast city centre.

**Glenbourne Antiques,** 27 Ballyclare Road,Glengormley BT36 8EZ TEL: 833833 OPEN: Mon-Sat 10-5 MIN: £5 MAX: £2000 PERIOD: 18th-20th century SPECIALIST: Furniture & objects.

### BELFAST (01232)

**Emerald Isle Books,** 539 Antrim Road, BT15 3BU TEL: 370798 FAX: 777288 ASSNS: ABA, ILAB PARKING: Easy OPEN: 10-5 PERIOD: 17th-20th century SPECIALIST: Ireland GENERAL: Travel, leather bound books.

**Kennedy Wolfenden & Co Ltd,** 218 Lisburn Road, BT9 6GD TEL: 381 775 FAX: 381147 PARKING: Easy OPEN: Mon-Sat 9-5.30 MIN: £15 MAX: £10,000 PERIOD: 19th-20th century GENERAL: Furniture, porcelain, paintings, large selection of antique & modern jewellery.

### HOLYWOOD (01232)

**Herbert Gould & Co,** 21-25A Church Road, BT18 9BU TEL: 428589 & 427916 FAX: 428396 PARKING: Easy OPEN: Mon-Sat 9-5.30 MIN: £5 MAX: £1000 PERIOD: 19th-20th century SPECIALIST: Antique pine GENERAL: Interior accessories, architectural OTHER INFO: We stock unusual gifts, comestibles, American folk art, teddy bears & gentrified goods. Superb coffee & bistro next door.

### BANGOR (01247)

**Goldenage Antiques,** 57A Gray's Hill, BT20 3BB TEL: 270938 PARKING: Easy OPEN: 12-5, closed Thurs & Sun MIN: £2 MAX: £2000 PERIOD: 19th-20th century SPECIALIST: Jewellery, silver, glass & porcelain GENERAL: Furniture & bric a brac.

### DONAGHADEE (01247)

**Furney Antiques & Interiors,** 2-4 Shore Street, BT21 0DG TEL: 883826 & 883517 FAX: 888729 PARKING: Easy OPEN: Wed-Sat 11-5.30 MIN: £1 MAX: £8000 PERIOD: 18th-19th century SPECIALIST: Georgian & Regency furniture GENERAL: Porcelain, silver, furniture OTHER INFO: Overlooking harbour in centre of village with the oldest pub in Ireland.

## GREYABBEY (01247)

**The Antique Shop,** 9 Main Street TEL: 738333 PARKING: Easy OPEN: Wed, Fri, Sat 2-5.30 MIN: £1 MAX: £2000 PERIOD: 18th-20th century SPECIALIST: Silver when available GENERAL: Furniture, porcelain, glass, linen, etc OTHER INFO: National Trust property, Mountstewart, 3 miles away.

**Phyllis Arnold Gallery Antiques,** Hoops Courtyard, BT22 2NE TEL: 788199 & 853322 OPEN: Wed, Fri, Sat 11-5 MIN: £10 MAX: £3000 PERIOD: 17th-20th century SPECIALIST: Antiquarian maps of Ireland from 1580, portrait miniatures GENERAL: Watercolours, paintings, engravings, small furniture OTHER INFO: Good restaurant in the courtyard. I am a member of the Royal Society of Miniatures & specialise in protraits for which I have won many major awards.

**Old Cross Antiques,** 3-5 Main Street, BT22 2NE TEL: 88346 & (0850) 183947 ASSNS: LAPADA PARKING: Easy OPEN: 11.30-5.30, closed Sun, & by appt MIN: £10 PERIOD: 18th-20th century GENERAL: Furniture, silver, pottery & porcelain.

**Old Priory Antiques,** 3-5 Main Street, BT22 2NE TEL: 88346 ASSNS: LAPADA PARKING: Easy OPEN: 11.30-5.30, closed Sun MIN: £10 MAX: £3000 PERIOD: 18th-19th century SPECIALIST: Jewellery GENERAL: Furniture, silver OTHER INFO: Greyabbey is a particularly attractive village situated on the shores of Strangford Lough.

## PORTAFERRY (012477)

**Rock Angus Antiques,** 2 Ferry Street, BT22 1PB TEL: 28935 PARKING: Easy OPEN: Wed, Fri-Sun 12-5.30 MIN: £25 MAX: £7500 PERIOD: 18th-20th century & 5000BC-500AD SPECIALIST: Egyptian, Roman, Persian antiquities. Clocks, watches, barometers & nautical memorabilia GENERAL: Furniture & objets d'art.

## SAINTFIELD (01238)

**Antiques at the Stile,** 52 Main Street, BT24 7AB TEL: 510385 PARKING: Easy OPEN: Wed-Sat 10.30-5 MIN: £35 MAX: £7500 PERIOD: 19th-20th century GENERAL: Victorian & Edwardian furniture, brass, clocks.

ATTIC ANTIQUES (CAESAR DOYLE) **90 MAIN STREET, BT24 7AB TEL: 511057 PARKING: MON-SAT 10-5 MIN: 50P MAX: £5000 PERIOD: 19TH-20TH CENTURY SPECIALIST: VICTORIAN & EDWARDIAN FURNITURE (MAHOGANY) GENERAL: STRIPPED PINE: BRASS, IRON BEDS, TABLES & SETS OF CHAIRS, TOYS, COUNTRY ITEMS, GLASS, JEWELLERY & BRIC A BRAC OTHER INFO: 3 FLOORS OF INTERESTING & VARIED STOCK, I.E. FROM JUNK TO JEWELS, SOMETHING FOR EVERYONE. FRIENDLY SHOP.**

**Albert Forsythe,** Mill House, 66 Carsonstown Road, BT24 7EB TEL: 510398 PARKING: Own carpark OPEN: 6 days, 9-5 MIN: £30 MAX: £3000 PERIOD: 18th-19th century SPECIALIST: Rare folk furniture, French provincial GENERAL: Antique pine country furniture OTHER INFO: Lots of good restaurants, Saintfield is a good centre for sailing on Strangford Lough, close to Downpatrick with cathedral, burial place of St Patrick, patron saint of Ireland.

## LISBURN (01846)

**Van-Lyn Antiques,** 300 Comber Road, BT27 6TA TEL: 638358 PARKING: Own carpark OPEN: Daily 9-9 MIN: £1 MAX: £2000 PERIOD: 19th-20th century GENERAL: Furniture, porcelain, brass, glass, clocks, books OTHER INFO: We are in pleasant countryside, spacious relaxed shop with coffee corner & everyone is welcome.

## HILLSBOROUGH (01846)

**John Cousans Architectural Antiques,** 263 Ballynahinch Road, Annahilt, BT26 6BP TEL: 638091PARKING: Own carpark OPEN: 9.30-5.30 MIN: £5 MAX: £5000 PERIOD: 18th-19th century SPECIALIST: Irish vernacular GENERAL: Architectural salvage & furniture.

## BANBRIDGE (01820)

**Cameo Antiques,** 41 Bridge Street TEL: 623241 PARKING: Easy OPEN: By appt MIN: £5 MAX: £5000 PERIOD: 19th-20th century SPECIALIST: Antique jewellery.

## NEWRY (01693)

**School House Antiques,** Seavers Road TEL:

250943 & 68694 PARKING: Own carpark OPEN: 6 days 1-6 MIN: £1 MAX: £1000 PERIOD: 18th-20th century SPECIALIST: Irish pine from brass beds, fireplaces, small collectables, lots of farmhouse bits & pieces OTHER INFO: Located just off main Dublin Road on the way from Newry. It's a cold spot on the way to the Mourne Mountains. If visiting during the winter visitors are advised to bring thermals, ski boots & snow shoes. During summer omit the boots & shoes but keep the thermals.

## WARRENPOINT (016937)

**Antiques & Fine Art Gallery,** 3 Charlotte Street, BT34 3LF TEL: 52905 PARKING: Easy OPEN: Tues, Thurs-Sat 10.30-5.30 PERIOD: 18th-20th century SPECIALIST: Irish paintings, Georgian furniture GENERAL: Paintings by Irish artists, Victorian & Edwardian furniture.

## PORTADOWN (01762)

**Moyallon Antiques,** 54 Moyallon Road TEL: 831615 PARKING: Easy OPEN: Mostly open MIN: £10 MAX: £1500 PERIOD: 19th-20th century SPECIALIST: Furniture, pine.

## STEWARTSTOWN (01868)

Silver Saddle Antiques, West St, BT80 8JG TEL: (01648) 762257 PARKING: Easy OPEN: Tues & Fri 6pm-9pm, Sat 1-7pm MIN: £20 MAX £1,000 PERIOD: 19th-20th century SPECIALIST: Victorian furniture & chandeliers GENERAL: Good range of quality collectables.

**PJ Smith (Antiques)1 North Street TEL: 738396 PARKING: Easy OPEN: Mon-Fri 10.45-5.30 (closed for lunch), Sat 12 noon-6.30 PERIOD: 18th-19th century SPECIALIST: Antique fireplaces, beds, stained glass GENERAL: Architectural antiques OTHER INFO: Small town, easily accessible, 3 antique shops within minutes of each other, one of the oldest towns in Ulster.**

## COOKSTOWN (01648)

**Cookstown Antiques,** 16 Oldtown Street, BT80 8EF TEL: 765279 FAX: 762946 PARKING: Easy OPEN: Thurs, Fri 2-5.30, Sat 10.30-1, 2-5.30 MIN: £5 MAX: £1500 PERIOD: 19th-20th century SPECIALIST: Jewellery, medals, china.

## DUNGANNON (01868)

**Hurst Antiques,** Cohannon House, 25 Bovean Road, BT71 6HR TEL: 723253 PARKING: Easy OPEN: Mon-Fri 2-6, Sat 10.30-6 & by appt MIN: £1 MAX: £3000 approx PERIOD: 19th-20th century GENERAL: Furniture, porcelain, clocks, Victorian oil lamps, ruby glass OTHER INFO: My shop is signposted from Exit 14 on M1 (not in town), restaurant, filling station, motel ° mile.

## LISBELLAW (01365)

**Forge Antiques,** 9 Brooke Street, BT94 5AS TEL: 387777 OPEN: Mon-Thurs 2-6, All day Fri & Sat MIN: £5 MAX: £2500 PERIOD: 19th-20th century GENERAL: Victorian & Edwardian furniture, Belleek china, silver, porcelain, country furniture OTHER INFO: On the gateway to Fermanagh lakeland. 1 hour from Belfast. Many good hotels & restaurants.

## LONDONDERRY (01504)

**Patrick Bradley Antiques**
**2 London Street, BT48 6RQ TEL: 267337 OPEN: Mon-Sat 11-5.30 MIN: £1 MAX: £1500 PERIOD: 19th-20th century SPECIALIST: Rugs, kilims, textiles GENERAL: Unpretentious & quirky furniture & objects OTHER INFO: City centre near 17th century St Columb's Cathedral, Derry city walls, award winning Tower Museum, close to other antique shops.**

**Bygones,** 71 Carlisle Road PARKING: Easy OPEN: Mon-Sat 11-5.30, closed Thurs Min: £1 MAX: £500 PERIOD: 19th-20th century GENERAL: Small antiques including jewellery.

**Cathedral Antiques,** 12 London Street, BT48 6RQ TEL: 373155 PARKING: Easy OPEN: 11.30-5, closed Thurs MIN: £5 MAX: £1500 PERIOD: 19th-20th century SPECIALIST: Iron & brass bedsteads, lighting, linen, lace GENERAL: General antiques.

**Fox's Corner Antique Market,** Upstairs, 4 London Street, BT48 6RQ TEL: 371551 PARKING: Fri, Sat 11-5 MIN: 50p MAX: £500 PERIOD: 19th-20th century GENERAL: 10 dealers, bric a brac, furniture, books, jewellery, silver, militaria, telephone cards, advertising, old pictures, ethnic pottery,etc.

**Frazer & Mitchell,** Carlisle Road OPEN: Sat 10-5 MIN: £5 MAX: £500 PERIOD: 19th-20th century GENERAL: Small antiques & collectables.

**Society Antiques,** 5 Society Street TEL: 265286 PARKING: Easy OPEN: Mon-Sat 10-5.30 MIN:

£40 MAX: £5000 PERIOD: 18th-20th century GENERAL: Furniture, lamps, etc.

**The Stamp Shop,** 33 Carlisle Road PARKING: Easy OPEN: Mon-Sat 11-5.30, closed Thurs MIN: 50p MAX: £250 PERIOD: 19th-20th century SPECIALIST: Stamps, postcards, railway ephemera GENERAL: Books, gramophone records, printed ephemera.

**The Whatnot,** 22 Bishop Street TEL: 265008 PARKING: Easy OPEN: Mon-Sat 11.30-5 MIN: £500 PERIOD: 18th-20th century GENERAL: A wide variety of general antiques & jewellery OTHER INFO: Close to other antique shops & tourist attractions in the historic area of the city.

## COLERAINE (01265)

**The Coleraine Bookshop,** 5 Stone Row, BT52 1EP TEL: 52557 PARKING: Easy OPEN: 10-1, 2-5 closed Thurs & Sat MIN: 50p MAX: £500 PERIOD: 18th-20th century GENERAL: Antiquarian , second hand & out of print books.

**Forge Antiques,** 24-26 Long Commons, BT52 1LH TEL: 51339 PARKING: Medium OPEN: 10-5.30, closed Thurs MIN: £1 MAX: £10,000 PERIOD: 19th-20th century SPECIALIST: Jewellery GENERAL: Paintings, silver, Belleek, Worcester, furniture.

## PORTSTEWART (01265)

**The Smithy,** 172 Coleraine Road, BT52 1RR TEL: 832209 & 52153 PARKING: Easy OPEN: £1 MAX: £1000 PERIOD: 19th-20th century SPECIALIST: Silver & jewellery GENERAL: Furniture, porcelain, 1950s & 60s glass & china OTHER INFO: I have 2 holiday homes to let June-Sept weekly, seaview, sleeps 7.

## PORTRUSH (01265)

**Alexander Antiques,** 108 Dunluce Road, BT56 8NB TEL: 822783 FAX: 822364 PARKING: Own carpark OPEN: Mon-Sat 10-6 MIN: £100 MAX: £5000 PERIOD: 19th-20th century SPECIALIST: Largest stock of antique furniture of antique furniture in N. Ireland OTHER INFO: Situated 1° miles from Portrush, one of N. Ireland's premiere seaside resorts, & 4 miles from the Devil's Causeway.

## BUSHMILLS (01265)

**Brian R Bolt Collectors' Antiques,** 88 Ballaghmore Road, Port Ballintrae, BT57 8RL TEL: 731129 ASSNS: IADA PARKING: Easy OPEN: Tues, Thurs, Sat 2-5.30 & other times by chance or by appt MIN: £10 MAX: £2500 PERIOD: 17th-20th century SPECIALIST: Antique & 20th century silver, glass, snuff boxes & unusual smalls GENERAL: Arts & Crafts, metalware, decorative art jewellery, pottery & studio glass OTHER INFO: I conduct business worldwide by post. Catalogues periodically available.

**Dunluce Antiques,** 33 Ballytober Road, BT57 8UU TEL: 31140 PARKING: Own carpark OPEN: Mon-Thurs, Sat 10-6 MIN: £5 MAX: £10,000 PERIOD: 18th-20th century SPECIALIST: Irish art GENERAL: Furniture, porcelain, glass, objets d'art, also porcelain restoration OTHER INFO: Dunluce Castle, Giants Causeway, Old Bushmills Distellery (oldest in world) all nearby. Award winning restaurants & B&Bs all here as well.

## BALLYMENA (01266)

**The Antique Shop,** 55 Ballymoney Street, BT43 6JH TEL: 652087 PARKING: Easy OPEN: 10.30-1, 2-5 MIN: £10 MAX: £1000 PERIOD: 19th-20th century GENERAL: China, silver, jewellery.

**The Dungeon,** 92 Lower Mill Street, BT43 5AF TEL: 44142 PARKING: Medium OPEN: 10-5, closed Wed MIN: £1 MAX: £700 PERIOD: 19th-early 20th century SPECIALIST: Antique brass & copper GENERAL: Oil lamps, jewellery.

## AHOGHILL (01266)

**Once Upon a Time Antiques**, 13 Church Street, BT42 2PA TEL: 871244 FAX: 656666 PARKING: Easy OPEN: 10-6 MIN: £5 MAX: £3500 PERIOD: 17th-20th century GENERAL: Furniture, porcelain, art, jewellery, coins, medals, militaria.

# Index of Specialist Dealers

# Furniture

# General Antiques

**HOTELS**



**ICONS & RUSSIAN ART**



**IRISH ART & ANTIQUES**



**KITCHENALIA**

# Index of Places

# Dealer & Shop Information for the 1997 Edition

All entries in *Touring British Antique Shops* are totally FREE of charge. To be included you must fill in our form and return it Carol Fisher Publishing, PO Box 531, Melksham, Wilts SN12 8SL. This ensures that the information in the book is accurate. If you know of other dealers and are doubtful whether they have received a form, please duplicate this page, before completing, and give it to them. Please try and include your postcode. If you are in a high street, please do try and include the street number. **If you do not want to cut up your book, please photocopy this page.**

BUSINESS NAME: ______________________________

ADDRESS: ______________________________

______________________________

______________________________

TEL NO: ______________ FAX No: ______________

TRADE ASSOCIATIONS: ______________________________

PARKING: Own carpark ☐ Easy ☐ Medium ☐ Difficult ☐

OPENING HOURS (days & times): ______________________________

MINIMUM PRICE OF STOCK: ______________ MAXIMUM PRICE: ______________

PERIOD: 17th century ☐ 18th century ☐ 19th century ☐ 20th century ☐

Other (please specify): ______________________________

SPECIALIST STOCK (if any) ______________________________

GENERAL STOCK: ______________________________

______________________________

Any information that you feel may be amusing, interesting or useful to visitors, i.e. good restaurants, hotels, B&Bs, places of interest, perhaps something unusual, strange or humorous about your local trade or area. Such items are much appreciated.

______________________________

______________________________

______________________________

I would like information on advertising in *Touring British Antique Shops.* **Yes/No**
I might be interested in stocking the book on a sale or return basis **Yes/No** (please circle)

The information supplied is accurate and may be used in *Touring British Antique Shops.*

SIGNED: ______________ NAME (Block Capitals) ______________

POSITION: ______________ DATE: ______________

# Readers' Remarks

We are very interested in your response to *Touring British Antiques Shops* so that future editions can be improved to reflect the needs of people using the book. Although there is space for your name and address, there is no compulsion to complete that part of the form if you would rather not. However, if you do include your name and address, you may rest assured that this information will not be divulged to anybody. We will only use it to send information on future editions if you request us to do so. **If you do not want to cut up your book please photocopy this form.**

NAME:

ADDRESS:

Do you want information on future editions? YES/NO

Have you experienced difficulties using the book? If yes, what were they?

What do you dislike most?

What do you like best?

Would you like more information on the dealers? YES/NO (please delete one)

Would you like more information on the places on the tours? YES/NO

If the answer to either of the last two questions was YES, please indicate the kind of information you would like to see.

Is there anything not covered in the book at the moment that you would like to see in future editions?

To give us an idea of how people use the book we would be glad if you would answer a few further questions.

Have you followed a complete tour? YES/NO (please delete one)

Do you use the book to find dealers when visiting a new place for some other purpose? YES/NO

If you run out of space, please use a plain sheet of paper to continue.
Please return this form to Carol Fisher Publishing, PO Box 531, Melksham Wilts SN12 8SL.
The best suggestion for improvements to future editions will receive a FREE copy of the next book.